The *Streeter/Hutchison* Series in Mathematics

Baratto | Kohlmetz | Bergman

intermediate algebra

The Streeter/Hutchison Series in Mathematics Intermediate Algebra

The *Streeter/Hutchison* Series in Mathematics

Baratto | Kohlmetz | Bergman

intermediate algebra

Stefan Baratto

Clackamas Community College

Kelly Kaiser Kohlmetz

University of Wisconsin–Milwaukee

Barry Bergman

Clackamas Community College

Boston Burr Ridge, IL Dubuque, IA New York San Francisco St. Louis
Bangkok Bogotá Caracas Kuala Lumpur Lisbon London Madrid Mexico City
Milan Montreal New Delhi Santiago Seoul Singapore Sydney Taipei Toronto

Higher Education

INTERMEDIATE ALGEBRA

Published by McGraw-Hill, a business unit of The McGraw-Hill Companies, Inc., 1221 Avenue of the Americas, New York, NY 10020.

This book is printed on recycled, acid-free paper containing 10% postconsumer waste.

1 2 3 4 5 6 7 8 9 0 QPD/QPD 0 9 8 7

ISBN 978–0–07–340613–8
MHID 0–07–340613–9

ISBN 978-0-07-327347-1
MHID 0-07-327347-3 (Annotated Instructor's Edition)

Publisher: *Elizabeth J. Haefele*
Sponsoring Editor: *Richard Kolasa*
Senior Developmental Editor: *Michelle L. Flomenhoft*
Marketing Manager: *Barbara Owca*
Project Manager: *Lora Kalb*
Senior Production Supervisor: *Kara Kudronowicz*
Senior Media Project Manager: *Sandra M. Schnee*
Media Producer: *Amber M. Huebner*
Senior Designer: *David W. Hash*
Cover/Interior Designer: *Asylum Studios, Mona Grigaliunas and Tom J. Nemoda*
Senior Photo Research Coordinator: *Lori Hancock*
Photo Research: *Connie Mueller*
Supplement Producer: *Melissa M. Leick*
Compositor: *Interactive Composition Corporation*
Typeface: *10/12 New Times Roman*
Printer: *Quebecor World Dubuque, IA*

Chapter 1
Opener: © F. Schussler/PhotoLink/Getty Images; p. 64: © Spacescapes/PhotoDisc/Getty Images; p. 68: © PhotoDisc/Vol. 54/Getty Images; p. 85: © F. Schussler/PhotoLink/Getty Images.

Chapter 2
Opener: © Hank Morgan/Photo Researchers, Inc.; p. 114: © Vol. 28/PhotoDisc/Getty Images; p. 121, 123: © Lifestyles Today/PhotoDisc/Getty Images; p. 147: © Vol. 28/PhotoDisc/Getty Images; p. 171: © AP Photo/Nick Ut.

Chapter 3
Opener: © Michelle D.Bridwell/PhotoEdit; p. 233: © Vol. 49/PhotoDisc/Getty Images; p. 322: © Vol. 76/Getty Images.

Chapter 4
Opener: © Royalty-Free/Getty Images; p. 405: Courtesy of John F. Price.

Chapter 5
Opener: © Paul Steel/Corbis; p. 521: © Vol. 166/ Corbis; p. 535: © 2006 Texas Instruments.

Chapter 6
Opener: © AP Photo/Greg Baker; p. 585: © Vol. 10/ PhotoDisc/Getty Images; p. 610: © Vol. 133/Corbis; p. 645: © Brand X Pictures/PunchStock.

Chapter 7
Opener: © Inga Spence/Visuals Unlimited; p. 705: © Vol. 26/Corbis; p.712: © Vol. 165/Corbis; p. 751: Museum of Science and Industry, Chicago Courtesy Museum of Science and Industry, Scott Brownell, photographer.

Chapter 8
Opener: © Comstock Images/Alamy; p. 791: © Vol. 41/PhotoDisc/Getty Images; p. 799: © Vol. 41/ PhotoDisc/Getty Images; p. 835: © Rubberball Productions/Index Stock.

Chapter 9
Opener: NASA; p. 852: © Vol. 102/Corbis; p. 928: NASA.

Chapter 10
Opener: © Wojnarowicz/The Image Works; p. 967: © Royalty-Free/Corbis.

Chapter 11
Opener: © Royalty-Free/Corbis; p. 1002: © Vol. 122/ Corbis; p. 1043: © Royalty-Free/Corbis

www.mhhe.com

dedications

My students inspired me; my colleagues challenged me; my friends encouraged me. Through them all, our work on this text comes to fruition. My deepest, heartfelt, gratitude to the students, colleagues, and friends with whom I have been blessed.

Stefan Baratto

To my parents, whose patience, understanding, and support helped form the teacher, and overall the person, that I am today. And to my sister Kerry, who was my very first student.

Kelly Kaiser Kohlmetz

To my beautiful wife Marcia, and to my two sons, Joel and Adam, who have developed into fine young men.

Barry Bergman

To the regular members of my book group: Tom, Grant, Joe, Paul, and Fred, who provide me with challenges, perspectives, and a better understanding of literature. Isn't it time for us to read a math book so that I can have an easy month?

Don Hutchison

about the authors

Stefan Baratto

Stefan currently enjoys teaching math at Clackamas Community College in Oregon. He has also taught at the University of Oregon, Southeast Missouri State University, York County Technical College (Maine), and in New York City middle schools.

Stefan is involved in many professional organizations, including AMATYC and ORMATYC, where he is a frequent presenter. He has also used statistics, technology, and Web design to apply math to various fields.

Stefan, and his wife Peggy, make their home in Portland and spend their time enjoying the wonders of Oregon and the Pacific Northwest.

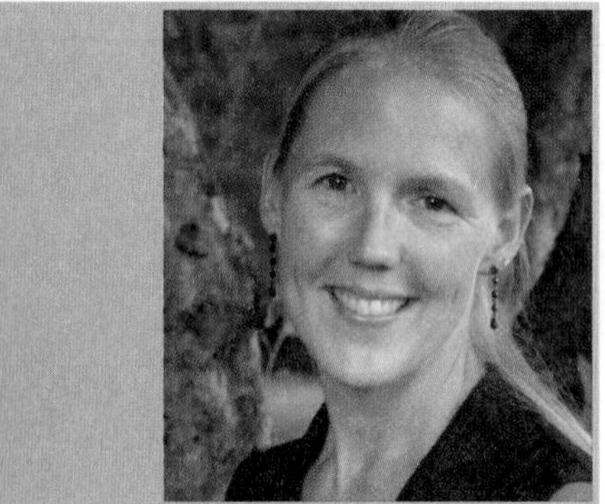

Kelly Kaiser Kohlmetz

Kelly began teaching mathematics as a graduate student at the University of Wisconsin–Milwaukee. She became so interested in helping the students at UWM that she stayed on after completing her degree. Currently she is the coordinator for Math 095, the last developmental course offered on campus.

Kelly's own education includes St. Olaf College (BA, Math and Spanish, 1993) and University of Wisconsin–Milwaukee (MS, Math, 1997). In addition, she has recently returned to graduate school to combine her two great loves, mathematics and teaching, by pursuing a doctorate in urban education, specializing in curriculum and instruction.

Kelly has been involved in numerous professional organizations including NCTM and MAA. Her areas of interest include dealing with math anxiety, helping underprepared students at postsecondary institutions find success in math, and understanding the role of technology in the teaching and learning of mathematics.

More personally, Kelly has recently gotten married and is looking forward to sharing each day with Bob, her partner, best friend, and biggest constant supporter.

Barry Bergman

Barry has enjoyed teaching mathematics to a wide variety of students over the years. He began in the field of adult basic education and moved into the teaching of high school mathematics in 1977. He taught at that level for 11 years, at which point he served as a K–12 mathematics specialist for his county. This work allowed him the opportunity to help promote the emerging NCTM Standards in his region.

In 1990 Barry began the present portion of his career, having been hired to teach at Clackamas Community College. He maintains a strong interest in the appropriate use of technology and visual models in the learning of mathematics.

Throughout the past 28 years, Barry has played an active role in professional organizations. As a member of OCTM, he contributed several articles and activities to the group's journal. He has made presentations at OCTM, NCTM, ORMATYC, and ICTCM conferences. Barry also served as an officer of ORMATYC for four years and participated on an AMATYC committee to provide feedback to revisions of NCTM's Standards.

Donald Hutchison

Don began teaching in a preschool while he was an undergraduate. He subsequently taught children with disabilities, adults with disabilities, high school mathematics, and college mathematics. Although all of these positions were challenging and satisfying, it was breaking a challenging lesson into teachable components that he most enjoyed.

It was at Clackamas Community College that he found his professional niche. The community college allowed him to focus on teaching within a department that constantly challenged faculty and students to expect more. Under the guidance of Jim Streeter, Don learned to present his approach to teaching in the form of a textbook.

Don has also been an active member of many professional organizations. He has been president of ORMATYC, AMATYC committee chair, and ACM curriculum committee member. He has presented at AMATYC, ORMATYC, AACC, MAA, ICTCM, and numerous other conferences.

contents

to the student

You are about to begin a course in mathematics. We made every attempt to provide a text that will help you understand what mathematics is about and how to use it effectively. We made no assumptions about your previous experience with mathematics. Your progress through the course will depend on the amount of time and effort you devote to the course and your previous background in math. There are some specific features in this book that will aid you in your studies. Here are some suggestions about how to use this book. (Keep in mind that a review of *all* the chapter and summary material will further enhance your ability to grasp later topics and to move more effectively through the text.)

1. If you are in a lecture class, make sure that you take the time to read the appropriate text section *before* your instructor's lecture on the subject. Then take careful notes on the examples that your instructor presents during class.
2. After class, work through similar examples in the text, making sure that you understand each of the steps shown. Examples are followed in the text by *Check Yourself* exercises. You can best learn mathematics by being involved in the process, and that is the purpose of these exercises. Always have a pencil and paper at hand, work out the problems presented, and check your results immediately. If you have difficulty, go back and carefully review the previous exercises. Make sure you understand what you are doing and why. The best test of whether you do understand a concept lies in your ability to explain that concept to one of your classmates. Try working together.
3. At the end of each chapter section you will find a set of exercises. Work these carefully to check your progress on the section you have just finished. You will find the solutions for the odd-numbered exercises following the problem set. If you have difficulties with any of the exercises, review the appropriate parts of the chapter section. If your questions are not completely cleared up, by all means do not become discouraged. Ask your instructor or an available tutor for further assistance. A word of caution: Work the exercises on a regular (preferably daily) basis. Again, learning mathematics requires becoming involved. As is the case with learning any skill, the main ingredient is practice.
4. When you complete a chapter, review by using the *Summary.* You will find all the important terms and definitions in this section, along with examples illustrating all the techniques developed in the chapter. Following the Summary are *Summary Exercises* for further practice. The exercises are keyed to chapter sections, so you will know where to turn if you are still having problems.
5. When you finish with the Summary Exercises, try the *Self-Test* that appears at the end of each chapter. It is an actual practice test you can work on as you review for in-class testing. Again, answers with section references are provided.
6. Finally, an important element of success in studying mathematics is the process of regular review. We provide a series of *Cumulative Reviews* throughout the textbook, beginning at the end of Chapter 2. These tests will help you review not only the concepts of the chapter that you have just completed but also those of previous chapters. Use these tests in preparation for any midterm or final exams. If it appears that you have forgotten some concepts that are being tested, don't worry. Go back and review the sections where the idea was initially explained or the appropriate chapter Summary. That is the purpose of the Cumulative Review.

We hope that you will find our suggestions helpful as you work through this material, and we wish you the best of luck in the course.

Stefan Baratto
Kelly Kaiser Kohlmetz
Barry Bergman
Donald Hutchison

preface

Message from the Authors

We believe the key to learning mathematics, at any level, is active participation—**Mastering Math Through Practice.** Students who are active participants in the learning process have the opportunity to construct their own mathematical ideas and make connections to previously studied material. Such participation leads to understanding, retention, success, and confidence. We developed this text with that philosophy in mind and integrated many features throughout the book to reflect that philosophy. Our goal is to provide *content in context.* The opening vignette for each chapter, the activity in that chapter, and several section exercises all relate to the same topic in order to engage students and allow them to see the relevance of mathematics. The Check Yourself exercises are designed to keep the students active and involved with every page of exposition. The optional calculator references involve students actively in the development of mathematical ideas.

The exercise sets are organized to showcase the different types of exercises available to the students: Basic Skills, Advanced Skills, Vocational-Technical Applications, Calculator/Computer, and Above and Beyond (which encompasses challenging exercises, writing exercises, and collaborative exercises). Answer blanks for these exercises appear in the margin allowing the student to actively use the text, making it more than just a reference tool. Many of these exercises are designed to awaken interest and insight in students: all are meant to provide continual practice and reinforcement of the topics being learned. For those seeking additional understanding, some exercises include icons next to them to indicate that a video stepping through that exercise is available. Not all the exercises will be appropriate for every student, but each one gives another opportunity for both the instructor and the student. Our hope is that every student who uses this text will become a better mathematical thinker as a result.

Overview

When preparing to write this text, the authors solicited feedback from the market about what types of pedagogical tools would better help students to understand and retain the key intermediate algebra concepts, in addition to what content should be updated or expanded. Being sure to have a significant number of applications and integrating them throughout the sections was one of the most prevalent responses. Based on this feedback, the authors focused on these themes as they wrote the text. It is by popular demand that we are now offering an intermediate algebra book in the series again. This book combines the best of earlier versions of *Intermediate Algebra,* along with new material requested by a cross-section of intermediate algebra instructors across the country. Author Kelly Kaiser Kohlmetz from the University of Wisconsin–Milwaukee is a welcome addition to the series, and her experience in academics helped bring this new edition to life.

In terms of pedagogical tools, this text seeks to provide carefully detailed explanations and accessible pedagogy to introduce intermediate algebra concepts to the students. The authors use a three-pronged approach to present the material and encourage critical thinking skills. The areas used to create the framework are communication, pattern recognition, and problem solving. Items such as Check Yourself exercises and activities represent this approach and the underlying philosophy of mastering math through practice. A key feature is Reading Your Text—these quick exercises presented at the end of each section quiz students' vocabulary knowledge and help strengthen their communication skills.

Market research has reinforced the importance of the exercise sets to the student's ability to process the content. To that end, the exercise sets in this book have been distinctly organized and clearly labeled (as previously outlined). Vocational and professional-technical exercises have been added throughout. In addition, exercises with fractions, decimals, and negative numbers have been added as appropriate. Repeated exposure to this consistent structure should help advance the student's skills in relating to mathematics.

Features

A number of features have contributed to the previous success of the Streeter-Hutchison texts. All of these features are also included in this text and help reinforce the authors' philosophy of *Mastering Math Through Practice.* Each feature was thoroughly discussed by the authors and review panels during the development of the text. More than ever, we are confident that the entire learning package is of value to your students and to you as an instructor. We will describe each of the key features of our package.

preface

> Make the Connection— Chapter-Opening Vignettes

The chapter-opening vignettes were written to provide students with interesting, relevant scenarios that will capture their attention and engage them in the upcoming material. Furthermore, exercises and activities related to the chapter-opening vignette were included in each chapter. These exercises are marked with a special icon next to them.

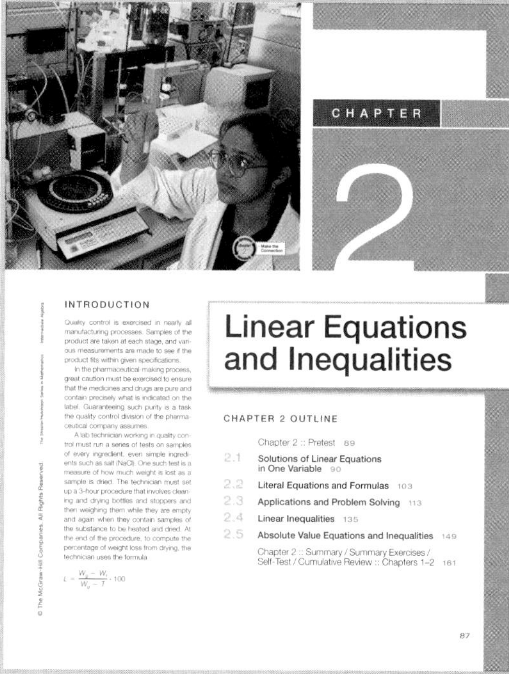

CHAPTER 2

INTRODUCTION

Quality control is exercised in nearly all manufacturing processes. Samples of the product are taken at each stage, and various measurements are made to see if the product fits within given specifications.

In the pharmaceutical-making process, great caution must be exercised to ensure that the medicines and drugs are pure and contain precisely what is indicated on the label. Guaranteeing such purity is a task the quality control division of the pharmaceutical company assumes.

A lab technician working in quality control must run a series of tests on samples of every ingredient, even simple ingredients such as salt (NaCl). One such test is a measure of how much weight is lost as a sample is dried. The technician must set up a 3-hour procedure that involves cleaning and drying bottles and stoppers and then weighing them while they are empty and again when they contain samples of the substance to be heated and dried. At the end of the procedure, to compute the percentage of weight loss from drying, the technician uses the formula

$$L = \frac{W_g - W_f}{W_g - T} \cdot 100$$

Linear Equations and Inequalities

CHAPTER 2 OUTLINE

87

> Activities

Activities are included in each chapter. They promote active learning by requiring students to find, interpret, and manipulate real world data. The activity in each chapter relates to the chapter-opening vignette, providing cohesiveness to the chapter. Students can complete the activities on their own, but these are best solved in small groups.

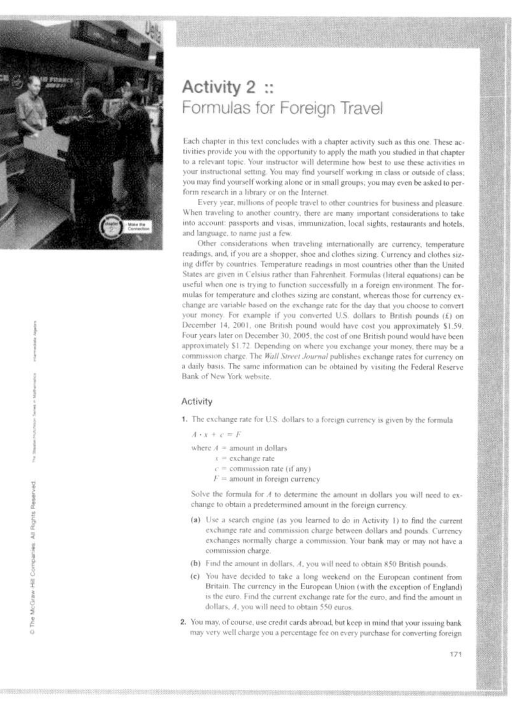

Activity 2 :: Formulas for Foreign Travel

Each chapter in this text concludes with a chapter activity such as this one. These activities provide you with the opportunity to apply the math you studied in that chapter to a relevant topic. Your instructor will determine how best to use these activities in your instructional setting. You may find yourself working in class or outside of class; you may find yourself working alone or in small groups; you may even be asked to perform research in a library or on the Internet.

Every year, millions of people travel to other countries for business and pleasure. When traveling to another country, there are many important considerations to take into account: passports and visas, immunization, local sights, restaurants and hotels, and language, to name just a few.

Other considerations when traveling internationally are currency, temperature readings, and, if you are a shopper, shoe and clothes sizing. Currency and clothes sizing differ by countries. Temperature readings in most countries other than the United States are given in Celsius rather than Fahrenheit. Formulas (literal equations) can be useful when one is trying to function successfully in a foreign environment. The formulas for temperature and clothes sizing are constant, whereas those for currency exchange are variable based on the exchange rate for the day that you choose to convert your money. For example if you converted U.S. dollars to British pounds (£) on December 14, 2001, one British pound would have cost you approximately $1.59. Four years later on December 30, 2005, the cost of one British pound would have been approximately $1.72. Depending on where you exchange your money, there may be a commission charge. The *Wall Street Journal* publishes exchange rates for currency on a daily basis. The same information can be obtained by visiting the Federal Reserve Bank of New York website.

Activity

1. The exchange rate for U.S. dollars to a foreign currency is given by the formula

$A \cdot x + c = F$

where A = amount in dollars
x = exchange rate
c = commission rate (if any)
F = amount in foreign currency

Solve the formula for A to determine the amount in dollars you will need to exchange to obtain a predetermined amount in the foreign currency.

(a) Use a search engine (as you learned to do in Activity 1) to find the current exchange rate and commission charge between dollars and pounds. Currency exchanges normally charge a commission. Your bank may or may not have a commission charge.

(b) Find the amount in dollars, A, you will need to obtain 850 British pounds.

(c) You have decided to take a long weekend on the European continent from Britain. The currency in the European Union (with the exception of England) is the euro. Find the current exchange rate for the euro, and find the amount in dollars, A, you will need to obtain 550 euros.

2. You may, of course, use credit cards abroad, but keep in mind that your issuing bank may very well charge you a percentage fee on every purchase for converting foreign

171

> Check Yourself Exercises

The Check Yourself exercises have been the hallmark of the Streeter-Hutchison series; they are designed to actively involve students throughout the learning process. Every example is followed by an exercise that encourages students to solve a problem similar to the one just presented and to check and practice what they have just learned. Answers are provided at the end of the section for immediate feedback.

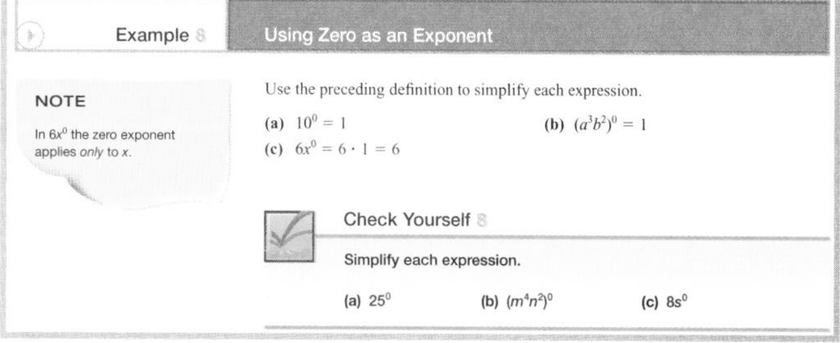

Example 8 Using Zero as an Exponent

NOTE

In $6x^0$ the zero exponent applies *only* to x.

Use the preceding definition to simplify each expression.

(a) $10^0 = 1$ (b) $(a^3b^2)^0 = 1$
(c) $6x^0 = 6 \cdot 1 = 6$

Check Yourself 8

Simplify each expression.

(a) 25^0 (b) $(m^4n^2)^0$ (c) $8s^0$

 The Streeter/Hutchison Series in Mathematics Intermediate Algebra

> Reading Your Text

The Reading Your Text feature is a set of quick exercises presented at the end of each section meant to quiz students' vocabulary knowledge. These exercises are designed to encourage careful reading of the text. If students do not understand the vocabulary, they cannot communicate effectively. The Reading Your Text exercises address the vocabulary issue that many students struggle with in learning and understanding mathematics. Answers to these exercises are provided at the end of the book.

Reading Your Text

The following fill-in-the-blank exercises are designed to ensure that you understand some of the key vocabulary used in this section.

SECTION 3.2

(a) The ______________ is a graphic test for identifying a function.

(b) Domain (and range) can be represented by an inequality or by using ______________ notation.

(c) A ______________ is a relation in which each element of the domain is paired with one and only one element of the range.

(d) Given that $y = f(x)$, x is called the ______________ and y is called the ______________.

> End-of-Section Exercises

The comprehensive end-of-section exercises have been organized to clearly identify the different types of exercises being presented. This structure highlights the progression in level and type of exercise for each section. This will not only provide clarity for students, but will also make it easier for the instructor to determine the exercises for their assignments. The application exercises that are integrated into every section are a crucial component of this organization.

6.6 exercises

37. Science and Medicine The electrical resistance of a wire varies directly as its length and inversely as the square of its diameter. If a wire with length 200 ft and diameter 0.1 in. has a resistance of 2 Ω, what will be the resistance in a wire of length 400 ft with diameter 0.2 in.?

38. Science and Medicine The frequency of a guitar string varies directly as the square root of the tension on the string and inversely as the length of the string. If a frequency of 440 cycles per second, or *hertz* (Hz), is produced by a tension of 36 lb on a string of length 60 cm, what frequency (in hertz) will be produced by a tension of 64 lb on a string of length 40 cm?

39. Science and Medicine The temperature of the steam from a geothermal source is inversely proportional to the distance it is transported. Write an algebraic equation relating temperature (t) to distance (d).

40. Science and Medicine Power available from a wind generator varies jointly as the square of the diameter of the rotor and the cube of the wind velocity. Write an algebraic equation relating power (p), rotor diameter (d), and wind speed (v).

Basic Skills | Advanced Skills | **Vocational-Technical Applications** | Calculator/Computer | Above and Beyond

Solve each variation application.

41. Allied Health If the temperature remains constant, then the pressure, P [measured in millimeters of mercury (mmHg)], being exerted on a gas is inversely proportional to the volume, V [measured in liters (L)], of the gas. Suppose that the initial volume of a gas is 6.3 L with an initial pressure of 725 mmHg. What is the new pressure if the volume changes to 4.75 L?

42. Allied Health The number of mAs, the product of the milliamperage and the time in seconds, varies directly with the square of the distance between the source of the radiation and the object receiving the radiation. If 10 mAs were used to produce a satisfactory radiograph at a distance of 30 inches, what mAs would be required at a distance of 45 inches?

43. Manufacturing Technology The tensile strength of a steel reinforcement rod varies directly with the square of the radius. If a $\frac{3}{8}$-in.-diameter rod has a tensile strength of 320 pounds, what is the tensile strength of a $\frac{1}{2}$-in.-diameter rod?

44. Manufacturing Technology The revolutions per minute (rpm) of a gear varies inversely with the number of teeth it has. If a gear with 8 teeth is spinning at 400 rpm, how many revolutions per minute is a gear with 5 teeth spinning?

Answers

37. ______
38. ______
39. ______
40. ______
41. ______
42. ______
43 ______
44. ______

SECTION 6.6 631

> Summary and Summary Exercises

The comprehensive Summaries at the end of each chapter enable students to review important concepts. The Summary Exercises provide an opportunity for students to practice these important concepts. The answers to odd-numbered exercises are provided in the Answers Appendix.

summary :: chapter 6

Definition/Procedure	Example	Reference
Simplification of Rational Expressions and Functions		Section 6.1
Rational expressions have the form $\frac{P}{Q}$ in which P and Q are polynomials and $Q(x) \neq 0$ for all x.	$\frac{x^2 - 5x}{x - 3}$ is a rational expression. The variable x cannot have the value 3.	p. 544
Fundamental Principle of Rational Expressions		
For polynomials P, Q, and R, $\frac{P}{Q} = \frac{PR}{QR}$ when $Q \neq 0$ and $R \neq 0$. This principle can be used in two ways. We can multiply or divide the numerator and denominator of a rational expression by the same nonzero polynomial.	This uses the fact that $\frac{R}{R} = 1$ when $R \neq 0$.	p. 546
Simplifying Rational Expressions		
To simplify a rational expression, use the following algorithm. **Step 1** Completely factor both the numerator and denominator of the expression. **Step 2** Divide the numerator and denominator by *all* common factors. **Step 3** The resulting expression will be in simplest form (or in lowest terms).	$\frac{x^2 - 4}{x^2 - 2x - 8} = \frac{(x - 2)(x + 2)}{(x - 4)(x + 2)} = \frac{x - 2}{x - 4}$	p. 548
Identifying Rational Functions		
A rational function is a function that is defined by a rational expression. It can be written as $f(x) = \frac{P}{Q}$ in which P and Q are polynomials, $Q \neq 0$		p. 548
Simplifying Rational Functions		
When we simplify a rational function, it is important that we note the x-values that need to be excluded, particularly when we are trying to draw the graph of a function. The set of ordered pairs of the simplified function will be exactly the same as the set of ordered pairs of the original function. If we plug the excluded value(s) for x into the simplified expression, we get a set of ordered pairs that represent "holes" in the graph. These holes are breaks in the curve. We use an open circle to designate them on a graph.		p. 549

Continued

> Icon Key

Make the Connection. Indicates the exercises, activity, and chapter opener that relate to each other.

Check Yourself. Indicates an exercise that is tied to the preceding example.

Calculator. Indicates an example that can be done using a calculator.

Video. Indicates an exercise that has a video walking through how to solve it.

Caution. Points out potential trouble spots.

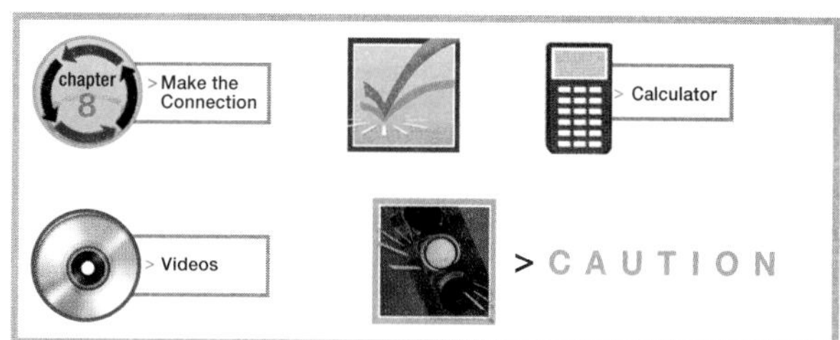

> Marginal Notes and Recall Notes

Marginal notes and Recall notes are provided throughout the text. Marginal notes are designed to help students focus on important topics and techniques, while Recall notes give students references to previously learned material.

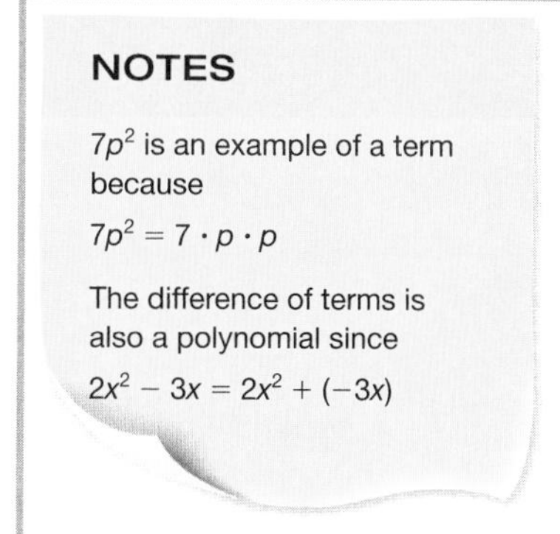

NOTES
$7p^2$ is an example of a term because
$7p^2 = 7 \cdot p \cdot p$
The difference of terms is also a polynomial since
$2x^2 - 3x = 2x^2 + (-3x)$

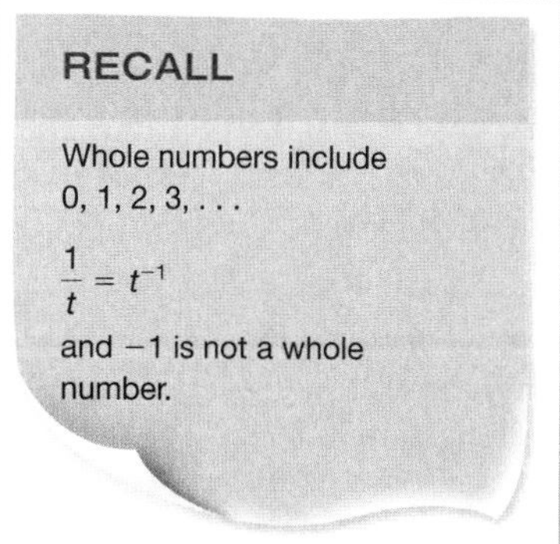

RECALL
Whole numbers include 0, 1, 2, 3, . . .
$\frac{1}{t} = t^{-1}$
and −1 is not a whole number.

> Learning Objectives

Learning objectives are clearly identified for each section. Annotations for the objectives appear next to examples, showing when a particular objective is about to be developed. References are also included within the exercise sets to help students quickly identify examples related to topics where they need more practice.

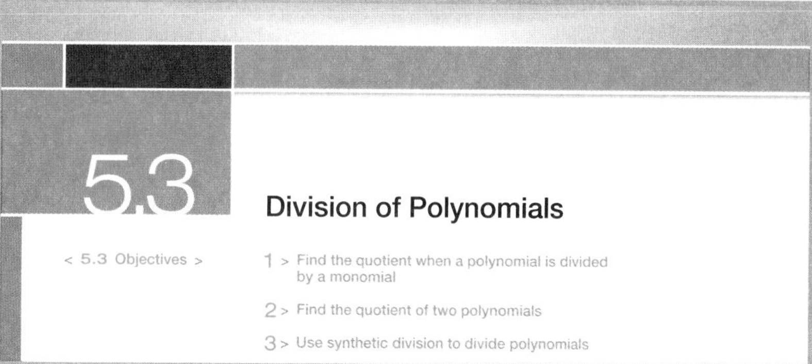

5.3
Division of Polynomials
< 5.3 Objectives >
1 > Find the quotient when a polynomial is divided by a monomial
2 > Find the quotient of two polynomials
3 > Use synthetic division to divide polynomials

> Self-Tests

Self-Tests appear in each chapter to provide students with an opportunity to check their progress and to review important concepts, as well as provide confidence and guidance in preparing for in-class tests or exams. The answers to the Self-Test exercises are given at the end of the book. Section references are given with the answers to help the student.

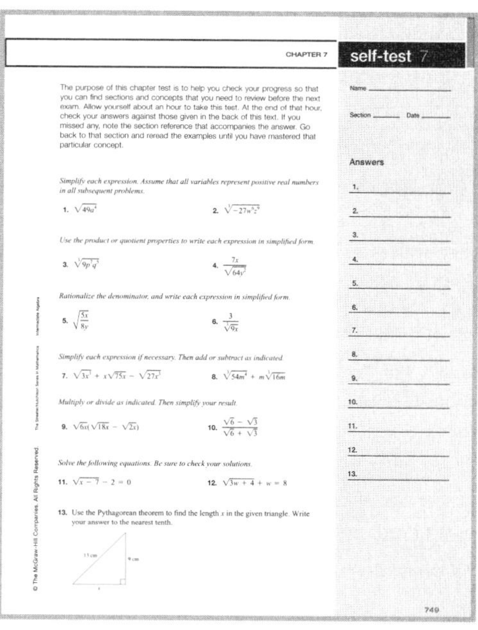

> Cumulative Reviews

Cumulative Reviews are included starting with Chapter 2, following the Self-Tests. These reviews help students build on previously covered material and give them an opportunity to reinforce the skills necessary in preparing for midterm and final exams. These reviews assist students with the retention of knowledge throughout the course. The answers to these exercises are also given at the end of the book, along with section references.

> Graph Paper Card

A graph paper card is bound into the back of the book. This perforated card can be torn out and copied as needed by the students and can be used any time they need to do graphing. An electronic version of the card is available through the book's Web site (www.mhhe.com/streeter) in the Information Center.

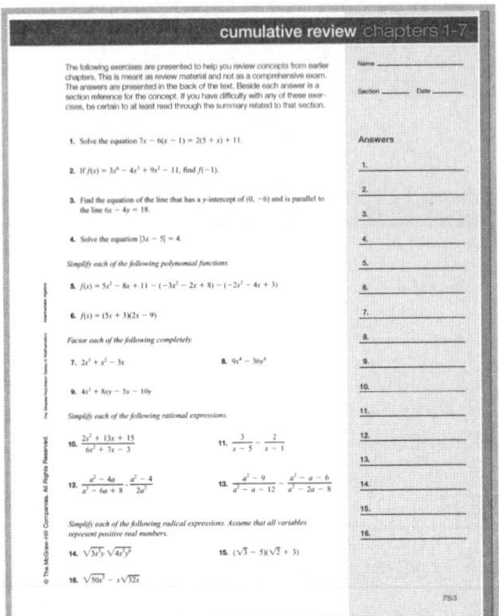

cumulative review chapters 1-7

The following exercises are presented to help you review concepts from earlier chapters. This is meant as review material and not as a comprehensive exam. The answers are presented in the back of the text. Beside each answer is a section reference for the concept. If you have difficulty with any of these exercises, be certain to at least read through the summary related to that section.

Name ________ Section ____ Date ____

1. Solve the equation $7x - 6(x - 1) = 2(5 + x) + 11$.
2. If $f(x) = 3x^4 - 4x^3 + 9x^2 - 11$, find $f(-1)$.
3. Find the equation of the line that has a y-intercept of $(0, -6)$ and is parallel to the line $6x - 4y = 18$.
4. Solve the equation $|3x - 5| = 4$.

Simplify each of the following polynomial functions.

5. $f(x) = 5x^2 - 8x + 11 - (-3x^2 - 2x + 8) - (-2x^2 - 4x + 3)$
6. $f(x) = (5x + 3)(2x - 9)$

Factor each of the following completely.

7. $2x^3 + x^2 - 3x$
8. $9x^4 - 36y^4$
9. $4x^2 + 8xy - 5x - 10y$

Simplify each of the following rational expressions.

10. $\dfrac{2x^2 + 13x + 15}{6x^2 + 7x - 3}$
11. $\dfrac{3}{x - 5} - \dfrac{2}{x - 1}$
12. $\dfrac{a^2 - 4a}{a^2 - 6a + 8} \cdot \dfrac{a^2 - 4}{2a^2}$
13. $\dfrac{a^2 - 9}{a^2 - a - 12} - \dfrac{a^2 - a - 6}{a^2 - 2a - 8}$

Simplify each of the following radical expressions. Assume that all variables represent positive real numbers.

14. $\sqrt{3x^3y}\sqrt{4x^3y^4}$
15. $(\sqrt{3} - 5)(\sqrt{2} + 3)$
16. $\sqrt{50x^3} - x\sqrt{32x}$

Answers

1. ____ 2. ____ 3. ____ 4. ____ 5. ____ 6. ____ 7. ____ 8. ____ 9. ____ 10. ____ 11. ____ 12. ____ 13. ____ 14. ____ 15. ____ 16. ____

753

Content Highlights Reflecting Reviewer Feedback

- *Chapter 1* contains a brief review of operations with real numbers in Section 1.1; translating statements using variables in Section 1.2; a section on algebraic expressions; and material on negative exponents in Section 1.5.
- *Chapter 2* features an introduction to interval notation in Section 2.4, as well as examples in Section 2.5 with "no solution" and an "all real numbers" solution.
- *Chapter 3* has graphing of linear equations introduced in Section 3.1; an introduction to functions including reading values from a graph and graphing linear functions in Section 3.2; a summary to review all situations for writing an equation of a line and material to interpret slope verbally for application problems in Section 3.4; along with graphing of vertically and horizontally shifted absolute value functions in Section 3.5.
- *Chapter 4* contains a section on solving linear systems using matrices.
- *Chapter 5* features coverage of the division of polynomials after multiplication of polynomials, but before factoring; coverage of synthetic division in Section 5.3; factoring trinomials using the trial-and-error method, as well as the *ac* method; and a section on strategies in factoring.
- *Chapter 6* contains up-to-date TI-84 calculator screen shots where appropriate, as do several other chapters.
- *Chapter 7* includes a discussion of rational and irrational numbers in Section 7.2; addition, subtraction, multiplication, and division of radicals in Section 7.3; and rational exponents near the end of the chapter.
- *Chapter 8* contains extensive coverage of solving rational inequalities.
- *Chapter 9* contains a discussion of the origination of the distance formula and its connection to the Pythagorean theorem in Section 9.2, as well as coverage of ellipses and hyperbolas which are not centered at the origin in Section 9.3.
- *Chapter 10* contains additional information of functions separate from other function work done in the chapter, including the composition of functions in Section 10.2 and inverse relations and functions in Section 10.3.
- *Chapter 11* contains up-to-date TI-84 calculator screen shots throughout and integrates applications of exponential and logarithmic functions into each section.

Supplements

Multimedia Supplements

MathZone

www.mathzone.com

McGraw-Hill's MathZone is a complete, online tutorial and course management system for mathematics and statistics, designed for greater ease of use than any other system available. Attainable with selected McGraw-Hill texts, the system allows instructors to create and share courses and assignments with colleagues and adjuncts with only a few clicks of the mouse. All assignments, questions, e-Professors, online tutoring, and video lectures are directly tied to text-specific materials.

MathZone courses are customized to your textbook, but you can edit questions and algorithms, import your own content, and create announcements and due dates for assignments.

MathZone has automatic grading and reporting of easy-to-assign algorithmically generated homework, quizzing, and testing. All student activity within MathZone is automatically recorded and available to you through a fully integrated grade book that can be downloaded to Excel.

MathZone offers:

- *Practice exercises* based on the text and generated in an unlimited number for as much practice as needed to master any topic you study.
- *Videos* of classroom instructors giving lectures and showing you how to solve exercises from the text.
- *e-Professors* to take you through animated, step-by-step instructions (delivered via on-screen text and synchronized audio) for solving exercises in the book, allowing you to digest each step at your own pace.
- *NetTutor,* which offers live, personalized tutoring via the Internet.

Instructor's Testing and Resource CD (Instructors Only)

This cross-platform CD-ROM includes a computerized test bank utilizing Brownstone Diploma algorithm-based testing software that enables users to create customized exams quickly. This user-friendly program enables instructors to search for questions by topic, format, or difficulty level; to edit existing questions or to add new ones; and to scramble questions and to create answer keys for multiple versions of the same test. Hundreds of text-specific open-ended and multiple-choice questions are included in the question bank. Sample chapter tests and final exams in Microsoft Word and PDF formats are also provided.

NetTutor

Available through MathZone, NetTutor is a revolutionary system that enables students to interact with a live tutor over the World Wide Web. NetTutor's Web-based, graphical chat capabilities enable students and tutors to use mathematical notation and even to draw graphs as they work through a problem together. Students can also submit questions and receive answers, browse previously answered questions, and view previous live-chat sessions. Tutors are familiar with the textbook's objectives and problem-solving styles.

Video Lectures on Digital Video Disk (DVD)

In the videos, qualified teachers work through selected exercises from the textbook, following the solution methodology employed in the text. The video series is available on DVD or online as an assignable element of MathZone. The DVDs are closed-captioned for the hearing impaired, subtitled in Spanish, and meet the Americans with Disabilities Act Standards for Accessible Design. Instructors may use them as resources in a learning center, for online courses, and/or to provide extra help for students who require extra practice.

ALEKS

ALEKS®

www.ALEKS.com

ALEKS (**A**ssessment and **LE**arning in **K**nowledge **S**paces) is an artificial intelligence–based system for individualized mathematics learning, available over the Web 24/7. ALEKS's unique adaptive questioning continually assesses each student's math knowledge. ALEKS then provides an individualized learning path, guiding the student in the selection of appropriate new study material. ALEKS 3.0 now links to text-specific video, multimedia tutorials, and textbook pages in PDF format. The system records each student's progress toward mastery of curricular goals in a robust classroom management system.

ALEKS improves students' performance by assessing what they know, guiding them to what they are ready to learn, and helping them master key mathematical concepts.

Printed Supplements

Annotated Instructor's Edition (Instructors Only)

This ancillary contains answers to exercises in the text, including answers to all section exercises, all Summary Exercises, Self-Tests, and Cumulative Reviews. These answers are printed in a special color for ease of use by the instructor and are located on the appropriate pages throughout the text. Exercises, Self-Tests, Summary Exercises, and Cumulative Reviews are annotated with section references to aid the instructor who may have omitted certain sections from study.

Instructor's Solutions Manual (Instructors Only)

The Instructor's Solutions Manual provides comprehensive, worked-out solutions to all exercises in the text. The methods used to solve the problems in the manual are the same as those used to solve the examples in the textbook.

Student's Solutions Manual

The Student's Solutions Manual provides comprehensive, worked-out solutions to all the odd-numbered exercises. The steps shown in the solutions match the style of solved examples in the textbook.

Acknowledgments

Putting together a text such as this one requires much more than an author team. There are three primary groups that make it possible to write and assemble the material. The most important of those groups is the set of end users, the students. Thanks to the many students who have contributed to the development of this text by telling us what worked (and didn't work) in helping them to learn the material.

At the other end of the process we have the many people who participated in the production of the text. The McGraw-Hill team includes our publisher Elizabeth Haefele who assembled this fine team, our editor Rich Kolasa who made certain that we had the resources and support that we needed to put the project together, and the project manager Lora Kalb. Gabrielle Andries has been invaluable as a writer, consultant, and coffee shop companion. Her experience and skills in both teaching and writing, as well as her willingness to make frequent trips between states, helped to shape this text. Other important contributors at or through McGraw-Hill include Barb Owca, David Hash, Kara Kudronowicz, Amber Huebner, Lori Hancock, Sandra Schnee, Harold (Hal) Whipple, Peter Hovanec, Robert Kohlmetz and Melissa Leick. Special thanks go to our developmental editor Michelle Flomenhoft. Michelle kept us on track and on time. She also ensured that we would never suffer the loneliness of waking up to an empty e-mail inbox.

The third group that made this edition possible was the set of reviewers who took the time to make observations and suggestions that helped improve this text. From TOC reviews to draft manuscript reviews to confirming reviews, the reviewer feedback has been invaluable.

Manuscript Reviewers

Andrew Mark Aberle, *Ozarks Technical Community College*

Enis Alpakin, *Kansas City Kansas Community College*

Jan Archibald, *Ventura College*

Ray Battee, *Cochise College—Douglas*

Lynn Beckett-Lemus, *El Camino College*

Kathleen Boehler, *Central Community College*

Bob Brown, *The Community College of Baltimore County—Essex*

Dorothy Brown, *Camden County College*

Jon Davidson, *Southern State Community College*

MaryRita Dennison, *University of Nebraska at Omaha*

Robert Diaz, *Fullerton College*

Steve Dostal, *College of the Desert*

Warrene Ferry, *Jones County Junior College*

Bernice Hersman, *Keiser College*

Peter Hovanec, *Okaloosa Walton College*

Christy Isakson, *The New England Institute of Art*

Benjamin Markham, *Ivy Tech Community College of Indiana*

Edgar Meyer, *Anoka Technical College*

Kim Miller, *Labette Community College*

Michael Montano, *Riverside Community College*

Priti Patel, *Tarrant County College—Southwest*

Marilyn Platt, *Gaston College*

Leesa Pohl, *Donnelly College*

Linda Pulsinelli, *Western Kentucky University*

Marc Sanchez, *Riverside Community College*

John Shirey, *Triangle Tech*

Jean Shutters, *Harrisburg Area Community College*

Abolhassan Taghavy, *Richard J. Daley College*

Wade Wells, *Bevill State Community College*

Kristi Whitehead, *Enterprise-Ozark Community College*

A commitment to accuracy

You have a right to expect an accurate textbook, and McGraw-Hill invests considerable time and effort to make sure that we deliver one. Listed below are the many steps we take to make sure this happens.

Our accuracy verification process

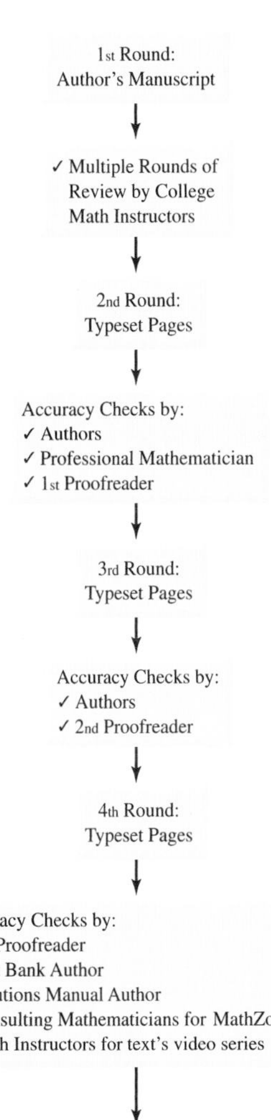

First Round

Step 1: Numerous **college math instructors** review the manuscript and report on any errors that they may find, and the authors make these corrections in their final manuscript.

Second Round

Step 2: Once the manuscript has been typeset, the **authors** check their manuscript against the first page proofs to ensure that all illustrations, graphs, examples, exercises, solutions, and answers have been correctly laid out on the pages, and that all notation is correctly used.

Step 3: An outside, **professional mathematician** works through every example and exercise in the page proofs to verify the accuracy of the answers.

Step 4: A **proofreader** adds a triple layer of accuracy assurance in the first pages by hunting for errors; then a second, corrected round of page proofs is produced.

Third Round

Step 5: The **author team** reviews the second round of page proofs for two reasons: (1) to make certain that any previous corrections were properly made, and (2) to look for any errors they might have missed on the first round.

Step 6: A **second proofreader** is added to the project to examine the new round of page proofs to double check the author team's work and to lend a fresh, critical eye to the book before the third round of paging.

Fourth Round

Step 7: A **third proofreader** inspects the third round of page proofs to verify that all previous corrections have been properly made and that there are no new or remaining errors.

Step 8: Meanwhile, in partnership with **independent mathematicians,** the text accuracy is verified from a variety of fresh perspectives:

- The **test bank author** checks for consistency and accuracy as they prepare the computerized test item file.
- The **solutions manual author** works every single exercise and verifies their answers, reporting any errors to the publisher.
- A **consulting group of mathematicians,** who write material for the text's MathZone site, notifies the publisher of any errors they encounter in the page proofs.
- A video production company employing **expert math instructors** for the text's videos will alert the publisher of any errors they might find in the page proofs.

Final Round

Step 9: The **project manager,** who has overseen the book from the beginning, performs a **fourth proofread** of the textbook during the printing process, providing a final accuracy review.

⇒ What results is a mathematics textbook that is as accurate and error-free as is humanly possible, and our authors and publishing staff are confident that our many layers of quality assurance have produced textbooks that are the leaders of the industry for their integrity and correctness.

applications index

CHAPTER

1

The Real Numbers

INTRODUCTION

Listen to any winter weather forecast in the northern United States, and you will probably hear something about the wind-chill factor. Just what is the wind-chill factor?

The speed of the wind does not actually affect the temperature, but it does affect how cold it feels. Scientists have conducted many studies to determine the relationship between the temperature, the wind speed, and how cold it actually feels outside. As a result of these studies, a formula has been developed that is used to compute the wind-chill factor. The following table uses that formula to calculate the effect. For example, if the actual temperature is 40 degrees Fahrenheit with a wind speed of 20 miles per hour (mph), the wind-chill factor is 18 degrees Fahrenheit.

The formula used to create this table has two inputs (temperature and wind speed) and one output (wind-chill factor). Equations of this type will be quite accessible for you by the time you finish this text.

CHAPTER 1 OUTLINE

Wind-Chill Factor in Degrees Fahrenheit

Wind Speed (mph)	Actual Temperature (Fahrenheit)								
	50	40	30	20	10	0	−10	−20	−30
5	48	37	27	16	6	−5	−15	−26	−36
10	40	28	16	4	−9	−21	−33	−46	−58
15	36	22	9	−5	−18	−36	−45	−58	−72
20	32	18	4	−10	−25	−39	−53	−67	−82
25	30	16	0	−15	−29	−44	−59	−74	−88
30	28	13	−2	−18	−33	−48	−53	−79	−94
35	27	11	−4	−20	−35	−49	−67	−82	−98
40	26	10	−6	−21	−37	−53	−69	−85	−100
45	25	10	−7	−22	−38	−54	−70	−86	−100

pretest 1

Name ______________________

Section __________ Date __________

This pretest provides a preview of the types of exercises you will encounter in each section of this chapter. The answers for these exercises can be found in the back of the text. If you are working on your own, or ahead of the class, this pretest can help you identify the sections in which you should focus more of your time.

1.1 Name all numeric sets to which each of the following numbers belong. The numeric sets consist of the natural numbers $\mathbb{N}$, integers $\mathbb{Z}$, rational numbers $\mathbb{Q}$, irrational numbers $\mathbb{Q}'$, and real numbers $\mathbb{R}$.

1. -5

2. 2π

3. $\frac{2}{3}$

4. -2.6

1.2 Evaluate each expression.

5. $6 - 3 \cdot 2$

6. $3 \cdot 5^2$

7. $(3.5)^2$

8. $-4 \cdot 2^2 - 5 \cdot 2$

9. $\frac{36}{-6 - 3}$

10. $-8^2 - (-3)^2$

Translate the following statements to symbols.

11. Twice the sum of n and 3

12. The product of 2 and x, divided by z

1.3 Graph the set.

13. $x \geq -4$

Write the expression without absolute value symbols.

14. $-(|2| + |-5|)$

1.4 Evaluate the expression if $a = 2$, $b = -1$, $c = 3$, and $d = -4$.

15. $\frac{3d + 2c}{b}$

16. $d^2 - b^2$

Answers

1. $\mathbb{Z}, \mathbb{Q}, \mathbb{R}$
2. $\mathbb{Q}', \mathbb{R}$
3. $\mathbb{Q}, \mathbb{R}$
4. $\mathbb{Q}, \mathbb{R}$
5. 0
6. 75
7. 12.25
8. −26
9. −4
10. −73
11. $2(n + 3)$
12. $\frac{2x}{z}$
13. 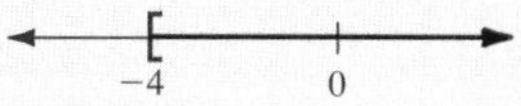

14. −7
15. 6
16. 15

Answers

17. $3x^2 - 8y$

18. $1.8m + 15$

19. $-\frac{2}{5}y$

20. 1

21. $\frac{1}{a^3}$

22. 0.00005

Simplify and combine like terms.

17. $2x^2 - 3y + x^2 - 5y$

18. $2.8m - 5(0.2m - 3)$

19. $\frac{1}{5}y - \frac{1}{5}(10 + 3y) + 2$

1.5 Simplify each expression.

20. $(2a^5b)^0$

21. $\frac{a^2b^{-4}}{a^5(b^{-2})^2}$

Compute using scientific notation. Then write the answer in decimal notation.

22. $\frac{3.5 \cdot 10^{-3}}{0.7 \cdot 10^2}$

1.1

The Set of Real Numbers

< 1.1 Objectives >

1 > Use set notation

2 > Recognize the basic subsets of the real numbers

3 > Plot numbers on a number line

4 > Review the four basic operations with real numbers

In the fall of 2000, there were approximately 3,200,000 people studying mathematics in 2-year and 4-year colleges and universities in the United States. One-half of these were studying in 2-year institutions. The following table, compiled by the National Science Foundation (www.nsf.gov), shows the mathematics enrollment in community colleges over 30 years.

Fall Enrollments in Math Programs; 2-Year Institutions (thousands)

Course level	1970	1980	1990	1995	2000
All math courses	555	900	1,241	1,384	1,600
Review courses	191	482	724	790	950
Precalculus	134	188	245	295	330
Calculus	59	97	128	139	150
Other	171	133	144	160	170

Note that, in the fall of 2000, there were approximately 950,000 students in 2-year colleges taking a course similar to the one in which you are enrolled. Why are all of these people taking these classes? Because it's required! This is a required class because both curriculum designers and employers have concluded that applied mathematics (courses for which this is a prerequisite) is important preparation for many, if not most, careers.

In 1998, the Bureau of Labor Statistics (stats.bls.gov), surveyed employers about the importance of mathematics. Following are just a few of the careers in which applied mathematics was considered important:

Accountants and auditors
Aircraft pilots and flight engineers
Computer programmers
Cost estimators
Dentists
Drafters
Electrical and electronic technicians
Engineering technicians
Financial managers
Insurance sales workers
Landscape architects
Management analysts and consultants
Optometrists
Pharmacists
Physicians
Psychologists

Real estate agents and brokers
Science technicians
Securities and financial services sales workers
Sociologists
Surveyors
Tool programmers, numerical control
Underwriters
Urban and regional planners
Veterinarians

Among the many mathematical topics that have applications in most of these fields is the idea of a set.

< Objective 1 >

A **set** is a collection of objects, symbols, or numbers. We often describe a set by enclosing its contents, or a description of its contents, in braces.

NOTES

Describing a set by listing its elements is called the *roster method* of defining a set.

The third set is read, "the set of all *x* such that *x* is a day of the week." This way of describing a set is called *set-builder notation.*

$\{1, 2, 3\}$ is a set containing the first three counting numbers.

$\{z, x, c, v, b, n, m\}$ is a set containing the letters found on the bottom row of a computer keyboard.

$\{x \mid x \text{ is a day of the week}\}$ is a set containing seven elements.

Frequently, we represent a set with a capital letter so that we may more easily refer to it. For example, we might say

$D = \{x \mid x \text{ is a day of the week}\}$

Any object or symbol that is contained in a set is called an **element,** or a **member,** of the set. The symbol $\in$ is used to indicate that an object is an element of a set.

NOTE

The symbol $\notin$ is used to indicate that an element is *not* a member of a set.

$3 \in \{1, 2, 3, 4\}$ indicates that 3 is contained in the set $\{1, 2, 3, 4\}$.

Saturday $\in D$ indicates that Saturday is an element of the set D previously named.

January $\notin D$ indicates that January is *not* an element of D.

Check Yourself 1

Complete each statement with the symbol $\in$ or $\notin$.

If $V = \{a, e, i, o, u\}$,

(a) a _____ V **(b)** t _____ V

Suppose that we define a set A as

$A = \{a, b, c, d\}$

and then a set B as

$B = \{d, c, b, a\}$

NOTES

The order in which we list the elements of a set doesn't matter.

This is read, "set *A* equals set *B*."

Here the two sets consist of the same elements—the first four letters of the alphabet. We can write

$A = B$

In general, we say that two sets, A and B, are equal whenever the two sets have exactly the same elements.

If the elements of a set can be ordered and we wish to indicate that a set continues as described, we use an ellipsis, three dots that mean "and so on."

{a, b, c, . . . , z}	describes the entire alphabet
{1, 2, 3, . . . , 100}	describes the first 100 counting numbers
{1, 3, 5, . . .}	describes the positive odd numbers

You will notice that the last set described *ends* with an **ellipsis** (three dots). This indicates that the elements continue without end. A set that has no end is said to be **infinite.**

A set that has some specific number of elements is said to be **finite.**

The set {a, b, c, d} is a finite set.

The set {2, 4, 6, . . . , 50} is a finite set.

But the set {2, 4, 6, . . .} is an infinite set.

NOTE

The set {2, 4, 6, . . .} is the set of positive even numbers. They continue without end.

RECALL

A prime number has *only* itself and 1 as factors.

Check Yourself 2

Describe each set as finite or infinite.

(a) {1, 3, 5, . . .} **(b)** {1, 2, 3, . . . , 99}
(c) {all prime numbers}

< Objective 2 >

NOTES

Including zero in the set of natural numbers, we have the set of whole numbers.

$W = \{0, 1, 2, 3, \ldots\}$

Every natural number is *also* an element of the set of integers.

Several numeric sets are used so commonly in mathematics that they have readily identifiable names. The rich history (or prehistory, in this case) of mathematics began with tallying or counting. The set of numbers used for counting is called the set of **natural numbers** and is designated by the capital letter $\mathbb{N}$. In set notation, we write

$$\mathbb{N} = \{1, 2, 3, \ldots\}$$

An equally important mathematical set is the set of **integers.** This is how we describe the set of integers:

$$\mathbb{Z} = \{\ldots, -2, -1, 0, 1, 2, \ldots\}$$

We see that the set continues without end in *both* the positive and negative directions. Also note the choice of the letter $\mathbb{Z}$ to designate this particular set. This comes from the word *Zahl,* the German word for "number."

We also will be referring to the set of **rational numbers.** A rational number is one that can be written as a fraction that is the ratio of two integers. Because ratios can be considered as **quotients** (and also because $\mathbb{R}$ will be used to designate a different set of numbers) we denote the set of rational numbers with the letter $\mathbb{Q}$.

NOTES

A rational number has the form

$\frac{p}{q}$

in which p and q are integers and q cannot be 0.

Because any integer can be written as the ratio of two integers, namely itself and 1, every integer is also a rational number.

Because we cannot list the rational numbers in any meaningful fashion, we define that set by *describing* the elements of that set instead:

$$\mathbb{Q} = \left\{ \frac{p}{q} \,\middle|\, p, q \in \mathbb{Z}, q \neq 0 \right\}$$

This is read "the set of elements of the form p over q, such that p and q are integers and q is not equal to zero."

NOTE

This is no surprise because

$0.45 = \frac{45}{100}$

which is the *ratio* of two integers.

$\frac{1}{3} = 0.\overline{3}$ (the bar denotes the repeating pattern)

$\frac{3}{11} = 0.\overline{27}$

There is another important characterization of the set of rational numbers. The decimal representation of any rational number is either a terminating decimal or a repeating decimal.

So 0.45 and 0.825 name rational numbers.

Also 0.3333. . . and 0.272727. . . name rational numbers.

Check Yourself 3

Complete each statement with the symbols $\in$ or $\notin$.

(a) 3 _____ $\mathbb{Z}$ **(b)** -3 _____ $\mathbb{N}$

(c) $\frac{2}{3}$ _____ $\mathbb{Z}$ **(d)** 0.25 _____ $\mathbb{Q}$

(e) $\frac{2}{3}$ _____ $\mathbb{N}$ **(f)** -5 _____ $\mathbb{Z}$

(g) $-\frac{3}{4}$ _____ $\mathbb{Q}$ **(h)** $0.\overline{35}$ _____ $\mathbb{Q}$

NOTES

The disturbing fact that $\sqrt{2}$ cannot be represented as the ratio of two integers was known to the Pythagoreans (400 B.C.), and it contradicted their belief that all lengths could be represented by ratios of integers.

$\mathbb{Q}'$ is read "$\mathbb{Q}$ prime."

Not every number can be expressed as the ratio of two integers. For example, it can be shown that the square root of 2 (denoted $\sqrt{2}$) cannot be written as the ratio of integers and is therefore *not* a rational number.

Numbers such as $\sqrt{2}$, $\sqrt[3]{7}$, and π are called **irrational numbers.** None of their decimal representations will ever repeat or terminate. The set of irrational numbers can be designated $\mathbb{Q}'$.

Now, if we combine the set of rational numbers with the set of irrational numbers, we call this new set the set of **real numbers** and use the letter $\mathbb{R}$ to designate the set. This is the set to which we refer most often in algebra.

Check Yourself 4

For the set $\left\{-4, 2.3, \sqrt{6}, -\pi, 0, \frac{3}{4}, 0.\overline{36}, 7\right\}$, which of the elements are

(a) Irrational numbers **(b)** Real numbers

(c) Natural numbers **(d)** Rational numbers

(e) Integers

< Objective 3 >

A convenient way to "picture" the set of real numbers is with a number line. This number line is constructed by drawing a straight line and then choosing a point to correspond to 0. This point is called the **origin** of the number line.

The standard convention is to allow positive numbers to increase to the right and negative numbers to decrease to the left. This is represented in the following number line.

NOTE

Zero is neither positive nor negative.

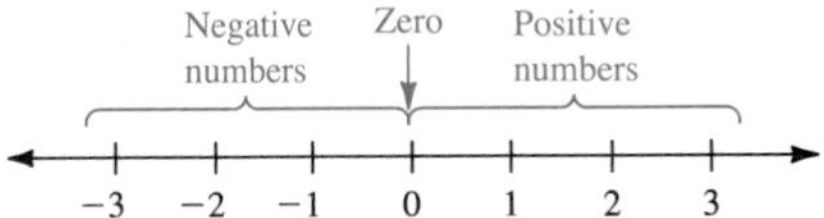

Each point on the line corresponds to a number called the **coordinate** of that point. The set of all numbers that correspond to a point on the number line makes up the set of real numbers.

NOTES

Later in the text, we will encounter numbers that cannot be represented on the real number line.

An approximation for $\sqrt{2}$ is 1.414, and for π, 3.14.

Every real number will correspond to exactly one point on the line, and every point corresponds to exactly one real number.

Locate the point corresponding to each element of the set

$$\left\{-1, \sqrt{2}, \frac{5}{2}, -2.5, \pi\right\}$$

on the real number line.

Check Yourself 5

Locate each element of set A on the number line, when

$$A = \left\{-\pi, -2, \sqrt{3}, -\frac{3}{4}, 3.5\right\}$$

The following diagram summarizes the relationships between the various numeric sets that have been introduced in this section.

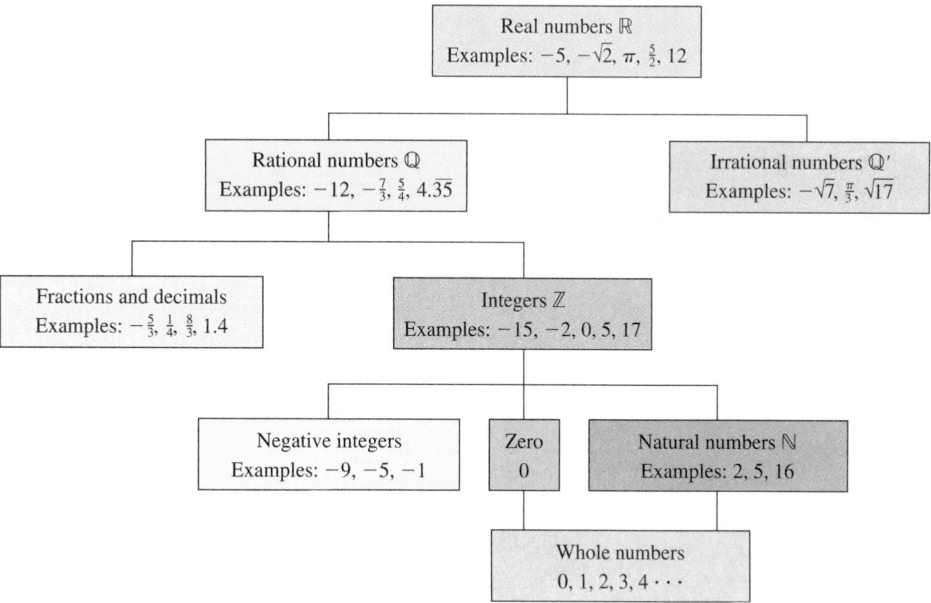

We now review the four arithmetic operations with real numbers. First we need to recall the concept of the absolute value of a number.

The **absolute value** of a number represents the distance of the point named by the number from the origin on the number line.

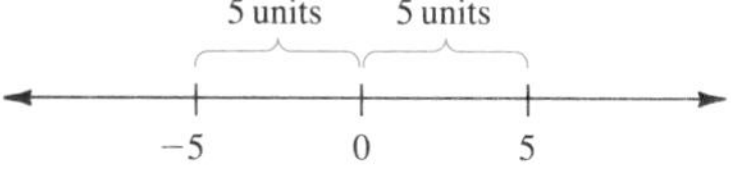

The absolute value of 5 is 5. The absolute value of -5 is also 5.

RECALL

The opposite of a number is the same distance from zero on the number line but in the opposite direction. The opposite of 3 is −3, and the opposite of −7 is 7.

The absolute value of a positive number or zero is itself. The absolute value of a negative number is its opposite.

In symbols we write

$|5| = 5$ and $|-5| = 5$

Read "the absolute value of 5." Read "the absolute value of negative 5."

The absolute value of a number does *not* depend on whether the number is to the right or to the left of the origin, but on its *distance* from the origin. We will review absolute value further in Section 1.3.

< Objective 4 >

Property

Adding Real Numbers

1. If two numbers have the same sign, add their absolute values. Give the result the sign of the original numbers.
2. If two numbers have different signs, subtract their absolute values, the smaller from the larger. Give the result the sign of the number with the larger absolute value.

Check Yourself 6

Add.

(a) $5 + (-14)$ **(b)** $-\frac{2}{3} + \left(-\frac{7}{3}\right)$

(c) $5.3 + (-2.3)$ **(d)** $-8 + 15$

Property

Subtracting Real Numbers

1. Rewrite the subtraction problem as an addition problem by
   (a) Changing the subtraction symbol to an addition symbol
   (b) Replacing the number being subtracted with its opposite
2. Add the resulting numbers as before.

Check Yourself 7

Subtract.

(a) $5 - (-13)$ **(b)** $-\frac{5}{7} - \frac{3}{7}$ **(c)** $5.6 - 7.8$

Property

Multiplying and Dividing Real Numbers

Multiply or divide the absolute values of the two numbers.

1. If the numbers have the same sign, the result is positive.
2. If the numbers have different signs, the result is negative.

Check Yourself 8

Multiply or divide.

(a) $(-8)(-9)$ **(b)** $\frac{7}{3} \cdot \frac{6}{7}$ **(c)** $-\frac{55}{11}$ **(d)** $\frac{-4.8}{-8}$

Check Yourself ANSWERS

1. **(a)** $a \in V$; **(b)** $t \notin V$ **2.** **(a)** Infinite; **(b)** finite; **(c)** infinite

3. **(a)** $3 \in \mathbb{Z}$; **(b)** $-3 \notin \mathbb{N}$; **(c)** $\frac{2}{3} \notin \mathbb{Z}$; **(d)** $0.25 \in \mathbb{Q}$; **(e)** $\frac{2}{3} \notin \mathbb{N}$; **(f)** $-5 \in \mathbb{Z}$; **(g)** $-\frac{3}{4} \in \mathbb{Q}$; **(h)** $0.\overline{35} \in \mathbb{Q}$

4. **(a)** $\sqrt{6}, -\pi$; **(b)** all; **(c)** 7; **(d)** $-4, 2.3, 0, \frac{3}{4}, 0.\overline{36}$, and 7; **(e)** $-4, 0, 7$

5. 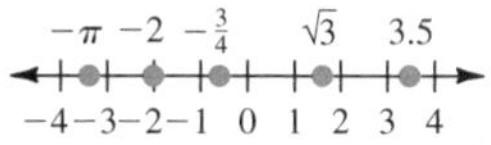 $-\pi$ -2 $-\frac{3}{4}$ $\sqrt{3}$ 3.5 (number line: -4 -3 -2 -1 0 1 2 3 4) **6.** **(a)** -9; **(b)** -3; **(c)** 3; **(d)** 7

7. **(a)** 18; **(b)** $-\frac{8}{7}$; **(c)** -2.2 **8.** **(a)** 72; **(b)** 2; **(c)** -5; **(d)** 0.6

Reading Your Text

The following fill-in-the-blank exercises are designed to ensure that you understand some of the key vocabulary used in this section.

SECTION 1.1

(a) A rational number is one that can be written as a fraction that is the ______________ of two integers.

(b) Numbers such as $\sqrt{2}$, $\sqrt[3]{7}$, and π are called ______________ numbers.

(c) The set of all numbers that correspond to a point on the number line makes up the set of ______________ numbers.

(d) Any object or symbol that is contained in a set is called an ______________ or a ______________ of the set.

1.1 exercises

Basic Skills | Advanced Skills | Vocational-Technical Applications | Calculator/Computer | Above and Beyond

Name ____________

Section ________ Date ________

< Objectives 1–3 >

Name all the numeric sets to which each of the following numbers belong. The numeric sets consist of the natural numbers $\mathbb{N}$, integers $\mathbb{Z}$, rational numbers $\mathbb{Q}$, irrational numbers $\mathbb{Q}'$, and real numbers $\mathbb{R}$.

1. 5

2. -3.4

3. -3

4. 3.2

5. $\sqrt{5}$ > Videos

6. 0

7. -3.1416

8. $-\sqrt{7}$

9. $\sqrt{4}$

10. $\frac{3}{4}$

11. π

12. $\sqrt{144}$

13. $-\frac{2}{5}$

14. $0.\overline{36}$

15. 2π

16. 2.35

On the number lines provided, graph the points named by each element of the set.

17. $\{3, 6, 9\}$

18. $\{-2, 0, 2\}$

19. $\left\{-\frac{1}{3}, 3, \frac{5}{2}\right\}$

20. $\left\{\frac{1}{2}, \frac{5}{4}, -\frac{7}{3}\right\}$

21. $\{-\sqrt{3}, \sqrt{2}\}$

22. $\{-\sqrt{5}, -\sqrt{3}, \sqrt{2}\}$

Answers

1. $\mathbb{N}, \mathbb{Z}, \mathbb{Q}, \mathbb{R}$
2. $\mathbb{Q}, \mathbb{R}$
3. $\mathbb{Z}, \mathbb{Q}, \mathbb{R}$
4. $\mathbb{Q}, \mathbb{R}$
5. $\mathbb{Q}', \mathbb{R}$
6. $\mathbb{Z}, \mathbb{Q}, \mathbb{R}$
7. $\mathbb{Q}, \mathbb{R}$
8. $\mathbb{Q}', \mathbb{R}$
9. $\mathbb{N}, \mathbb{Z}, \mathbb{Q}, \mathbb{R}$
10. $\mathbb{Q}, \mathbb{R}$
11. $\mathbb{Q}', \mathbb{R}$
12. $\mathbb{N}, \mathbb{Z}, \mathbb{Q}, \mathbb{R}$
13. $\mathbb{Q}, \mathbb{R}$
14. $\mathbb{Q}, \mathbb{R}$
15. $\mathbb{Q}', \mathbb{R}$
16. $\mathbb{Q}, \mathbb{R}$
17. See exercise
18. See exercise
19. See exercise
20. See exercise
21. See exercise
22. See exercise

1.1 exercises

Describe each set as finite or infinite.

23. $\{3, 6, 9, \ldots\}$

24. $\{4, 8, 12, 16, \ldots\}$

25. $\{4, 8, 12, 16, 20, \ldots, 48\}$

26. $\{5, 10, 15, 25, 30, \ldots\}$

27. {all even numbers}

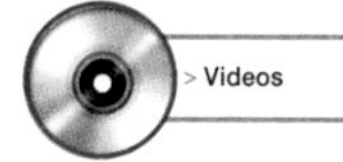

28. $\{1, 2, 3, 5, 8, 13, \ldots, 55\}$

Insert $\in$ or $\notin$ so that the statement is true.

29. 2 _____ $\mathbb{Z}$

30. 3.4 _____ $\mathbb{Z}$

31. -3 _____ $\mathbb{N}$

32. $\sqrt{3}$ _____ $\mathbb{Z}$

33. $\frac{5}{3}$ _____ $\mathbb{Z}$

34. -4 _____ $\mathbb{Z}$

35. $-\frac{2}{7}$ _____ $\mathbb{Q}$

36. $\frac{23}{6}$ _____ $\mathbb{Q}$

37. $\sqrt{3}$ _____ $\mathbb{R}$

38. $\sqrt{3}$ _____ $\mathbb{Q}'$

39. $\frac{8}{0}$ _____ $\mathbb{R}$

40. $\sqrt{25}$ _____ $\mathbb{R}$

41. 0 _____ $\mathbb{N}$

42. $0.\overline{24}$ _____ $\mathbb{Q}'$

From the set $\left\{-4, -\frac{5}{3}, 0, \frac{4}{3}, \sqrt{3}, 3\pi, 4.5, 0.\overline{21}, 8\right\}$, *list the elements that are*

43. Natural numbers

44. Rational numbers

45. Irrational numbers

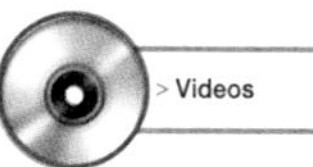

46. Real numbers

47. Integers

Determine whether the given statements are **true** *or* **false.**

48. All odd integers are real numbers.

49. All even integers are rational numbers.

50. Every negative real number is a natural number.

Answers

23. Infinite
24. Infinite
25. Finite
26. Infinite
27. Infinite
28. Finite
29. $\in$
30. $\notin$
31. $\notin$
32. $\notin$
33. $\notin$
34. $\in$
35. $\in$
36. $\in$
37. $\in$
38. $\in$
39. $\notin$
40. $\in$
41. $\notin$
42. $\notin$
43. 8
44. $-4, -\frac{5}{3}, 0, \frac{4}{3}, 4.5, 0.\overline{21}, 8$
45. $\sqrt{3}, 3\pi$
46. All are real numbers.
47. $-4, 0, 8$
48. True
49. True
50. False

Answers

51. True
52. True
53. False
54. False
55. False
56. 16
57. 15
58. $-\frac{7}{8}$
59. $-\frac{11}{14}$
60. 6
61. 6
62. $-\frac{7}{20}$
63. $-\frac{17}{12}$
64. 2
65. 2.3
66. 0
67. −1
68. −2
69. −3
70. −3
71. −11
72. −2
73. −5
74. −3.8
75. −23
76. $\frac{9}{4}$
77. 39.1
78. 3.2
79. 40
80. 42
81. −6
82. −6

51. Every integer is a real number.

52. All natural numbers are integers.

53. Every real number is an integer.

54. All integers are natural numbers.

55. Zero is not a rational number.

< Objective 4 >

Add.

56. $11 + 5$

57. $8 + 7$

58. $\left(-\frac{1}{2}\right) + \left(-\frac{3}{8}\right)$

59. $\left(-\frac{4}{7}\right) + \left(-\frac{3}{14}\right)$

60. $9 + (-3)$

61. $10 + (-4)$

62. $\left(-\frac{4}{5}\right) + \frac{9}{20}$

63. $\left(-\frac{11}{6}\right) + \frac{5}{12}$

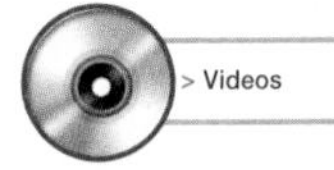

64. $-11.4 + 13.4$

65. $-2.6 + 4.9$

66. $-4.5 + 4.5$

67. $(-4) + 6 + (-3) + 0$

68. $7 + (-3) + 5 + (-11)$

69. $-\frac{6}{5} + \left(-\frac{13}{5}\right) + \frac{4}{5}$

70. $-\frac{3}{2} + \left(-\frac{7}{4}\right) + \frac{1}{4}$

71. $-5.4 + (-2.1) + (-3.5)$

Subtract.

72. $8 - 10$

73. $14 - 19$

74. $7.8 - 11.6$

75. $-15 - 8$

76. $\frac{3}{4} - \left(-\frac{3}{2}\right)$

77. $14.5 - (-24.6)$

78. $-6.9 - (-10.1)$

Multiply.

79. $4 \cdot 10$

80. $3 \cdot 14$

81. $(4)\left(-\frac{3}{2}\right)$

82. $\left(-\frac{3}{2}\right)(4)$

83. $(3.25)(-4)$

84. $(5.4)(-5)$

85. $(-9)\left(-\frac{2}{3}\right)$

86. $(-6)\left(-\frac{3}{2}\right)$

87. $(0)(-18)$

88. $(0)(25)$

89. $\left(-\frac{3}{2}\right)\left(-\frac{2}{3}\right)$

90. $\left(-\frac{4}{5}\right)\left(-\frac{5}{4}\right)$

Divide if possible.

91. $\frac{48}{6}$

92. $\frac{-24}{8}$

93. $\frac{50}{-5}$

94. $\frac{56}{-7}$

95. $\frac{0}{-8}$

96. $\frac{-10}{0}$

97. $\frac{18}{0}$

98. $\frac{0}{8}$

99. $\frac{-29.4}{4.9}$ > Videos

100. $\frac{-25.9}{-3.7}$

101. $\frac{-8}{32}$

102. $\frac{-6}{-30}$

Solve each problem.

103. **Statistics** On four consecutive running plays, Ricky Watters of the Seattle Seahawks gained 23 yards, lost 5 yards, gained 15 yards, and lost 10 yards. What was his net yardage change for the series of plays?

104. **Statistics** The temperature at noon on a June day was 82 degrees Fahrenheit (°F). It fell by 12°F in the next 4 hours. What was the temperature at 4:00 P.M.?

105. **Business and Finance** Omar's checking account was overdrawn by $72. He wrote another check for $23.50. How much was his checking account overdrawn after writing the check?

106. **Business and Finance** Angelo owed his sister $15. He later borrowed another $10. What positive or negative number represents his current financial condition?

Answers

83. −13
84. −27
85. 6
86. 9
87. 0
88. 0
89. 1
90. 1
91. 8
92. −3
93. −10
94. −8
95. 0
96. Undefined
97. Undefined
98. 0
99. −6
100. 7
101. $-\frac{1}{4}$
102. $\frac{1}{5}$
103. 23 yards
104. 70°F
105. $95.50
106. −25

Answers

107. 1,175 students

108. 3°F

109. $43.75

110. $126

111. −22°F

112. −2.4°F

113. Above and Beyond

114. Above and Beyond

107. STATISTICS A local community college had a decrease in enrollment of 750 students in the fall of 2002. In the spring of 2003, there was another decrease of 425 students. What was the total decrease in enrollment for both semesters?

108. STATISTICS At 7 A.M., the temperature was −15°F. By 1 P.M., the temperature had increased by 18°F. What was the temperature at 1 P.M.?

109. BUSINESS AND FINANCE Suppose you own 35 shares of stock. If the price increases $1.25 per share, how much money have you made?

110. BUSINESS AND FINANCE Your bank charges a flat service charge of $3.50 per month on your checking account. You have had the account for 3 years. How much have you paid in service charges?

111. STATISTICS The temperature is −6°F at 5:00 in the evening. If the temperature drops 2°F every hour, what is the temperature at 1:00 A.M.?

112. STATISTICS Suppose that the temperature outside is dropping at a constant rate. At noon, the temperature is 70°F and it drops to 58°F at 5:00 P.M. How much did the temperature change each hour?

Basic Skills | Advanced Skills | Vocational-Technical Applications | Calculator/Computer | **Above and Beyond**

113. Complete the following statement: "3 − (−7) is the same as ______ because . . . ". Write a problem that might be answered by doing this subtraction.

114. Explain the difference between the two phrases: "a number subtracted from 5" and "a number less than 5." Use algebra and English to explain the meaning of these phrases. Write other ways to express subtraction in English. Which ones are confusing?

Answers

1. $\mathbb{N}, \mathbb{Z}, \mathbb{Q}, \mathbb{R}$ **3.** $\mathbb{Z}, \mathbb{Q}, \mathbb{R}$ **5.** $\mathbb{Q}', \mathbb{R}$ **7.** $\mathbb{Q}, \mathbb{R}$ **9.** $\mathbb{N}, \mathbb{Z}, \mathbb{Q}, \mathbb{R}$
11. $\mathbb{Q}', \mathbb{R}$ **13.** $\mathbb{Q}, \mathbb{R}$ **15.** $\mathbb{Q}', \mathbb{R}$ **17.** 

19. 

21. 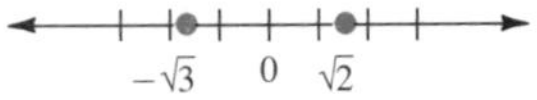

23. Infinite
25. Finite **27.** Infinite **29.** $\in$ **31.** $\notin$ **33.** $\notin$ **35.** $\in$
37. $\in$ **39.** $\notin$ **41.** $\notin$ **43.** 8 **45.** $\sqrt{3}, 3\pi$ **47.** −4, 0, 8
49. True **51.** True **53.** False **55.** False **57.** 15 **59.** $-\frac{11}{14}$
61. 6 **63.** $-\frac{17}{12}$ **65.** 2.3 **67.** −1 **69.** −3 **71.** −11
73. −5 **75.** −23 **77.** 39.1 **79.** 40 **81.** −6 **83.** −13
85. 6 **87.** 0 **89.** 1 **91.** 8 **93.** −10 **95.** 0
97. Undefined **99.** −6 **101.** $-\frac{1}{4}$ **103.** 23 yards **105.** $95.50
107. 1,175 students **109.** $43.75 **111.** −22°F **113.** Above and Beyond

1.2 Operations and Properties

< 1.2 Objectives >

1 > Represent the four arithmetic operations using variables

2 > Evaluate expressions using the order of operations

3 > Recognize and apply the properties of addition and multiplication

4 > Recognize and apply the distributive property

NOTES

François Viète (1540–1603), a French mathematician, first introduced the practice of using letters to represent known and unknown quantities.

We do not use a multiplication sign $\times$ because of the possible confusion with the letter *x*.

The symbols $+$ and $-$ first appeared in print in a book by Johann Widman (1489). The symbol $\times$ dates to a text by William Oughtred (1631).

The process of combining two elements of a set to produce a third element is called a **binary operation.** There are four basic binary operations: addition, subtraction, multiplication, and division. In algebra, we write these operations as follows:

$x + y$ is called the sum of x and y, x plus y, x more than y, or x increased by y.

$x - y$ is called the difference of x and y, x minus y, x decreased by y, or y less than x.

xy (or $x \cdot y$) is the product of x and y, or x times y.

$\frac{x}{y}$ (or $x \div y$) is the quotient of x and y, or x divided by y.

Each of the preceding is an example of an **expression.** An expression is a meaningful collection of numbers, variables, and operations.

Example 1 illustrates expressions with one more operations.

Example 1 Translating Statements Using Variables

< Objective 1 >

(a) 5 more than m is written as $m + 5$.

(b) 4 less than a is written as $a - 4$.

(c) The product of 5 and a is written as $5 \cdot a$, $(5)(a)$, or $5a$.

(d) The quotient of a plus b and 5 is written as $\frac{a + b}{5}$, or $(a + b) \div 5$.

(e) Twice the sum of x and y is written as $2(x + y)$.

The Streeter/Hutchison Series in Mathematics Intermediate Algebra

Check Yourself 1

Translate each of the following statements using symbols.

(a) x increased by 7
(b) x decreased by 8
(c) The product of 2, s, and t
(d) y more than the product of 6 and x
(e) The quotient of 3 and the difference m minus n

Algebraic expressions frequently involve more than one of the operation symbols that we have seen thus far in this section. For instance, when we are given an expression to evaluate such as

$2 + 3 \cdot 4$

we must agree on the order in which the indicated operations are to be performed. If we don't, we can end up with different results after the evaluation. For instance, if we were to add first, in this case we would have

$\underbrace{2 + 3}_{\text{Add first}} \cdot 4 = \underbrace{5 \cdot 4}_{\text{Then multiply}} = 20$

However, if we multiply first, we have

$2 + \underbrace{3 \cdot 4}_{\text{Multiply}} = \underbrace{2 + 12}_{\text{Then add}} = 14$

Because we get different answers depending on the order in which we do the operations, the language of algebra would not be clear unless we agreed on which of the methods of evaluation shown is correct.

To avoid this difficulty, we will agree that the multiplication in an expression such as

$2 + 3 \cdot 4$

should always be done *before* the addition.

We refer to our procedure as the **order of operations.** The following algorithm gives us a set of rules, defining the order in which the operations should be performed.

NOTES

The order of operations tells us that $2 + 3 \cdot 4 = 14$ and the second approach shown is the correct one.

An algorithm is a step-by-step process for solving a problem.

The most common grouping symbols are parentheses, brackets, fraction bars, absolute value signs, and radicals.

Property

Order of Operations

1. Simplify operations within the innermost grouping symbols, and work outward until all grouping symbols are removed.
2. Evaluate any expressions involving exponents.
3. Perform any multiplication and division, working from left to right.
4. Then do any addition and subtraction, again working left to right.

Example 2 Evaluating Expressions

< Objective 2 >

Evaluate each expression.

(a) $2 \cdot 4 + 3 = 8 + 3$ Multiply first.

$= 11$ Then do the addition.

NOTE

Remember:

$7^2 = 7 \cdot 7 = 49$ ← Two factors

$2^3 = 2 \cdot 2 \cdot 2 = 8$ ← Three factors

(b) $2(4 + 3) = 2 \cdot 7$ Simplify within the grouping symbol.

$= 14$ Then multiply.

(c) $2(4 + 3)^2 = 2(7)^2$ Add inside the parentheses.

$= 2 \cdot 49$ Evaluate the power.

$= 98$ Multiply.

(d) $3 + 5 \cdot 2^3 - 3 = 3 + 5 \cdot 8 - 3$ Evaluate the power.

$= 3 + 40 - 3$ Multiply.

$= 43 - 3$ Add and then subtract—from left to right.

$= 40$

Check Yourself 2

Evaluate each expression.

(a) $50 - 6 \cdot 8$ **(b)** $3(25 - 20)$
(c) $3(25 - 20)^2$ **(d)** $17 + 2 \cdot 3^3$

Graphing calculators correctly interpret the order of operations. This is demonstrated in Example 3.

Example 3 Using a Calculator to Evaluate Expressions

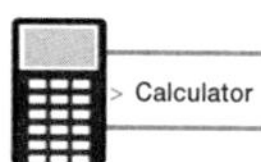

Use your graphing calculator to evaluate each expression. Round answers to the nearest tenth.

(a) $24.3 + 6.2 \cdot 3.53$

When evaluating expressions by hand, you must consider the order of operations. In this case, the multiplication must be done first, and then the addition. With a calculator, you need only enter the expression correctly. The calculator is programmed to follow the order of operations.

Entering 24.3 [+] 6.2 [×] 3.53 [ENTER]

yields the evaluation 46.186. Rounding to the nearest tenth, we have 46.2.

(b) $2.45^3 - 49 \div 8000 + 12.2 \cdot 1.3$

Graphing calculators use the carat (^) to designate powers.

Entering 2.45 [^] 3 [−] 49 [÷] 8000 [+] 12.2 [×] 1.3 [ENTER]

yields the evaluation 30.56. Rounding to the nearest tenth, we have 30.6.

Check Yourself 3

Use your graphing calculator to evaluate each expression.

(a) $67.89 - 4.7 \cdot 12.7$ **(b)** $4.3 \cdot 55.5 - 3.75^3 + 8{,}007 \div 1{,}600$

There are several properties of the two primary operations, addition and multiplication, that are very important in the study of algebra. The following table describes several of those properties for real numbers a, b, and c.

NOTE

The multiplicative inverse of a is also called the *reciprocal* of a. This is the property that allows us to *define division* by any nonzero number.

Property	Addition	Multiplication
Closure	$a + b \in \mathbb{R}$	$a \cdot b \in \mathbb{R}$
Associative	$(a + b) + c = a + (b + c)$	$(a \cdot b) \cdot c = a \cdot (b \cdot c)$
Commutative	$a + b = b + a$	$a \cdot b = b \cdot a$
Identity	$a + 0 = a$	$a \cdot 1 = a$
Inverse	$a + (-a) = 0$	$a \cdot \frac{1}{a} = 1$

Example 4 illustrates the use of the properties introduced.

Example 4 Identifying Properties of Multiplication

< Objective 3 >

State the property used to justify each statement.

(a) $2 + (3 + b) = (2 + 3) + b$
Associative property of addition

(b) $\left(\frac{2}{3}\right)\left(\frac{3}{2}\right) = 1$
Multiplicative inverse

(c) $(-3)(-4)$ is a real number
Closure property of multiplication

(d) $1(5) = 5$
Multiplicative identity

(e) $2 + (x + y) = 2 + (y + x)$
Commutative property of addition

NOTES

In part (a), the *grouping* has been changed, but the position of the terms is the same.

Because $\frac{3}{2}$ is the reciprocal of $\frac{2}{3}$, part (b) is true.

In part (e), only the position of the terms has been changed.

Check Yourself 4

State the property used to justify each statement.

(a) $(9)(-7)$ is a real number

(b) $2 + x + y = 2 + y + x$

(c) $\left(\frac{1}{3} \cdot 3\right)xy = 1 \cdot xy$

(d) $0 + x + y = x + y$

(e) $12(3ab) = (12 \cdot 3)ab$

We have one property that involves both addition and multiplication.

Property

Distributive Property

For any real numbers a, b, and c,

$a(b + c) = ab + ac$

In words, multiplication distributes *over* addition.

Example 5 illustrates the use of the distributive property.

Example 5 **Using the Distributive Property**

< Objective 4 >

Use the distributive property to simplify each expression.

(a) $4(3x + 7) = 4(3x) + 4(7)$

$= 12x + 28$

(b) $7(3x + 2y + 5) = 7(3x) + 7(2y) + 7(5)$

$= 21x + 14y + 35$

NOTE

In part **(a),** we "distribute" the multiplication by 4 over $3x$ and 7.

Simplify.

Check Yourself 5

Use the distributive property to simplify each expression.

(a) $5(4a + 5)$ **(b)** $4(2x^2 + 5x)$
(c) $6(4a + 3b + 7c)$ **(d)** $5(p + 5q)$

The fraction bar serves as a *grouping symbol.* This means that all operations in the numerator and denominator should be performed separately. Then the division is done as the last step. Example 6 illustrates this property.

Example 6 **Dividing Real Numbers**

Evaluate each expression.

(a) $\frac{(-6)(-7)}{3} = \frac{42}{3} = 14$ Multiply in the numerator, and then divide.

(b) $\frac{3 + (-12)}{3} = \frac{-9}{3} = -3$ Add in the numerator, and then divide.

(c) $\frac{-4 + (2)(-6)}{-6 - 2} = \frac{-4 + (-12)}{-6 - 2}$ Multiply in the numerator. Then add in the numerator and subtract in the denominator.

$= \frac{-16}{-8} = 2$ Divide as the last step.

NOTE

Part **(b)** can also be written as $[3 + (-12)] \div 3$

Check Yourself 6

Evaluate each expression.

(a) $\dfrac{-4 + (-8)}{6}$ (b) $\dfrac{3 - (2)(-6)}{-5}$ (c) $\dfrac{(-2)(-4) - (-6)(-5)}{(-4)(11)}$

Evaluating fractions with a calculator poses a special problem. Example 7 illustrates this problem.

Example 7 Using a Calculator to Divide

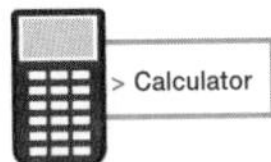

Use your graphing calculator to evaluate each fraction.

(a) $\dfrac{4}{2 - 3}$

The correct answer should be -4. To get this answer with your calculator, you must place the denominator in parentheses. The key stroke sequence will be

4 [÷] [(] 2 [−] 3 [)] [ENTER]

(b) $\dfrac{-7 - 7}{3 - 10}$

In this problem, the correct answer is 2. This can be found on your calculator by placing the numerator in parentheses and then placing the denominator in parentheses. The key stroke sequence will be

[(] [(−)] 7 [−] 7 [)] [÷] [(] 3 [−] 10 [)] [ENTER]

When evaluating a fraction with a calculator, it is safest to use parentheses in both the numerator and the denominator.

Check Yourself 7

Evaluate using your calculator.

(a) $\dfrac{-8}{5 - 7}$ (b) $\dfrac{-3 - 2}{-13 + 23}$

Check Yourself ANSWERS

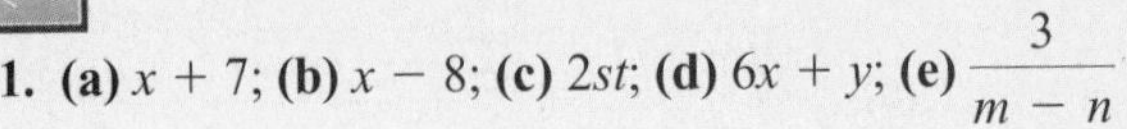

1. (a) $x + 7$; **(b)** $x - 8$; **(c)** $2st$; **(d)** $6x + y$; **(e)** $\dfrac{3}{m - n}$
2. (a) 2; **(b)** 15; **(c)** 75; **(d)** 71 **3. (a)** 8.2; **(b)** 190.92
4. (a) Closure property of multiplication; **(b)** commutative property of addition; **(c)** multiplicative inverse; **(d)** additive identity; **(e)** associative property of multiplication **5. (a)** $20a + 25$; **(b)** $8x^2 + 20x$; **(c)** $24a + 18b + 42c$; **(d)** $5p + 25q$ **6. (a)** -2; **(b)** -3; **(c)** $\dfrac{1}{2}$ **7. (a)** 4; **(b)** -0.5

Reading Your Text

The following fill-in-the-blank exercises are designed to ensure that you understand some of the key vocabulary used in this section.

SECTION 1.2

(a) The process of combining two elements of a set to produce a third element is called a ____________ operation.

(b) $\frac{x}{y}$ (or $x \div y$) is called the ____________ of x and y.

(c) Following the order of operations, we perform any multiplication and division working from ____________ to ____________.

(d) The distributive property distributes multiplication over ____________.

1.2 exercises

Basic Skills | Advanced Skills | Vocational-Technical Applications | Calculator/Computer | Above and Beyond

MathZone

Boost your grade at mathzone.com!
> Practice Problems
> NetTutor
> Self-Tests
> e-Professors
> Videos

Name ____________

Section ________ Date ________

Answers

1.	$10 + x$	2.	$x + 5$
3.	$p + 12$	4.	$m + 25$
5.	$n + 1$	6.	$s + 3$
7.	$m - 14$	8.	$b - 5$
9.	$x - 1$	10.	$25 - a$
11.	mn	12.	$\frac{b}{2}$
13.	$\frac{s}{4}$	14.	$7b$
15.	$2(c - d)$	16.	$2(a + b)$
17.	$rs - 4$	18.	$2w + 11$
19.	$\frac{c + 4}{d}$	20.	$\frac{m - 2}{n}$
21.	29	22.	22
23.	42	24.	15
25.	96	26.	144
27.	56	28.	44

< Objective 1 >

Translate each of the following statements, using symbols.

1. The sum of 10 and x

2. x plus 5

3. 12 more than p

4. The sum of m and 25

5. n increased by 1

6. s increased by 3

7. m minus 14

8. 5 less than b

9. Subtract 1 from x.

10. 25 minus a

11. The product of m and n

12. The quotient of b and 2

13. s divided by 4

14. 7 times b

15. 2 times the difference of c and d

16. Twice the sum of a and b

17. 4 less than the product of r and s

18. 11 more than 2 times w

19. The sum of c and 4, divided by d

20. The difference of m and 2, divided by n

< Objective 2 >

Apply the order-of-operations algorithm to evaluate the following expressions.

21. $5 + 4 \cdot 6$

22. $7 + 5 \cdot 3$

23. $7(8 - 2)$

24. $3(12 - 7)$

25. $6(8 - 4)^2$

26. $4(12 - 6)^2$

27. $(4 + 3)(5 + 3)$

28. $(5 + 6)(3 + 1)$

29. $4 + 3 \cdot 5 + 2$

30. $5 + 6 \cdot 2 + 1$

31. $(7 + 5)(7 - 5)$

32. $(12 + 3)(12 - 3)$

33. $7 + 5 \cdot 7 - 5$

34. $11 + 2 \cdot 11 - 3$

35. $9^2 - 5^2$

36. $12^2 - 3^2$

37. $(9 - 5)^2$

38. $(11 - 2)^2$

39. $16 \div 2^3 \cdot 2 - 3 + 11$

40. $10 - 3 \cdot 8 \div 4 + 3$

41. $-12 - 8 \div 4$

42. $48 \div 8 - 14 \div 2$

43. $(2^3 + 3)^2 + 12 \div 3 \cdot 2$

44. $(4 \cdot 3 + 13) \div 5 \cdot 3^2$

45. $3[35 - 3(6 - 2)^2]$

46. $3[14 - 2(5 - 3)^3]$

47. $\dfrac{5 - 15}{2 + 3}$

48. $\dfrac{4 - (-8)}{2 - 5}$

49. $\dfrac{-6 + 18}{-2 - 4}$

50. $\dfrac{-4 - 21}{3 - 8}$

51. $\dfrac{(5)(-12)}{(-3)(5)}$

52. $\dfrac{(-8)(-3)}{(2)(-4)}$

< Objective 3 >

In each exercise, apply the commutative and associative properties to rewrite the expression. Then simplify the result.

53. $8 + (6 + a)$

54. $10 + (2 + y)$

55. $(2x + 5) + 12$

56. $(2w + 2) + 10$

57. $8 + (p + 6)$

58. $6 + (2m + 12)$

Answers

29. 21
30. 18
31. 24
32. 135
33. 37
34. 30
35. 56
36. 135
37. 16
38. 81
39. 12
40. 7

41. −14	42. −1
43. 129	44. 45
45. −39	46. −6
47. −2	48. −4
49. −2	50. 5
51. 4	52. −3
53. $14 + a$	54. $12 + y$
55. $2x + 17$	56. $2w + 12$
57. $p + 14$	58. $2m + 18$

Answers

59. a
60. p
61. $16x$
62. $12b$
63. w
64. p
65. 1
66. b
67. $10m + 15$
68. $8p + 10$
69. $4a^2 + 16a$
70. $6b^2 + 30b$
71. $2a + 5$
72. $2y + 5$
73. $15a + 10b + 20$
74. $18m + 36n + 42$
75. $2a + 3b + c$
76. $2x + 4y + 6z$
77. Commutative property of addition
78. Closure property of multiplication
79. Distributive property
80. Associative property of multiplication
81. Associative property of addition
82. Commutative property of addition
83. Commutative property of addition
84. Associative property of addition
85. Distributive property
86. Multiplicative inverse

59. $(8 + a) + (-8)$

60. $-2 + (p + 2)$

61. $2(8x)$

62. $6(2b)$

63. $\frac{1}{4}(4w)$

64. $6p\left(\frac{1}{6}\right)$

65. $\left(\frac{2}{7}\right)\left(\frac{7}{2}\right)\left(\frac{1}{m}\right)m$

66. $\left(\frac{3}{4}\right)(b)\left(\frac{4}{3}\right)$

< Objective 4 >

In each exercise apply the distributive property to rewrite the expression. Then simplify the result when possible.

67. $5(2m + 3)$

68. $2(4p + 5)$

69. $4a(a + 4)$

70. $6b(b + 5)$

71. $\frac{1}{2}(4a + 10)$

72. $\frac{1}{3}(6y + 15)$

73. $5(3a + 2b + 4)$

74. $6(3m + 6n + 7)$

75. $\frac{1}{2}(4a + 6b + 2c)$ > Videos

76. $\frac{2}{3}(3x + 6y + 9z)$

< Objectives 3, 4 >

State the property used to justify the following statements.

77. $2 + 8 = 8 + 2$

78. $3 \cdot 6$ is a real number

79. $2(y + 5) = 2y + 10$

80. $6(2x) = (6 \cdot 2)x$

81. $4 + (5 + 6) = (4 + 5) + 6$

82. $4 + (5 + 6) = (5 + 6) + 4$

83. $18b + 6 + 12b = 18b + 12b + 6$

84. $18b + (12b + 6) = (18b + 12b) + 6$

85. $(18b + 12b) + 6 = (18 + 12)b + 6$

86. $\left(\frac{2}{7}\right)\left(\frac{7}{2}\right) = 1$

87. $\frac{3}{5} + \left(-\frac{3}{5}\right) = 0$

88. $(y + 3)(y + 2) = y(y + 2) + 3(y + 2)$

Basic Skills | **Advanced Skills** | Vocational-Technical Applications | Calculator/Computer | Above and Beyond

89. **Business and Finance** A local baker observed that the sales in her store in May were twice the sales in April. She also observed that the sales in June were three-fourths the sales in April. Use variables to describe the sales of the bakery in each of the 3 months.

> Videos

90. **Business and Finance** Computer Corner noted that the sales of computers in August were three-fourths of the sales of computers in July. The sales of computers in September were five-sixths of the sales of computers in July. Use variables to describe the number of computers sold in each of the 3 months.

Basic Skills | Advanced Skills | Vocational-Technical Applications | **Calculator/Computer** | Above and Beyond

Evaluate using your calculator. Round your answer to the nearest tenth.

91. $(1.2)^3 \div 2.0736 \cdot 2.4 + 1.6935 - 2.4896$

92. $(5.21 \cdot 3.14 - 6.2154) \div 5.12 - 0.45625$

Basic Skills | Advanced Skills | Vocational-Technical Applications | Calculator/Computer | **Above and Beyond**

Determine whether each statement is **true** *or* **false.** *If it is false, rewrite the right side of the equation to make it a true statement.*

93. $3 + 5(y + 4) = 3 + 5y + 4$

94. $10 + 5x + 5 = 5(2 + x + 5)$

95. $7b + 8b = 15b$

96. $3a + (10 + 2a) = (3a + 2a) + 10$

97. $4(3w + 3) = 12w + 7$

98. $\frac{1}{5}y + \frac{2}{5}y = \frac{3}{10}y$

99. $3m + 4m + 1 = 7m + 1$

100. $3b + 2b + 5 = 10b$

Answers

87. Additive inverse

88. Distributive property

89. April: x; May: $2x$; June: $\frac{3}{4}x$

90. July: x; August: $\frac{3}{4}x$; September: $\frac{5}{6}x$

91. 1.2

92. 1.5

93. False; $3 + 5y + 20$

94. False; $5(2 + x + 1)$

95. True

96. True

97. False; $12w + 12$

98. False; $\frac{3}{5}y$

99. True

100. False; $5b + 5$

Answers

101. True

102. False; 0

103. False; 8n

104. False; 4a

105. Above and Beyond

106. Above and Beyond

101. $6y + (-6)y = 0$

102. $4b + (-4b) = b$

103. $2n + 6n = 8n^2$

104. $3a + a = 3a^2$

105. Create an example to show that subtraction of signed numbers is *not* commutative.

106. Create an example to show that division of signed numbers is *not* associative.

Answers

1. $10 + x$ **3.** $p + 12$ **5.** $n + 1$ **7.** $m - 14$ **9.** $x - 1$
11. mn **13.** $\frac{s}{4}$ **15.** $2(c - d)$ **17.** $rs - 4$ **19.** $\frac{c+4}{d}$
21. 29 **23.** 42 **25.** 96 **27.** 56 **29.** 21 **31.** 24 **33.** 37
35. 56 **37.** 16 **39.** 12 **41.** -14 **43.** 129 **45.** -39
47. -2 **49.** -2 **51.** 4 **53.** $14 + a$ **55.** $2x + 17$
57. $p + 14$ **59.** a **61.** $16x$ **63.** w **65.** 1 **67.** $10m + 15$
69. $4a^2 + 16a$ **71.** $2a + 5$ **73.** $15a + 10b + 20$ **75.** $2a + 3b + c$
77. Commutative property of addition **79.** Distributive property
81. Associative property of addition **83.** Commutative property of addition
85. Distributive property **87.** Additive inverse
89. April: x; May: $2x$; June: $\frac{3}{4}x$ **91.** 1.2 **93.** False; $3 + 5y + 20$
95. True **97.** False; $12w + 12$ **99.** True **101.** True
103. False; $8n$ **105.** Above and Beyond

1.3 Inequalities and Absolute Value

< 1.3 Objectives >

1 > Use the notation of inequalities

2 > Graph inequalities

3 > Use the absolute value notation

Let's now consider two relations on the set of real numbers. These are the relations of order or inequality known as **less than** or **greater than.**

The set of real numbers is an ordered set. Given any two numbers, we can determine whether one number is less than, equal to, or greater than the other. Let's see how this is expressed symbolically.

We use the **inequality symbol** $<$ to represent "less than," and we write

$a < b$ This is read "a is less than b."

to indicate that a is less than b. The number line gives us a clear picture of the meaning of this statement. The point corresponding to a must lie *to the left* of the point corresponding to b.

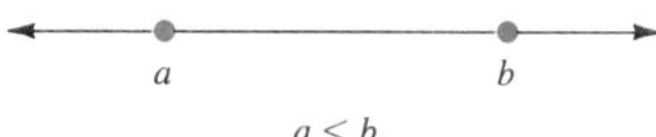

Similarly, the inequality symbol $>$ represents "greater than," and the statement

$a > b$ This is read "a is greater than b."

indicates that a is greater than b and means that the point corresponding to a on the number line lies *to the right* of the point corresponding to b.

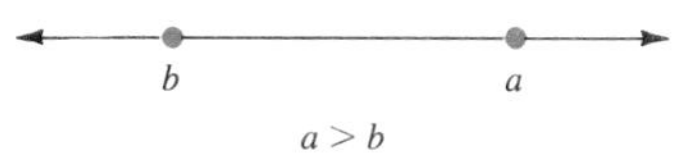

NOTE

$a > b$

and

$b < a$

are equivalent statements. The symbol "points to" the smaller quantity.

Example 1 illustrates the use of the inequality symbols.

Example 1 Establishing the Direction of Inequalities

< Objective 1 >

Complete each statement by inserting the symbol $<$ or $>$ between the given numbers.

(a) 2 ______ 8

$2 < 8$

(b) 2.786 ______ 2.78

$2.786 > 2.78$

(c) -23 ______ -5

$-23 < -5$

(d) $\sqrt{2}$ ______ 1.4

$\sqrt{2} > 1.4$ Recall that 1.414 is an approximation for $\sqrt{2}$.

Check Yourself 1

Insert an inequality symbol that makes each of the following a true statement.

(a) 5 ______ −2 **(b)** 3.14 ______ π

(c) −10 ______ −15 **(d)** $\sqrt{15}$ ______ 4

(e) 9.78 ______ 9.87 **(f)** −1.3 ______ $-\frac{4}{3}$

Suppose we are given an inequality of the form

$x > -1$

The **solution** for an inequality (similar as for an equation) is the set of all values for the variable that makes the inequality a true statement. A convenient way to picture that solution set is by a graph on a number line. Example 2 illustrates.

Example 2 Graphing Inequalities

< Objective 2 >

NOTE

The parenthesis at 4 means that the point corresponding to 4 is *not included* in the graph. Such a graph is called an *open half line.*

Graph the inequality.

$x < 4$

We want to include all real numbers less than 4, that is, *to the left* of 4 on the number line.

Check Yourself 2

Graph the inequalities.

(a) $x < 5$ **(b)** $x > -3$

NOTES

This combines the symbols < and = and means that either $a < b$ or $a = b$.

Here either $a > b$ or $a = b$.

Two other symbols, ≤ and ≥, are also used in writing inequalities. In each case they combine the inequality symbols for less than or greater than with the symbol for equality. The following shows the use of these new symbols. The statement

$a \leq b$

is read "*a* is less than or equal to *b*." Similarly,

$a \geq b$

is read "*a* is greater than or equal to *b*." We consider the graph of inequalities involving these symbols in Example 3.

Example 3 Graphing Inequalities

NOTE

Here the bracket at $\frac{7}{2}$ means that the point corresponding to $\frac{7}{2}$ *is included* in the graph. Such a graph is called a *closed half line.*

Graph the inequality.

$$x \geq \frac{7}{2}$$

Here we want all numbers to the right of $\frac{7}{2}$ *and including* $\frac{7}{2}$.

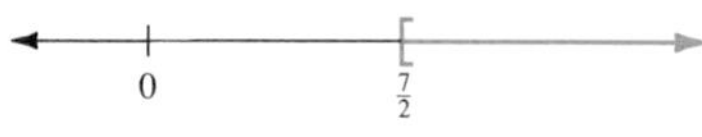

Check Yourself 3

Graph the inequalities.

(a) $x \leq 7$ **(b)** $x \geq -\frac{4}{3}$

NOTES

The open circle is used to indicate the *open* half line, extending to the right, and *not including* 3.

The closed circle is used to indicate the *closed* half line, extending to the left, and *including* −2.

The word *and* is implied in any double-inequality statement.

Note: You may very well encounter a different notation for indicating the graphs of inequalities. This involves the use of circles to represent open and closed half lines. For example, the graph of $x > 3$ can be drawn as

and the graph of $x \leq -2$ as

Our subsequent work with inequalities in Chapters 2, 4, and 8 involves the use of a **double-inequality** statement such as

$$-3 < x < 4$$

This statement combines the two inequalities

$$x > -3 \qquad and \qquad x < 4$$

That is why it is sometimes called a **compound inequality.**

In Example 4 we look at the graphs of inequalities that have this form.

Example 4 Graphing Compound Inequalities

NOTE

The parentheses indicate that the endpoints, −3 and 4, are *not included* in the graph. This is called an *open interval.*

Graph the inequality.

$$-3 < x < 4$$

For the solution set of this double inequality, we want all points that lie to the right of -3 $(x > -3)$ and to the left of 4 $(x < 4)$. This means that we should include all points that lie *between* -3 and 4.

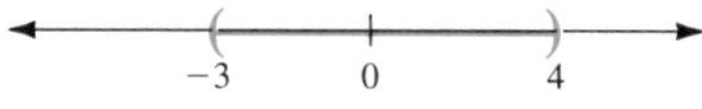

Check Yourself 4

Graph the inequalities.

(a) $-1 < x < 6$ **(b)** $-2 \le x < 8$

Once again, we refer to the number line to introduce our final topic of this section. If we locate the number 4 and its additive inverse, -4, on the number line, we see that both numbers correspond to points that are the same distance (4 units) from the origin.

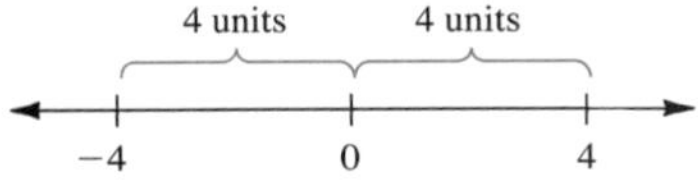

NOTE

If a is *negative,* then its additive inverse, $-a$, must be *positive* and we want a *positive* absolute value. Say $a = -2$; then $|-2| = -(-2) = 2$

When we are concerned not with the direction (left or right) of a number from the origin, but only with the distance from the origin, we refer to that number's absolute value.

An **absolute value** is the distance (on the number line) between the point named by that real number and the origin. We indicate the absolute value of a number with vertical bars.

In general, we can define the absolute value of any real number a as

$$|a| = \begin{cases} a & \text{if } a \text{ is positive} \\ 0 & \text{if } a \text{ is zero} \\ -a & \text{if } a \text{ is negative} \end{cases}$$

The use of the absolute value notation is illustrated in Example 5.

Example 5 Evaluating Absolute Value Expressions

< Objective 3 >

NOTE

$|-5|$ is 5, so $-|-5|$ must be -5.

Evaluate each of the following expressions.

(a) $|32| = 32$ **(b)** $|-2.5| = 2.5$

(c) $|\sqrt{2}| = \sqrt{2}$ **(d)** $|-\sqrt{2}| = \sqrt{2}$

(e) $-|-5| = -5$ **(f)** $|-3| + |-7| = 3 + 7 = 10$

Check Yourself 5

Evaluate each of the following expressions.

(a) $|121|$ **(b)** $|-3.4|$ **(c)** $|\sqrt{3}|$

(d) $|-\sqrt{5}|$ **(e)** $-|-8|$ **(f)** $|-9| + |-2|$

Check Yourself ANSWERS

1. **(a)** $5 > -2$; **(b)** $3.14 < \pi$; **(c)** $-10 > -15$; **(d)** $\sqrt{15} < 4$; **(e)** $9.78 < 9.87$; **(f)** $-1.3 > -\frac{4}{3}$

2. **(a)** $x < 5$

(b) $x > -3$

3. **(a)** $x \le 7$ **(b)** $x \ge -\frac{4}{3}$

4. **(a)** $-1 < x < 6$

(b) $-2 \le x < 8$

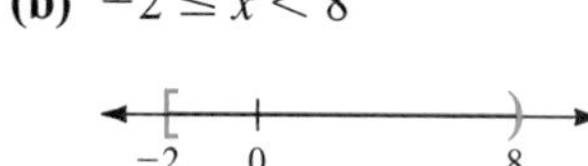

(This is a *half open* interval.)

5. **(a)** 121; **(b)** 3.4; **(c)** $\sqrt{3}$; **(d)** $\sqrt{5}$; **(e)** -8; **(f)** 11

Reading Your Text

The following fill-in-the-blank exercises are designed to ensure that you understand some of the key vocabulary used in this section.

SECTION 1.3

(a) The inequality symbol $<$ represents ______________.

(b) The set values for the variable that make the inequality a ______________ statement is the solution for the inequality.

(c) A statement that combines two inequalities is called a ______________ inequality.

(d) The distance on the number line between the point named by a real number and the origin is called its ______________.

1.3 exercises

Basic Skills | Advanced Skills | Vocational-Technical Applications | Calculator/Computer | Above and Beyond

MathZone

Boost your grade at mathzone.com!
> Practice Problems
> NetTutor
> Self-Tests
> e-Professors
> Videos

Name ______

Section ______ Date ______

< Objective 1 >

Insert an inequality symbol or an equal sign to make each of the following a true statement.

1. 8 ______ 3

2. -3 ______ 7

3. -6 ______ -4

4. -2 ______ -3

5. -2.6 ______ -3.8

6. -7.40 ______ -7.4

7. $-\frac{5}{3}$ ______ $-\frac{5}{4}$

8. -1.2 ______ $-\frac{4}{3}$

9. $\sqrt{2}$ ______ 1.4

10. $-\sqrt{3}$ ______ -1.4

11. 1.75 ______ $\frac{7}{4}$

12. $\frac{8}{3}$ ______ 2.33

13. $|-3|$ ______ -3

14. $|-3|$ ______ $|-1|$

15. $-|5|$ ______ $|-5|$

16. $|4|$ ______ $-|-4|$

Write each of the following inequalities in words.

17. $y \geq 2$

18. $x > 3$

19. $m < -3$

20. $n \leq 5$

21. $a \geq b$

22. $r < s$

23. $b > 0$

24. $y \leq 0$

25. $-3 < p < 7$

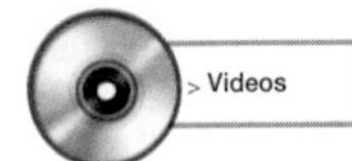

26. $-4 \leq y \leq -2$

Answers

1. >
2. <
3. <
4. >
5. >
6. =
7. <
8. >
9. >
10. <
11. =
12. >
13. >
14. >
15. <
16. >
17. *y* is greater than or equal to 2.
18. *x* is greater than 3.
19. *m* is less than −3.
20. *n* is less than or equal to 5.
21. *a* is greater than or equal to *b*.
22. *r* is less than *s*.
23. *b* is greater than 0.
24. *y* is less than or equal to 0.
25. −3 is less than *p* and *p* is less than 7.
26. −4 is less than or equal to *y* and *y* is less than or equal to −2.

< Objective 2 >

Graph the inequalities. Assume x represents a real number.

27. $x < 4$

28. $x \geq 5$

29. $x > -4$

30. $x \leq -2$

31. $-4 \geq x$

> Videos

32. $4 < x$

33. $x \geq 4$

34. $0 \geq x$

35. $1 < x < 2$

36. $-3 \leq x \leq 5$

37. $-4 < x \leq -1$

38. $2 \leq x < 5$

Rewrite each of the following statements, using inequality symbols. Then graph the inequality. Assume that x represents a real number.

39. x is less than 3

40. x is more than -2

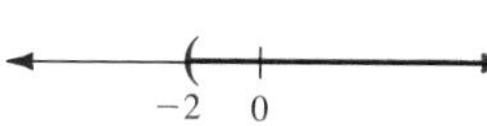

41. x is at least -1

> Videos

42. x is no more than 5

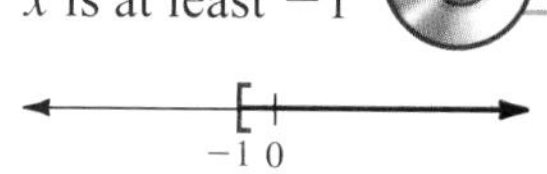

43. x is greater than 4

44. x is at least 2

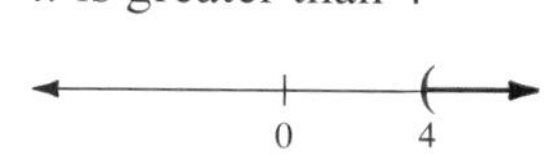

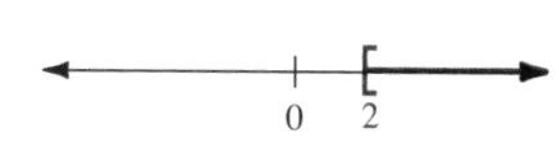

Answers

27. See exercise
28. See exercise
29. See exercise
30. See exercise
31. See exercise
32. See exercise
33. See exercise
34. See exercise
35. See exercise
36. See exercise
37. See exercise
38. See exercise
39. $x < 3$
40. $x > -2$
41. $x \geq -1$
42. $x \leq 5$
43. $x > 4$
44. $x \geq 2$

45. x is no more than -2

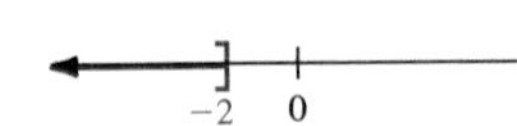

46. x is not less than -2

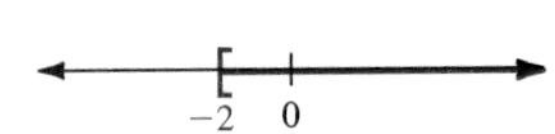

47. 2 is less than x and x is less than 4

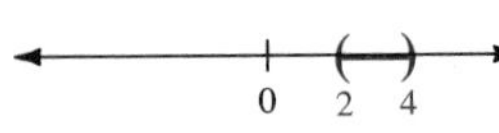

48. -4 is less than or equal to x and x is less than -2

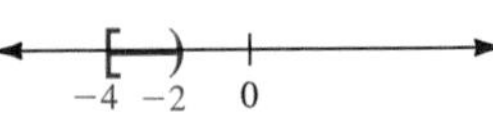

< Objective 3 >

Write each of the following expressions without the absolute value symbol.

49. $|5|$

50. $|-5|$

51. $|-2.5|$

52. $|4.5|$

53. $\left|\frac{5}{6}\right|$

54. $-\left|\frac{7}{8}\right|$

55. $-|1.2|$

56. $|-4.5|$

57. $-|-3|$ > Videos

58. $-|-6|$

59. $-\left|\frac{2}{3}\right|$

60. $\left|-\frac{7}{2}\right|$

61. $|-3| + |-5|$

62. $|-2| + |-6|$

63. $-(|3| + |-4|)$

64. $-(|-4| + |-8|)$

Basic Skills | Advanced Skills | Vocational-Technical Applications | Calculator/Computer | **Above and Beyond**

Label each statement as **true** *or* **false.** *If it is false, explain.*

65. $|-2| \geq 2$

66. $|0| = 0$

67. $|-12| = |12|$

68. $|2 - 3| > |0 - 1|$

69. $|-x| = x$ *Hint:* For this statement to be true, it must be true for all values of the variable.

70. $-|a| = -a$

Answers

45. $x \leq -2$
46. $x \geq -2$
47. $2 < x < 4$
48. $-4 \leq x < -2$
49. 5
50. 5
51. 2.5
52. 4.5
53. $\frac{5}{6}$
54. $-\frac{7}{8}$
55. -1.2
56. 4.5
57. -3
58. -6
59. $-\frac{2}{3}$
60. $\frac{7}{2}$
61. 8
62. 8
63. -7
64. -12
65. True
66. True
67. True
68. False; both sides are equal to 1.
69. False; it would not be true for negative values of x, for example, $|-(-1)| \neq -1$.
70. False; this is not true for negative values of a, for example, $-|(-1)| \neq -(-1)$.

71. The absolute value of any real number is positive or zero.

72. Some real numbers have no absolute value.

73. The absolute value of any real number is equal to the absolute value of its additive inverse.

74. There is only one real number that is equal to its own absolute value.

75. Do you think that the following statement is true?

$|a + b| = |a| + |b|$ for all numbers a and b

When we don't know whether such a statement is true, we refer to the statement as a **conjecture.** We may "test" the conjecture by substituting specific numbers for the variables.

Test the conjecture using two positive numbers for a and b.

Test again using a positive number for a and 0 for b.

Test again using two negative numbers.

Now try using one positive number and one negative number.

Summarize your results in a rule that you think is true.

In exercises 76 *to* 80, *test the given conjecture, as you did in exercise* 75.

76. Do you think that the following statement is true?

$|a - b| = |a| - |b|$ for all numbers a and b

77. Do you think that the following statement is true?

$|a \cdot b| = |a| \cdot |b|$ for all numbers a and b

78. Do you think that the following statement is true?

$|a - b| = |b - a|$ for all numbers a and b

79. Do you think that the following statement is true?

$\left|\frac{a}{b}\right| = \frac{|a|}{|b|}$ for all numbers a and b

80. Do you think that the following statement is true?

$|a| = |-a|$ for any number a

81. If a represents a positive number and b represents a negative number, determine whether the given expression is positive or negative.

(a) $|b| + a$ **(b)** $b + (-a)$ **(c)** $(-b) + a$ **(d)** $-b + |-a|$

Answers

71. True

72. False; every real number has an absolute value.

73. True

74. False; every nonnegative real number is equal to its absolute value.

75. Above and Beyond

76. Above and Beyond

77. Above and Beyond

78. Above and Beyond

79. Above and Beyond

80. Above and Beyond

81. (a) Positive; (b) negative; (c) positive; (d) positive

Answers

1. > **3.** < **5.** > **7.** < **9.** > **11.** = **13.** >
15. < **17.** y is greater than or equal to 2. **19.** m is less than -3.
21. a is greater than or equal to b. **23.** b is greater than 0.
25. -3 is less than p and p is less than 7.

27. 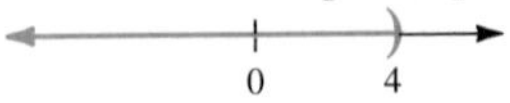

$x < 4$

29. 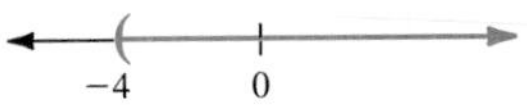

$x > -4$

31. 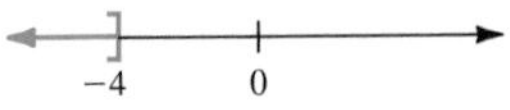

$-4 \geq x$

33. 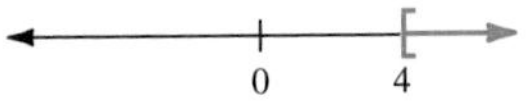

$x \geq 4$

35. 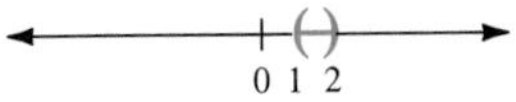

$1 < x < 2$

37. 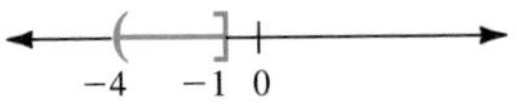

$-4 < x \leq -1$

39. 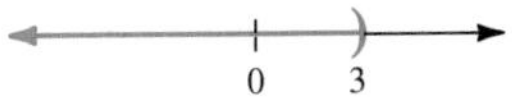

$x < 3$

41. 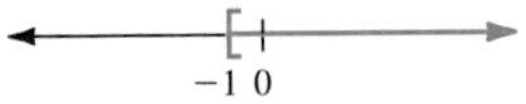

$x \geq -1$

43. 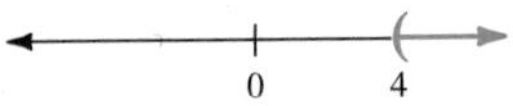

$x > 4$

45. 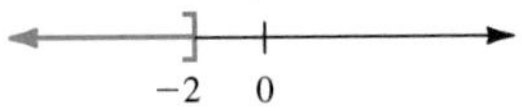

$x \leq -2$

47. 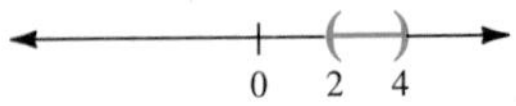

$2 < x < 4$

49. 5 **51.** 2.5 **53.** $\frac{5}{6}$
55. -1.2 **57.** -3 **59.** $-\frac{2}{3}$ **61.** 8 **63.** -7 **65.** True
67. True
69. False; it would not be true for negative values of x, for example, $|-(-1)| \neq -1$.
71. True **73.** True **75.** Above and Beyond **77.** Above and Beyond
79. Above and Beyond **81.** **(a)** Positive; **(b)** negative; **(c)** positive; **(d)** positive

1.4 Algebraic Expressions

< 1.4 Objectives >

1 > Evaluate algebraic expressions given values for the variables

2 > Identify terms and like terms

3 > Combine like terms

Previously we defined an expression as a meaningful collection of numbers, variables, and operations (see Section 1.2).

In applying algebra to problem solving, you will often want to find the value of an algebraic expression given certain values for the variables in the expression.

To evaluate an algebraic expression, replace each variable by the given number value for that variable. Then do the necessary arithmetic operations following the rules for the order of operations (see Section 1.2).

Example 1 Evaluating Algebraic Expressions

< Objective 1 >

Evaluate the following expressions if $a = 2$, $b = 3$, $c = 4$, and $d = 5$.

(a) $5a + 7b = 5 \cdot 2 + 7 \cdot 3$ Multiply first.

$= 10 + 21 = 31$ Then add.

> CAUTION

Part (b) is different from

$(3c)^2 = (3 \cdot 4)^2$

$= 12^2 = 144$

(b) $3c^2 = 3 \cdot 4^2$ Evaluate the power.

$= 3 \cdot 16 = 48$ Then multiply.

(c) $7(c + d) = 7(4 + 5)$ Add inside the parentheses.

$= 7 \cdot 9 = 63$

(d) $5a^4 - 2d^2 = 5 \cdot 2^4 - 2 \cdot 5^2$ Evaluate the powers.

$= 5 \cdot 16 - 2 \cdot 25$ Multiply.

$= 80 - 50 = 30$ Subtract.

Check Yourself 1

If $x = 3$, $y = 2$, $z = 4$, and $w = 5$, evaluate the expressions.

(a) $4x^2 + 2$ **(b)** $5(z + w)$ **(c)** $7(z^2 - y^2)$

We will follow the same steps we used in Example 1 to evaluate algebraic expressions when a fraction bar is used.

Example 2 Evaluating Algebraic Expressions

If $p = 2$, $q = 3$, and $r = 4$, evaluate:

(a) $\dfrac{8p}{r}$

RECALL

The fraction bar is a grouping symbol, like parentheses. Work first in the numerator and then in the denominator, then divide.

Replace p with 2 and r with 4.

$$\frac{8p}{r} = \frac{8 \cdot 2}{4} = \frac{16}{4} = 4$$

Divide as the last step.

(b) $\dfrac{7q + r}{p + q} = \dfrac{7 \cdot 3 + 4}{2 + 3}$

Evaluate the top and bottom separately.

$$= \frac{21 + 4}{2 + 3} = \frac{25}{5} = 5$$

Check Yourself 2

Evaluate each expression if $c = 5$, $d = 8$, and $e = 3$.

(a) $\dfrac{6c}{e}$ **(b)** $\dfrac{4d + e}{c}$ **(c)** $\dfrac{10d - e}{d + e}$

In Examples 3 to 5 the variables sometimes represent negative values.

Example 3 Evaluating Expressions

RECALL

The rules for the order of operations tell us here to multiply first, and then add.

Evaluate $5a + 4b$ if $a = -2$ and $b = 3$.

Replace a with -2 and b with 3.

$$\begin{aligned} 5a + 4b &= 5(-2) + 4(3) \\ &= -10 + 12 \\ &= 2 \end{aligned}$$

Check Yourself 3

Evaluate $3x + 5y$ if $x = -2$ and $y = -5$.

Example 4 Evaluating Expressions

Evaluate the expressions if $a = -4$, $b = 2$, $c = -5$, and $d = 6$.

This becomes $-(-20)$, or $+20$.

(a) $$\begin{aligned} 7a - 4c &= 7(-4) - 4(-5) \\ &= -28 + 20 \\ &= -8 \end{aligned}$$

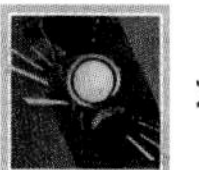

> CAUTION

When a squared variable is replaced by a negative number, square the negative.

$(-5)^2 = (-5)(-5) = 25$

The exponent applies to -5!

$-5^2 = -(5 \cdot 5) = -25$

The exponent applies only to 5!

(b) $7c^2 = 7(-5)^2 = 7 \cdot 25$
$= 175$

Evaluate the power first, and then multiply by 7.

(c) $b^2 - 4ac = 2^2 - 4(-4)(-5)$
$= 4 - 4(-4)(-5)$
$= 4 - 80$
$= -76$

Add inside the parentheses first.

(d) $b(a + d) = 2(-4 + 6)$
$= 2(2)$
$= 4$

Check Yourself 4

Evaluate if $p = -4$, $q = 3$, and $r = -2$.

(a) $5p - 3r$ **(b)** $2p^2 + q$ **(c)** $p(q + r)$
(d) $-q^2$ **(e)** $(-q)^2$

If an expression involves a fraction, remember that the fraction bar is a grouping symbol.

Example 5 Evaluating Expressions

Evaluate the expressions if $x = 4$, $y = -5$, $z = 2$, and $w = -3$.

(a) $\dfrac{z - 2y}{x} = \dfrac{2 - 2(-5)}{4} = \dfrac{2 + 10}{4}$
$= \dfrac{12}{4} = 3$

(b) $\dfrac{3x - w}{2x + w} = \dfrac{3(4) - (-3)}{2(4) + (-3)} = \dfrac{12 + 3}{8 + (-3)}$
$= \dfrac{15}{5} = 3$

Check Yourself 5

Evaluate if $m = -6$, $n = 4$, and $p = -3$.

(a) $\dfrac{m + 3n}{p}$ **(b)** $\dfrac{4m + n}{m + 4n}$

Example 6 shows how a graphing calculator can be used to evaluate algebraic expressions.

Example 6 Using a Calculator to Evaluate Expressions

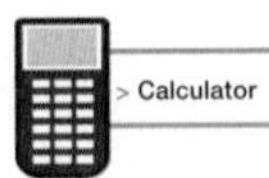

Use a graphing calculator to evaluate the expression if $x = 2$, $y = 6$, and $z = 2$.

$$\frac{7x - y}{3z - x} = \frac{7 \cdot 2 - 6}{3 \cdot 2 - 2}$$

Use these keystrokes:

[(] 7 [×] 2 [−] 6 [)] [÷] [(] 3 [×] 2 − 2 [)] [ENTER]

The display will read 2.

NOTE

As an alternative, you could store the values in the variable locations

2 [STO→] [ALPHA] *x* [ENTER]

6 [STO→] [ALPHA] *y* [ENTER]

2 [STO→] [ALPHA] *z* [ENTER]

Then enter

$(7x - y) \div (3z - x)$

Check Yourself 6

Use a graphing calculator to evaluate the expressions if $x = 2$, $y = 6$, and $z = 5$.

(a) $\frac{2x + y}{z}$ **(b)** $\frac{4y - 2z}{x}$

In algebraic expressions, the addition and subtraction signs break the expressions into smaller parts called *terms.*

Definition

Term A **term** is a number, or the product of a number and one or more variables, raised to a whole number power.

In an expression, each sign (+ or −) is a part of the term that follows the sign.

Example 7 Identifying Terms

< Objective 2 >

(a) $5x^2$ has one term.

(b) $\underbrace{3a}_{\text{Term}} + \underbrace{2b}_{\text{Term}}$ has two terms: $3a$ and $2b$.

(c) $\underbrace{4x^3}_{\text{Term}} + \underbrace{(-2y)}_{\text{Term}} + \underbrace{1}_{\text{Term}}$ has three terms: $4x^3$, $-2y$, and 1.

NOTE

This is usually written as $4x^3 - 2y + 1$.

Check Yourself 7

List the terms of each expression.

(a) $2b^4$ **(b)** $5m + 3n$ **(c)** $2s^2 - 3t - 6$

Note that a term in an expression may have any number of factors. For instance, $5xy$ is a term. It has factors of 5, x, and y. The number factor of a term is called the **numerical coefficient.** So for the term $5xy$, the numerical coefficient is 5.

Example 8 Identifying the Numerical Coefficient

(a) $4a$ has the numerical coefficient 4.

(b) $6a^3b^4c^2$ has the numerical coefficient 6.

(c) $-7m^2n^3$ has the numerical coefficient -7.

(d) Because $1 \cdot x = x$, the numerical coefficient of x is understood to be 1.

Check Yourself 8

Give the numerical coefficient for each of the terms.

(a) $8a^2b$ **(b)** $-5m^3n^4$ **(c)** y

If terms contain exactly the *same letters* (or variables) raised to the *same powers,* they are called **like terms.**

Example 9 Identifying Like Terms

(a) The following are like terms.

$6a$ and $7a$

$5b^2$ and b^2

$10x^2y^3z$ and $-6x^2y^3z$

$-3m^2$ and m^2

Each pair of terms has the same letters, with each letter raised to the same power—the numerical coefficients can be any number.

(b) The following are *not* like terms.

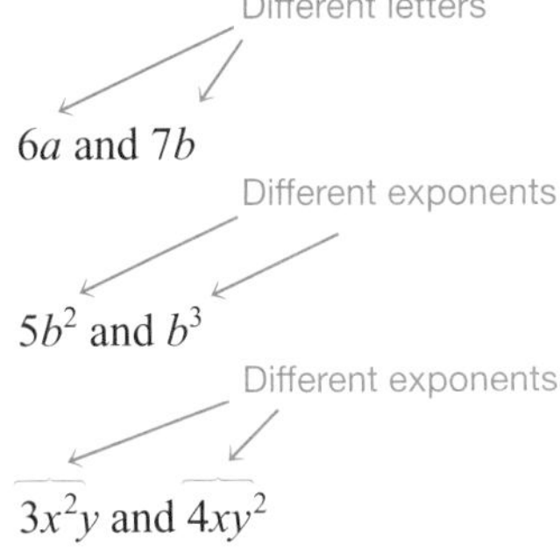

Check Yourself 9

Circle the like terms.

$5a^2b$ ab^2 a^2b $-3a^2$ $4ab$ $3b^2$ $-7a^2b$

Like terms of an expression can always be combined into a single term. Look at the following:

$$\underbrace{x + x}_{2x} + \underbrace{x + x + x + x + x}_{5x} = \underbrace{x + x + x + x + x + x + x}_{7x}$$

NOTES

Here we use the distributive property from Section 1.2.

You don't have to write all this out—just do it mentally!

Rather than having to write out all those x's, try

$2x + 5x = (2 + 5)x = 7x$

In the same way,

$9b + 6b = (9 + 6)b = 15b$

and

$10a + (-4a) = [10 + (-4)]a = 6a$

This leads us to the following rule.

Step by Step

To Combine Like Terms

To combine like terms, use the following steps.

Step 1 Add or subtract the numerical coefficients.

Step 2 Attach the common variables.

Example 10 Combining Like Terms

< Objective 3 >

RECALL

When any factor is multiplied by 0, the product is 0.

Combine like terms.

(a) $8m + 5m = (8 + 5)m = 13m$

(b) $5pq^3 - 4pq^3 = 5pq^3 + (-4pq^3) = 1pq^3 = pq^3$

(c) $7a^3b^2 - 7a^3b^2 = 7a^3b^2 + (-7a^3b^2) = 0a^3b^2 = 0$

Check Yourself 10

Combine like terms.

(a) $6b + 8b$ **(b)** $12x^2 - 3x^2$ **(c)** $8xy^3 - 7xy^3$ **(d)** $9a^2b^4 - 9a^2b^4$

For expressions involving more than two terms, Examples 11 and 12 demonstrate that the idea is just the same.

Example 11 Combining Like Terms

Combine like terms.

(a) $5ab - 2ab + 3ab$

$= 5ab + (-2ab) + 3ab$

$= [5 + (-2) + 3]ab = 6ab$

NOTE

The distributive property can be used over any number of like terms.

NOTE

With practice you won't be writing out these steps, but doing them mentally.

Only like terms can be combined.

(b) $8x - 2x + 5y$
$= [8 + (-2)]x + 5y$
$= 6x + 5y$

Like terms Like terms

(c) $5m + 8n + 4m - 3n$
$= (5m + 4m) + [8n + (-3n)]$
$= 9m + 5n$

Here we have used the associative and commutative properties.

(d) $4x^2 + 2x - 3x^2 + x$
$= [4x^2 + (-3x^2)] + (2x + x)$
$= x^2 + 3x$

As these examples illustrate, combining like terms often means changing the grouping and the order in which the terms are written. Again all this is possible because of the properties of addition that we reviewed in Section 1.2.

Check Yourself 11

Combine like terms.

(a) $4m^2 - 3m^2 + 8m^2$ **(b)** $9ab + 3a - 5ab$
(c) $4p + 7q + 5p - 3q$

As you have seen in arithmetic, subtraction can be performed directly. As this is the form used for most of mathematics, we will use that form throughout this text. Just remember, by using negative numbers, you can always rewrite a subtraction problem as an addition problem.

Example 12 Combining Like Terms

Combine like terms.

(a) $2xy - 3xy + 5xy$
$= (2 - 3 + 5)xy$
$= 4xy$

(b) $5a - 2b + 7b - 8a$
$= (5a - 8a) + (-2b + 7b)$
$= -3a + 5b$

Check Yourself 12

Combine like terms.

(a) $4ab + 5ab - 3ab - 7ab$ **(b)** $2x - 7y - 8x - y$

Check Yourself ANSWERS

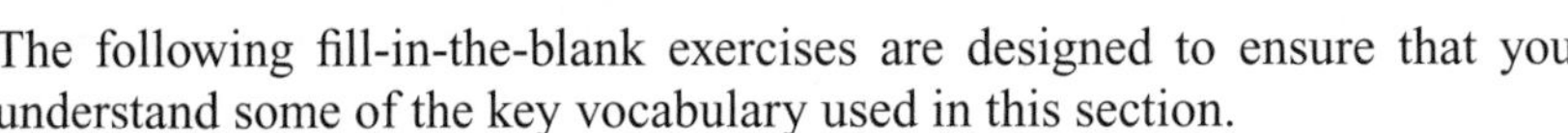

1. **(a)** 38; **(b)** 45; **(c)** 84 **2.** **(a)** 10; **(b)** 7; **(c)** 7 **3.** −31 **4.** **(a)** −14; **(b)** 35; **(c)** −4; **(d)** −9; **(e)** 9 **5.** **(a)** −2; **(b)** −2 **6.** **(a)** 2; **(b)** 7 **7.** **(a)** $2b^4$; **(b)** $5m$, $3n$; **(c)** $2s^2$, $-3t$, -6 **8.** **(a)** 8; **(b)** −5; **(c)** 1 **9.** The like terms are $5a^2b$, a^2b, and $-7a^2b$. **10.** **(a)** $14b$; **(b)** $9x^2$; **(c)** xy^3; **(d)** 0 **11.** **(a)** $9m^2$; **(b)** $4ab + 3a$; **(c)** $9p + 4q$ **12.** **(a)** $-ab$; **(b)** $-6x - 8y$

Reading Your Text

The following fill-in-the-blank exercises are designed to ensure that you understand some of the key vocabulary used in this section.

SECTION 1.4

(a) To evaluate an algebraic expression, first replace each ____________ by the given numerical value.

(b) The ____________ factor of a term is called the coefficient.

(c) Terms that contain exactly the same variables raised to the same respective powers are called ____________ terms.

(d) The ____________ property enables us to combine like terms into a single term.

Basic Skills | Advanced Skills | Vocational-Technical Applications | Calculator/Computer | Above and Beyond

1.4 exercises

MathZone

Boost your grade at mathzone.com!
- Practice Problems
- NetTutor
- Self-Tests
- e-Professors
- Videos

Name ______

Section ______ Date ______

< Objective 1 >

Evaluate each expression if $a = -2$, $b = 5$, $c = -4$, and $d = 6$.

1. $8b + 2c$

2. $7a - 2c$

3. $-b^2 + b$

4. $(-b)^2 + b$

5. $3a^2$

6. $6c^2$

7. $c^2 - 2d$

8. $3a^2 + 4c$

9. $4(2a - d)$

10. $6(3c - d)$

11. $\frac{6d}{c}$

12. $\frac{8b}{5c}$

13. $\frac{3d + 2c}{b}$

14. $\frac{2b + 3d}{2a}$

15. $\frac{2b - 3a}{c + 2d}$

16. $\frac{3d - 2b}{5a + d}$

17. $d^2 - b^2$

18. $c^2 - a^2$

19. $(d - b)^2$

20. $(c - a)^2$

21. $(d - b)(d + b)$

22. $(c - a)(c + a)$

23. $d^3 - b^3$

24. $c^3 + a^3$

25. $(d - b)^3$

26. $(c + a)^3$

27. $(d - b)(d^2 + db + b^2)$

28. $(c + a)(c^2 - ac + a^2)$

29. $b^2 + a^2$ 

30. $d^2 - a^2$

Answers

1. 32
2. −6
3. −20
4. 30
5. 12
6. 96
7. 4
8. −4
9. −40
10. −108
11. −9
12. −2
13. 2
14. −7
15. 2
16. −2
17. 11
18. 12
19. 1
20. 4
21. 11
22. 12
23. 91
24. −72
25. 1
26. −216
27. 91
28. −72
29. 29
30. 32

31. $(b + a)^2$ 

32. $(d - a)^2$

33. $b^2 + 2ab + a^2$

34. $d^2 - 2ad + a^2$

< Objective 2 >

List the terms of each expression.

35. $5a + 2$

36. $7a - 4b$

37. $3x^2 + 3x - 7$

38. $2a^3 - a^2 + a$

Circle the like terms in each group of terms.

39. $5ab, 3b, 3a, 4ab$

40. $8a^2b, 4a^2, 3ab^2, -5a^2b, 3ab, 5a^2b$

< Objective 3 >

Combine the like terms.

41. $3m + 7m$

42. $6a^2 + 8a^2$

43. $7b^3 + 10b^3$

44. $7rs + 13rs$

45. $9z^2 - 3z^2$

46. $7m - 6m$

47. $5a^3 - 5a^3$

48. $13xy - 9xy$

49. $21p^2q - 6p^2q$

50. $17r^3s^2 - 8r^3s^2$

51. $10x^2 - 7x^2 + 3x^2$

52. $13uv + 5uv - 12uv$

53. $4a + 7b + 3 - 2a + 3b - 2$

54. $5p^2 + 2p + 8 + 4p^2 + 5p - 6$

55. $\frac{2}{3}m + 3 + \frac{4}{3}m$

56. $\frac{1}{5}a - 2 + \frac{4}{5}a$

57. $2.3a + 7 + 4.7a + 3$

58. $5.8m + 4 - 2.8m + 11$

In each exercise, simplify the expression and combine like terms.

59. $6x + (2 + 3x)$

60. $5p + (3 + 9p)$

61. $8y + (2y + 5)$

62. $8m + (3 + 4m)$

Answers

31. 9
32. 64
33. 9
34. 64
35. $5a$, 2
36. $7a$, $-4b$
37. $3x^2$, $3x$, -7
38. $2a^3$, $-a^2$, a
39. $5ab$, $4ab$
40. $8a^2b$, $-5a^2b$, $5a^2b$
41. $10m$
42. $14a^2$
43. $17b^3$
44. $20rs$
45. $6z^2$
46. m
47. 0
48. $4xy$
49. $15p^2q$
50. $9r^3s^2$
51. $6x^2$
52. $6uv$
53. $2a + 10b + 1$
54. $9p^2 + 7p + 2$
55. $2m + 3$
56. $a - 2$
57. $7a + 10$
58. $3m + 15$
59. $9x + 2$
60. $14p + 3$
61. $10y + 5$
62. $12m + 3$

63. $2x + 9 + 4x + 6$

64. $2a + 1 + 9a + 7$

65. $3b + 2b + 5 + 4b$

66. $6x + 7 + 8x + 10$

67. $3 + 7y + (-3) + y$

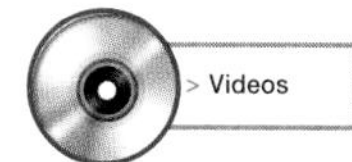

68. $w + (-7) + 2w + 7$

69. $2 + 3(2y + 1) + 3y$

70. $5 + 2(3b + 3) + 4b$

71. $2y + 3(2 + y) + 3y$

72. $5n + 3(n + 2) + 2n$

Basic Skills | **Advanced Skills** | Vocational-Technical Applications | Calculator/Computer | Above and Beyond

73. **Electronics** The formula for the total resistance in a parallel circuit is given by the formula $R_T = R_1R_2/(R_1 + R_2)$. Find the total resistance if $R_1 = 6$ ohms (Ω) and $R_2 = 10\ \Omega$.

> Videos

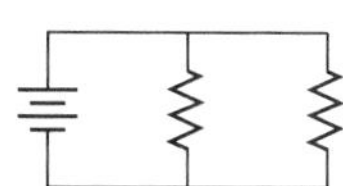

74. **Geometry** The formula for the area of a triangle is given by $A = \frac{1}{2}ab$. Find the area of a triangle if $a = 4$ centimeters (cm) and $b = 8$ cm.

75. **Geometry** The perimeter of a rectangle of length L and width W is given by the formula $P = 2L + 2W$. Find the perimeter when $L = 10$ inches (in.) and $W = 5$ in.

> Videos

Answers

63. $6x + 15$
64. $11a + 8$
65. $9b + 5$
66. $14x + 17$
67. $8y$
68. $3w$
69. $9y + 5$
70. $10b + 11$
71. $8y + 6$
72. $10n + 6$
73. $3.75\ \Omega$
74. $16\ \text{cm}^2$
75. 30 in.

Answers

76. $1,440

77. 14°F

78. 28.26 m^2

79. $6H - 254$

80. $5H - 195$

81. −15.3

82. −11.4

83. 1.1

84. −0.8

76. **Business and Finance** The simple interest I on a principal of P dollars at interest rate r for time t, in years, is given by $I = Prt$. Find the simple interest on a principal of $6,000 at 8 percent for 3 years. (**Note:** 8% = 0.08.)

77. **Science and Medicine** The formula that relates Celsius and Fahrenheit temperature is $F = \frac{9}{5}C + 32$. If the temperature of the day is $-10°C$, what is the Fahrenheit temperature?

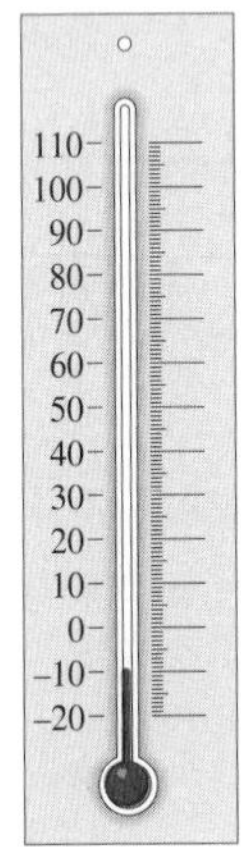

78. **Geometry** If the area of a circle whose radius is r is given by $A = \pi r^2$, where $\pi \approx 3.14$, approximate the area when $r = 3$ m.

Basic Skills | Advanced Skills | **Vocational-Technical Applications** | Calculator/Computer | Above and Beyond

79. **Allied Health** The ideal body weight, in pounds, for a man is determined by plugging his height (H), in inches, into the expression $106 + 6(H - 60)$. Simplify this expression.

80. **Allied Health** The ideal body weight, in pounds, for a woman is determined by plugging her height (H), in inches, into the expression $105 + 5(H - 60)$. Simplify this expression.

Basic Skills | Advanced Skills | Vocational-Technical Applications | **Calculator/Computer** | Above and Beyond

Use your calculator to evaluate each expression if $x = -2.34$, $y = -3.14$, and $z = 4.12$. Round your answer to the nearest tenth.

81. $x + yz$

82. $y - 2z$

83. $\dfrac{xy}{z - x}$

84. $\dfrac{y^2}{zy}$

Basic Skills | Advanced Skills | Vocational-Technical Applications | Calculator/Computer | **Above and Beyond**

In each problem, decide if the given values make the statement **true** *or* **false.**

85. $x - 7 = 2y + 5; x = 22, y = 5$

86. $3(x - y) = 6; x = 5, y = -3$

87. $2(x + y) = 2x + y; x = -4, y = -2$

88. $x^2 - y^2 = x - y; x = 4, y = -3$

89. Write an English interpretation of each of the algebraic expressions.

(a) $(2x^2 - y)^3$

(b) $3n - \frac{n - 1}{2}$

(c) $(2n + 3)(n - 4)$

90. Is $a^n + b^n = (a + b)^n$? Try a few numbers and decide if you think this is true for all numbers, for some numbers, or never true. Write an explanation of your findings and give examples.

91. Enjoyment of patterns in art, music, and language is common to all cultures, and many cultures also delight in and draw spiritual significance from patterns in numbers. One such set of patterns is that of the "magic" square. One of these squares appears in a famous etching by Albrecht Dürer, who lived from 1471 to 1528 in Europe. He was one of the first artists in Europe to use geometry to give perspective, a feeling of three dimensions, in his work.

The magic square in his work is this one:

16	3	2	13
5	10	11	8
9	6	7	12
4	15	14	1

Why is this square "magic"? It is magic because every row, every column, and both diagonals add to the same number. In this square there are sixteen spaces for the numbers 1 through 16.

Answers

85. True
86. False
87. False
88. True
89. Above and Beyond
90. Above and Beyond
91. Above and Beyond

Part 1: What number does each row and column add to?

Write the square that you obtain by adding -17 to each number. Is this still a magic square? If so, what number does each column and row add to? If you add 5 to each number in the original magic square, do you still have a magic square? You have been studying the operations of addition, multiplication, subtraction, and division with integers and with rational numbers. What operations can you perform on this magic square and still have a magic square? Try to find something that will not work. Use algebra to help you decide what will work and what won't. Write a description of your work and explain your conclusions.

Part 2: Here is the oldest published magic square. It is from China, about 250 B.C.E. Legend has it that it was brought from the River Lo by a turtle to the Emperor Yii, who was a hydraulic engineer.

4	9	2
3	5	7
8	1	6

Check to make sure that this is a magic square. Work together to decide what operation might be done to every number in the magic square to make the sum of each row, column, and diagonal the *opposite* of what it is now. What would you do to every number to cause the sum of each row, column, and diagonal to equal 0?

Answers

1. 32 **3.** -20 **5.** 12 **7.** 4 **9.** -40 **11.** -9 **13.** 2
15. 2 **17.** 11 **19.** 1 **21.** 11 **23.** 91 **25.** 1 **27.** 91
29. 29 **31.** 9 **33.** 9 **35.** $5a, 2$ **37.** $3x^2, 3x, -7$ **39.** $5ab, 4ab$
41. $10m$ **43.** $17b^3$ **45.** $6z^2$ **47.** 0 **49.** $15p^2q$ **51.** $6x^2$
53. $2a + 10b + 1$ **55.** $2m + 3$ **57.** $7a + 10$ **59.** $9x + 2$
61. $10y + 5$ **63.** $6x + 15$ **65.** $9b + 5$ **67.** $8y$ **69.** $9y + 5$
71. $8y + 6$ **73.** $3.75\ \Omega$ **75.** 30 in. **77.** 14°F **79.** $6H - 254$
81. -15.3 **83.** 1.1 **85.** True **87.** False **89.** Above and Beyond
91. Above and Beyond

1.5 Properties of Exponents and Scientific Notation

< 1.5 Objectives >

1 > Use the properties of exponents

2 > Use scientific notation

Exponents are used as a short-hand form for repeated multiplication. Instead of writing

$a \cdot a \cdot a \cdot a \cdot a$

we write

a^5

which we read as "*a* to the fifth power."

Definition

Exponential Form

In general, for any real number *a* and any natural number *n*,

$$a^n = \underbrace{a \cdot a \cdot \cdots \cdot a}_{n \text{ factors}}$$

NOTES

We expand the expressions and apply the associative property to regroup.

This is our *first property of exponents*

$a^m \cdot a^n = a^{m+n}$

An expression of this type is said to be in **exponential form.** We call *a* the **base** of the expression and *n* the **exponent,** or the **power.**

Let's consider what happens when we multiply two expressions in exponential form with the same base.

$$a^4 \cdot a^5 = \underbrace{(a \cdot a \cdot a \cdot a)}_{4 \text{ factors}}\underbrace{(a \cdot a \cdot a \cdot a \cdot a)}_{5 \text{ factors}}$$

$$= \underbrace{a \cdot a \cdot a \cdot a \cdot a \cdot a \cdot a \cdot a \cdot a}_{9 \text{ factors}}$$

$$= a^9$$

Notice that the product is simply the base taken to the power that is the sum of the two original exponents.

In fact, in general, the following holds:

Property

Product Property

For any real number *a* and natural numbers *m* and *n*,

$$a^m \cdot a^n = \underbrace{(a \cdot a \cdot \cdots \cdot a)}_{m \text{ factors}}\underbrace{(a \cdot a \cdot \cdots \cdot a)}_{n \text{ factors}}$$

$$= \underbrace{a \cdot a \cdot \cdots \cdot a}_{m + n \text{ factors}}$$

$$= a^{m+n}$$

Example 1 Simplifying Expressions

< Objective 1 >

Simplify each expression.

(a) $b^4 \cdot b^6 = b^{10}$

(b) $(2a)^3 \cdot (2a)^4 = (2a)^7$

(c) $(-2)^5(-2)^4 = (-2)^9$

(d) $10^7 \cdot 10^{11} = 10^{18}$

Check Yourself 1

Simplify each product.

(a) $(5b)^6(5b)^5$

(b) $(-3)^4(-3)^3$

(c) $10^8 \cdot 10^{12}$

(d) $(xy)^2(xy)^3$

Applying the commutative and associative properties of multiplication, we know that a product such as

$2x^3 \cdot 3x^2$

can be rewritten as

$(2 \cdot 3)(x^3 \cdot x^2)$

or as

$6x^5$

We expand on these illustrated ideas in Example 2.

Example 2 Simplifying Expressions

NOTE

Multiply the coefficients and *add* the exponents by the product property. With practice you will *not need to write* the regrouping step.

Using the product property of exponents together with the commutative and associative properties, simplify each product.

(a) $(5x^4)(3x^2) = (5 \cdot 3)x^4x^2 = 15x^6$

(b) $(x^2y^3)(x^2y^4) = (x^2 \cdot x^2)(y^3 \cdot y^4) = x^4y^7$

(c) $(4c^5d^3)(3c^2d^2) = (4 \cdot 3)(c^5c^2)(d^3d^2) = 12c^7d^5$

Check Yourself 2

Simplify each expression.

(a) $(4a^2b)(2a^3b^4)$

(b) $(3x^4)(2x^3y)$

We now consider a second property of exponents that can be used to simplify quotients of expressions in exponential form that have the same base.

NOTES

Divide the numerator and denominator by the four common factors of *a*.

$\frac{a}{a} = 1$, when $a \neq 0$.

Consider the quotient

$$\frac{a^6}{a^4}$$

If we write this in expanded form, we have

$$\frac{\overbrace{a \cdot a \cdot a \cdot a \cdot a \cdot a}^{\text{6 factors}}}{\underbrace{a \cdot a \cdot a \cdot a}_{\text{4 factors}}}$$

NOTE

This is our *second property of exponents.* We write $a \neq 0$ to avoid division by zero.

This can be reduced to

$$\frac{a \cdot a \cdot a \cdot a \cdot a \cdot a}{a \cdot a \cdot a \cdot a} \quad \text{or} \quad a^2$$

This means that

$$\frac{a^6}{a^4} = a^2$$

Property

Quotient Property

In general, for any real number a ($a \neq 0$) and natural numbers m and n, $m > n$,

$$\frac{a^m}{a^n} = a^{m-n}$$

Example 3 Simplifying Expressions

NOTES

Subtract the exponents, applying the quotient property.

$a^1 = a$; there is no need to write the exponent of 1 because it is understood.

We *divide* the coefficients and subtract the exponents.

Divide the coefficients and subtract the exponents for *each* variable.

Simplify each expression.

(a) $\frac{x^{10}}{x^4} = x^{10-4} = x^6$

(b) $\frac{a^8}{a^7} = a^{8-7} = a$

(c) $\frac{63w^8}{7w^5} = 9w^{8-5} = 9w^3$

(d) $\frac{-32a^4b^5}{8a^2b} = -4a^{4-2}b^{5-1} = -4a^2b^4$

(e) $\frac{10^{16}}{10^6} = 10^{16-6} = 10^{10}$

Check Yourself 3

Simplify each expression.

(a) $\frac{y^{12}}{y^5}$ (b) $\frac{x^9}{x^8}$ (c) $\frac{45r^8}{-9r^6}$

(d) $\frac{49a^6b^7}{7ab^3}$ (e) $\frac{10^{13}}{10^5}$

Suppose that we have an expression of the form

$(a^2)^4$

This can be written as

$\underbrace{(a \cdot a)(a \cdot a)(a \cdot a)(a \cdot a)}_{2 \cdot 4 \text{ or } 8 \text{ factors}}$ or a^8

NOTE

This is our *third property of exponents.*

This suggests, in general, the following:

Property

Power to a Power Property

For any real number a and natural numbers m and n,

$(a^m)^n = a^{mn}$

Example 4 illustrates the use of this third property of exponents.

Example 4 Simplifying Expressions

Using the power to a power property of exponents, simplify each expression.

NOTE

We *multiply* the exponents.

(a) $(x^3)^5 = x^{3 \cdot 5} = x^{15}$

(b) $(a^2)^8 = a^{2 \cdot 8} = a^{16}$

(c) $(10^2)^3 = 10^{2 \cdot 3} = 10^6$

Be Careful! Students sometimes confuse $(x^3)^5$ or x^{15} with $x^3 \cdot x^5$ or x^8. In the first case we *multiply* the exponents; in the second we *add!*

Check Yourself 4

Simplify each expression.

(a) $(b^4)^7$ (b) $(10^3)^3$ (c) b^4b^7

Let's develop another property for exponents. An expression such as

$$(2x)^5$$

can be written in expanded form as

$$\underbrace{(2x)(2x)(2x)(2x)(2x)}_{\text{5 factors}}$$

NOTES

Each factor of the base has been raised to the fifth power.

This is our *fourth property of exponents.*

We could use the commutative and associative properties to write this product as

$$(2 \cdot 2 \cdot 2 \cdot 2 \cdot 2)(x \cdot x \cdot x \cdot x \cdot x)$$

or

$$2^5x^5$$

This suggests our fourth property of exponents.

Property

Product to a Power Property

For any real numbers *a* and *b* and any natural number *m*,

$$(ab)^m = a^mb^m$$

The use of this product to a power property is illustrated in Example 5.

Example 5 Simplifying Expressions

NOTE

We also apply the power to a power property in simplifying this expression.

Simplify each expression.

(a) $(xy)^5 = x^5y^5$

(b) $(10a)^4 = 10^4 \cdot a^4 = 10{,}000a^4$

(c) $(2p^2q^3)^3 = 2^3(p^2)^3(q^3)^3$
$= 8p^6q^9$

Check Yourself 5

Simplify each expression.

(a) $(ab)^7$ **(b)** $(4p)^3$ **(c)** $(3m^4n^2)^2$

Our fifth (and final) property of exponents can be established in a similar fashion to the product to a power property. It deals with the power of a quotient rather than the power of a product.

Property

Quotient to a Power Property

For any real numbers *a* and *b* ($b \neq 0$) and natural number *m*,

$$\left(\frac{a}{b}\right)^m = \frac{a^m}{b^m}$$

Example 6 shows the application of this property.

Example 6 Simplifying Expressions

NOTE

This is our *fifth property of exponents.*

Simplify each expression.

(a) $\left(\frac{x^2}{y}\right)^3 = \frac{(x^2)^3}{y^3} = \frac{x^6}{y^3}$ Quotient to a power property, power to a power property

(b) $\left(\frac{2a}{b^3}\right)^4 = \frac{(2a)^4}{(b^3)^4}$ Quotient to a power property

$= \frac{2^4a^4}{b^{12}} = \frac{16a^4}{b^{12}}$ Product to a power property, power to a power property

Check Yourself 6

Simplify each expression.

(a) $\left(\frac{m^3}{n}\right)^4$ (b) $\left(\frac{3t^2}{s^3}\right)^3$

As we have seen, more complicated expressions require the use of more than one of our properties, for simplification. Example 7 illustrates other such cases.

Example 7 Simplifying Expressions

Use the properties of exponents to simplify the following expressions.

(a) $(2x)^2(2x)^4 = (2x)^{2+4} = (2x)^6$ Product property

$= 2^6x^6 = 64x^6$ Product to a power property

(b) $\frac{(x^4)^3}{(x^3)^2} = \frac{x^{12}}{x^6} = x^{12-6} = x^6$ Power to a power property, quotient property

(c) $\frac{6a^4b^5}{3a^2b} = 2a^{4-2}b^{5-1} = 2a^2b^4$ Quotient property, division

(d) $\frac{7.5 \times 10^{14}}{2.5 \times 10^3} = \frac{7.5}{2.5} \times 10^{14-3}$ Quotient property

$= 3 \times 10^{11}$ Divide.

Check Yourself 7

Simplify each expression.

(a) $(3y)^2(3y)^3$ (b) $\frac{(3a^2)^3}{9a^3}$ (c) $\frac{25x^3y^4}{5x^2y}$

The following table summarizes the five properties of exponents introduced in this section.

General Form	Example
I. $a^m a^n = a^{m+n}$	$x^2 \cdot x^3 = x^5$
II. $\dfrac{a^m}{a^n} = a^{m-n} \quad a \neq 0, m > n$	$\dfrac{5^7}{5^3} = 5^4$
III. $(a^m)^n = a^{mn}$	$(z^5)^4 = z^{20}$
IV. $(ab)^m = a^m b^m$	$(4x)^3 = 4^3x^3 = 64x^3$
V. $\left(\dfrac{a}{b}\right)^m = \dfrac{a^m}{b^m} \quad b \neq 0$	$\left(\dfrac{2}{3}\right)^6 = \dfrac{2^6}{3^6} = \dfrac{64}{729}$

NOTES

With this definition

$\dfrac{a^m}{a^n} = a^{m-n}$ when $m \geq n$.

We must have $a \neq 0$ because the form 0^0 is called *indeterminate.* It is considered in later mathematics classes.

Before leaving the properties of exponents, we would like to make an important extension of one of the properties. In the quotient property, suppose that we now allow *m to equal n.* We then have

$$\frac{a^m}{a^m} = a^{m-m} = a^0$$

But we know that it is also true that

$$\frac{a^m}{a^m} = 1$$

Comparing the first and second equations, it then seems reasonable to make the following definition.

Definition

The Zero Exponent

For any real number a, $a \neq 0$,

$a^0 = 1$

Example 8 Using Zero as an Exponent

NOTE

In $6x^0$ the zero exponent applies *only* to x.

Use the preceding definition to simplify each expression.

(a) $10^0 = 1$

(b) $(a^3b^2)^0 = 1$

(c) $6x^0 = 6 \cdot 1 = 6$

Check Yourself 8

Simplify each expression.

(a) 25^0 **(b)** $(m^4n^2)^0$ **(c)** $8s^0$

RECALL

$\frac{a^m}{a^n} = a^{m-n}$

The quotient property of exponents allows us to define a negative exponent. Suppose that the exponent in the denominator is *greater than* the exponent in the numerator. Consider the expression $\frac{x^2}{x^5}$.

Divide the numerator and denominator by the two common factors of x.

$$\frac{x^2}{x^5} = \frac{x \cdot x}{x \cdot x \cdot x \cdot x \cdot x} = \frac{1}{x^3}$$

However, if we extend the quotient property to let n be greater than m, we have

$$\frac{x^2}{x^5} = x^{2-5} = x^{-3}$$

Now, by comparing these two equations, it seems reasonable to define x^{-3} as $\frac{1}{x^3}$.

In general, we have this result:

Definition

Negative Powers

For any number a, $a \neq 0$, and any positive integer n,

$$a^{-n} = \frac{1}{a^n}$$

Example 9 **Rewriting Expressions That Contain Negative Exponents**

NOTE

John Wallis (1616–1703), an English mathematician, was the first to fully discuss the meaning of 0 and negative exponents.

Rewrite each expression, using only positive exponents.

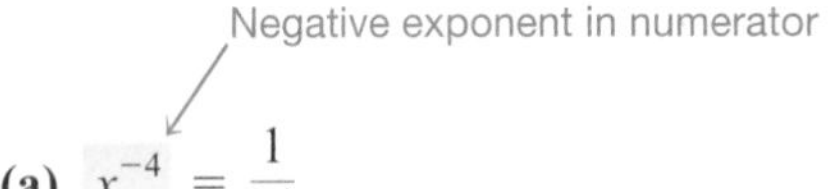

Negative exponent in numerator

(a) $x^{-4} = \frac{1}{x^4}$

Positive exponent in denominator

(b) $m^{-7} = \frac{1}{m^7}$

(c) $3^{-2} = \frac{1}{3^2}$ or $\frac{1}{9}$

(d) $10^{-3} = \frac{1}{10^3}$ or $\frac{1}{1,000}$

> CAUTION

$2x^{-3} \neq (2x)^{-3}$

(e) $2x^{-3} = 2 \cdot \frac{1}{x^3} = \frac{2}{x^3}$

The -3 exponent applies only to x, because x is the base.

(f) $(2x)^{-3} = \frac{1}{(2x)^3} = \frac{1}{8x^3}$

(g) $\frac{a^5}{a^9} = a^{5-9} = a^{-4} = \frac{1}{a^4}$

(h) $-4x^{-5} = -4 \cdot \frac{1}{x^5} = -\frac{4}{x^5}$

Check Yourself 9

Write, using only positive exponents.

(a) a^{-10} **(b)** 4^{-3} **(c)** $3x^{-2}$ **(d)** $\frac{x^5}{x^8}$

Example 10 Simplifying Expressions Containing Exponents

NOTE

$a^m \cdot a^n = a^{m+n}$ for *any* integers *m* and *n*. So add the exponents.

Simplify (write an equivalent expression that uses only positive exponents).

(a) $x^5x^{-2} = x^{5+(-2)} = x^3$

Note: An alternative approach would be

$$x^5x^{-2} = x^5 \cdot \frac{1}{x^2} = \frac{x^5}{x^2} = x^3$$

(b) $a^7a^{-5} = a^{7+(-5)} = a^2$

(c) $y^5y^{-9} = y^{5+(-9)} = y^{-4} = \frac{1}{y^4}$

NOTE

By definition

$x^{-2} = \frac{1}{x^2}$

Check Yourself 10

Simplify (write an equivalent expression that uses only positive exponents).

(a) x^7x^{-2} **(b)** b^3b^{-8}

Example 11 shows that all the properties of exponents introduced previously in this section can be extended to expressions with negative exponents.

Example 11 Simplifying Expressions Containing Exponents

Simplify each expression. Write answers with positive exponents only.

(a) $\frac{m^{-3}}{m^4} = m^{-3-4}$ Quotient property

$= m^{-7} = \frac{1}{m^7}$

NOTE

This could also be done by using product to a power property first, so

$(2x^4)^{-3} = 2^{-3} \cdot (x^4)^{-3}$
$= 2^{-3}x^{-12}$
$= \frac{1}{2^3x^{12}}$
$= \frac{1}{8x^{12}}$

(b) $\frac{a^{-2}b^6}{a^5b^{-4}} = a^{-2-5}b^{6-(-4)}$ Apply the quotient property to each variable.

$= a^{-7}b^{10} = \frac{b^{10}}{a^7}$

(c) $(2x^4)^{-3} = \frac{1}{(2x^4)^3}$ Definition of the negative exponent

$= \frac{1}{2^3(x^4)^3}$ Product to a power property

$= \frac{1}{8x^{12}}$ Power to a power property

(d) $\frac{(y^{-2})^4}{(y^3)^{-2}} = \frac{y^{-8}}{y^{-6}}$ Power to a power property

$= y^{-8-(-6)}$ Quotient property

$= y^{-2} = \frac{1}{y^2}$

Check Yourself 11

Simplify each expression.

(a) $\frac{x^5}{x^{-3}}$ (b) $\frac{m^3n^{-5}}{m^{-2}n^3}$ (c) $(3a^3)^{-4}$ (d) $\frac{(r^3)^{-2}}{(r^{-4})^2}$

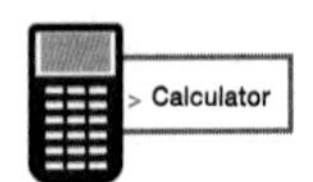

We will now take a look at an important use of exponents, scientific notation.

We begin the discussion with a calculator exercise. On most calculators, if you multiply 2.3 times 1,000, the display will read

2300

Multiply by 1,000 a second time. Now you will see

2300000

Multiplying by 1,000 a third time will result in the display

2300000000

And multiplying by 1,000 again yields

2.3E12 which must represent 2,300,000,000,000.

NOTE

Consider the following equations:

$2.3 = 2.3 \times 10^0$
$23 = 2.3 \times 10^1$
$230 = 2.3 \times 10^2$
$2300 = 2.3 \times 10^3$
$23{,}000 = 2.3 \times 10^4$
$230{,}000 = 2.3 \times 10^5$

Can you see what is happening? This is the way calculators display very large numbers. The number on the left is always between 1 and 10, and the number on the right indicates the number of places the decimal point must be moved to the right to put the answer in standard (or decimal) form.

This notation is used frequently in science. It is not uncommon in scientific applications of algebra to find yourself working with very large or very small numbers. Even in the time of Archimedes (287–212 B.C.E.), the study of such numbers was not unusual. Archimedes estimated that the universe was 23,000,000,000,000,000 meters (m) in diameter, which is the approximate distance light travels in $2\frac{1}{2}$ years. By

NOTE

When displaying a number in scientific notation, we use "×" instead of "·" for multiplication.

comparison, Polaris (the North Star) is actually 680 light-years from the Earth. Example 13 will discuss the idea of light-years.

In scientific notation, Archimedes's estimate for the diameter of the universe would be

2.3×10^{16} m

In general, we can define scientific notation as follows.

Definition

Scientific Notation

Any number written in the form

$a \times 10^n$

in which $1 \le a < 10$ and n is an integer, is written in scientific notation.

Example 12 Using Scientific Notation

< Objective 2 >

NOTES

This is the pattern for writing a number in scientific notation.

The exponent of the base 10 shows the *number of places* we must move the decimal point. A positive exponent tells us to move right, and a negative exponent indicates to move left.

To convert back to standard or decimal form, the process is simply reversed.

Write each of the numbers in scientific notation.

(a) $120{,}000. = 1.2 \times 10^5$

5 places — The power is 5.

(b) $88{,}000{,}000. = 8.8 \times 10^7$

7 places — The power is 7.

(c) $520{,}000{,}000. = 5.2 \times 10^8$

8 places

(d) $4{,}000{,}000{,}000. = 4 \times 10^9$

9 places

(e) $0.0005 = 5 \times 10^{-4}$

4 places

If the decimal point is to be moved to the left, the exponent will be negative.

(f) $0.0000000081 = 8.1 \times 10^{-9}$

9 places

Check Yourself 12

Write in scientific notation.

(a) 212,000,000,000,000,000 **(b)** 0.00079
(c) 5,600,000 **(d)** 0.0000007

Example 13 An Application of Scientific Notation

> **NOTE**
>
> $9.6075 \times 10^{15} \approx 10 \times 10^{15} = 10^{16}$

(a) Light travels at a speed of 3.05×10^8 meters per second (m/s). There are approximately 3.15×10^7 s in a year. How far does light travel in a year?

We multiply the distance traveled in 1 s by the number of seconds in a year. This yields

$$(3.05 \times 10^8)(3.15 \times 10^7) = (3.05 \cdot 3.15)(10^8 \cdot 10^7)$$

Multiply the coefficients, and add the exponents.

$$= 9.6075 \times 10^{15}$$

For our purposes we round the distance light travels in 1 year to 10^{16} m. This unit is called a **light-year,** and it is used to measure astronomical distances.

(b) The distance from Earth to the star Spica (in Virgo) is 2.2×10^{18} m. How many light-years is Spica from Earth?

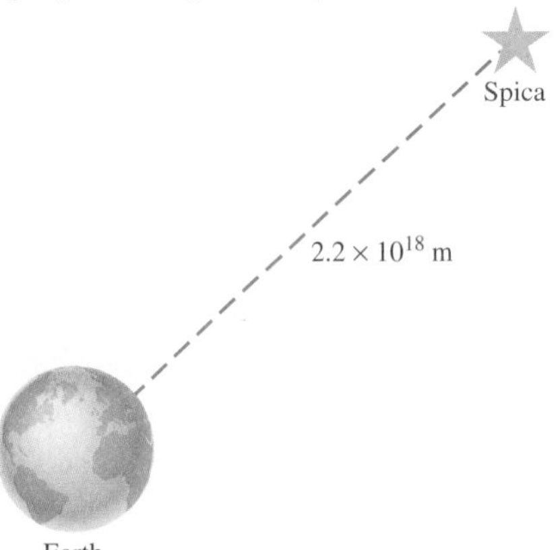

> **NOTE**
>
> We divide the distance (in meters) by the number of meters in 1 light-year.

$$\frac{2.2 \times 10^{18}}{10^{16}} = 2.2 \times 10^{18-16}$$

$$= 2.2 \times 10^2 = 220 \text{ light-years}$$

Check Yourself 13

The farthest object that can be seen with the unaided eye is the Andromeda galaxy. This galaxy is 2.3×10^{22} m from Earth. What is this distance in light-years?

Check Yourself ANSWERS

1. (a) $(5b)^{11}$; **(b)** $(-3)^7$; **(c)** 10^{20}; **(d)** $(xy)^5$ **2. (a)** $8a^5b^5$; **(b)** $6x^7y$
3. (a) y^7; **(b)** x; **(c)** $-5r^2$; **(d)** $7a^5b^4$; **(e)** 10^8 **4. (a)** b^{28}; **(b)** 10^9; **(c)** b^{11}
5. (a) a^7b^7; **(b)** $64p^3$; **(c)** $9m^8n^4$ **6. (a)** $\frac{m^{12}}{n^4}$; **(b)** $\frac{27t^6}{s^9}$
7. (a) $243y^5$; **(b)** $3a^3$; **(c)** $5xy^3$ **8. (a)** 1; **(b)** 1; **(c)** 8
9. (a) $\frac{1}{a^{10}}$; **(b)** $\frac{1}{4^3}$ or $\frac{1}{64}$; **(c)** $\frac{3}{x^2}$; **(d)** $\frac{1}{x^3}$ **10. (a)** x^5; **(b)** $\frac{1}{b^5}$
11. (a) x^8; **(b)** $\frac{m^5}{n^8}$; **(c)** $\frac{1}{81a^{12}}$; **(d)** r^2 **12. (a)** 2.12×10^{17}; **(b)** 7.9×10^{-4}; **(c)** 5.6×10^6; **(d)** 7×10^{-7} **13.** 2,300,000 or 2.3×10^6 light-years

Reading Your Text

The following fill-in-the-blank exercises are designed to ensure that you understand some of the key vocabulary used in this section.

SECTION 1.5

(a) The exponential, 3^6, means that the base, 3, is used as a __________ 6 times.

(b) Any expression, except zero, raised to the zero power is __________.

(c) To multiply two exponentials with the same base, we keep the common base and __________ the exponents.

(d) Any number written in the form $a \times 10^n$ in which $1 \le a < 10$ and n is an integer is written in __________.

1.5 exercises

Basic Skills | Advanced Skills | Vocational-Technical Applications | Calculator/Computer | Above and Beyond

Name ____________

Section ________ Date ________

< Objective 1 >

Write each expression in exponential form.

1. $7 \cdot 7 \cdot 7 \cdot 7$

2. $2 \cdot 2 \cdot 2 \cdot 2 \cdot 2 \cdot 2$

3. $15 \cdot 15 \cdot 15 \cdot 15 \cdot 15 \cdot 15$

4. $31 \cdot 31 \cdot 31 \cdot 31 \cdot 31 \cdot 31 \cdot 31 \cdot 31 \cdot 31 \cdot 31$

Simplify each expression.

5. $(x^2)^3$

6. $(p^7)^2$

7. $(2^4)^2$

8. $(3^3)^2$

Use the five properties of exponents to simplify each expression.

9. $(3x)^3$

10. $(5pq)^3$

11. $5(3ab)^3$

12. $4(2rs)^4$

13. $\left(\frac{3}{4}\right)^2$

14. $\left(\frac{a}{2}\right)^5$

15. $(2x^2)^4$

16. $(3y^2)^5$

17. $(a^8b^6)^2$

18. $(4m^4n^4)^2$

19. $(3m^2)^4(m^3)^2$

20. $(y^4)^3(4y^3)^2$

21. $\frac{(x^4)^3}{x^2}$

22. $\frac{(y^5)^3(y^3)^2}{(y^4)^4}$

23. $\left(\frac{m^3}{n^2}\right)^3$

24. $\left(\frac{x^5y^2}{z^4}\right)^3$

Answers

1. 7^4
2. 2^6
3. 15^6
4. 31^{10}
5. x^6
6. p^{14}
7. 2^8 or 256
8. 3^6 or 729
9. $27x^3$
10. $125p^3q^3$
11. $135a^3b^3$
12. $64r^4s^4$
13. $\frac{9}{16}$
14. $\frac{a^5}{32}$
15. $16x^8$
16. $243y^{10}$
17. $a^{16}b^{12}$
18. $16m^8n^8$
19. $81m^{14}$
20. $16y^{18}$
21. x^{10}
22. y^5
23. $\frac{m^9}{n^6}$
24. $\frac{x^{15}y^6}{z^{12}}$

Evaluate (assume the variables are nonzero).

25. 4^0

26. $(-7)^0$

27. $(x^3y^2)^0$

28. $7m^0$

29. $(-3p^6q^8)^0$

30. $-7x^0$

Write each expression using a positive exponent; simplify when possible.

31. b^{-8}

32. 2^{-5}

33. 5^{-2}

34. 10^{-5}

35. $-2x^{-5}$ > Videos

36. $3x^{-4}$

37. $(-2x)^{-5}$

38. $(3x)^{-4}$

Simplify each expression. Write your answers with positive exponents only.

39. a^5a^3

40. m^5m^7

41. x^8x^{-2}

42. $a^{12}a^{-8}$

43. x^0x^5

44. $r^{-3}r^0$

45. $\frac{a^8}{a^5}$

46. $\frac{m^9}{m^4}$

47. $\frac{x^7}{x^9}$

48. $\frac{a^3}{a^{10}}$

49. $\frac{r^{-3}}{r^5}$

50. $\frac{x^3}{x^{-5}}$

51. $\frac{x^{-4}}{x^{-5}}$

52. $\frac{p^{-6}}{p^{-3}}$

Simplify each expression. Write your answers with positive exponents only.

53. $\frac{m^5n^{-3}}{m^{-4}n^5}$

54. $\frac{p^{-3}q^{-2}}{p^4q^{-3}}$

55. $(2a^{-3})^4$

56. $(3x^2)^{-3}$

Answers

25. 1
26. 1
27. 1
28. 7
29. 1
30. −7
31. $\frac{1}{b^8}$
32. $\frac{1}{32}$
33. $\frac{1}{25}$
34. $\frac{1}{100,000}$
35. $-\frac{2}{x^5}$
36. $\frac{3}{x^4}$
37. $-\frac{1}{32x^5}$
38. $\frac{1}{81x^4}$
39. a^8
40. m^{12}
41. x^6
42. a^4
43. x^5
44. $\frac{1}{r^3}$
45. a^3
46. m^5
47. $\frac{1}{x^2}$
48. $\frac{1}{a^7}$
49. $\frac{1}{r^8}$
50. x^8
51. x
52. $\frac{1}{p^3}$
53. $\frac{m^9}{n^8}$
54. $\frac{q}{p^7}$
55. $\frac{16}{a^{12}}$
56. $\frac{1}{27x^6}$

Answers

57. $\frac{x^4}{y^6}$

58. $\frac{b^9}{a^{15}}$

59. $\frac{1}{r^2}$

60. $\frac{1}{m^4}$

61. $\frac{1}{a^{11}}$

62. 1

63. 1.41×10^8

64. 1.86×10^8

65. 8.8×10^4

66. 1.5×10^{21}

67. 20 zeros

68. 22 zeros

57. $(x^{-2}y^3)^{-2}$

58. $(a^5b^{-3})^{-3}$

59. $\frac{(r^{-2})^3}{r^{-4}}$

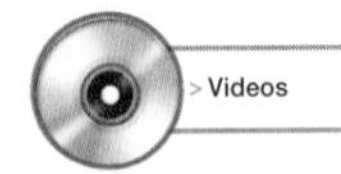

60. $\frac{(m^4)^{-3}}{(m^{-2})^4}$

61. $\frac{(a^{-3})^2(a^4)}{(a^{-3})^{-3}}$

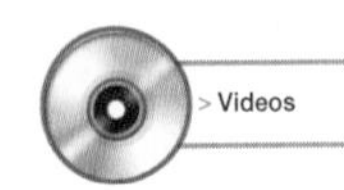

62. $\frac{(x^2)^{-3}(x^{-2})}{(x^2)^{-4}}$

< Objective 2 >

Express each number in scientific notation.

63. **Science and Medicine** The distance from Mars to the sun: 141,000,000 miles (mi)

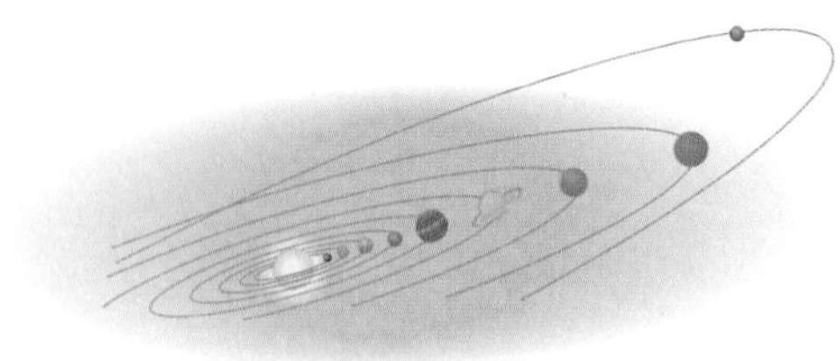

64. **Science and Medicine** The diameter of Earth's orbit: 186,000,000 mi

65. **Science and Medicine** The diameter of Jupiter: 88,000 mi

66. **Science and Medicine** The amount of free oxygen on Earth: 1,500,000,000,000,000,000,000 grams (g)

67. **Science and Medicine** The mass of the moon is approximately 7.37×10^{22} kilograms (kg). If this were written in standard or decimal form, how many zeros would follow the second digit 7?

68. **Science and Medicine** Scientists estimate the mass of our sun to be 1.98×10^{24} kg. If this number were written in standard or decimal form, how many zeros would follow the digit 8?

69. **Science and Medicine** The distance from Pluto to the sun is 5.91×10^{12} mi. If this number were written in standard or decimal form, how many zeros would follow the digit 1?

70. **Science and Medicine** The distance light travels in 100 years is 5.8×10^{14} mi. If this number were written in standard or decimal form, how many zeros would follow the digit 8?

In the following expressions, perform the indicated calculations. Write your result in scientific notation.

71. $(2 \times 10^5)(3 \times 10^3)$

72. $(3.3 \times 10^7)(2 \times 10^4)$

73. $\dfrac{9 \times 10^9}{3 \times 10^6}$

74. $\dfrac{7.5 \times 10^{11}}{1.5 \times 10^7}$

75. $\dfrac{(3.3 \times 10^{15})(9 \times 10^{10})}{(1.1 \times 10^8)(3 \times 10^6)}$

76. $\dfrac{(6 \times 10^{12})(4.8 \times 10^6)}{(1.6 \times 10^7)(3 \times 10^2)}$

77. **Science and Medicine** Alkaid, the most distant star in the Big Dipper, is 2.1×10^{18} meters (m) from Earth. Approximately how long does it take light, traveling at 10^{16} m/year, to travel from Alkaid to Earth?

78. **Science and Medicine** Megrez, the nearest of the Big Dipper stars, is 6.6×10^{17} m from Earth. Approximately how long does it take light, traveling at 10^{16} m/year, to travel from Megrez to Earth?

79. **Statistics** If there are 6×10^9 people on Earth and there is enough freshwater to provide each person with 8×10^5 liters (L), how much freshwater is on Earth?

80. **Statistics** The United States uses an average of 2.6×10^6 L of water per person each year. The United States has approximately 3.2×10^8 people. How many liters of water does the United States use each year?

Basic Skills | Advanced Skills | **Vocational-Technical Applications** | Calculator/Computer | Above and Beyond

81. **Electronics** Convert 234.8 MΩ to ohms (Ω) with the answer represented in scientific notation.

Note: "M" is the symbol for *mega,* the metric prefix for 10^6.

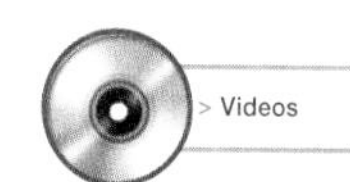

82. **Allied Health** In calculating a red blood cell (RBC) count, using a hemacytometer, medical lab technicians must multiply the number of red blood cells counted in the diluted blood sample by 5 times the dilution correction factor times 10^7 to get the total RBC count in cells per liter (cells/L). Determine the RBC count, in cells per liter, if 340 red blood cells were counted in a sample with a dilution factor of 500.

Answers

69. 10 zeros
70. 13 zeros
71. 6×10^8
72. 6.6×10^{11}
73. 3×10^3
74. 5×10^4
75. 9×10^{11}
76. 6×10^9
77. 210 years
78. 66 years
79. 4.8×10^{15} L
80. 8.32×10^{14} L
81. 2.348×10^8 Ω
82. 8.5×10^{12} cells/L

Basic Skills | Advanced Skills | Vocational-Technical Applications | Calculator/Computer | **Above and Beyond**

Answers

83. 2^9
84. 2^{24}
85. 3^{24}
86. 3^{32}
87. 9^4
88. 27^6
89. 8^3
90. 100^{10}
91. a^{6n}
92. x^{3n+1}
93. r^3
94. w^{4n^2}
95. a^{n^2+2n}
96. x^3
97. w^5
98. Above and Beyond

Do each of the following problems.

83. Write 8^3 as a power of 2. (Remember that $8 = 2^3$.)

84. Write 16^6 as a power of 2.

85. Write 9^{12} as a power of 3.

86. Write 81^8 as a power of 3.

87. Write 3^8 as a power of 9.

88. Write 3^{18} as a power of 27.

89. Write 2^9 as a power of 8.

90. Write 10^{20} as a power of 100.

Assume that n is an integer such that all exponents are positive numbers. Then simplify each of the following expressions.

91. $a^{2n} \cdot a^{4n}$

92. $x^{n+1} \cdot x^{2n}$

93. $\dfrac{r^{n+4}}{r^{n+1}}$

94. $(w^n)^{4n}$

95. $(a^{n+2})^n$

96. $\dfrac{(x^{3n})(x^{n+3})}{x^{4n}}$

97. $\dfrac{(w^n)(w^{4n+5})}{w^{5n}}$

98. Do some research to discover the meaning of the word *googol*. What are the origins of this term? What connection does it have with this section?

Answers

1. 7^4 **3.** 15^6 **5.** x^6 **7.** 2^8 or 256 **9.** $27x^3$ **11.** $135a^3b^3$ **13.** $\frac{9}{16}$ **15.** $16x^8$ **17.** $a^{16}b^{12}$ **19.** $81m^{14}$ **21.** x^{10} **23.** $\frac{m^9}{n^6}$ **25.** 1 **27.** 1 **29.** 1 **31.** $\frac{1}{b^8}$ **33.** $\frac{1}{25}$ **35.** $-\frac{2}{x^5}$ **37.** $-\frac{1}{32x^5}$ **39.** a^8 **41.** x^6 **43.** x^5 **45.** a^3 **47.** $\frac{1}{x^2}$ **49.** $\frac{1}{r^8}$ **51.** x **53.** $\frac{m^9}{n^8}$ **55.** $\frac{16}{a^{12}}$ **57.** $\frac{x^4}{y^6}$ **59.** $\frac{1}{r^2}$ **61.** $\frac{1}{a^{11}}$ **63.** 1.41×10^8 **65.** 8.8×10^4 **67.** 20 zeros **69.** 10 zeros **71.** 6×10^8 **73.** 3×10^3 **75.** 9×10^{11} **77.** 210 years **79.** 4.8×10^{15} L **81.** $2.348 \times 10^8\ \Omega$ **83.** 2^9 **85.** 3^{24} **87.** 9^4 **89.** 8^3 **91.** a^{6n} **93.** r^3 **95.** a^{n^2+2n} **97.** w^5

Definition/Procedure	Example	Reference
The Set of Real Numbers		**Section 1.1**
A *set* is a collection of objects, symbols, or numbers. We can describe a set by listing its contents in braces. Sets are often named by capital letters.	$A = \{1, 2, 3, 4\}$ is a set containing the first four counting numbers.	p. 6
Any object contained in a set is called an *element,* or a *member,* of that set. We write	For the given set A,	
$a \in A$	$3 \in A$	
to indicate that a is an element of set A. We can also write $a \notin A$	$5 \notin A$	
to indicate that a is *not* an element of set A. Two sets are *equal* if they have exactly the same elements. We write $A = B$	If $B = \{4, 3, 2, 1\}$, $A = B$	
to indicate that set A is equal to set B. A set whose elements continue indefinitely is said to be an *infinite* set, and ellipses (. . .) are often used in describing infinite sets.	$E = \{2, 4, 6, \ldots\}$, the set of positive even numbers, is an infinite set.	
A set that has some specific number of elements is called a *finite* set.	$A = \{1, 2, 3, 4\}$ is a finite set. It has four elements.	
Numeric Sets		
The set of *natural numbers* is denoted $\mathbb{N}$, and $\mathbb{N} = \{1, 2, 3, \ldots\}$	$5 \in \mathbb{N}$ $-3 \notin \mathbb{N}$ $\frac{2}{3} \notin \mathbb{N}$	p. 7
The set of *integers* is denoted $\mathbb{Z}$, and $\mathbb{Z} = \{\ldots, -2, -1, 0, 1, 2, \ldots\}$	$7 \in \mathbb{Z}$ $-8 \in \mathbb{Z}$ $\frac{3}{4} \notin \mathbb{Z}$	
The set of *rational numbers* is denoted $\mathbb{Q}$, and $\mathbb{Q} = \left\{\frac{p}{q} \middle\| p, q \in \mathbb{Z}, q \neq 0\right\}$	$-\frac{3}{4} \in \mathbb{Q}$ $-5 \in \mathbb{Q}$ $\sqrt{2} \notin \mathbb{Q}$	
The set of *irrational numbers* is denoted $\mathbb{Q}'$, and $\mathbb{Q}'$ consists of all numbers that *cannot* be expressed as the ratio of two integers—that is, they are *not* rational.	$\sqrt{2} \in \mathbb{Q}'$ $\sqrt[3]{5} \in \mathbb{Q}'$ $\pi \in \mathbb{Q}'$ $\frac{4}{5} \notin \mathbb{Q}'$	
The set of *real numbers* is denoted $\mathbb{R}$, and $\mathbb{R}$ combines the set of rational numbers with the set of irrational numbers.	$\frac{2}{3} \in \mathbb{R}$ $-8 \in \mathbb{R}$ $\sqrt{3} \in \mathbb{R}$ $\sqrt{-2} \notin \mathbb{R}$	
The set of real numbers can be pictured on the *real number line.* 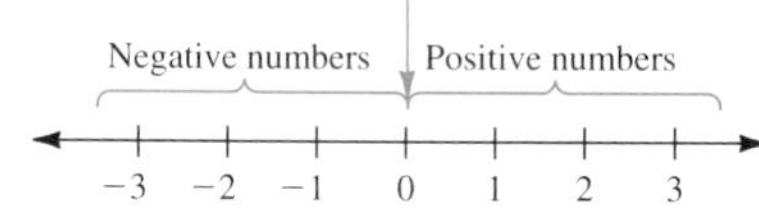	Zero is neither positive nor negative.	
Every real number corresponds to exactly one point on the number line, and every point on that line corresponds to exactly one real number.		

Continued

Definition/Procedure	Example	Reference
Adding Real Numbers		
1. If two numbers have the same sign, add their absolute values.* Give the result the sign of the original numbers. **2.** If two numbers have different signs, subtract their absolute values, the smaller from the larger. Give the result the sign of the number with the larger absolute value. * The *absolute value* of a number represents the distance of the point named by the number from the origin on the number line. Distance is always positive.	$9 + 7 = 16$ $-9 + (-7) = -16$ $15 + (-10) = 5$ $-12 + 9 = -3$	p. 10
Subtracting Real Numbers		
1. Rewrite the subtraction problem as an addition problem by **a.** Changing the subtraction symbol to an addition symbol **b.** Replacing the number being subtracted with its opposite **2.** Add the resulting numbers as before.	$16 - 8 = 16 + (-8)$ $= 8$ $8 - 15 = 8 + (-15)$ $= -7$ $-9 - (-7) = -9 + 7$ $= -2$	p. 10
Multiplying Real Numbers		
Multiply the absolute values of the two numbers. **1.** If the numbers have different signs, the product is negative. **2.** If the numbers have the same sign, the product is positive.	$5(-7) = -35$ $(-10)(9) = -90$ $8 \cdot 7 = 56$ $(-9)(-8) = 72$	p. 10
Dividing Real Numbers		
Divide the absolute values of the two numbers. **1.** If the numbers have different signs, the quotient is negative. **2.** If the numbers have the same sign, the quotient is positive.	$\frac{-32}{4} = -8$ $\frac{75}{-5} = -15$ $\frac{20}{5} = 4$ $\frac{-18}{-9} = 2$	p. 10
Operations and Properties		**Section 1.2**
Addition		
$x + y$ means the **sum** of x and y or x **plus** y. Some other words indicating addition are "more than" and "increased by."	The sum of x and 5 is $x + 5$. 7 more than a is $a + 7$. b increased by 3 is $b + 3$.	p. 17

Definition/Procedure	Example	Reference
Subtraction		
$x - y$ means the **difference** of x and y or x **minus** y. Some other words indicating subtraction are "less than" and "decreased by."	The difference of x and 3 is $x - 3$. 5 less than p is $p - 5$. a decreased by 4 is $a - 4$.	p. 17
Multiplication		
$x \cdot y$, $(x)(y)$, xy — These all mean the **product** of x and y or x **times** y.	The product of m and n is mn. The product of 2 and the sum of a and b is $2(a + b)$.	p. 17
Division		
$\frac{x}{y}$ means x **divided by** y or the **quotient** when x is divided by y.	n divided by 5 is $\frac{n}{5}$. The sum of a and b, divided by 3, is $\frac{a + b}{3}$.	p. 17
Order of Operations		
1. Simplify within the innermost grouping symbol, and then work outward until all grouping symbols are removed. **2.** Evaluate any expressions involving exponents. **3.** Perform any multiplication and division, working from left to right. **4.** Then do any addition and subtraction, again working from left to right.	$4(5 - 2)^2 + 7 = 4(3)^2 + 7$ $= 4 \cdot 9 + 7$ $= 36 + 7$ $= 43$	p. 18
For any real numbers a, b, and c:		
Closure Properties		
$a + b$ is a real number $a \cdot b$ is a real number	$3 + 4$ is a real number. $3 \cdot 4$ is a real number.	p. 20
Commutative Properties		
$a + b = b + a$ $a \cdot b = b \cdot a$	$7 + 5 = 5 + 7$ $7 \cdot 5 = 5 \cdot 7$	p. 20

Continued

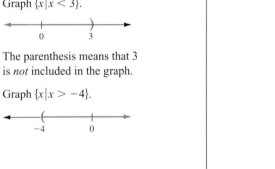

Definition/Procedure	Example	Reference
Associative Properties		
$(a + b) + c = a + (b + c)$ $(a \cdot b) \cdot c = a \cdot (b \cdot c)$	$(2 + 7) + 4 = 2 + (7 + 4)$ $(2 \cdot 7) \cdot 4 = 2 \cdot (7 \cdot 4)$	*p.* 20
Identities		
There exists a unique real number 0 such that $a + 0 = 0 + a = a$ The number 0 is called the *additive identity.*	$7 + 0 = 7$ $-8 + 0 = -8$	*p.* 20
There exists a unique real number 1 such that $a \cdot 1 = 1 \cdot a = a$ The number 1 is called the *multiplicative identity.*	$3 \cdot 1 = 3$ $(-5)(1) = -5$	
Inverse Properties		
For any real number a, there exists a unique real number $-a$ such that $a + (-a) = (-a) + a = 0$ and $-a$ is called the *additive inverse,* or the *opposite,* of a.	$3 + (-3) = 0$	*p.* 20
For any real number $a (a \neq 0)$, there exists a unique number $\frac{1}{a}$ such that $a \cdot \frac{1}{a} = \frac{1}{a} \cdot a = 1$ $\frac{1}{a}$ is called the *multiplicative inverse,* or the *reciprocal,* of a.	$(3)\left(\frac{1}{3}\right) = 1$	
Distributive Property		
$a(b + c) = ab + ac$	$5(4 + 3) = 5 \cdot 4 + 5 \cdot 3$	*p.* 21
Inequalities and Absolute Value		**Section 1.3**
Inequalities		
The inequality relations are as follows:		*p.* 29
1. *Less than,* which we denote with the symbol $<$. We write $a < b$ to indicate that a is less than b. Graphically this means that the point corresponding to a must lie *to the left* of the point corresponding to b. 	Graph $\{x \mid x < 3\}$.  The parenthesis means that 3 is *not* included in the graph.	
2. *Greater than,* which we denote with the symbol $>$. We write $a > b$ to indicate that a is greater than b. Graphically this means that the point corresponding to a must lie *to the right* of the point corresponding to b. 	Graph $\{x \mid x > -4\}$. 	

Definition/Procedure	Example	Reference

Two other symbols, ≤ and ≥, are also used in writing inequalities.

The statement $a \leq b$ is read "a is less than or equal to b."

The statement $a \geq b$ is read "a is greater than or equal to b."

Graph $\{x \mid x \leq -1\}$.

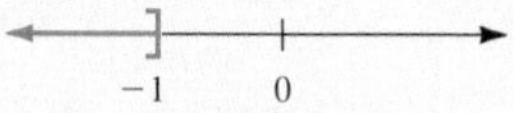

The bracket means that −1 is included in the graph.

p. 30

Double Inequalities

An inequality of the form

$-4 < x < 3$

is called a *double-inequality* and combines the two inequality statements

$x > -4$ and $x < 3$

Graph $\{x \mid -4 < x < 3\}$.

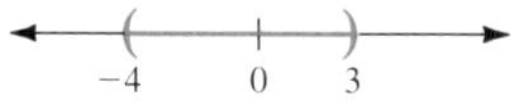

p. 31

Absolute Value

The *absolute value* of a real number is the distance (on the number line) between the point named by that real number and the origin. The absolute value of a number a is denoted $|a|$. In general, we can define the absolute value of any real number a as

$$|a| = \begin{cases} a & \text{if } a \text{ is positive} \\ 0 & \text{if } a \text{ is zero} \\ -a & \text{if } a \text{ is negative} \end{cases}$$

$|7| = 7$

$|0| = 0$

$|-7| = -(-7) = 7$

p. 32

Algebraic Expressions

Section 1.4

Algebraic Expressions

An expression that contains numbers, letters (called *variables*), and operations.

p. 39

Evaluating Algebraic Expressions

To evaluate an algebraic expression:

1. Replace each variable or letter with its number value.
2. Do the necessary arithmetic.

Evaluate $x - y$ if $x = 5$ and $y = -2$.

$x - y$

$= 5 - (-2)$

$= 5 + 2 = 7$

p. 39

Continued

Definition/Procedure	Example	Reference
Term		
A number or the product of a number and one or more variables.	5, $2a$, and $3x^2$ are all terms.	p. 42
Combining Like Terms		
To combine like terms (terms containing the same variables raised to the same powers): **1.** Add or subtract the coefficients (the numbers multiplying the variables). **2.** Attach the common variable.	$5x + 2x = 7x$ (5 + 2) $8a - 5a = 3a$ (8 − 5)	p. 44
Properties of Exponents and Scientific Notation		**Section 1.5**
Using Exponents		
Base The number that is raised to a power. **Exponent** The exponent is written to the right and above the base. The exponent tells the number of times the base is to be used as a factor.	$5^3 = 5 \cdot 5 \cdot 5 = 125$ (Exponent; Base; Three factors) This is read "5 to the third power" or "5 cubed."	p. 53
Properties of Exponents		
1. $a^m \cdot a^n = a^{m+n}$ **2.** $\frac{a^m}{a^n} = a^{m-n}$ **3.** $(a^m)^n = a^{mn}$ **4.** $(ab)^m = a^m b^m$ **5.** $\left(\frac{a}{b}\right)^m = \frac{a^m}{b^m}$	$3^3 \cdot 3^4 = 3^7$ $\frac{10^6}{10^2} = 10^4$ $(2^3)^5 = 2^{15}$ $(3x)^2 = 9x^2$ $\left(\frac{2}{3}\right)^3 = \frac{8}{27}$	pp. 53–57
The Zero Power		
Any nonzero expression taken to the power zero equals 1.	$3^0 = 1$ $(5x)^0 = 1$	p. 59
Negative Powers		
An expression taken to a negative power equals its reciprocal taken to the opposite of its power.	$x^{-1} = \frac{1}{x}$	p. 60
Scientific Notation		
Any number written in the form $a \times 10^n$ in which $1 \le a < 10$ and n is an integer, is written in scientific notation.	$6.02 \times 10^6 = 6{,}020{,}000$	p. 63

summary exercises :: chapter 1

This summary exercise set is provided to give you practice with each of the objectives of this chapter. Each exercise is keyed to the appropriate chapter section. When you are finished, you can check your answers to the odd-numbered exercises against those presented in the back of the text. If you have difficulty with any of these questions, go back and reread the examples from that section. The answers to the even-numbered exercises appear in the *Instructor's Solutions Manual.* Your instructor will give you guidelines on how to best use these exercises in your instructional setting.

1.1 *Name all the numeric sets to which each of the following numbers belong. The numeric sets consist of the natural numbers* $\mathbb{N}$, *integers* $\mathbb{Z}$, *rational numbers* $\mathbb{Q}$, *irrational numbers* $\mathbb{Q}'$, *and real numbers* $\mathbb{R}$.

1. 0 $\mathbb{Z}, \mathbb{Q}, \mathbb{R}$

2. -9 $\mathbb{Z}, \mathbb{Q}, \mathbb{R}$

3. $-\sqrt{3}$ $\mathbb{Q}', \mathbb{R}$

4. $\frac{4}{3}$ $\mathbb{Q}, \mathbb{R}$

5. 3π $\mathbb{Q}', \mathbb{R}$

6. $-\frac{5}{8}$ $\mathbb{Q}, \mathbb{R}$

7. $1.\overline{74}$ $\mathbb{Q}, \mathbb{R}$

8. 3.25 $\mathbb{Q}, \mathbb{R}$

On the number line provided, graph the points corresponding to the elements of each of the given sets.

9. $\{1, 4, 7\}$

0 1 4 7

10. $\{-4, 0, 4\}$

−4 0 4

11. $\left\{-\frac{2}{3}, \frac{5}{3}, \frac{7}{3}\right\}$

$-\frac{2}{3}$ 0 $\frac{5}{3}$ $\frac{7}{3}$

12. $\{-\sqrt{5}, -\sqrt{2}, \sqrt{3}\}$

$-\sqrt{5}$ $-\sqrt{2}$ 0 $\sqrt{3}$

Add.

13. $-3 + (-8)$ −11

14. $10 + (-4)$ 6

15. $6 + (-6)$ 0

16. $-16 + (-16)$ −32

17. $-18 + 0$ −18

18. $\frac{3}{8} + \left(-\frac{11}{8}\right)$ −1

19. $5.7 + (-9.7)$ −4

20. $-18 + 7 + (-3)$ −14

Subtract.

21. $8 - 13$ −5

22. $-7 - 10$ −17

23. $10 - (-7)$ 17

24. $-5 - (-1)$ −4

25. $-9 - (-9)$ 0

26. $0 - (-2)$ 2

27. $-\frac{5}{4} - \left(-\frac{17}{4}\right)$ 3

28. $7.9 - (-8.1)$ 16

Multiply.

29. $(10)(-7)$ −70

30. $(-8)(-5)$ 40

31. $(-3)(-15)$ 45

32. $(1)(-15)$ −15

33. $(0)(-8)$ 0

34. $\left(\frac{2}{3}\right)\left(-\frac{3}{2}\right)$ −1

35. $(-4)\left(\frac{3}{8}\right)$ $-\frac{3}{2}$

36. $\left(-\frac{5}{4}\right)(-1)$ $\frac{5}{4}$

Divide.

37. $\frac{80}{16}$ 5

38. $\frac{-63}{7}$ −9

39. $\frac{-81}{-9}$ 9

40. $\frac{0}{-5}$ 0

41. $\frac{32}{-8}$ −4

42. $\frac{-7}{0}$ Undefined

1.2 *Translate the following statements to symbols.*

43. a increased by 4 $a + 4$

44. 6 times y $6y$

45. 8 less than w $w - 8$

46. b decreased by 7 $b - 7$

47. Twice the difference of n and 2 $2(n - 2)$

48. The product of 3 and a, divided by b $\frac{3a}{b}$

49. The quotient of the sum of x and y, divided by 3 $\frac{x + y}{3}$

50. 4 less than the product of s and t $st - 4$

Evaluate each of the following expressions.

51. $2 + 5 \cdot 3$ 17

52. $5(4 - 3)$ 5

53. $5 + 3 \cdot 5 - 3$ 17

54. $(5 + 3)(5 - 3)$ 16

55. $6^2 - 2^2$ 32

56. $2 + 4 \cdot 3^2$ 38

57. $(3 + 4)4^2$ 112

58. $2 + (3 \cdot 5)^2$ 227

State the property that is used to justify each of the following statements.

59. $25x + (-25x) = 0$

Additive inverse

60. $(25x)\left(\frac{1}{25x}\right) = 1$

Multiplicative inverse

61. $a + (3a + 4) = (a + 3a) + 4$

Associative property of addition

62. $2x + 4 + 6x = 2x + 6x + 4$

Commutative property of addition

63. $3(2x) = (3 \cdot 2)x$

Associative property of multiplication

64. $4(2a + 1) = 4 \cdot 2a + 4 \cdot 1$

Distributive property

65. $5y + 0 = 5y$

Additive identity

66. $(1)(4w) = 4w$

Multiplicative identity

1.3 *Graph each of the following inequalities.*

67. $x > 3$

0 3

68. $x \le 5$

0 5

69. $x < \frac{7}{2}$

0 $\frac{7}{2}$

70. $x \geq -6$

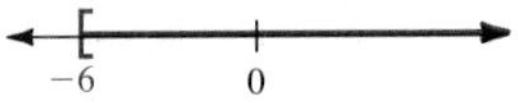

71. $-3 < x < 6$

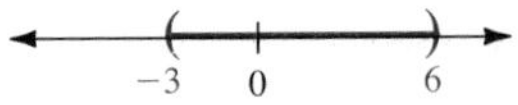

72. $-5 \leq x < -1$

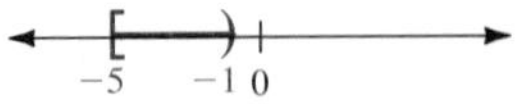

Write each of the following expressions without absolute value symbols.

73. $|9|$ 9

74. $|-4.3|$ 4.3

75. $-|3|$ −3

76. $-|-3.5|$ −3.5

77. $|4| + |-4|$ 8

78. $|-3| + |-5|$ 8

79. $-(|3| + |-4|)$ −7

80. $-(|-7| + |-9|)$ −16

1.4 *Evaluate the expressions if* $x = -3$, $y = 6$, $z = -4$, *and* $w = 2$.

81. $3x + w$ −7

82. $5y - 4z$ 46

83. $x + y - 3z$ 15

84. $5z^2$ 80

85. $3x^2 - 2w^2$ 19

86. $3x^3$ −81

87. $5(x^2 - w^2)$ 25

88. $\dfrac{6z}{2w}$ −6

89. $\dfrac{2x - 4z}{y - z}$ 1

90. $\dfrac{3x - y}{w - x}$ −3

91. $\dfrac{x(y^2 - z^2)}{(y + z)(y - z)}$ −3

92. $\dfrac{y(x - w)^2}{x^2 - 2xw + w^2}$ 6

List the terms of the expressions.

93. $4a^3 - 3a^2$ $4a^3, -3a^2$

94. $5x^2 - 7x + 3$ $5x^2, -7x, 3$

Circle like terms.

95. $5m^2, -3m, -4m^2, 5m^3, m^2$ $5m^2, -4m^2, m^2$

96. $4ab^2, 3b^2, -5a, ab^2, 7a^2, -3ab^2, 4a^2b$ $4ab^2, ab^2, -3ab^2$

Combine like terms.

97. $5c + 7c$ $12c$

98. $2x + 5x$ $7x$

99. $\frac{1}{3}a - 4a + \frac{2}{3}a$ $-3a$

100. $\frac{4}{7} - 3y + \frac{3}{7} - 2y$ $1 - 5y$

101. $1.3x + 8 - 4.3x + 2$ $-3x + 10$

102. $5ab^2 + 2ab^2$ $7ab^2$

103. $7a + 3b + 12a - 2b$ $19a + b$

104. $6x - 2x + 5y - 3x$ $x + 5y$

105. $5x^3 + 17x^2 - 2x^3 - 8x^2$ $3x^3 + 9x^2$

106. $3a^3 + 5a^2 + 4a - 2a^3 - 3a^2 - a$ $a^3 + 2a^2 + 3a$

1.5 *Write each product in exponential form. Identify the base and the exponent.*

107. $b \cdot b \cdot b \cdot b \cdot b$ b^5, base b, exponent 5

108. $(6w)(6w)(6w)(6w)$ $(6w)^4$, base $6w$, exponent 4

Simplify each expression, using the properties of exponents.

109. $w^3 \cdot w^8$ w^{11}

110. $(-2)^2(-2)^4$ $(-2)^6$

111. $(x^3y^2)(x^7y^4)$ $x^{10}y^6$

112. $(5a^0b^3)(-2a^2b^4)$ $-10a^2b^7$

113. $\frac{a^{14}}{a^8}$ a^6

114. $\frac{(3x + 1)^7}{(3x + 1)^3}$ $(3x + 1)^4$

115. $(m^2n)^4$ m^8n^4

116. $(3a^2b^5)^3$ $27a^6b^{15}$

117. $(3b^2)^0(-2b^5)^2$ $4b^{10}$

118. $\left(\frac{c}{d^3}\right)^2$ $\frac{c^2}{d^6}$

119. $\left(\frac{2a^2b^4}{c^3}\right)^3$ $\frac{8a^6b^{12}}{c^9}$

120. $\left(\frac{x^8}{y^5}\right)\left(\frac{y^3}{3x^2}\right)^2$ $\frac{x^4y}{9}$

Evaluate each expression.

121. 4^0 1

122. $(3a)^0$ 1

123. $6x^0$ 6

124. $(3a^4b)^0$ 1

Simplify each expression using positive exponents.

125. x^{-5} $\frac{1}{x^5}$

126. 3^{-3} $\frac{1}{3^3} = \frac{1}{27}$

127. 10^{-4} $\frac{1}{10^4}$

128. $4x^{-4}$ $\frac{4}{x^4}$

129. $\frac{x^6}{x^8}$ $\frac{1}{x^2}$

130. m^7m^{-9} $\frac{1}{m^2}$

131. $\frac{a^{-4}}{a^{-9}}$ a^5

132. $\frac{x^2y^{-3}}{x^{-3}y^2}$ $\frac{x^5}{y^5}$

133. $(3m^{-3})^2$ $\frac{9}{m^6}$

134. $\frac{(a^4)^{-3}}{(a^{-2})^{-3}}$ $\frac{1}{a^{18}}$

Express each number in scientific notation.

135. The average distance from Earth to the sun is 150,000,000,000 m. 1.5×10^{11} m

136. A bat emits a sound with a frequency of 51,000 cycles per second (cps). 5.1×10^4 cps

137. The diameter of a grain of salt is 0.000062 m. 6.2×10^{-5} m

Compute the expression using scientific notation and express your answers in that form.

138. $(2.3 \times 10^{-3})(1.4 \times 10^{12})$ 3.22×10^9

139. $(4.8 \times 10^{-10})(6.5 \times 10^{34})$ 3.12×10^{25}

140. $\frac{(8 \times 10^{23})}{(4 \times 10^6)}$ 2×10^{17}

141. $\frac{(5.4 \times 10^{-12})}{(4.5 \times 10^{16})}$ 1.2×10^{-28}

self-test 1

The purpose of this chapter test is to help you check your progress so that you can find sections and concepts that you need to review before the next exam. Allow yourself about an hour to take this test. At the end of that hour, check your answers against those given in the back of this text. If you missed any, note the section reference that accompanies the answer. Go back to that section and reread the examples until you have mastered that particular concept.

Name ______________

Section ________ Date ________

1.1

For the set of numbers

$$\left\{-6, -\frac{2}{3}, 4.1, -\sqrt{3}, 0, \pi, 9, \frac{5}{4}, 0.\overline{78}\right\}$$

which numbers belong to the following numeric sets?

1. **(a)** Natural numbers $\mathbb{N}$ **(b)** Integers $\mathbb{Z}$
(c) Rational numbers $\mathbb{Q}$ **(d)** Irrational numbers $\mathbb{Q}'$
(e) Real numbers $\mathbb{R}$

1.2

Translate each of the following statements, using symbols.

2. 2 times the sum of x and y

3. 8 less than p, divided by t

Evaluate each of the following expressions.

4. $2 + 5 \cdot 3^2$

5. $(2 - 5)4^2$

State the property that is used to justify each of the following statements.

6. $y + (2y + 5) = (y + 2y) + 5$

7. $4(2c + 7) = 4 \cdot 2c + 4 \cdot 7$

1.3

Graph each of the following sets.

8. $x > -5$

9. $-1 \le x \le 4$

Write the following expressions without absolute value symbols.

10. $|-3| - |-6|$

11. $-|5| + |-7|$

1.4

12. If $x = 2$, $y = -1$, and $z = 3$, evaluate the expression $\dfrac{9x^2y}{3z}$.

Answers

1. (a) 9; (b) −6, 0, 9; (c) $-6, -\frac{2}{3}, 4.1, 0, 9, \frac{5}{4}, 0.\overline{78}$; (d) $-\sqrt{3}, \pi$; (e) All are real numbers.
2. $2(x + y)$
3. $\dfrac{p - 8}{t}$
4. 47
5. −48
6. Associative property of addition
7. Distributive property
8. See exercise
9. See exercise
10. −3
11. 2
12. −4

Answers

13. $21a + 13$

14. $-\frac{1}{3}x$

15. $15x^3y^7$

16. $4ab^3$

17. $\frac{4w^4}{9t^6}$

18. $16x^{18}y^{17}$

19. 1

20. 6

21. $\frac{3}{b^7}$

22. $\frac{1}{y^4}$

23. 3.12×10^{-10}

Simplify each expression by combining like terms.

13. $6a + 5(3a + 4) - 7$

14. $\frac{1}{3}x - \frac{1}{3}(9 + 2x) + 3$

1.5

Simplify each expression.

15. $3x^2y^3 \cdot 5xy^4$

16. $\frac{20a^3b^5}{5a^2b^2}$

17. $\left(\frac{2w^2}{3t^3}\right)^2$

18. $(2x^3y^2)^4(x^2y^3)^3$

Evaluate (assume the variables are nonzero).

19. 8^0

20. $6x^0$

Simplify and rewrite, using positive exponents.

21. $3b^{-7}$

22. y^4y^{-8}

Compute and answer using scientific notation.

23. $(6 \times 10^{-23})(5.2 \times 10^{12})$

Activity 1 :: An Introduction to Searching

Each chapter in this text concludes with a chapter activity such as this one. These activities provide you with the opportunity to apply the math you studied in that chapter to a relevant topic. Your instructor will determine how best to use these activities in your instructional setting. You may find yourself working in class or outside of class; you may find yourself working alone or in small groups; you may even be asked to perform research in a library or on the Internet.

Many (though not all) of these activities will require you to use the Internet. This activity is designed to familiarize you with searching the Internet for information.

If you are new to computers or the Internet, your instructor (or perhaps a friend) can help you get started. You will need to access the Internet through one of the many Web browsers, such as Microsoft's Internet Explorer, Netscape Navigator, Mozilla Firefox, or AOL's browser.

We will ask that you "bookmark" various websites—some browsers refer to bookmarks as "favorites" or "preferences." Bookmarking a website allows you to return to the site at a later time by choosing it from a list of bookmarked sites. This way, you do not have to search for it every time you wish to visit that site.

Most Web browsers provide you with a way to bookmark a website. When you are looking at a website that you wish to bookmark, click on the menu that says Bookmarks (or Favorites, Preferences, or whatever name your browser uses), and click on the menu item Add Bookmark (or Add to Favorites, Create Preference, etc.). The next time you want to look at the website that you bookmarked, you need only click on the Bookmark menu and then click on the title of the site saved.

Activity

First, you will need to connect to the Internet. Next, you will need to access a page containing a *search engine* that searches the World Wide Web at large (rather than just doing an internal search). Many *default* home pages (such as www.msn.com and www.aol.com) contain a *search* field. If yours does not, several of the more popular sites that do are listed here:

www.yahoo.com

www.altavista.com

www.google.com

www.lycos.com

Access one of these websites or use some other search engine, as you see fit. Now we are ready to continue.

I.

1. Locate your state government home page. You may accomplish this by typing your state name into the search field and clicking on Go or Find. A (long) list of "matches" will appear. Read the blurbs to determine which belongs to the state government. **Note:** You should not need to go through more than the first page or two of listings. Bookmark this site (as previously described).
2. Find an official e-mail address for the governor of your state. Find the names of the senators for your state. See if you can locate e-mail addresses for the senators of your state. **Note:** If their e-mail addresses are not provided, then we will find them later.

3. Locate the home page of your college or university, or the flagship university in your state.
4. Repeat steps 1 to 3 for a different state.

II.

1. Search for the White House in Washington D.C. Find an official e-mail address for the President of the United States.
2. Find the home page for the U.S. Congress. If you could not find e-mail addresses for senators on the state pages (step I.2), then find one through the U.S. Congress website.
3. Locate the home page of the U.S. Census Bureau and bookmark this site. Find the census data for your state. How many people live in your state, according to the most recent census? How many people live in your city or hometown?
4. Repeat step 3 for the second state that you used in part I (choose the state capital as the city).

III.

1. Search for the National Weather Service's Weather Forecast Office for Sioux Falls, South Dakota (SD). (Use Google.com or Lycos.com for your search engine.) Find the temperature chart for past highs and lows for the month of January. What was the record high for January over the past 100 years? What was the record low?
2. Locate the wind-chill index chart and the wind-chill calculator. Using the mathematical formula given, calculate the wind-chill factor for the highs and lows with wind speeds of 10, 20, and 30 miles per hour (mi/h). Check your answers with the index chart or wind-chill calculator.

chapter 1 >Make the Connection

IV.

1. Choose a country on some other continent. Can you locate the name and e-mail address of that nation's leader? Census data? Weather?
2. Locate a home page for a university in the country found in step 1.
3. Locate the home page for the United Nations (UN) and bookmark this site. Does the UN site provide some of the information asked for in step 1? Does the UN data differ from the data provided by the nation itself?

V.

1. Locate two different images of the so-called Mandelbrot fractal. These can be the same image with different colors, or they can be two different views of the fractal.
2. Locate an image of a different fractal.
3. Locate information on fractals in general. (What are they?) Write a paragraph describing fractals in general and express your thoughts on the fractals you found in steps 1 and 2.

VI.

1. Search for a business or an organization that hires people in your field; if you are not already on a career path, determine a potential career for yourself. Bookmark this site.
2. Write a paragraph describing the organization as it has presented itself on its website.
3. Find the name and an e-mail address of a person whom you would contact if you were applying for a job.
4. Find information describing the application process for someone seeking employment with this business or organization.
5. Are there forms that the site provides for job seekers? Can you download them (using Save As or a link)? If forms exist, what format are these forms in (Adobe pdf files, Microsoft Word documents, or some other format)?

You have now searched through the World Wide Web for information. Later, you will be asked to use the skills gained here to complete some of the other activities in this text.

Linear Equations and Inequalities

INTRODUCTION

Quality control is exercised in nearly all manufacturing processes. Samples of the product are taken at each stage, and various measurements are made to see if the product fits within given specifications.

In the pharmaceutical-making process, great caution must be exercised to ensure that the medicines and drugs are pure and contain precisely what is indicated on the label. Guaranteeing such purity is a task the quality control division of the pharmaceutical company assumes.

A lab technician working in quality control must run a series of tests on samples of every ingredient, even simple ingredients such as salt (NaCl). One such test is a measure of how much weight is lost as a sample is dried. The technician must set up a 3-hour procedure that involves cleaning and drying bottles and stoppers and then weighing them while they are empty and again when they contain samples of the substance to be heated and dried. At the end of the procedure, to compute the percentage of weight loss from drying, the technician uses the formula

$$L = \frac{W_g - W_f}{W_g - T} \cdot 100$$

CHAPTER 2 OUTLINE

in which L = percentage loss in drying

W_g = weight of container and sample

W_f = weight of container and sample after drying process completed

T = weight of empty container

This equation is more useful when solved for one of the variables, here W_f or T. In Section 2.2 of this chapter, you will learn how to solve such an equation. At the end of the chapter, you will find a more in-depth activity involving formulas for foreign travel.

pretest 2

Name ____________

Section ________ Date ________

This pretest will provide a preview of the types of exercises you will encounter in each section of this chapter. The answers for these exercises can be found in the back of the text. If you are working on your own, or ahead of the class, this pretest can help you identify the sections in which you should focus more of your time.

2.1 Solve the following equations.

1. $8 - 2x = 2$

2. $7x - 5 = 6x - 4$

3. $4(2x + 3) = 7x + 5$

4. $\dfrac{x - 2}{3} + \dfrac{x}{5} = \dfrac{-2}{15}$

2.2 Solve the following literal equations for the indicated variable.

5. $ax + by = c$ (for x)

6. $A = \dfrac{1}{2}bh$ (for b)

2.3 Solve the following applications.

7. Alicia earns \$130 per month more than Dane. If they earn a combined total of \$2,690 per month, what are their monthly salaries?

8. The area of a triangle with a height of 5 centimeters (cm) is 30 cm^2. Find the base.

9. The sum of two consecutive integers is 85. Find the two integers.

2.4 Solve the following inequalities. Then graph the solution.

10. $5x - 3 \geq -18$

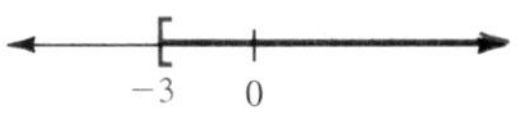

11. $3(x + 5) < 6x + 9$

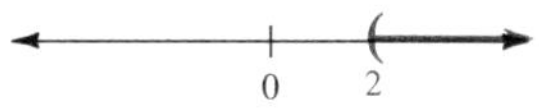

12. $\dfrac{x + 1}{3} + \dfrac{1}{2} > \dfrac{x + 10}{6}$

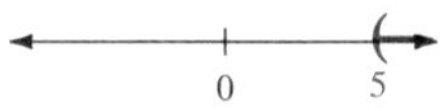

13. $-6 < 2 - 4x \leq 10$

2.5 Solve the following absolute value equations and inequalities.

14. $|2x - 1| = 5$

15. $|3x - 2| = |x + 2|$

16. $|4x - 3| \geq 9$

17. $|5 - 4x| < 13$

Answers

1. $x = 3$
2. $x = 1$
3. $x = -7$
4. $x = 1$
5. $x = \dfrac{c - by}{a}$
6. $b = \dfrac{2A}{h}$
7. Dane: \$1,280, Alicia: \$1,410
8. 12 cm
9. 42, 43
10. $x \geq -3$; See exercise
11. $x > 2$; See exercise
12. $x > 5$; See exercise
13. $-2 \leq x < 2$; See exercise
14. $x = -2$ or $x = 3$
15. $x = 0$ or $x = 2$
16. $x \leq -\dfrac{3}{2}$ or $x \geq 3$
17. $-2 < x < \dfrac{9}{2}$

2.1 Solutions of Linear Equations in One Variable

< 2.1 Objectives >

1 > Apply the properties of equations

2 > Combine like terms to solve an equation

RECALL

An equation is a mathematical statement in which two expressions represent the same quantity.

We begin this chapter by considering one of the most important tools of mathematics—the equation. The ability to recognize and solve various types of equations and inequalities is probably the most useful algebraic skill. In this section we review solving linear equations in one variable. Let us start with the following definition.

Definition

Linear Equation in One Variable

A **linear equation in one variable** is any equation that can be written in the form

$ax + b = 0$

in which a and b are any real numbers and

$a \neq 0$

NOTE

We also say the solution *satisfies* the equation.

Linear equations are also called **first-degree equations** because the highest power of the variable is the first power, or first degree.

The **solution** of an equation in one variable is any number that will make the equation a true statement. To find the solution to such an equation requires using **equivalent equations.**

Definition

Equivalent Equations

Two equations are *equivalent* if they have the same solution.

NOTE

You can verify that −3 is a solution by replacing x with −3 in each equation.

For example, the three equations

$$5x + 5 = 2x - 4 \qquad 3x = -9 \qquad x = -3$$

are all equivalent because they all have the same solution, −3. Note that replacing x with −3 will give a true statement in the third equation, but it is not as clear that −3 is a solution for the other two equations. This leads us to an equation-solving strategy of *isolating* the variable, as is the case in the equation $x = -3$.

To form equivalent equations that will lead to the solution of a linear equation, we need two properties of equations: addition and multiplication. The addition property is defined here.

Property

Addition Property of Equations

If $a = b$

then $a + c = b + c$

NOTE

Adding the same quantity to both sides of an equation gives an equivalent equation, which holds true whether c is positive or negative.

Recall that subtraction can always be defined in terms of addition, so

$$a - c = a + (-c)$$

The addition property also allows us to *subtract* the same quantity from both sides of an equation.

The multiplication property is defined here.

Property

Multiplication Property of Equations

If $a = b$

then $ac = bc$ when $c \neq 0$

NOTE

Multiplying both sides of an equation by the same nonzero quantity gives an equivalent equation.

It is also the case that division can be defined in terms of multiplication, so

$$\frac{a}{c} = a \cdot \frac{1}{c} \qquad c \neq 0$$

The multiplication property allows us to *divide* both sides of an equation by the same nonzero quantity.

Example 1 Applying the Properties of Equations

< Objective 1 >

Solve for x.

$$3x - 5 = 4$$

$$3x - 5 + 5 = 4 + 5 \qquad \text{Apply the addition property. Add 5 to both sides.}$$

$$3x = 9$$

$$\frac{1}{3}(3x) = \frac{1}{3}(9) \qquad \text{Apply the multiplication property. Multiply both sides by } \frac{1}{3}.$$

$$\left(\frac{1}{3} \cdot 3\right)(x) = 3$$

So, $x = 3$.

NOTES

Why did we add 5 when we started solving? We added 5 because it is the *opposite* of -5, and the resulting equation will have the variable term on the left and the constant term on the right.

When applying the multiplication property, we chose $\frac{1}{3}$ because $\frac{1}{3}$ is the *reciprocal* of 3 and $\frac{1}{3} \cdot 3 = 1$.

Because any application of the addition or multiplication properties leads to an equivalent equation, each of the preceding equations in Example 1 has the same solution, 3.

To check this result, we can replace x with 3 in the original equation:

$$3(3) - 5 \stackrel{?}{=} 4$$
$$9 - 5 \stackrel{?}{=} 4$$
$$4 = 4 \quad \text{A true statement.}$$

You may prefer a slightly different approach in the last step of the preceding solution. From the second equation,

$$3x = 9$$

The multiplication property can be used to *divide* both sides of the equation by 3. Then,

$$\frac{3x}{3} = \frac{9}{3}$$
$$x = 3$$

Of course, the result is the same.

Check Yourself 1

Solve for x.

$$4x - 7 = 17$$

The steps involved in using the addition and multiplication properties to solve an equation are the same if more terms are involved in an equation.

Example 2 Applying the Properties of Equations

NOTES

Adding 11 puts the constant term on the right.

If you prefer, write

$5x - 2x = 2x - 2x + 4$

Again:

$3x = 4$

This is the same as dividing both sides by 3. So

$\frac{3x}{3} = \frac{4}{3}$

$x = \frac{4}{3}$

Solve for x.

$$5x - 11 = 2x - 7$$

Our objective is to use the properties of equations to isolate x on one side of an equivalent equation.

$$5x - 11 + 11 = 2x - 7 + 11 \quad \text{Apply the addition property. Add 11 to both sides.}$$
$$5x = 2x + 4$$
$$5x + (-2x) = 2x + (-2x) + 4 \quad \text{Apply the addition property to combine the } x \text{ terms. Add } -2x \text{ to both sides.}$$

We have now isolated the variable term on the left side of the equation.

$$3x = 4$$
$$\frac{1}{3}(3x) = \frac{1}{3}(4) \quad \text{Apply the multiplication property to isolate } x. \text{ Multiply both sides by } \frac{1}{3}.$$
$$x = \frac{4}{3}$$

We leave it to you to check this result by substitution.

Check Yourself 2

Solve for x.

$7x - 12 = 2x - 9$

Both sides of an equation should be simplified as much as possible *before* the addition and multiplication properties are applied. If like terms are involved on one side (or on both sides) of an equation, they should be combined before an attempt is made to isolate the variable. Example 3 illustrates this approach.

Example 3 Applying the Properties of Equations with Like Terms

< Objective 2 >

NOTE

There are like terms on the left and right sides of the equation.

Solve for x.

$$8x + 2 - 3x = 8 + 3x + 2$$

Here we combine the like terms $8x$ and $-3x$ on the left and the like terms 8 and 2 on the right as our first step. We then have

$$5x + 2 = 3x + 10$$

We can now solve as before.

$$5x + 2 - 2 = 3x + 10 - 2 \quad \text{Apply the addition property. Subtract 2 from both sides.}$$

$$5x = 3x + 8$$

$$5x - 3x = 3x - 3x + 8 \quad \text{Apply the addition property. Subtract } 3x \text{ from both sides.}$$

$$2x = 8$$

$$\frac{2x}{2} = \frac{8}{2} \quad \text{Apply the multiplication property. Divide both sides by 2.}$$

$$x = 4$$

The solution is 4, which can be checked by returning to the *original equation.*

Check Yourself 3

Solve for x.

$7x - 3 - 5x = 10 + 4x + 3$

If parentheses are involved on one or both sides of an equation, the parentheses should be removed by applying the distributive property as the first step. Like terms should then be combined before an attempt is made to isolate the variable. Consider Example 4.

Example 4 Applying the Properties of Equations with Parentheses

Solve for x.

$$x + 3(3x - 1) = 4(x + 2) + 4$$

$$x + 9x - 3 = 4x + 8 + 4 \quad \text{Apply the distributive property.}$$

$$10x - 3 = 4x + 12 \quad \text{Combine like terms on each side.}$$

RECALL

To isolate the x, we must get x alone on the left side with a coefficient of 1.

Now, isolate variable x on the left side.

$10x - 3 + 3 = 4x + 12 + 3$ Apply the addition property. Add 3 to both sides.

$10x = 4x + 15$

$10x - 4x = 4x - 4x + 15$ Apply the addition property. Subtract $4x$ from both sides.

$6x = 15$

$\frac{6x}{6} = \frac{15}{6}$ Apply the multiplication property. Divide both sides by 6.

$x = \frac{5}{2}$

The solution is $\frac{5}{2}$. Again, this can be checked by returning to the original equation.

Check Yourself 4

Solve for x.

$x + 5(x + 2) = 3(3x - 2) + 18$

If grouping symbols (parentheses, brackets, braces) are "nested," we simplify by working from the inside out as demonstrated in Example 5.

Example 5 **Applying the Properties of Equations with Nested Grouping Symbols**

Solve for x.

$4 - 3[x - 3(x + 2)] = -6 + 16$

$4 - 3[x - 3x - 6] = -6 + 16$ Apply the distributive property to the parentheses inside the brackets.

$4 - 3[-2x - 6] = 10$ Combine like terms inside the brackets and to the right of the equal sign.

$4 + 6x + 18 = 10$ Apply the distributive property to the brackets.

$6x + 22 = 10$ Combine like terms on the left.

$6x + 22 - 22 = 10 - 22$ Apply the addition property. Subtract 22 from both sides.

$6x = -12$

$\frac{6x}{6} = \frac{-12}{6}$ Apply the multiplication property. Divide both sides by 6.

$x = -2$

The solution is -2. This can be checked by returning to the original equation.

Check Yourself 5

Solve for x.

$6 - [x - 4(x - 3)] = 1 - 10$

To solve an equation involving fractions, the first step is to multiply both sides of the equation by the **least common multiple (LCM)** of all denominators in the equation. This will clear the equation of fractions, and we can proceed as before.

Example 6 Applying the Properties of Equations with Fractions

NOTE

The LCM of a set of denominators is also called the **lowest common denominator (LCD).**

Solve for x.

$$\frac{x}{2} - \frac{2}{3} = \frac{5}{6}$$

First, multiply each side by 6, the least common multiple of 2, 3, and 6.

$$6\left(\frac{x}{2} - \frac{2}{3}\right) = 6\left(\frac{5}{6}\right)$$

$$6\left(\frac{x}{2}\right) - 6\left(\frac{2}{3}\right) = 6\left(\frac{5}{6}\right) \quad \text{Apply the distributive property.}$$

$$\overset{3}{\cancel{6}}\left(\frac{x}{\underset{1}{\cancel{2}}}\right) - \overset{2}{\cancel{6}}\left(\frac{2}{\underset{1}{\cancel{3}}}\right) = \overset{1}{\cancel{6}}\left(\frac{5}{\underset{1}{\cancel{6}}}\right) \quad \text{Simplify.}$$

NOTE

The equation is now cleared of fractions.

$$3x - 4 = 5$$

$$3x - 4 + 4 = 5 + 4 \quad \text{Apply the addition property. Add 4 to both sides.}$$

$$3x = 9$$

$$x = 3$$

The solution, 3, can be checked as before by returning to the original equation.

Check Yourself 6

Solve for x.

$$\frac{x}{4} - \frac{4}{5} = \frac{19}{20}$$

Be sure that the distributive property is applied properly so that *every term* of the equation is multiplied by the LCM.

Example 7 Applying the Properties of Equations with Fractions

Solve for x.

$$\frac{2x - 1}{5} + 1 = \frac{x}{2}$$

First, multiply each side by 10, the LCM of 5 and 2.

$$10\left(\frac{2x-1}{5}+1\right) = 10\left(\frac{x}{2}\right)$$

$$\overset{2}{\cancel{10}}\left(\frac{2x-1}{\underset{1}{\cancel{5}}}\right) + 10(1) = \overset{5}{\cancel{10}}\left(\frac{x}{\underset{1}{\cancel{2}}}\right)$$ Apply the distributive property on the left.

$$2(2x-1) + 10 = 5x$$

$$4x - 2 + 10 = 5x$$ Apply the distributive property.

$$4x + 8 = 5x$$ Combine like terms.

$$4x - 4x + 8 = 5x - 4x$$ Apply the addition property to isolate x on the right. Subtract $4x$ from both sides.

$$8 = x$$

The solution for the original equation is 8.

Check Yourself 7

Solve for x.

$$\frac{3x+1}{4} - 2 = \frac{x+1}{3}$$

Thus far, we have considered only equations of the form $ax + b = 0$, in which $a \neq 0$. If we allow the possibility that $a = 0$, two additional equation forms arise. The resulting equations can be classified into three types depending on the nature of their solutions.

1. An equation that is true for only particular values of the variable is called a **conditional equation.** Here the equation can be written in the form

   $ax + b = 0$

   in which $a \neq 0$. This case was illustrated in all our previous examples and exercises.
2. An equation that is true for all possible values of the variable is called an **identity.** In this case, *both* a and b are 0, so we get the equation $0 = 0$. This will be the case if both sides of the equation reduce to the same expression (a true statement).
3. An equation that is never true, no matter what the value of the variable, is called a **contradiction.** For example, if a is 0 but b is nonzero, we end up with something like $4 = 0$. This will be the case if both sides of the equation reduce to a false statement.

Example 8 illustrates the second and third cases.

Example 8 Identities and Contradictions

NOTE

See the earlier definition of an identity. By adding 6 to both sides of this equation, we have $0 = 0$.

(a) Solve for x.

$$2(x-3) - 2x = -6$$

$$2x - 6 - 2x = -6$$ Apply the distributive property.

$$-6 = -6$$ Combine like terms.

Because the two sides reduce to the true statement $-6 = -6$, the original equation is an *identity,* and the solution is the set of all real numbers.

(b) Solve for x.

$$
\begin{aligned}
3(x + 1) - 2x &= x + 4 \\
3x + 3 - 2x &= x + 4 && \text{Apply the distributive property.} \\
x + 3 &= x + 4 && \text{Combine like terms.} \\
x - x + 3 &= x - x + 4 && \text{Apply the addition property. Subtract } x \text{ from both sides.} \\
3 &= 4 && \text{A \textit{false} statement.}
\end{aligned}
$$

Because the two sides reduce to the false statement $3 = 4$, the original equation is a contradiction. There are no values of the variable that can satisfy the equation. There is no solution. This is sometimes referred to as the **empty set** or $\varnothing$.

NOTE

See the earlier definition of a contradiction. Subtracting 3 from both sides, we have $0 = 1$.

Check Yourself 8

Determine whether each of the following equations is a conditional equation, an identity, or a contradiction.

(a) $2(x + 1) - 3 = x$ **(b)** $2(x + 1) - 3 = 2x + 1$
(c) $2(x + 1) - 3 = 2x - 1$

NOTES

An **algorithm** is a step-by-step process for problem solving.

If the equation derived in step 5 is always true, the original equation was an identity. If the equation is always false, the original equation was a contradiction.

An organized step-by-step procedure is the key to an effective equation-solving strategy. The following algorithm summarizes our work in this section and gives you guidance in approaching the problems that follow.

Step by Step

Solving Linear Equations in One Variable

Step 1 Remove any grouping symbols by applying the distributive property.
Step 2 Multiply both sides of the equation by the LCM of any denominators, to clear the equation of fractions.
Step 3 Combine any like terms that appear on either side of the equation.
Step 4 Apply the addition property of equations to write an equivalent equation with the variable term on *one side* of the equation and the constant term on the *other side.*
Step 5 Apply the multiplication property of equations to write an equivalent equation with the variable isolated on one side of the equation.
Step 6 Check the solution in the *original* equation.

When you are solving an equation for which a calculator is recommended, *it is often easiest to do all calculations as the last step.*

Example 9 Evaluating Expressions Using a Calculator

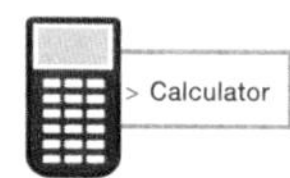

Solve the following equation for x.

$$\frac{185(x - 3.25) + 1{,}650}{500} = 159.44$$

Following the steps of the algorithm, we get

$$\frac{185x - 185 \cdot 3.25 + 1{,}650}{500} = 159.44$$ Apply the distributive property.

$$185x - 185 \cdot 3.25 + 1{,}650 = 159.44 \cdot 500$$ Multiply by the LCM, 500.

$$185x = 159.44 \cdot 500 + 185 \cdot 3.25 - 1{,}650$$ Apply the addition property. Add $185 \cdot 3.25$ and subtract 1,650 on both sides.

$$x = \frac{159.44 \cdot 500 + 185 \cdot 3.25 - 1{,}650}{185}$$ Apply the multiplication property. Divide both sides by 185.

Now, remembering to insert parentheses around the numerator, we use a calculator to simplify the expression on the right.

$x = 425.25$

Check Yourself 9

Solve the following equation for x.

$$\frac{2{,}200(x + 17.5) - 1{,}550}{75} = 2{,}326$$

Check Yourself ANSWERS

1. $x = 6$ **2.** $x = \frac{3}{5}$ **3.** $x = -8$ **4.** $x = -\frac{2}{3}$ **5.** $x = -1$ **6.** $x = 7$
7. $x = 5$ **8.** **(a)** Conditional; **(b)** contradiction; **(c)** identity **9.** $x = 62.5$

Reading Your Text

The following fill-in-the-blank exercises are designed to ensure that you understand some of the key vocabulary used in this section.

SECTION 2.1

(a) A linear equation in one variable is any equation that can be written in the form __________ in which a and b are any real numbers and $a \neq 0$.

(b) Solving linear equations in one variable requires using __________ equations.

(c) An equation that is true for all possible values of the variable is called an __________.

(d) A __________ is an equation that is never true, no matter what the value of the variable.

2.1 exercises

MathZone

Boost your grade at mathzone.com!
> Practice Problems
> NetTutor
> Self-Tests
> e-Professors
> Videos

Name ______________________

Section __________ Date __________

< Objectives 1, 2 >

Solve each equation, and check your results.

1. $5x - 8 = 17$

2. $4x + 9 = -11$

3. $8 - 7x = -41$

4. $-7 - 4x = 21$

5. $7x - 5 = 6x + 6$

6. $9x + 4 = 8x - 3$

7. $8x - 4 = 3x - 24$

8. $5x + 2 = 2x - 5$

9. $7x - 4 = 2x + 26$

10. $11x - 3 = 4x - 31$

11. $4x - 3 = 1 - 2x$

12. $8x + 5 = -19 - 4x$

13. $2x + 8 = 7x - 37$

14. $3x - 5 = 9x + 22$

Simplify and then solve each equation.

15. $5x - 2 + x = 9 + 3x + 10$

16. $5x + 5 - x = -7 + x - 2$

17. $7x - 3 - 4x = 5 + 5x - 13$

18. $8x - 3 - 6x = 7 + 5x + 17$

19. $5x = 3(x - 6)$

20. $2(x - 15) = 7x$

21. $5(8 - x) = 3x$

22. $7x = 7(6 - x)$

23. $2(2x - 1) = 3(x + 1)$

24. $3(3x - 1) = 4(3x + 1)$

25. $8x - 3(2x - 4) = 17$

26. $7x - 4(3x + 4) = 9$

27. $7(3x + 4) = 8(2x + 5) + 13$

28. $-4(2x - 1) + 3(3x + 1) = 9$

Answers

1. $x = 5$	**2.** $x = -5$
3. $x = 7$	**4.** $x = -7$
5. $x = 11$	**6.** $x = -7$
7. $x = -4$	**8.** $x = -\frac{7}{3}$
9. $x = 6$	**10.** $x = -4$
11. $x = \frac{2}{3}$	**12.** $x = -2$
13. $x = 9$	**14.** $x = -\frac{9}{2}$
15. $x = 7$	**16.** $x = -\frac{14}{3}$
17. $x = \frac{5}{2}$	**18.** $x = -9$
19. $x = -9$	**20.** $x = -6$
21. $x = 5$	**22.** $x = 3$
23. $x = 5$	**24.** $x = -\frac{7}{3}$
25. $x = \frac{5}{2}$	**26.** $x = -5$
27. $x = 5$	**28.** $x = 2$

Answers

29. $x = -\frac{4}{3}$
30. $x = \frac{3}{5}$
31. $x = -13$
32. $x = -3$
33. $x = 7$
34. $x = 5$
35. $x = 30$
36. $x = 24$
37. $x = 6$
38. $x = \frac{5}{9}$
39. $x = 15$
40. $x = 12$
41. $x = 3$
42. $x = 6$
43. $x = \frac{3}{2}$
44. $x = -\frac{2}{3}$
45. $x = 20$
46. $x = 5$
47. Conditional
48. Identity
49. Contradiction
50. Conditional

29. $9 - 4(3x + 1) = 3(6 - 3x) - 9$

30. $13 - 4(5x + 1) = 3(7 - 5x) - 15$

31. $5 - 2[x - 2(x + 1)] = 63 - 4[x - 3(x + 2)]$

32. $7 - 5[x - 3(x + 2)] = 25 - 2[x - 2(x - 3)]$

Clear fractions and then solve each equation.

33. $\frac{2x}{3} - \frac{5}{3} = 3$

34. $\frac{3x}{4} + \frac{1}{4} = 4$

35. $\frac{x}{6} + \frac{x}{5} = 11$

36. $\frac{x}{6} - \frac{x}{8} = 1$

37. $\frac{2x}{3} - \frac{x}{4} = \frac{5}{2}$

38. $\frac{5x}{6} + \frac{2x}{3} = \frac{5}{6}$

39. $\frac{x}{5} - \frac{x - 7}{3} = \frac{1}{3}$

40. $\frac{x}{6} + \frac{3}{4} = \frac{x - 1}{4}$

41. $\frac{5x - 3}{4} - 2 = \frac{x}{3}$

42. $\frac{6x - 1}{5} - \frac{2x}{3} = 3$

43. $\frac{2x + 3}{5} - \frac{2x - 1}{3} = \frac{8}{15}$

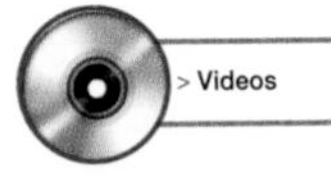

44. $\frac{3x}{5} - \frac{3x - 1}{2} = \frac{11}{10}$

45. $0.5x - 6 = 0.2x$

46. $0.7x - 7 = 0.3x - 5$

Classify each equation as a conditional equation, an identity, or a contradiction.

47. $3(x - 1) = 2x + 3$

48. $2(x + 3) = 2x + 6$

49. $3(x - 1) = 3x + 3$

50. $2(x + 3) = x + 5$

51. $3(x - 1) = 3x - 3$

52. $2(x + 3) = 3x + 5$

53. $3x - (x - 3) = 2(x + 1) + 2$

54. $5x - (x + 4) = 4(x - 2) + 4$

55. $\frac{x}{2} - \frac{x}{3} = \frac{x}{6}$

56. $\frac{3x}{4} - \frac{2x}{3} = \frac{x}{6}$

Label the exercises **true** *or* **false.**

57. Adding the same value to both sides of an equation creates an equivalent equation.

58. Multiplying both sides of an equation by 0 creates an equivalent equation.

59. To clear an equation of fractions, we multiply both sides by the least common multiple (LCM) of the numerators.

60. The multiplication property of equations allows us to divide both sides by the same nonzero quantity.

61. Some equations have more than one solution.

62. No matter what value is substituted for x, the expressions on either side of the equal sign have the same value.

Basic Skills | Advanced Skills | Vocational-Technical Applications | **Calculator/Computer** | Above and Beyond

Use a calculator to solve the given equations for x. Round your answer to two decimal places.

63. $\frac{63(x - 2.45) + 325}{200} = 3$

64. $\frac{47(x + 3.15) - 263}{315} = 11$

65. $\frac{-23x - 14(x - 9.75)}{23.46} = 15.75$

66. $\frac{-15.25x + 12(2x - 11.23)}{-15.6} = 8.4$

Answers

51. Identity

52. Conditional

53. Contradiction

54. Identity

55. Identity

56. Conditional

57. True

58. False

59. False

60. True

61. True

62. False

63. $x = 6.82$

64. $x = 76.17$

65. $x = -6.30$

66. $x = 0.43$

Answers

67. Solutions are the same.

68. A value for which the original equation is true.

69. (a) An equation that is true for all possible values of the variable.
(b) An equation that is never true, no matter what the variable's value.

70. Multiplying by 0 would always give 0 = 0.

Basic Skills | Advanced Skills | Vocational-Technical Applications | Calculator/Computer | **Above and Beyond**

67. What is the common characteristic of equivalent equations?

68. What is meant by a *solution* to a linear equation?

69. Define **(a)** identity and **(b)** contradiction.

70. Why does the multiplication property of equations not include multiplying both sides of an equation by 0?

Answers

1. $x = 5$ **3.** $x = 7$ **5.** $x = 11$ **7.** $x = -4$ **9.** $x = 6$ **11.** $x = \frac{2}{3}$ **13.** $x = 9$ **15.** $x = 7$ **17.** $x = \frac{5}{2}$ **19.** $x = -9$ **21.** $x = 5$ **23.** $x = 5$ **25.** $x = \frac{5}{2}$ **27.** $x = 5$ **29.** $x = -\frac{4}{3}$ **31.** $x = -13$ **33.** $x = 7$ **35.** $x = 30$ **37.** $x = 6$ **39.** $x = 15$ **41.** $x = 3$ **43.** $x = \frac{3}{2}$ **45.** $x = 20$ **47.** Conditional **49.** Contradiction **51.** Identity **53.** Contradiction **55.** Identity **57.** True **59.** False **61.** True **63.** $x = 6.82$ **65.** $x = -6.30$ **67.** Solutions are the same. **69. (a)** An equation that is true for all possible values of the variable. **(b)** An equation that is never true, no matter what the variable's value.

2.2 Literal Equations and Formulas

< 2.2 Objective >

1 > Solve a literal equation for a specified variable

Many problems in algebra require the use of **formulas** for their solution. Formulas are simply equations that express a relationship between more than one variable or letter. You are already familiar with a number of examples. For instance,

$$P = R \cdot B \qquad A = \frac{1}{2}bh \qquad P = 2L + 2W$$

are formulas for percentage, the area of a triangle, and the perimeter of a rectangle, respectively.

One useful application of the equation-solving skills we considered in Section 2.1 is in rewriting these formulas, also called **literal equations,** in more convenient equivalent forms.

NOTE

A *literal equation* is any equation that involves more than one variable or letter.

Generally, that more convenient form is one in which the original formula or equation is solved for a particular variable or letter. This is called **solving the equation for a variable,** and the steps used in the process are very similar to those you saw earlier in solving linear equations.

Consider Example 1.

Example 1 Solving a Literal Equation Involving Distance

< Objective 1 >

Solve the formula

$d = r \cdot t$ for t

This formula gives distance d in terms of a rate r and time t.

To solve for t means to isolate t on one side of the equation. This can be done by dividing both sides by r. Given

$$d = r \cdot t$$

$$\frac{d}{r} = \frac{r \cdot t}{r} \qquad \text{Apply the multiplication property. Divide by } r.$$

$$\frac{d}{r} = t$$

We usually write the equation in the equivalent form with the desired variable on the left. So

$$t = \frac{d}{r}$$

We now have t in terms of d and r, as required.

Check Yourself 1

Solve the formula $C = 2\pi r$ for r.

Solving a formula for a particular variable may require the use of both properties of equations, as Example 2 illustrates.

Example 2 Solving a Literal Equation Involving Geometry

Solve the formula

$P = 2L + 2W \quad \text{for } L$

This formula gives the perimeter of a rectangle P in terms of its width W and its length L.

To solve for L, subtract $2W$ from both sides.

NOTE

We want to isolate the term with the variable we are solving for—here L.

$$P = 2L + 2W$$

$$P - 2W = 2L + 2W - 2W \qquad \text{Apply the addition property. Subtract } 2W.$$

$$P - 2W = 2L$$

$$\frac{P - 2W}{2} = \frac{2L}{2} \qquad \text{Apply the multiplication property. Divide by 2.}$$

$$\frac{P - 2W}{2} = L$$

$$L = \frac{P - 2W}{2}$$

This gives L in terms of P and W, as desired.

NOTE

This result can also be written as

$L = \frac{P}{2} - W$

Check Yourself 2

Solve the formula $ax + by = c$ for y.

You may also have to apply the distributive property in solving for a variable. Consider Example 3.

Example 3 Solving a Literal Equation Involving Money

Solve the formula

$A = P(1 + rt) \quad \text{for } r$

This formula gives the amount A in an account earning simple interest, with principal P, interest rate r, and time t.

$$A = P(1 + rt) = P + Prt \qquad \text{Apply the distributive property.}$$

$$A - P = P - P + Prt \qquad \text{Apply the addition property. Subtract } P.$$

$$A - P = Prt$$

$$\frac{A - P}{Pt} = \frac{Prt}{Pt}$$ Apply the multiplication property. Divide by Pt.

$$\frac{A - P}{Pt} = r$$

$$r = \frac{A - P}{Pt}$$

Check Yourself 3

Solve the equation for n.

$S = 180(n - 2)$

Often it is necessary to apply the multiplication property, to clear the literal equation of fractions, as the first step of the solution process. This is illustrated in Example 4.

Example 4 Solving a Literal Equation Involving Money

Solve the formula for C.

$$D = \frac{C - S}{n}$$

This formula gives the yearly depreciation D for an item in terms of its cost C, its salvage value S, and the number of years n.

As our first step, we multiply both sides of the given equation by n to clear of fractions.

NOTE

On the *right* we have

$\frac{n}{n} = 1$

and multiplying by 1 leaves $C - S$.

$$D = \frac{C - S}{n}$$

$$nD = n\left(\frac{C - S}{n}\right)$$

$$nD = C - S$$

$$nD + S = C - S + S$$ Apply the addition property. Add S.

$$nD + S = C$$

$$C = nD + S$$

The cost C is now represented in terms of n, D, and S.

Check Yourself 4

Solve the formula $V = \frac{1}{3}\pi r^2 h$ for h.

You may have to apply both the addition and the multiplication properties when solving a formula for a specified variable. Example 5 illustrates this property.

Example 5 Solving a Literal Equation Involving Geometry

NOTE

This is a linear equation in two variables. You will see this again in Chapter 3.

Solve the equation for x.

$$y = mx + b$$

Remember that we want to end up with x alone on one side of the equation.

$$y = mx + b$$

$$y - b = mx + b - b \qquad \text{Apply the addition property. Subtract } b.$$

$$y - b = mx$$

$$\frac{y - b}{m} = \frac{mx}{m} \qquad \text{Apply the multiplication property. Divide by } m.$$

$$\frac{y - b}{m} = x$$

or

$$x = \frac{y - b}{m}$$

Check Yourself 5

Solve $v = v_0 + gt$ for t.

We now summarize the steps illustrated by our examples.

Step by Step

Solving a Formula or Literal Equation

Step 1 Remove any grouping symbols by applying the distributive property.

Step 2 If necessary, multiply both sides of the equation by the same term to clear it of fractions.

Step 3 Add or subtract the same term on both sides of the equation so that all terms involving the variable that you are solving for are on one side of the equation and all other terms are on the other side.

Step 4 Divide both sides of the equation by the coefficient of the variable that you are solving for.

We end this section by looking at an application of solving a literal equation.

Example 6 Solving a Literal Equation Involving Money

Suppose that the amount in an account, 3 years after a principal of \$5,000 was invested, is \$6,050. What was the interest rate?

From Example 3,

$$A = P + Prt$$

NOTE

Do you see the advantage of having our equation solved for the desired variable?

in which A is the amount in the account, P is the principal, r is the interest rate, and t is the time that the money has been invested. By the result of Example 3 we have

$$r = \frac{A - P}{Pt}$$

and we can substitute the known values into the second equation.

$$r = \frac{6{,}050 - 5{,}000}{(5{,}000)(3)}$$

$$r = \frac{1{,}050}{15{,}000} = 0.07 = 7\%$$

The interest rate is 7%.

Check Yourself 6

Suppose that the amount in an account, 4 years after a principal of \$3,000 was invested, is \$3,720. What was the interest rate?

Check Yourself ANSWERS

1. $r = \dfrac{C}{2\pi}$ **2.** $y = \dfrac{c - ax}{b}$ **3.** $n = \dfrac{S + 360}{180}$ **4.** $h = \dfrac{3V}{\pi r^2}$

5. $t = \dfrac{v - v_0}{g}$ **6.** 6%

Reading Your Text

The following fill-in-the-blank exercises are designed to ensure that you understand some of the key vocabulary used in this section.

SECTION 2.2

(a) Equations that express a relationship between more than one variable or letter are called ______________ or ______________.

(b) The steps involved in solving an equation for a specified variable are very similar to those used in solving ______________ equations.

(c) To solve the formula $d = r \cdot t$ for t means to ______________ t on one side of the equation.

(d) When solving an application of a literal equation, there is an advantage in having the equation solved for the desired ______________ first.

2.2 exercises

Basic Skills | Advanced Skills | Vocational-Technical Applications | Calculator/Computer | Above and Beyond

MathZone

Boost your grade at mathzone.com!
- Practice Problems
- NetTutor
- Self-Tests
- e-Professors
- Videos

Name ______________

Section ________ Date ________

Answers

1. $s = \frac{P}{4}$
2. $B = \frac{V}{h}$
3. $R = \frac{E}{I}$
4. $r = \frac{I}{Pt}$
5. $H = \frac{V}{LW}$
6. $h = \frac{V}{\pi r^2}$
7. $B = 180 - A - C$
8. $R = \frac{P}{I^2}$
9. $x = -\frac{b}{a}$
10. $m = \frac{y - b}{x}$
11. $g = \frac{2s}{t^2}$
12. $m = \frac{2K}{v^2}$
13. $L = \frac{P - 2W}{2}$ or $L = \frac{P}{2} - W$
14. $y = \frac{c - ax}{b}$
15. $T = \frac{PV}{K}$
16. $h = \frac{3V}{\pi r^2}$

< Objective 1 >

Solve each literal equation for the indicated variable.

1. $P = 4s$ (for s) Perimeter of a square
2. $V = Bh$ (for B) Volume of a prism
3. $E = IR$ (for R) Voltage in an electric circuit
4. $I = Prt$ (for r) Simple interest
5. $V = LWH$ (for H) Volume of a rectangular solid

6. $V = \pi r^2 h$ (for h) Volume of a cylinder
7. $A + B + C = 180$ (for B) Measure of angles in a triangle
8. $P = I^2R$ (for R) Power in an electric circuit
9. $ax + b = 0$ (for x) Linear equation in one variable

10. $y = mx + b$ (for m) Slope-intercept form for a line
11. $s = \frac{1}{2}gt^2$ (for g) Distance

12. $K = \frac{1}{2}mv^2$ (for m) Energy
13. $P = 2L + 2W$ (for L) Perimeter of a rectangle
14. $ax + by = c$ (for y) Linear equation in two variables
15. $V = \frac{KT}{P}$ (for T) Volume of a gas
16. $V = \frac{1}{3}\pi r^2 h$ (for h) Volume of a cone

17. $x = \frac{a + b}{2}$ (for b) Mean of two numbers

18. $D = \frac{C - s}{n}$ (for s) Depreciation

19. $F = \frac{9}{5}C + 32$ (for C) Celsius/Fahrenheit conversion

20. $A = P + Prt$ (for t) Amount at simple interest

21. $S = 2\pi r^2 + 2\pi rh$ (for h) Total surface area of a cylinder

22. $A = \frac{1}{2}h(B + b)$ (for b) Area of a trapezoid

23. $R = C(1 + r)$ (for r) Retail sales

24. $V = \frac{1}{3}Bh$ (for B) Volume of a pyramid

Solve each of the following exercises using the indicated formula from exercises 1 to 24.

25. **Geometry** A rectangular solid has a base with length 8 centimeters (cm) and width 5 cm. If the volume of the solid is 120 cubic centimeters (cm^3), find the height of the solid. (See exercise 5.)

26. **Geometry** A cylinder has a radius of 4 inches (in.). If the volume of the cylinder is 48π cubic inches (in.^{3}), what is the height of the cylinder? (See exercise 6.)

27. **Business and Finance** A principal of $3,000 was invested in a savings account for 3 years. If the interest earned for the period was $450, what was the interest rate? (See exercise 4.)

28. **Geometry** If the perimeter of a rectangle is 60 feet (ft) and the width is 12 ft, find its length. (See exercise 13.)

29. **Science and Medicine** The high temperature in New York for a particular day was reported at 77°F. How would the same temperature have been given in degrees Celsius? (See exercise 19.)

Answers

17. $b = 2x - a$

18. $s = C - nD$

19. $C = \frac{5}{9}(F - 32)$ or $C = \frac{5(F - 32)}{9}$

20. $t = \frac{A - P}{Pr}$ or $t = \frac{A}{Pr} - \frac{1}{r}$

21. $h = \frac{S - 2\pi r^2}{2\pi r}$ or $h = \frac{S}{2\pi r} - r$

22. $b = \frac{2A - hB}{h}$ or $b = \frac{2A}{h} - B$

23. $r = \frac{R - C}{C}$ or $r = \frac{R}{C} - 1$

24. $B = \frac{3V}{h}$

25. 3 cm

26. 3 in.

27. 5%

28. 18 ft

29. 25°C

Answers

30. 8 m

31. 3 cm

32. 9 in.

33. 6%

34. 15%

35. 8 cm

36. 15 in.^{2}

30. **GEOMETRY** Rose's garden is in the shape of a trapezoid. If the height of the trapezoid is 16 meters (m), one base is 20 m, and the area is 224 square meters (m^2), find the length of the other base. (See exercise 22.)

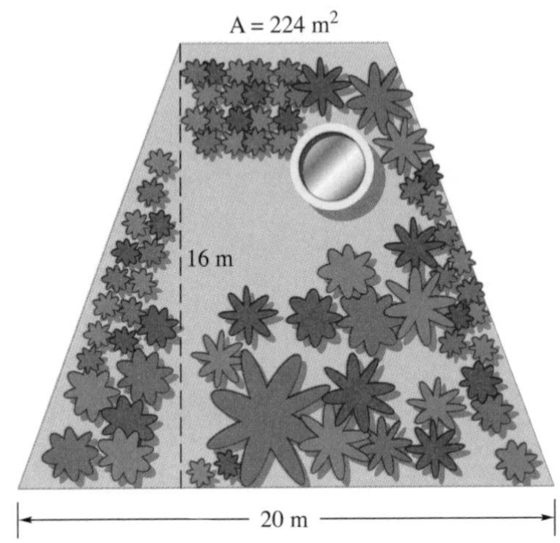

31. **GEOMETRY** A rectangular solid has a base with length 6 cm and width 4 cm. If the volume of the solid is 72 cm^3, find the height of the solid. (See exercise 5.) > Videos

32. **GEOMETRY** A cylinder has a radius of 4 in. If its volume is 144π in.^{3}, what is the height of the cylinder? (See exercise 6.)

33. **BUSINESS AND FINANCE** A principal of $2,000 was invested in a savings account for 4 years. If the interest earned for that period was $480, what was the interest rate? (See exercise 4.)

34. **BUSINESS AND FINANCE** The retail selling price of an item, R, was $20.70. If its cost, C, to the store was $18, what was the markup rate, r? (See exercise 23.)

35. **GEOMETRY** The radius of the base of a cone is 3 cm. If the volume of the cone is 24π cm^3, find the height of the cone. (See exercise 16.)

36. **GEOMETRY** The volume of a pyramid is 30 in.^{3} If the height of the pyramid is 6 in., find the area of its base, B. (See exercise 24.)

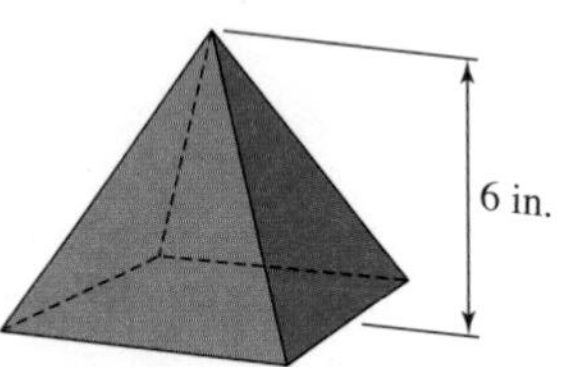

37. Geometry If the perimeter of a rectangle is 60 ft and its length is 18 ft, find its width. (See exercise 13.)

38. Business and Finance The yearly depreciation, D, for a piece of machinery was \$1,500 over 8 years. If the cost of the machinery was \$15,000, what was its salvage value, S? (See exercise 18.)

39. Business and Finance A principal of \$5,000 was invested in a time-deposit account paying 9% annual interest. If the amount in the account at the end of a certain period was \$7,250, for how long was the money invested? (See exercise 20.)

40. Geometry The area of a trapezoid is 36 in.^{2} If its height is 4 in. and the length of one of the bases is 11 in., find the length of the other base. (See exercise 22.)

Basic Skills | Advanced Skills | **Vocational-Technical Applications** | Calculator/Computer | Above and Beyond

41. Electronics The kinetic energy of an object is given by the formula

$$KE = \frac{mv^2}{2} \qquad m = \text{mass, } v = \text{velocity}$$

Find the kinetic energy [in joules (J)] of an object that has a mass of 46 kilograms (kg) and is moving at a velocity of 16 meters per second (m/s).

42. Electronics The power of a circuit can be given by any of the following formulas:

$$P = IV \qquad I = \text{current, } V = \text{voltage}$$

$$P = \frac{V^2}{R} \qquad R = \text{resistance}$$

$$P = I^2R$$

Find the power [in watts (W)] for each of the following circuits:

(a) Voltage = 110 volts (V), current = 13 amperes (A)

(b) Voltage = 220 V, resistance = 22 ohms (Ω)

(c) Current = 25 A, resistance = 9 Ω

43. Allied Health In radiographic procedures, two important factors are the milliamperage (mA), or amount of radiation used, and the time, s, in seconds, of exposure to the radiation. Generally, the radiographer keeps a constant mAs, which is equal to the milliamperage multiplied by the time: mAs = mA $\times$ s. Since the mAs tends to be held constant, it is often more useful to have the formula solved for one of the other variables. Rewrite this equation to give a formula for the exposure time, s.

Answers

37. 12 ft

38. \$3,000

39. 5 years

40. 7 in.

41. 5,888 J

42. (a) 1,430 W; (b) 2,200 W; (c) 5,625 W

43. $s = \frac{\text{mAs}}{\text{mA}}$

Answers

44. $t = \dfrac{d}{v}$; 5 sec

44. **Information Technology** Pat is downloading a 1,920,000-byte file from a server at a bandwidth of 384,000 bytes per second (bytes/s) over a DSL connection. To figure out how much time, t, it will take, she needs to calculate the quotient of the size of the file, d, and the bandwidth, v, of the connection. Write the formula for the time, and calculate the time.

Answers

1. $s = \dfrac{P}{4}$ **3.** $R = \dfrac{E}{I}$ **5.** $H = \dfrac{V}{LW}$ **7.** $B = 180 - A - C$

9. $x = -\dfrac{b}{a}$ **11.** $g = \dfrac{2s}{t^2}$ **13.** $L = \dfrac{P - 2W}{2}$ or $L = \dfrac{P}{2} - W$

15. $T = \dfrac{PV}{K}$ **17.** $b = 2x - a$ **19.** $C = \dfrac{5}{9}(F - 32)$ or $C = \dfrac{5(F - 32)}{9}$

21. $h = \dfrac{S - 2\pi r^2}{2\pi r}$ or $h = \dfrac{S}{2\pi r} - r$ **23.** $r = \dfrac{R - C}{C}$ or $r = \dfrac{R}{C} - 1$

25. 3 cm **27.** 5% **29.** 25°C **31.** 3 cm **33.** 6% **35.** 8 cm

37. 12 ft **39.** 5 years **41.** 5,888 J **43.** $s = \dfrac{\text{mA}s}{\text{mA}}$

2.3 Applications and Problem Solving

< 2.3 Objectives >

1 > Apply the five-step strategy for solving an application

2 > Solve applications using a linear equation

"I have a problem!"

How often have you, or a friend, started a conversation with this statement? And, more important, what do you do to solve the problem? George Polya, in his book *How to Solve It,* contends that there are four parts to solving any problem.

1. Understand the problem.
2. Devise a plan.
3. Carry out the plan.
4. Look back.

This approach is useful for solving any problem. One of the reasons that mathematics is a required course in most programs is that, in a math class, you are constantly practicing the art of problem solving. To help you remember to use Polya's approach on problems that you encounter outside of the classroom, we will consistently use a series of steps similar to those he prescribed.

Recall that an **algorithm** is a series of steps that, when followed, solves a problem. The following five-step algorithm is essentially the same as Polya's approach, but for one thing. We have divided the "devise a plan" step into two steps that are more directly relevant to solving mathematical problems. Here is our five-step approach:

Step by Step

Solving Applications

Step 1 Read the problem carefully to determine the unknown quantities.

Step 2 Choose a variable to represent the unknown. Express all other unknowns in terms of this variable.

Step 3 Translate the problem to the language of algebra to form an equation.

Step 4 Solve the equation, and answer the question of the original problem.

Step 5 Verify your solution by returning to the original problem.

Our first two applications fall into the category of **uniform-motion problems.** Uniform motion means that the speed of an object does not change over a certain distance or time. To solve these problems, we will need a relationship between the distance traveled, represented by d; the rate (or speed) of travel, r; and the time of that travel, t. In general, the relationship for the distance traveled d, rate r, and time t, is expressed as

$$d = r \cdot t$$

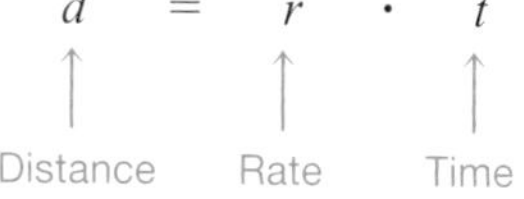

The Streeter/Hutchison Series in Mathematics Intermediate Algebra

This is the key relationship, and it will be used in all motion problems. We will see how it is applied in Example 1.

Example 1 Solving a Motion Problem

< Objectives 1 and 2 >

On Friday morning Ricardo drove from his house to the beach in 4 h. In coming back on Sunday afternoon, heavy traffic slowed his speed by 10 mi/h, and the trip took 5 h. What was his average speed (rate) in each direction?

Step 1 We want the speed or rate in each direction.

Step 2 Let x be Ricardo's speed to the beach. Then $x - 10$ is his return speed.

It is always a good idea to sketch the given information in a motion problem. Here we would have

Going —— $x$mi/h for 4 h ——→

Returning ←—— $(x - 10)$mi/h for 5 h ——

Step 3 Because we know that the distance is the same each way, we can write an equation, using the fact that the product of the rate and the time each way must be the same.

A chart can help summarize the given information. We begin by filling in the information given in the problem.

	Rate	Time	Distance
Going	x	4	
Returning	$x - 10$	5	

Now we fill in the missing information. Here we use the fact that $d = rt$ to complete the chart.

	Rate	Time	Distance
Going	x	4	$4x$
Returning	$x - 10$	5	$5(x - 10)$

So

Distance (going) = distance (returning)

Time · rate (going) = time · rate (returning)

$$\underbrace{4x}_{\text{Time · rate (going)}} = \underbrace{5(x - 10)}_{\text{Time · rate (returning)}}$$

Step 4 Solve.

$$4x = 5(x - 10)$$
$$4x = 5x - 50$$
$$-x = -50$$
$$x = 50$$
$$\text{Rate going } (x) = 50 \text{ mi/h}$$
$$\text{Rate returning } (x - 10) = 40 \text{ mi/h}$$

So Ricardo's rate going to the beach was 50 mi/h, and his rate returning was 40 mi/h.

Step 5 To check, you should verify that the product of the time and the rate is the same in each direction. Going, the distance is

$50 \text{ mi/h} \cdot 4 \text{ h} = 200 \text{ mi}$

Returning

$(50 - 10) \text{ mi/h} \cdot 5 \text{ h} = 40 \text{ mi/h} \cdot 5 \text{ h} = 200 \text{ mi}$

Check Yourself 1

A plane made a flight (with the wind) between two towns in 2 h. Returning against the wind, the plane's speed was 60 mi/h slower, and the flight took 3 h. What was the plane's speed in each direction?

Example 2 illustrates another way of using the distance relationship.

Example 2 Solving a Motion Problem

Katy leaves Las Vegas for Los Angeles at 10 A.M., driving at 50 mi/h. At 11 A.M. Jensen leaves Los Angeles for Las Vegas, driving at 55 mi/h along the same route. If the cities are 260 mi apart, at what time will they meet?

Step 1 We will find the time that Katy travels until they meet.

Step 2 Let x be Katy's time.

Then $x - 1$ is Jensen's time. Jensen left 1 h later.

Again, you should draw a sketch of the given information.

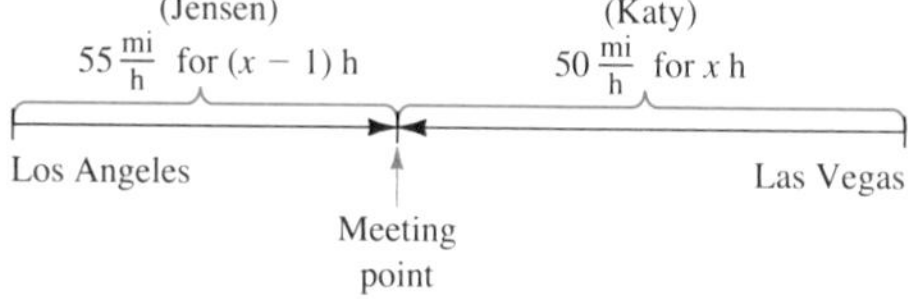

Step 3 To write an equation, we will again need the relationship $d = rt$. From this equation, we can write

$$\text{Katy's distance} = 50x$$
$$\text{Jensen's distance} = 55(x - 1)$$

As before, we can use a table to organize the information.

	Rate	Time	Distance
Katy	50	x	$50x$
Jensen	55	$x - 1$	$55(x - 1)$

From the original problem, the sum of those distances is 260 mi, so

$$50x + 55(x - 1) = 260$$

Step 4

$$50x + 55(x - 1) = 260$$
$$50x + 55x - 55 = 260$$
$$105x - 55 = 260$$
$$105x = 315$$
$$x = 3$$

Katy's time (x) = 3 h

NOTE

Be sure to answer the question asked in the problem.

Finally, because Katy left at 10 A.M., the two will meet at 1 P.M. (10 A.M. + 3 h). We leave the check of this result to you.

Check Yourself 2

At noon a jogger leaves one point, running at 8 mi/h. One hour later a bicyclist leaves the same point, traveling at 20 mi/h in the opposite direction. At what time will they be 36 mi apart?

Next, we consider an application from business. But we will need some new terminology. The total cost of manufacturing an item consists of two types of costs. The **fixed cost,** sometimes called the **overhead,** includes costs such as product design, rent, and utilities. In general, this cost is constant and does not change with the number of items produced. The **variable cost,** which is a cost per item, includes costs such as material, labor, and shipping. The variable cost depends on the number of items being produced.

A typical cost equation might be

$$C = 3.30x + 5{,}000$$

Variable cost (3.30) Fixed cost (5,000)

in which total cost, C, equals variable cost times the number of items produced, x, plus the fixed cost.

The total **revenue** is the income the company makes. It is calculated as the product of the selling price of the item and the number of items sold. A typical revenue equation might be

$$R = 7.50x$$

Selling price per item (7.50) Number of items sold (x)

and total revenue equals an item's selling price times the number sold.

The **break-even point** is that value at which the revenue equals the cost (the company would exactly break even without a profit or a loss).

We will apply these concepts in Example 3.

Example 3 Finding the Break-Even Point

A firm producing DVDs finds that its fixed cost is \$5,000 per month and that its variable cost is \$3.50 per DVD. The cost of producing x DVDs is then given by

$$C = 3.50x + 5{,}000$$

The firm can sell the units at \$7.50 each, so the revenue from selling x units is

$$R = 7.50x$$

Find the break-even point.

Because the break-even point is that point at which the revenue equals the cost, or $R = C$, from our given equations we have

$$\underset{\text{Revenue}}{7.50x} = \underset{\text{Cost}}{\underbrace{3.50x + 5{,}000}}$$

Solving as before gives

$$4x = 5{,}000$$
$$x = 1{,}250$$

The firm will break even (no profit or loss) by producing and selling exactly 1,250 DVDs each month.

Check Yourself 3

A firm producing lawn chairs has fixed costs of \$525 per week. The variable cost is \$8.50 per chair, and the revenue per chair is \$15.50. This means that the cost equation is

$$C = 8.50x + 525$$

and the revenue equation is

$$R = 15.50x$$

Find the break-even point.

Definition

Consecutive Integers

Consecutive integers are integers that follow one another, such as 10, 11, and 12. To represent them in algebra:

If x is an integer, then $x + 1$ is the next consecutive integer, $x + 2$ is the next, and so on.

We'll need this idea in Example 4.

Example 4 Solving an Application

The sum of two consecutive integers is 41. What are the two integers?

RECALL

Remember the steps! Read the problem carefully. What do you need to find? Assign letters to the unknown or unknowns. (This should be done before you try to write an equation!)

Step 1 We want to find the two consecutive integers.

Step 2 Let x be the first integer. Then $x + 1$ must be the next.

Step 3

The first integer (points to x); The second integer (brace over $x + 1$)

$$x + x + 1 = 41$$

The sum (points to $+$); Is (points to $=$)

NOTES

Steps 3–5:

Write an equation. Solve the equation.

Check.

Step 4

$$x + x + 1 = 41$$
$$2x + 1 = 41$$
$$2x = 40$$
$$x = 20$$

First integer $(x) = 20$

Second integer $(x + 1) = 21$

Step 5 The sum of the two integers 20 and 21 is 41.

Check Yourself 4

The sum of three consecutive integers is 51. What are the three integers?

Sometimes algebra is used to reconstruct missing information. Example 5 does just that with some election information.

Example 5 Solving an Application

There were 55 more yes votes than no votes on an election measure. If 735 votes were cast in all, how many yes votes were there? How many no votes?

NOTES

What do you need to find?

Assign letters to the unknowns.

Write an equation.

Step 1 We want to find the number of yes votes and the number of no votes.

Step 2 Let x be the number of no votes. Then

$$\underbrace{x + 55}_{\text{55 more than } x}$$

is the number of yes votes.

Step 3

$$\underset{\text{No votes}}{x} + \underset{\text{Yes votes}}{\underbrace{x + 55}} = 735$$

Step 4

$$x + x + 55 = 735$$
$$2x + 55 = 735$$
$$2x = 680$$
$$x = 340$$
$$\text{No votes } (x) = 340$$
$$\text{Yes votes } (x + 55) = 395$$

NOTES

Solve the equation.

Check.

Step 5 Thus 340 no votes plus 395 yes votes equals 735 total votes. The solution checks.

Check Yourself 5

Francine earns $120 per month more than Rob. If they earn a total of $2,680 per month, what are their monthly salaries?

Similar methods will allow you to solve a variety of word problems. Example 6 includes three unknown quantities but uses the same basic solution steps.

Example 6 Solving an Application

> **NOTE**
>
> There are other choices for x, but choosing the smallest quantity will usually give the easiest equation to write and solve.

Juan worked twice as many hours as Jerry. Marcia worked 3 more hours than Jerry. If they worked a total of 31 hours, find out how many hours each worked.

Step 1 We want to find the hours each worked, so there are three unknowns.

Step 2 Let x be the hours that Jerry worked.

Twice Jerry's hours ↘

Then $2x$ is Juan's hours worked

3 more hours than Jerry worked ↘

and $\overline{x + 3}$ is Marcia's hours.

Step 3

Jerry ↙, Juan ↙, Marcia ↓

$$x + 2x + \overline{x + 3} = 31$$

↑ Sum of their hours

Step 4

$$x + 2x + x + 3 = 31$$
$$4x + 3 = 31$$
$$4x = 28$$
$$x = 7$$

Jerry's hours $(x) = 7$

Juan's hours $(2x) = 14$

Marcia's hours $(x + 3) = 10$

Step 5 The sum of their hours $(7 + 14 + 10)$ is 31, and the solution is verified.

Check Yourself 6

Lucy jogged twice as many miles as Paul but 3 less than Isaac. If the three ran a total of 23 mi, how far did each person run?

As we saw in Examples 1 and 2, many applications lead to equations involving parentheses.

Example 7 Solving Applications Using Parentheses

One number is 5 more than a second number. If 3 times the smaller number plus 4 times the larger is 104, find the two numbers.

Step 1 What are you asked to find? You must find the two numbers.

Step 2 Represent the unknowns. Let x be the smaller number. Then

$x + 5$

is the larger number.

Step 3 Write an equation.

$$3x + 4(x + 5) = 104$$

3 times the smaller — Plus — 4 times the larger

Step 4 Solve the equation.

$$3x + 4(x + 5) = 104$$
$$3x + 4x + 20 = 104$$
$$7x + 20 = 104$$
$$7x = 84$$
$$x = 12$$

Smaller number $(x) = 12$

Larger number $(x + 5) = 17$

Step 5 Check the solution: 12 is the smaller number, and 17 is the larger number.

$3 \cdot 12 + 4 \cdot 17 = 104$ (True)

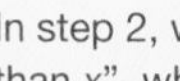

NOTES

In step 2, we have "5 more than x", which is $x + 5$.

In step 3, the parentheses are *essential* in writing the correct equation. "$x + 5$" represents a single value, which is indicated by using the parentheses.

Check Yourself 7

One number is 4 more than another. If 6 times the smaller minus 4 times the larger is 4, what are the two numbers?

The solutions for many problems from geometry will also yield equations involving parentheses. Consider Example 8.

Example 8 Solving a Geometry Application

> **NOTE**
>
> Whenever you are working on an application involving geometric figures, you should draw a sketch of the problem, including the labels assigned in step 2.

The length of a rectangle is 1 cm less than 3 times the width. If the perimeter is 54 cm, find the dimensions of the rectangle.

Step 1 You want to find the dimensions (the width and length).

Step 2 Let x be the width.

Then $3x - 1$ is the length.

(3 times the width → $3x$; 1 less than → $- 1$)

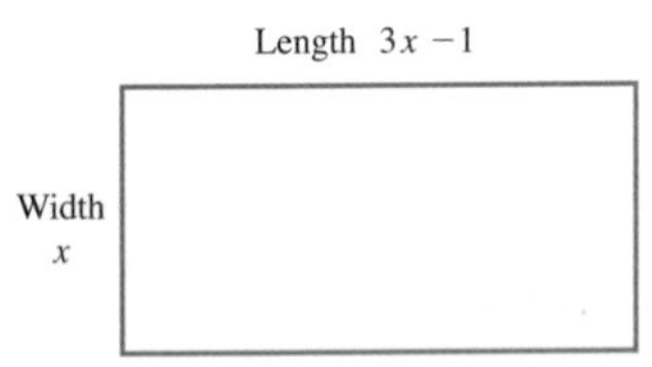

Step 3 To write an equation, we use this formula for the perimeter of a rectangle:

$$P = 2W + 2L$$

So

$$2x + 2(3x - 1) = 54$$

(Twice the width → $2x$; Twice the length → $2(3x - 1)$; Perimeter → 54)

> **NOTE**
>
> The parentheses are essential here in that the difference "$3x - 1$" represents a single value and must be treated as such by placing the parentheses around it.

Step 4 Solve the equation.

$$\begin{aligned} 2x + 2(3x - 1) &= 54 \\ 2x + 6x - 2 &= 54 \\ 8x &= 56 \\ x &= 7 \\ \text{Width } (x) &= 7 \text{ cm} \\ \text{Length } (3x - 1) &= 20 \text{ cm} \end{aligned}$$

We leave step 5, the check, to you.

> **NOTE**
>
> Be sure to return to the original statement of the problem when checking your result.

Check Yourself 8

The length of a rectangle is 5 in. more than twice the width. If the perimeter of the rectangle is 76 in., what are the dimensions of the rectangle?

You will also often use parentheses in solving *mixture problems.* Mixture problems involve combining things that have a different value, rate, or strength. Look at Example 9.

Example 9 Solving a Mixture Problem

Four hundred tickets were sold for a school play. General admission tickets were $4, and student tickets were $3. If the total ticket sales were $1,350, how many of each type of ticket were sold?

NOTE

We subtract x, the number of general admission tickets, from 400, the total number of tickets, to find the number of student tickets.

Step 1 You want to find the number of each type of ticket sold.

Step 2 Let x be the number of general admission tickets.

Then $\underbrace{400 - x}$ student tickets were sold.

↑ 400 tickets were sold in all.

Step 3 The sales value for each kind of ticket is found by multiplying the price of the ticket by the number sold.

General admission tickets:	$4x$	\$4 for each of the x tickets
Student tickets:	$3(400 - x)$	\$3 for each of the $400 - x$ tickets

So to form an equation, we have

$$4x + \underbrace{3(400 - x)} = 1{,}350$$

Value of general admission tickets — Value of student tickets — Total value

Step 4 Solve the equation.

$$\begin{aligned} 4x + 3(400 - x) &= 1{,}350 \\ 4x + 1{,}200 - 3x &= 1{,}350 \\ x + 1{,}200 &= 1{,}350 \\ x &= 150 \end{aligned}$$

So 150 general admission and 250 student tickets were sold. We leave the check to you.

Check Yourself 9

Beth bought 35¢ stamps and 25¢ stamps at the post office. If she purchased 60 stamps at a cost of \$19, how many of each kind did she buy?

Check Yourself ANSWERS

1. 180 mi/h with the wind and 120 mi/h against **2.** At 2 P.M.
3. 75 chairs **4.** The integers are 16, 17, and 18.
5. Rob's salary is \$1,280, and Francine's is \$1,400.
6. Paul: 4 mi; Lucy: 8 mi; Isaac: 11 mi **7.** The numbers are 10 and 14.
8. The width is 11 in.; the length is 27 in. **9.** 40 at 35¢, and 20 at 25¢

Reading Your Text

The following fill-in-the-blank exercises are designed to ensure that you understand some of the key vocabulary used in this section.

SECTION 2.3

(a) An ______________ is a series of steps, that when followed, solves a problem.

(b) When solving a problem, we choose a ______________ to represent the unknown.

(c) In solving business applications, the ______________ point is the point at which the revenue equals the cost.

(d) For a consecutive integer problem, if x is an integer, then ______________ is the next consecutive integer.

2.3 exercises

< Objectives 1, 2 >

Solve the applications.

1. **Science and Medicine** On her way to a business meeting, Kim took the freeway, and the trip took 3 h. Returning, she decided to take a side road, and her speed along that route averaged 9 mi/h slower than on the freeway. If Kim's return trip took $3\frac{1}{2}$ h and the distance driven was the same each way, find her average speed in each direction.

2. **Science and Medicine** Beth was required to make a cross-country flight in training for her pilot's license. When she flew from her home airport, a steady 30-mi/h wind was behind her, and the trip took 5 h. When she returned against the same wind, the flight took 7 h. Find the plane's speed in still air and the distance traveled each way.

3. **Science and Medicine** On Tuesday, Malia drove to a conference and averaged 54 mi/h for the trip. When she returned on Thursday, road construction slowed her average speed by 9 mi/h. If her total driving time was 11 h, what was her driving time each way, and how far away from her home was the conference?

4. **Science and Medicine** Robert can drive to work in 45 min, whereas if he decides to take the bus, the same trip takes 1 h 15 min. If the average rate of the bus is 16 mi/h slower than his driving rate, how far does he travel to work?

5. **Science and Medicine** At 9 A.M., Tom left Boston for Baltimore, traveling at 45 mi/h. One hour later, Andrea left Baltimore for Boston, traveling at 50 mi/h along the same route. If the cities are 425 mi apart, at what time did Tom and Andrea meet? > Videos

6. **Science and Medicine** A passenger bus left a station at 1 P.M., traveling north at an average rate of 50 mi/h. One hour later, a second bus left the same station, traveling south at a rate of 55 mi/h. At what time will the two buses be 260 mi apart?

MathZone

Boost your grade at mathzone.com!
- > Practice Problems
- > NetTutor
- > Self-Tests
- > e-Professors
- > Videos

Name ______________

Section ________ Date ________

Answers

1. 63 mi/h going, 54 mi/h returning
2. Speed: 180 mi/h, distance: 1,050 mi
3. 5 h going, 6 h returning, 270 mi
4. 30 mi
5. 2 P.M.
6. 4 P.M.

Answers

7. 800 pairs of gloves

8. 252 calculators

9. 180 calculators

10. 4,000 books

11. $21

7. **Business and Finance** A firm producing gloves finds that its fixed cost is $4,000 per week and its variable cost is $8.50 per pair. The revenue is $13.50 per pair of gloves, so that cost and revenue equations are, respectively,

$C = 8.50x + 4{,}000 \quad \text{and} \quad R = 13.50x$

Find the break-even point for the firm.

8. **Business and Finance** A company that produces calculators determines that its fixed cost is $8,820 per month. The variable cost is $70 per calculator and the revenue is $105 per calculator. The cost and revenue equations, respectively, are given by

$C = 70x + 8{,}820 \quad \text{and} \quad R = 105x$

Find the number of calculators the company must produce and sell to break even.

9. **Business and Finance** A firm that produces scientific calculators has a fixed cost of $1,260 per week and a variable cost of $6.50 per calculator. If the company can sell the calculators for $13.50, find the break-even point.

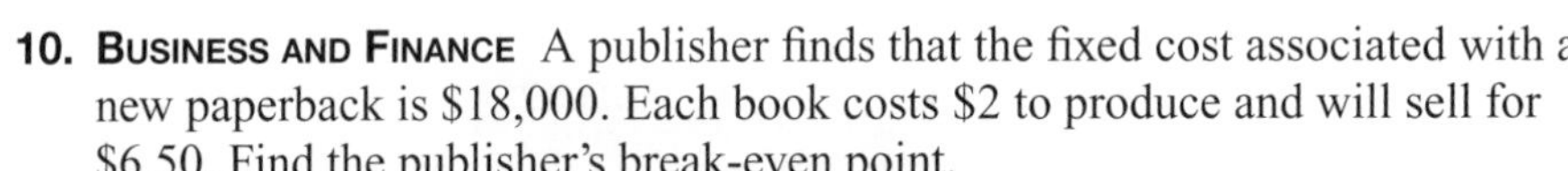

10. **Business and Finance** A publisher finds that the fixed cost associated with a new paperback is $18,000. Each book costs $2 to produce and will sell for $6.50. Find the publisher's break-even point.

11. **Business and Finance** An important economic application involves supply and demand. The number of units of a commodity that manufacturers are willing to **supply,** S, is related to the market price, p, in dollars. A typical supply equation is

$S = 40p - 285$

(Generally the supply increases as the price increases.)

The number of units that consumers are willing to buy, D, is called the **demand,** and it is also related to the market price. A typical demand equation is

$D = -45p + 1{,}500$

(Generally the demand decreases as the price increases.)

The price at which the supply and demand are equal (or $S = D$) is called the **equilibrium price** for the commodity. The supply and demand equations for a certain model portable radio are given in the preceding equations. Find the equilibrium price for the radio.

12. **Business and Finance** The supply and demand equations for a certain type of computer modem are

$S = 25p - 2{,}500$ and $D = -40p + 5{,}300$

where p is the market price, in dollars.

Find the equilibrium price for the modem.

13. **Number Problem** The sum of two consecutive integers is 71. Find the two integers.

14. **Number Problem** The sum of two consecutive integers is 145. Find the two integers.

15. **Number Problem** The sum of three consecutive integers is 63. What are the three integers?

16. **Number Problem** If the sum of three consecutive integers is 93, find the three integers.

17. **Number Problem** The sum of two consecutive even integers is 66. What are the two integers? (*Hint:* Consecutive even integers such as 10, 12, and 14 can be represented by $x, x + 2, x + 4$, and so on.)

18. **Number Problem** If the sum of two consecutive even integers is 86, find the two integers.

19. **Number Problem** If the sum of two consecutive odd integers is 52, what are the two integers? (*Hint:* Consecutive odd integers such as 21, 23, and 25 can be represented by $x, x + 2, x + 4$, and so on.)

20. **Number Problem** The sum of two consecutive odd integers is 88. Find the two integers.

21. **Number Problem** The sum of three consecutive odd integers is 105. What are the three integers? > Videos

22. **Number Problem** The sum of three consecutive even integers is 126. What are the three integers?

Answers

12. $120
13. 35, 36
14. 72, 73
15. 20, 21, 22
16. 30, 31, 32
17. 32, 34
18. 42, 44
19. 25, 27
20. 43, 45
21. 33, 35, 37
22. 40, 42, 44

Answers

23. 12, 13

24. 20, 22

25. Winner: 1,710 votes, loser: 1,550 votes

26. Jody: $1,450, Frank: $1,310

27. Washer: $360, dryer: $290

28. 44 in., 54 in.

29. 9 years old

30. Diane: 18 years old, Dan: 9 years old

23. NUMBER PROBLEM 4 times an integer is 9 more than 3 times the next consecutive integer. What are the two integers?

24. NUMBER PROBLEM 4 times an even integer is 30 less than 5 times the next consecutive even integer. Find the two integers.

25. SOCIAL SCIENCE In an election, the winning candidate had 160 more votes than the loser. If the total number of votes cast was 3,260, how many votes did each candidate receive?

26. BUSINESS AND FINANCE Jody earns $140 more per month than Frank. If their monthly salaries total $2,760, what amount does each earn?

27. BUSINESS AND FINANCE A washer-dryer combination costs $650. If the washer costs $70 more than the dryer, what does each appliance cost?

28. CRAFTS Yuri has a board that is 98 in. long. He wishes to cut the board into two pieces so that one piece will be 10 in. longer than the other. What should be the length of each piece?

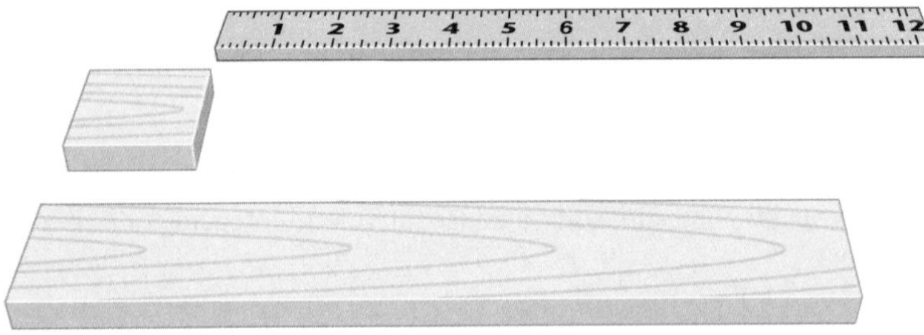

29. SOCIAL SCIENCE Yan Ling is 1 year less than twice as old as his sister. If the sum of their ages is 14 years, how old is Yan Ling?

30. SOCIAL SCIENCE Diane is twice as old as her brother Dan. If the sum of their ages is 27 years, how old are Diane and her brother?

31. **Social Science** Maritza is 3 years less than 4 times as old as her daughter. If the sum of their ages is 37, how old is Maritza?

32. **Social Science** Mrs. Jackson is 2 years more than 3 times as old as her son. If the difference between their ages is 22 years, how old is Mrs. Jackson?

33. **Business and Finance** On her vacation in Europe, Jovita's expenses for food and lodging were \$60 less than twice as much as her airfare. If she spent \$2,400 in all, what was her airfare?

34. **Business and Finance** Rachel earns \$6,000 less than twice as much as Tom. If their two incomes total \$48,000, how much does each earn?

35. **Statistics** There are 99 students registered in three sections of algebra. There are twice as many students in the 10 A.M. section as the 8 A.M. section and 7 more students at 12 P.M. than at 8 A.M. How many students are in each section?

> Videos

36. **Business and Finance** The Randolphs used 12 more gallons (gal) of fuel oil in October than in September and twice as much oil in November as in September. If they used 132 gal for the 3 months, how much was used during each month?

37. **Number Problem** One number is 8 more than another. If the sum of the smaller number and twice the larger number is 46, find the two numbers.

38. **Number Problem** One number is 3 less than another. If 4 times the smaller number minus 3 times the larger number is 4, find the two numbers.

39. **Number Problem** Find two consecutive integers such that the sum of twice the first integer and 3 times the second integer is 28.

40. **Number Problem** Find two consecutive odd integers such that 3 times the first integer is 5 more than twice the second. (*Hint:* If x represents the first integer, $x + 2$ represents the next consecutive odd integer.)

Answers

31. 29 years old
32. 32 years old
33. \$820
34. Tom: \$18,000, Rachel: \$30,000
35. 8 A.M.: 23 students, 10 A.M.: 46 students, 12 P.M.: 30 students
36. September: 30 gal, October: 42 gal, November: 60 gal
37. 10, 18
38. 13, 16
39. 5, 6
40. 9, 11

Answers

41. 12 in., 25 in.

42. 7 cm, 16 cm

43. 6 m, 22 m

44. 75 m, 40 m

45. Legs: 13 cm, base: 10 cm

46. Legs: 11 in., base: 7 in.

47. 200 \$6 tickets, 300 \$8 tickets

48. 850 student, 600 nonstudent

41. **Geometry** The length of a rectangle is 1 in. more than twice its width. If the perimeter of the rectangle is 74 in., find the dimensions of the rectangle.

42. **Geometry** The length of a rectangle is 5 cm less than 3 times its width. If the perimeter of the rectangle is 46 cm, find the dimensions of the rectangle.

43. **Geometry** The length of a rectangular garden is 4 m more than 3 times its width. The perimeter of the garden is 56 m. What are the dimensions of the garden? > Videos

44. **Geometry** The length of a rectangular playing field is 5 m less than twice its width. If the perimeter of the playing field is 230 m, find the length and width of the field.

45. **Geometry** The base of an isosceles triangle is 3 cm less than the length of the equal sides. If the perimeter of the triangle is 36 cm, find the length of each of the sides.

46. **Geometry** The length of one of the equal legs of an isosceles triangle is 3 in. less than twice the length of the base. If the perimeter is 29 in., find the length of each of the sides.

47. **Business and Finance** Tickets for a play cost \$8 for the main floor and \$6 in the balcony. If the total receipts from 500 tickets were \$3,600, how many of each type of ticket were sold? > Videos

48. **Business and Finance** Tickets for a basketball tournament were \$6 for students and \$9 for nonstudents. Total sales were \$10,500, and 250 more student tickets were sold than nonstudent tickets. How many of each type of ticket were sold?

49. **Business and Finance** Maria bought 70 stamps at the post office in 40¢ and 25¢ denominations. If she paid $25 for the stamps, how many of each denomination did she buy?

50. **Business and Finance** A bank teller had a total of 125 $10 bills and $20 bills to start the day. If the value of the bills was $1,650, how many of each denomination did he have?

51. **Business and Finance** There are 500 Douglas fir and hemlock trees in a section of forest bought by Hoodoo Logging Co. The company paid an average of $250 for each Douglas fir and $300 for each hemlock. If the company paid $132,000 for the trees, how many of each kind did the company buy?

52. **Business and Finance** There are 850 Douglas fir and ponderosa pine trees in a section of forest bought by Sawz Logging Co. The company paid an average of $300 for each Douglas fir and $225 for each ponderosa pine. If the company paid $217,500 for the trees, how many of each kind did the company buy?

Basic Skills | Advanced Skills | **Vocational-Technical Applications** | Calculator/Computer | Above and Beyond

53. **Manufacturing Technology** The elastic modulus of a material, E, is given by

$$E = \frac{PL}{eA}$$

Solve for the elongation, e.

54. **Allied Health** Solve the linear equation $130 = 105 + 5(H - 60)$ to determine what height, H, in inches, for a woman corresponds to an ideal body weight of 130 pounds.

Answers

49. 20 25¢ stamps, 50 40¢ stamps
50. 85 $10 bills, 40 $20 bills
51. 360 Douglas fir, 140 hemlock
52. 350 Douglas fir, 500 ponderosa pine
53. $e = \frac{PL}{EA}$
54. 65 in.

Answers

55. 76 in.

56. $B = 99.99 + 0.20\,(M - 1{,}000)$, $B = \$199.99$

57. Above and Beyond

58. Above and Beyond

55. Allied Health Solve the linear equation $202 = 106 + 6(H - 60)$ to determine what height, H, in inches, for a man corresponds to an ideal body weight of 202 pounds.

> Videos

56. Information Technology Amir has a cell phone for his field service technician job. His contract with his cell phone company is \$99.99 per month for 1,000 minutes (M). Each minute after 1,000 is 20¢ a minute. Last month he used 1,500 minutes. Give a linear equation that represents the bill (B) for last month and calculate the amount of the bill.

Basic Skills | Advanced Skills | Vocational-Technical Applications | Calculator/Computer | **Above and Beyond**

57. You find a new bicycle that you like, and you plan to ride it for exercise several days a week. You are also happy to find that this very model is on sale for 22% off. You speak to the salesclerk, who begins writing up the sale by first adding on your state's 7.8% sales tax. He then takes off the 22%. "No!", you object, "You should take the 22% off first and then add the sales tax." The salesclerk says he is sorry, but he has been instructed to first calculate the amount of tax. Who is correct? Defend your position using algebra.

58. You have probably heard the question, "Which weighs more, a ton of feathers or a ton of bricks?" The usual response of "bricks" is, of course, incorrect. A ton of anything weighs 2,000 pounds. Why do people miss this question so often? We know from experience that bricks are heavier than feathers. However, what we mean is that bricks have a much higher *density* than feathers (they weigh more per unit volume). A cubic meter of bricks weighs far more than a cubic meter of feathers.

We often compare the density of a substance to the density of water. Water has a density of 1 gram per cubic centimeter (g/cm^3). Things denser than water (such as body muscle and bone) sink, whereas things less dense (such as body fat) float.

The concept of density is important in analyzing the significance of the percentage of body fat you have. There are many ways to measure, or estimate, your percentage of body fat. Most health clubs and many college health classes offer the opportunity to find this percentage. By multiplying percentage of body fat times your weight, you can calculate the actual pounds of fat in your body.

However, we are looking for a more useful measure. Body density, D, can be calculated using the following formula.

$$D = \frac{1}{\dfrac{A}{a} + \dfrac{B}{b}}$$

in which A = proportion of body fat
B = proportion of lean body tissue $(1 - A)$
a = density of fat body tissue in g/cm^3 (approximately 0.9 g/cm^3)
b = density of lean body tissue in g/cm^3 (approximately 1.1 g/cm^3)

Use this formula to compute parts **(a)** to **(c)**.

(a) Substituting $1 - A$ for B, 0.9 for a, and 1.1 for b, solve the formula so that D is expressed in terms of A.

(b) Find the values associated with body fat proportions of 0.1, 0.15, 0.2, 0.25, and 0.3.

(c) Use other resources (health professionals, health clubs, the Internet, and the library) to find another measure of body density. How do the two methods compare?

59. "I make \$2.50 an hour more in my new job." If $x =$ the amount I used to make per hour and $y =$ the amount I now make, which of equations **(a)** to **(f)** say the same thing as the statement? Explain your choices by translating the equations into English and comparing with the original statement.

(a) $x + y = 2.50$ **(b)** $x - y = 2.50$

(c) $x + 2.50 = y$ **(d)** $2.50 + y = x$

(e) $y - x = 2.50$ **(f)** $2.50 - x = y$

60. "The river rose 4 ft above flood stage last night." If $a =$ the river's height at flood stage, $b =$ the river's height now (the morning after), which of equations **(a)** to **(f)** say the same thing as the statement? Explain your choices by translating the equations into English and comparing the meaning with the original statement.

(a) $a + b = 4$ **(b)** $b - 4 = a$

(c) $a - 4 = b$ **(d)** $a + 4 = b$

(e) $b + 4 = b$ **(f)** $b - a = 4$

61. Maxine lives in Pittsburgh, Pennsylvania, and pays 8.33¢ per kilowatt hour (kWh) for electricity. During the 6 months of cold winter weather, her household uses about 1,500 kWh of electric power per month. During the two hottest summer months, the usage is also high because the family uses electricity to run an air conditioner. During these summer months, the usage is 1,200 kWh per month; the rest of the year, usage averages 900 kWh per month.

(a) Write an expression for the total yearly electric bill.

(b) Maxine is considering spending \$2,000 for more insulation for her home so that it is less expensive to heat and to cool. The insulation company claims that "with proper installation the insulation will reduce heating and cooling bills by 25%." If Maxine invests the money in insulation, how long will it take her to get her money back in saving on her electric bill? Write to her about what information she needs to answer this question. Give her your opinion about how long it will take to save \$2,000 on heating and cooling bills, and explain your reasoning. What is your advice to Maxine?

62. Here is a common mistake made when solving equations:

The equation: $2(x - 2) = x + 3$

First step in solving: $2x - 2 = x + 3$

Write a clear explanation of what error has been made. What could be done to avoid this error?

Answers

59. Above and Beyond

60. Above and Beyond

61. Above and Beyond

62. Above and Beyond

Answers

63. Above and Beyond

64. Above and Beyond

65. Above and Beyond

66. $542.03

67. Above and Beyond

63. Another very common mistake is made when solving this equation:

The equation: $6x - (x + 3) = 5 + 2x$

First step in solving: $6x - x + 3 = 5 + 2x$

Write a clear explanation of what error has been made and what could be done to avoid the mistake.

64. Write an algebraic equation for the English statement "Subtract 5 from the sum of x and 7 times 3 and the result is 20." Compare your equation with those of other students. Did you all write the same equation? Are all the equations correct even though they don't look alike? Do all the equations have the same solution? What is wrong? The English statement is *ambiguous*. Write another English statement that leads correctly to more than one algebraic equation. Exchange with another student and see if he or she thinks the statement is ambiguous. Notice that the algebra is *not* ambiguous!

65. There is a universally agreed on "order of operations" used to simplify expressions. Explain how the order of operations is used in solving equations. Be sure to use complete sentences.

66. Angel invests in the currency market by purchasing US$10,000 worth of Japanese yen at an exchange rate of 134.2. If he sells the yen when the exchange rate is 127.3 yen per US dollar, how much profit does he make?

67. If Angel were to sell his yen (refer to exercise 66) at the current exchange rate, how much profit (or loss) would he make?

Answers

1. 63 mi/h going, 54 mi/h returning **3.** 5 h going, 6 h returning, 270 mi
5. 2 P.M. **7.** 800 pairs of gloves **9.** 180 calculators **11.** $21
13. 35, 36 **15.** 20, 21, 22 **17.** 32, 34 **19.** 25, 27 **21.** 33, 35, 37
23. 12, 13 **25.** Winner: 1,710 votes, loser: 1,550 votes
27. Washer: $360, dryer: $290 **29.** 9 years old **31.** 29 years old
33. $820 **35.** 8 A.M.: 23 students, 10 A.M.: 46 students, 12 P.M.: 30 students
37. 10, 18 **39.** 5, 6 **41.** 12 in., 25 in. **43.** 6 m, 22 m
45. Legs: 13 cm, base: 10 cm **47.** 200 $6 tickets, 300 $8 tickets
49. 20 25¢ stamps, 50 40¢ stamps **51.** 360 Douglas fir, 140 hemlock
53. $e = \dfrac{PL}{EA}$ **55.** 76 in. **57.** Above and Beyond
59. Above and Beyond **61.** Above and Beyond **63.** Above and Beyond
65. Above and Beyond **67.** Above and Beyond

2.4 Linear Inequalities

< 2.4 Objectives >

1 > Solve and graph the solution set for a linear inequality

2 > Solve and graph the solution set for a compound inequality

In Section 2.1 we defined a linear equation in one variable as an equation that could be written in the form

$$ax + b = 0$$

in which a and b are real numbers and $a \neq 0$.

A linear inequality in one variable is defined in a similar fashion.

Definition

Linear Inequality

A *linear inequality* can be written in the form

$$ax + b < 0$$

in which a and b are real numbers and $a \neq 0$.

The inequality symbol $<$ can be replaced with any of the other inequality symbols $>$, $\leq$, or $\geq$, so that

$$ax + b > 0 \qquad ax + b \leq 0 \qquad \text{and} \qquad ax + b \geq 0$$

are also linear inequalities.

NOTES

We can also say that a solution *satisfies* the inequality.

Adding the same quantity to both sides of an inequality gives an equivalent inequality.

Fortunately your experience with linear equations in Section 2.1 provides the groundwork for solving linear inequalities. You will see many similarities.

A **solution** for a linear inequality in one variable is any real number that will make the inequality a true statement when the variable is replaced by that number. The **solution set** for a linear inequality is the set of all solutions.

Our strategy for solving linear inequalities is, for the most part, identical to that used for solving linear equations. We write a sequence of equivalent inequalities to isolate the variable on one side of the inequality symbol.

Writing equivalent inequalities for this purpose requires two properties. First:

Property

Addition Property of Inequalities

If $a < b$, then $a + c < b + c$.

This addition property is similar to that seen earlier in solving equations. As before, because subtraction is defined in terms of addition, the property also allows us to subtract the same quantity from both sides of an inequality without changing the solutions.

Our second property, dealing with multiplication, has an important difference. We begin by writing the true inequality

$$2 < 3$$

Multiplying both sides of that inequality by the same *positive* number, say 3, gives

$$3(2) < 3(3)$$

$$6 < 9 \qquad \text{Another true statement!}$$

NOTES

Multiplying both sides of an inequality by a positive number gives an equivalent inequality.

Multiplying both sides of an inequality by a negative number and reversing the sense gives an equivalent inequality.

Note that the new inequality has the same sense (points in the same direction) as the original inequality.

However, if we multiply both sides of the original inequality by a *negative* number, say -3, we have

$$-3(2) < -3(3)$$

$$-6 < -9 \qquad \text{A } \textit{false} \text{ statement!}$$

To make this a true statement, we must *reverse the sense* of the inequality to write

$$-6 > -9$$

This suggests that if we multiply both sides of an inequality by a negative number, we must reverse the sense of the inequality to form an equivalent inequality. From this discussion we can now state our second property.

Property

Multiplication Property of Inequalities

If $a < b$

then $ac < bc$ when c is a *positive* number ($c > 0$)

and $ac > bc$ when c is a *negative* number ($c < 0$)

Again, because division is defined in terms of multiplication, this property also allows us to divide both sides of an inequality by the same nonzero number, reversing the sense of the inequality if that number is negative.

We will use these properties in solving inequalities in much the same way as we did in solving equations, with the one significant difference pointed out earlier.

Examples 1 to 4 illustrate the solution process for linear inequalities.

Example 1 Solving a Linear Inequality

< Objective 1 >

NOTE

As in solving equations, we apply the addition property and *then* the multiplication property, to isolate the variable.

Solve and graph the inequality.

$$4x - 3 < 5$$

$$4x - 3 + 3 < 5 + 3 \qquad \text{Add 3 to both sides.}$$

$$4x < 8$$

$$\frac{4x}{4} < \frac{8}{4} \qquad \text{Divide both sides by 4.}$$

$$x < 2$$

RECALL

The parenthesis means 2 is *not* included in the solution.

NOTES

Parentheses are always used to enclose ∞ and $-\infty$.

The symbol $\cup$ represents "or" in interval notation.

Because all the inequalities are equivalent, the solution set for the original inequality consists of all numbers that are less than 2. That set can be written

$x < 2$

The graph of the solution set is

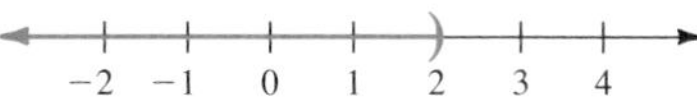

The graphing notation used here is similar to **interval notation,** which is another way of indicating the solution to an inequality. The solution set to the preceding inequality can be represented in interval notation as $(-\infty, 2)$. Notice that all values less than 2, which are indicated by a solid line to the left of 2 on the number line, are represented by $-\infty$. The negative sign indicates direction, left, and the infinity sign indicates *all* values less than 2.

The following table summarizes interval notation.

Inequality Solution	Graph	Interval Notation
All real numbers greater than b	(at b, shaded to the right	(b, ∞)
All real numbers less than or equal to b	] at b, shaded to the left	$(-\infty, b]$
All real numbers greater than a and less than b	(at a,) at b	(a, b)
All real numbers greater than or equal to a and less than b	[at a,) at b	$[a, b)$
All real numbers less than a or greater than or equal to b	) at a, [at b	$(-\infty, a) \cup [b, \infty)$

Check Yourself 1

Solve and graph the inequality. Then write the solution set in interval notation.

$5x + 7 > 22$

Example 2 Solving a Linear Inequality

Solve and graph the inequality. Then write the solution set in interval notation.

$$3x - 5 \geq 5x + 3$$

$$3x - 5 + 5 \geq 5x + 3 + 5 \quad \text{Add 5.}$$

$$3x \geq 5x + 8$$

$$3x - 5x \geq 5x - 5x + 8 \quad \text{Subtract } 5x.$$

$$-2x \geq 8$$

$$\frac{-2x}{-2} \leq \frac{8}{-2} \quad \text{Divide by } -2 \text{, reversing the sense of the inequality.}$$

$$x \leq -4$$

NOTE

Here we use the bracket to indicate that -4 is included in the solution set.

The solution set consists of all numbers that are less than or equal to -4.

$x \leq -4$ or $(-\infty, -4]$ Interval notation.

The graph of the solution set is

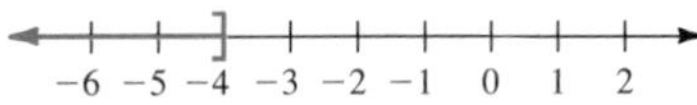

Check Yourself 2

Solve and graph. Then write the solution set in interval notation.

$4x + 3 \leq 7x - 12$

In working with more complicated inequalities, as was the case with equations, any signs of grouping must be removed, and like terms combined, before the properties of inequalities are applied to isolate the variable.

Example 3 Solving a Linear Inequality

Solve and graph. Then write the solution set in interval notation.

$$5 - 3(x - 2) \leq 1 - x$$

$$5 - 3x + 6 \leq 1 - x$$ Apply the distributive property on the left.

$$-3x + 11 \leq 1 - x$$ Combine like terms on the left.

$$-3x + 11 - 11 \leq 1 - 11 - x$$ Subtract 11.

$$-3x \leq -10 - x$$

$$-3x + x \leq -10 - x + x$$ Add x.

$$-2x \leq -10$$

$$\frac{-2x}{-2} \geq \frac{-10}{-2}$$ Divide by -2, reversing the sense of the inequality.

$$x \geq 5$$

The solution set is

$x \geq 5$ or $[5, \infty)$

The graph of the solution set is

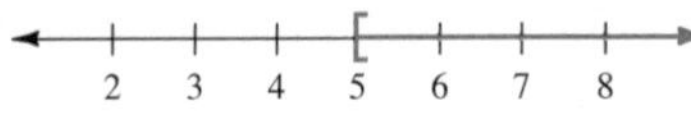

Check Yourself 3

Solve and graph. Then write the solution set in interval notation.

$4 - 2(x + 5) \geq -9 - 4x$

If fractions are involved in an inequality, you should apply the multiplication property to clear the inequality of fractions as your first step.

Example 4 Solving a Linear Inequality

Solve and graph the inequality. Then write the solution set in interval notation.

> **NOTE**
>
> Apply the distributive property on the left.

$$\frac{3x+2}{6} - 1 < \frac{x}{3}$$

$$6\left(\frac{3x+2}{6} - 1\right) < 6\left(\frac{x}{3}\right) \qquad \text{Multiply by 6, the LCM of 6 and 3.}$$

$$6\left(\frac{3x+2}{6}\right) - 6(1) < 6\left(\frac{x}{3}\right) \qquad \text{Apply the distributive property on the left.}$$

$$3x + 2 - 6 < 2x$$

$$3x - 4 < 2x \qquad \text{Combine like terms on the left.}$$

$$3x - 2x < 2x + 4 - 2x \qquad \text{Subtract } 2x \text{ and add 4.}$$

$$x < 4$$

The solution set is

$x < 4$ or $(-\infty, 4)$

The graph of the solution set is

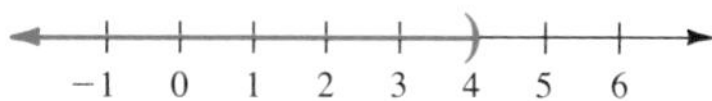

Check Yourself 4

Solve and graph the inequality. Then write the solution set in interval notation.

$$\frac{5x-1}{4} - 2 > \frac{x}{2}$$

The following algorithm summarizes our work thus far in this section in solving linear inequalities.

Step by Step

Solving Linear Inequalities in One Variable

- **Step 1** Remove any grouping symbols by applying the distributive property.
- **Step 2** Clear the inequality statement of any fractions by multiplying both sides by the LCM of all denominators.
- **Step 3** Combine any like terms that appear on either side of the equation.
- **Step 4** Apply the addition property to write an equivalent inequality with the variable term on one side of the inequality and the constant term on the other.
- **Step 5** Apply the multiplication property to write an equivalent inequality with the variable isolated on one side of the inequality. Be sure to reverse the sense of the inequality if you multiply or divide by a negative number.
- **Step 6** Graph the solution set of the original inequality.

Let us now consider two types of inequality statements that arise frequently in mathematics. Consider a statement such as

$$-2 < x < 5$$

NOTE

In the compound inequality the word *and* is understood.

As we saw in Section 1.3, it is called a **double** or **compound inequality** because it combines the two inequalities

$$-2 < x \quad \text{and} \quad x < 5$$

It is read "x is greater than -2 and less than 5."

To solve a compound inequality means to isolate the variable in the middle term, as Example 5 illustrates.

Example 5 Solving a Compound Inequality

< Objective 2 >

Solve and graph the compound inequality. Then write the solution set in interval notation.

$$-3 \le 2x + 1 \le 7$$

NOTE

We are really applying the addition property to each of the *two* inequalities that make up the compound inequality statement.

We want to isolate x in the middle term.

$$-3 - 1 \le 2x + 1 - 1 \le 7 - 1$$

Subtract 1 from the middle and both sides of the compound inequality.

$$-4 \le 2x \le 6$$

$$\frac{-4}{2} \le \frac{2x}{2} \le \frac{6}{2}$$

Divide the middle and both sides of the inequality by 2.

$$-2 \le x \le 3$$

The solution set consists of all numbers between -2 and 3, including -2 and 3, and is written

$$-2 \le x \le 3 \quad \text{or} \quad [-2, 3]$$

NOTE

Because the points at both ends of the interval are included, we sometimes call this a *closed interval.*

The graph of the solution set is

−3 −2 −1 0 1 2 3 4

Check Yourself 5

Solve and graph the inequality. Then write the solution set in interval notation.

$$-5 \le 2x - 3 \le 3$$

When the coefficient of the variable is a negative number, care must be taken in isolating the variable.

Example 6 Solving a Compound Inequality

Solve and graph the compound inequality. Then write the solution set in interval notation.

$$-3 < 4 - 3x < 13$$

$$-7 < -3x < 9$$ Subtract 4 from the middle and both sides of the inequality.

$$\frac{-7}{-3} > \frac{-3x}{-3} > \frac{9}{-3}$$ Divide the middle and both sides by −3, reversing the inequality.

$$\frac{7}{3} > x > -3$$

$$-3 < x < \frac{7}{3}$$ Rewrite the inequality in standard smallest-to-largest format.

The solution consists of all numbers between −3 and $\frac{7}{3}$ and is written

$$-3 < x < \frac{7}{3} \quad \text{or} \quad \left(-3, \frac{7}{3}\right)$$

NOTE

This is called an *open interval.*

The graph of the solution set is

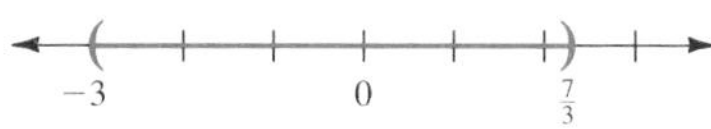

Check Yourself 6

Solve and graph the double inequality. Then write the solution set in interval notation.

$$-5 < 3 - 2x < 5$$

A compound inequality may also consist of two inequality statements connected by the word *or*. Example 7 illustrates the solution of that type of compound inequality.

Example 7 Solving a Compound Inequality

Solve and graph the inequality. Then write the solution set in interval notation.

$$2x - 3 < -5 \quad \text{or} \quad 2x - 3 > 5$$

In this case we must work with each of the inequalities *separately.*

$$2x - 3 < -5 \quad \text{or} \quad 2x - 3 > 5$$

$$2x - 3 + 3 < -5 + 3 \qquad 2x - 3 + 3 > 5 + 3$$ Add 3.

$$2x < -2 \qquad 2x > 8$$

$$\frac{2x}{2} < -\frac{2}{2} \qquad \frac{2x}{2} > \frac{8}{2}$$ Divide by 2.

$$x < -1 \qquad x > 4$$

RECALL

The symbol ∪ represents "or" in interval notation.

The solution set is

$x < -1$ or $x > 4$ or $(-\infty, -1) \cup (4, \infty)$

The graph of the solution set is

Check Yourself 7

Solve and graph the inequality. Then write the solution set in interval notation.

$3x - 4 \le -7$ or $3x - 4 \ge 7$

The following chart summarizes our discussion of solving linear inequalities and the nature of the solution sets of the types of inequalities we have considered in this section. The variables r and s in the solution set are the real numbers.

Type of Inequality	Solution Set	Graph
	If $a > 0$:	
$ax + b < c$	$x < r$ or $(-\infty, r)$	r
	If $a < 0$:	
	$x > r$ or (r, ∞)	r
$-c < ax + b < c$	$r < x < s$ or (r, s)	r s
$ax + b < -c$ or $ax + b > c$	$x < r$ or $x > s$ or $(-\infty, r) \cup (s, \infty)$	r s

Check Yourself ANSWERS

1. $x > 3$ (1 2 3 4 5) $(3, \infty)$
2. $x \ge 5$ (3 4 5 6 7) $[5, \infty)$
3. $x \ge -\frac{3}{2}$ ($-\frac{3}{2}$; −2 −1 0 1 2) $\left[-\frac{3}{2}, \infty\right)$
4. $x > 3$ (1 2 3 4 5) $(3, \infty)$
5. $-1 \le x \le 3$ (−1 0 1 2 3) $[-1, 3]$
6. $-1 < x < 4$ (−2 −1 0 1 2 3 4 5) $(-1, 4)$
7. $x \le -1$ or $x \ge \frac{11}{3}$ ($\frac{11}{3}$; −3 −2 −1 0 1 2 3 4 5) $(-\infty, -1] \cup \left[\frac{11}{3}, \infty\right)$

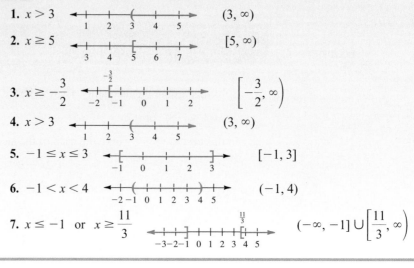

Reading Your Text

The following fill-in-the-blank exercises are designed to ensure that you understand some of the key vocabulary used in this section.

SECTION 2.4

(a) Multiplying both sides of an inequality by a negative number and ______________ the sense gives an equivalent inequality.

(b) In graphing the solution to a linear inequality, we use a ______________ to indicate that a number is included in the solution.

(c) If fractions are involved in an inequality, we should apply the ______________ property to clear the inequality of the fractions as a first step.

(d) An inequality that combines two inequalities is called a ____________ or ____________ inequality.

2.4 exercises

Basic Skills | Advanced Skills | Vocational-Technical Applications | Calculator/Computer | Above and Beyond

Name ____________

Section ________ Date ________

Answers

1. $x < 7$
2. $x > -7$
3. $x \ge -2$
4. $x \le 2$
5. $x > 5$
6. $x < -3$
7. $x \ge 5$
8. $x < -3$
9. $x < \frac{7}{2}$
10. $x \le 4$
11. $x \le -6$
12. $x > \frac{8}{3}$
13. $x > -3$
14. $x \le -4$
15. $x > 9$
16. $x \le 8$
17. $x \le \frac{4}{3}$
18. $x > \frac{5}{2}$
19. $x > -2$
20. $x \ge -3$
21. $x \ge -4$
22. $x \ge \frac{5}{3}$
23. $x < \frac{2}{5}$
24. $x < 2$
25. $x \le 3$
26. $x > -2$
27. $x > 1$
28. $x \ge 3$
29. $x > -3$
30. $x \le 6$
31. $x < 5$
32. $x \le -4$

< Objective 1 >

Solve each of the following inequalities. Then graph the solution set.

1. $x - 2 < 5$

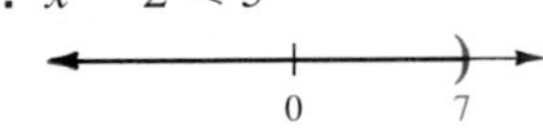

2. $x + 3 > -4$

3. $x + 5 \ge 3$

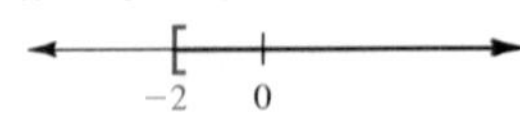

4. $x - 4 \le -2$

5. $5x > 25$

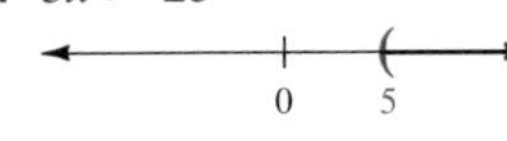

6. $4x < -12$

7. $-3x \le -15$

8. $-7x > 21$

9. $2x + 3 < 10$

10. $5x - 3 \le 17$

11. $-2x - 7 \ge 5$

12. $-3x + 4 < -4$

13. $5 - 3x < 14$

14. $2 - 5x \ge 22$

15. $3x - 4 > 2x + 5$

16. $4x + 3 \le 3x + 11$

17. $8x + 2 \le 2x + 10$

18. $5x - 1 > x + 9$

19. $7x - 3 > 2x - 13$

20. $9x + 2 \ge 2x - 19$

21. $4x - 3 \le 6x + 5$

> Videos

22. $7x - 1 \le 10x - 6$

23. $5 - 3x > 2x + 3$

24. $7 - 5x > 3x - 9$

Simplify and then solve each of the following inequalities.

25. $5(2x - 1) \le 25$

26. $3(3x + 1) > -15$

27. $4(5x + 1) > 3(3x + 5)$

28. $3(2x + 4) \le 5(3x - 3)$

29. $3(x - 1) - 4 < 2(3x + 1)$

30. $3(3x - 1) - 4(x + 3) \le 15$

31. $3(x + 7) - 11 > 2(3x - 5) + x$

32. $3(2x + 7) - 5 \le 4(x + 1) - x$

Clear of fractions and then solve each of the following inequalities.

33. $\frac{x-4}{3} < 5$

34. $\frac{x+5}{2} \geq -3$

35. $\frac{x+2}{-3} \leq 3$

36. $\frac{x-2}{-4} > -6$

37. $\frac{x}{2} - \frac{x}{3} \geq 2$

38. $\frac{x}{4} - 2 < \frac{x}{5}$

39. $\frac{x}{5} - \frac{x-7}{3} < \frac{1}{3}$

40. $\frac{x}{4} - \frac{4x+3}{20} < \frac{1}{5}$

41. $\frac{x-3}{2} - \frac{x+5}{5} \leq \frac{1}{2}$

42. $\frac{x+5}{4} - \frac{x+1}{3} \leq \frac{2}{3}$

< Objective 2 >

Solve and graph each of the following compound inequalities. Then write the solution set in interval notation.

43. $3 \leq x + 1 \leq 5$

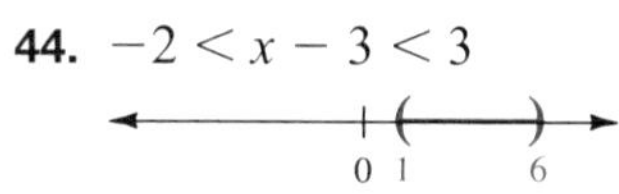

44. $-2 < x - 3 < 3$

45. $-8 < 2x < 4$

46. $-6 \leq 3x \leq 9$

47. $1 \leq 2x - 3 \leq 6$

48. $-2 < 3x - 5 < 4$

49. $-1 < 5 - 3x < 8$

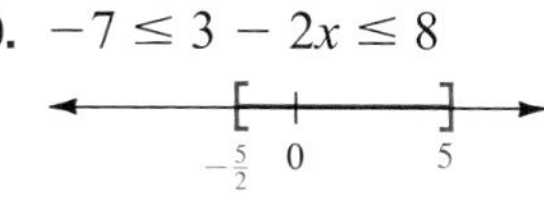

50. $-7 \leq 3 - 2x \leq 8$

Solve and graph each of the following compound inequalities. Then write the solution set in interval notation.

51. $x - 1 < -3$ or $x - 1 > 3$

52. $x + 2 < -5$ or $x + 2 > 5$

53. $2x - 1 < -7$ or $2x - 1 > 7$

54. $2x + 3 < -3$ or $2x + 3 > 3$

55. $3x - 1 < -7$ or $3x - 1 > 7$

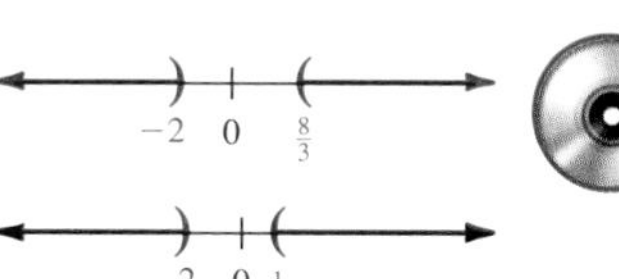

56. $4x + 3 < -5$ or $4x + 3 > 5$

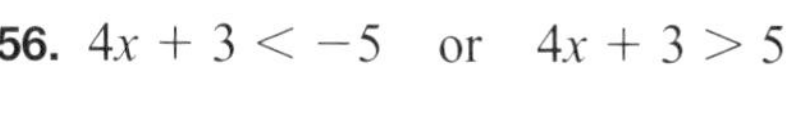

Answers

33. $x < 19$
34. $x \geq -11$
35. $x \geq -11$
36. $x < 26$
37. $x \geq 12$
38. $x < 40$
39. $x > 15$
40. $x < 7$
41. $x \leq 10$
42. $x \geq 3$
43. $2 \leq x \leq 4$, $[2, 4]$
44. $1 < x < 6$, $(1, 6)$
45. $-4 < x < 2$, $(-4, 2)$
46. $-2 \leq x \leq 3$, $[-2, 3]$
47. $2 \leq x \leq \frac{9}{2}$, $\left[2, \frac{9}{2}\right]$
48. $1 < x < 3$, $(1, 3)$
49. $-1 < x < 2$, $(-1, 2)$
50. $-\frac{5}{2} \leq x \leq 5$, $\left[-\frac{5}{2}, 5\right]$
51. $x < -2$ or $x > 4$, $(-\infty, -2) \cup (4, \infty)$
52. $x < -7$ or $x > 3$, $(-\infty, -7) \cup (3, \infty)$
53. $x < -3$ or $x > 4$, $(-\infty, -3) \cup (4, \infty)$
54. $x < -3$ or $x > 0$, $(-\infty, -3) \cup (0, \infty)$
55. $x < -2$ or $x > \frac{8}{3}$, $(-\infty, -2) \cup \left(\frac{8}{3}, \infty\right)$
56. $x < -2$ or $x > \frac{1}{2}$, $(-\infty, -2) \cup \left(\frac{1}{2}, \infty\right)$

Basic Skills | Advanced Skills | Vocational-Technical Applications | Calculator/Computer | **Above and Beyond**

Answers

57. $x > 50$ items

58. $x > 80$ items

59. $x \geq 92$ points

60. $x \geq 84$ points

61. $x \geq 12$ sections

62. $x \geq 8$ buses

63. $190 \leq m \leq 230$

Suppose that the revenue a company will receive from producing and selling x items is given by R and the cost of those items by C. The company will make a profit only if the revenue is greater than the cost, that is, when $R > C$. Use this information to find the number of items that must be produced and sold for the company to make a profit.

57. $R = 50x, \quad C = 1{,}000 + 30x$

58. $R = 800x, \quad C = 24{,}000 + 500x$

Recall that the average *of a group of test scores is the sum of those test scores divided by the number of scores. Use this information to solve the following problems.*

59. Suppose that Kim has scores of 83, 94, and 91 on three 100-point tests in her chemistry class thus far. Describe the set of scores on the 100-point final test that will give her an average of 90 or above, so that she will receive an A for the course.

(*Hint:* If x represents her final score, then

$83 + 94 + 91 + x$

will give her total score for the four tests.)

60. Robert has scores of 78, 85, 70, and 83 on four tests. Describe the set of scores he must have on the 100-point final to average 80 or above for the course.

Solve each of the following problems.

61. A college must decide how many sections of intermediate algebra to offer during the fall quarter. Each section should contain a maximum of 35 students, and the college anticipates that a total of 400 students will enroll for the sections. How many sections should be offered?

(*Hint:* If x represents the number of sections, then $400/x$ will give the number of students per section. Establish an inequality from the given information. Note that you can clear the inequality of fractions by multiplying by x because x is the number of sections and must be a positive number. Also keep in mind that x must be a *whole* number.)

62. A student-activities director must order buses for a football game. He anticipates that 300 students will sign up, and the capacity of each bus is 40 people. How many buses should he have available?

63. The mileage markers on a freeway begin at marker 0 at the southern border of a state and continue to increase toward the northern border. The legal maximum speed on the freeway is 65 mi/h, and the legal minimum speed is 45 mi/h. If you enter the freeway at marker 100 and travel north for 2 h, what is the possible range of values for the nearest marker you could legally reach?

(*Hint:* Because distance = rate · time, the minimum distance can be calculated as (45)(2) and the maximum distance as (65)(2). Let m be the marker you could legally reach, and establish a double-inequality statement for the solution.)

64. You enter the freeway at marker 240 and now travel south for 3 h. What is the possible range of values for the nearest marker you could legally reach?

65. A new landfill must last at least 30 years for it to receive an operating permit from the local community. The proposed site is capable of receiving 570×10^6 metric tons (t) of refuse over its lifespan. How much refuse can the landfill accept each year and still meet the conditions of its permit?

66. A garbage burner must receive at least 1,350 tons of trash per day to be economical enough for a community to build it. Local laws restrict truck weight to a 15-ton limit. How many truck deliveries per day will be necessary to supply the burner with its daily requirement of trash?

Answers

64. $45 \le m \le 105$

65. $x \le 19 \times 10^6$ t

66. $x \ge 90$ deliveries per day

Answers

1. $x < 7$

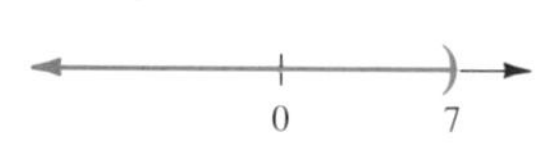

3. $x \ge -2$

5. $x > 5$

7. $x \ge 5$

9. $x < \frac{7}{2}$

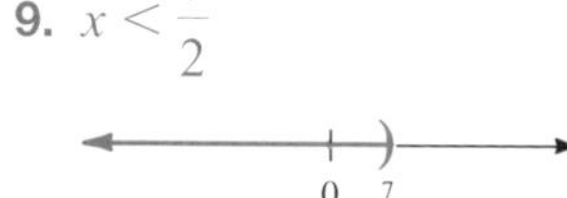

11. $x \le -6$

13. $x > -3$

15. $x > 9$

17. $x \le \frac{4}{3}$

19. $x > -2$

21. $x \ge -4$

23. $x < \frac{2}{5}$

25. $x \le 3$ **27.** $x > 1$ **29.** $x > -3$ **31.** $x < 5$ **33.** $x < 19$

35. $x \geq -11$ **37.** $x \geq 12$ **39.** $x > 15$ **41.** $x \leq 10$

43. $2 \leq x \leq 4$, $[2, 4]$

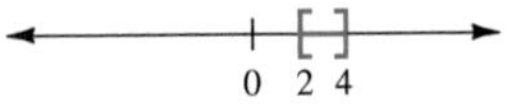

0 2 4

45. $-4 < x < 2$, $(-4, 2)$

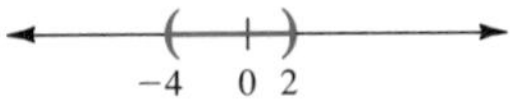

−4 0 2

47. $2 \leq x \leq \frac{9}{2}$, $\left[2, \frac{9}{2}\right]$

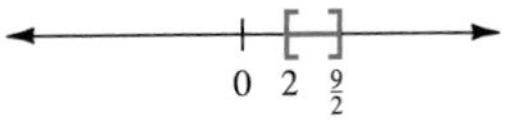

0 2 $\frac{9}{2}$

49. $-1 < x < 2$, $(-1, 2)$

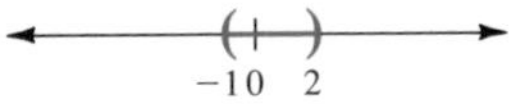

−1 0 2

51. $x < -2$ or $x > 4$, $(-\infty, -2) \cup (4, \infty)$

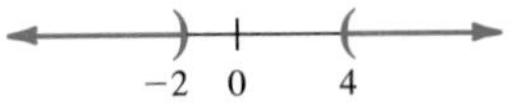

−2 0 4

53. $x < -3$ or $x > 4$, $(-\infty, -3) \cup (4, \infty)$

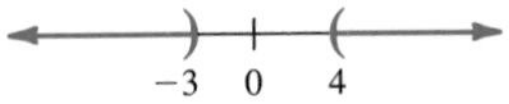

−3 0 4

55. $x < -2$ or $x > \frac{8}{3}$, $(-\infty, -2) \cup \left(\frac{8}{3}, \infty\right)$

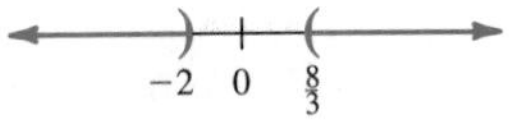

−2 0 $\frac{8}{3}$

57. $x > 50$ items **59.** $x \geq 92$ points **61.** $x \geq 12$ sections

63. $190 \leq m \leq 230$ **65.** $x \leq 19 \times 10^6$ t

2.5 Absolute Value Equations and Inequalities

< 2.5 Objectives >

1 > Solve an absolute value equation in one variable

2 > Solve an absolute value inequality in one variable

NOTE

Technically we mean the distance between the *point corresponding* to x and the *point corresponding* to 0, the origin.

Equations and inequalities may involve the absolute value notation in their statements. In this section we build on the tools developed in Sections 2.1, 2.2, and 2.4 and on our earlier work with absolute value for the necessary solution techniques.

Recall from Section 1.3 that the absolute value of x, written $|x|$, is the distance between x and 0 on the number line. Consider, for example, the absolute value equation

$$|x| = 4$$

This means that the distance between x and 0 is 4, as is pictured here.

> CAUTION

In property 1 below, p must be positive because an equation such as $|x - 2| = -3$ has no solution. The absolute value of a quantity must always be equal to a nonnegative number.

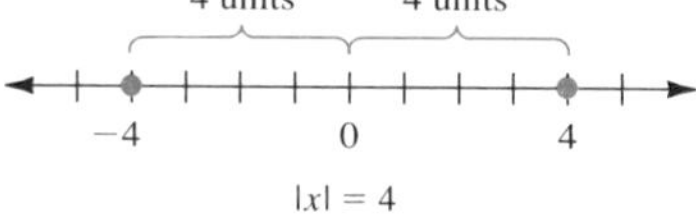

As the sketch illustrates, $x = 4$ and $x = -4$ are the two solutions for the equation.

This observation suggests the more general statement.

Property

Absolute Value Equations—Property 1

For any positive number p, if

$$|x| = p$$

then

$$x = p \quad \text{or} \quad x = -p$$

This property allows us to "translate" an equation involving absolute value to two linear equations that we can then solve separately. Example 1 illustrates.

Example 1 **Solving an Absolute Value Equation**

< Objective 1 >

Solve for x.

$$|3x - 2| = 4$$

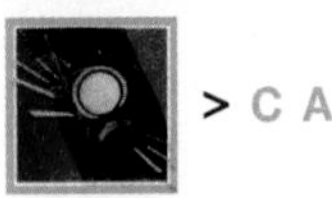

> CAUTION

Be Careful! A common mistake is to solve *only* the equation $3x - 2 = 4$. You must solve *both* of the equivalent equations to find the two required solutions.

From Property 1 we know that $|3x - 2| = 4$ is equivalent to the equations

$$\begin{aligned} 3x - 2 &= 4 \quad \text{or} \quad & 3x - 2 &= -4 \\ 3x &= 6 & 3x &= -2 \quad & \text{Add 2.} \\ x &= 2 & x &= -\frac{2}{3} \quad & \text{Divide by 3.} \end{aligned}$$

The solutions are $-\frac{2}{3}$ and 2. These solutions are easily checked by replacing x with $-\frac{2}{3}$ and 2 in the original absolute value equation.

Check Yourself 1

Solve for x.

$|4x + 1| = 9$

An equation involving absolute value may have to be rewritten before you can apply Property 1. Consider Example 2.

Example 2 Solving an Absolute Value Equation

Solve for x.

$|2 - 3x| + 5 = 10$

To use Property 1, we must first isolate the absolute value on the left side of the equation. This is done by subtracting 5 from both sides for the result:

$|2 - 3x| = 5$

We can now proceed as before by using Property 1.

$$\begin{aligned} 2 - 3x &= 5 \quad \text{or} \quad & 2 - 3x &= -5 \\ -3x &= 3 & -3x &= -7 \quad & \text{Subtract 2.} \\ x &= -1 & x &= \frac{7}{3} \quad & \text{Divide by } -3. \end{aligned}$$

The solutions are -1 and $\frac{7}{3}$.

Check Yourself 2

Solve for x.

$|5 - 2x| - 4 = 7$

Some absolute value equations have no solution. One such equation is illustrated in Example 3.

Example 3 Solving an Absolute Value Equation

Solve for x.

$$|3x - 1| = -2$$

By Property 1, we can write

$$\begin{aligned} 3x - 1 &= -2 \quad \text{or} \quad 3x - 1 = 2 \\ 3x &= -1 \qquad\qquad 3x = 3 \qquad \text{Add 1.} \\ x &= -\frac{1}{3} \qquad\qquad x = 1 \qquad \text{Divide by 3.} \end{aligned}$$

The necessity of checking the solutions in the original equation is demonstrated here.

For $x = -\frac{1}{3}$:

$$\left|3\left(-\frac{1}{3}\right) - 1\right| = -2$$

$$|-1 - 1| = -2$$

$$|-2| = -2$$

$$2 = -2 \quad \text{False}$$

For $x = 1$:

$$|3(1) - 1| = -2$$

$$|3 - 1| = -2$$

$$|2| = -2$$

$$2 = -2 \quad \text{False}$$

Since both equations reduce to a false statement, $2 = -2$, the original equation is a contradiction (Section 2.1). Therefore, there is no solution.

Would it have been necessary for us to apply Property 1 and solve the equations to determine there is no solution? Look carefully at the original equation. Can the absolute value of any number or expression be negative?

Check Yourself 3

Solve for x.

$$|4x + 2| = -6$$

In some applications more than one absolute value is involved in an equation. Consider an equation of the form

$$|x| = |y|$$

Because the absolute values of x and y are equal, x and y are the same distance from 0. This means they are either *equal* or *opposite in sign.* This leads to a second general property of absolute value equations.

Property

Absolute Value Equations—Property 2

If

$$|x| = |y|$$

then

$$x = y \quad \text{or} \quad x = -y$$

We will look at an application of this second property in Example 4.

Example 4 Solving an Absolute Value Equation

Solve for x.

$|3x - 4| = |x + 2|$

By Property 2, we can write

$3x - 4 = x + 2$ or $3x - 4 = -(x + 2)$

$3x - 4 = -x - 2$ Apply the distributive property.

$3x = x + 6$ $\quad$ $3x = -x + 2$

$2x = 6$ $\quad$ $4x = 2$

$x = 3$ $\quad$ $x = \frac{1}{2}$

The solutions are $\frac{1}{2}$ and 3.

Check Yourself 4

Solve for x.

$|4x - 1| = |x + 5|$

Some absolute value equations have a solution set of all real numbers. One such equation is illustrated in Example 5.

Example 5 Solving an Absolute Value Equation

Solve for x.

$|x - 3| = |3 - x|$

By Property 2, we can write

$x - 3 = 3 - x$ or $x - 3 = -(3 - x)$

$x = 6 - x$ $\quad$ $x - 3 = -3 + x$ Apply the distributive property first, for equation on right.

$2x = 6$ $\quad$ $x = 0 + x$

$x = 3$ $\quad$ $0 = 0$ $\quad$ $0 = 0$ is an identity.

RECALL

An identity is an equation that is true for all possible values of the variable.

The necessity of checking the solution $x = 3$ in the original equation is demonstrated here.

For $x = 3$:

$|(3) - 3| = |3 - (3)|$

$|0| = |0|$

$0 = 0$ True

Again, we have $0 = 0$, which is an identity (see Section 2.1). Therefore, the solution for the absolute value equation is all real numbers.

Check Yourself 5

Solve for *x*.

$|x + 4| = |4 + x|$

You may encounter an absolute value equation with only one solution as shown in Example 6.

Example 6 Solving an Absolute Value Equation

Solve for *x*.

$|x - 6| = |x + 2|$

By Property 2, we can write

$$x - 6 = x + 2 \quad \text{or} \quad x - 6 = -(x + 2)$$

$$x - 6 = -x - 2 \qquad \text{Apply the distributive property.}$$

$$x = x + 8 \qquad x = -x + 4$$

$$2x = 4$$

$$0 = 8 \quad \text{False} \qquad x = 2$$

The resulting false statement for the first equation yields no solution. Checking the solution $x = 2$ in the original equation, we have

For $x = 2$:

$$|(2) - 6| = |(2) + 2|$$

$$|-4| = |4|$$

$$4 = 4 \qquad \text{True}$$

There is one solution for the given equation, $x = 2$.

Check Yourself 6

Solve for *x*.

$|x + 3| = |x - 5|$

We started this section by noting that the solution for the equation

$|x| = 4$

consists of those numbers whose distance from the origin is equal to 4. Similarly, the solution set for the absolute value inequality

$|x| < 4$

consists of those numbers whose distance from the origin is *less than* 4, that is, all numbers between -4 and 4. The solution set is pictured here.

−4 0 4

$|x| < 4$

NOTE

The solution set would be $-4 < x < 4$

The solution set can be described by the compound inequality

$$-4 < x < 4$$

and this suggests the following general statement.

Property

Absolute Value Inequalities—Property 1

For any positive number p, if

$$|x| < p$$

then

$$-p < x < p$$

We will look at an application of Property 1 in solving an absolute value inequality.

Example 7 Solving an Absolute Value Inequality

< Objective 2 >

Solve and graph the solution set. Then, write the solution set in interval notation.

$$|2x - 3| < 5$$

NOTE

With Property 1 we can *translate* an absolute value inequality to an inequality *not* involving absolute value that can be solved by methods developed earlier in section 2.4.

From Property 1, we know that the given absolute value inequality is equivalent to the compound inequality

$$-5 < 2x - 3 < 5$$

Solving as before, we isolate the variable in the center term.

$-2 < 2x < 8$ We added 3 to all three parts. Now divide by 2.

$-1 < x < 4$

The solution set in interval notation is

$$(-1, 4)$$

The graph is shown here.

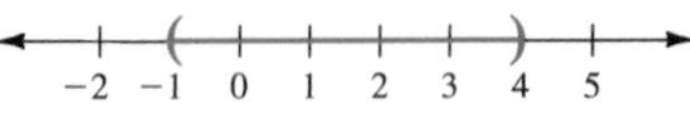

NOTE

The solution is an open interval on the number line.

Check Yourself 7

Solve and graph the solution set. Then, write the solution set in interval notation.

$$|3x - 4| \le 8$$

We know that the solution set for the absolute value inequality

$$|x| < 4$$

consists of those numbers whose distance from the origin is *less than* 4. Now consider the solution set for

$$|x| > 4$$

It must consist of those numbers whose distance from the origin is *greater than* 4. The solution set is pictured here.

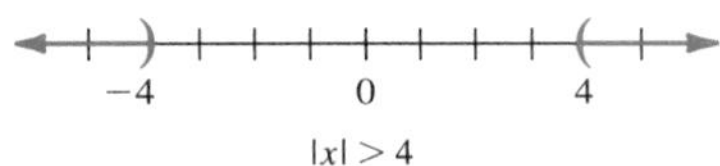

The solution set can be translated into the compound inequality

$$x < -4 \quad \text{or} \quad x > 4$$

and this suggests the following general statement.

Property

Absolute Value Inequalities—Property 2

For any positive number p, if

$$|x| > p$$

then

$$x < -p \quad \text{or} \quad x > p$$

We will apply Property 2 to the solution of an absolute value inequality.

Example 8 Solving an Absolute Value Inequality

> **NOTE**
>
> Again we *translate* the absolute value inequality to a compound inequality *not* involving absolute value.

Solve and graph the solution set. Then write the solution set in interval notation.

$$|5x - 2| > 8$$

From Property 2, we know that the given absolute value inequality is equivalent to the compound inequality

$$5x - 2 < -8 \quad \text{or} \quad 5x - 2 > 8$$

Solving as before, we have

$$5x < -6 \quad \text{or} \quad 5x > 10 \qquad \text{Add 2.}$$

$$x < -\frac{6}{5} \qquad x > 2 \qquad \text{Divide by 5.}$$

The solution set is $x < -\frac{6}{5}$ or $x > 2$, or $\left(-\infty, -\frac{6}{5}\right) \cup (2, \infty)$. The graph is shown here.

$-\frac{6}{5}$

−3 −2 −1 0 1 2 3 4

Check Yourself 8

Solve and graph the solution set. Then write the *set* solution in interval notation.

$|3 - 2x| \geq 9$

It is important to note that, just as with absolute value equations (see Examples 3 and 5), absolute value inequalities can have a result of "no solution," when the solution yields a false statement, or "all real numbers," when the solution is true for all possible values of the variable.

The following chart summarizes our discussion of absolute value inequalities.

NOTE

As before, p must be a positive number.

Type of Inequality	Equivalent Inequality	Direction of Parentheses
$\lvert ax + b\rvert < p$	$-p < ax + b < p$	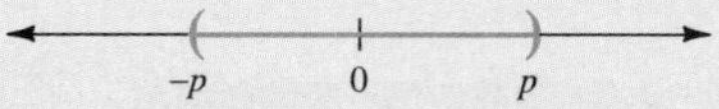
$\lvert ax + b\rvert > p$	$ax + b < -p$ or $ax + b > p$	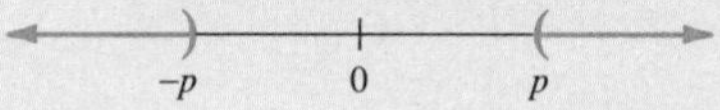

Check Yourself ANSWERS

1. $x = -\frac{5}{2}, x = 2$ **2.** $x = -3, x = 8$ **3.** No solution **4.** $x = -\frac{4}{5}, x = 2$

5. All real numbers **6.** $x = 1$

7. $-\frac{4}{3} \leq x \leq 4$ 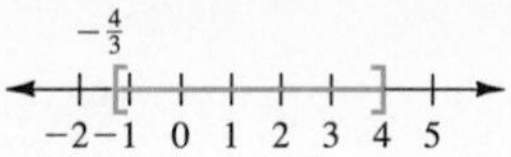 $\left[-\frac{4}{3}, 4\right]$

8. $x \leq -3$ or $x \geq 6$ 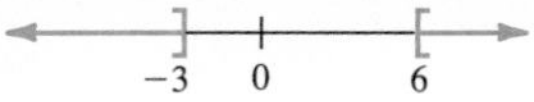 $(-\infty, -3] \cup [6, \infty)$

Reading Your Text

The following fill-in-the-blank exercises are designed to ensure that you understand some of the key vocabulary used in this section.

SECTION 2.5

(a) To solve an absolute value equation, we must "translate" the equation to ______________ linear equations that we can then solve separately.

(b) In solving an absolute value equation, we must first ______________ the absolute value on the left side of the equation.

(c) The solution set for an absolute value inequality of the form $|p| < 0$ or $|p| > 0$ is a ______________ inequality.

(d) If $|x| = |y|$, then $x =$ ______________ or $x =$ ______________.

Basic Skills | Advanced Skills | Vocational-Technical Applications | Calculator/Computer | Above and Beyond

2.5 exercises

< Objective 1 >

Solve each of the absolute value equations. Verify the solutions.

1. $|x| = 5$

2. $|x| = 7$

3. $|x - 2| = 3$

4. $|x + 5| = 6$

5. $|x + 6| = 0$

6. $|x - 3| = 0$

7. $|3 - x| = 7$

8. $|5 - x| = 4$

9. $|2x - 3| = 9$

10. $|3x + 5| = 11$

11. $|5 - 4x| = 1$

12. $|3 - 6x| = 9$

13. $\left|\frac{1}{2}x + 5\right| = 7$

14. $\left|\frac{2}{3}x - 4\right| = 6$

15. $\left|4 - \frac{3}{4}x\right| = 8$

16. $\left|3 - \frac{2}{5}x\right| = 9$

17. $|3x + 1| = -2$

18. $|5x - 2| = -3$

Rewrite each of the absolute value equations, and then solve the equations.

19. $|x| - 3 = 2$

20. $|x| + 4 = 6$

21. $|x - 2| + 3 = 5$

22. $|x + 5| - 2 = 5$

23. $|2x - 3| - 1 = 6$

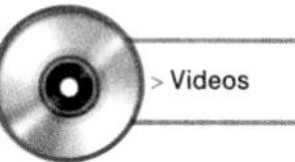

24. $|3x + 5| + 2 = 4$

25. $\left|\frac{1}{2}x + 2\right| - 3 = 5$

26. $\left|\frac{1}{3}x - 4\right| + 3 = 9$

Name ____________

Section ________ Date ________

Answers

1. $x = -5, x = 5$
2. $x = -7, x = 7$
3. $x = -1, x = 5$
4. $x = -11, x = 1$
5. $x = -6$
6. $x = 3$
7. $x = -4, x = 10$
8. $x = 1, x = 9$
9. $x = -3, x = 6$
10. $x = -\frac{16}{3}, x = 2$
11. $x = 1, x = \frac{3}{2}$
12. $x = -1, x = 2$
13. $x = -24, x = 4$
14. $x = -3, x = 15$
15. $x = -\frac{16}{3}, x = 16$
16. $x = -15, x = 30$
17. No solution
18. No solution
19. $x = -5, x = 5$
20. $x = -2, x = 2$
21. $x = 0, x = 4$
22. $x = -12, x = 2$
23. $x = -2, x = 5$
24. $x = -\frac{7}{3}, x = -1$
25. $x = -20, x = 12$
26. $x = -6, x = 30$

Answers

27. $x = 1, x = 7$

28. $x = -4, x = 3$

29. No solution

30. No solution

31. $x = -\frac{2}{3}, x = 4$

32. $x = -4, x = \frac{2}{5}$

33. $x = -\frac{2}{7}, x = 2$

34. $x = -\frac{4}{9}, x = 2$

35. $x = \frac{1}{2}$

36. $x = -\frac{1}{2}$

37. $x = 2$

38. $x = 0$

39. All real numbers

40. All real numbers

41. $-5 < x < 5$, $(-5, 5)$

42. $x < -3$ or $x > 3$, $(-\infty, -3) \cup (3, \infty)$

43. $x \le -7$ or $x \ge 7$, $(-\infty, -7] \cup [7, \infty)$

44. $-4 \le x \le 4$, $[-4, 4]$

45. $x < 2$ or $x > 6$, $(-\infty, 2) \cup (6, \infty)$

46. $-8 < x < -2$, $(-8, -2)$

47. $-10 \le x \le -2$, $[-10, -2]$

48. $x \le 2$ or $x \ge 12$, $(-\infty, 2] \cup [12, \infty)$

49. $x < -2$ or $x > 8$, $(-\infty, -2) \cup (8, \infty)$

50. $2 < x < 8$, $(2, 8)$

27. $8 - |x - 4| = 5$

28. $10 - |2x + 1| = 3$

29. $|3x - 2| + 4 = 3$

30. $|5x - 3| + 5 = 3$

Solve each of the absolute value equations.

31. $|2x - 1| = |x + 3|$

32. $|3x + 1| = |2x - 3|$

33. $|5x - 2| = |2x + 4|$

34. $|7x - 3| = |2x + 7|$

35. $|x - 2| = |x + 1|$

36. $|x + 3| = |x - 2|$

37. $|2x - 5| = |2x - 3|$

38. $|3x + 1| = |3x - 1|$

39. $|x - 2| = |2 - x|$

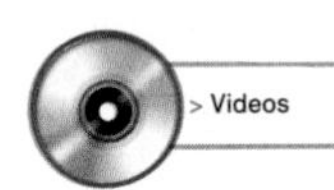

40. $|x - 4| = |4 - x|$

< Objective 2 >

Find and graph the solution set for each of the absolute value inequalities. Then write the solution set in interval notation.

41. $|x| < 5$

−5 0 5

42. $|x| > 3$

−3 0 3

43. $|x| \ge 7$

−7 0 7

44. $|x| \le 4$

−4 0 4

45. $|x - 4| > 2$

0 2 6

46. $|x + 5| < 3$

−8 −2 0

47. $|x + 6| \le 4$

−10 −2 0

48. $|x - 7| \ge 5$

0 2 12

49. $|3 - x| > 5$

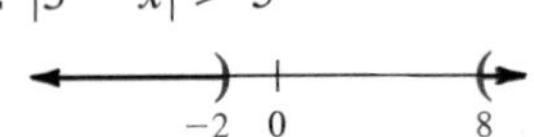

50. $|5 - x| < 3$

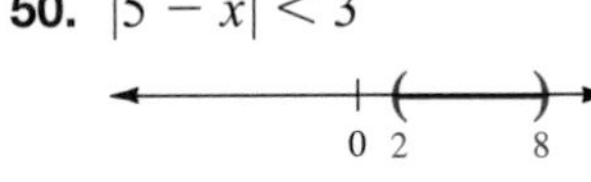

51. $|x - 7| < 0$ > Videos

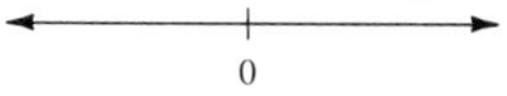

52. $|x + 5| \geq 0$

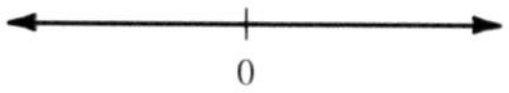

53. $|2x - 5| < 3$

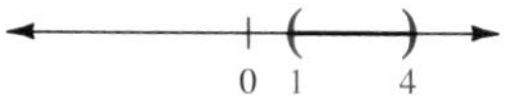

54. $|3x - 1| > 8$

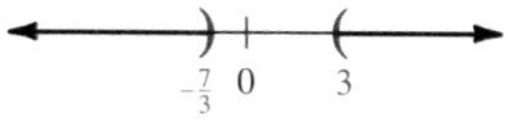

55. $|3x + 4| \geq 5$

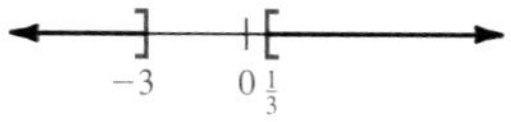

56. $|2x + 3| \leq 9$

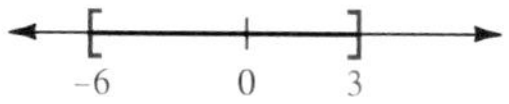

57. $|5x - 3| > 7$

58. $|6x - 5| < 13$

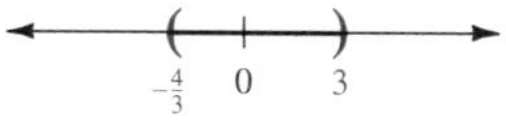

59. $|2 - 3x| < 11$

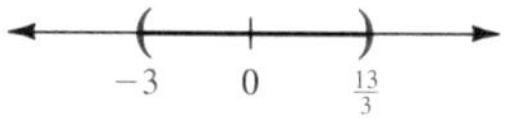

60. $|3 - 2x| \geq 11$

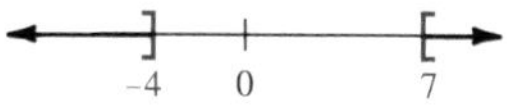

61. $|3 - 5x| \geq 7$

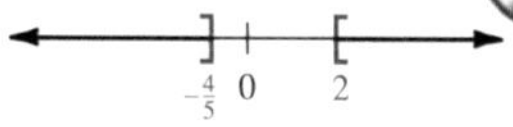

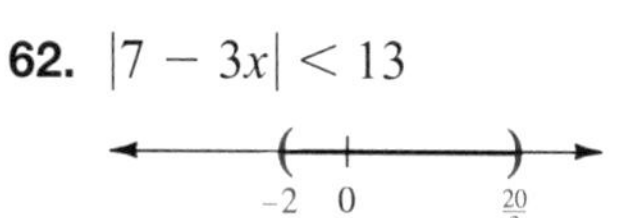

62. $|7 - 3x| < 13$

63. $\left|\frac{3}{4}x - 5\right| < 7$

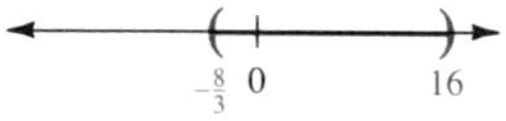

64. $\left|\frac{2}{3}x + 5\right| \geq 3$

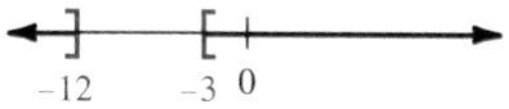

Basic Skills | Advanced Skills | Vocational-Technical Applications | **Calculator/Computer** | Above and Beyond

On some popular calculators, there is a special absolute value function key. It is usually labeled "abs." To register an absolute value, you press this key and then put the desired expression in parentheses. For the expression $|x + 3|$, enter abs($x + 3$). To access the absolute value function on the TI-84 calculator, use the following path:

MATH

NUM

1:abs(

These same calculators display multiplication using the symbol "*".

Rewrite each expression in calculator form.

65. $|x + 2|$

66. $|x - 2|$

67. $|2x - 3|$

68. $|5x + 7|$

Answers

51. No solution
52. All real numbers
53. $1 < x < 4$, $(1, 4)$
54. $x < -\frac{7}{3}$ or $x > 3$, $\left(-\infty, -\frac{7}{3}\right) \cup (3, \infty)$
55. $x \leq -3$ or $x \geq \frac{1}{3}$, $(-\infty, -3] \cup \left[\frac{1}{3}, \infty\right)$
56. $-6 \leq x \leq 3$, $[-6, 3]$
57. $x < -\frac{4}{5}$ or $x > 2$, $\left(-\infty, -\frac{4}{5}\right) \cup (2, \infty)$
58. $-\frac{4}{3} < x < 3$, $\left(-\frac{4}{3}, 3\right)$
59. $-3 < x < \frac{13}{3}$, $\left(-3, \frac{13}{3}\right)$
60. $x \leq -4$, or $x \geq 7$ $(-\infty, -4] \cup [7, \infty)$
61. $x \leq -\frac{4}{5}$ or $x \geq 2$, $\left(-\infty, -\frac{4}{5}\right] \cup [2, \infty)$
62. $-2 < x < \frac{20}{3}$, $\left(-2, \frac{20}{3}\right)$
63. $-\frac{8}{3} < x < 16$, $\left(-\frac{8}{3}, 16\right)$
64. $x \leq -12$ or $x \geq -3$, $(-\infty, -12] \cup [-3, \infty)$
65. abs(x + 2)
66. abs(x − 2)
67. abs(2 * x − 3)
68. abs(5 * x + 7)

Answers

69. abs(3 * x + 2) − 4

70. abs(4 * x − 7) + 2

71. 2 * abs(3 * x − 1)

72. −3 * abs(2 * x + 8)

69. $|3x + 2| - 4$ **70.** $|4x - 7| + 2$

71. $2|3x - 1|$ **72.** $-3|2x + 8|$

Answers

1. $x = -5, x = 5$ **3.** $x = -1, x = 5$ **5.** $x = -6$ **7.** $x = -4, x = 10$ **9.** $x = -3, x = 6$ **11.** $x = 1, x = \frac{3}{2}$ **13.** $x = -24, x = 4$ **15.** $x = -\frac{16}{3}, x = 16$ **17.** No solution **19.** $x = -5, x = 5$ **21.** $x = 0, x = 4$ **23.** $x = -2, x = 5$ **25.** $x = -20, x = 12$ **27.** $x = 1, x = 7$ **29.** No solution **31.** $x = -\frac{2}{3}, x = 4$ **33.** $x = -\frac{2}{7}, x = 2$ **35.** $x = \frac{1}{2}$ **37.** $x = 2$ **39.** All real numbers

41. $-5 < x < 5, (-5, 5)$
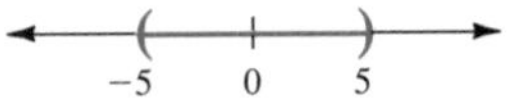

43. $x \le -7$ or $x \ge 7, (-\infty, -7] \cup [7, \infty)$
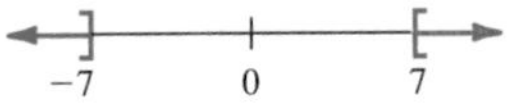

45. $x < 2$ or $x > 6, (-\infty, 2) \cup (6, \infty)$
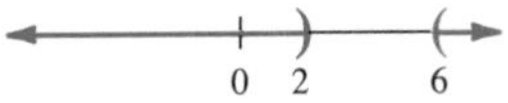

47. $-10 \le x \le -2, [-10, -2]$
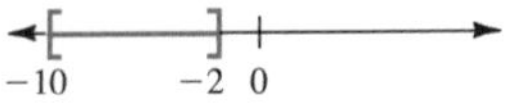

49. $x < -2$ or $x > 8, (-\infty, -2) \cup (8, \infty)$
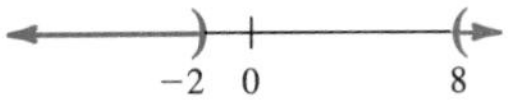

51. No solution **53.** $1 < x < 4, (1, 4)$
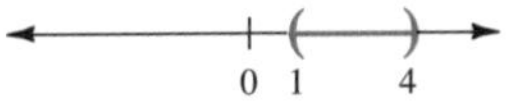

55. $x \le -3$ or $x \ge \frac{1}{3}, (-\infty, -3] \cup \left[\frac{1}{3}, \infty\right)$
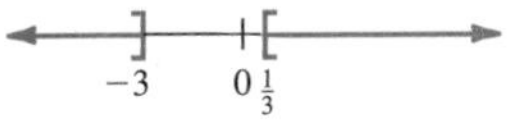

57. $x < -\frac{4}{5}$ or $x > 2, \left(-\infty, -\frac{4}{5}\right) \cup (2, \infty)$

59. $-3 < x < \frac{13}{3}, \left(-3, \frac{13}{3}\right)$
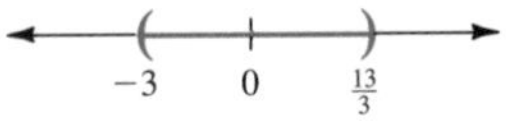

61. $x \le -\frac{4}{5}$ or $x \ge 2, \left(-\infty, -\frac{4}{5}\right] \cup [2, \infty)$
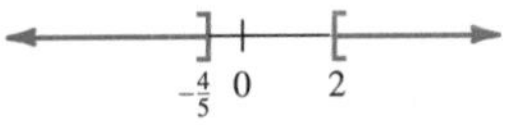

63. $-\frac{8}{3} < x < 16, \left(-\frac{8}{3}, 16\right)$
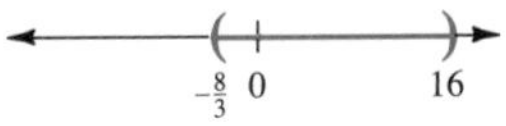

65. abs(x + 2) **67.** abs(2 * x − 3) **69.** abs(3 * x + 2) − 4 **71.** 2 * abs(3 * x − 1)

Definition/Procedure	Example	Reference
Solutions of Linear Equations in One Variable		**Section 2.1**
A **linear equation in one variable** is any equation that can be written in the form $ax + b = 0$ in which a and b are any real numbers and $a \neq 0$.	$5x - 6 = 3x + 2$ is a linear equation. The variable appears only to the first power.	*pp.* 90–91
To solve a linear equation means to find its solution. A **solution** of an equation in one variable is any number that will make the equation a true statement. Two equations are **equivalent** if they have the same solution set.	The solution for the preceding equation is 4 because $5 \cdot 4 - 6 \stackrel{?}{=} 3 \cdot 4 + 2$ $14 = 14$ is a true statement.	
Forming a sequence of equivalent equations that will lead to the solution of a linear equation involves two properties of equations.	$5x - 6 = 3x + 2$ and $2x = 8$ are equivalent equations. Both have 4 as the solution.	
Addition Property of Equations		
If $a = b$, then $a + c = b + c$. In words, adding the same quantity to both sides of an equation gives an equivalent equation.	If $x - 3 = 7$, then $x - 3 + 3 = 7 + 3$.	*p.* 91
Multiplication Property of Equations		
If $a = b$, then $ac = bc$, $c \neq 0$. In words, multiplying both sides of an equation by the same nonzero quantity gives an equivalent equation.	If $2x = 8$, then $\frac{1}{2}(2x) = \frac{1}{2}(8)$.	*p.* 91
Solving Linear Equations in One Variable		
Step 1 Remove any grouping symbols by applying the distributive property.	Solve. $4(x + 1) - 5x = 1$	*p.* 97
Step 2 Multiply both sides of the equation by the LCM of all denominators, to clear the equation of fractions.	Remove grouping symbols. $4x + 4 - 5x = 1$	
Step 3 Combine any like terms that appear on either side of the equation.	Combine like terms. $-x + 4 = 1$	
Step 4 Apply the addition property of equations to write an equivalent equation with the variable term on *one side* of the equation and the constant term on the *other side*.	Subtract 4. $-x = -3$	
Step 5 Apply the multiplication property of equations to write an equivalent equation with the variable isolated on one side of the equation.	Divide by -1. $x = 3$	
Step 6 Check the solution in the *original* equation.	To check: $4(3 + 1) - 5(3) \stackrel{?}{=} 1$	

Continued

Definition/Procedure	Example	Reference
Literal Equations and Formulas		**Section 2.2**
Formulas and **literal equations** express a relationship between more than one variable or letter. Solving a formula or literal equation for a variable means isolating that specified variable on one side of the equation. The steps used in the process are very similar to those used in solving linear equations.	$P = 2L + 2W$ is a formula or a literal equation. To solve for L: $P - 2W = 2L$ $L = \frac{P - 2W}{2}$	*p.* 103
Applications and Problem Solving		**Section 2.3**
Solving Applications	One number is 3 less than twice another. If the sum of the numbers is 27, find the two numbers.	*p.* 113
Step 1 Read the problem carefully to determine the unknown quantities.	**1.** The unknowns are the two numbers.	
Step 2 Choose a variable to represent the unknown or unknowns.	**2.** Let x be the first number. Then $2x - 3$ is the second.	
Step 3 Translate the problem to the language of algebra to form an equation.	**3.** $\underbrace{x + 2x - 3}_{\text{Sum of the numbers}} = 27$	
Step 4 Solve the equation and answer the question of the original problem.	**4.** Solving as before gives $x = 10$ and $2x - 3 = 17$	
Step 5 Verify your solution by returning to the original problem.	**5.** The sum of the numbers is 27, and 17 is 3 less than twice 10.	
Linear Inequalities		**Section 2.4**
A linear inequality in one variable is any inequality that can be written in the form $ax + b < 0$ in which a and b are real numbers and $a \neq 0$.	$5x - 7 < 2x + 4$ is a linear inequality. The inequalities $ax + b > 0$ $ax + b \le 0$ and $ax + b \ge 0$ are also linear inequalities.	*p.* 135
Addition Property of Inequalities		
If $a < b$, then $a + c < b + c$.	If $x - 3 < 7$, $x - 3 + 3 < 7 + 3$ $x < 10$	*p.* 135

Definition/Procedure	Example	Reference
Multiplication Property of Inequalities		
If $a < b$ then $ac < bc$ when c is a *positive* number and $ac > bc$ when c is a *negative* number Solving linear inequalities involves essentially the same procedures as solving linear equations. The following algorithm is applied.	If $\frac{1}{3}x < 5$, $3\left(\frac{1}{3}\right)x < 3(5)$ $x < 15$ If $-x < 4$, $x > -4$	p. 136
Interval Notation		
(b, ∞) is read "all real numbers greater than b."	$(2, \infty)$ indicates all real numbers greater than 2.	p. 137
$(-\infty, b]$ is read "all real numbers less than or equal to b."	$(-\infty, -4]$ indicates all real numbers less than or equal to -4.	
(a, b) is read "all real numbers greater than a and less than b."	$(-1, 7)$ indicates all real numbers greater than -1 and less than 7.	
$[a, b)$ is read "all real numbers greater than or equal to a and less than b."	$[0, 5)$ indicates all real numbers greater than or equal to 0 and less than 5.	
$(-\infty, a] \cup (b, \infty)$ is read "all real numbers less than or equal to a or all real numbers greater than b."	$(-\infty, 3] \cup (8, \infty)$ indicates all real numbers less than or equal to 3 or greater than 8.	
Solving Linear Inequalities in One Variable		
Step 1 Remove any grouping symbols and combine like terms by applying the distributive property.		p. 139
Step 2 Clear the inequality statement of any fractions by multiplying both sides by the LCM of all denominators.	$2x - 5 \geq 7x + 15$	
Step 3 Combine any like terms that appear on either side of the equation.		
Step 4 Apply the addition property to write an equivalent inequality with the variable term on *one side* of the inequality and the constant term on the *other side.*	Add 5 to both sides. $2x \geq 7x + 20$ Subtract $7x$ from both sides.	
Step 5 Apply the multiplication property to write an equivalent inequality with the variable isolated on one side of the inequality. Be sure to reverse the sense of the inequality if you multiply or divide by a negative number.	$-5x \geq 20$ Divide both sides by -5. $x \leq -4$	

Continued

Definition/Procedure	Example	Reference
Step 6 Graph the solution set of the original inequality.	Note that we *reverse the sense* of the inequality. The graph of the solution set $x \le -4$, or $(-\infty, -4]$, is 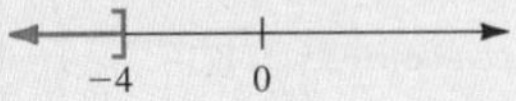	
The **compound inequalities** considered here fall into two categories: **1.** $ax + b > -c$ and $ax + b < c$ which can be written in the double-inequality form as $-c < ax + b < c$ This type of inequality statement is solved by isolating the variable in the middle term. **2.** $ax + b < -c$ or $ax + b > c$ This type of inequality statement is solved by considering each inequality separately.	$-5 < 3x < 7$ means that $-5 < 3x$ and $3x < 7$ So $-\frac{5}{3} < x$ and $x < \frac{7}{3}$	*p.* 140
Absolute Value Equations and Inequalities		**Section 2.5**
To solve absolute value equations, the following properties are applied. ***Absolute Value Equations—Properties 1 and 2*** **1.** For any positive number p, if $\|x\| = p$ then $x = -p$ or $x = p$ To solve an equation involving absolute value, translate the equation to the two equivalent linear equations. Those equations can then be solved separately. **2.** If $\|x\| = \|y\|$, then $x = y$ or $x = -y$ To solve an absolute value equation of this form, translate the equation to the two equivalent linear equations. Those equations can then be solved separately.	$\|2x - 5\| = 7$ is equivalent to $2x - 5 = -7$ or $2x - 5 = 7$ so $x = -1$ or $x = 6$ $\|3x - 1\| = \|x + 5\|$ $3x - 1 = x + 5$ or $3x - 1 = -(x + 5)$ so $x = 3$ or $x = -1$	*pp.* 149–151

Definition/Procedure	Example	Reference

Absolute Value Inequalities—Properties 1 and 2

1. For any positive number p, if

   $|x| < p$

   then

   $-p < x < p$

   To solve this form of inequality, translate to the equivalent compound inequality and then solve as before.

2. For any positive number p, if

   $|x| > p$

   then

   $x < -p \quad \text{or} \quad x > p$

   To solve this form of inequality, translate to the equivalent compound inequality and then solve as before.

Example

$|3x - 5| < 7$ is equivalent to

$-7 < 3x - 5 < 7$

This yields

$-2 < 3x < 12$

$-\frac{2}{3} < x < 4$

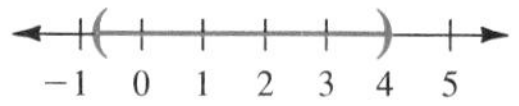

$|2 - 5x| \geq 12$ is equivalent to

$2 - 5x \leq -12$

or

$2 - 5x \geq 12$

This yields

$x \geq \frac{14}{5} \quad \text{or} \quad x \leq -2$

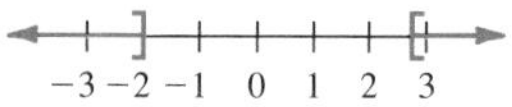

Reference

pp. 154–155

summary exercises :: chapter 2

This summary exercise set is provided to give you practice with each of the objectives of this chapter. Each exercise is keyed to the appropriate chapter section. When you are finished, you can check your answers to the odd-numbered exercises against those presented in the back of the text. If you have difficulty with any of these questions, go back and reread the examples from that section. The answers to the even-numbered exercises appear in the *Instructor's Solutions Manual.* Your instructor will give you guidelines on how to best use these exercises in your instructional setting.

2.1 *Solve the following equations.*

1. $4x - 5 = 23$ $x = 7$

2. $7 - 3x = -8$ $x = 5$

3. $5x + 2 = 6 - 3x$ $x = \frac{1}{2}$

4. $7x - 3 = 2x + 12$ $x = 3$

5. $2x - 7 = 9x - 35$ $x = 4$

6. $5 - 3x = 2 - 6x$ $x = -1$

7. $7x - 3 + 2x = 5 + 6x + 4$ $x = 4$

8. $2x + 5 - 4x = 3 - 6x + 10$ $x = 2$

9. $3(x - 5) = x + 1$ $x = 8$

10. $4(2x - 1) = 6x + 5$ $x = \frac{9}{2}$

11. $7x - 3(x - 2) = 30$ $x = 6$

12. $8x - 5(x + 3) = -10$ $x = \frac{5}{3}$

13. $7(3x + 1) - 13 = 8(2x + 3)$ $x = 6$

14. $3(2x - 5) - 2(x - 3) = 11$ $x = 5$

15. $\frac{2x}{3} - \frac{x}{4} = 5$ $x = 12$

16. $\frac{3x}{4} - \frac{2x}{5} = 7$ $x = 20$

17. $\frac{x}{2} - \frac{x + 1}{3} = \frac{1}{6}$ $x = 3$

18. $\frac{x + 1}{5} - \frac{x - 6}{3} = \frac{1}{3}$ $x = 14$

2.2 *Solve for the indicated variable.*

19. $P = RB$ for R $R = \frac{P}{B}$

20. $I = Prt$ for t $t = \frac{I}{Pr}$

21. $S = 2\pi rh$ for h $h = \frac{S}{2\pi r}$

22. $S = \frac{1}{2}gt^2$ for g $g = \frac{2S}{t^2}$

23. $y = mx + b$ for m $m = \frac{y - b}{x}$

24. $A = P(1 + rt)$ for r $r = \frac{A - P}{Pt}$

2.3 *Solve each of the following problems.*

25. A principal of \$5,000 was invested in a savings account paying 6% annual interest. If the interest earned over a certain period was \$1,200, for how long was the money invested? See exercise 20. 4 yr

26. A cylinder has a lateral surface area of 96π square inches (in.^{2}). If the radius of the cylinder is 6 in., find the height of the cylinder. See exercise 21. 8 in.

27. A principal of \$3,000 was invested in a money market fund. If the amount in the account was \$3,720 at the end of 3 years, what was the annual interest rate? See exercise 24. 8%

Solve each of the following applications.

28. Lisa left Friday morning, driving on the freeway to visit friends for the weekend. Her trip took 4 h. When she returned on Sunday, heavier traffic slowed her average speed by 6 mi/h, and the trip took $4\frac{1}{2}$ h. What was her average speed in each direction, and how far did she travel each way? Going 54 mi/h, returning 48 mi/h, 216 mi each way

29. A bicyclist started on a 132-mi trip and rode at a steady rate for 3 h. He began to tire at that point and slowed his speed by 4 mi/h for the remaining 2 h of the trip. What was his average speed for each part of the journey? 3 h at 28 mi/h, 2 h at 24 mi/h

30. At noon, Jan left her house, jogging at an average rate of 8 mi/h. Two hours later, Stanley left on his bicycle along the same route, averaging 20 mi/h. At what time will Stanley catch up with Jan? 3:20 P.M.

31. At 9 A.M., David left New Orleans for Tallahassee, averaging 47 mi/h. Two hours later, Gloria left Tallahassee for New Orleans along the same route, driving 5 mi/h faster than David. If the two cities are 391 mi apart, at what time will David and Gloria meet? 2:00 P.M.

32. A firm producing running shoes finds that its fixed costs are \$3,900 per week, and its variable cost is \$21 per pair of shoes. If the firm can sell the shoes for \$47 per pair, how many pairs of shoes must be produced and sold each week for the company to break even? 150 pairs

2.4 *Solve each of the following inequalities. Then graph the solution set and write the answer in interval notation.*

33. $3x - 2 > 10$ $x > 4, (4, \infty)$

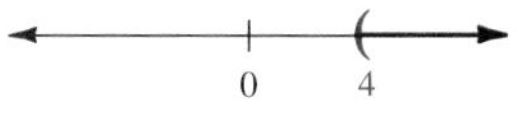

0 4

34. $5x - 3 \le -18$ $x \le -3, (-\infty, -3]$

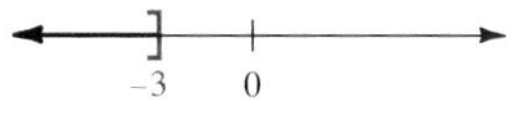

-3 0

35. $5 - 3x \le 3$ $x \ge \frac{2}{3}, \left[\frac{2}{3}, \infty\right)$

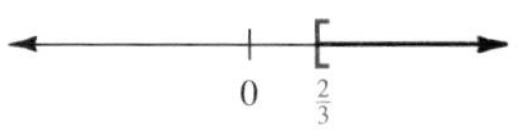

0 $\frac{2}{3}$

36. $7 - 4x \ge 15$ $x \le -2, (-\infty, -2]$

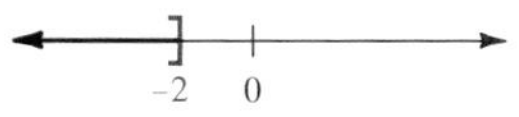

-2 0

37. $9x - 3 < 7x - 13$ $x < -5, (-\infty, -5)$

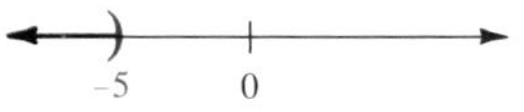

-5 0

38. $5 - 3x > 2 - 6x$ $x > -1, (-1, \infty)$

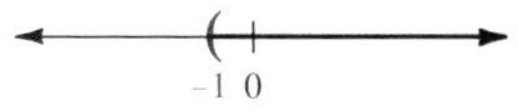

-1 0

39. $2x - 5 \geq 7x - 10$ $x \leq 1, (-\infty, 1]$

40. $4 - 3x < 14 + 2x$ $x > -2, (-2, \infty)$

41. $4(5x - 4) \geq 3(3x + 2)$ $x \geq 2, [2, \infty)$

42. $3(2x - 1) > 2(x - 4) - 11$ $x > -4, (-4, \infty)$

43. $\frac{x}{2} - \frac{x + 8}{5} < \frac{1}{2}$ $x < 7, (-\infty, 7)$

44. $\frac{x + 3}{4} - \frac{x - 1}{3} > \frac{2}{3}$ $x < 5, (-\infty, 5)$

Solve each of the following compound inequalities. Then graph the solution set and write the answer in interval notation.

45. $3 < x + 5 < 7$ $-2 < x < 2, (-2, 2)$

46. $-2 \leq 3x + 4 \leq 10$ $-2 \leq x \leq 2, [-2, 2]$

47. $-5 \leq 3 - 2x \leq 5$ $-1 \leq x \leq 4, [-1, 4]$

48. $-4 < 5 - 3x < 4$ $\frac{1}{3} < x < 3, \left(\frac{1}{3}, 3\right)$

49. $3x - 1 < -7$ or $3x - 1 > 7$
$x < -2$ or $x > \frac{8}{3}, (-\infty, -2) \cup \left(\frac{8}{3}, \infty\right)$

50. $2x + 5 \leq -9$ or $2x + 5 \geq 9$
$x \leq -7$ or $x \geq 2, (-\infty, -7] \cup [2, \infty)$

2.5 *Solve each of the absolute value equations.*

51. $|x + 3| = 5$ $x = -8, x = 2$

52. $|3x - 2| = 7$ $x = -\frac{5}{3}, x = 3$

53. $|7 - x| = 3$ $x = 4, x = 10$

54. $|5 - 3x| = 14$ $x = -3, x = \frac{19}{3}$

55. $|2x + 1| - 3 = 6$ $x = -5, x = 4$

56. $7 - |x - 3| = 5$ $x = 1, x = 5$

57. $|3x - 1| = |x + 5|$ $x = -1, x = 3$

58. $|x - 5| = |x + 3|$ $x = 1$

Solve each of the absolute value inequalities. Then graph the solution set and write the answer in interval notation.

59. $|x| \leq 3$ $-3 \leq x \leq 3, [-3, 3]$

60. $|x + 3| > 5$ $x < -8$ or $x > 2, (-\infty, -8) \cup (2, \infty)$

61. $|x - 7| > 4$ $x < 3$ or $x > 11$, $(-\infty, 3) \cup (11, \infty)$

62. $|3 - x| < 6$ $-3 < x < 9$, $(-3, 9)$

63. $|2x + 7| > 5$ $x < -6$ or $x > -1$, $(-\infty, -6) \cup (-1, \infty)$

64. $|3x - 1| < 14$ $-\frac{13}{3} < x < 5$, $\left(-\frac{13}{3}, 5\right)$

65. $|3x + 4| < 11$ $-5 < x < \frac{7}{3}$, $\left(-5, \frac{7}{3}\right)$

66. $|5x + 2| \geq 12$ $x \leq -\frac{14}{5}$ or $x \geq 2$, $\left(-\infty, -\frac{14}{5}\right] \cup [2, \infty)$

67. $|3 - 2x| \geq 15$ $x \leq -6$ or $x \geq 9$, $(-\infty, -6] \cup [9, \infty)$

68. $|5 - 3x| < 11$ $-2 < x < \frac{16}{3}$, $\left(-2, \frac{16}{3}\right)$

69. $\left|\frac{2x - 1}{3}\right| < 5$ $-7 < x < 8$, $(-7, 8)$

70. $\left|\frac{2x + 1}{3}\right| \geq 5$ $x \leq -8$ or $x \geq 7$, $(-\infty, -8] \cup [7, \infty)$

self-test 2

Name ______________________

Section ________ Date ________

Answers

1. $x = \frac{4}{5}$
2. $x = 2$
3. $x = 2$
4. $x = \frac{3}{2}$
5. $r = \frac{A - P}{Pt}$
6. $h = \frac{2A}{B + b}$
7. 3:30 P.M.
8. 800 flashlights
9. $x \le 4$, $(-\infty, 4]$
10. $x > \frac{17}{2}$, $\left(\frac{17}{2}, \infty\right)$
11. $x > 1$, $(1, \infty)$
12. $-2 \le x \le 4$, $[-2, 4]$
13. $x = -\frac{2}{3}$, $x = 4$
14. $x = \frac{2}{3}$, $x = 4$
15. $-\frac{3}{2} < x < 3$
16. $x \le -2$ or $x \ge \frac{9}{2}$

The purpose of this chapter test is to help you check your progress so that you can find sections and concepts that you need to review before the next exam. Allow yourself about an hour to take this test. At the end of that hour, check your answers against those given in the back of this text. If you missed any, note the section reference that accompanies the answer. Go back to that section and reread the examples until you have mastered that particular concept.

2.1

Solve each of the following equations.

1. $7 - 5x = 3$

2. $7x + 8 = 30 - 4x$

3. $5x - 3(x - 5) = 19$

4. $\frac{x + 3}{4} - \frac{x}{2} = \frac{3}{8}$

2.2

Solve each of the following literal equations for the indicated variables.

5. $A = P(1 + rt)$ for r

6. $A = \frac{1}{2}h(B + b)$ for h

2.3

Solve the following applications.

7. At 10 A.M., Sandra left her house on a business trip and drove at an average rate of 45 mi/h. One hour later, Adam discovered that Sandra had left her briefcase behind, and he began driving at 55 mi/h along the same route. When will Adam catch up with Sandra?

8. A firm producing flashlights finds that its fixed cost is \$2,400 per week and its variable cost is \$4.50 per flashlight. The revenue is \$7.50 per flashlight, so the cost and revenue equations are, respectively,

$C = 4.50x + 2{,}400$ and $R = 7.50x$

Find the break-even point for the firm.

2.4

Solve each of the following inequalities and graph the solution set. Then write the answer in interval notation.

9. $5x - 3 \le 17$

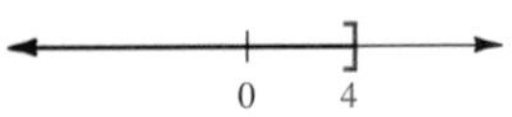

10. $3x + 7 < 5(x - 2)$

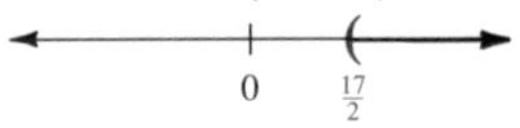

11. $\frac{x + 1}{2} - \frac{1}{3} > \frac{x + 3}{6}$

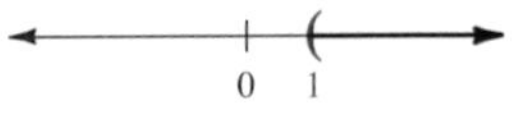

12 $-5 \le 3 - 2x \le 7$

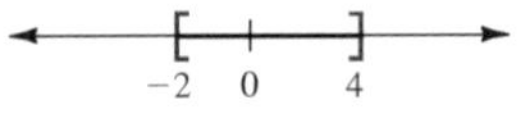

2.5

Solve each of the following equations and inequalities.

13. $|3x - 5| = 7$

14. $|2x - 3| = |x + 1|$

15. $|4x - 3| < 9$

16. $|5 - 4x| \ge 13$

Activity 2 ::
Formulas for Foreign Travel

Each chapter in this text concludes with a chapter activity such as this one. These activities provide you with the opportunity to apply the math you studied in that chapter to a relevant topic. Your instructor will determine how best to use these activities in your instructional setting. You may find yourself working in class or outside of class; you may find yourself working alone or in small groups; you may even be asked to perform research in a library or on the Internet.

Every year, millions of people travel to other countries for business and pleasure. When traveling to another country, there are many important considerations to take into account: passports and visas, immunization, local sights, restaurants and hotels, and language, to name just a few.

Other considerations when traveling internationally are currency, temperature readings, and, if you are a shopper, shoe and clothes sizing. Currency and clothes sizing differ by countries. Temperature readings in most countries other than the United States are given in Celsius rather than Fahrenheit. Formulas (literal equations) can be useful when one is trying to function successfully in a foreign environment. The formulas for temperature and clothes sizing are constant, whereas those for currency exchange are variable based on the exchange rate for the day that you choose to convert your money. For example if you converted U.S. dollars to British pounds (£) on December 14, 2001, one British pound would have cost you approximately \$1.59. Four years later on December 30, 2005, the cost of one British pound would have been approximately \$1.72. Depending on where you exchange your money, there may be a commission charge. The *Wall Street Journal* publishes exchange rates for currency on a daily basis. The same information can be obtained by visiting the Federal Reserve Bank of New York website.

Activity

1. The exchange rate for U.S. dollars to a foreign currency is given by the formula

$$A \cdot x + c = F$$

where A = amount in dollars
x = exchange rate
c = commission rate (if any)
F = amount in foreign currency

Solve the formula for A to determine the amount in dollars you will need to exchange to obtain a predetermined amount in the foreign currency.

(a) Use a search engine (as you learned to do in Activity 1) to find the current exchange rate and commission charge between dollars and pounds. Currency exchanges normally charge a commission. Your bank may or may not have a commission charge.

(b) Find the amount in dollars, A, you will need to obtain 850 British pounds.

(c) You have decided to take a long weekend on the European continent from Britain. The currency in the European Union (with the exception of England) is the euro. Find the current exchange rate for the euro, and find the amount in dollars, A, you will need to obtain 550 euros.

2. You may, of course, use credit cards abroad, but keep in mind that your issuing bank may very well charge you a percentage fee on every purchase for converting foreign

 The Streeter/Hutchison Series in Mathematics Intermediate Algebra

currency charges to dollars. You will also encounter extra charges if you use your credit card in an ATM to obtain that country's currency. One bank, if you use a credit card, will charge 2% of the purchase price of an item or service in dollars for currency conversion. The formula $C = p + 0.02p$ can be used to determine what the cost, C (in dollars), of an item priced at p (in dollars) will be.

You decide to pay a hotel bill of 174 British pounds with your credit card.

(a) Convert the bill in British pounds to U.S. dollars.

(b) Determine what the total cost on your credit card will be based on the given formula.

3. The formula $C = \frac{5}{9}(F - 32)$ can be used to convert Fahrenheit temperatures, F, to Celsius temperatures, C. Solve the formula for F in order to determine the given Celsius temperature in Fahrenheit.

(a) Use a search engine to find the 5-day weather forecast for London, England, and the extended forecast for Rome, Italy.

(b) Convert the Celsius temperatures to Fahrenheit.

4. You have packed your bags based on the temperatures. However, you know that weather can be variable and forecasts are not always accurate. So you have put aside some extra money to buy some needed clothes to accommodate the weather if necessary. The following formulas convert clothing sizes from American to Italian standards (and most European standards).

Men's shirts	$M_{\text{shirts}} = 2(s + 4)$	M is Italian size, s is American
Men's shoes	$M_{\text{shoes}} = 2s + 25$	
Women's shoes	$W_{\text{shoes}} = s + 31$	W is Italian size, s is American
Women's dress	$W_{\text{dress}} = 2(s + 10)$	

Determine the comparable sizes by Italian standards that you will need to purchase clothing for

(a) Yourself

(b) A friend or relative

cumulative review chapters 1-2

Name ______________________

Section __________ Date __________

The following exercises are presented to help you review concepts from earlier chapters. This is meant as review material and not as a comprehensive exam. The answers are presented in the back of the text. Beside each answer is a section reference for the concept. If you have difficulty with any of these exercises, be certain to at least read through the summary related to that section.

1.1

1. For the set of numbers $\{-5, 3, 4.1, 5, 0, \sqrt{3}, -7\}$, which belong to **(a)** the natural numbers, **(b)** the integers?

1.2

2. Translate the statement "5 less than p, divided by s" into symbols.

3. Name the property that justifies the statement $x + (3w + 5) = (x + 3w) + 5$.

4. Evaluate the expression $34 + 24 \div 6 \cdot 4 - 5^2$.

1.3

5. Write $-|7| - |-7|$ without using absolute value symbols.

6. Graph the compound inequality $-2 < x \le 5$.

1.4

7. Combine like terms in the expression $7x - 2(2x - 5) - 7$.

1.5

8. Simplify the expressions: **(a)** $(x^3y^5)^2$ **(b)** $\dfrac{(x^4y^7)^2}{x^9y^6}$

9. Write 4,370,000,000 in scientific notation.

2.1

Solve each of the following equations and check the results.

10. $5c - 7 = 3c - 2$

11. $3t + 11 = 5(t - 2)$

12. $\dfrac{1}{3}y - 5 = 8 - \dfrac{5}{6}y$

2.2

Solve each of the following equations for the indicated variable.

13. $A = \dfrac{1}{2}h(B + b)$ for B

14. $7p - 4y + 12 = 0$ for p

Answers

1. (a) 3, 5; (b) −7, −5, 0, 3, 5

2. $\dfrac{p-5}{s}$

3. Associative property of addition

4. 25

5. −14

6. 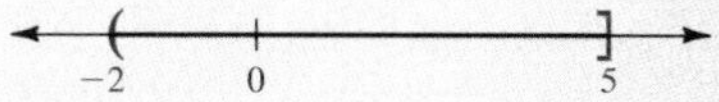

7. $3x + 3$

8. (a) x^6y^{10}; (b) $\dfrac{y^8}{x}$

9. 4.37×10^9

10. $c = \dfrac{5}{2}$

11. $t = \dfrac{21}{2}$

12. $y = \dfrac{78}{7}$

13. $B = \dfrac{2A - hb}{h}$

14. $p = \dfrac{4y - 12}{7}$

Answers

15. $3\frac{2}{3}$ h

16. 30 mi

17. $x < -7$, $(-\infty, -7)$

18. $2 \le x \le 5$, $[2, 5]$

19. $x = 1, x = 7$

20. All real numbers

21. $x < 0$ or $x > 5$

22. $-10 \le x \le -2$

2.3

Solve the following applications.

15. Carla and Jake leave town at the same time, traveling in opposite directions. If Carla travels at 55 mi/h and Jake travels at 35 mi/h, how long will it take for them to be 330 mi apart?

16. Randolph can drive to work in 45 minutes (min) whereas if he decides to take the bus, the same trip takes 1 h 15 min. If the average rate of the bus is 16 mi/h slower than his driving rate, how far does he travel to work?

2.4

Solve each inequality, and graph its solution set. Then write the answer in interval notation.

17. $3x - 5 > 5x + 9$

18. $-11 \le -3x + 4 \le -2$

2.5

Solve each of the following equations or inequalities.

19. $8 - |x - 4| = 5$

20. $|x - 4| = |4 - x|$

21. $|5 - 2x| > 5$

22. $|x + 6| \le 4$

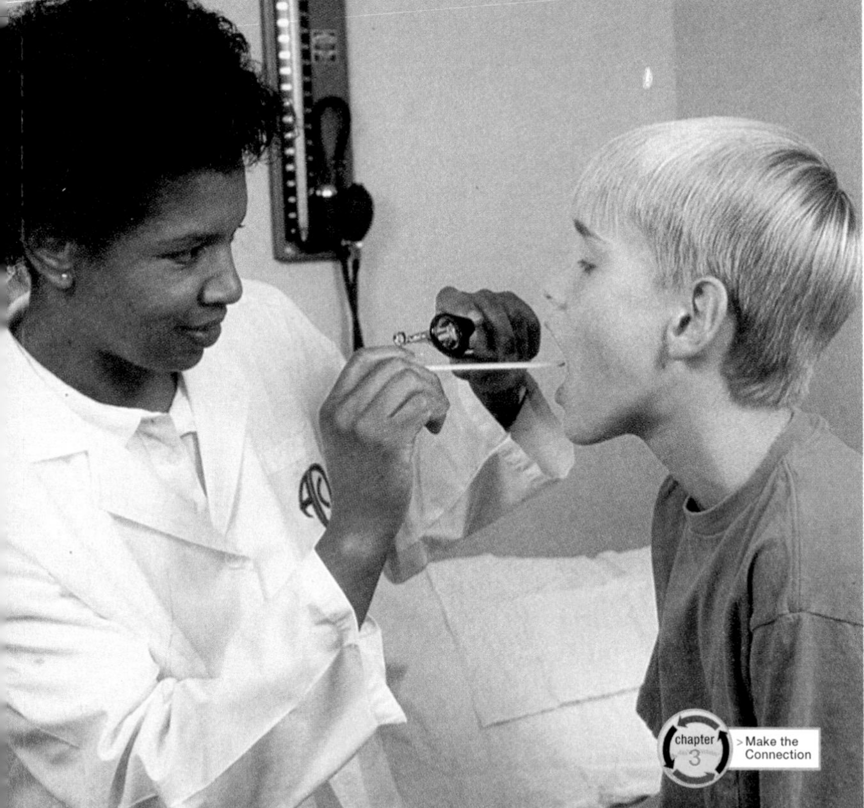

CHAPTER

3

Graphs of Linear Relations and Functions

INTRODUCTION

Graphs are used to discern patterns and trends that may be difficult to see when looking at a list of numbers or other kinds of data. The word *graph* comes from Latin and Greek roots and means "to draw a picture." This is just what a graph does in mathematics: it draws a picture of a relationship between two or more variables. But, as in art, these graphs can be difficult to interpret without a little practice and training. This chapter is the beginning of that training. And the training is important because graphs are used in every field in which numbers are used.

In the field of pediatric medicine, there has been controversy about the use of somatotropin (human growth hormone) to help children whose growth has been impeded by various health problems. The reason for the controversy is that many doctors are giving this expensive drug therapy to children who are simply shorter than average or shorter than their parents want them to be. The question of which children are not growing normally because of some serious health defect and need the therapy and which children are healthy and simply small of stature and thus should not be subjected to this treatment has been vigorously argued by professionals here and in Europe, where the therapy is being used.

CHAPTER 3 OUTLINE

Some of the measures used to distinguish between the two groups are blood tests and age and height measurements. The age and height measurements are graphed and monitored over several years of a child's life to monitor the rate of growth. If during a certain period the child's rate of growth slows to below 4.5 centimeters per year, this indicates that something may be seriously wrong. The graph can also indicate if the child's size fits within a range considered normal at each age of the child's life.

Throughout this chapter we will explore different types of graphs. At the end of the chapter, you will find a more in-depth activity involving fitting a linear graph to data.

pretest 3

Name ______________

Section ________ Date ________

This pretest provides a preview of the types of exercises you will encounter in each section of this chapter. The answers for these exercises can be found in the back of the text. If you are working on your own, or ahead of the class, this pretest can help you identify the sections in which you should focus more of your time.

3.1 **1.** Graph the set of ordered pairs.

$\{(5, 3), (6, 0), (0, -2), (-4, 5)\}$

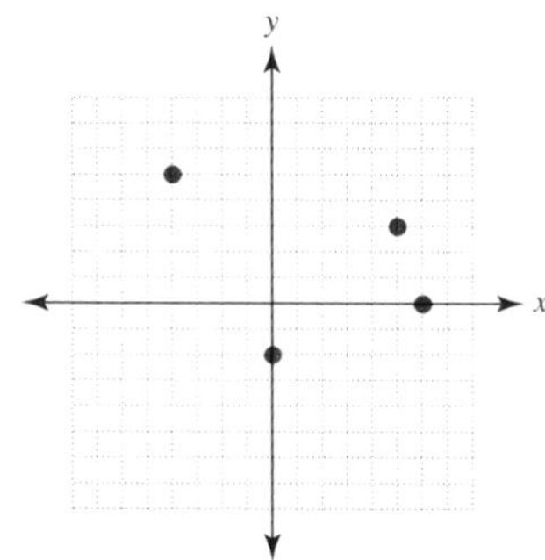

2. Find three ordered pairs that are solutions to $2x - 3y = 6$.

3. Graph the equation $3x + 4y = 12$.

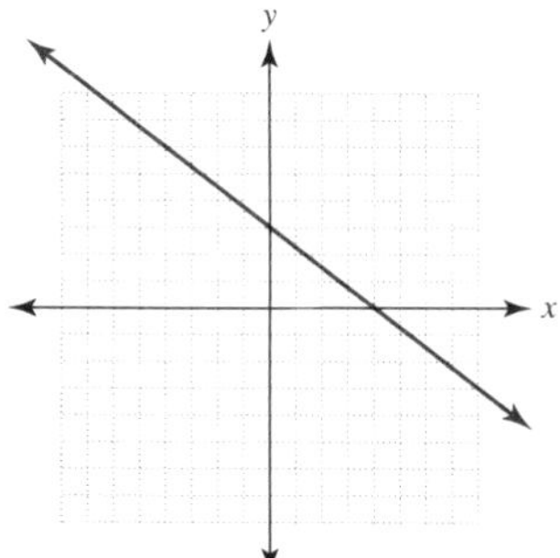

3.2 **4.** Evaluate the function $f(x) = x^2 - 2x + 2$ for the values specified.

(a) $f(0)$ **(b)** $f(-1)$ **(c)** $f\left(\frac{1}{2}\right)$

5. Determine whether the relation is a function. Also provide the domain and the range.

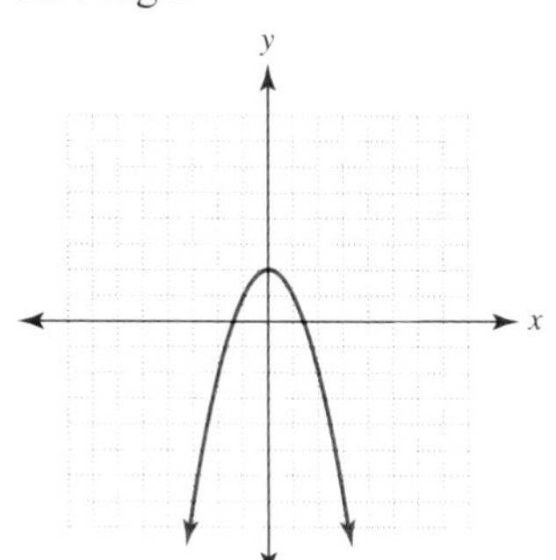

Answers

1. See exercise
2. Answers will vary; sample: $(0, -2), (3, 0), (6, 2)$
3. See exercise
4. (a) 2; (b) 5; (c) $\frac{5}{4}$
5. Function; D: $\mathbb{R}$; R: $\{y|y \le 2\}$

Answers

6. See exercise

7. Parallel

8. See exercise

9. $x = 3$

10. $y = 2x - 8$

11. See exercise

12. See exercise

6. Graph the linear function $f(x) = -2x - 5$.

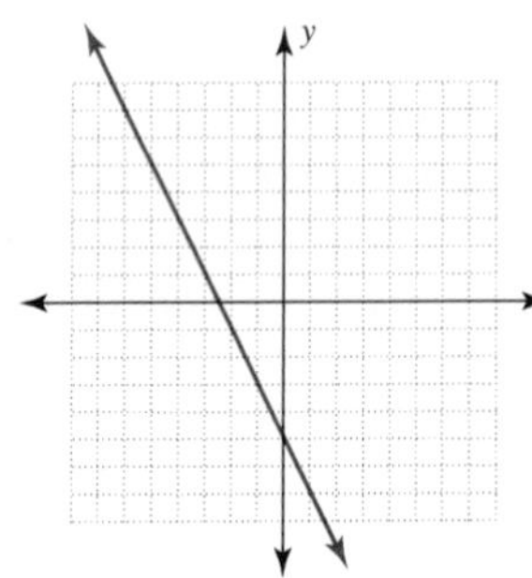

3.3 **7.** Without graphing, determine whether the pair of lines is parallel, perpendicular, or neither.

L_1 through (3, 4) and (−3, −2); L_2 through (5, 3) and (7, 5)

8. Graph the line through (2, 5) with slope $-\frac{1}{2}$.

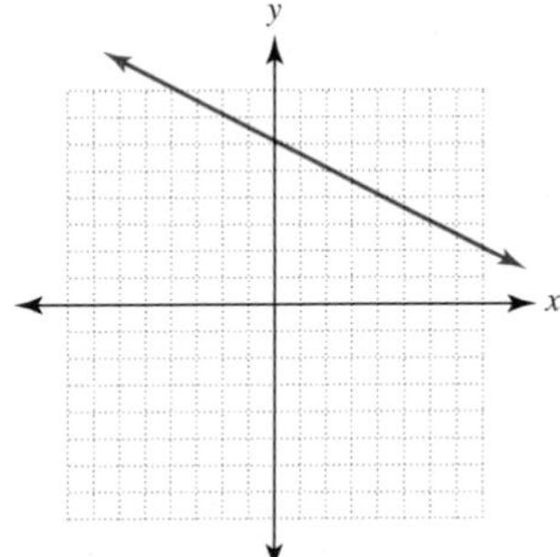

3.4 **9.** Write the equation of the line through the point (3, 6) with undefined slope.

10. Write the equation of the line passing through the points (3, −2) and (6, 4).

3.5 **11.** Graph the absolute value function $f(x) = |x - 2|$.

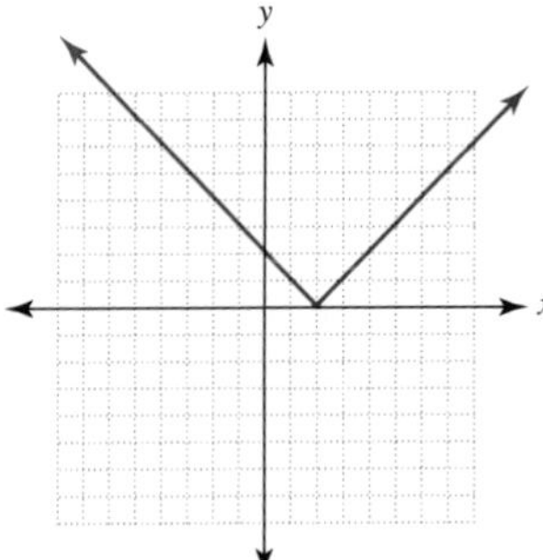

12. Graph the linear inequality $3y > 9$.

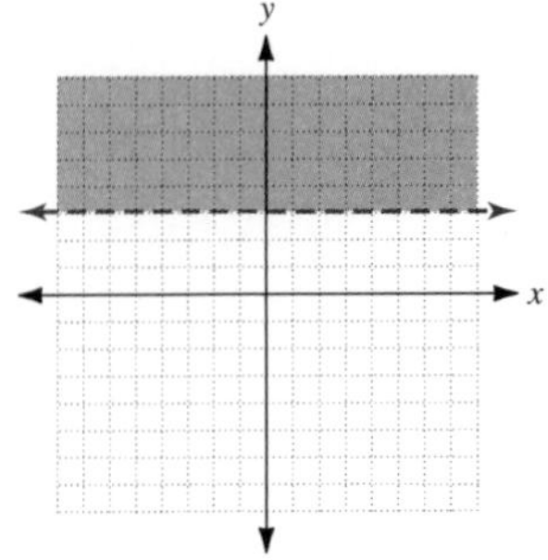

3.1 Graphing Linear Equations

< 3.1 Objectives >

1 > Graph the points corresponding to a set of ordered pairs

2 > Find solutions of two-variable equations

3 > Graph a linear equation

4 > Solve an application involving a linear equation

In Chapter 1, we introduced the idea of a set of numbers. We also graphed real numbers and sets of real numbers on the number line. In this chapter, we will begin by looking at how to graph pairs of numbers as points in a plane.

NOTE

We read $\{(x, y) | x \in \mathbb{R}, y \in \mathbb{R}\}$ as, "the set of ordered pairs, (x, y) in which x is a real number and y is a real number." Remember that sets always use braces to enclose their contents.

The material in this first section may be review from other algebra courses you have taken. However, it is very important as the foundation for graphing with two variables. Therefore, we will begin with basic definitions and start to build our way to more complicated graphing in later chapters.

Given the two related values x and y, we write the pair as (x, y). The set of all possible ordered pairs of real numbers is written as $\{(x, y) | x \in \mathbb{R}, y \in \mathbb{R}\}$.

The ordered pair $(2, -3)$ is different from the ordered pair $(-3, 2)$. By contrast, the set $\{2, -3\}$ is identical to the set $\{-3, 2\}$.

Example 1 Identifying Ordered Pairs

NOTE

(c) is called an ordered triple and will be studied in Chapter 4.

Which of the following are ordered pairs?

(a) $(2, -\pi)$ **(b)** $\{2, -4\}$ **(c)** $(1, 3, -1)$

(d) $\{(1, -5), (9, 0)\}$ **(e)** $2, 5$

Only **(a)** is an ordered pair. **(b)** is a set (it uses braces instead of parentheses), **(c)** has three numbers instead of two, **(d)** is a set of ordered pairs, and **(e)** is simply a list of two numbers.

Check Yourself 1

Which of the following are ordered pairs?

(a) $\left\{\frac{1}{2}, -3\right\}$ **(b)** $\left(-3, \frac{1}{3}\right)$ **(c)** $\{(5, 0)\}$

(d) $(1, -5)$ **(e)** $-3, 6$

Now that we know what ordered pairs are, we next want to find a way to locate and visualize them. In Chapter 1, we used a number line to locate and visualize real numbers. Such a line has been used by mathematicians for so many years that we do not know who gets credit for creating the number line. Locating and visualizing ordered pairs is a different story.

Since an ordered pair consists of two real numbers (one for x and one for y), we will need two number lines to describe it with a graph. One number line is drawn horizontally, and the other is drawn vertically; their point of intersection (at their respective zero points) is called the *origin*. Together the lines form the **rectangular coordinate system.** If the two lines have the same scale, we sometimes refer to the system as a Cartesian coordinate system in honor of René Descartes.

NOTES

In the seventeenth century, René Descartes, a French philosopher and mathematician, created a way of graphing ordered pairs.

The development of the **coordinate system** was part of an effort to combine the knowledge of geometry with that of algebra.

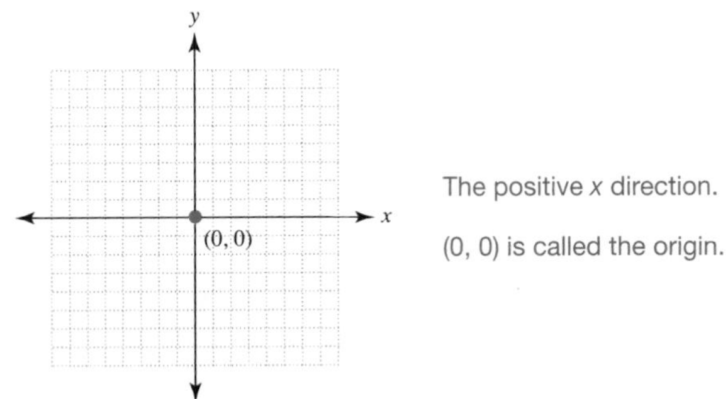

Definition

Axes

The horizontal line is called the **x-axis.** The vertical line is the **y-axis.** Together they are called the x- and y-axes (pronounced "axees").

Definition

Coordinate Plane

The plane (a flat surface that continues forever in every direction) containing the x- and y-axes is called the **coordinate plane.**

The axes divide the plane into four regions called **quadrants,** which are numbered (usually by Roman numerals) counterclockwise from the upper right.

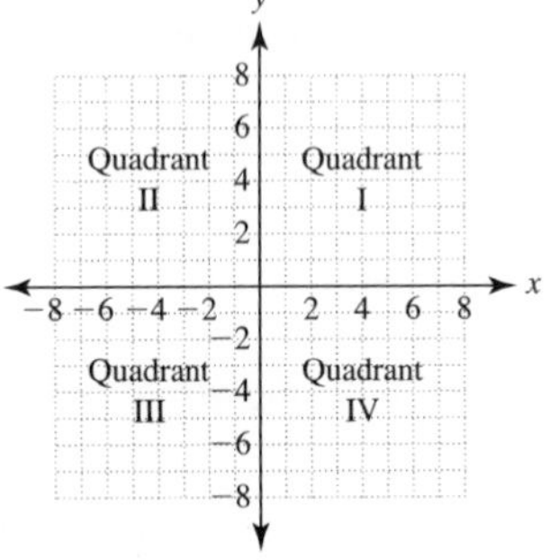

Every point in the coordinate plane can be described using an ordered pair of real numbers. And, conversely, every ordered pair can be plotted as a point in the plane.

Given an ordered pair (2, 4), 2 is called the x-coordinate and 4 is called the y-coordinate. If either coordinate of an ordered pair is equal to 0, the associated point lies on one of the axes. Every point that does not lie on the x- or y-axis can be plotted in one of the four quadrants.

Example 2 Graphing Ordered Pairs

< Objective 1 >

Graph the ordered pair $(3, -5)$.

Beginning at the origin, we move 3 units in the x direction (positive is to the right) and -5 units in the y direction (negative is down).

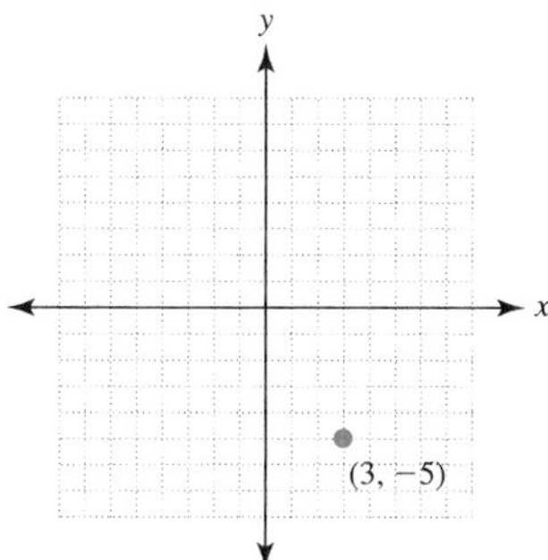

Check Yourself 2

Graph the ordered pairs: (0, 3), (−2, −4), (3, −1).

To find the ordered pair associated with a plotted point, we move vertically from the point to find the x-coordinate and horizontally from the point to find the y-coordinate.

Example 3 Identifying Plotted Points

Find the ordered pair associated with each point.

NOTE

When no scale appears on the grid, we assume that each division on each axis is one unit.

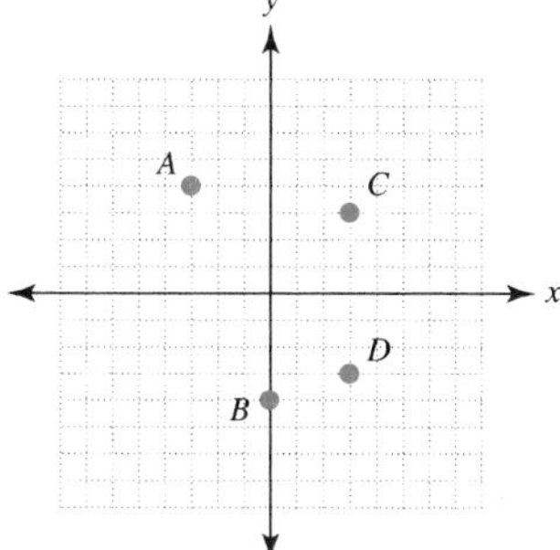

From point A, a vertical line meets the x-axis at -3. A horizontal line meets the y-axis at 4. The ordered pair is $(-3, 4)$. B is associated with $(0, -4)$, C with $(3, 3)$, and D with $(3, -3)$.

Check Yourself 3

Find the ordered pair associated with each point.

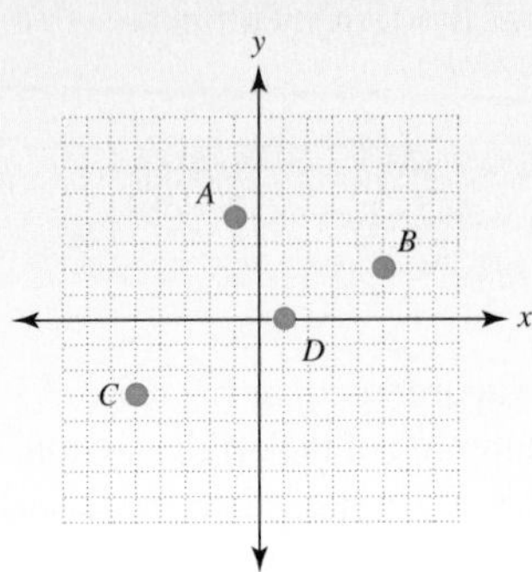

So far we have been working with ordered pairs. It is useful to now consider where ordered pairs might come from. In Chapter 2 you solved equations in one variable such as $3x - 2 = 5x + 4$.

Solving such an equation required finding the value of the variable, in this case x, that made the equation a true statement. In this case, that value is $x = -3$, because

$$3(-3) - 2 = 5(-3) + 4$$

This is a true statement because each side of the equation is equal to -11; no other value for x makes this statement true.

What if we have an equation in two variables, such as $3x + y = 6$? A solution for an equation in two variables is an ordered pair. Typically, there will be an infinite number of ordered pairs that make an equation a true statement. We can find some of these ordered pairs by substituting a value for x and then solving the remaining equation for y. We will use that technique in Example 4.

Example 4 Finding Ordered-Pair Solutions

< Objective 2 >

Find three ordered pairs that are solutions for each equation.

(a) $3x + y = 6$

We will pick three values for x, set up a table for ordered pairs, and then determine the related value for y.

x	y
-1	
0	
1	

Substituting -1 for x, we get

$$3(-1) + y = 6$$
$$-3 + y = 6$$
$$y = 9$$

The ordered pair $(-1, 9)$ is a solution to the equation $3x + y = 6$.

Substituting 0 for x, we get

$$3(0) + y = 6$$
$$0 + y = 6$$
$$y = 6$$

The ordered pair (0, 6) is a solution to the equation $3x + y = 6$.

Substituting 1 for x, we get

$$3(1) + y = 6$$
$$3 + y = 6$$
$$y = 3$$

The ordered pair (1, 3) is a solution to the equation $3x + y = 6$.

Completing the table gives us the following:

x	y
−1	9
0	6
1	3

(b) $2x - y = 1$

Let's try a different set of values for x. We will use the following table.

x	y
−5	
0	
5	

Substituting −5 for x, we get

$$2(-5) - y = 1$$
$$-10 - y = 1$$
$$-y = 11$$
$$y = -11$$

The ordered pair (−5, −11) is a solution to the equation $2x - y = 1$.

Substituting 0 for x, we get

$$2(0) - y = 1$$
$$0 - y = 1$$
$$-y = 1$$
$$y = -1$$

The ordered pair (0, −1) is a solution to the equation $2x - y = 1$.

Substituting 5 for x, we get

$$2(5) - y = 1$$
$$10 - y = 1$$
$$-y = -9$$
$$y = 9$$

The ordered pair (5, 9) is a solution to the equation $2x - y = 1$.

NOTE

In the definition of a linear equation, why can *A* and *B* not both be zero? First, recall that, although *x* and *y* are variables, *A*, *B*, and *C* are constants. With that in mind, look at the equation if *A* and *B* are both zero.

$$(0)x + (0)y = C$$
$$0 + 0 = C$$
$$0 = C$$

Because zero must be a constant, we are left with the statement

$$0 = 0$$

This would be a true statement regardless of the values of *x* and *y*. Its graph would be every point in the plane.

Completing the table gives us the following:

x	y
-5	-11
0	-1
5	9

Check Yourself 4

Find three ordered pairs that are solutions for each equation.

(a) $2x - y = 6$ **(b)** $3x + y = 2$

The **graph of an equation** is the set of all points with coordinates (x, y) that satisfy the equation.

In this chapter, we are primarily interested in a particular kind of equation in x and y and the graph of that equation. The equations we refer to involve x and y to the first power, and they are called **linear equations.**

Definition

Linear Equations

An equation of the form

$$Ax + By = C$$

in which *A* and *B* cannot both be zero, is called the **standard form for a linear equation.** Its graph is always a line.

We are now ready to combine our knowledge of solutions of equations in two variables with our work with ordered pairs. We just learned to write the solutions of equations in two variables as ordered pairs. Earlier, ordered pairs were graphed in the plane. We can put these ideas together to graph certain equations. Example 5 illustrates this approach.

Example 5 Graphing a Linear Equation

< Objective 3 >

NOTE

We are going to find *three* solutions for the equation. We'll point out why shortly.

Graph $x + 2y = 4$.

Step 1 Find some solutions for $x + 2y = 4$. To find solutions, we choose any convenient values for x, say $x = 0$, $x = 2$, and $x = 4$. Given these values for x, we can substitute and then solve for the corresponding value for y. So

If $x = 0$, then $y = 2$, so $(0, 2)$ is a solution.

If $x = 2$, then $y = 1$, so $(2, 1)$ is a solution.

If $x = 4$, then $y = 0$, so $(4, 0)$ is a solution.

Next, make a table using these values.

x	y
0	2
2	1
4	0

Step 2 We now graph the solutions found in step 1.

$x + 2y = 4$

x	y
0	2
2	1
4	0

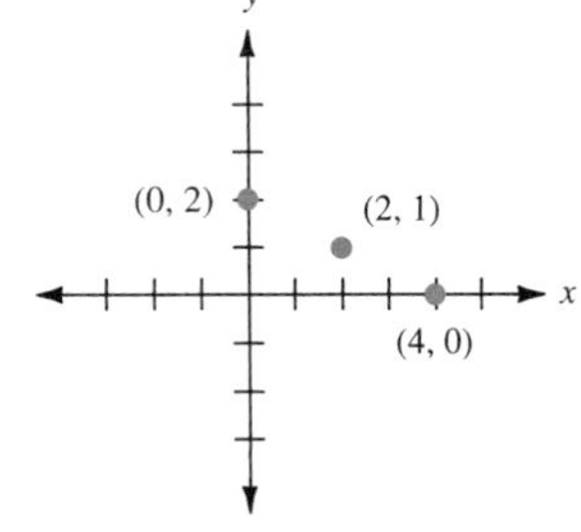

What pattern do you see? It appears that the three points lie on a straight line, and that is in fact the case.

Step 3 Draw a straight line through the three points graphed in step 2.

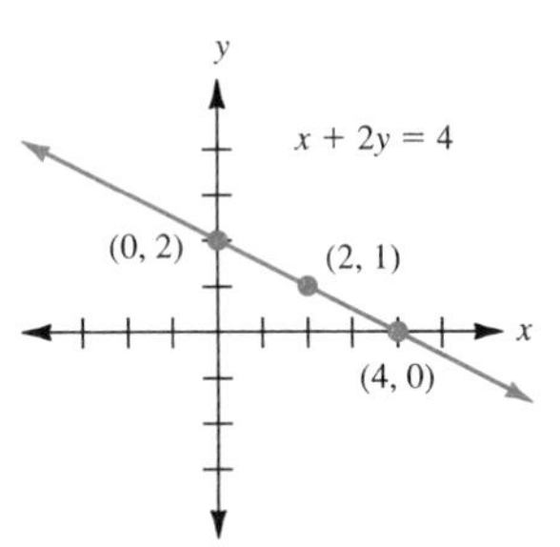

The line shown is the **graph** of the equation $x + 2y = 4$. It represents *all* the ordered pairs that are solutions (an infinite number) for that equation.

Every ordered pair that is a solution will have its graph on this line. Any point on the line will have coordinates that are a solution for the equation.

Why did we suggest finding *three* solutions in step 1? Two points determine a line, so technically you need only two. The third point that we find is a check to catch any possible errors.

NOTE

If you first rewrite an equation so that y is isolated on the left side, it can be easily entered and graphed with a graphing calculator. In this case, graph the equation

$y = -\frac{1}{2}x + 2$

NOTES

The arrows on the ends of the line mean that the line extends indefinitely in either direction.

The graph is a "picture" of the solutions for the given equation.

Check Yourself 5

Graph $2x - y = 6$, using the steps shown in Example 5.

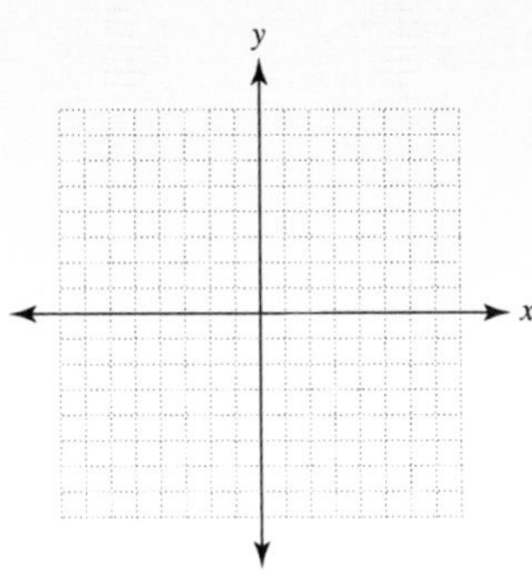

The following algorithm summarizes our first approach to **graphing a linear equation in two variables.**

Step by Step

To Graph a Linear Equation

Step 1 Find at least three solutions for the equation, and write your results in a table of values.

Step 2 Graph the points associated with the ordered pairs found in step 1.

Step 3 Draw a line through the points plotted in step 2 to form the graph of the equation.

Two particular points are often used in graphing an equation because they are very easy to find. The ***x*-intercept** of a line is the point at which the line crosses the x-axis. If the x-intercept exists, it can be found by setting $y = 0$ in the equation and solving for x. The ***y*-intercept** is the point at which the line crosses the y-axis. If the y-intercept exists, it is found by letting $x = 0$ and solving for y.

Example 6 Graphing by the Intercept Method

Use the intercepts to graph the equation

$x - 2y = 6$

To find the x-intercept, let $y = 0$.

$$x - 2 \cdot 0 = 6$$
$$x = 6$$

The x-intercept is (6, 0).

To find the y-intercept, let $x = 0$.

$$0 - 2y = 6$$
$$-2y = 6$$
$$y = -3$$

The y-intercept is (0, −3).

Again, a third point is useful as a check point. Let $x = 2$.

$$2 - 2y = 6$$
$$-2y = 4$$
$$y = -2$$

A third point is (2, −2).

Graphing these ordered pairs, we have the desired graph.

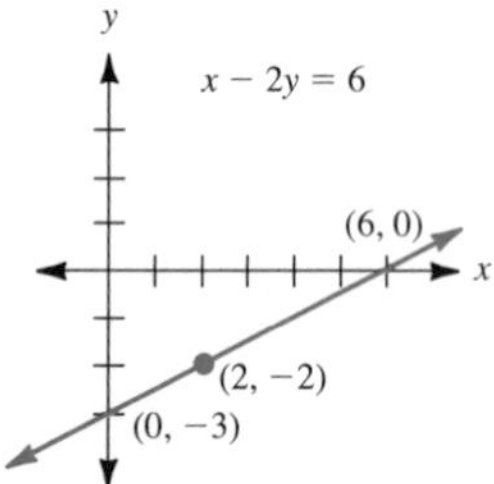

NOTE

Solving for y, we get

$$y = \frac{1}{2}x - 3$$

To graph this result on your calculator, you can enter

$Y_1 = (1 \div 2)x - 3$

using the [x, T, θ, n] key for x.

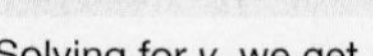

Check Yourself 6

Graph, using the intercept method.

$4x + 3y = 12$

The following algorithm summarizes the steps of graphing a line by the **intercept method.**

Step by Step

Graphing by the Intercept Method

Step 1 Find the x-intercept. Let $y = 0$, and solve for x.
Step 2 Find the y-intercept. Let $x = 0$, and solve for y.
Step 3 Plot the two intercepts determined in steps 1 and 2.
Step 4 Draw a line through the intercepts.

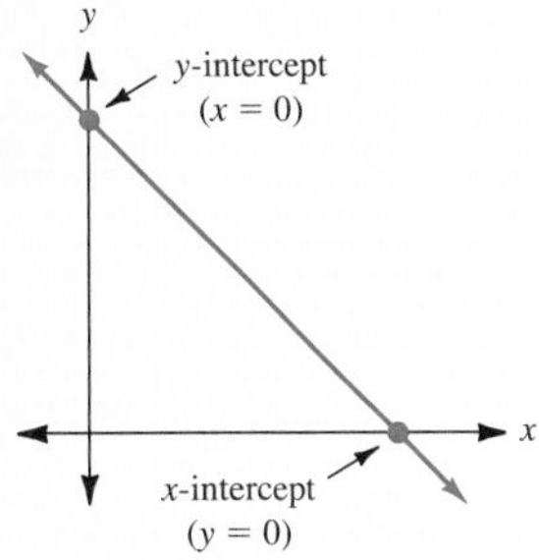

Are there any instances in which the intercept method cannot be used? Well, some lines have only one intercept. For instance, the graph of $x + 2y = 0$ passes through the origin. In this case, we can use the single intercept as one point, but then we also need to find other points. Therefore, the intercept method can be used, but the intercept alone is not enough to graph the line.

NOTE

The equation of the y-axis itself is $x = 0$. The equation of the x-axis itself is $y = 0$.

Two types of linear equations are worthy of special attention. Their graphs are lines that are parallel to the x- or y-axis, and the equations are special cases of the general form

$$Ax + By = C$$

in which either $A = 0$ or $B = 0$.

Definition

Vertical and Horizontal Lines

1. The graph of $x = a$ is a **vertical line** crossing the x-axis at $(a, 0)$.
2. The graph of $y = b$ is a **horizontal line** crossing the y-axis at $(0, b)$.

Example 7 illustrates both cases.

Example 7 Graphing Horizontal and Vertical Lines

(a) Graph the line with equation

$y = 3$

You can think of the equation in the equivalent form

$0 \cdot x + y = 3$

NOTE

Horizontal lines are parallel to the x-axis.

Note that any ordered pair of the form (__, 3) will satisfy the equation. Because x is multiplied by 0, y will always be equal to 3. So for any value of x, y will be 3.

For instance, $(-2, 3)$, $(0, 3)$, and $(3, 3)$ are on the graph. The graph, a horizontal line, is shown here.

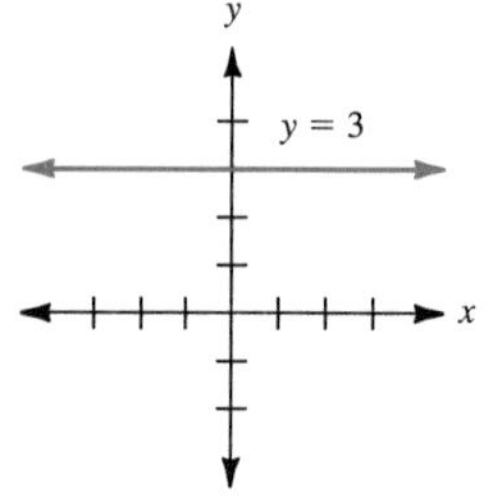

(b) Graph the line with equation

$x = -2$

In this case, you can think of the equation in the equivalent form

$x + 0 \cdot y = -2$

NOTE

Vertical lines are parallel to the y-axis.

Now any ordered pair of the form $(-2, \_\_)$ will satisfy the equation. Examples are $(-2, -1)$, $(-2, 0)$, and $(-2, 3)$. The graph, a vertical line, is shown here.

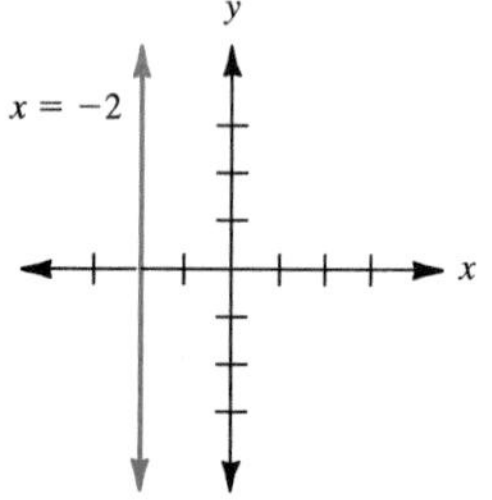

Check Yourself 7

Graph each equation.

(a) $y = -3$ **(b)** $x = 5$

We have studied two-variable graphs. Where might you find such things in your daily life—outside of the mathematics classroom? It is unusual to find a newspaper that does not have several two-variable graphs. Each of the following graphs was found in a daily newspaper.

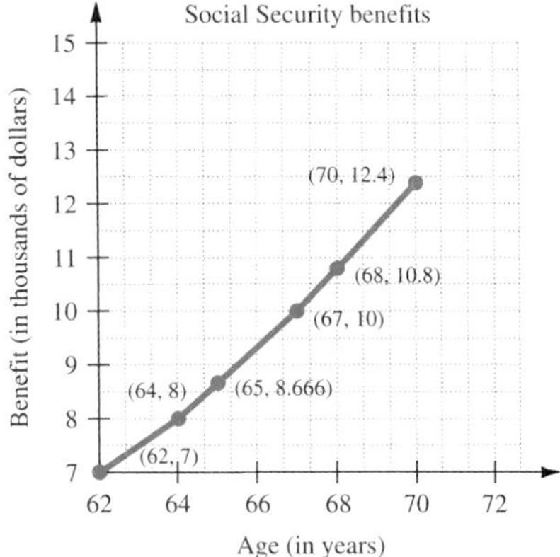

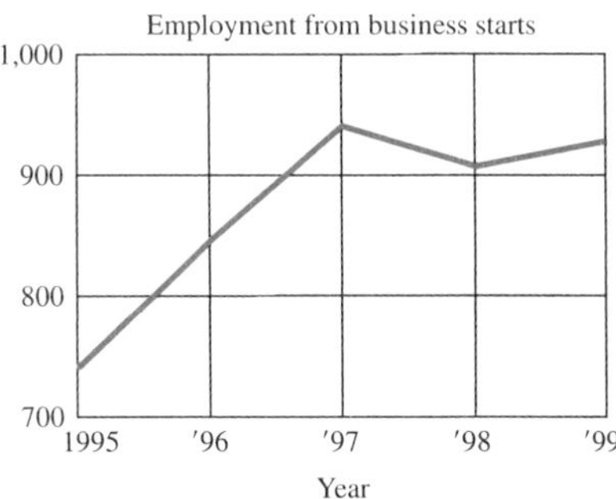

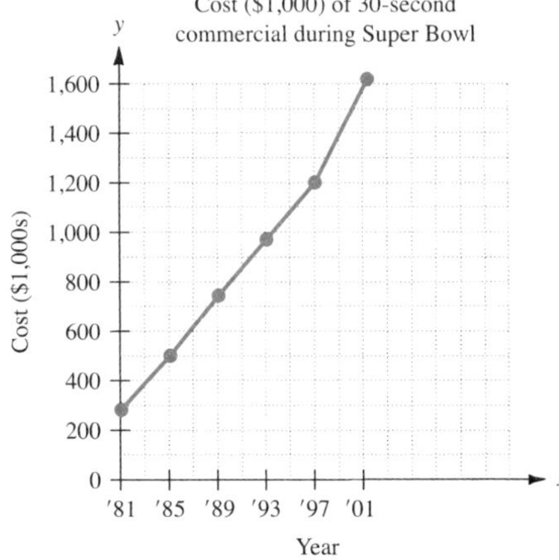

All three of the graphs use the principles described in this section. There are, however, a few noticeable differences. Notice the units on the x- and y-axes for each graph. This leads to the following rule of graphing applications.

Property

Graphing Applications When graphing an application, each axis must be labeled with appropriate units.

Note also that none of the graphs use equal units for the two axes. This is usually the case with an application. That observation leads to Example 8.

Example 8 Adjusting the Scale on the x- and y-Axes

< Objective 4 >

A car rental agency advertises daily rates for a midsized automobile at $20 per day plus 10¢ per mile. The cost per day, C, and the distance driven in miles, s, are then related by the following linear equation:

$$C = 0.10s + 20$$

Graph the relationship between s and C.

First, we proceed by finding three points on the graph.

s	C
0	20
100	30
200	40

So as the distance s varies from 0 to 200 mi, the cost C changes from $20 to $40. To draw a "reasonable" graph, it makes sense to choose a different scale for the horizontal (or s) axis than for the vertical (or C) axis.

NOTE

Before you graph this on your calculator, adjust the scales on both axes. This is done from the WINDOW menu.

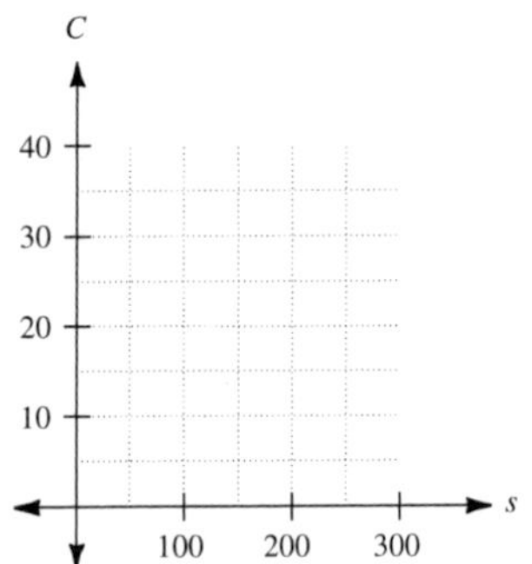

We have chosen units of 100 for the s-axis and units of 10 for the C-axis. The graph can then be completed, as shown.

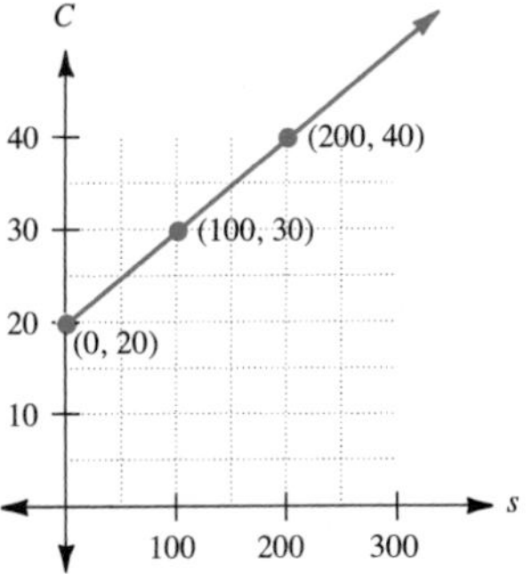

Note that the graph does not extend beyond the first quadrant because of the nature of our problem, in which solutions are only realistic when $s \geq 0$.

Check Yourself 8

A salesperson's monthly salary, S, is based on a fixed salary of \$1,200 plus 8% of all monthly sales, x. The linear equation relating S and x is

$$S = 0.08x + 1{,}200$$

Graph the relationship between x and S. *Hint:* Find the monthly salary for sales of \$0, \$10,000, and \$20,000.

Check Yourself ANSWERS

1. (b) and (d) are ordered pairs **2.**

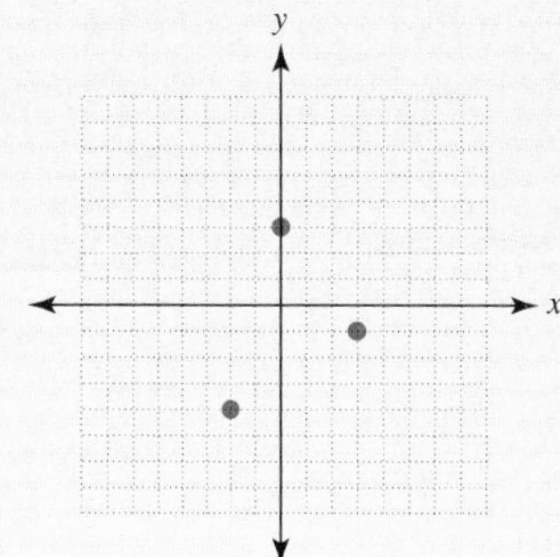

3. $A(-1, 4)$, $B(5, 2)$, $C(-5, -3)$, $D(1, 0)$ **4.** **(a)** Answers will vary; sample: $(-1, -8)$, $(0, -6)$, $(1, -4)$; **(b)** Answers will vary; sample: $(-1, 5)$, $(0, 2)$, $(1, -1)$.

5.

x	y
0	−6
1	−4
2	−2

6.

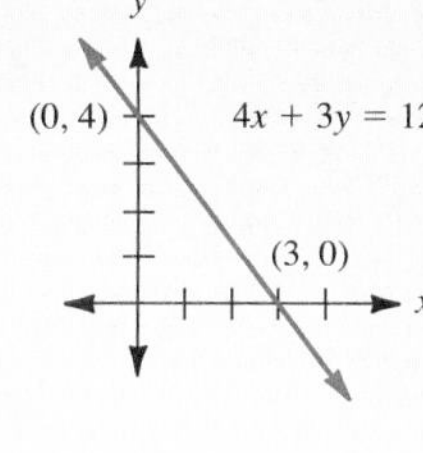

7. **(a)**

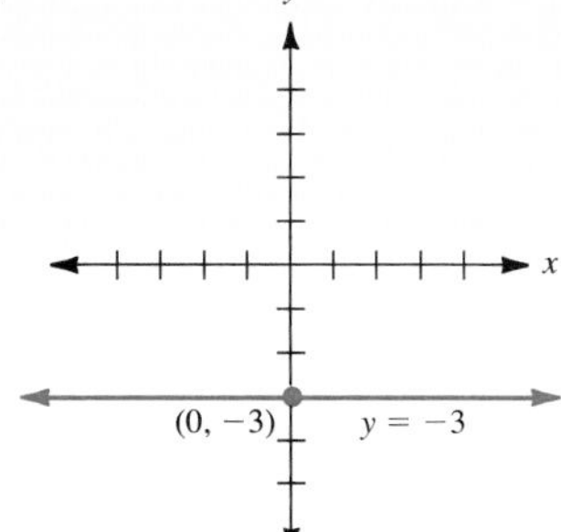

(b)

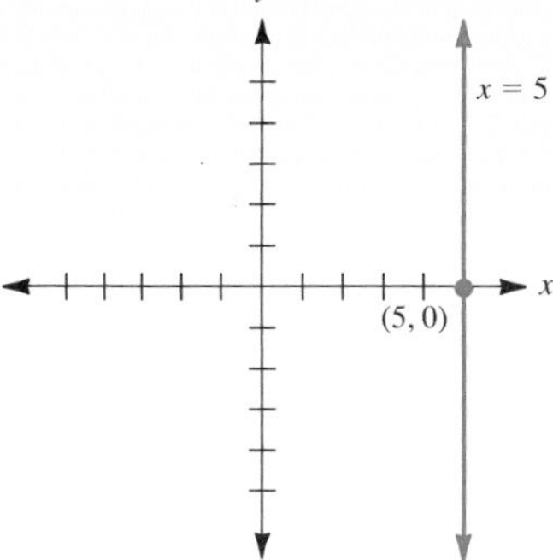

8.

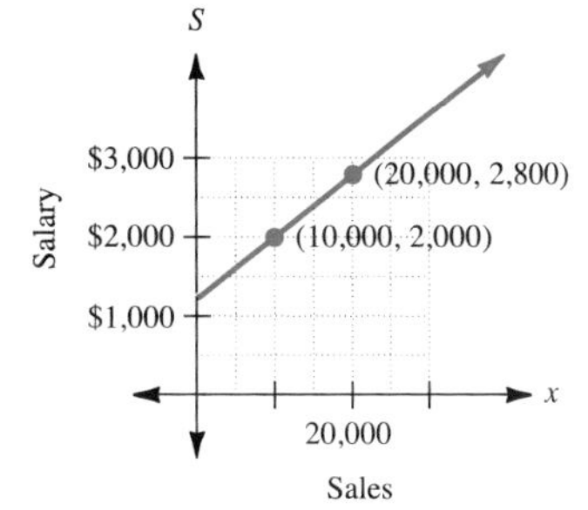

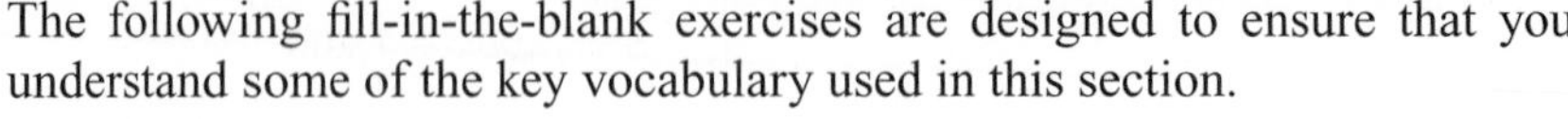

Reading Your Text

The following fill-in-the-blank exercises are designed to ensure that you understand some of the key vocabulary used in this section.

SECTION 3.1

(a) Given the ordered pair (2, 4), 2 is called the ______________ and 4 is called the ______________.

(b) The ______________ is the set of all points with coordinates (x, y) that satisfy the equation.

(c) An equation of the form $Ax + By = C$, in which A and B cannot both be zero, is called the ______________.

(d) The graph of $x = a$ is a ______________ crossing the x-axis at $(a, 0)$, and the graph of $y = b$ is a ______________ crossing the y-axis at $(0, b)$.

Basic Skills | Advanced Skills | Vocational-Technical Applications | Calculator/Computer | Above and Beyond

3.1 exercises

MathZone

Boost your grade at mathzone.com!
> Practice Problems
> NetTutor
> Self-Tests
> e-Professors
> Videos

Name ______________

Section ________ Date ________

Identify the ordered pairs.

1. **(a)** $(3, -5)$ **(b)** $\{7, 9\}$ **(c)** $(2, 5)$
   (d) $5, 2$ **(e)** $((3, 1), 4)$

2. **(a)** $\{7, 23\}$ **(b)** $(1, 0, (5, 6))$ **(c)** $\left(\frac{1}{2}, -1\right)$
   (d) $[5, 6]$ **(e)** $(23, 7)$

3. **(a)** $18, 67$ **(b)** $(-3, -9)$ **(c)** $\{3, 9\}$
   (d) $(3, 7, -3)$ **(e)** $[12, 56]$

4. **(a)** $\{45, 67]$ **(b)** $(9, 3)$ **(c)** $5, 8$
   (d) $(11, -3, 9)$ **(e)** $[5, 2]$

< Objective 1 >

Graph each set of ordered pairs.

5. $\{(3, 5), (-4, 6), (-2, 6), (5, -6)\}$

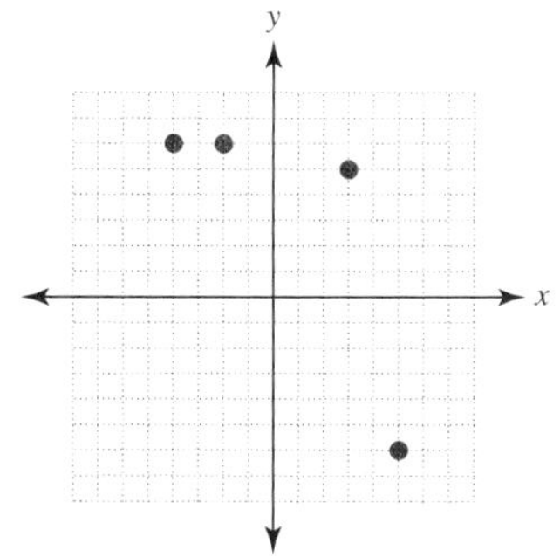

6. $\left\{(0, -5), (2, -3), \left(-1, \frac{5}{2}\right), \left(-5, \frac{3}{4}\right)\right\}$

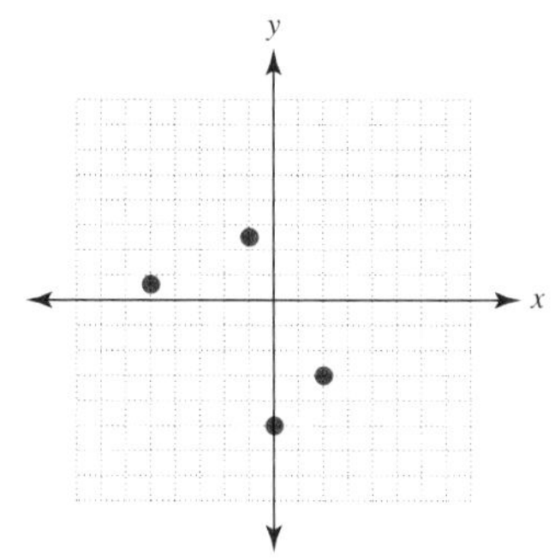

Answers

1. (a) and (c)
2. (c) and (e)
3. (b)
4. (b)
5. See exercise
6. See exercise

Answers

7. See exercise
8. See exercise
9. See exercise
10. See exercise
11. See exercise
12. See exercise
13. See exercise
14. See exercise

7. $\{(-1, 6), (3, -5), (-2, -5), (1, 4)\}$

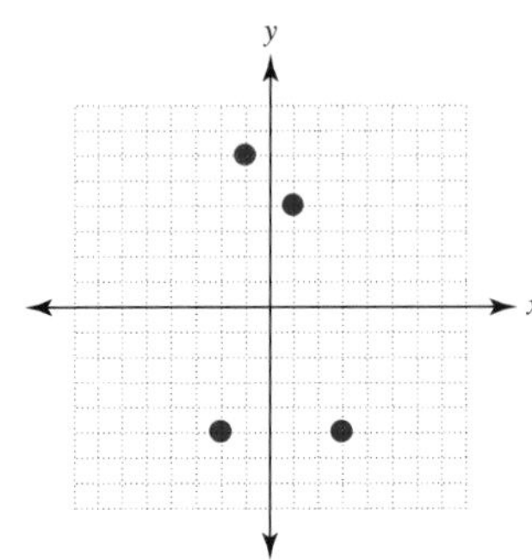

Give the coordinates (ordered pairs) associated with the points indicated in the figure.

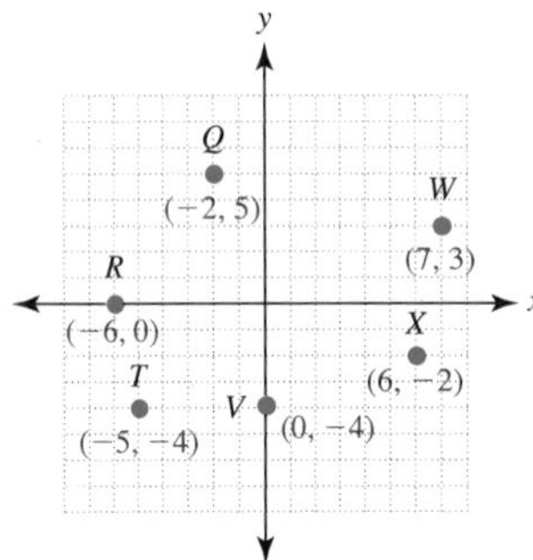

8. Q **9.** R

10. T **11.** V

12. W 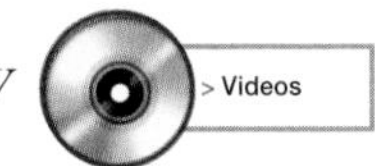

13. X

14. In the following figure, points correspond to an ordered-pair relationship between height and age in which the first number represents age and the second number represents height. Estimate each ordered pair represented. In your own words, state the meaning of the graph.

chapter 3 > Make the Connection

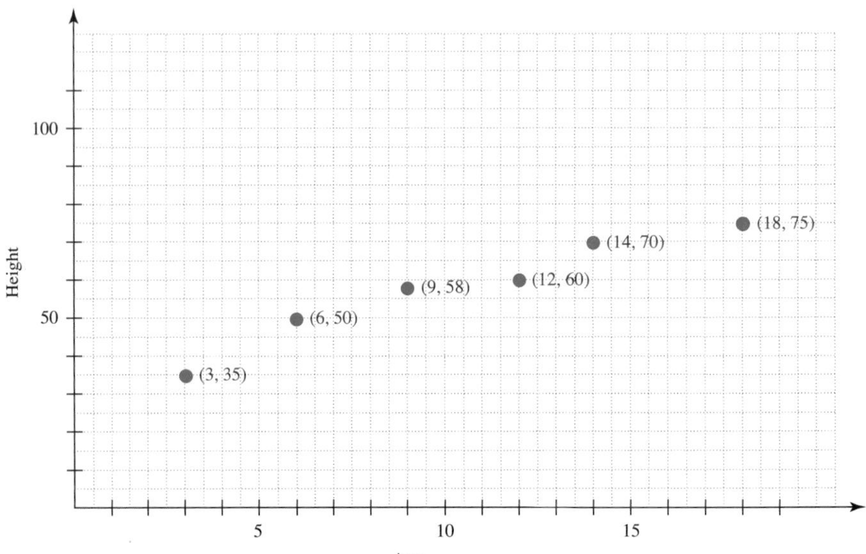

Plot the points whose coordinates are given in the table. Scale the axes appropriately.

15. STATISTICS The table gives the time, x, in hours invested in studying for four different algebra exams and the resulting grade, y.

x	4	3	2	8	1
y	85	80	70	95	60

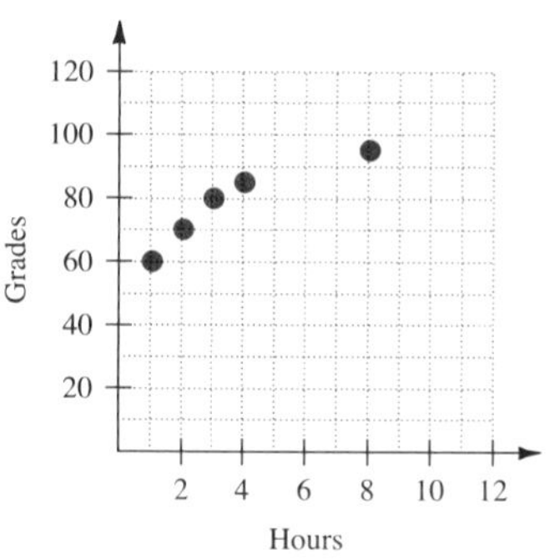

16. SCIENCE AND MEDICINE The table gives the speed, x, of a car in miles per hour and the approximate fuel efficiency, y, in miles per gallon.

x	45	55	60	65	70
y	30	25	20	20	15

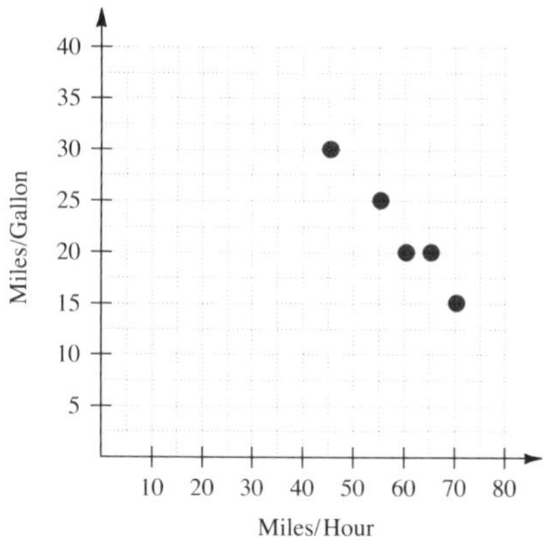

Answers

15. See exercise

16. See exercise

< Objective 2 >

Find three ordered pairs that are solutions to the given equations.

17. $2x + y = 5$

18. $7x - y = 8$

19. $4x + 5y = 20$

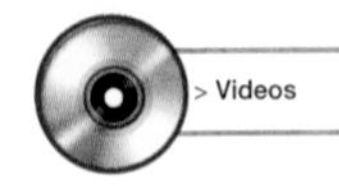

20. $3x + y = 0$

21. $2x - y = 0$

< Objective 3 >

Graph each of the equations.

22. $x + y = 6$

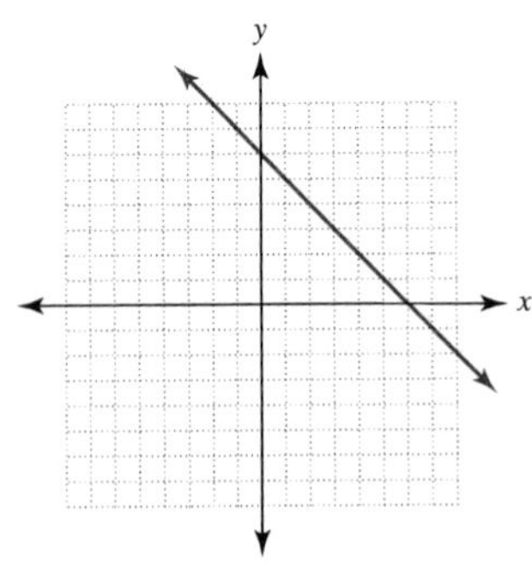

23. $y = x - 2$

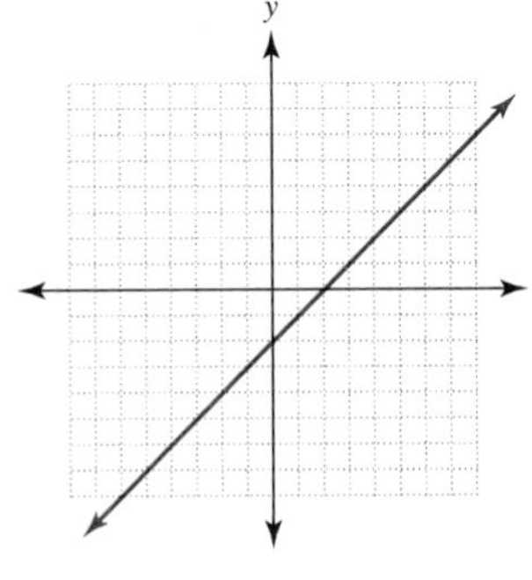

24. $y = -2x + 1$

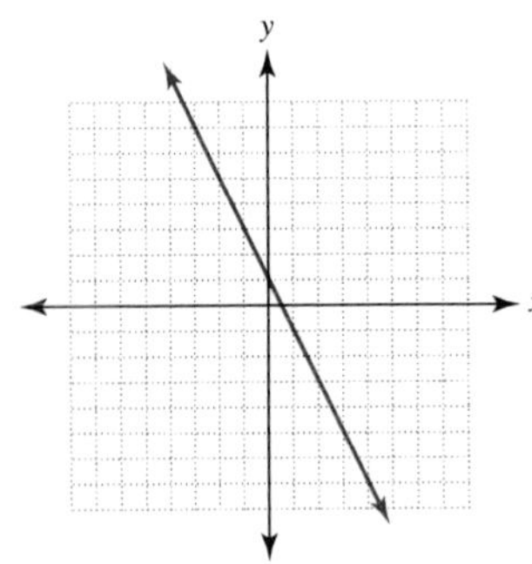

25. $y = \frac{1}{2}x - 3$

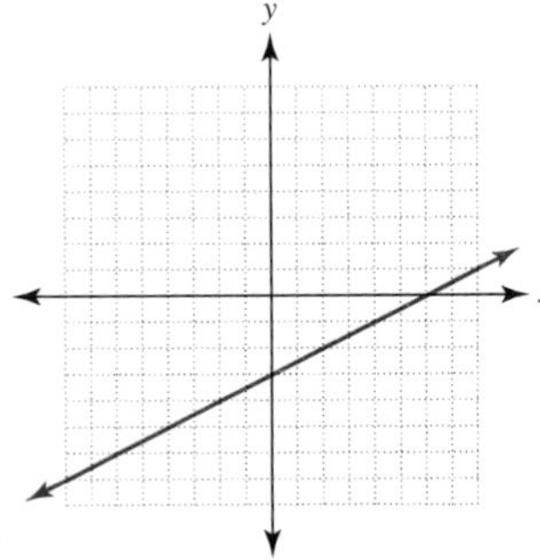

26. $y = 2x - 4$

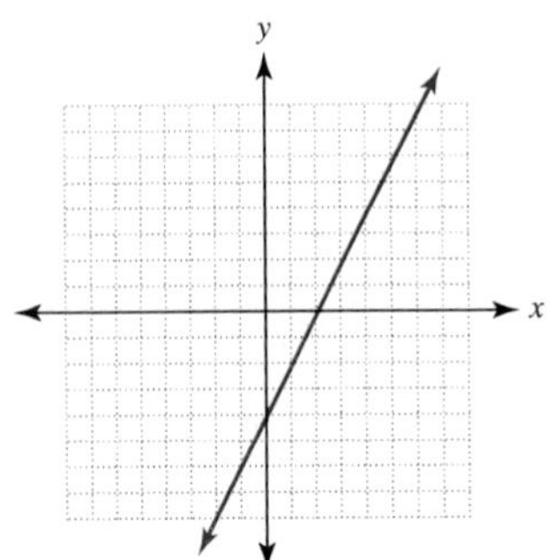

27. $x + 2y = 0$

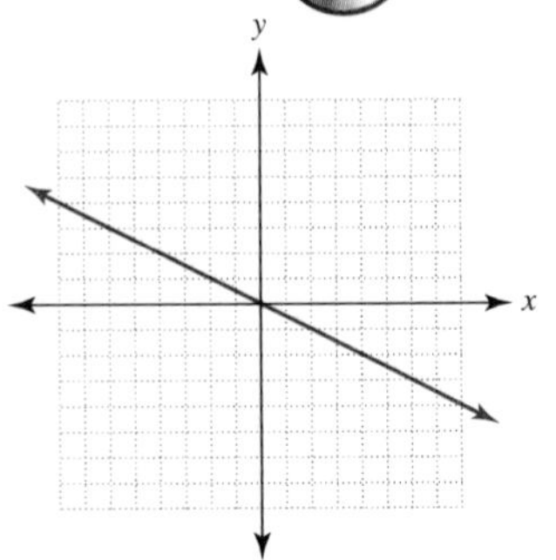

Answers

17. Answers will vary; sample: (0, 5), (1, 3), (−1, 7)

18. Answers will vary; sample: (0, −8), (1, −1), (−1, −15)

19. Answers will vary; sample: (0, 4), (5, 0), $\left(-1, \frac{24}{5}\right)$

20. Answers will vary; sample: (0, 0), (1, −3), (−1, 3)

21. Answers will vary; sample: (0, 0), (−1, −2), (2, 4)

22. See exercise

23. See exercise

24. See exercise

25. See exercise

26. See exercise

27. See exercise

28. $x - 2y = 0$

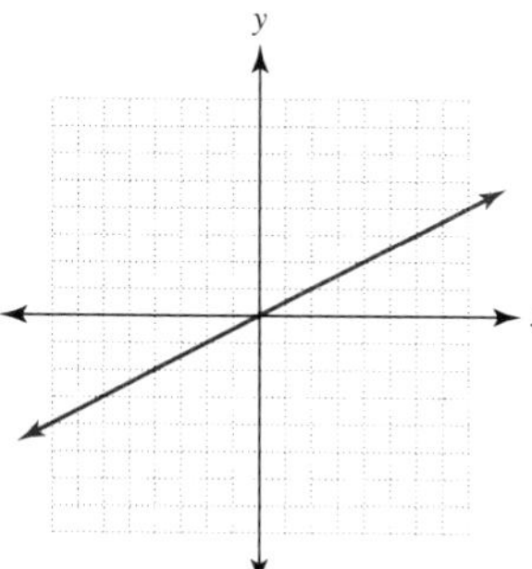

29. $x = 4$

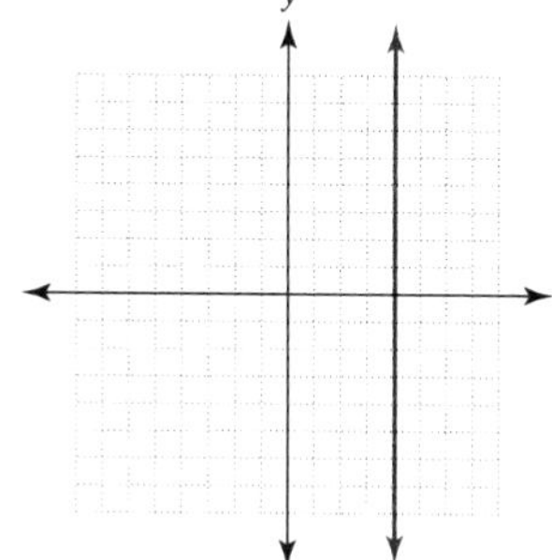

30. $x = -4$

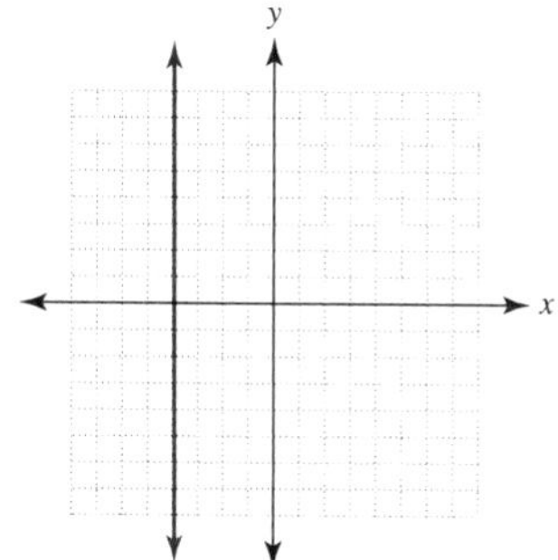

31. $y = 4$

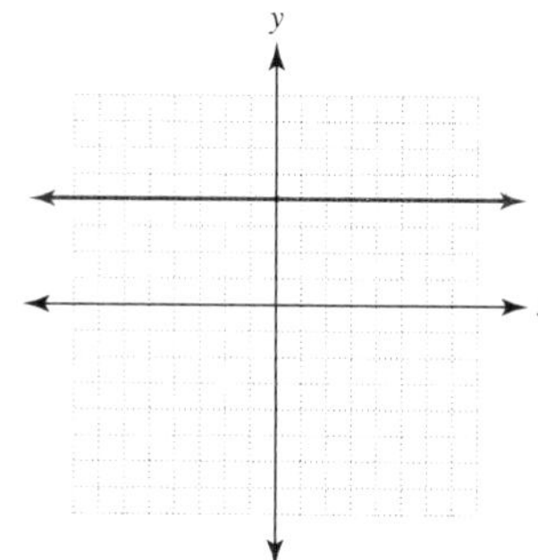

Find the x- and y-intercepts and then graph each equation.

32. $x + 3y = 6$

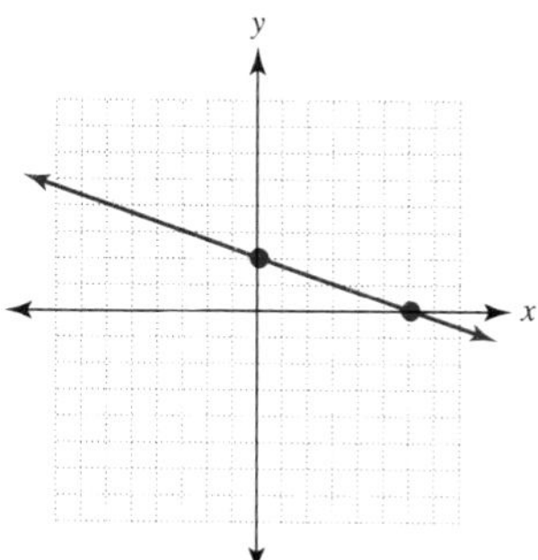

33. $2x + 5y = 10$

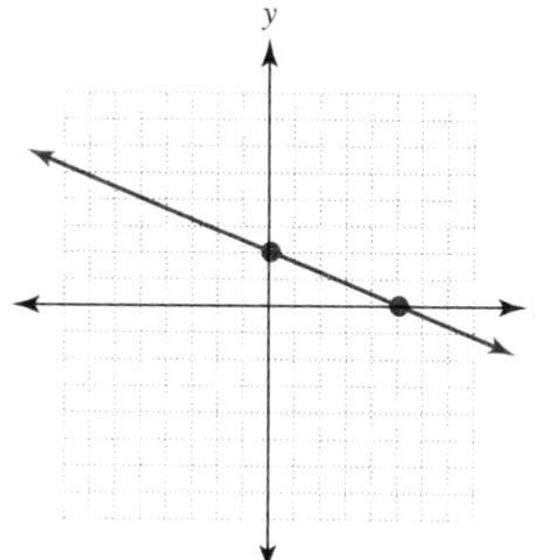

34. $2x + 7y = 0$

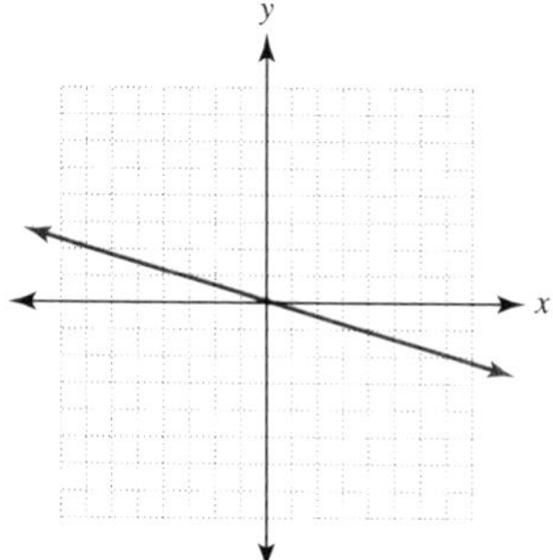

35. $x + 4y + 8 = 0$

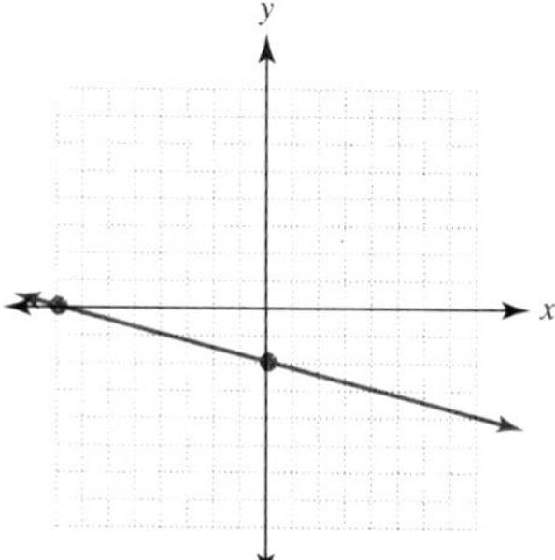

Answers

28. See exercise

29. See exercise

30. See exercise

31. See exercise

32. *y*-int: (0, 2); *x*-int: (6, 0)

33. *y*-int: (0, 2); *x*-int: (5, 0)

34. Intercepts: (0, 0)

35. *y*-int: (0, −2); *x*-int: (−8, 0)

Answers

36. y-int: (0, 6); x-int: (−3, 0)

37. Intercepts: (0, 0)

38. Intercepts: (0, 0)

39. sometimes

40. always

41. sometimes

42. never

43. See exercise

36. $2x - y + 6 = 0$

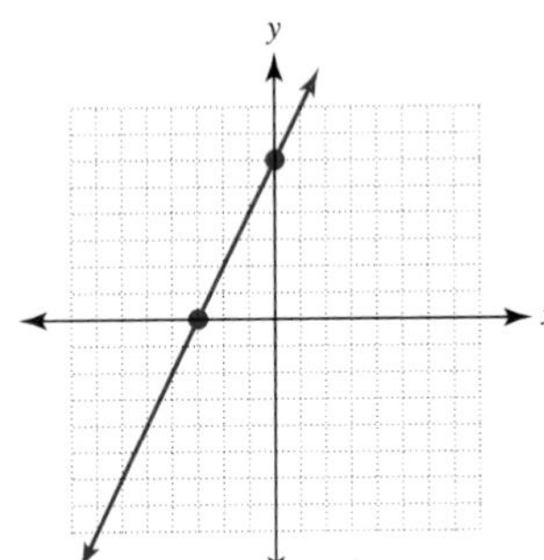

37. $8x = 4y$

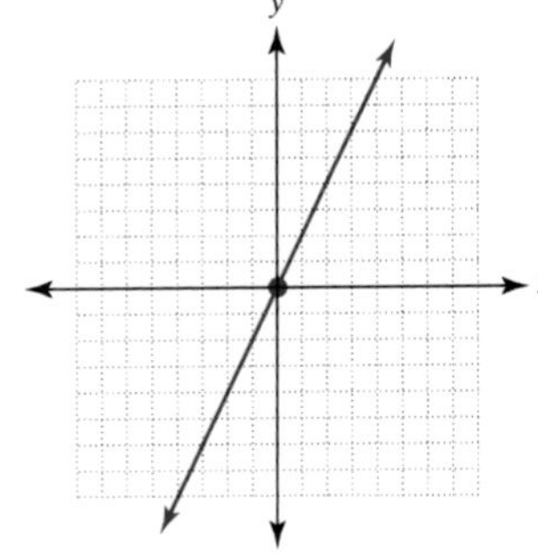

38. $6x = -7y$

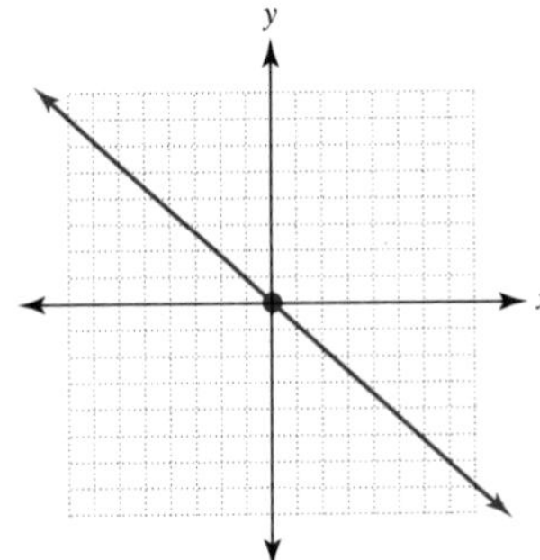

In the following statement, fill in the blank with **always, sometimes,** *or* **never.**

39. If the ordered pair (a, b) is a solution to a linear equation, then the ordered pair (b, a) is ________ a solution as well.

40. If the graph of a linear equation $Ax + By = C$ passes through the origin, then C ________ equals zero.

41. The graph of a linear equation ________ has an x-intercept.

42. The graph of $y = b$ is ________ a vertical line.

< Objective 4 >

43. **Business and Finance** A car rental agency charges \$20 per day and 20¢ per mile for the use of a compact automobile. The cost of the rental, C, and the number of miles driven per day, m, are related by the equation

$$C = 0.20m + 20$$

Graph the relationship between m and C. Be sure to select appropriate scaling for the m- and C-axes.

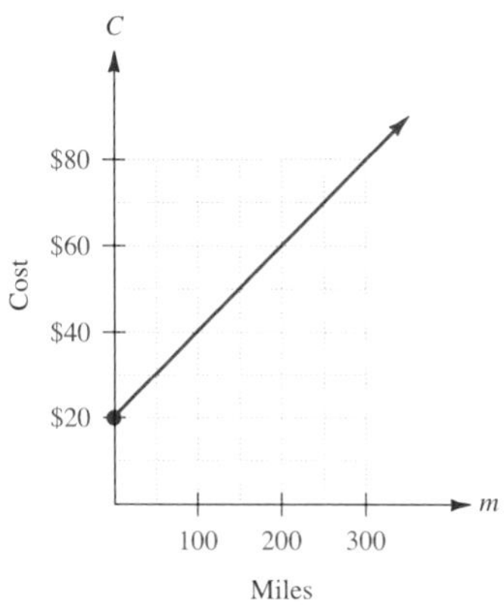

44. Business and Finance A bank has the following structure for charges on checking accounts. The monthly charge consists of a fixed amount of \$8 and an additional charge of 12¢ per check. The monthly cost of an account, C, and the number of checks written per month, n, are related by the equation

$C = 0.12n + 8$

Graph the relationship between n and C.

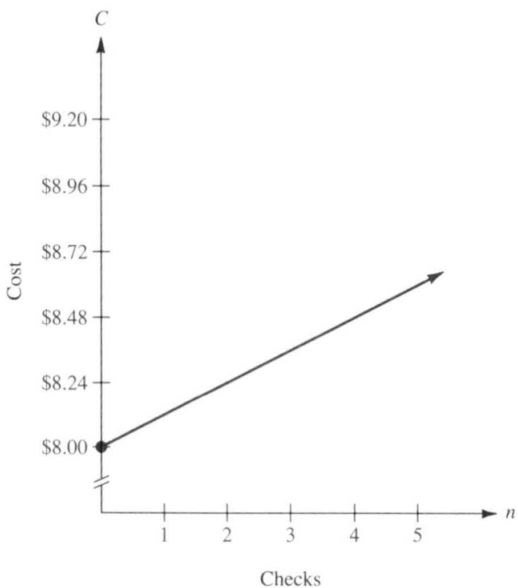

Answers

44. See exercise

Basic Skills | **Advanced Skills** | Vocational-Technical Applications | Calculator/Computer | Above and Beyond

Answers

45. Scatter plot: Final exam score vs. Mid-term exam score

46. 20,000 units sold and $20,000 profit

47. 40,000 units sold and $30,000 profit

48. $22,500 profit

49. $27,500 profit

In many applications, we are not given x- and y-values. In the following problem, consider column one as x-values and column two as y-values. Then plot the points whose coordinates are given in the table. The resulting graph is often called a "scatter plot." Notice that by plotting the data points, we can see the relationship between two sets of data (x-values and y-values).

45. Statistics In a statistics class, the midterm and final exam scores were collected for 10 students. Each exam was worth a total of 100 points.

Mid-Term Exam Scores	Final Exam Scores
71	80
79	85
84	88
76	81
62	75
93	90
88	87
91	96
68	82
77	83

Use the graph below to answer exercises 46 to 51.

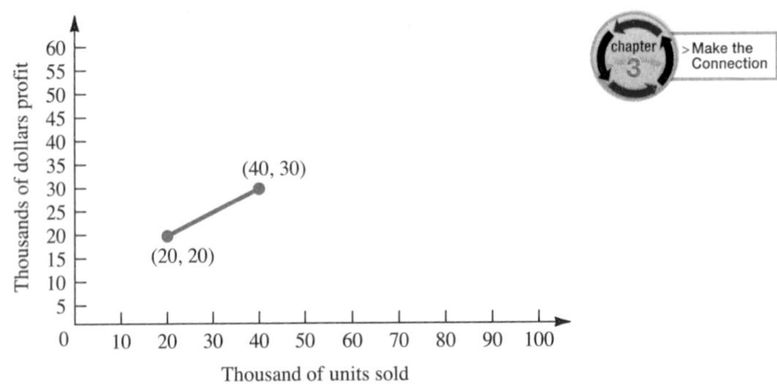

chapter 3 > Make the Connection

46. Describe the meaning of the point (20, 20).

47. Describe the meaning of the point (40, 30).

48. What prediction would you make from the graph for the profit if 25,000 units were sold?

49. What prediction would you make from the graph for the profit if 35,000 units were sold?

50. What prediction would you make from the graph for the profit if 10,000 units were sold? (*Hint:* Extend the line segment beyond the two given points.)

51. What prediction would you make from the graph for the profit if 50,000 units were sold? (*Hint:* Extend the line segment beyond the two given points.)

Basic Skills | Advanced Skills | **Vocational-Technical Applications** | Calculator/Computer | Above and Beyond

52. **Information Technology** Since 1994, the number of children online has increased every year. Provide the ordered pairs for Internet use from any location from 1994–1998.

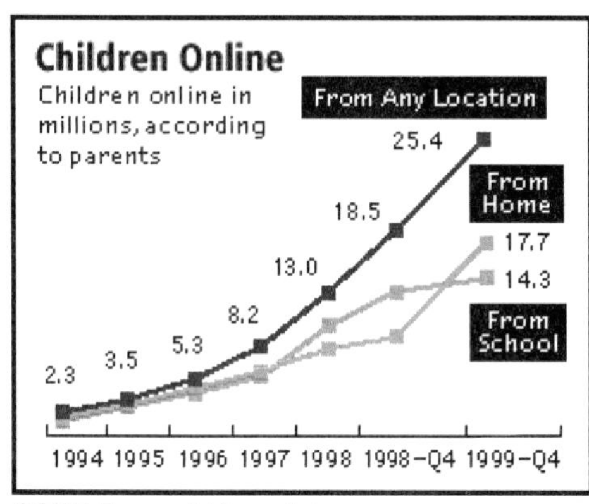

53. **Manufacturing Technology** A CAD operator has located three corners of a rectangle. The corners are at: (5, 9), (−2, 9), and (5, 2). Find the location of the fourth corner.

54. **Allied Health** The recommended dosage (d), in milligrams (mg), of the antibiotic ampicillin sodium for children weighing less than 40 kilograms is given by the linear equation $d = 7.5w$, where w represents the child's weight in kilograms (kg).

(a) What dose should be given to a child weighing 30 kg?

(b) Sketch a graph of the linear equation.

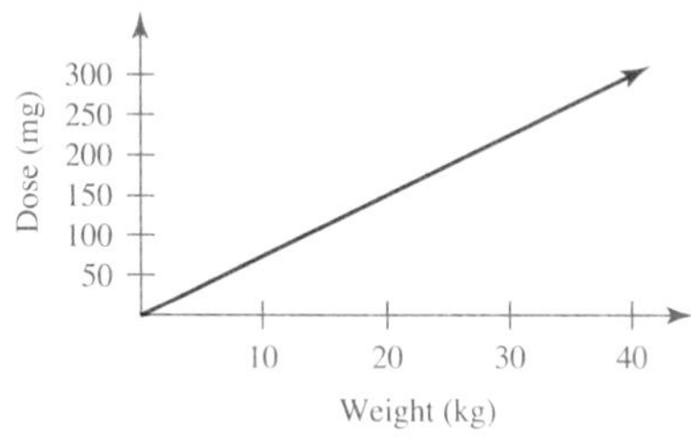

(c) What size child requires a dose of 150 mg?

Answers

50. $15,000 profit

51. $35,000 profit

52. (1994, 2.3), (1995, 3.5), (1996, 5.3), (1997, 8.2), (1998, 13.0)

53. (−2, 2)

54. (a) 225 mg; (b) See exercise; (c) 20 kg

Answers

55. (a) See exercise; (b) 32 kg; (c) 20 days

56. X max > 80, Y min < −80

57. X max > 450, Y max > 300

58. X min < −18, Y max > 90

59. Any viewing window that shows the origin

60. Y max > 200

61. See exercise

62. See exercise

63. See exercise

64. See exercise

65. y = 6

66. x = −5

67. The y-coordinate is 1 more than the x-coordinate; (4, 5) is one example (y = x + 1)

68. The y-coordinate equals −3 times the x-coordinate; (2, −6) is one example

55. **ALLIED HEALTH** The weight (w), in kilograms, of an abdominal tumor is related to the number of days (d) of chemotherapy treatment and given by the linear equation $w = -1.6d + 32$.

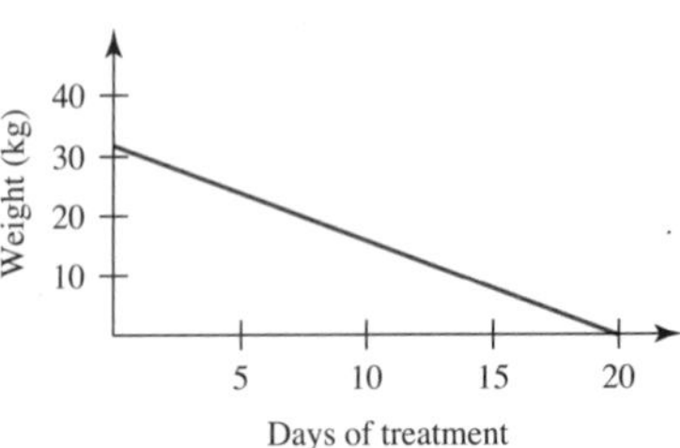

(a) Sketch a graph of the linear equation.

(b) What was the original size of the tumor?

(c) How many days of chemotherapy are required to eliminate the tumor?

Basic Skills | Advanced Skills | Vocational-Technical Applications | **Calculator/Computer** | Above and Beyond

Select a window that allows you to see both the x- and y-intercepts on your calculator. If that is not possible, explain why not.

56. $x - y = 80$

57. $2x + 3y = 900$

58. $y = 5x + 90$

59. $y = 30x$

60. $y = 200$

Use your graphing utility to graph each of the following equations.

61. $y = -3$

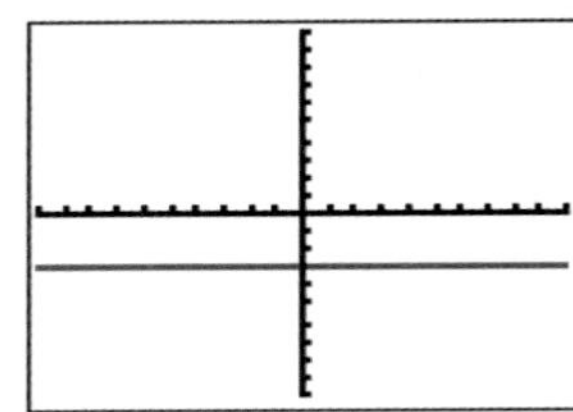

62. $y = 2$

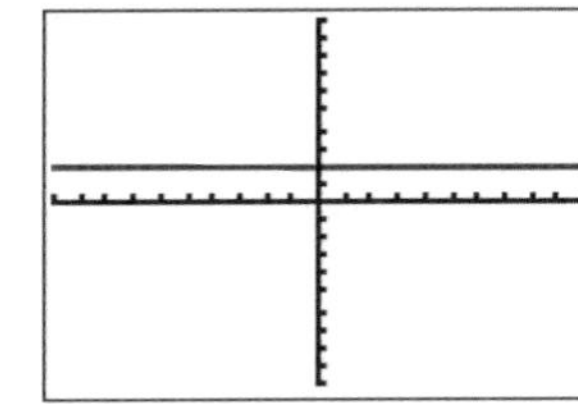

63. $y = 3x - 1$

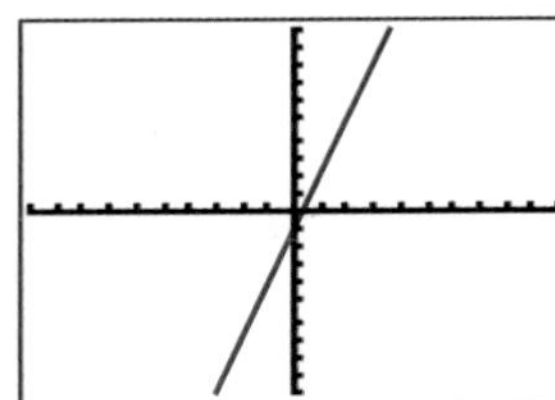

64. $y = -2x + 2$

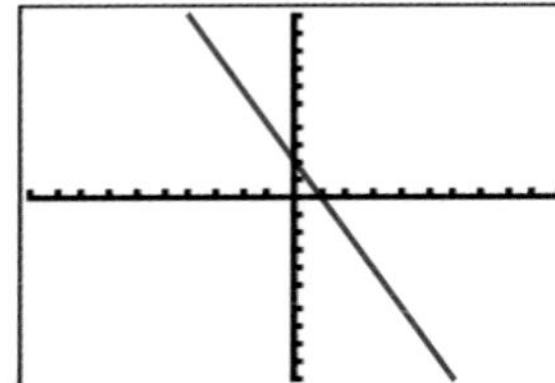

65. Write an equation whose graph will have no x-intercept but will have a y-intercept at (0, 6).

66. Write an equation whose graph will have no y-intercept but will have an x-intercept at (−5, 0).

Basic Skills | Advanced Skills | Vocational-Technical Applications | Calculator/Computer | **Above and Beyond**

67. Graph the points with coordinates (1, 2), (2, 3), and (3, 4). What do you observe? Give the coordinates of another point with the same property.

68. Graph points with coordinates (−1, 3), (0, 0), and (1, −3). What do you observe? Give the coordinates of another point with the same property.

Two distinct lines in the plane either are parallel or they intersect. In exercises 69 to 72, graph each pair of equations on the same set of axes, and find the point of intersection, where possible.

69. $x + y = 6, x - y = 4$

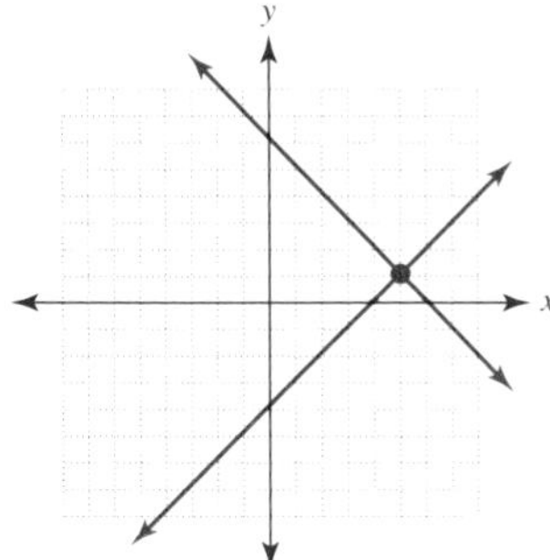

70. $y = x + 3, y = -x + 1$

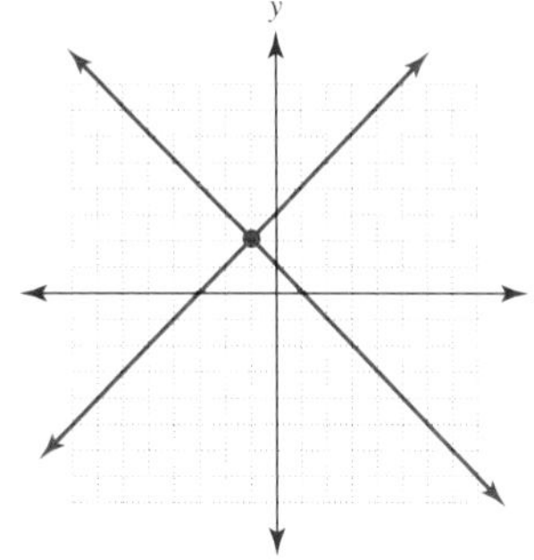

71. $y = 2x, y = x + 1$

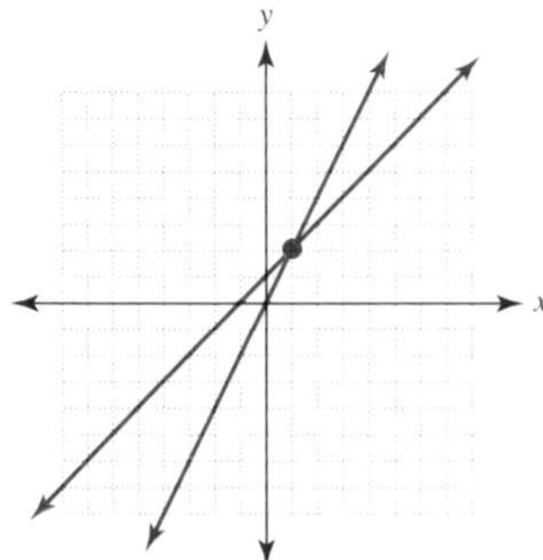

72. $2x + y = 3, 2x + y = 5$

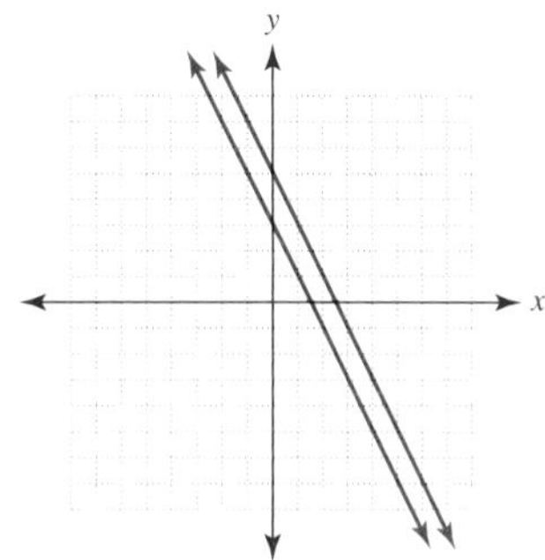

73. Graph $y = x$ and $y = 2x$ on the same set of axes. What do you observe?

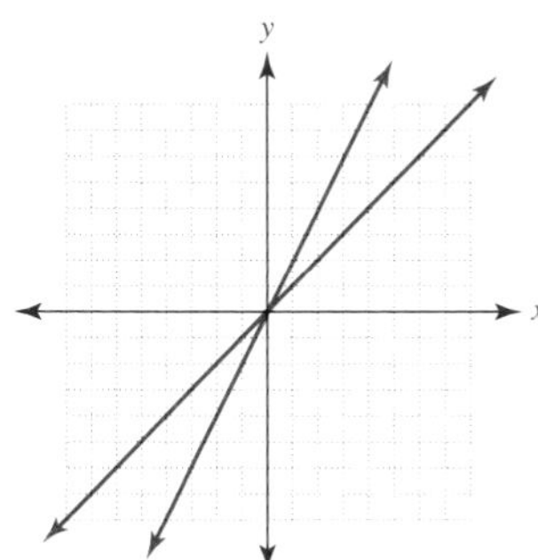

74. Graph $y = 2x + 1$ and $y = -2x + 1$ on the same set of axes. What do you observe?

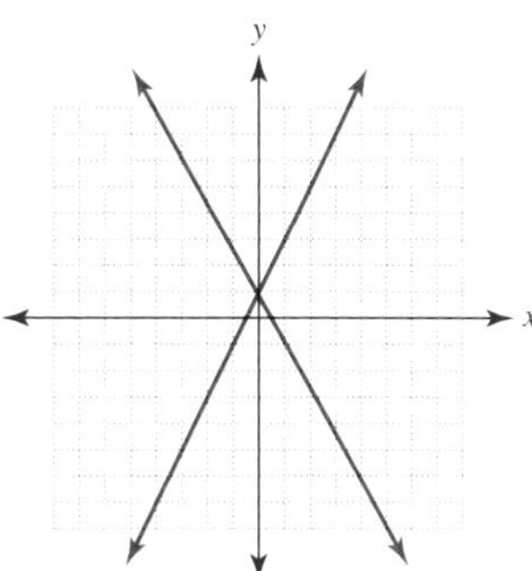

75. Graph $y = 2x$ and $y = 2x + 1$ on the same set of axes. What do you observe?

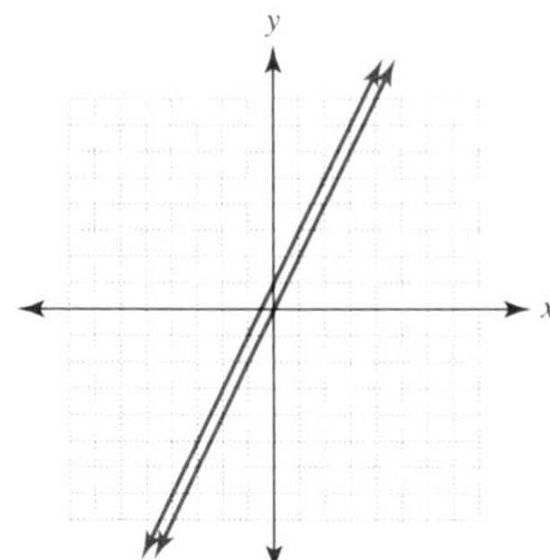

76. Graph $y = 3x + 1$ and $y = 3x - 1$ on the same set of axes. What do you observe?

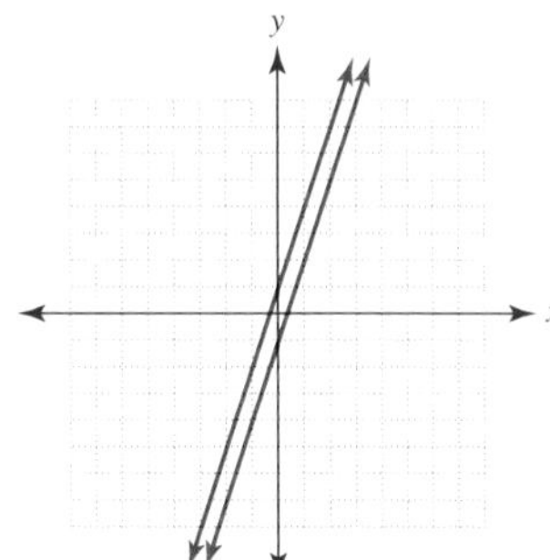

Answers

69. Intersection: (5, 1)

70. Intersection: (−1, 2)

71. Intersection: (1, 2)

72. Parallel

73. The line corresponding to $y = 2x$ is steeper than that corresponding to $y = x$. See exercise.

74. The line corresponding to $y = 2x + 1$ rises from left to right, and the other line falls. See exercise.

75. The lines appear to be parallel. See exercise.

76. The lines appear to be parallel See exercise.

Answers

77. The lines appear to be perpendicular. See exercise.

78. The lines appear to be perpendicular. See exercise.

77. Graph $y = 2x$ and $y = -\frac{1}{2}x$ on the same set of axes. What do you observe?

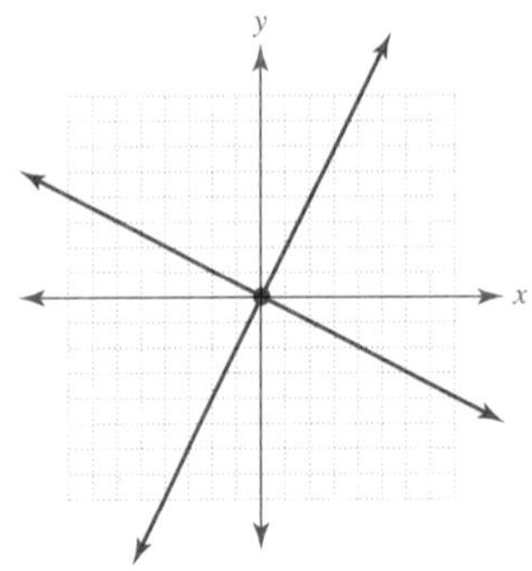

78. Graph $y = \frac{1}{3}x + \frac{7}{3}$ and $y = -3x + 2$ on the same set of axes. What do you observe?

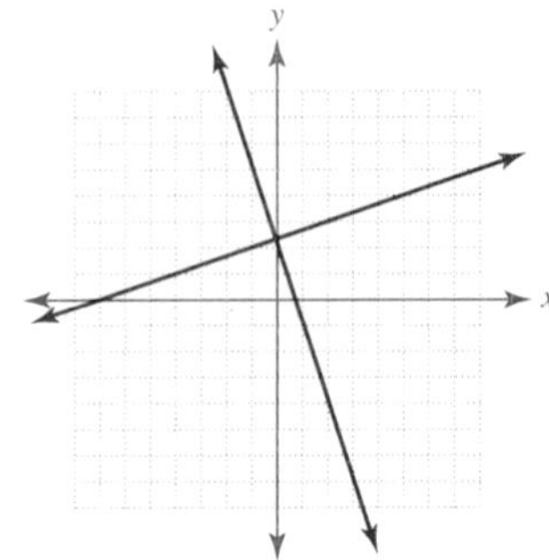

Answers

1. (a) and (c) **3.** (b)

5.

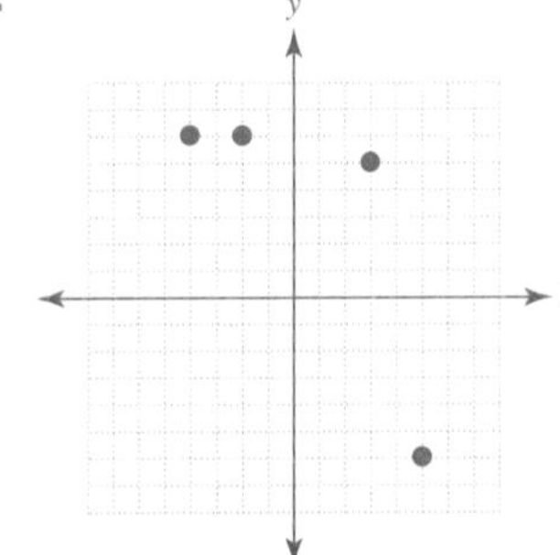

7.

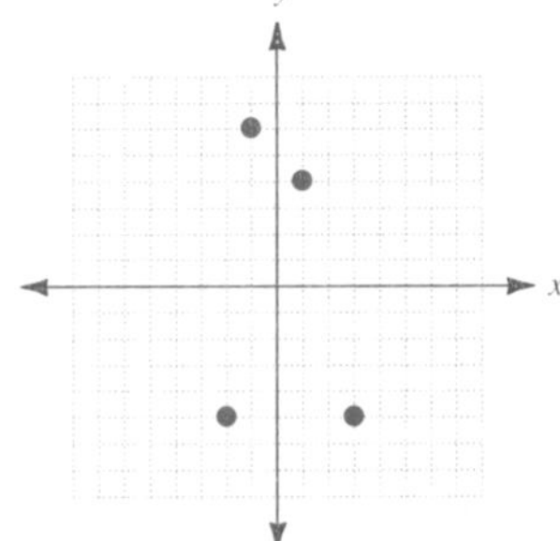

9. $(-6, 0)$ **11.** $(0, -4)$ **13.** $(6, -2)$

15.

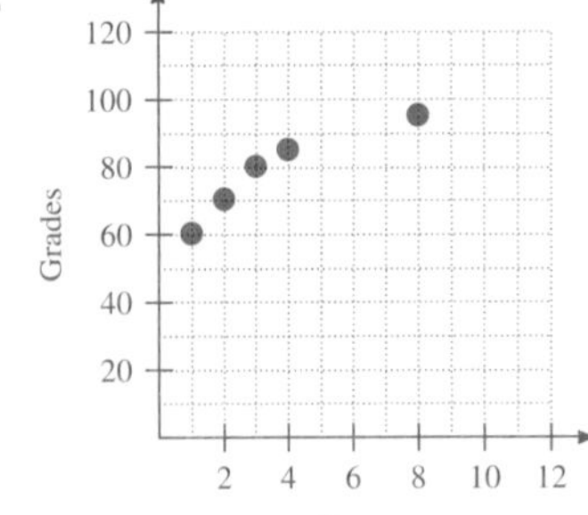

17. Answers will vary; sample: $(0, 5), (1, 3), (-1, 7)$

19. Answers will vary; sample: $(0, 4), (5, 0), \left(-1, \frac{24}{5}\right)$

21. Answers will vary; sample: $(0, 0), (-1, -2), (2, 4)$

23. $y = x - 2$

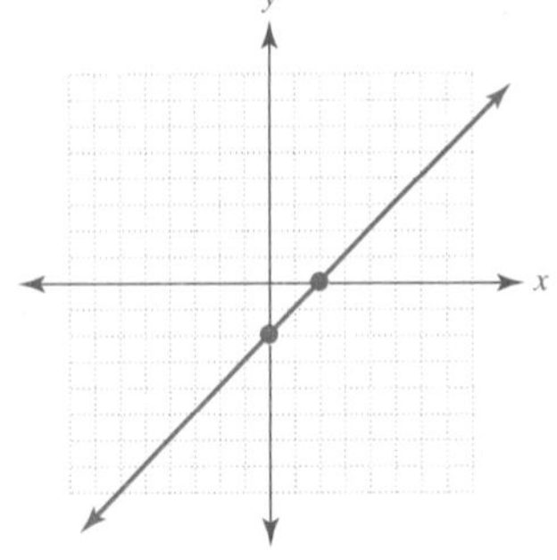

25. $y = \frac{1}{2}x - 3$

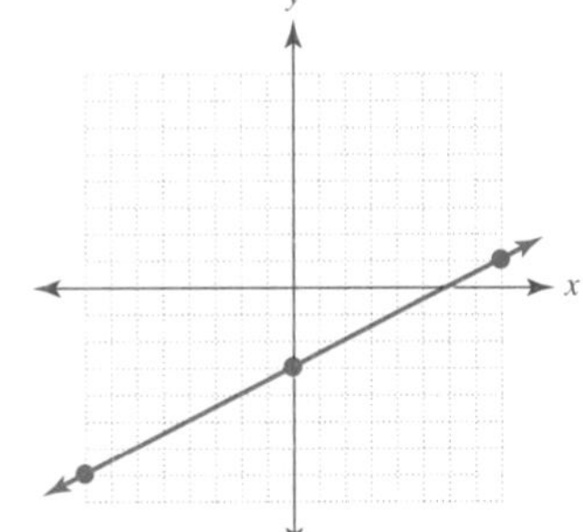

27. $x + 2y = 0$

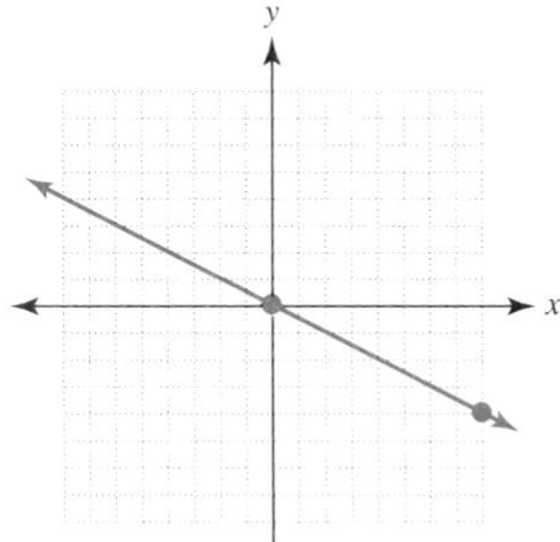

29. $x = 4$

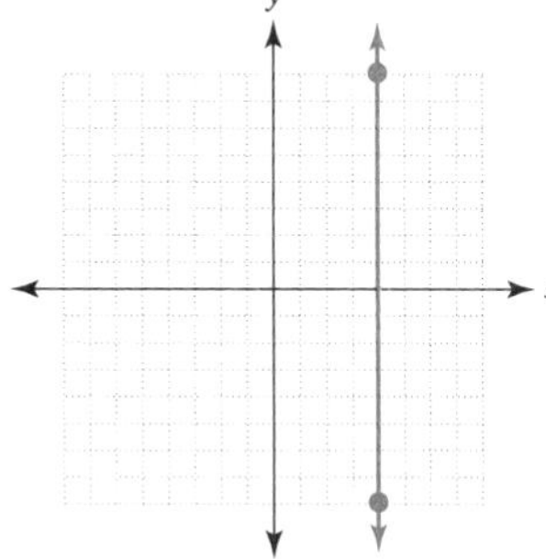

31. $y = 4$

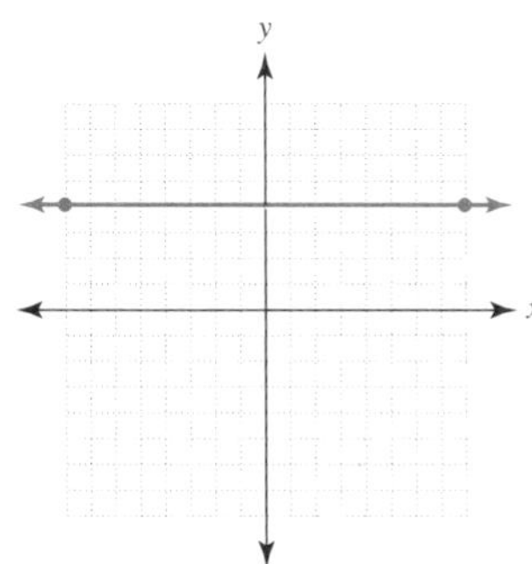

33. $2x + 5y = 10$; y-int: $(0, 2)$; x-int: $(5, 0)$

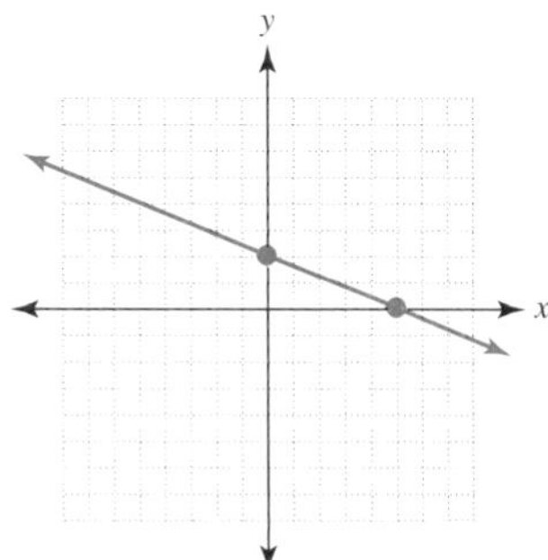

35. $x + 4y + 8 = 0$; y-int: $(0, -2)$; x-int: $(-8, 0)$

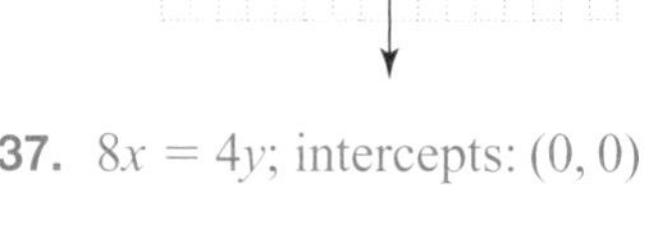

37. $8x = 4y$; intercepts: $(0, 0)$

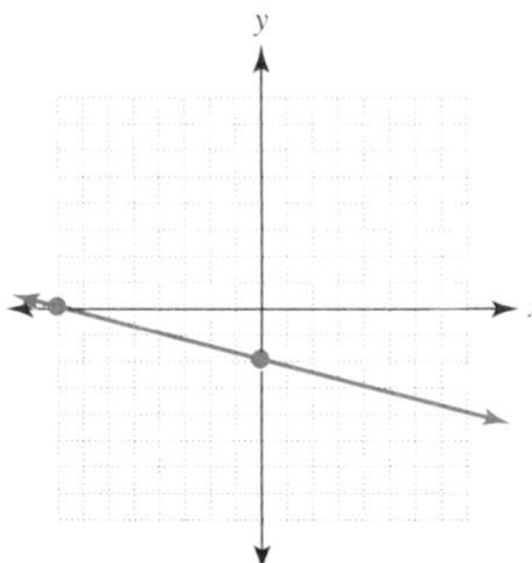

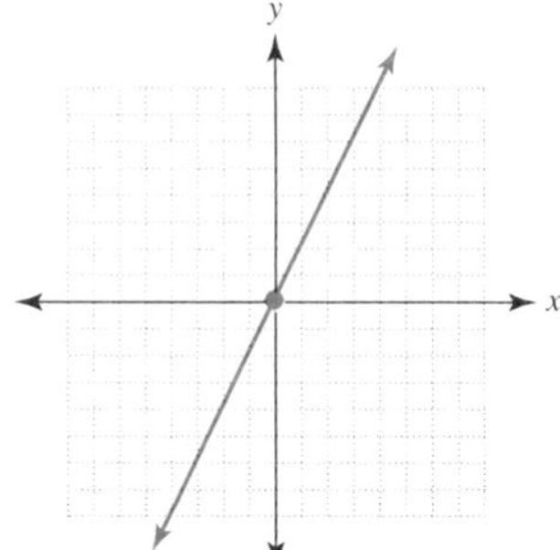

39. sometimes **41.** sometimes

43. $C = 0.20m + 20$

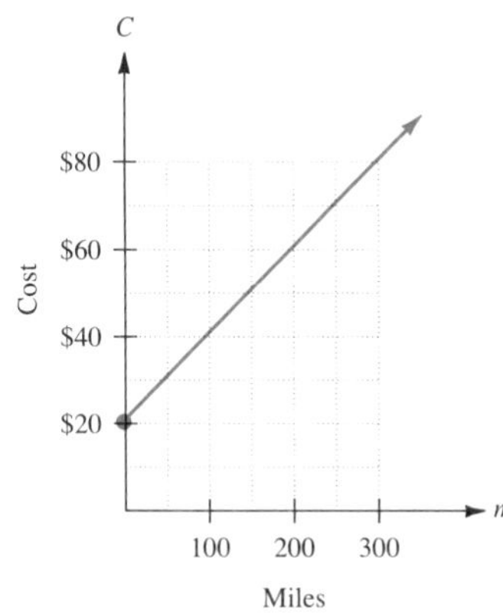

45.

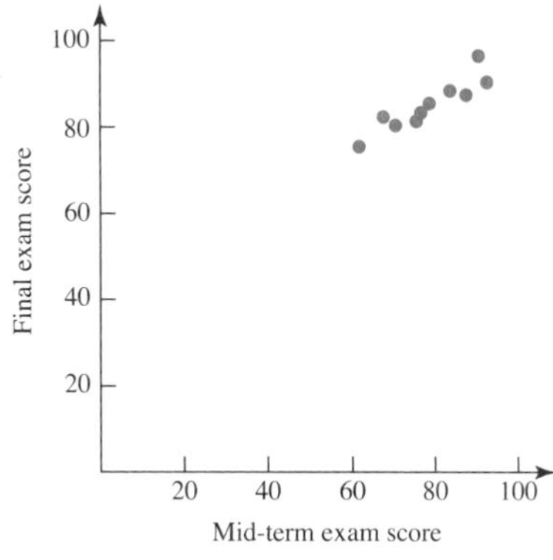

47. 40,000 units sold and \$30,000 profit **49.** \$27,500 profit

51. \$35,000 profit **53.** $(-2, 2)$

55. (a)

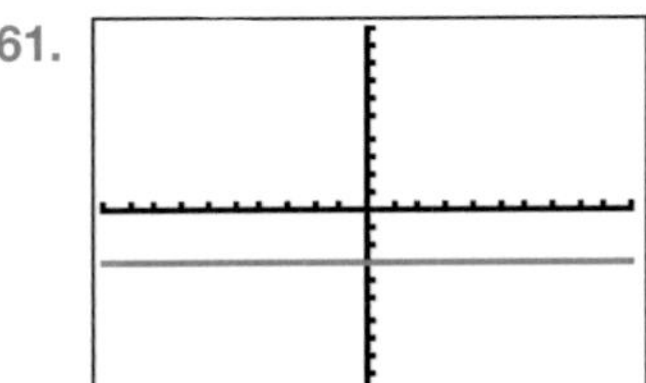

(b) 32 kg; **(c)** 20 days

57. X max > 450; Y max > 300 **59.** Any viewing window that shows the origin

61.

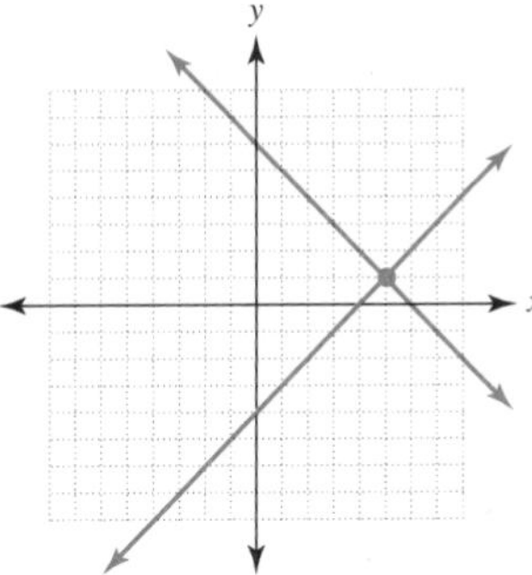

63.

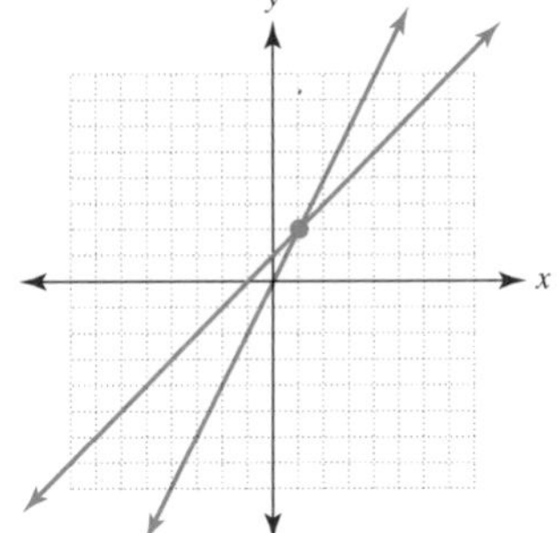

65. $y = 6$

67. The y-coordinate is one more than the x-coordinate; (4, 5) is one example ($y = x + 1$)

69. Intersection: (5, 1)

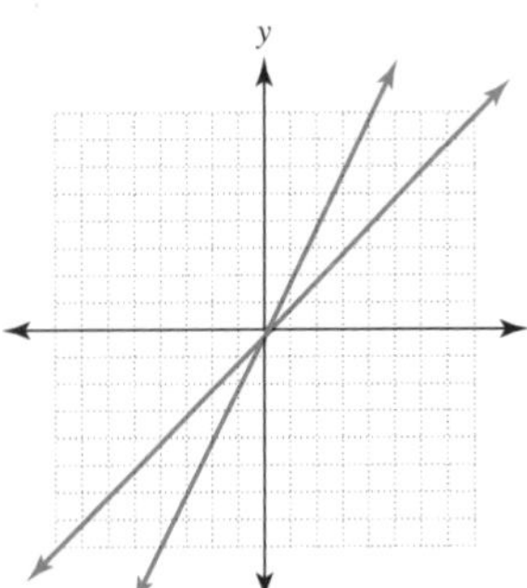

71. Intersection: (1, 2)

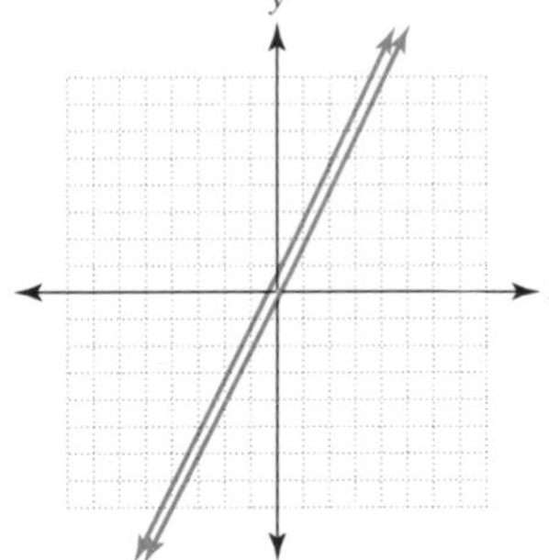

73. The line corresponding to $y = 2x$ is steeper than that corresponding to $y = x$.

75. The lines appear to be parallel.

77. The lines appear to be perpendicular.

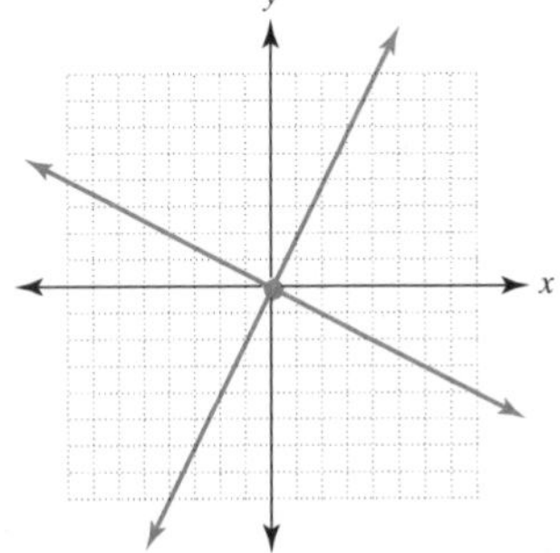

3.2 Introduction to Functions

< 3.2 Objectives >

1 > Identify domain and range

2 > Define and evaluate a function

3 > Graph a function

4 > Reading values from a graph

5 > Identify the dependent and independent variables for an application

In Section 3.1, we discussed ordered pairs. All of the ordered pairs we considered consisted of two numbers. However, ordered pairs are not always made up of two numbers. Given something like (John Doe, 987-65-4321), we have an ordered pair. In this case, it is a name paired with that person's Social Security number (SSN).

Definition

Relation A set of ordered pairs is called a **relation.**

We usually denote a relation with a capital letter. Given S = {(John Doe, 987-65-4321), (Jacob Smith, 112-23-3445), (Julia Jones, 111-22-3333)} we have a relation, which we call S. In this case, there are three ordered pairs in the relation S.

Within this relation, there are two interesting sets. The first is the set of names, which happens to be the set of first elements. The second is the set of SSNs, which is the set of second elements. Each of these sets has a name.

Definition

Domain The set of first elements in a relation is called the **domain** of the relation.

Definition

Range The set of second elements in a relation is called the **range** of the relation.

Example 1 Finding the Domain and Range of a Relation

< Objective 1 >

NOTE

$X \rightarrow$ Domain
$Y \rightarrow$ Range
Many students find it helpful to remember that domain and range occur in alphabetical order.

Find the domain and range for each relation.

(a) $A = \{$(Ben Bender, 58), (Carol Clairol, 32), (David Duval, 29)$\}$
The domain of A is {Ben Bender, Carol Clairol, David Duval}.
The range of A is $\{58, 32, 29\}$.

(b) $B = \left\{\left(5, \frac{1}{2}\right), (-4, -5), (-12, 10), (-16, \pi)\right\}$

The domain of B is $\{5, -4, -12, -16\}$.

The range of B is $\left\{\frac{1}{2}, -5, 10, \pi\right\}$.

Check Yourself 1

Find the domain and range of each relation.

(a) $H = \{$(Secretariat, 10), (Seattle Slew, 8), (Charismatic, 5), (Gallant Man, 7)$\}$

(b) $N = \left\{\left(-\frac{1}{2}, \frac{3}{4}\right), (0, 0), (1, 5), (\pi, \pi)\right\}$

RECALL

To evaluate an expression, replace each variable by its given number value.

One special type of relation is a **function.** Being a relation, a function is also a set of ordered pairs, but with certain restrictions.

In Chapter 1, we introduced algebraic expressions and learned how to evaluate them. We could design a machine whose purpose would be to crank out the value of an expression for each given value of x. We could call this machine something simple such as f, our **function machine.** Our machine might look like this.

For example, when we put -1 into the machine, the machine would substitute -1 for x in the expression, and 5 would come out the other end because

$$2(-1)^3 + 3(-1)^2 - 5(-1) - 1 = -2 + 3 + 5 - 1 = 5$$

Note that, with this function machine, an input of -1 will always result in an output of 5. One of the most important aspects of a function machine is that each input has a unique output.

In fact, the idea of the function machine is very useful in mathematics. Your graphing calculator can be used as a function machine. You can enter the expression into the calculator as Y_1 and then evaluate Y_1 for different values of x.

Generally, in mathematics, we do not write $Y_1 = 2x^3 + 3x^2 - 5x - 1$. Instead, we write $f(x) = 2x^3 + 3x^2 - 5x - 1$, which is read "$f$ of x is equal to . . .". Instead of calling f a function machine, we say that f is a function of x. The greatest benefit of this notation is that it lets us easily note the input value of x along with the output of the function. Instead of "the value of Y_1 is 155 when $x = 4$," we can write $f(4) = 155$.

Example 2 Evaluating a Function

< Objective 2 >

Given $f(x) = x^3 + 3x^2 - x + 5$, find the following.

(a) $f(0)$

Substituting 0 for x in the expression on the right, we get

$$(0)^3 + 3(0)^2 - (0) + 5 = 5$$

So $f(0) = 5$.

(b) $f(-3)$

Substituting -3 for x in the expression on the right, we get

$$\begin{aligned}(-3)^3 + 3(-3)^2 - (-3) + 5 &= -27 + 27 + 3 + 5\\ &= 8\end{aligned}$$

So $f(-3) = 8$.

(c) $f\left(\frac{1}{2}\right)$

Substituting $\frac{1}{2}$ for x in the expression on the right, we get

$$\begin{aligned}\left(\frac{1}{2}\right)^3 + 3\left(\frac{1}{2}\right)^2 - \left(\frac{1}{2}\right) + 5 &= \frac{1}{8} + 3\left(\frac{1}{4}\right) - \frac{1}{2} + 5\\ &= \frac{1}{8} + \frac{3}{4} - \frac{1}{2} + 5\\ &= \frac{1}{8} + \frac{6}{8} - \frac{4}{8} + 5\\ &= \frac{3}{8} + 5\\ &= 5\frac{3}{8} \text{ or } \frac{43}{8}\end{aligned}$$

So $f\left(\frac{1}{2}\right) = \frac{43}{8}$.

(d) $f(0.4)$

Substituting 0.4 for x in the expression on the right, we get

$$\begin{aligned}(0.4)^3 + 3(0.4)^2 - (0.4) + 5 &= 0.064 + 3(0.16) - 0.4 + 5\\ &= 0.064 + 0.48 - 0.4 + 5\\ &= 5.144\end{aligned}$$

So $f(0.4) = 5.144$.

Check Yourself 2

Given $f(x) = 2x^3 - x^2 + 3x - 2$, find the following.

(a) $f(0)$ **(b)** $f(3)$ **(c)** $f\left(-\frac{1}{2}\right)$ **(d)** $f(0.2)$

We can rewrite the relationship between x and $f(x)$ in Example 2 as a series of ordered pairs.

$$f(x) = x^3 + 3x^2 - x + 5$$

From this we found that

$$f(0) = 5, \quad f(-3) = 8, \quad f\left(\frac{1}{2}\right) = \frac{43}{8}, \quad \text{and} \quad f(0.4) = 5.144$$

NOTE

Because $y = f(x)$, $(x, f(x))$ is another way of writing (x, y).

There is an ordered pair, which we could write as $(x, f(x))$, associated with each of these. Those three ordered pairs are

$$(0, 5), \quad (-3, 8), \quad \left(\frac{1}{2}, \frac{43}{8}\right), \quad \text{and} \quad (0.4, 5.144)$$

Example 3 Finding Ordered Pairs

Given the function $f(x) = 2x^2 - 3x + 5$, find the ordered pair $(x, f(x))$ associated with each given value for x.

(a) $x = 0$

$f(0) = 2(0)^2 - 3(0) + 5 = 5$, so the ordered pair is $(0, 5)$.

(b) $x = -1$

$f(-1) = 2(-1)^2 - 3(-1) + 5 = 10$, so the ordered pair is $(-1, 10)$.

(c) $x = \frac{1}{4}$

$f\left(\frac{1}{4}\right) = 2\left(\frac{1}{4}\right)^2 - 3\left(\frac{1}{4}\right) + 5 = \frac{35}{8}$, so the ordered pair is $\left(\frac{1}{4}, \frac{35}{8}\right)$.

(d) $x = 0.9$

$f(0.9) = 2(0.9)^2 - 3(0.9) + 5 = 3.92$, so the ordered pair is $(0.9, 3.92)$.

Check Yourself 3

Given $f(x) = 2x^3 - x^2 + 3x - 2$, find the ordered pair associated with each given value of x.

(a) $x = 0$ **(b)** $x = 3$ **(c)** $x = -\frac{1}{2}$ **(d)** $x = 0.2$

Now that both relations and functions have been introduced, let us now learn more about how they differ. We defined a relation as a set of ordered pairs. In Example 3, we found ordered pairs from a function. This illustrates that a function (since it produces ordered pairs) is also a relation. However, not all relations are functions. In other words, some sets of ordered pairs do not have what it takes to be a function. In Example 4, we will determine which relations actually can be modeled by a function machine.

Example 4 Modeling with a Function Machine

Determine which relations can be modeled by a function machine.

(a) The set of all ordered pairs in which the input is the year and the output is the U.S. Open golf champion of that year.

This relation can be modeled with the function machine. Each input has a unique output. In the picture, an input of 2000 gives an output of Tiger Woods. Every time the input is 2000, the output will be Tiger Woods.

(b) The set of all possible ordered pairs in which the first element is a U.S. state and the second element is a U.S. senator from that state.

We cannot model this relation with a function machine. Because there are two senators from each state, each input does not have a unique output. In the picture, New Jersey is the input, but New Jersey has two different senators.

(c) The set of all ordered pairs in the relation **L,** when

$\mathbf{L} = \{(1, 3), (2, 5), (2, 7), (3, -4)\}$

This relation cannot be modeled with a function machine. An input of 2 can result in two different outputs, either 5 or 7.

(d) The set of all ordered pairs in the relation **M,** when

$\mathbf{M} = \{(-1, 3), (0, 3), (3, 5), (5, -2)\}$

This relation can be modeled with a function machine. Each input has a unique output. For example, an input of 0 gives an output of 3.

Check Yourself 4

Determine which relations can be modeled by a function machine.

(a) The set of all ordered pairs in which the first element is a U.S. city and the second element is the mayor of that city.

(b) The set of all ordered pairs in which the first element is a street name and the second element is a U.S. city in which a street of that name is found.

(c) The relation $P = \{(-2, 3), (-4, 9), (9, -4)\}$.

(d) The relation $Q = \{(1, 2), (3, 4), (3, 5)\}$.

The idea of a function machine and ordered pairs leads us to a definition of a function.

Definition

Function (Ordered Pairs)

A **function** is a set of distinct ordered pairs (a relation) in which no two first coordinates are equal.

We have defined a function in terms of ordered pairs. A set of ordered pairs can be specified in several ways; here are the most common.

Property

Ordered Pairs

1. We can present ordered pairs in a list or table.
2. We can give a rule or equation that will generate ordered pairs.
3. We can use a graph to indicate ordered pairs. The graph can show distinct ordered pairs, or it can show all the ordered pairs on a line or curve.

So far we have looked at functions and relations defined by ordered pairs. We have also considered functions that are equations that generate ordered pairs. We now want to consider functions and relations that use graphs to indicate ordered pairs.

Graphs are a very useful way to discuss functions and relations. For instance, by studying the graph of a relation, not only can we find ordered pairs, but we can also determine the domain and range, as shown in Example 5. Recall that the domain is the set of x-values (first elements) that appear in ordered pairs, while the range is the set of y-values (second elements).

Example 5 Identifying Functions, Domain, and Range

Determine whether or not each is the graph of a function. Also provide the domain and range in each case.

(a)

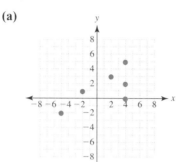

This is not a function. The value $x = 4$ has three corresponding y-values: (4, 0), (4, 2), and (4, 5). The domain of this relation is

D: $\{-5, -2, 2, 4\}$

and the range is

R: $\{-2, 0, 1, 2, 3, 5\}$

(b)

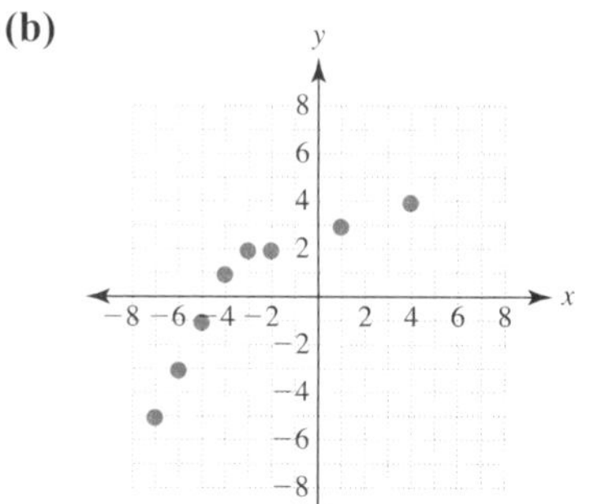

This is a function. Each x-value has a unique y-value corresponding to it. The domain is

D: $\{-7, -6, -5, -4, -3, -2, 1, 4\}$

and the range is

R: $\{-5, -3, -1, 1, 2, 3, 4\}$

Check Yourself 5

Determine whether or not each is the graph of a function. Also provide the domain and range in each case.

(a)

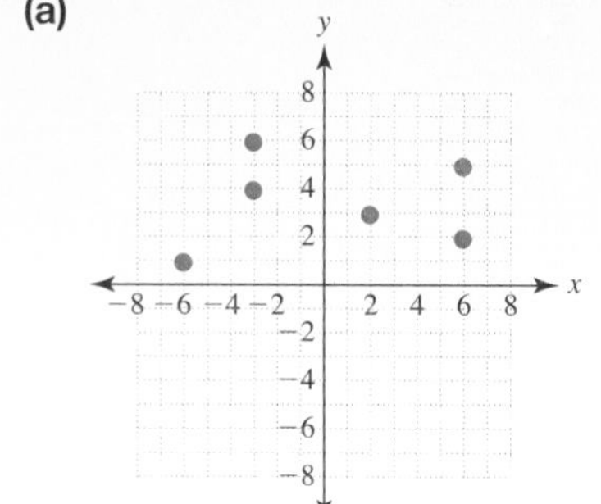

(b)

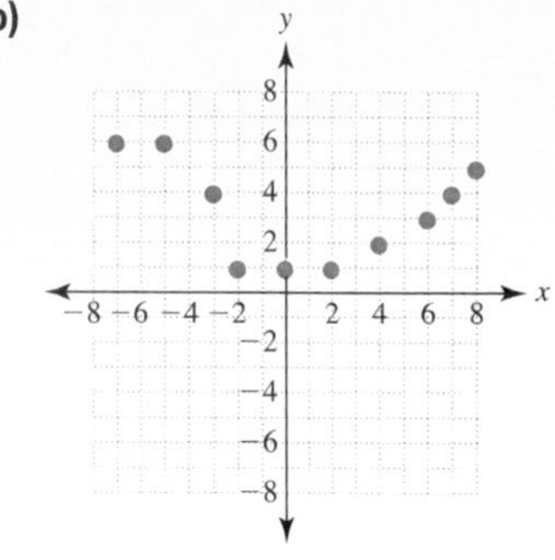

We have been examining relations and functions as described by ordered pairs, and now as graphs. If we are given a graph, we have one more way to help us determine if it is the graph of a function.

As we have seen, a graph of a relation can be found by plotting the set of distinct ordered pairs. This graph will be a function if no two first coordinates are equal. On the graph, this will occur if a vertical line, at any place on the graph, passes through the graph at only one point. This vertical line test gives us a graphic way for identifying a function.

Definition

Vertical Line Test

A relation is a function if no vertical line intersects the graph at two or more points.

Before continuing, let us return again to Example 5. Notice that in part **(a)** a vertical line at $x = 4$ passes through three points: (4, 0), (4, 2), and (4, 5). This vertical line test gives us another way to determine that part **(a)** is not a function.

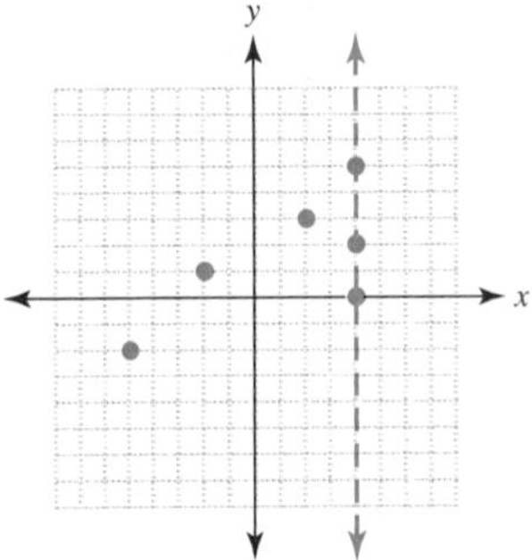

For part **(b),** no vertical line passes through more than one point. Therefore, as we had previously determined, part **(b)** is a function.

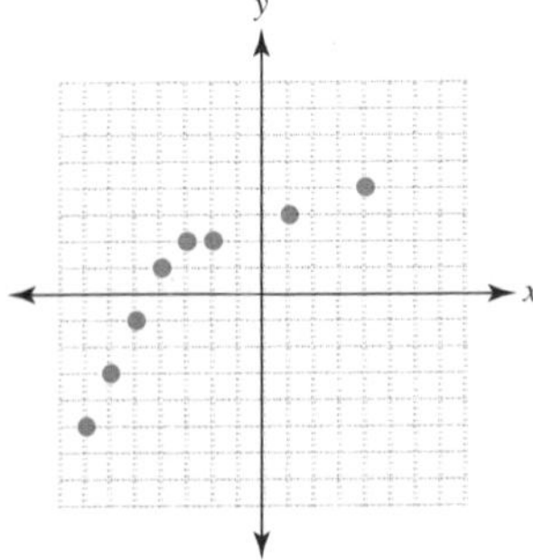

Putting together the ideas of Example 5, we have a more formal definition of a function.

Definition

Function (Domain and Range)

A **function** is a relation in which each element of the domain is paired with one and only one element of the range.

Example 5 shows that this definition is equivalent to our earlier definition as well as the vertical line test. We introduce this more formal definition since it can be useful when considering graphs that are more complicated than *finite* sets of ordered pairs (also called *scatter plots*).

We want to expand our idea of relations and functions to consider graphs comprised of line segments, lines, or curves. Graphs of these types represent an *infinite* collection of points. First, we will consider how to create graphs of relations and functions. Then, we will look at given graphs in more detail.

As we have seen, a relation is a set of ordered pairs. From our work in Section 3.1, we know how to graph ordered pairs. Therefore, we already know how to graph relations. However, can we graph functions?

The answer is yes! Since functions are just a special type of relation, we can graph functions as well. Some functions will consist of a finite set of points (as we saw in Example 5); others will be much more complicated graphs. For instance, the process of finding the graph of a linear function is identical to the process of finding the graph of a linear equation, which we did in Section 3.1.

Example 6 Graphing a Linear Function

< Objective 3 >

Graph the function $f(x) = 2x - 1$.

From our work in Section 3.1, we know we need to find three points (the third is just a check point) and draw the line through them. In Example 2 we found ordered pairs associated with given values of x. We can do the same here to find three ordered pairs $(x, f(x))$ to use for graphing the function $f(x) = 2x - 1$.

$f(0) = -1 \qquad f(1) = 1 \qquad f(2) = 3$

Therefore, the three points are $(0, -1)$, $(1, 1)$, and $(2, 3)$.

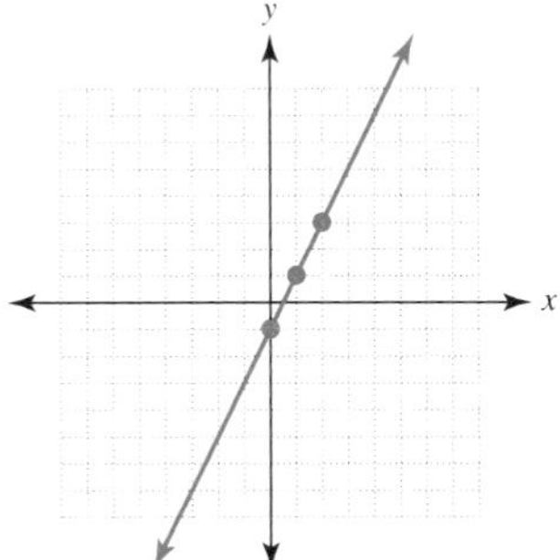

Check Yourself 6

Graph the function

$f(x) = 4x + 5$

NOTE

Keep in mind that although we usually say something like "Find the coordinates of the point . . .", sometimes when we read a graph we are able to only *estimate* the coordinates.

All functions can be graphed in this manner, by finding points. However, we will learn later in the course that there are other, faster ways to do graphing as well.

Now that we know how to create graphs of relations and functions, let us next learn how to find the coordinates (x- and y-values) of a point on a graph.

Finding the coordinates of any point on a graph of an infinite collection of points is exactly the same as finding the coordinates of an isolated point. Consider Example 7.

Example 7 Reading Values from a Graph

< Objective 4 >

Find the coordinates of the labeled points.

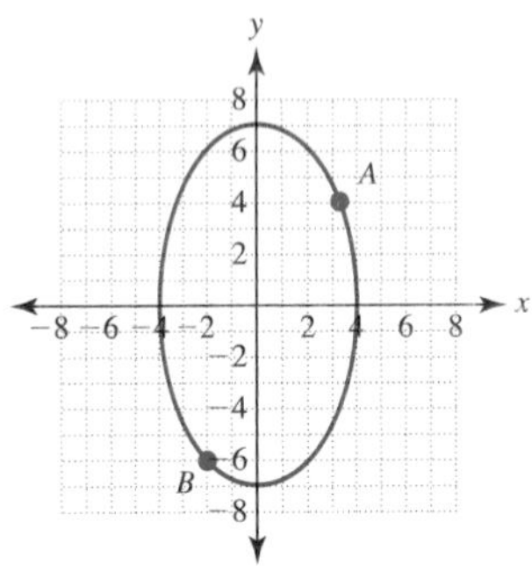

Point A has an x-coordinate of 3 and a y-coordinate of 4. Point A represents the ordered pair (3, 4). Point B represents the ordered pair (−2, −6).

Check Yourself 7

Find the coordinates of the labeled points.

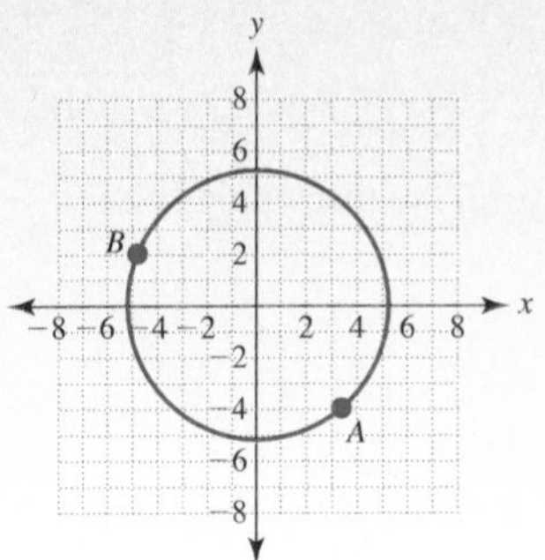

If a graph is the graph of a function, then every ordered pair (x, y) can be thought of as $(x, f(x))$.

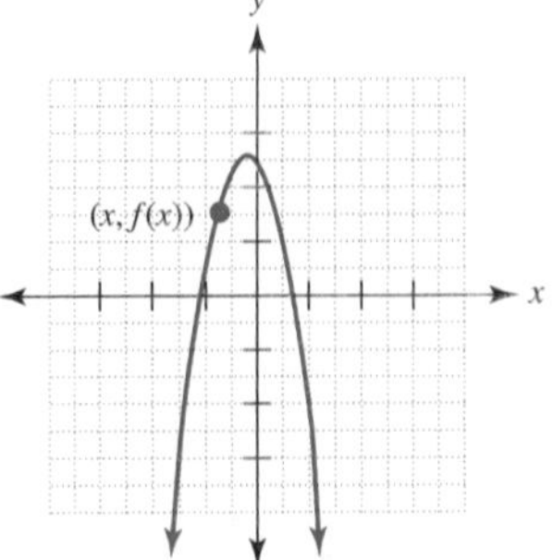

For a specific value of x, let us call it a, we can find $f(a)$ with the following algorithm (a sequence of steps that solve a problem).

Step by Step

Reading Function Values from Graphs

Step 1 Draw a vertical line through a on the x-axis.
Step 2 Find the point of intersection of that line with the graph.
Step 3 Draw a horizontal line through the graph at that point.
Step 4 Find the intersection of the horizontal line with the y-axis.
Step 5 $f(a)$ is that y-value.

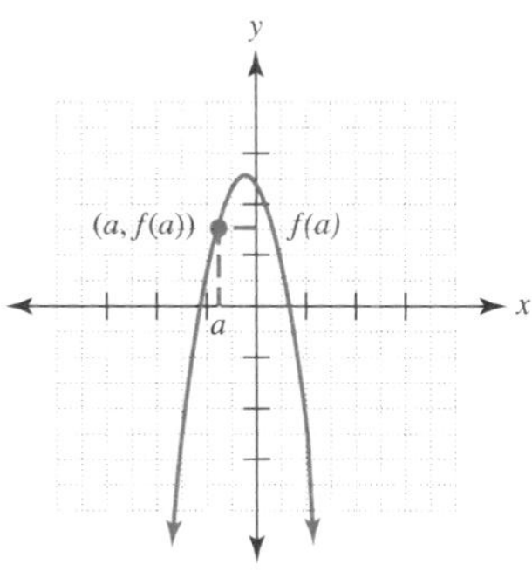

Example 8 illustrates this algorithm.

Example 8 Finding the Function Value on a Graph Given x

Consider the following graph of the function f. Find $f(2)$.

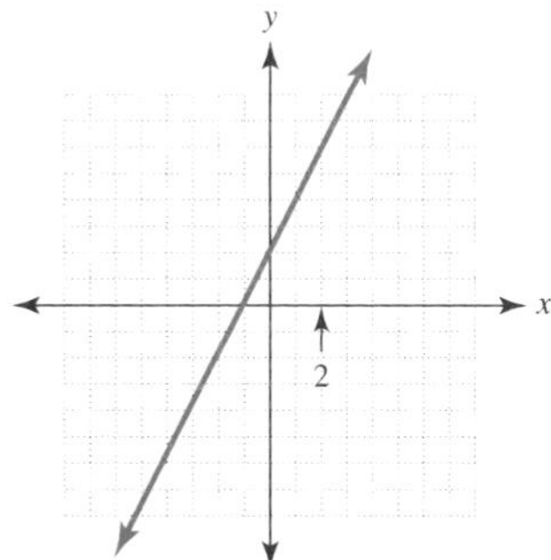

$f(2)$ is a y-value. It is the y-value that is paired with an x-value of 2. Locate the number 2 on the x-axis; draw a vertical line to the graph of the function, and then draw a horizontal line to the y-axis, as shown in the following graph.

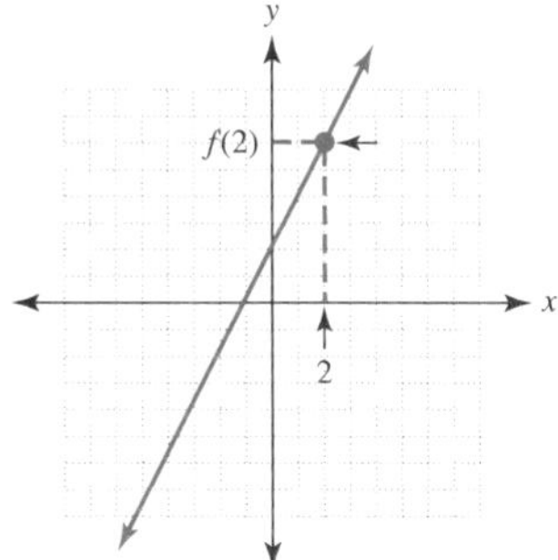

The coordinates of the point are $(2, f(2))$. The y-value of the point is $f(2)$. Read the y-value of this point on the y-axis. $f(2)$, the y-value of the point, is 6. Therefore, $f(2) = 6$.

Check Yourself 8

Use the graph of the function *f* in Example 8, to find each of the following.

(a) $f(1)$
(b) $f(-0)$
(c) $f(-1)$

In Example 8, you were given the x-value and were asked to find the corresponding function value or y-value. Now you will do the opposite. You will be given the function value and then you will need to find the corresponding x-value(s).

If given the function value, we can find the associated x-value by using the following algorithm.

Step by Step

Finding x-Values from Function Values

Step 1 Find the given function value on the y-axis.
Step 2 Draw a horizontal line through that point.
Step 3 Find every point on the graph that intersects the horizontal line.
Step 4 Draw a vertical line through each of those points of intersection.
Step 5 Each point of intersection of the vertical lines and the x-axis gives an x-value.

Example 9 Finding the x-Value from a Graph Given the Function Value

Use the following graph of the function f to find all values of x such that $f(x) = -5$.

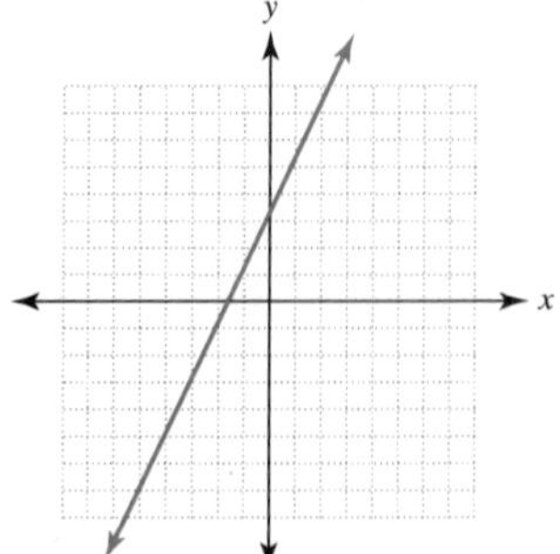

This time -5 is a function value, or y-value. Locate -5 on the y-axis, and draw a horizontal line to the graph of the function, followed by a vertical line to the x-axis, as shown in the following graph.

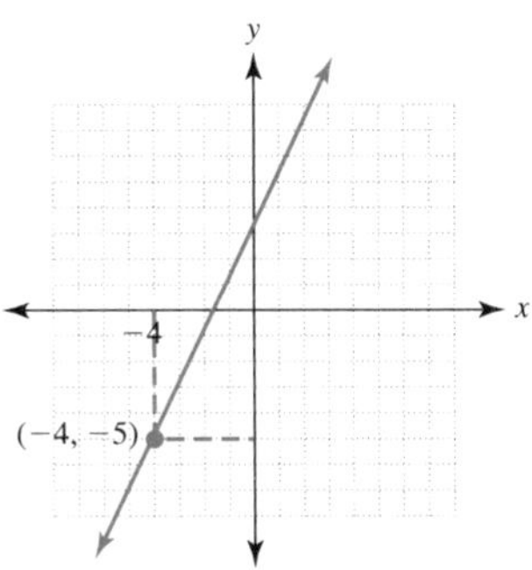

The solution of $f(x) = -5$ is $x = -4$. In particular, $f(-4) = -5$.

Check Yourself 9

Use the following graph to find all values of *x* such that

(a) $f(x) = 1$ **(b)** $f(x) = 5$ **(c)** $f(x) = -1$

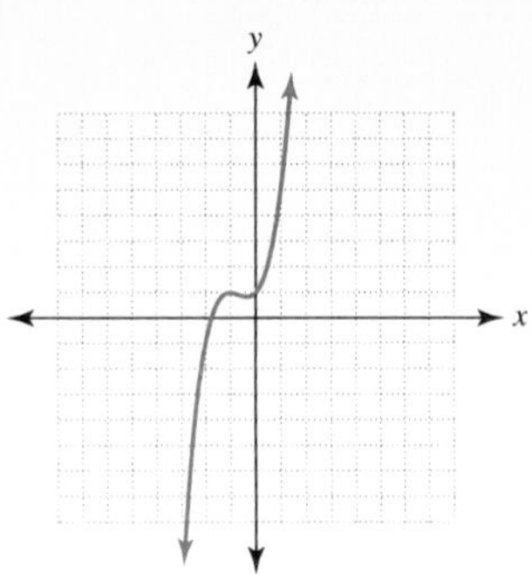

Among the most important values that can be read from graphs are the values of the *x*- and *y*-intercepts.

Example 10 Finding *x*- and *y*-Intercepts

Find the *x*- and *y*-intercepts from the graph.

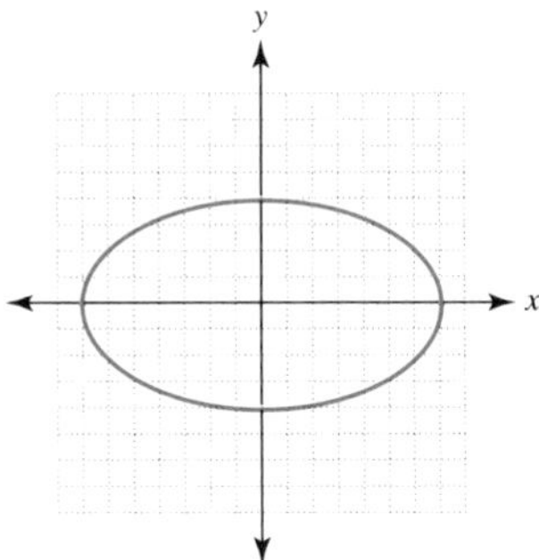

The x-coordinate of the x-intercept is the value of x for which $y = 0$. It is the x-value of any point on the graph that touches the x-axis. This graph touches the x-axis at x-values of 7 and -7. The x-intercepts are $(7, 0)$ and $(-7, 0)$.

The y-coordinate of the y-intercept is the value of y when $x = 0$. It is the y-value of any point that touches the y-axis. This graph touches the y-axis at y-values of 4 and -4. The y-intercepts are $(0, 4)$ and $(0, -4)$.

Check Yourself 10

Find the x- and y-intercepts from the graph.

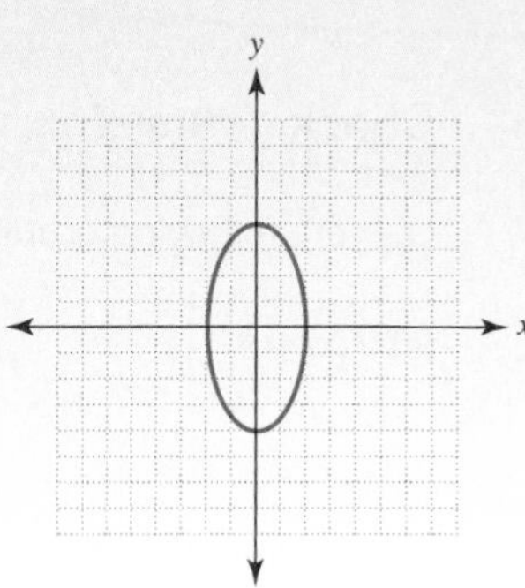

Often in mathematics, we need to read more than a finite number of values from a graph. In order to represent an infinite number of values for x or for y, we need to use something other than a list. (Do you see why?) Let us assume that we want to represent all the x-values between (but not including) 2 and 5. We can certainly use the inequality

$$2 < x < 5$$

The convention sometimes used in mathematics texts is called **set-builder notation.** The preceding set of values is written

$$\{x|2 < x < 5\}$$

We read this, "the set of all x-values that are greater than two and less than five."

Now we have a way to represent the domain and range for graphs that represent an infinite collection of points.

Example 11 Identifying Functions, Domain, and Range

Determine whether or not each is the graph of a function. Also provide the domain and range in each case.

NOTE

When you see the statement $-2 \le x \le 4$ think: "all real numbers between -2 and 4, including -2 and 4."

(a)

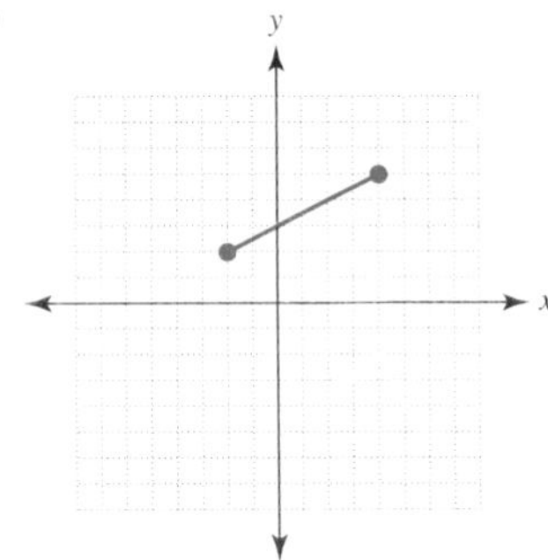

NOTE

"Inclusive" means the end points are included.

Because no vertical line will pass through more than one point, this is a function. The x-values that are used in the ordered pairs extend from -2 to 4, inclusive. Using set-builder notation, the domain is then

D: $\{x \mid -2 \le x \le 4\}$

The y-values that occur include all values from 2 to 5, inclusive. The range is

R: $\{y \mid 2 \le y \le 5\}$

(b)

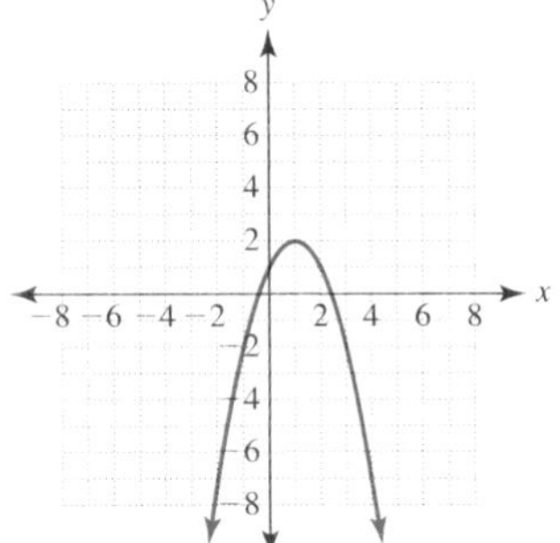

NOTE

Depicted here is a curve called a *parabola.*

Because no vertical line will pass through more than one point, this is a function. Note that the arrows on the ends of the graph indicate that the pattern continues indefinitely. The x-values that are used in this graph therefore consist of all real numbers. The domain is

RECALL

$\mathbb{R}$ is the symbol for the set of all real numbers.

D: $\{x \mid x \text{ is a real number}\}$

or simply $D = \mathbb{R}$. The y-values, however, are never higher than 2. The range is the set of all real numbers less than or equal to 2, so

R: $\{y \mid y \le 2\}$

(c)

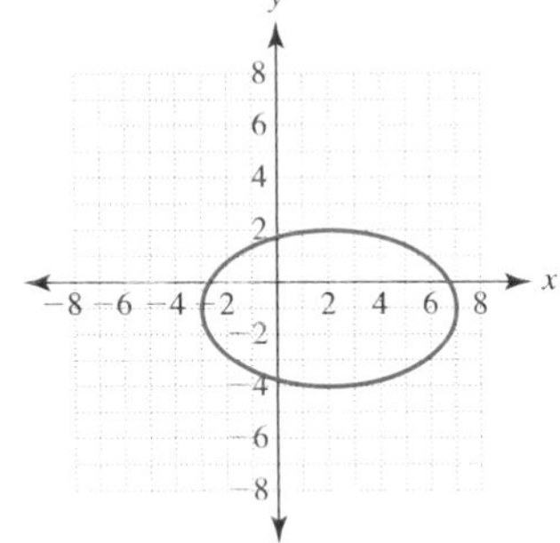

NOTE

This curve is called an *ellipse.*

This relation is not a function. A vertical line, drawn anywhere between -3 and 7, will pass through two points. The x-values that are used run from -3 to 7, inclusive, so

D: $\{x \mid -3 \leq x \leq 7\}$

The y-values used in the ordered pairs range from -4 to 2, inclusive, so

R: $\{y \mid -4 \leq y \leq 2\}$

Check Yourself 11

Determine whether or not each is the graph of a function. Also provide the domain and range in each case.

(a)

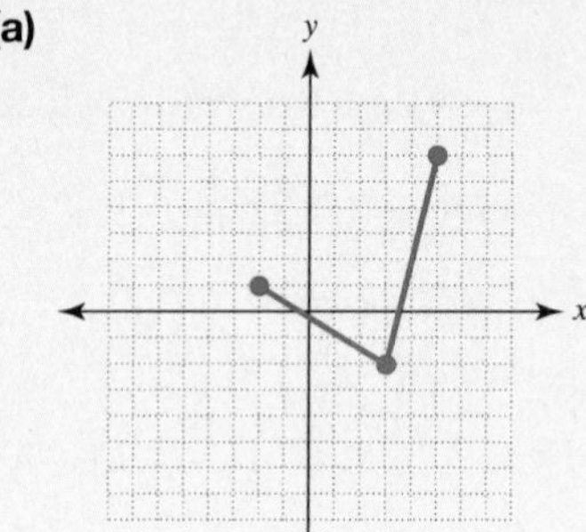

(b)

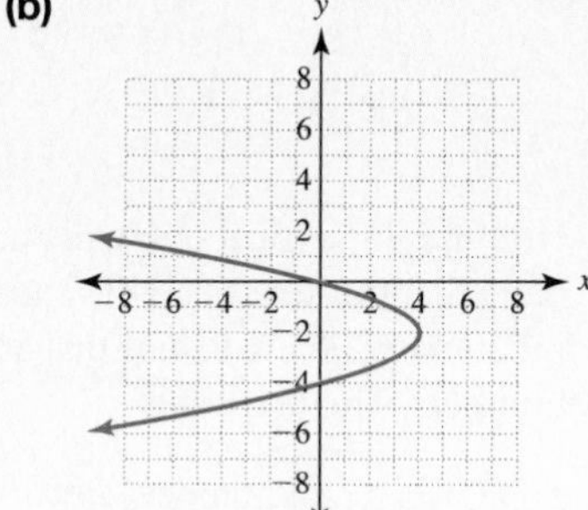

(c)

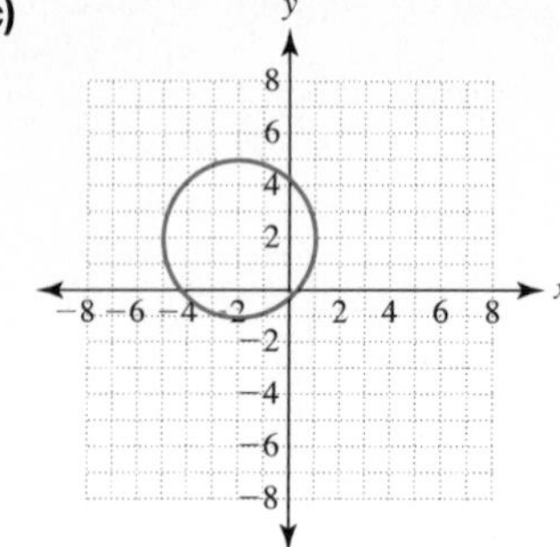

At this point, you may be wondering how the concept of function relates to anything outside the study of mathematics. A function is a relation that yields a single output (y-value) each time a specific input (x-value) is given. Any field in which predictions are made builds on the idea of functions. Here are a few examples:

- A physicist looks for the relationship that uses a planet's mass to predict its gravitational pull.
- An economist looks for the relationship that uses the tax rate to predict the employment rate.
- A business marketer looks for the relationship that uses an item's price to predict the number that will be sold.
- A college board looks for the relationship between tuition costs and the number of students enrolled at the college.
- A biologist looks for the relationship that uses temperature to predict a body of water's nutrient level.

Another important application of functions involves the idea of independent and dependent variables. When an equation is written such that on one side is y and the other side is an expression involving the variable x, such as

$$y = 3x - 2$$

we can rewrite the equation as a function. In this case, we have

$$f(x) = 3x - 2$$

NOTE

The value of y depends on x.

This implies that

$$y = f(x)$$

We can say that y is a function of x, or y is dependent on x. That leads to the following definitions.

Definition

Independent Variable and Dependent Variable

Given that $y = f(x)$,

x is called the **independent variable** and y is called the **dependent variable.**

Identifying which variable is independent and which is dependent is important in many applications in real-world situations.

Example 12 Identifying the Dependent Variable

< Objective 5 >

From each pair, identify which variable is dependent on the other.

(a) The age of a car and its resale value.

The resale value depends on the age, so we would assign the age of the car the independent variable (x) and the resale value the dependent variable (y).

NOTE

If you think about it, you will see that time will be the independent variable in most ordered pairs. Most everything depends on time rather than the reverse.

(b) The amount of interest earned in a bank account and the amount of time the money has been in the bank.

The interest depends on the time, so interest is the dependent variable (y) and time is the independent variable (x).

(c) The number of cigarettes you have smoked and the probability of dying from a smoking-related disease.

The number of cigarettes is the independent variable (x), and the probability of dying from a smoking-related disease is the dependent variable (y).

Check Yourself 12

From each pair, identify which variable is dependent on the other.

(a) The number of credits taken and the amount of tuition paid.
(b) The temperature of a cup of coffee and the length of time since it was poured.

In your future study of mathematics, you will see functions applied in these ways. In those applications, you will find that you put to good use the basic skills developed in this section.

Check Yourself ANSWERS

1. (a) The domain of H is {Secretariat, Seattle Slew, Charismatic, Gallant Man}; The range of H is $\{10, 8, 5, 7\}$
(b) The domain of N is $\left\{-\frac{1}{2}, 0, 1, \pi\right\}$; The range of N is $\left\{\frac{3}{4}, 0, 5, \pi\right\}$
2. (a) -2; **(b)** 52; **(c)** -4; **(d)** -1.424 **3. (a)** $(0, -2)$; **(b)** $(3, 52)$; **(c)** $\left(-\frac{1}{2}, -4\right)$; **(d)** $(0.2, -1.424)$ **4. (a)** function; **(b)** not a function; **(c)** function; **(d)** not a function **5. (a)** not a function; D: $\{-6, -3, 2, 6\}$; R: $\{1, 2, 3, 4, 5, 6\}$; **(b)** function; D: $\{-7, -5, -3, -2, 0, 2, 4, 6, 7, 8\}$; R: $\{1, 2, 3, 4, 5, 6\}$
6.

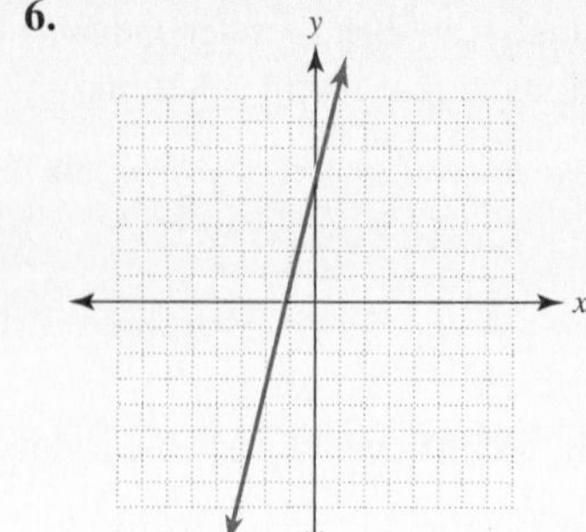

7. A: $(3, -4)$; B: $(-5, 2)$ **8. (a)** $f(1) = 4$; **(b)** $f(-0) = 2$; **(c)** $f(-1) = -0$ **9. (a)** $x = -1, x = 0$; **(b)** $x = 1$; **(c)** $x = -2$ **10.** x-int: $(-2, 0), (2, 0)$; y-int: $(0, -4), (0, 4)$ **11. (a)** function; D: $\{x|-2 \le x \le 5\}$; R: $\{y|-2 \le y \le 6\}$; **(b)** not a function; D: $\{x|x \le 4\}$; R: $\mathbb{R}$; **(c)** not a function; D: $\{x|-5 \le x \le 1\}$, R: $\{y|-1 \le y \le 5\}$ **12. (a)** Tuition is dependent and number of credits is independent; **(b)** The temperature is dependent and time since the coffee was poured is independent

Reading Your Text

The following fill-in-the-blank exercises are designed to ensure that you understand some of the key vocabulary used in this section.

SECTION 3.2

(a) The ______________ is a graphic test for identifying a function.

(b) Domain (and range) can be represented by an inequality or by using ______________ notation.

(c) A ______________ is a relation in which each element of the domain is paired with one and only one element of the range.

(d) Given that $y = f(x)$, x is called the ______________ and y is called the ______________.

3.2 exercises

Basic Skills | Advanced Skills | Vocational-Technical Applications | Calculator/Computer | Above and Beyond

MathZone

Boost your grade at mathzone.com!
- > Practice Problems
- > NetTutor
- > Self-Tests
- > e-Professors
- > Videos

Name ____________

Section ________ Date ________

Answers

1. D: {Colorado, Edmonton, Calgary, Vancouver}; R: {21, 5, 18, 17}
2. D: {Eric Lindros, Mark Recchi, John LeClair, Keith Primeau}; R: {88, 8, 10, 25}
3. D: {John Adams, John Kennedy, Richard Nixon, Harry Truman}; R: {−16, −23, −5, −11}
4. D: {Chamber, Testament, Rainmaker, Street Lawyer}; R: $\left\{\pi, 2\pi, \frac{1}{2}, 6\right\}$
5. D: {St. Louis, Denver, Green Bay, Dallas}; R: $\left\{\frac{1}{2}, -\frac{3}{4}, \frac{7}{8}, -\frac{4}{5}\right\}$
6. D: {2, 3, 4, 5, 6}; R: {3, 5, 7, 9, 11}
7. D: {1}; R: {2, 3, 4, 5, 6}
8. D: $\left\{0.2, 0.4, \frac{1}{2}, \frac{3}{4}\right\}$; R: {4, 5, 6}
9. D: {−3, −2, −1, 4, 5}; R: {3, 4, 5, 6}
10. D: {−3, −2, 1, 5, 7}; R: {4}
11. (a) −2; (b) 4; (c) $-\frac{20}{9}$
12. (a) 9; (b) −1; (c) 3
13. (a) −62; (b) −2; (c) −1.519

< Objective 1 >

Find the domain, D, and range, R, of each relation.

1. $A = \{$(Colorado, 21), (Edmonton, 5), (Calgary, 18), (Vancouver, 17)$\}$

2. $B = \{$(Eric Lindros, 88), (Mark Recchi, 8), (John LeClair, 10), (Keith Primeau, 25)$\}$

3. $C = \{$(John Adams, −16), (John Kennedy, −23), (Richard Nixon, −5), (Harry Truman, −11)$\}$

4. $G = \left\{(\text{Chamber}, \pi), (\text{Testament}, 2\pi), \left(\text{Rainmaker}, \frac{1}{2}\right), (\text{Street Lawyer}, 6)\right\}$

5. $F = \left\{\left(\text{St. Louis}, \frac{1}{2}\right), \left(\text{Denver}, -\frac{3}{4}\right), \left(\text{Green Bay}, \frac{7}{8}\right), \left(\text{Dallas}, -\frac{4}{5}\right)\right\}$

6. $\{(2, 3), (3, 5), (4, 7), (5, 9), (6, 11)\}$

7. $\{(1, 2), (1, 3), (1, 4), (1, 5), (1, 6)\}$

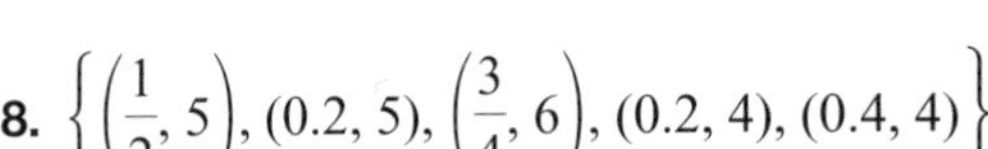

8. $\left\{\left(\frac{1}{2}, 5\right), (0.2, 5), \left(\frac{3}{4}, 6\right), (0.2, 4), (0.4, 4)\right\}$

9. $\{(-1, 3), (-2, 4), (-3, 5), (4, 4), (5, 6)\}$

10. $\{(-2, 4), (1, 4), (-3, 4), (5, 4), (7, 4)\}$

< Objective 2 >

Evaluate each function for the value specified.

11. $f(x) = x^2 - x - 2$; find **(a)** $f(0)$, **(b)** $f(-2)$, and **(c)** $f\left(\frac{1}{3}\right)$.

12. $f(x) = 3x^2 + x - 1$; find **(a)** $f(-2)$, **(b)** $f(0)$, and **(c)** $f(1)$.

13. $f(x) = x^3 - 2x^2 + 5x - 2$; find **(a)** $f(-3)$, **(b)** $f(0)$, and **(c)** $f(0.1)$.

14. $f(x) = -3x^3 + 2x^2 - 5x + 3$; find **(a)** $f(-2)$, **(b)** $f(0)$, and **(c)** $f(3)$.

15. $f(x) = 2x^3 + 4x^2 + 5x + 2$; find **(a)** $f(-1)$, **(b)** $f(0)$, and **(c)** $f\left(\frac{1}{2}\right)$.

16. $f(x) = -x^3 + 2x^2 - 7x + 9$; find **(a)** $f(-2)$, **(b)** $f(0)$, and **(c)** $f(2)$.

Determine which of the relations are also functions.

17. $\{(1, 6), (2, 8), (3, 9)\}$

18. $\{(2, 3), (3, 4), (5, 9)\}$

19. $\{(-1, 4), (-2, 5), (-3, 7)\}$

20. $\{(-2, 1), (-3, 4), (-4, 6)\}$

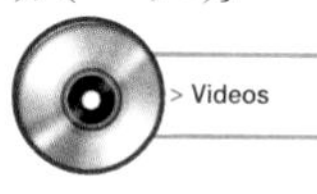

21. $\{(1, 3), (1, 2), (1, 1)\}$

22. $\{(2, 4), (2, 5), (3, 6)\}$

23. $\{(-1, 1), (2, 1), (2, 3)\}$

< Objective 3 >

Graph the functions.

24. $f(x) = 3x + 7$

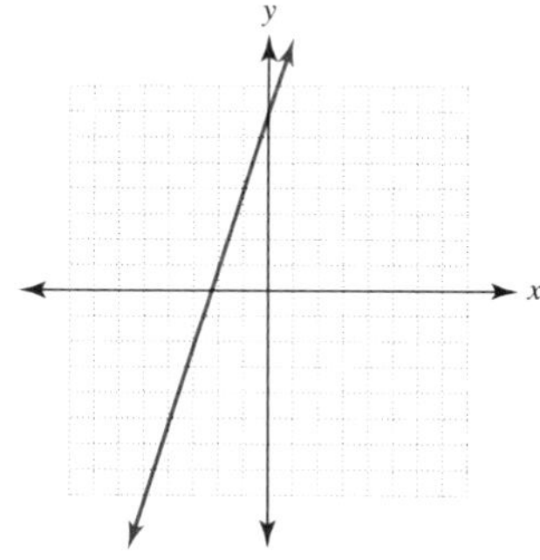

25. $f(x) = -2x + 7$

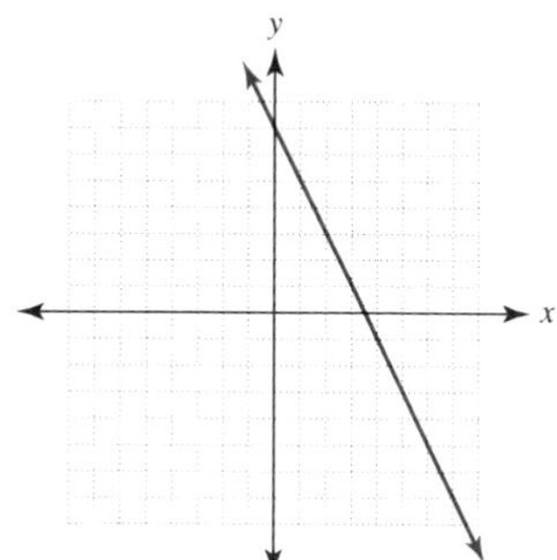

26. $f(x) = -3x + 8$

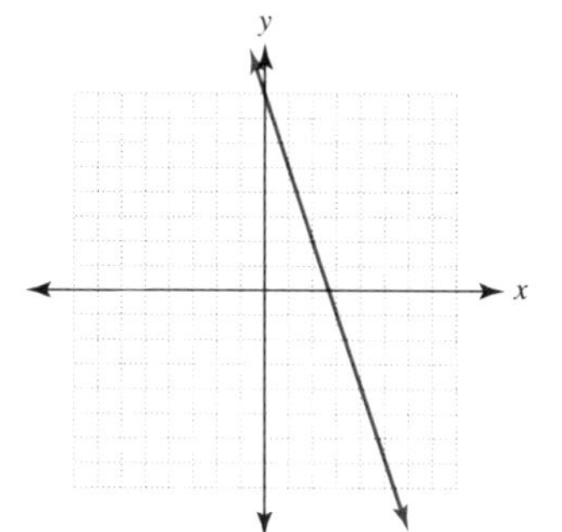

27. $f(x) = -x - 1$

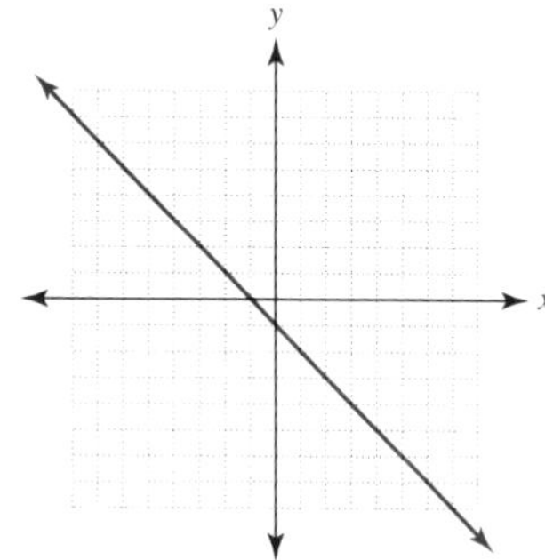

Answers

14. (a) 45; (b) 3; (c) −75

15. (a) −1; (b) 2; (c) $\frac{23}{4}$

16. (a) 39; (b) 9; (c) −5

17. Function

18. Function

19. Function

20. Function

21. Not a function

22. Not a function

23. Not a function

24. See exercise

25. See exercise

26. See exercise

27. See exercise

Answers

28. See exercise

29. A: (−4, 1), B: (1, −4)

30. A: (0, 5), B: (3, 0)

31. A: (2, 0), B: (6, 4)

32. A: (3, 3), B: (−3, −3)

33. A: (3, 6), B: (3, 0)

34. A: (6, 4), B: (−5, 2)

28. $f(x) = -2x - 5$

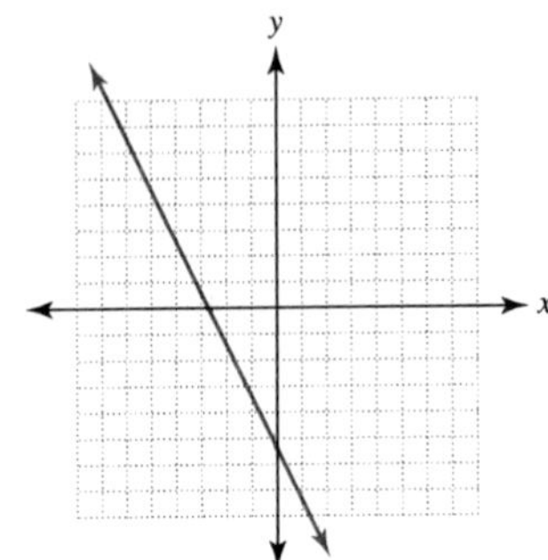

< Objective 4 >

Find the coordinates of the labeled points. Assume that each small square is a 1-unit square.

29.

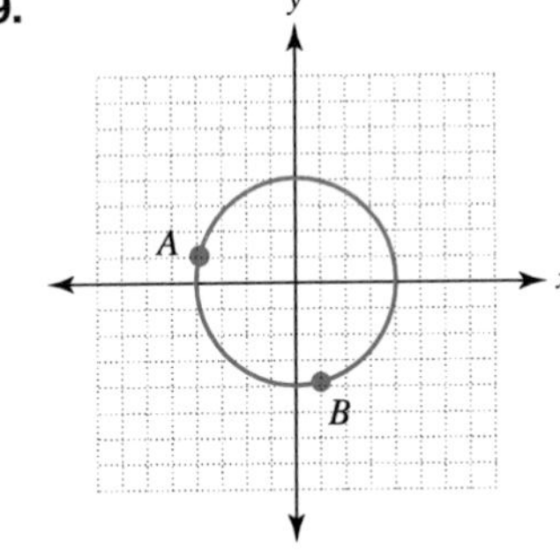

30.

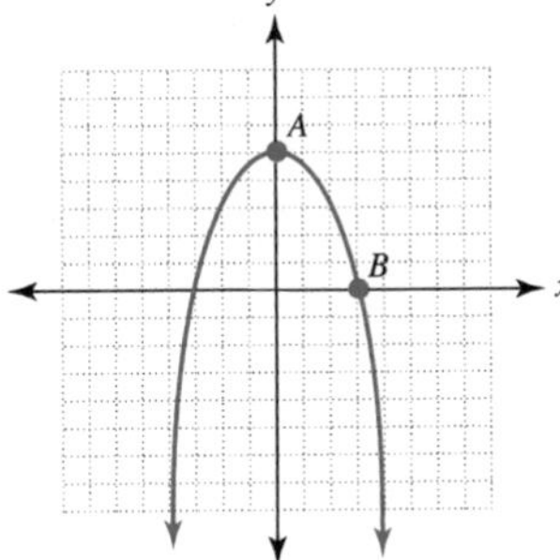

31.

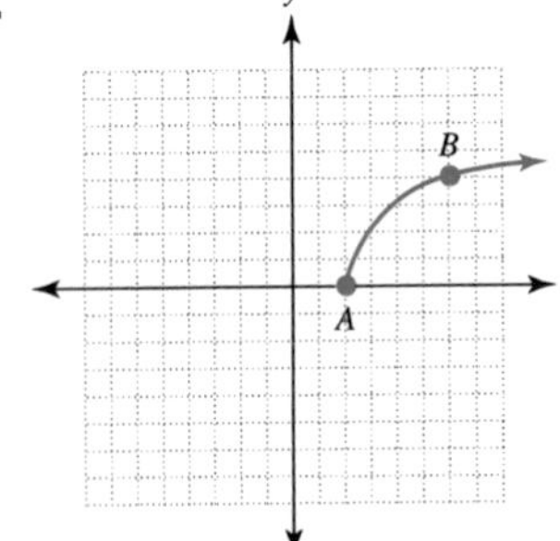

32.

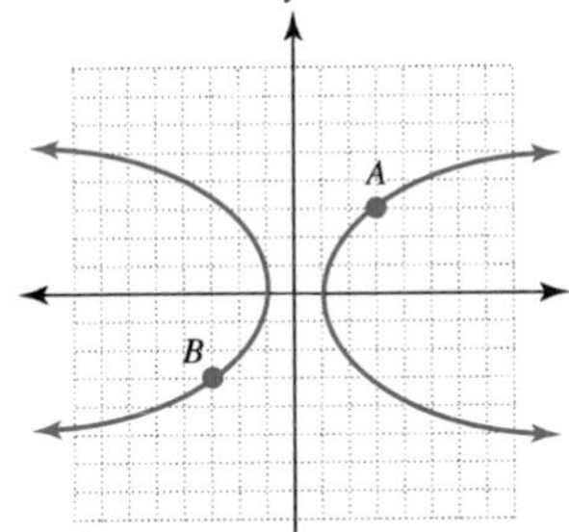

33.

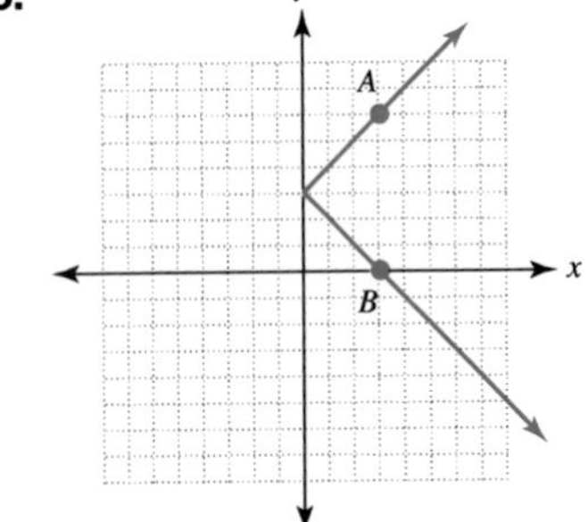

34.

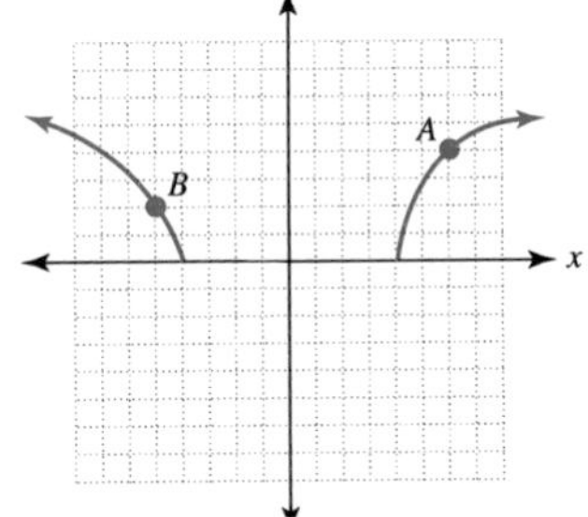

Use the graph of the function to find each of the following values: **(a)** $f(1)$, **(b)** $f(-1)$, **(c)** $f(0)$, **(d)** $f(3)$, *and* **(e)** $f(-2)$.

35.

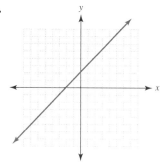

36.

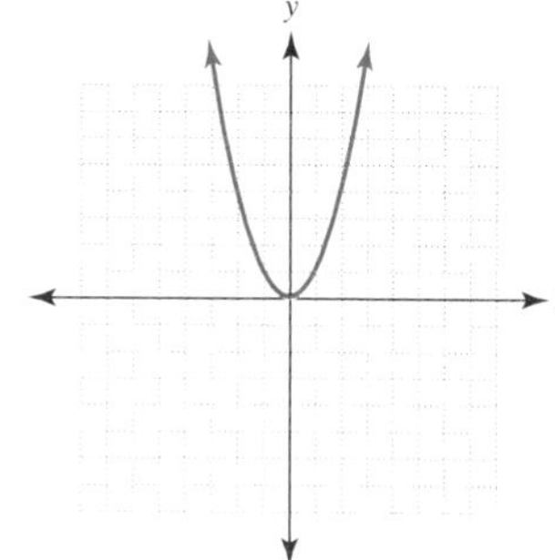

37.

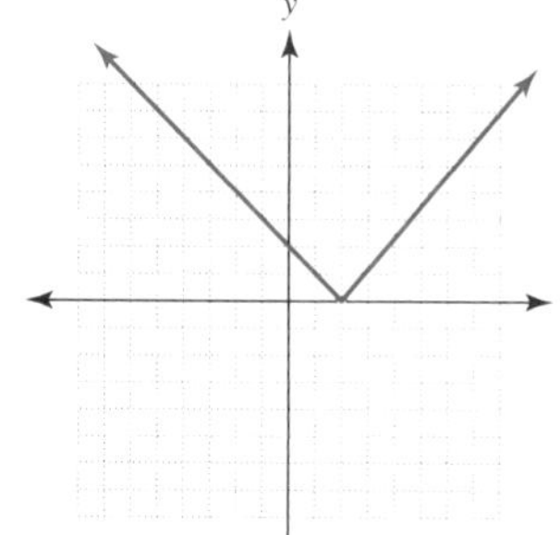

38.

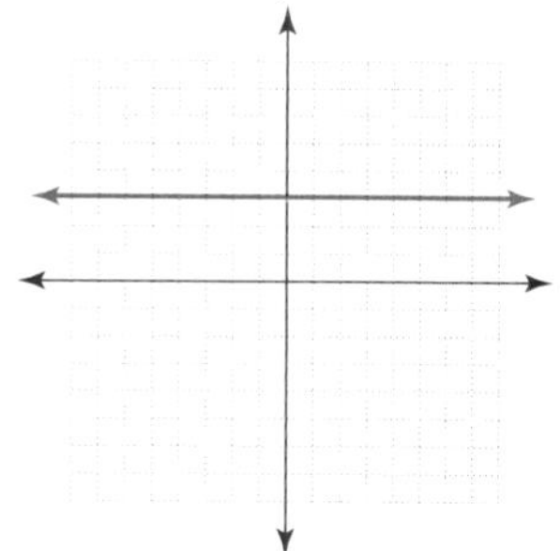

Use the graph of $f(x)$ *to find all values of x such that* **(a)** $f(x) = -1$, **(b)** $f(x) = 0$, *and* **(c)** $f(x) = 2$.

39.

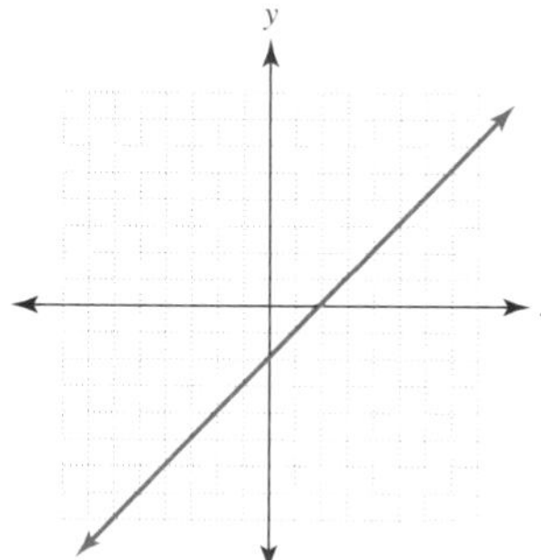

40.

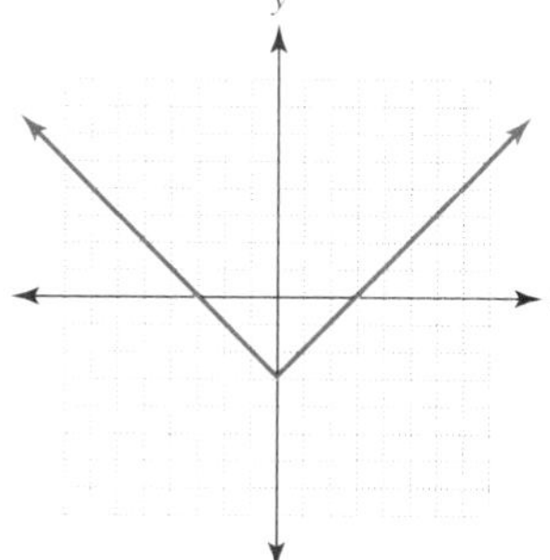

41.

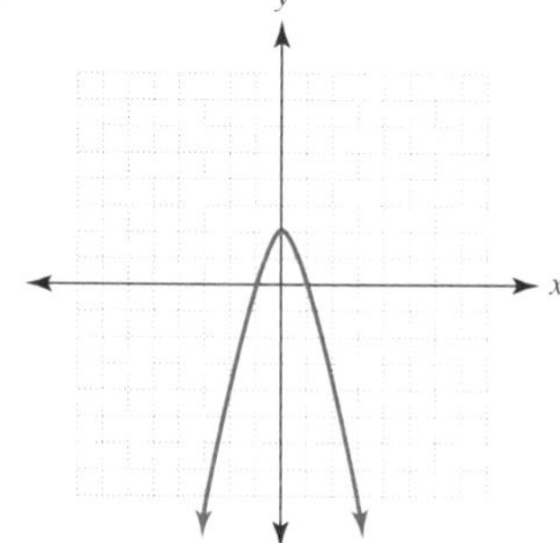

42.

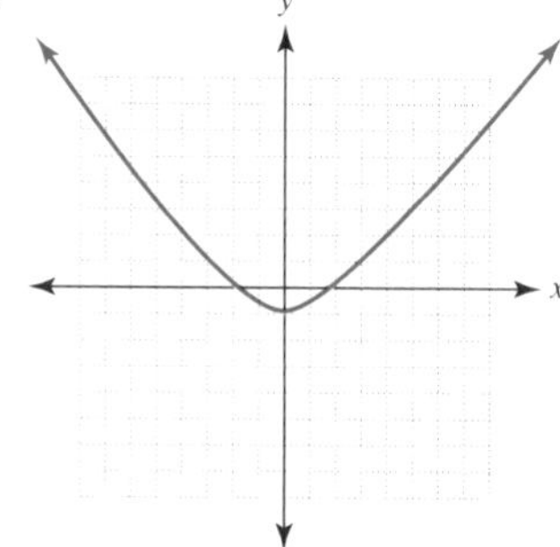

Answers

35. (a) 3; (b) 1; (c) 2; (d) 5; (e) 0

36. (a) 1; (b) 1; (c) 0; (d) 9; (e) 4

37. (a) 1; (b) 3; (c) 2; (d) 1; (e) 4

38. (a) 3; (b) 3; (c) 3; (d) 3; (e) 3

39. (a) 1; (b) 2; (c) 4

40. (a) −2, 2; (b) −3, 3; (c) −5, 5

41. (a) −1.5, 1.5; (b) 1, −1; (c) 0

42. (a) 0; (b) −2, 2; (c) −4, 4

Answers

43. x-int: none; y-int: (0, 3)

44. x-int: (−6, 0) and (6, 0); y-int: (0, −6) and (0, 6)

45. Function; D: {−2, −1, 0, 1, 2, 3}; R: {−1, 0, 1, 2, 3, 4}

46. Not a function; D: {−5, −3, 1, 3, 5}; R: {−2, 1, 2, 3, 4}

47. Function; D: $\{x \mid -4 \le x \le 3\}$; R: {−2}

48. Not a function; D: {2}; R: $\{y \mid -1 \le y \le 7\}$

49. Not a function; D: $\{x \mid -3 \le x \le 3\}$; R: $\{y \mid -3 \le y \le 4\}$

50. Function; D: $\{x \mid -5 \le x \le 5\}$; R: $\{y \mid -3 \le y \le 5\}$

Find the x- and y-intercepts from the graph.

43.

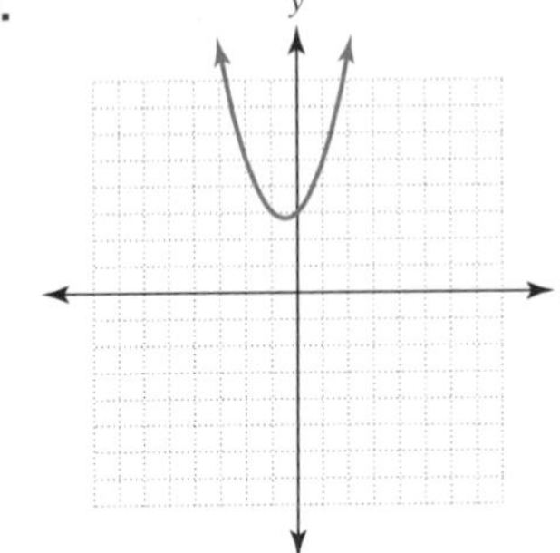

44.

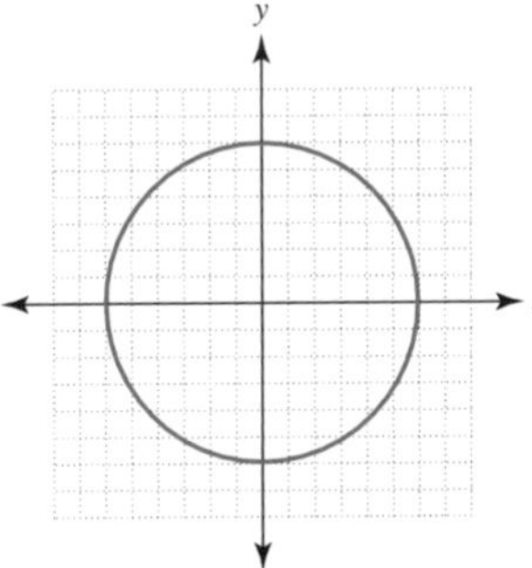

Determine whether the relation is a function. Also provide the domain and the range.

45.

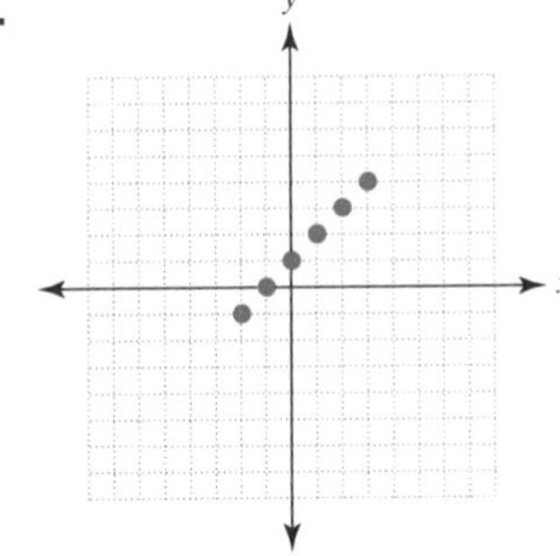

46.

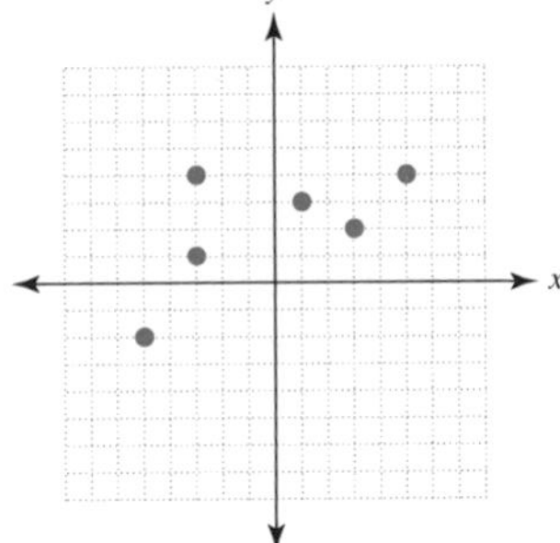

> Videos

47.

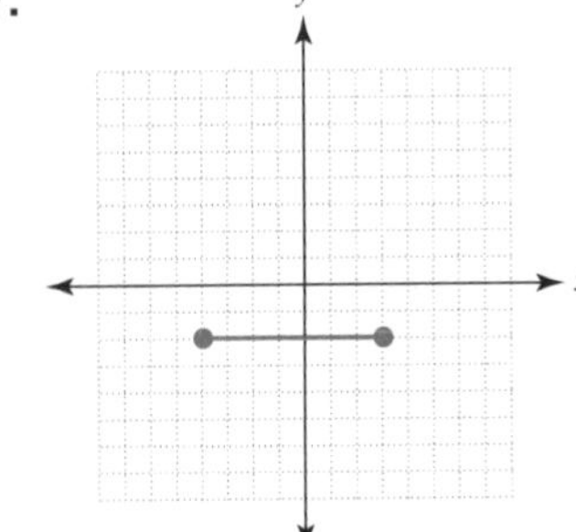

48.

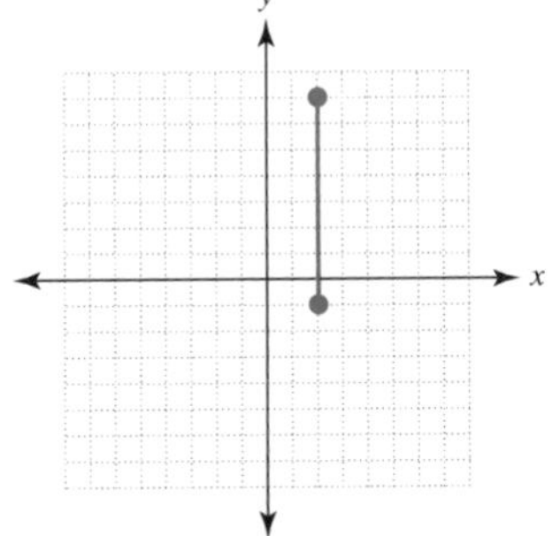

49.

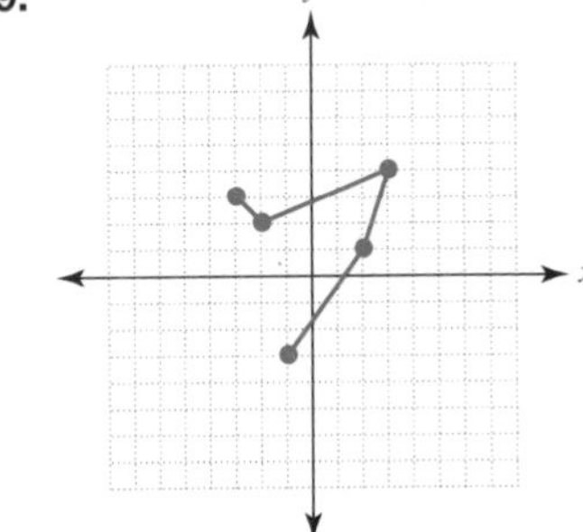

50.

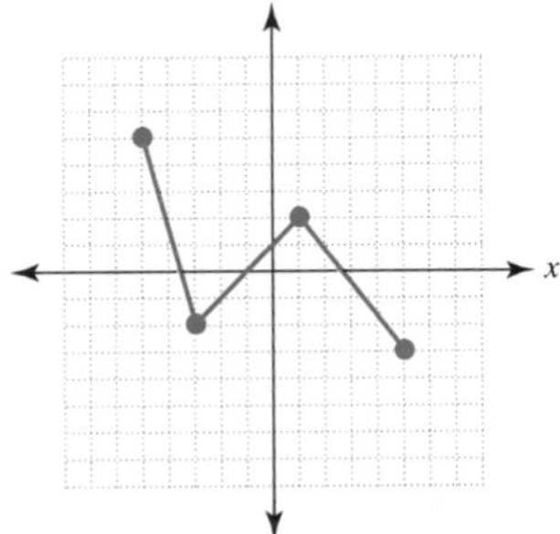

51.

52.

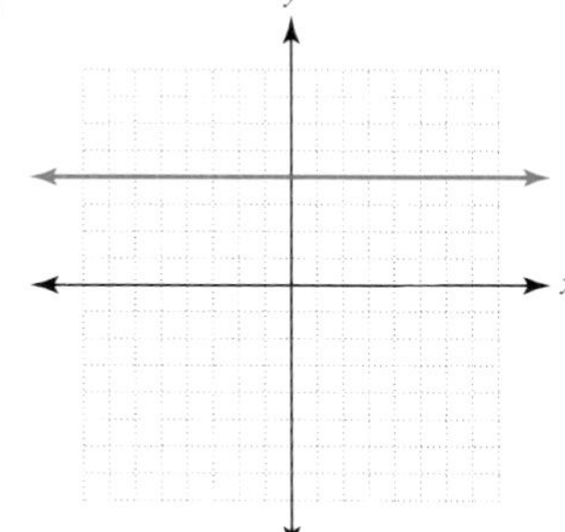

53.

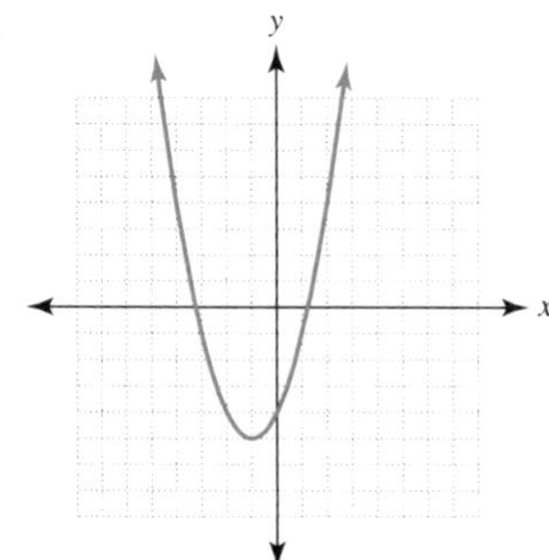

54.

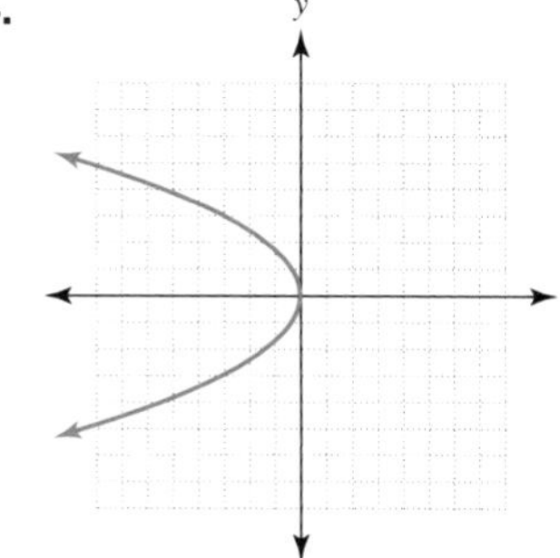

55.

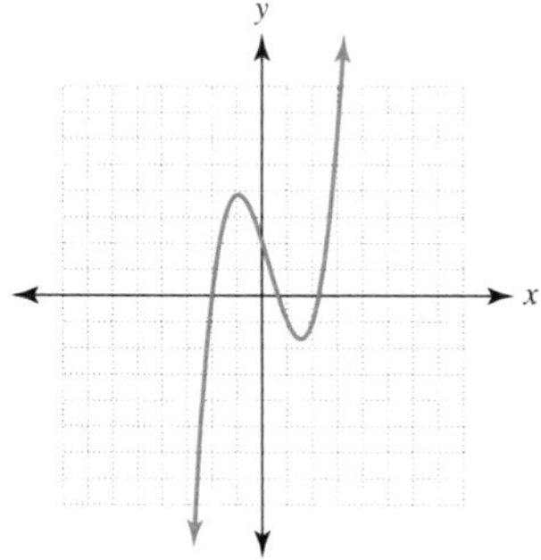

> Videos

56.

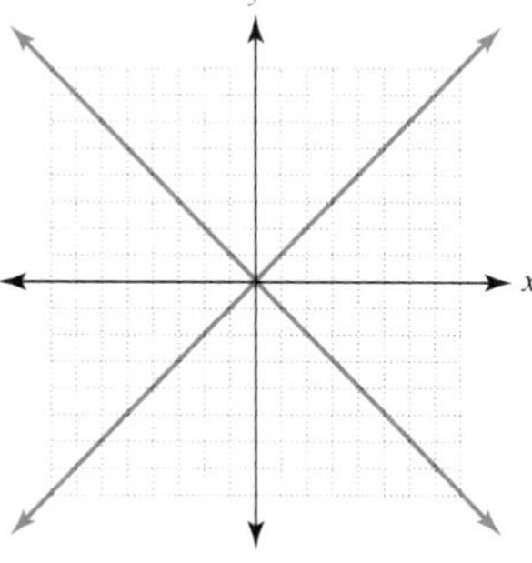

57.

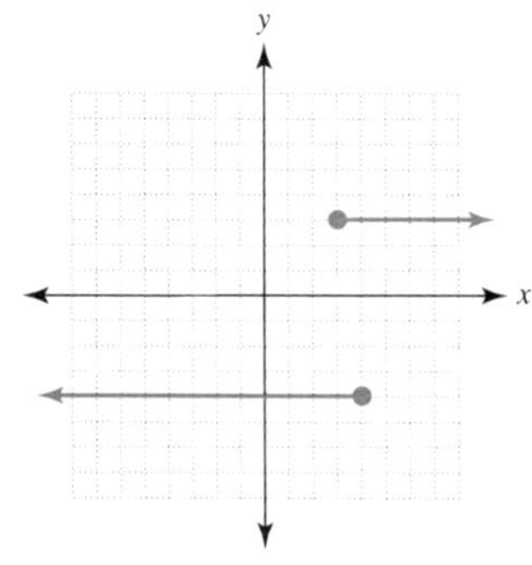

Answers

51. Not a function; D: $\{-3\}$; R: $\mathbb{R}$

52. Function; D: $\mathbb{R}$; R: $\{4\}$

53. Function; D: $\mathbb{R}$; R: $\{y \mid y \geq -5\}$

54. Not a function; D: $\{x \mid x \leq 0\}$; R: $\mathbb{R}$

55. Function; D: $\mathbb{R}$; R: $\mathbb{R}$

56. Not a function; D: $\mathbb{R}$; R: $\mathbb{R}$

57. Not a function; D: $\mathbb{R}$; R: $\{-4, 3\}$

Answers

58. Independent: length of call; dependent: amount of bill

59. Independent: time in air; dependent: height of ball

60. Independent: length of time; dependent: amount of penalty

61. Independent: number of credits; dependent: time to graduate

62. Independent: length of winter; dependent: amount of snowfall

63. $1,275

64. $10,500

65. (a) $4.12; (b) $2.73

< Objective 5 >

Identify which variable is dependent and which is independent.

58. The amount of a phone bill and the length of the call.

59. The height of a ball thrown in the air and the time in the air.

60. The amount of penalty on an unpaid tax bill and the length of the time unpaid.

61. The length of time needed to graduate from college and the number of credits taken per semester.

62. The amount of snowfall in Boston and the length of the winter.

Basic Skills | **Advanced Skills** | Vocational-Technical Applications | Calculator/Computer | Above and Beyond

Solve the following application problems.

63. Business and Finance The marketing department of a company has determined that the profit for selling x units of a product is approximated by the function

$$f(x) = 50\sqrt{x} - 0.25x - 600$$

Find the profit in selling 2,500 units.

64. Business and Finance The inventor of a new product believes that the cost of producing the product is given by the function

$$C(x) = 1.75x + 7,000$$

What would be the cost of producing 2,000 units of the product?

65. Business and Finance A phone company has two different rates for calls made at different times of the day. These rates are given by the following function

$$C(x) = \begin{cases} 24x + 33 & \text{between 5 P.M. and 11 P.M.} \\ 36x + 52 & \text{between 8 A.M. and 5 P.M.} \end{cases}$$

when x is the number of minutes of a call and C is the cost of a call in cents.

(a) What is the cost of a 10-minute call at 10:00 A.M.?

(b) What is the cost of a 10-minute call at 10:00 P.M.?

66. **Statistics** The number of accidents in 1 month involving drivers x years of age can be approximated by the function

$$f(x) = 2x^2 - 125x + 3{,}000$$

Find the number of accidents in 1 month that involved **(a)** 17-year-olds and **(b)** 25-year-olds.

67. **Science and Medicine** The distance d (in feet) that a car will skid on a certain road surface after the brakes are applied is a function of the car's velocity v [in miles per hour (mi/h)]. The function can be approximated by

$$d = f(v) = 0.017v^2$$

How far will the car skid if the brakes are applied at **(a)** 55 mi/h? **(b)** 70 mi/h?

68. **Science and Medicine** An object is thrown upward with an initial velocity of 128 ft/s. Its height h after t seconds is given by the function

$$h(t) = -16t^2 + 128t$$

What is the height of the object at **(a)** 2 s? **(b)** 4 s? **(c)** 6 s?

69. The cost of a taxi ride is shown in the following graph:

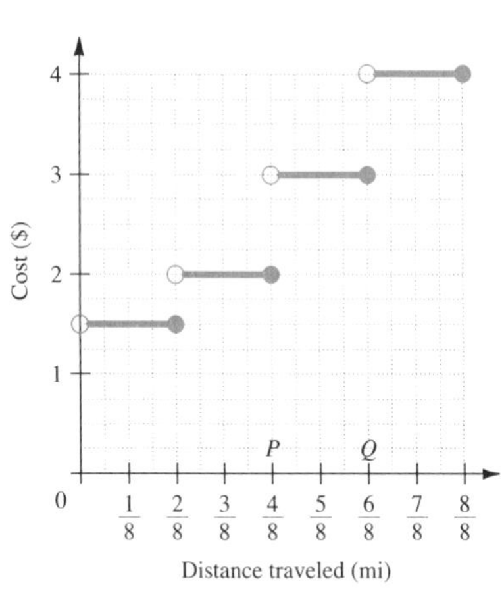

(a) How much does it cost to ride the taxi for $\frac{3}{4}$ of a mile?

(b) If the cost of the taxi ride is \$2, how far was the ride?

(c) What is the cost of the ride between points P and Q?

Answers

66. (a) 1,453 accidents; (b) 1,125 accidents

67. (a) 51.425 ft; (b) 83.3 ft

68. (a) 192 ft; (b) 256 ft; (c) 192 ft

69. (a) \$3; (b) $\frac{1}{4}$ mi < distance $\le \frac{1}{2}$ mi; (c) \$3.00

Answers

70. (a) $P(t) = t/6$; (b) pitch = 5

71. (a) $f(x) = 4x$; (b) 20 mg; (c) 362.5 kg

72. (a) $F(a) = 90a + 12{,}000$; (b) \$174,000

73. (a) 107; (b) 57; (c) 379

74. (a) −1,107; (b) 621; (c) 3,309

75. (a) 406; (b) 399; (c) 5,226

76. (a) −80,029; (b) −10,381; (c) 719

Basic Skills | Advanced Skills | **Vocational-Technical Applications** | Calculator/Computer | Above and Beyond

70. Manufacturing Technology The pitch of a 6-inch gear is the number of teeth divided by 6.

(a) Write a function to describe this relationship. Let t be the number of teeth.

(b) What is the pitch of a 6-inch gear with 30 teeth?

71. Allied Health Dimercaprol (BAL) is used to treat arsenic poisoning in mammals. The recommended dose is 4 milligrams (mg) per kilogram (kg) of the animal's weight.

(a) Write a function describing the relationship between the recommended dose, in milligrams, and the animal's weight, x, in kilograms.

(b) How much BAL must be administered to a 5-kg cat?

(c) What size cow requires a 1,450-mg dose of BAL?

72. Construction The cost of building a house is \$90 per square foot plus \$12,000 for the foundation.

(a) Create a function to represent the cost of building a house of a square feet.

(b) What is the cost of a house that is 1,800 square feet?

Basic Skills | Advanced Skills | Vocational-Technical Applications | **Calculator/Computer** | Above and Beyond

Your graphing calculator can be used to evaluate a function for a specific value of x. If $f(x) = 3x^2 - 7$, and you wish to find $f(-3)$,

1. Use the [Y =] key to enter $Y_1 = 3x^2 - 7$.
2. Select [TABLE] ([2nd] [GRAPH]), and choose −3 for x.
3. The table will give you a value of 20 for Y_1.

Use that technique to evaluate the functions in exercises 73 to 76.

73. $f(x) = 3x^2 - 5x + 7$; find **(a)** $f(-5)$, **(b)** $f(5)$, and **(c)** $f(12)$.

74. $f(x) = 4x^3 - 7x^2 + 9$; find **(a)** $f(-6)$, **(b)** $f(6)$, and **(c)** $f(10)$.

75. $f(x) = 3x^4 - 6x^3 + 2x^2 - 17$; find **(a)** $f(-3)$, **(b)** $f(4)$, and **(c)** $f(7)$.

76. $f(x) = 5x^7 + 8x^4 - 9x^2 - 13$; find **(a)** $f(-4)$, **(b)** $f(-3)$, and **(c)** $f(2)$.

Basic Skills | Advanced Skills | Vocational-Technical Applications | Calculator/Computer | Above and Beyond

77. The following table shows the average hourly earnings for blue collar workers from 1947 to 1993. These figures are given in "real" wages, which means that the *purchasing power* of the money is given rather than the actual dollar amount. In other words, the amount earned for 1947 is not the actual amount listed here; in fact, it was much lower. The amount you see here is the amount in dollars that 1947 earnings could buy in 1947 compared to what 1993 wages could buy in 1993.

Year	Average Hourly Earnings (in 1993 dollars)
1947	$ 6.75
1967	10.67
1973	12.06
1979	12.03
1982	11.61
1989	11.26
1991	10.95
1993	10.83

Make a Cartesian coordinate graph of this data, using the year as the domain and the hourly earnings as the range. You will have to decide how to set up the axes so that the data all fit on the graph nicely. (*Hint:* Do not start the year at 0!) In complete sentences, answer the following questions: What are the trends that you notice from reading the table? What additional information does the graph show? Is this relation a function? Why or why not?

78. Your friend Sam Weatherby is a salesperson and has just been offered two new jobs, one for $280 a month plus 9% of the amount of all his sales over $20,000. The second job offer is $280 a month plus 3% of the amount of his sales.

Sam and his spouse are about to have a child, and he feels that he has to make $4,000 a month just to make ends meet. He has called you to ask for your help in deciding which job to take. To help him picture his options, graph both offers on the same graph, and add a graph of the income of $4,000.

Next, write an explanation that answers these questions: How much does he have to sell in each position to earn $4,000? When is the first offer better? When is the second better? What sales would he have made to make less than $3,500 in each position? Which job should he take?

Answers

77. Above and Beyond

78. Above and Beyond

Answers

1. D: {Colorado, Edmonton, Calgary, Vancouver}; R: $\{21, 5, 18, 17\}$

3. D: {John Adams, John Kennedy, Richard Nixon, Harry Truman}; R: $\{-16, -23, -5, -11\}$

5. D: {St. Louis, Denver, Green Bay, Dallas}; R: $\left\{\frac{1}{2}, -\frac{3}{4}, \frac{7}{8}, -\frac{4}{5}\right\}$

7. D: $\{1\}$; R: $\{2, 3, 4, 5, 6\}$ **9.** D: $\{-3, -2, -1, 4, 5\}$; R: $\{3, 4, 5, 6\}$

11. **(a)** -2; **(b)** 4; **(c)** $-\frac{20}{9}$ **13.** **(a)** -62; **(b)** -2; **(c)** -1.519

15. **(a)** -1; **(b)** 2; **(c)** $\frac{23}{4}$ **17.** Function **19.** Function

21. Not a function **23.** Not a function

25.

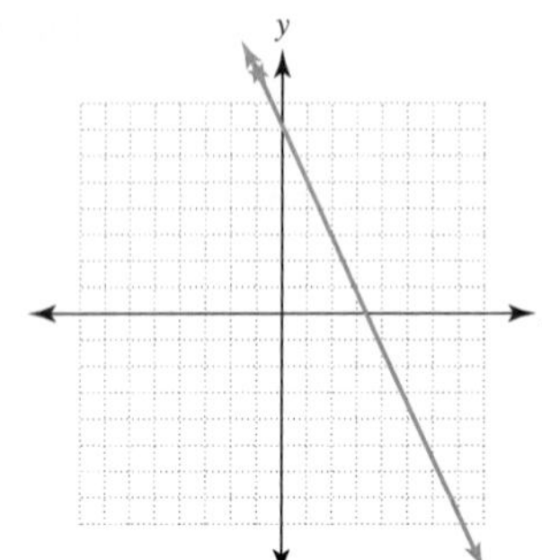

27.

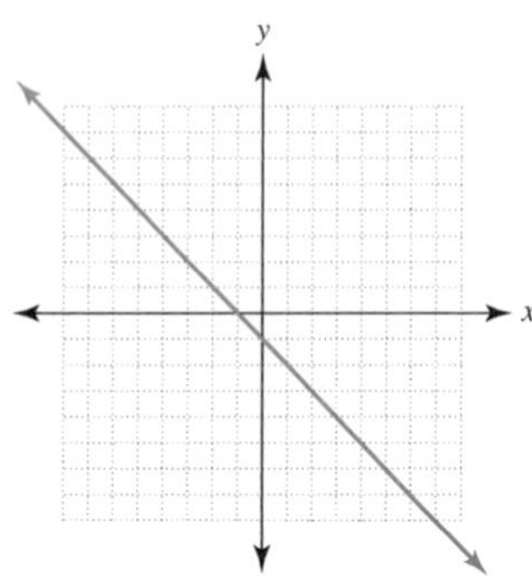

29. A: $(-4, 1)$, B: $(1, -4)$ **31.** A: $(2, 0)$, B: $(6, 4)$ **33.** A: $(3, 6)$, B: $(3, 0)$
35. **(a)** 3; **(b)** 1; **(c)** 2; **(d)** 5; **(e)** 0 **37.** **(a)** 1; **(b)** 3; **(c)** 2; **(d)** 1; **(e)** 4
39. **(a)** 1; **(b)** 2; **(c)** 4 **41.** **(a)** $-1.5, 1.5$; **(b)** $1, -1$; **(c)** 0
43. x-int: none; y-int: $(0, 3)$ **45.** Function; D: $\{-2, -1, 0, 1, 2, 3\}$; R: $\{-1, 0, 1, 2, 3, 4\}$ **47.** Function; D: $\{x | -4 \le x \le 3\}$; R: $\{-2\}$
49. Not a function; D: $\{x | -3 \le x \le 3\}$; R: $\{y | -3 \le y \le 4\}$
51. Not a function; D: $\{-3\}$; R: $\mathbb{R}$ **53.** Function; D: $\mathbb{R}$; R: $\{y | y \ge -5\}$
55. Function; D: $\mathbb{R}$; R: $\mathbb{R}$ **57.** Not a function; D: $\mathbb{R}$; R: $\{-4, 3\}$
59. Independent: time in air; dependent: height of ball
61. Independent: number of credits; dependent: time to graduate
63. \$1,275 **65.** **(a)** \$4.12; **(b)** \$2.73 **67.** **(a)** 51.425 ft; **(b)** 83.3 ft
69. **(a)** \$3; **(b)** $\frac{1}{4}$ mi < distance $\le \frac{1}{2}$ mi; **(c)** \$3.00
71. **(a)** $f(x) = 4x$; **(b)** 20 mg; **(c)** 362.5 kg **73.** **(a)** 107; **(b)** 57; **(c)** 379
75. **(a)** 406; **(b)** 399; **(c)** 5,226 **77.** Above and Beyond

3.3 The Slope of a Line

< 3.3 Objectives >

1 > Find the slope of a line

2 > Find the slopes of parallel and perpendicular lines

3 > Graph a line given a point and a slope

On the coordinate system shown, plot a point.

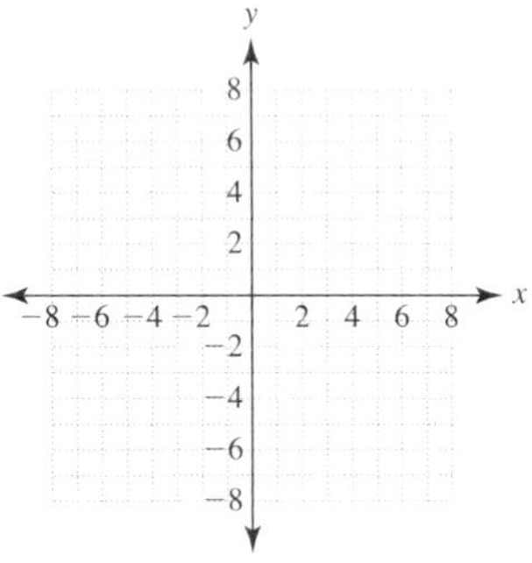

How many different lines can you draw through that point? Hundreds? Thousands? Millions? Actually, there is no limit to the number of different lines that pass through that point.

Now, plot a second point on the coordinate system. How many different lines can you draw through the pair of points? Only one! The two points were enough to define the line.

In Section 3.4, we will see how we can find the equation of a line if we are given two of its points. The first part of finding that equation is finding the **slope** of the line, which is a way of describing the steepness of a line. You may have noticed that lines often have different slopes. How could we define the slope of a line?

NOTES

The slope of a line is like the incline (or decline) of a hill.

When a number is written after and below a variable, it is called a **subscript.**

First, we choose any two distinct points on the line, say, P with coordinates (x_1, y_1) and Q with coordinates (x_2, y_2). As we move along the line from P to Q, the x-value, or coordinate, changes from x_1 to x_2. That change in x, also called the **horizontal change,** is $x_2 - x_1$. Similarly, as we move from P to Q, the corresponding change in y, called the **vertical change,** is $y_2 - y_1$. The *slope* is then defined as the ratio of the vertical change to the horizontal change. This is often described as the rate of change. The letter m is used to represent the slope, which we now define.

Definition

Slope of a Line

The **slope** of a line through two distinct points $P(x_1, y_1)$ and $Q(x_2, y_2)$ is given by

$$m = \frac{\text{change in } y}{\text{change in } x} = \frac{y_2 - y_1}{x_2 - x_1}$$

when $x_1 \neq x_2$.

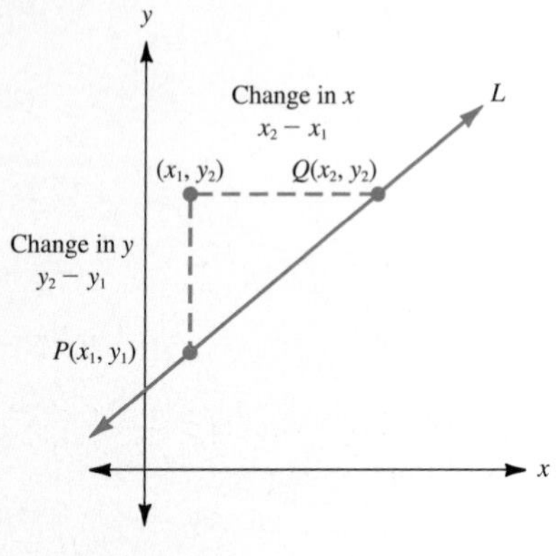

The difference $x_2 - x_1$ is often called the **run.** The difference $y_2 - y_1$ is the **rise.** So the slope can be thought of as "rise over run."

Note that $x_1 \neq x_2$ or $x_2 - x_1 \neq 0$ ensures that the denominator is nonzero, so that the slope is defined. It also means the line cannot be vertical.

We will look at some examples using the definition.

Example 1 Finding the Slope Through Two Points

< Objective 1 >

Find the slope of the line through the points $(-3, 2)$ and $(3, 5)$.

Let $(x_1, y_1) = (-3, 2)$ and $(x_2, y_2) = (3, 5)$. From the definition we have

$$m = \frac{\text{change in } y\text{-values}}{\text{change in } x\text{-values}} = \frac{5 - 2}{3 - (-3)} = \frac{3}{6} = \frac{1}{2}$$

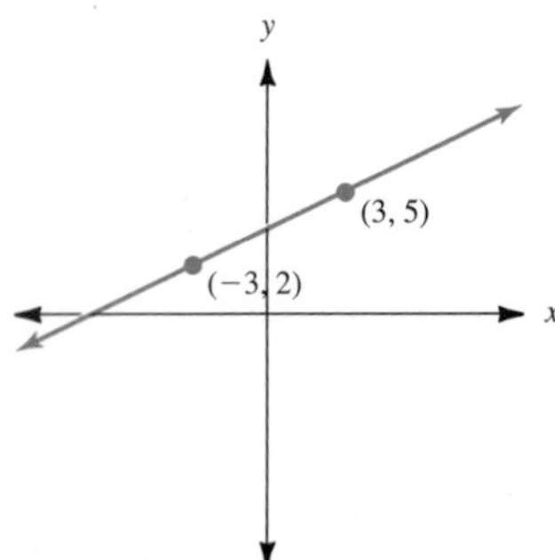

Note that if the pairs are reversed, so that

$(x_1, y_1) = (3, 5)$ and $(x_2, y_2) = (-3, 2)$

then we have

$$m = \frac{\text{change in } y\text{-values}}{\text{change in } x\text{-values}} = \frac{2 - 5}{-3 - 3} = \frac{-3}{-6} = \frac{1}{2}$$

The slope in either case is the same.

The work in Example 1 suggests that no matter which point is chosen as (x_1, y_1) or (x_2, y_2), the slope formula will give the same result. Simply stay with your choice once it is made, and use the same order of subtraction in the numerator and the denominator.

Also notice that since the slope is $\frac{1}{2}$, the *rate of change* is a vertical change of 1 unit for every horizontal change of 2 units.

Check Yourself 1

Find the slope of the line through the points (−2, −1) and (1, 1).

The slope indicates both the direction of a line and its steepness. We will compare the steepness of the lines in Examples 1, 2, and 3.

Example 2 Finding the Slope

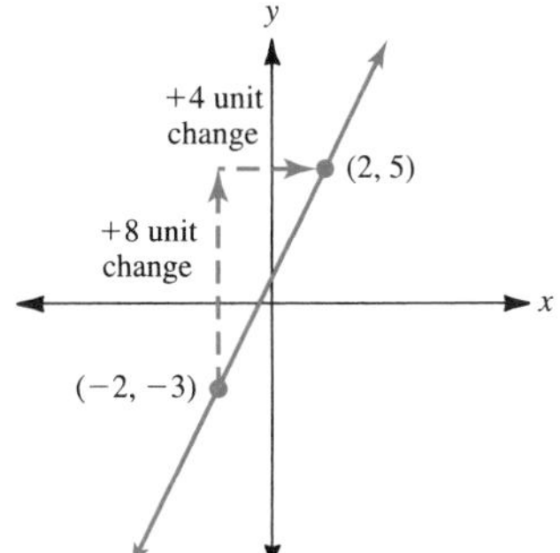

Find the slope of the line through (−2, −3) and (2, 5).

Again, from the definition,

$$m = \frac{5 - (-3)}{2 - (-2)} = \frac{8}{4} = 2$$

Compare the lines in Examples 1 and 2. In Example 1 the line has slope $\frac{1}{2}$. The slope here is 2. Now look at the two lines. Do you see the idea of slope as measuring steepness? The greater the absolute value of the slope, the steeper the line.

Check Yourself 2

Find the slope of the line through the points (−1, 2) and (2, 7). Draw a sketch of this line and the line in the Check Yourself 1 exercise on the same coordinate axes. Compare the lines and the two slopes.

The sign of the slope indicates in which direction the line tilts, as Example 3 illustrates.

Example 3 Finding the Slope

Find the slope of the line through the points (−1, 2) and (4, −3).

We see that

$$m = \frac{-3 - 2}{4 - (-1)} = \frac{-5}{5} = -1$$

y
(−1, 2)
x
−5 unit change
(4, −3)
+5 unit change

Now the slope is negative.

Comparing this with Examples 1 and 2, we see that

(a) In Examples 1 and 2, the lines were rising from left to right, and the slope was **positive.** The y-value increases from left to right. If you were walking along the line from left to right, you would be walking uphill.

(b) In Example 3, the line is falling from left to right, and the slope is **negative.** The y-value decreases from left to right. If you were walking along the line from left to right, you would be walking downhill.

Check Yourself 3

Find the slope of the line through the points (−2, 5) and (4, −1).

We continue by looking at the slopes of lines in two particular cases.

Example 4 Finding the Slope of a Horizontal Line

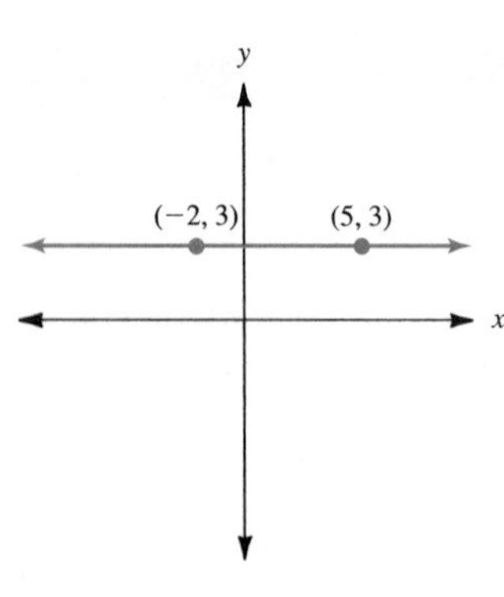

Find the slope of the line through (−2, 3) and (5, 3).

$$m = \frac{3 - 3}{5 - (-2)} = \frac{0}{7} = 0$$

The slope of the line is 0. Note that the line is parallel to the x-axis and $y_2 - y_1 = 0$. *The slope of any horizontal line will be* 0. The y-value does not change.

Check Yourself 4

Find the slope of the line through the points (−2, −4) and (3, −4).

Example 5 Finding the Slope of a Vertical Line

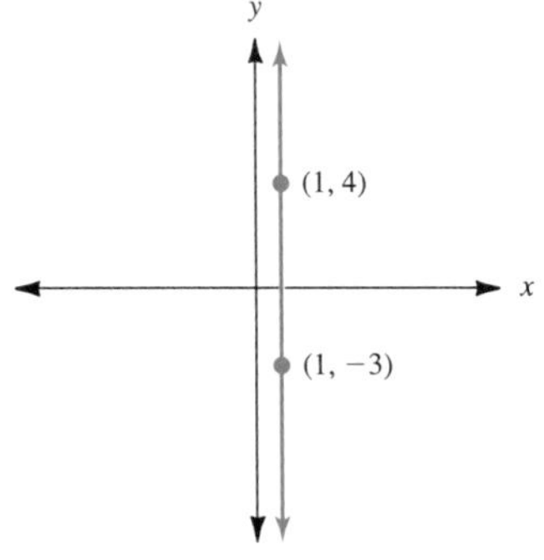

Find the slope of the line through the points (1, −3) and (1, 4).

$$m = \frac{4 - (-3)}{1 - 1} = \frac{7}{0}, \quad \text{which is undefined.}$$

Here the line is parallel to the *y*-axis, and $x_2 - x_1$ (the denominator of the slope formula) is 0. Because division by 0 is undefined, we say that the slope is **undefined,** as will be the case for *any vertical line.*

Be very careful not to confuse a slope of 0 (in the case of a horizontal line) with an undefined slope (in the case of a vertical line). From the vertical line test in Section 3.2, we know that horizontal lines are functions but vertical lines are not. In fact, any line with a slope of any value (not undefined) will be a function.

Check Yourself 5

Find the slope of the line through the points (2, −3) and (2, 7).

Here is a summary of our work in Examples 1 to 5.

1. If the slope of a line is *positive,* the line is rising from left to right.

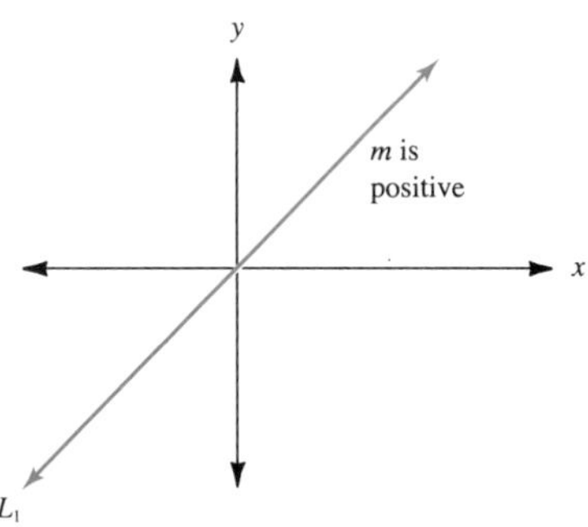

2. If the slope of a line is *negative,* the line is falling from left to right.

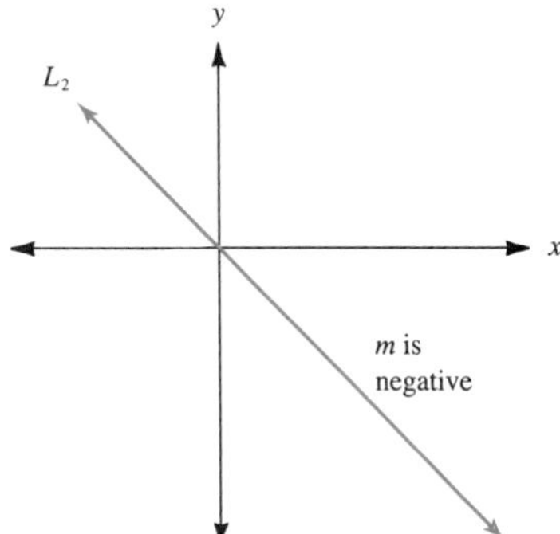

3. If the slope of a line is 0, the line is *horizontal.*

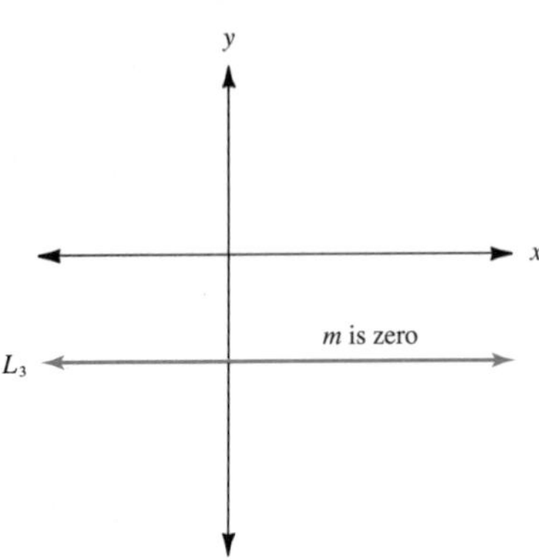

4. If the slope of a line is undefined, the line is *vertical.*

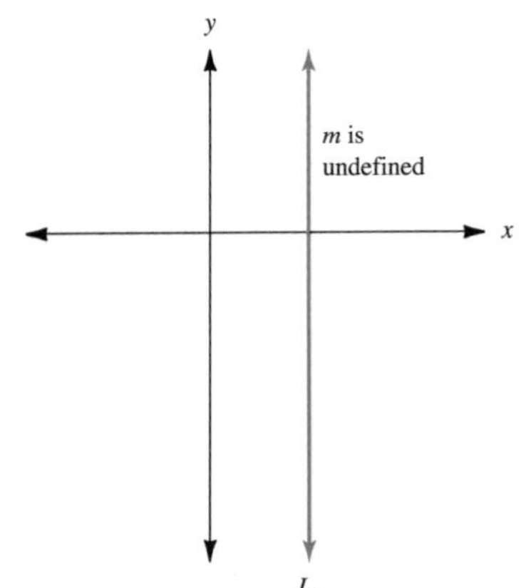

NOTES

The definition below means that if the lines are parallel, then their slopes are equal. Conversely, if the slopes are equal, then the lines are parallel.

Mathematicians use the symbol ⇔ to represent "if and only if."

All vertical lines are parallel to each other.

There are two more important results regarding the slope. Recall that two distinct lines in the plane either intersect at a point or never intersect. Two lines in the plane that do not intersect are called **parallel lines.** It can be shown that two distinct parallel lines will always have the same slope, and we can state the following.

Definition

Slopes of Parallel Lines

For nonvertical lines L_1 and L_2, if line L_1 has slope m_1 and line L_2 has slope m_2, then

L_1 is **parallel** to L_2 if and only if $m_1 = m_2$

Example 6 Parallel Lines

< Objective 2 >

NOTE

Are L_1 and L_2 the same line? A quick sketch will show that the lines are distinct.

Are lines L_1 through (2, 3) and (4, 6) and L_2 through (−4, 2) and (0, 8) parallel, or do they intersect?

$$m_1 = \frac{6 - 3}{4 - 2} = \frac{3}{2}$$

$$m_2 = \frac{8 - 2}{0 - (-4)} = \frac{6}{4} = \frac{3}{2}$$

Because the slopes of the lines are equal, the lines are parallel. They do *not* intersect.

Check Yourself 6

Are lines L_1 through (−2, −1) and (1, 4) and L_2 through (−3, 4) and (0, 8) parallel, or do they intersect?

NOTE

Horizontal lines are perpendicular to vertical lines.

Two lines are **perpendicular** if they intersect at right angles. Also, if two lines (which are not vertical or horizontal) are perpendicular, their slopes are the negative reciprocals of each other. We can then state the following result for perpendicular lines.

Definition

Slopes of Perpendicular Lines

For nonvertical lines L_1 and L_2, if line L_1 has slope m_1 and line L_2 has slope m_2, then

L_1 is **perpendicular** to L_2 if and only if $m_1 = -\dfrac{1}{m_2}$

or, equivalently,

$m_1 \cdot m_2 = -1$

Example 7 Perpendicular Lines

Are lines L_1 through points (−2, 3) and (1, 7) and L_2 through points (2, 4) and (6, 1) perpendicular?

NOTE

$\left(\frac{4}{3}\right)\left(-\frac{3}{4}\right) = -1$

$$m_1 = \frac{7-3}{1-(-2)} = \frac{4}{3}$$

$$m_2 = \frac{1-4}{6-2} = -\frac{3}{4}$$

Because the slopes are negative reciprocals of each other, the lines are perpendicular.

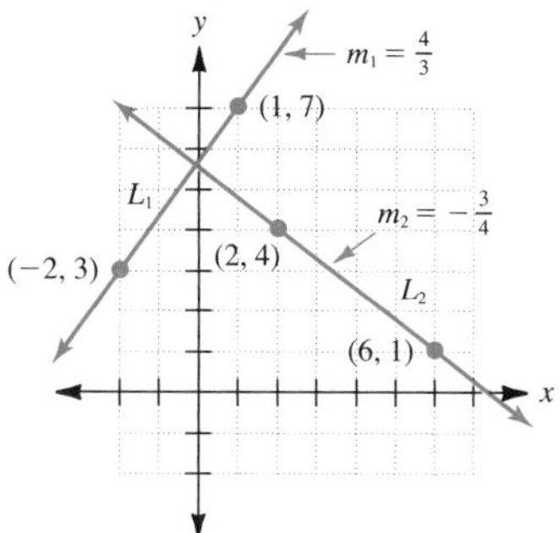

Check Yourself 7

Are lines L_1 through points (1, 3) and (4, 1) and L_2 through points (−2, 4) and (2, 10) perpendicular?

Given the equation of a line, we can also find its slope, as Example 8 illustrates.

Example 8 Finding the Slope from an Equation

NOTE

Try solving the original equation for y:

$3x + 2y = 6$

$2y = -3x + 6$

$y = -\frac{3}{2}x + 3$

Consider the coefficient of x. What do you observe?

Find the slope of the line with equation $3x + 2y = 6$.

First, find any two points on the line. In this case, (2, 0) and (0, 3), the x- and y-intercepts, will work and are easy to find. From the slope formula,

$$m = \frac{0 - 3}{2 - 0} = \frac{-3}{2} = -\frac{3}{2}$$

The slope of the line with equation $3x + 2y = 6$ is $-\frac{3}{2}$.

Check Yourself 8

Find the slope of the line with equation $3x - 4y = 12$.

Every line has constant slope. That is, choosing a different pair of points results in the same slope. In Example 8, the point $(4, -3)$ is also a solution to the equation $3x + 2y = 6$. If we use this point along with the y-intercept (0, 3) to compute the slope of the line, we have

$$m = \frac{3 - (-3)}{0 - 4} = \frac{6}{-4} = -\frac{3}{2}$$

which is the same as the slope we calculated in Example 8.

We can find the slope of a graphed line by identifying two points on the line. We will use that technique in Example 9.

Example 9 Finding the Slope from a Graph

Determine the slope of the line from its graph.

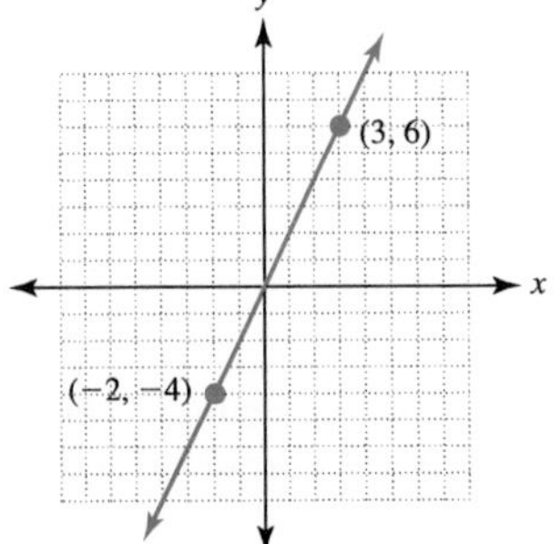

We can choose any two points to determine the slope of the line. Here we pick (3, 6) and (−2, −4). We find the slope by the usual method. There is a vertical change of +10 units and a horizontal change of +5 units, or by using the definition:

$$m = \frac{6 - (-4)}{3 - (-2)} = \frac{10}{5} = 2$$

The slope of the line is 2.

Check Yourself 9

Determine the slope of the line from its graph.

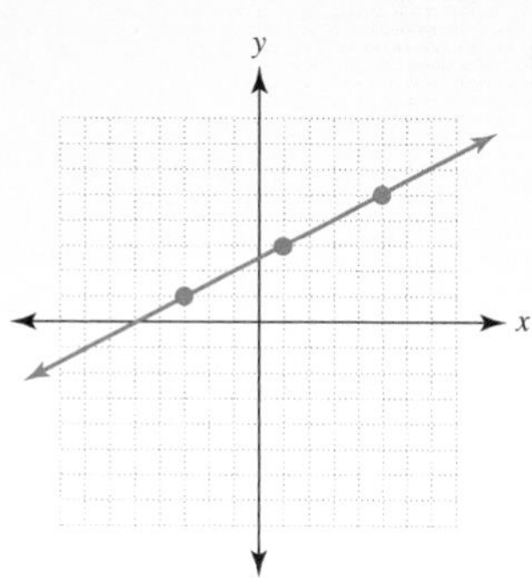

The slope of a line can also be useful in graphing a line. In Example 10, the slope of a line is used in sketching its graph.

Example 10 Graphing a Line with a Given Slope

< Objective 3 >

Suppose a line has slope $\frac{3}{2}$ and passes through the point (5, 2). Graph the line.

First, locate the point (5, 2) in the coordinate system. Now, because the slope, $\frac{3}{2}$, is the ratio of the change in y to the change in x, move 3 units up in the y direction and then 2 units to the right in the x direction. This determines a second point, here (7, 5), and we can draw our graph.

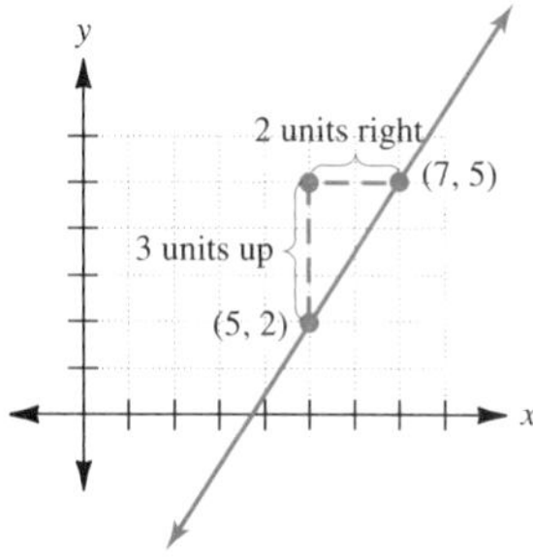

Check Yourself 10

Graph the line with slope $-\frac{3}{4}$ that passes through the point (2, 3).

Hint: Consider the *y* change as −3 units (down) and the *x* change as 4 units (right).

Because, given a point on a line and its slope, we can graph the line, we also should be able to write its equation. That is, in fact, the case, as we will see in Section 3.4.

Check Yourself ANSWERS

1. $m = \frac{2}{3}$ **2.** $m = \frac{5}{3}$. This line is steeper than the line of Check Yourself 1.

3. $m = -1$ **4.** $m = 0$ **5.** Undefined **6.** The lines intersect.

7. The lines are perpendicular. **8.** $m = \frac{3}{4}$ **9.** $m = \frac{1}{2}$

10.

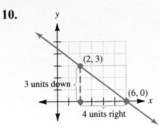

Reading Your Text

The following fill-in-the-blank exercises are designed to ensure that you understand some of the key vocabulary used in this section.

SECTION 3.3

(a) The ____________ of a line is a way of describing the steepness of that line.

(b) The change in *x*, also called the ____________, is $x_2 - x_1$, and the corresponding change in *y*, called the ____________, is $y_2 - y_1$.

(c) The slopes of two parallel lines will be ____________.

(d) Two lines are ____________ if they intersect at right angles.

Basic Skills	Advanced Skills	Vocational-Technical Applications	Calculator/Computer	Above and Beyond

3.3 exercises

MathZone

Boost your grade at mathzone.com!
- > Practice Problems
- > NetTutor
- > Self-Tests
- > e-Professors
- > Videos

Name ____________

Section ________ Date ________

< Objective 1 >

Find the slope (if it exists) of the line determined by the given pairs of points. Sketch each line so that you can compare the slopes.

1. (2, 3) and (4, 7)

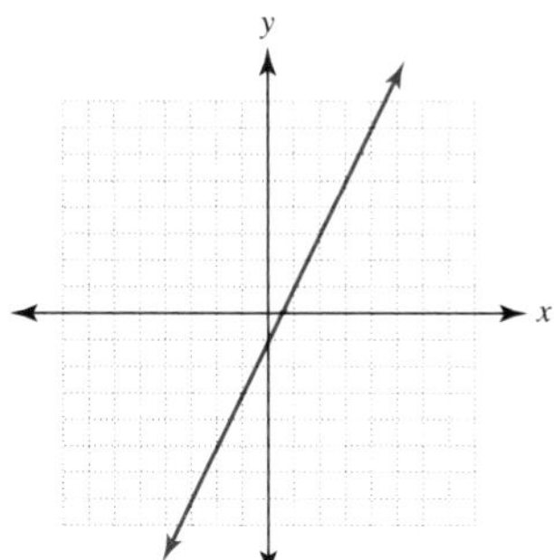

2. (2, −3) and (−2, −5)

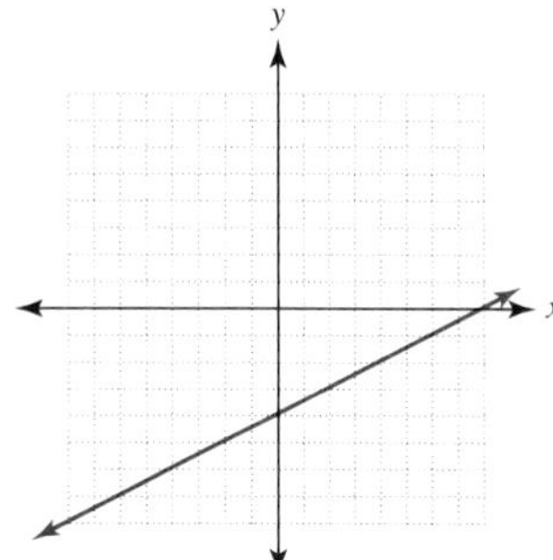

3. (2, 5) and (−3, 5)

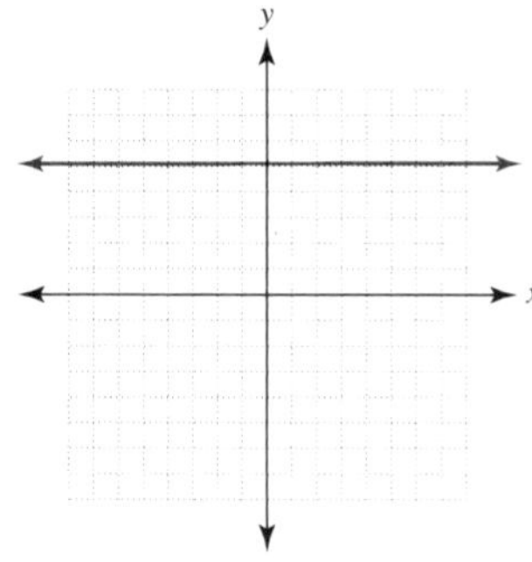

4. (−1, 4) and (−1, 7)

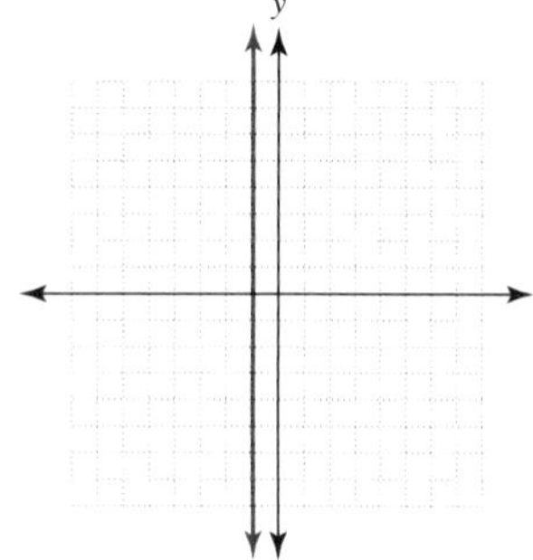

5. (8, −3) and (−2, −5)

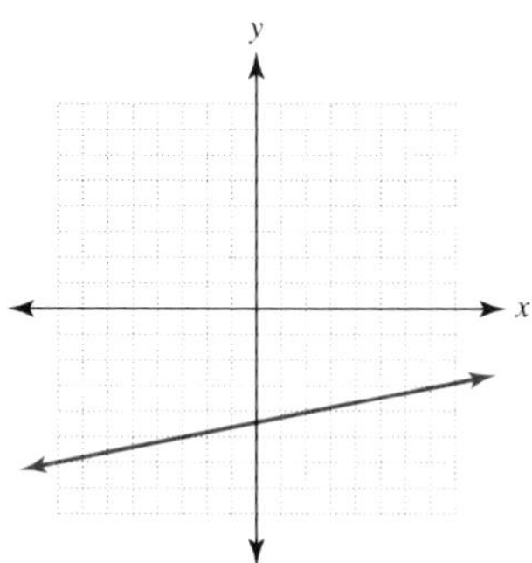

6. (−4, −3) and (2, −7)

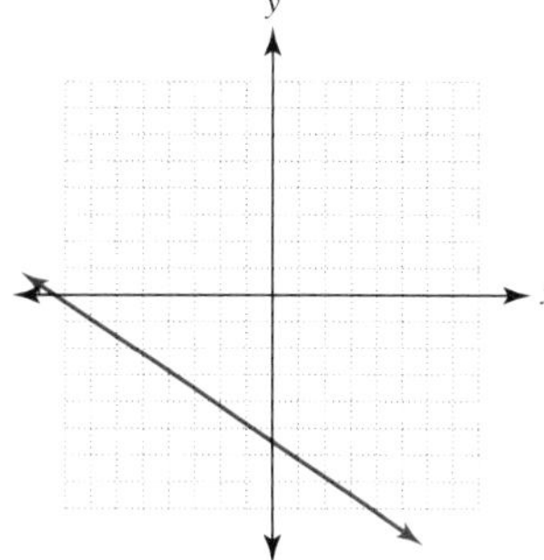

Find the slope of the line determined by each equation.

7. $y = -3x - \frac{1}{2}$

8. $y = \frac{1}{4}x + 3$

9. $y + \frac{1}{2}x = 2$

10. $2y - 3x + 5 = 0$

11. $2x - 3y = 6$

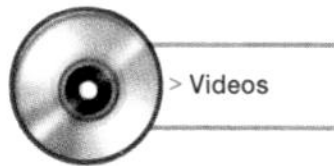

12. $3x + 4y = 12$

Answers

1. 2
2. $\frac{1}{2}$
3. 0
4. Undefined
5. $\frac{1}{5}$
6. $-\frac{2}{3}$
7. −3
8. $\frac{1}{4}$
9. $-\frac{1}{2}$
10. $\frac{3}{2}$
11. $\frac{2}{3}$
12. $-\frac{3}{4}$

Answers

13. 2

14. −3

15. 3

16. −3

17. Parallel

18. Perpendicular

19. Neither

20. Parallel

21. See exercise

22. See exercise

Use the graph to determine the slope of the line.

13.

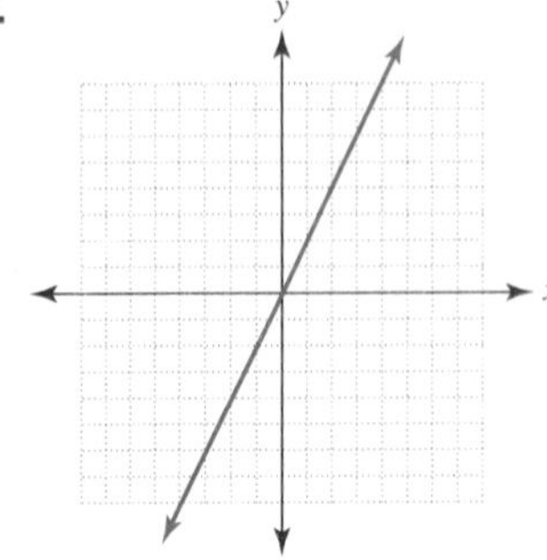

14.

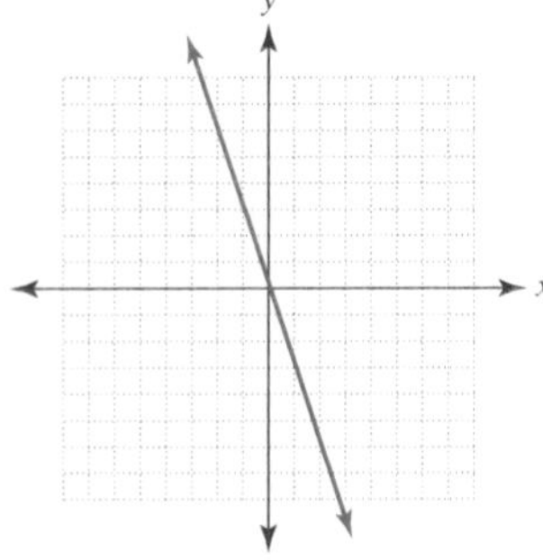

15.

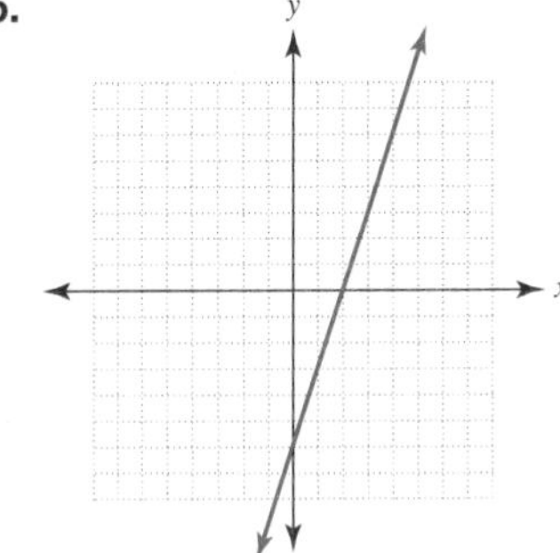

16.

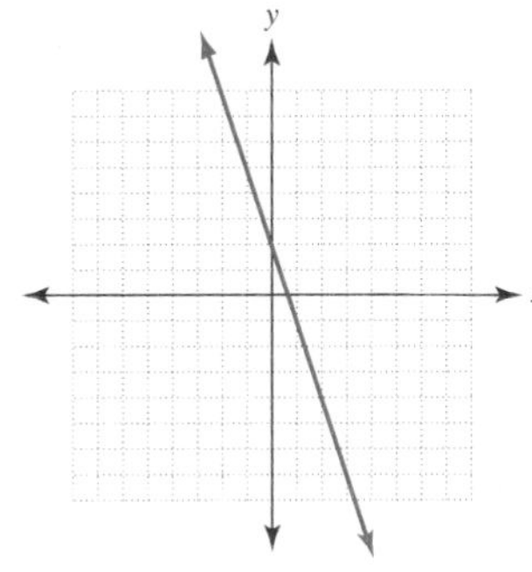

< Objective 2 >

Without graphing, determine whether each pair of lines is **parallel, perpendicular,** *or* **neither.**

17. L_1 through $(-2, -3)$ and $(4, 3)$; L_2 through $(3, 5)$ and $(5, 7)$

18. L_1 through $(-2, 4)$ and $(1, 8)$; L_2 through $(-1, -1)$ and $(-5, 2)$

19. L_1 through $(8, 5)$ and $(3, -2)$; L_2 through $(-2, 4)$ and $(4, -1)$

20. L_1 through $(-2, -3)$ and $(3, -1)$; L_2 through $(-3, 1)$ and $(7, 5)$

< Objective 3 >

Graph the lines through each of the specified points having the given slope.

21. $(0, 1)$, $m = 3$

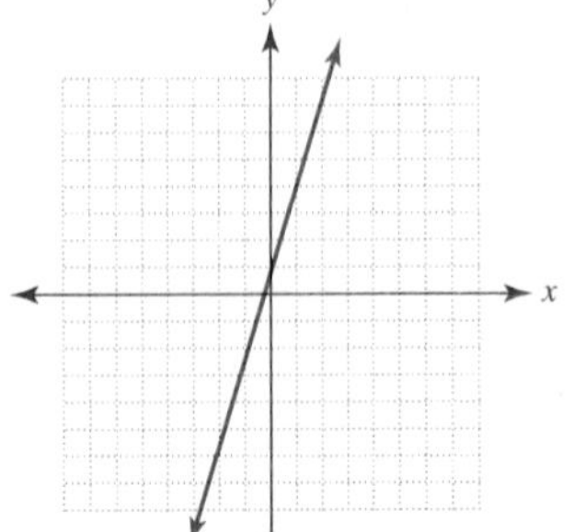

22. $(0, -2)$, $m = -2$

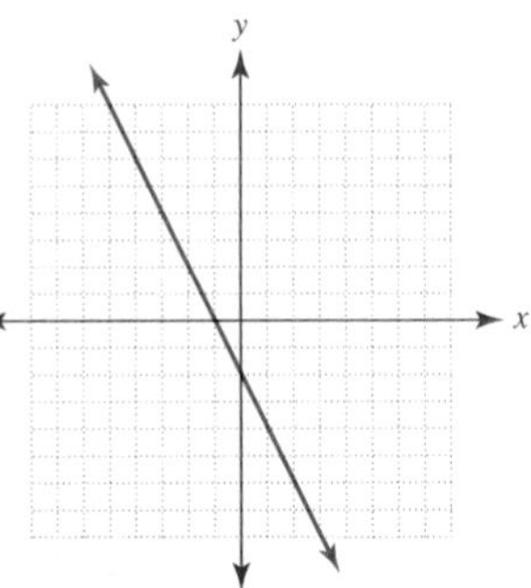

23. $(3, -1)$, $m = 2$

24. $(2, -3)$, $m = -3$

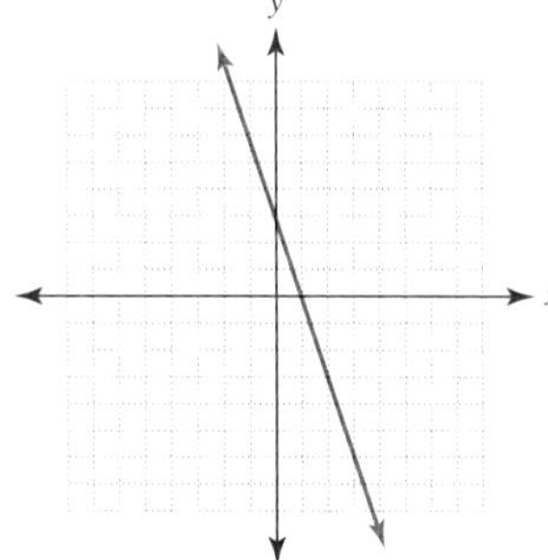

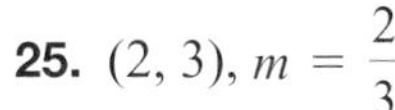

25. $(2, 3)$, $m = \frac{2}{3}$

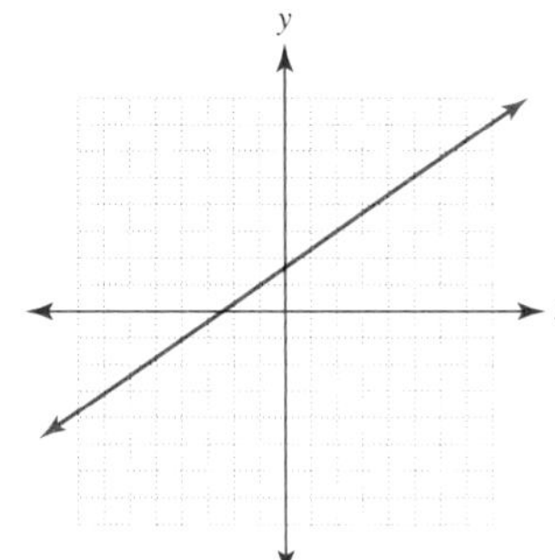

26. $(-2, 1)$, $m = -\frac{3}{4}$

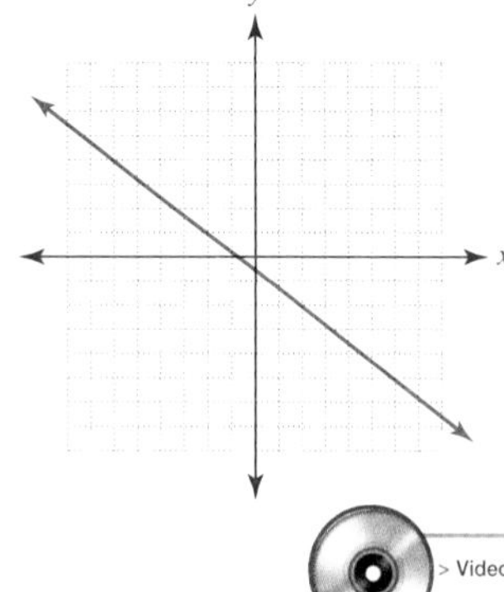

> Videos

27. $(4, 2)$, $m = 0$

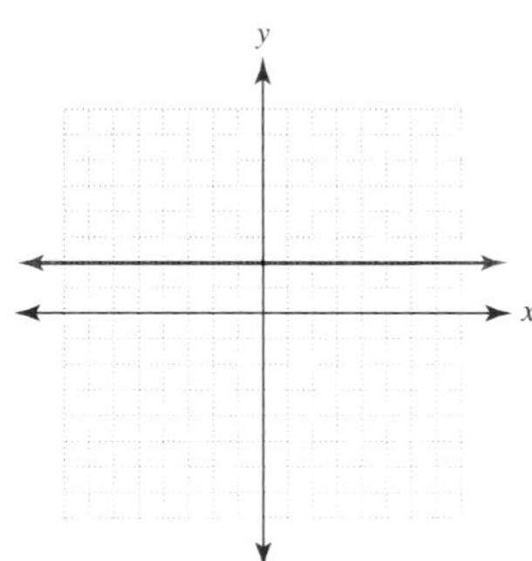

28. $(3, 0)$, m is undefined

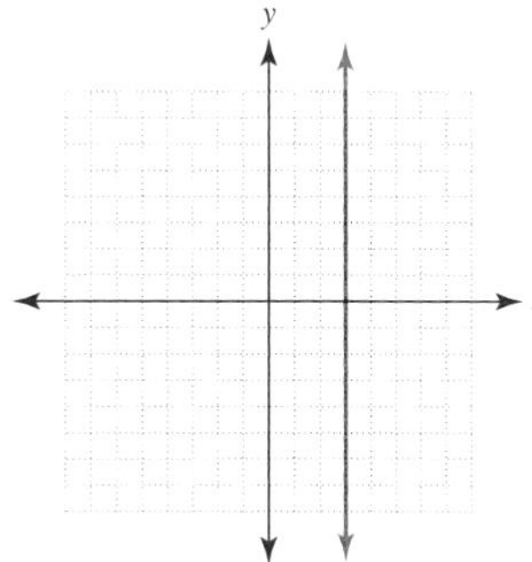

Determine whether the following statements are **true** *or* **false.**

29. The slope of a horizontal line is undefined.

30. Vertical lines are not parallel to each other.

31. If the slope of one line is $\frac{c}{d}$, then the slope of a line that is perpendicular is $-\frac{d}{c}$.

Answers

23. See exercise

24. See exercise

25. See exercise

26. See exercise

27. See exercise

28. See exercise

29. False

30. False

31. True

Answers

32. always

33. sometimes

34. never

35. 12.5¢/year

36. 2°/h

37. $5\frac{1}{3}$ ft or 5 ft 4 in.

38. Perpendicular

39. Parallel

In the following statement, fill in the blank with **always, sometimes,** *or* **never.**

32. The graph of $y = mx$ ________ passes through the origin.

33. Two lines that are perpendicular will ________ pass through the origin.

34. Parallel lines will ________ intersect.

35. BUSINESS AND FINANCE In 1995, the cost of a soft drink was 75¢. By 1999, the cost of the same soft drink had risen to \$1.25. During this period, what was the rate of change of the cost of the soft drink? (*Hint:* Assume a linear growth rate for the price as the years go by. Find the slope of the line.)

36. SCIENCE AND MEDICINE On a certain February day in Philadelphia, the temperature at 6:00 A.M. was 10°F. By 2:00 P.M. the temperature was up to 26°F. What was the average hourly rate of temperature change? (*Hint:* Assume a linear growth rate for the temperature as the hours go by, and find the slope.)

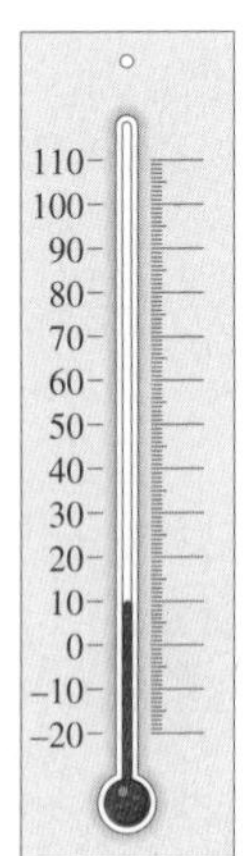

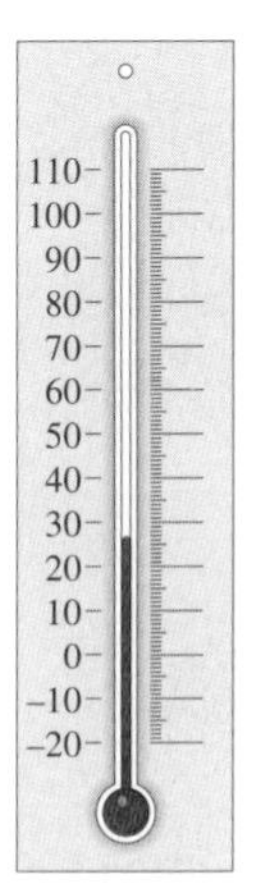

37. CONSTRUCTION The rise-to-run ratio used to describe the steepness of the roof on a certain house is 4 to 12. Determine the maximum height of the attic if the house is 32 ft wide.

Basic Skills | **Advanced Skills** | Vocational-Technical Applications | Calculator/Computer | Above and Beyond

38. L_1 with equation $x - 3y = 6$; L_2 with equation $3x + y = 3$. Are L_1 and L_2 parallel or perpendicular?

> Videos

39. L_1 with equation $x + 2y = 4$; L_2 with equation $2x + 4y = 5$. Are L_1 and L_2 parallel or perpendicular?

40. Find the slope of any line parallel to the line through points (−2, 3) and (4, 5).

41. Find the slope of any line perpendicular to the line through points (0, 5) and (−3, −4).

42. A line passing through (−1, 2) and (4, y) is parallel to a line with slope 2. What is the value of y?

43. A line passing through (2, 3) and (5, y) is perpendicular to a line with slope $\frac{3}{4}$. What is the value of y?

If the slope of the line through P and Q equals the slope of the line through Q and R, then the points P, Q, and R are collinear (lie on the same line). In exercises 44 to 49, use the slope concept to determine whether the sets of points are collinear.

44. $P(-2, -3)$, $Q(3, 2)$, and $R(4, 3)$

45. $P(-5, 1)$, $Q(-2, 4)$, and $R(4, 9)$

46. $P(0, 0)$, $Q(2, 4)$, and $R(-3, 6)$

47. $P(-2, 5)$, $Q(-5, 2)$, and $R(1, 12)$

48. $P(2, 4)$, $Q(-3, -6)$, and $R(-4, 8)$

49. $P(-1, 5)$, $Q(2, -4)$, and $R(-2, 8)$

50. On the same graph, sketch lines with slope 2 through each of the following points: (−1, 0), (2, 0), and (5, 0).

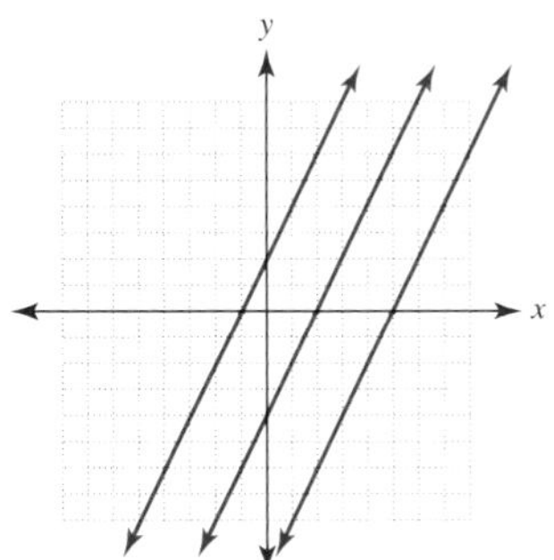

51. On the same graph, sketch one line with slope $\frac{1}{3}$ and one line with slope −3, having both pass through point (2, 3).

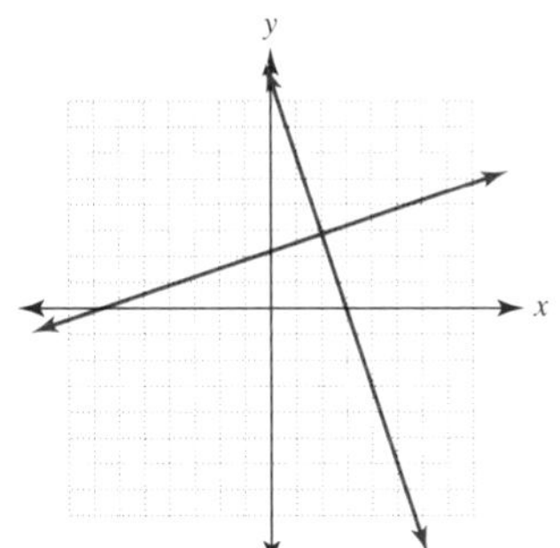

Answers

40. $\frac{1}{3}$

41. $-\frac{1}{3}$

42. $y = 12$

43. $y = -1$

44. Collinear

45. Not collinear

46. Not collinear

47. Not collinear

48. Not collinear

49. Collinear

50. See exercise

51. See exercise

Answers

52. Parallelogram, rectangle

53. Parallelogram, not a rectangle

54. Parallelogram, not a rectangle

55. Parallelogram, rectangle

56. No

57. Yes

58. 29.5 mi/gal

59. 16 parts per hour

60. $\frac{2,700 - 2,450}{5 - 40} = -\frac{50}{7}$ degrees per min

A four-sided figure (quadrilateral) is a parallelogram if the opposite sides have the same slope. If the adjacent sides are perpendicular, the figure is a rectangle. In exercises 52 to 55, for each quadrilateral ABCD, determine whether it is a parallelogram; then determine whether it is a rectangle.

52. $A(0, 0), B(2, 0), C(2, 3), D(0, 3)$

53. $A(-3, 2), B(1, -7), C(3, -4), D(-1, 5)$

54. $A(0, 0), B(4, 0), C(5, 2), D(1, 2)$

55. $A(-3, -5), B(2, 1), C(-4, 6), D(-9, 0)$

Basic Skills | Advanced Skills | **Vocational-Technical Applications** | Calculator/Computer | Above and Beyond

56. Manufacturing Technology A slot is to be machined into a part from the coordinates (4, 9) to (48, 64). The machinist is to machine a second slot parallel to this one. She decides the second slot should be cut from (7, 23) to (49, 71). Will this produce parallel slots?

57. Manufacturing Technology A corner is machined into a part. The cut is made from $(-40, 0)$ to $(0, 24)$ and then to $(12, 4)$. Is this a square corner?

58. Automotive Technology A car drives 84 miles and uses 3 gallons of gas. When the same car drives 261 miles, it uses 9 gallons of gas. What is the rate of change (in miles per gallon) over this range? (*Hint:* Use the slope definition on the two points.)

59. Construction Technology During a welder's shift, at the end of hour 3, she had completed 46 parts. At the end of 10 hours, she had finished 158 parts. Find the slope of her production level (in parts per hour).

60. Manufacturing Technology What is the average rate of change in the temperature between 5 and 40 minutes for this graph? (**Hint:** Compute the slope between the two indicated points.)

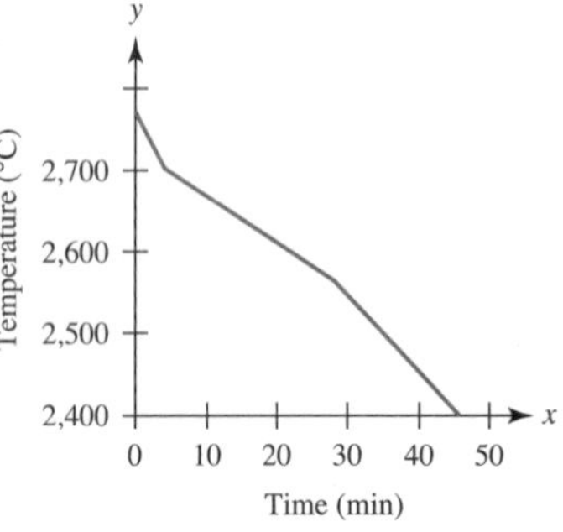

Basic Skills | Advanced Skills | Vocational-Technical Applications | **Calculator/Computer** | Above and Beyond

Solve each equation for y; then use your graphing utility to graph each equation.

61. $2x + 5y = 10$

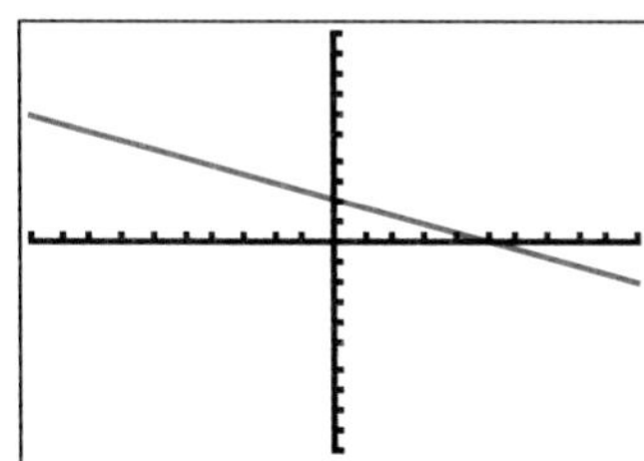

62. $5x - 3y = 12$

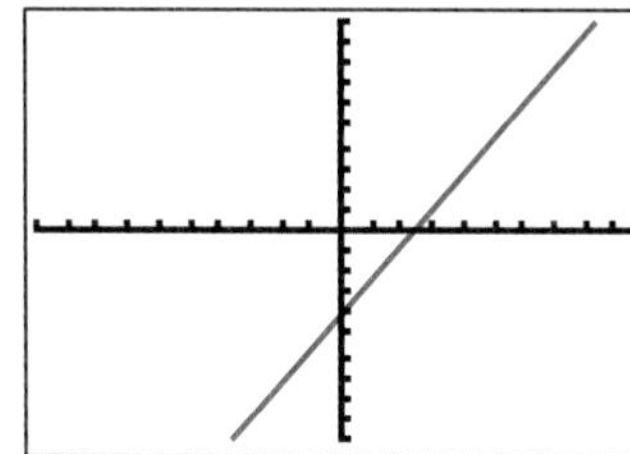

63. $x + 7y = 14$

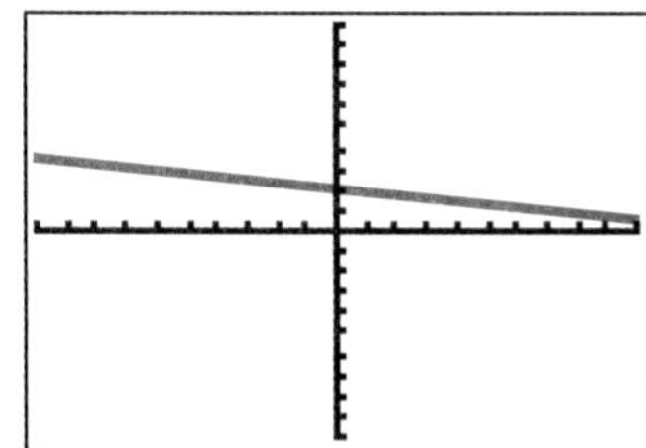

64. $-2x - 3y = 9$

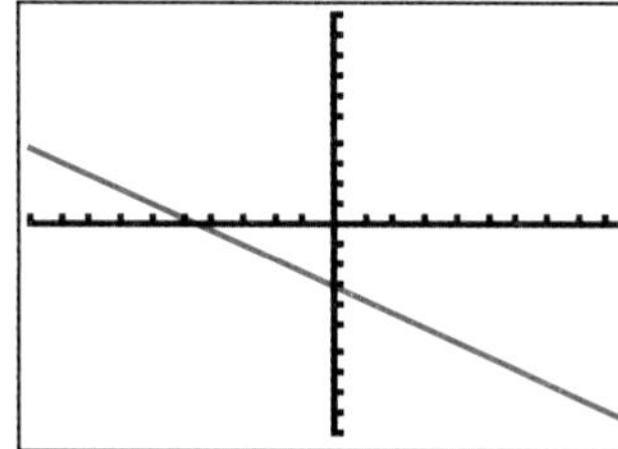

Basic Skills | Advanced Skills | Vocational-Technical Applications | Calculator/Computer | **Above and Beyond**

65. Consider the equation $y = 2x + 3$.

(a) Complete the table of values, and plot the resulting points.

Point	x	y
A	5	
B	6	
C	7	
D	8	
E	9	

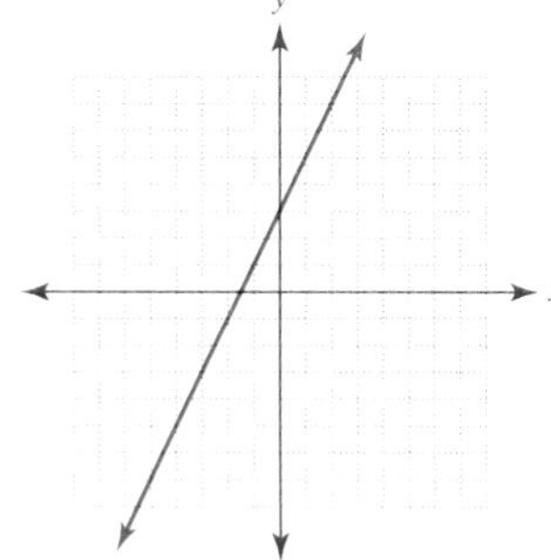

(b) As the x-coordinates change by 1 (for example, as you move from point A to point B), by how much does the corresponding y-coordinate change?

(c) Is your answer to part **(b)** the same if you move from B to C? from C to D? from D to E?

(d) Describe the "growth rate" of the line using these observations. Complete the following statement: When the x-value grows by 1 unit, the y-value ________________.

Answers

61. $y = -\frac{2}{5}x + 2$

62. $y = \frac{5}{3}x - 4$

63. $y = -\frac{1}{7}x + 2$

64. $y = -\frac{2}{3}x - 3$

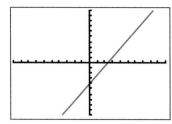

65. (a) y-coordinates: 13, 15, 17, 19, 21; (b) y increases by 2; (c) yes, same; (d) grows by 2 units

Answers

66. (a) y-coordinates: 15, 17, 19, 21, 23; (b) y increases by 2; (c) yes, same; (d) grows by 2 units

67. (a) y-coordinates: 13, 16, 19, 22, 25; (b) y increases by 3; (c) yes, same; (d) grows by 3 units

68. (a) y-coordinates: 11, 14, 17, 20, 23; (b) y increases by 3; (c) yes, same; (d) grows by 3 units

69. (a) y-coordinates: 30, 26, 22, 18, 14; (b) y decreases by 4; (c) yes, same; (d) drops by 4 units

70. (a) y-coordinates: 20, 16, 12, 8, 4; (b) y decreases by 4; (c) yes, same; (d) drops by 4 units

71. Above and Beyond

66. Repeat exercise 65 using $y = 2x + 5$.

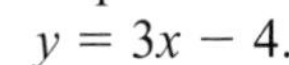

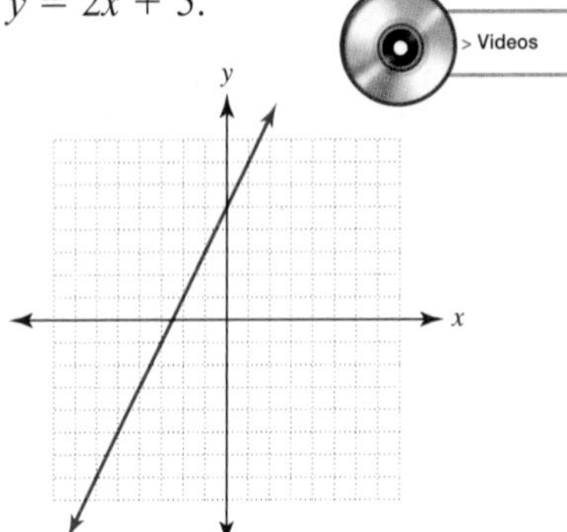

67. Repeat exercise 65 using $y = 3x - 2$.

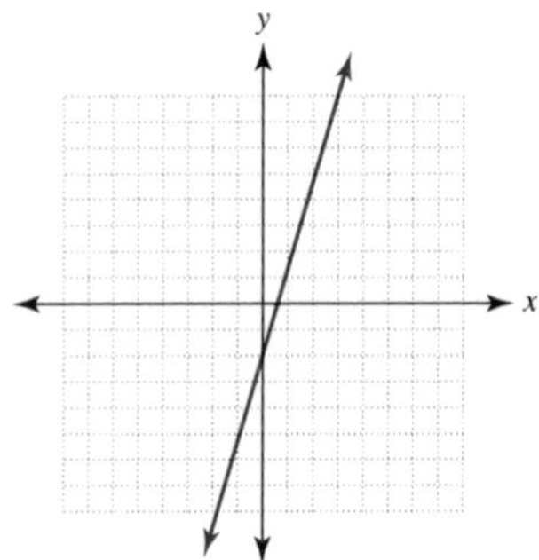

68. Repeat exercise 65 using $y = 3x - 4$.

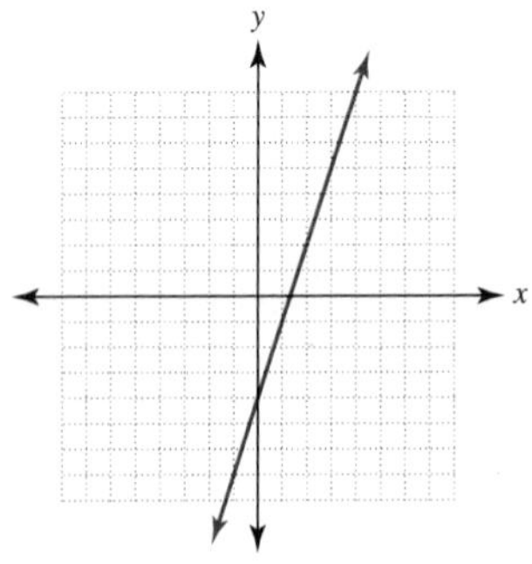

69. Repeat exercise 65 using $y = -4x + 50$.

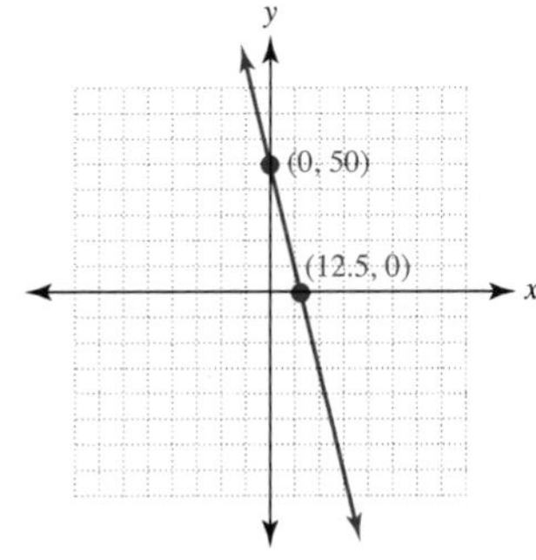

70. Repeat exercise 65 using $y = -4x + 40$.

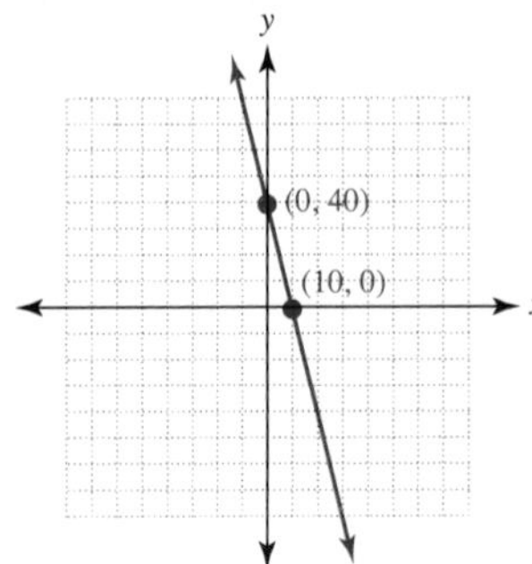

71. Summarize the results of exercises 65 to 70. In particular, how does the concept of "growth rate" connect to the concept of slope?

Answers

1. 2

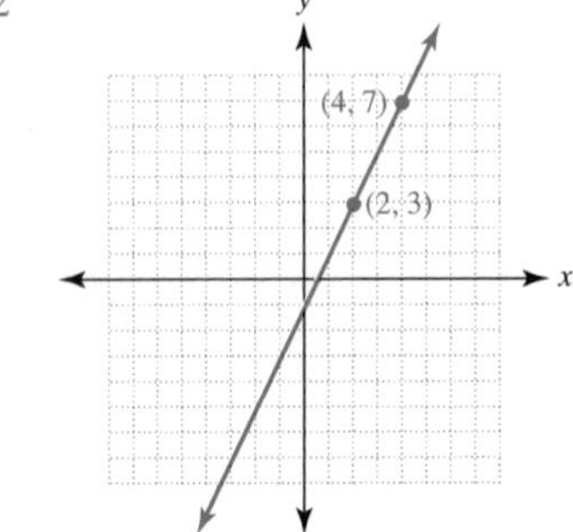

3. 0

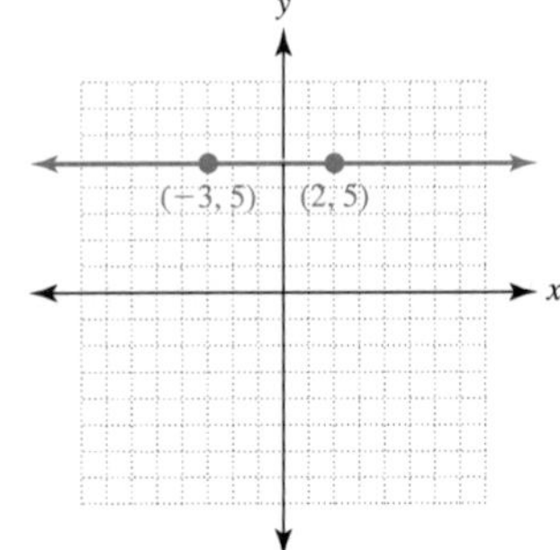

5. $\frac{1}{5}$ 7. -3 9. $-\frac{1}{2}$ 11. $\frac{2}{3}$ 13. 2

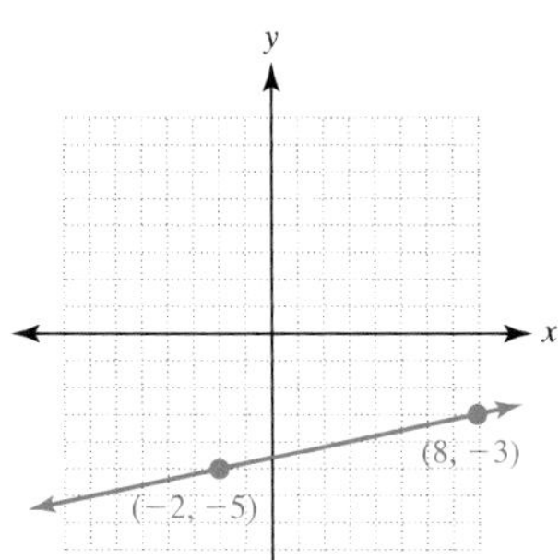

15. 3 17. Parallel 19. Neither

21.

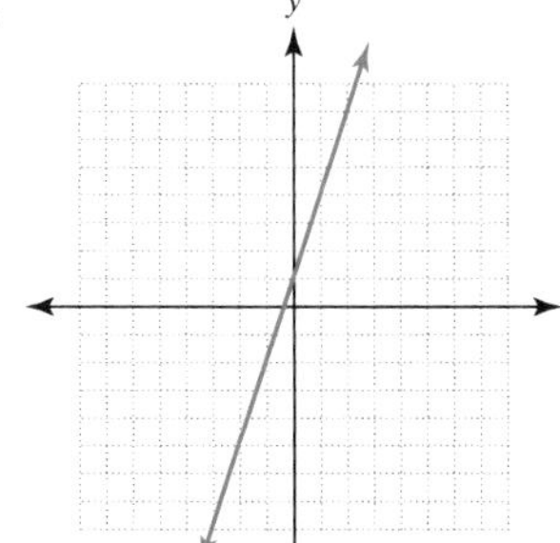

23.

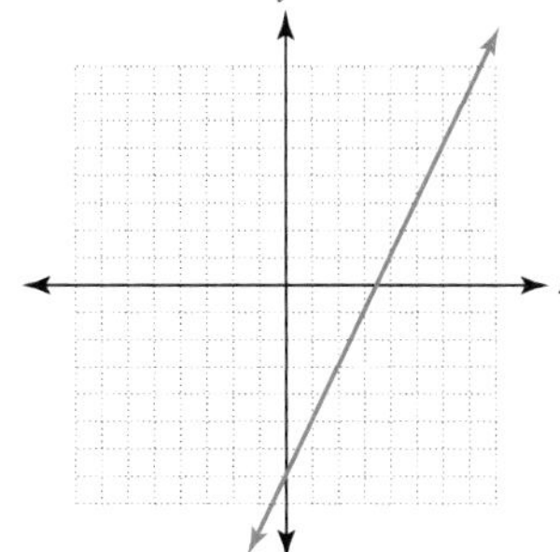

25.

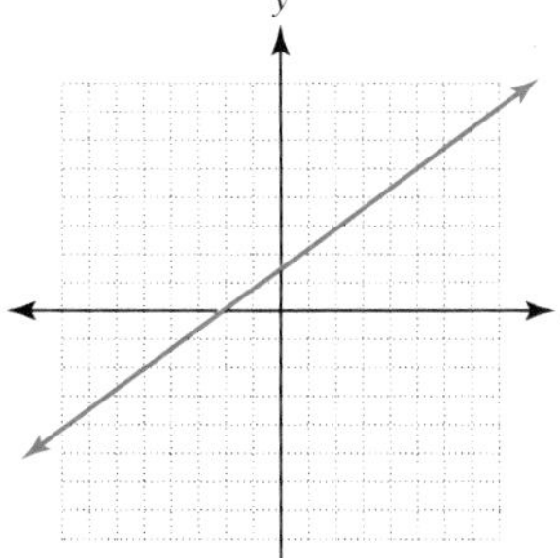

27.

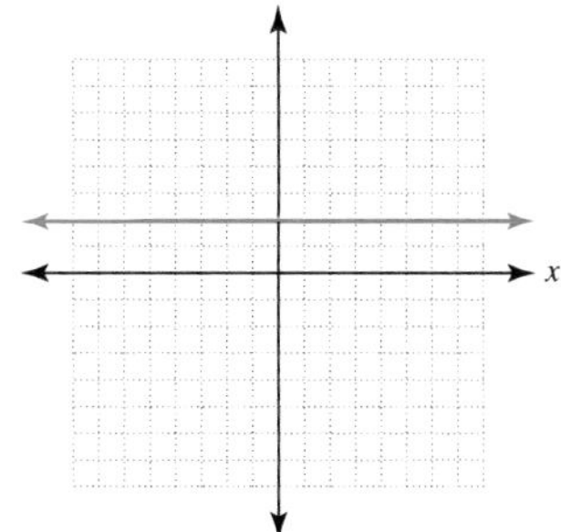

29. False 31. True 33. sometimes 35. 12.5 ¢/year
37. $5\frac{1}{3}$ ft or 5 ft 4 in. 39. Parallel 41. $-\frac{1}{3}$ 43. $y = -1$
45. Not collinear 47. Not collinear 49. Collinear

51.

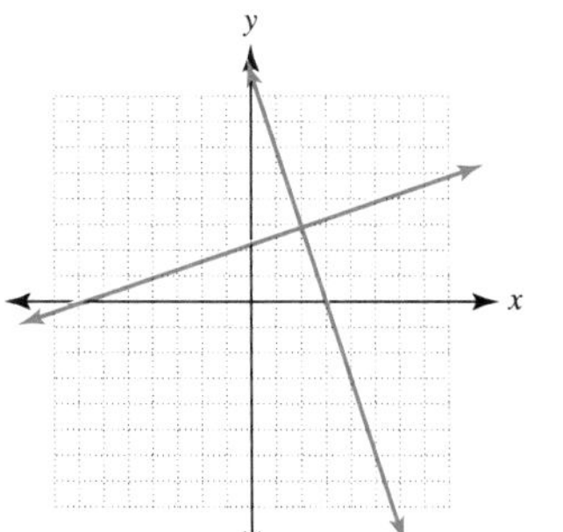

53. Parallelogram, not a rectangle

55. Parallelogram, rectangle 57. Yes 59. 16 parts per hour

61.

63.

65.

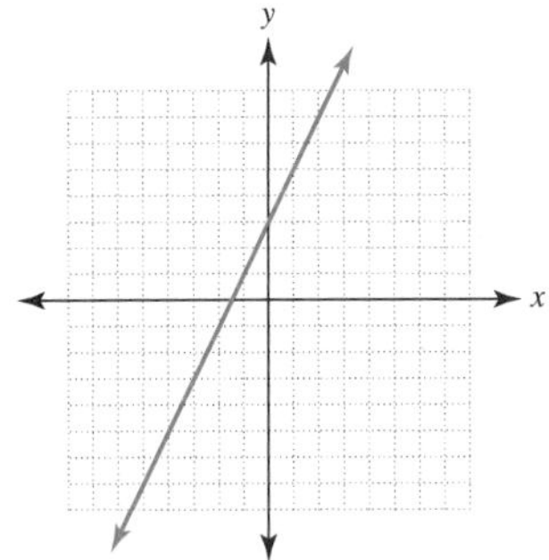

(a) y-coordinates: 13, 15, 17, 19, 21; **(b)** y increases by 2; **(c)** yes, same; **(d)** grows by 2 units

67.

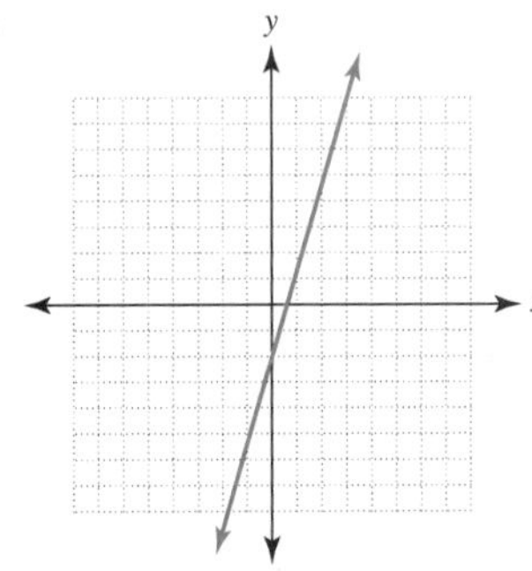

(a) y-coordinates: 13, 16, 19, 22, 25; **(b)** y increases by 3; **(c)** yes, same; **(d)** grows by 3 units

69.

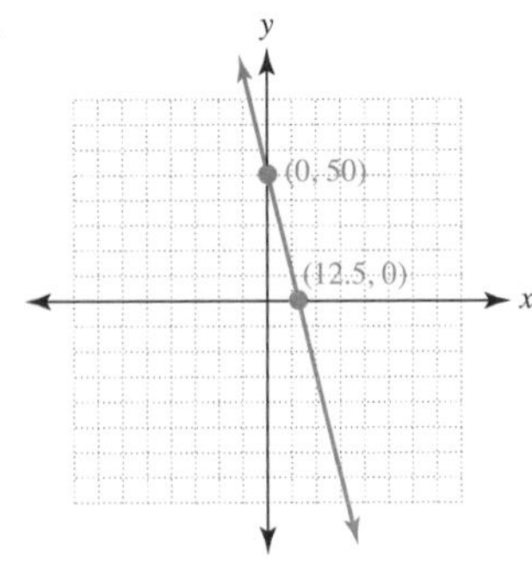

(a) y-coordinates: 30, 26, 22, 18, 14; **(b)** y decreases by 4; **(c)** yes, same; **(d)** drops by 4 units

71. Above and Beyond

3.4

Forms of Linear Equations

< 3.4 Objectives >

1 > Write the equation of a line

2 > Solve an application involving a linear equation

3 > Linear equations as functions

We have seen that the special form

$$Ax + By = C$$

in which A and B cannot both be zero, is called the **standard form for a linear equation.** In Section 3.3, we determined the slope of a line from two ordered pairs. In this section, we will look at several forms for a linear equation. For the first of these forms, we use the concept of slope to write the equation of a line.

> **NOTE**
>
> The coordinates of the y-intercept are $(0, b)$ because the x-coordinate on the y-axis is zero and the y-coordinate of the intercept is b.

First, suppose we know the y-intercept $(0, b)$ of a line L, and its slope m. Let $P(x, y)$ be any other point on that line. Using $(0, b)$ as (x_1, y_1) and (x, y) as (x_2, y_2) in the slope formula, we have

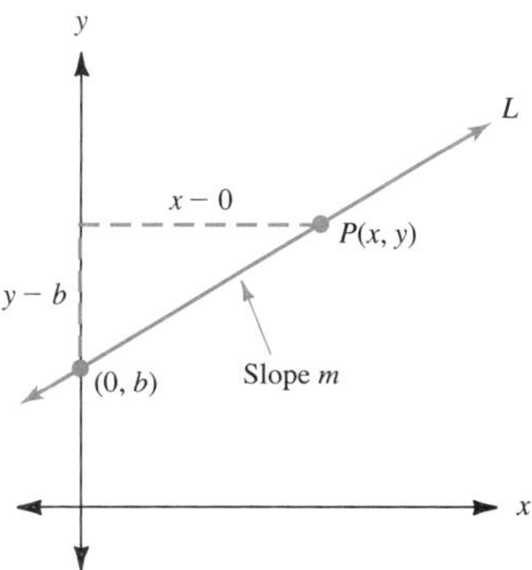

$$m = \frac{y - b}{x - 0}$$

or

$$m = \frac{y - b}{x}$$

> **NOTE**
>
> The slope-intercept form for the equation of a line is the most convenient form for entering an equation into the calculator.

Multiplying both sides of this equation by x gives

$$mx = y - b$$

or

$$y = mx + b$$

This equation will be satisfied by any point on line L, including $(0, b)$. It is called the **slope-intercept form** for a line, and we can state the following general result.

Definition

Slope-Intercept Form for the Equation of a Line

The equation of a line with y-intercept $(0, b)$ and with slope m can be written as

$$y = mx + b$$

Example 1 Finding the Equation of a Line

< Objective 1 >

Write the equation of the line with slope 2 and y-intercept $(0, 3)$.

Here $m = 2$ and $b = 3$. Applying the slope-intercept form, we have

$$y = 2x + 3$$

as the equation of the specified line.

NOTE

The x-coefficient is 2; the y-intercept is $(0, 3)$.

It is easy to see that whenever a linear equation is written in slope-intercept form, the slope of the line is simply the x-coefficient and the y-intercept is determined by the constant.

Check Yourself 1

Write the equation of the line with slope $-\frac{2}{3}$ and y-intercept $(0, -3)$.

Note that the slope-intercept form now gives us a second (and generally more efficient) means of finding the slope of a line whose equation is written in standard form. Recall that we determined two specific points on the line and then applied the slope formula. Now, rather than using specific points, we can simply solve the given equation for y to rewrite the equation in the slope-intercept form and identify the slope of the line as the x-coefficient.

Example 2 Finding the Slope and y-Intercept of a Line

Find the slope and y-intercept of the line with equation

$$2x + 3y = 3$$

To write the equation in slope-intercept form, we solve for y.

$$2x + 3y = 3$$

$$3y = -2x + 3 \quad \text{Subtract } 2x \text{ from both sides.}$$

$$y = -\frac{2}{3}x + 1 \quad \text{Divide by 3.}$$

We now see that the slope of the line is $-\frac{2}{3}$ and the y-intercept is $(0, 1)$.

Check Yourself 2

Find the slope and y-intercept of the line with equation.

$3x - 4y = 8$

We can also use the slope-intercept form to determine whether the graphs of given equations will be parallel, intersecting, or perpendicular lines.

Example 3 Verifying That Two Lines Are Perpendicular

RECALL

Two lines are perpendicular if their slopes are negative reciprocals, so

$m_1 = -\frac{1}{m_2}$

or, equivalently

$m_1 \cdot m_2 = -1$

Without graphing, show that the graphs of $3x + 4y = 4$ and $-4x + 3y = 12$ are perpendicular lines.

First, we solve each equation for y.

$$3x + 4y = 4$$
$$4y = -3x + 4$$
$$y = -\frac{3}{4}x + 1$$

$$-4x + 3y = 12$$
$$3y = 4x + 12$$
$$y = \frac{4}{3}x + 4$$

We now look at the product of the two slopes: $-\frac{3}{4} \cdot \frac{4}{3} = -1$. Any two lines whose slopes have a product of -1 are perpendicular lines. These two lines are perpendicular.

Check Yourself 3

Without graphing show that the graphs of the equations

$-3x + 2y = 4$ **and** $2x + 3y = 9$

are perpendicular lines.

The slope-intercept form can also be used in graphing a line, as Example 4 illustrates.

Example 4 Graphing the Equation of a Line

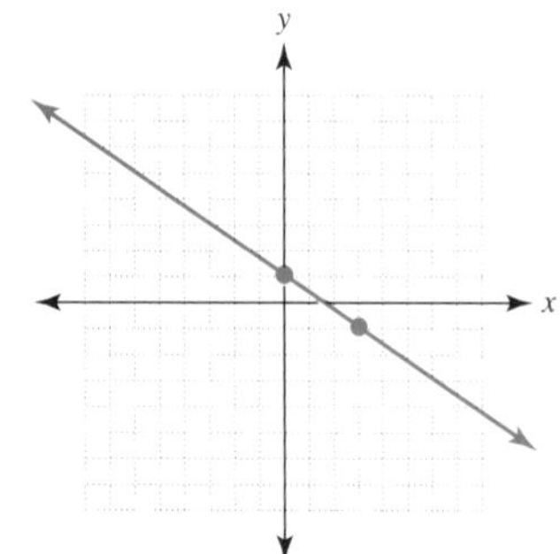

Graph the line $2x + 3y = 3$.

In Example 2, we found that the slope-intercept form for this equation is

$$y = -\frac{2}{3}x + 1$$

To graph the line, plot the y-intercept at (0, 1). Now, because the slope m is equal to $-\frac{2}{3}$, from (0, 1) we move *down* 2 units and then to the *right* 3 units, to locate a second point on the graph of the line, here (3, −1). We can now draw a line through the two points to complete the graph.

Check Yourself 4

Graph the line with equation

$3x - 4y = 8$

***Hint:* You worked with this equation in Check Yourself 2.**

In Example 4, we treated $-\frac{2}{3}$ as $\frac{-2}{+3}$ to move down from (0, 1) 2 units and to the right 3 units to get to (3, −1).

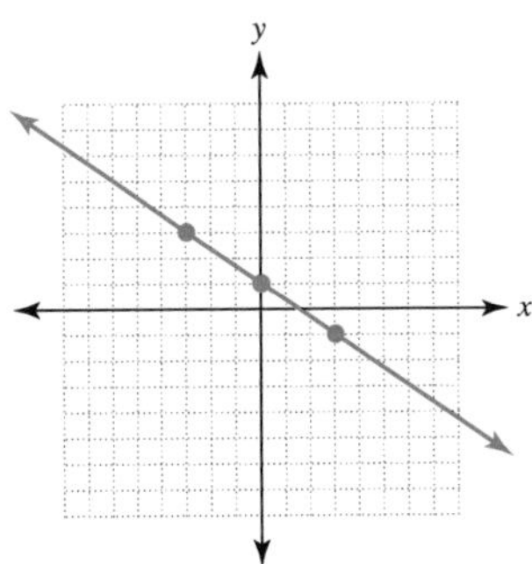

The sign property of fractions also allows us to consider $-\frac{2}{3}$ as $\frac{+2}{-3}$. This would mean starting at (0, 1) and moving up two units and then left three units to get to (−3, 3). Notice this gives us another way to get a point on the same line.

The following algorithm summarizes the use of graphing with the slope-intercept form.

Step by Step

Graphing by Using the Slope-Intercept Form

Step 1 Write the original equation of the line in slope-intercept form.
Step 2 Determine the slope m and the y-intercept $(0, b)$.
Step 3 Plot the y-intercept at $(0, b)$.
Step 4 Use m (the change in y over the change in x) to determine a second point on the desired line.
Step 5 Draw a line through the two points determined in steps 2 and 4 to complete the graph.

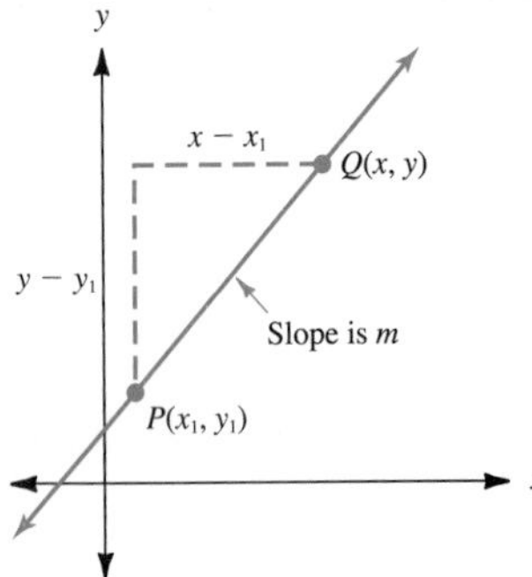

Often in mathematics it is useful to be able to write the equation of a line, given its slope and *any* point on the line. We will now derive a third special form for a line for this purpose.

Suppose a line has slope m and passes through the known point $P(x_1, y_1)$. Let $Q(x, y)$ be any other point on the line. Once again we can use the definition of slope and write

$$m = \frac{y - y_1}{x - x_1}$$

Multiplying both sides of this equation by $x - x_1$, we have

$$m(x - x_1) = y - y_1$$

or

$$y - y_1 = m(x - x_1)$$

This equation is called the **point-slope form** for the equation of a line, and all points lying on the line [including (x_1, y_1)] will satisfy this equation. We can state the following general result.

Definition

Point-Slope Form for the Equation of a Line

The equation of a line with slope m that passes through point (x_1, y_1) is given by

$$y - y_1 = m(x - x_1)$$

Example 5 Finding the Equation of a Line

RECALL

A vertical line has undefined slope. The equation of a line with *undefined* slope passing through the point (x_1, y_1) is given by $x = x_1$. For example, the equation of a line with undefined slope passing through (3, 5) is $x = 3$. We will consider this special case again in Example 7.

Write the equation for the line that passes through point $(3, -1)$ with a slope of 3.

Letting $(x_1, y_1) = (3, -1)$ and $m = 3$ in point-slope form, we have

$$y - (-1) = 3(x - 3)$$

or

$$y + 1 = 3x - 9$$

We can write the final result in slope-intercept form as

$$y = 3x - 10$$

Check Yourself 5

Write the equation of the line that passes through point $(-2, 4)$ with a slope of $\frac{3}{2}$. Write your result in slope-intercept form.

Because we know that two points determine a line, it is natural that we should be able to write the equation of a line passing through two given points. Using the point-slope form together with the slope formula will allow us to write such an equation.

Example 6 Finding the Equation of a Line

NOTE

We could just as well have chosen to let

$(x_1, y_1) = (4, 7)$

The resulting equation will be the same in either case. Take time to verify this for yourself.

Write the equation of the line passing through (2, 4) and (4, 7).

First, we find m, the slope of the line. Here

$$m = \frac{7 - 4}{4 - 2} = \frac{3}{2}$$

Now we apply the point-slope form with $m = \frac{3}{2}$ and $(x_1, y_1) = (2, 4)$:

$$y - 4 = \frac{3}{2}(x - 2) \quad \text{Distribute the } \frac{3}{2}.$$

$$y - 4 = \frac{3}{2}x - 3 \quad \text{Write the result in slope-intercept form.}$$

$$y = \frac{3}{2}x + 1$$

Check Yourself 6

Write the equation of the line passing through (−2, 5) and (1, 3). Write your result in slope-intercept form.

A line with slope zero is a horizontal line. A line with an undefined slope is vertical. Example 7 illustrates the equations of such lines.

Example 7 Finding the Equation of a Line

(a) Find the equation of a line passing through $(7, -2)$ with a slope of zero.

We could find the equation by letting $m = 0$. Substituting into the slope-intercept form, we can solve for b.

$$y = mx + b$$
$$-2 = 0(7) + b$$
$$-2 = b$$

So,

$$y = 0x - 2 \qquad y = -2$$

It is far easier to remember that any line with a zero slope is a horizontal line and has the form

$$y = b$$

The value for b will always be the y-coordinate for the given point.

(b) Find the equation of a line with undefined slope passing through $(4, -5)$.

A line with undefined slope is vertical. It will always be of the form $x = a$, in which a is the x-coordinate for the given point. The equation is

$$x = 4$$

Check Yourself 7

(a) Find the equation of a line with zero slope that passes through point (−3, 5).
(b) Find the equation of a line passing through (−3, −6) with undefined slope.

Alternate methods for finding the equation of a line through two points do exist and have particular significance in other fields of mathematics, such as statistics. Example 8 shows such an alternate approach.

Example 8 Finding the Equation of a Line

Write the equation of the line through points $(-2, 3)$ and $(4, 5)$.

First, we find m, as before.

$$m = \frac{5 - 3}{4 - (-2)} = \frac{2}{6} = \frac{1}{3}$$

We now make use of the slope-intercept equation, but in a slightly different form.

Because $y = mx + b$, we can write

$$b = y - mx$$

NOTE

We substitute these values because the line must pass through $(-2, 3)$.

Now, letting $x = -2$, $y = 3$, and $m = \frac{1}{3}$, we can calculate b.

$$b = 3 - \left(\frac{1}{3}\right)(-2)$$

$$= 3 + \frac{2}{3} = \frac{11}{3}$$

With $m = \frac{1}{3}$ and $b = \frac{11}{3}$, we can apply the slope-intercept form to write the equation of the desired line. We have

$$y = \frac{1}{3}x + \frac{11}{3}$$

Check Yourself 8

Repeat the Check Yourself 6 exercise, using the technique illustrated in Example 8.

We now know that we can write the equation of a line once we have been given appropriate geometric conditions, such as a point on the line and the slope of that line. Let us now consider some applications of linear equations. In some applications, the slope may be given not directly but through specified parallel or perpendicular lines.

Example 9 Finding the Equation of a Line

NOTE

The slope of the given line is $-\frac{3}{4}$.

Find the equation of the line passing through $(-4, -3)$ and parallel to the line determined by $3x + 4y = 12$.

First, we find the slope of the given parallel line, as before.

$$3x + 4y = 12$$

$$4y = -3x + 12$$

$$y = -\frac{3}{4}x + 3$$

RECALL

Parallel lines have the same slope.

Now, because the slope of the desired line must also be $-\frac{3}{4}$, we can use the point-slope form to write the required equation.

$$y - (-3) = -\frac{3}{4}[x - (-4)]$$

NOTE

The line must pass through $(-4, -3)$, so let $(x_1, y_1) = (-4, -3)$.

This simplifies to

$$y = -\frac{3}{4}x - 6$$

and we have our equation in slope-intercept form.

Check Yourself 9

Find the equation of the line passing through (5, 4) and perpendicular to the line with equation $2x - 5y = 10$. (*Hint:* Recall that the slopes of perpendicular lines are negative reciprocals of each other.)

In Example 10 we will consider a business application of a linear equation.

Example 10 An Application of a Linear Equation

< Objective 2 >

In producing a new product, a manufacturer predicts that the number of items produced, x, and the cost, C, of producing those items will be related by a linear equation.

Suppose that the cost of producing 100 items will be \$5,000 and the cost of producing 500 items will be \$15,000. Find a linear equation relating x and C.

To solve this problem, we must find the equation of the line passing through points (100, 5,000) and (500, 15,000).

Although the numbers are considerably larger than we encountered so far in this section, the process is exactly the same.

First, we find the slope:

$$m = \frac{15{,}000 - 5{,}000}{500 - 100} = \frac{10{,}000}{400} = 25$$

We can now use the point-slope form as before to find the desired equation.

$$C - 5{,}000 = 25(x - 100)$$
$$C - 5{,}000 = 25x - 2{,}500$$
$$C = 25x + 2{,}500$$

To graph the equation we just derived, we must choose the scaling on the x- and C-axes carefully to get a reasonable picture. Here we choose increments of 100 on the x-axis and 2,500 on the C-axis because those seem appropriate for the given information.

NOTE

See how the change in scaling "distorts" the slope of the line? Also notice that the graph does not extend to the left of the y-axis since we cannot produce a negative number of items (x-values must be zero or greater).

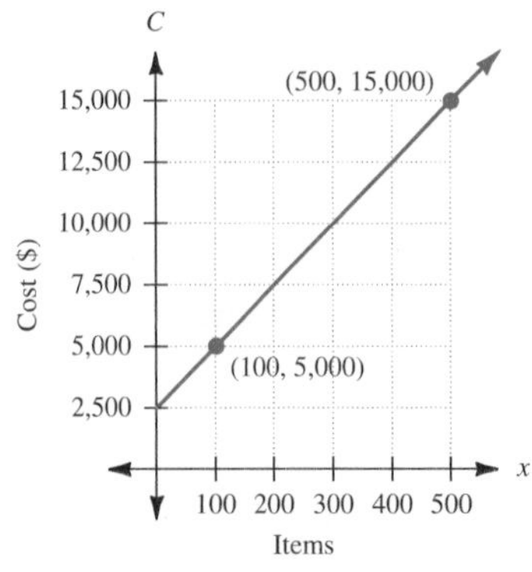

Check Yourself 10

A company predicts that the value in dollars, *V*, and the time that a piece of equipment has been in use, *t*, are related by a linear equation. Given that the equipment is valued at $1,500 after 2 years and at $300 after 10 years, find the linear equation relating *t* and *V*.

We have seen that to write the equation of a line, all we need to know is one point on the line and the slope of the line. We will not always be given a point and the slope directly. Nevertheless, if we can find these two things, we will be able to write the equation of the line. How we actually find a point and a slope will differ depending on the information given in the problem. For instance, consider the following situations:

1. We are given a graph of a line.

   We can find a point on the line from the graph.
   We can also find the slope of the line from the graph.

   This is all we need. We can now use the point-slope form (or slope-intercept form) to write the equation of our line.

2. We are given two points.

   We can choose one of the two points we are given.
   We can find the slope by using the definition of slope.

   This is all we need. We can now use the point-slope form (or slope-intercept form) to write the equation of our line.

3. We are given one point and the equation of a parallel or perpendicular line.

   We can use the point we are given.
   We can find the slope of the line we are given. Using the relationship of the second line to our line, we can find the slope.

   This is all we need. We can now use the point-slope form (or slope-intercept form) to write the equation of our line.

RECALL

The *vertical line test* is used to determine whether a graph is the graph of a function.

Putting together everything we have done in this chapter so far, we can further explore the connection between linear equations and functions. Because a vertical line cannot pass through a line with defined slope more than once, any nonvertical line can be represented as a function.

Example 11 Writing Equations as Functions

< Objective 3 >

Rewrite each linear equation as a function of x.

(a) $y = 3x - 4$

This can be rewritten as

$$f(x) = 3x - 4$$

(b) $2x - 3y = 6$

We must first solve the equation for y (recall that this will give us the slope-intercept form).

$$-3y = -2x + 6$$

$$y = \frac{2}{3}x - 2$$

This can be rewritten as

$$f(x) = \frac{2}{3}x - 2$$

Check Yourself 11

Rewrite each equation as a function of *x*.

(a) $y = -2x + 5$ **(b)** $3x + 5y = 15$

RECALL

Another benefit is that $f(x)$ can be entered easily into a graphing calculator.

One benefit of having a function written in $f(x)$ form is that it makes it fairly easy to substitute values for x. Sometimes it is useful to substitute nonnumeric values for x.

Example 12 Substituting Nonnumeric Values for x

Let $f(x) = 2x + 3$. Evaluate f as indicated.

(a) $f(a)$

Substituting a for x in our equation, we see that

$$f(a) = 2a + 3$$

(b) $f(2 + h)$

Substituting $2 + h$ for x in our equation, we get

$$f(2 + h) = 2(2 + h) + 3$$

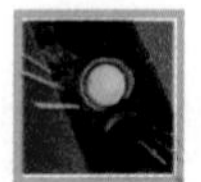

> CAUTION

f indicates our function. Do *not* distribute *f*.

Distributing the 2 and then simplifying, we have

$$f(2 + h) = 4 + 2h + 3$$
$$= 2h + 7$$

Check Yourself 12

Let $f(x) = 4x - 2$. Evaluate f as indicated.

(a) $f(b)$ **(b)** $f(4 + h)$

Check Yourself ANSWERS

1. $y = -\frac{2}{3}x - 3$ **2.** $m = \frac{3}{4}$ and the y-intercept is $(0, -2)$.

3. $m_1 = \frac{3}{2}$ and $m_2 = -\frac{2}{3}$; $m_1 \cdot m_2 = -1$

4.

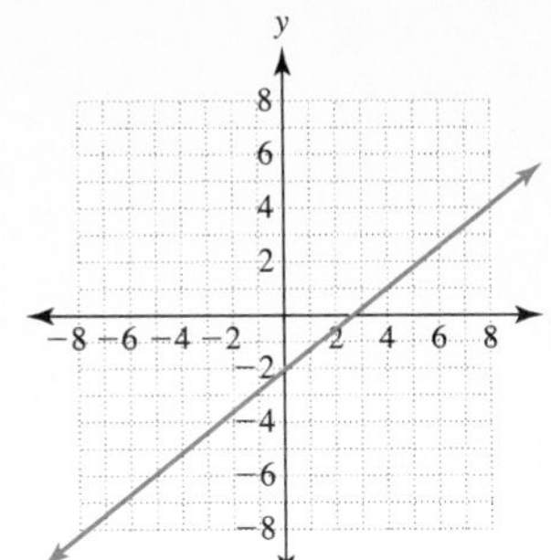

5. $y = \frac{3}{2}x + 7$ **6.** $y = -\frac{2}{3}x + \frac{11}{3}$

7. **(a)** $y = 5$; **(b)** $x = -3$ **8.** $y = -\frac{2}{3}x + \frac{11}{3}$ **9.** $y = -\frac{5}{2}x + \frac{33}{2}$

10. $V = -150t + 1{,}800$ **11.** **(a)** $f(x) = -2x + 5$; **(b)** $f(x) = -\frac{3}{5}x + 3$

12. **(a)** $4b - 2$; **(b)** $4h + 14$

Reading Your Text

The following fill-in-the-blank exercises are designed to ensure that you understand some of the key vocabulary used in this section.

SECTION 3.4

(a) The special form $Ax + By = C$, in which A and B cannot both be zero, is called the ______________.

(b) The equation $y = mx + b$ is called the ______________ for a line.

(c) The equation $y - y_1 = m(x - x_1)$ is called the ______________ for the equation of a line.

(d) In any situation, only two things need to be known to write the equation of a line: ______________ and ______________.

3.4 exercises

Basic Skills | Advanced Skills | Vocational-Technical Applications | Calculator/Computer | Above and Beyond

MathZone

Boost your grade at mathzone.com!
- Practice Problems
- NetTutor
- Self-Tests
- e-Professors
- Videos

Name ______________

Section ________ Date ________

In exercises 1 to 8, match the graph with one of these equations: **(a)** $y = 2x$; **(b)** $y = x + 1$; **(c)** $y = -x + 3$; **(d)** $y = 2x + 1$; **(e)** $y = -3x - 2$; **(f)** $y = \frac{2}{3}x + 1$; **(g)** $y = -\frac{4}{3}x + 1$; *and* **(h)** $y = -4x$.

1.

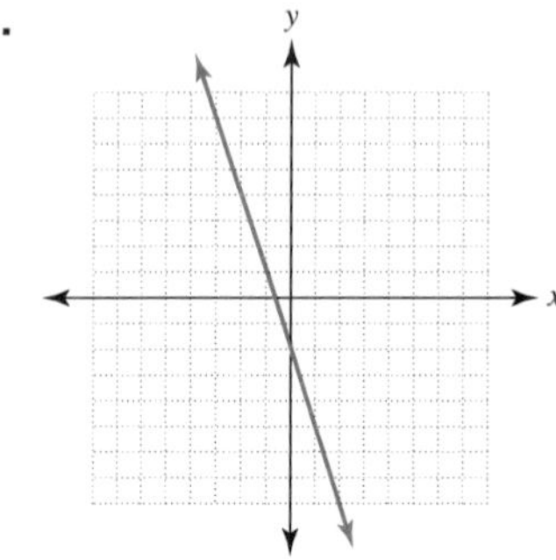

2.

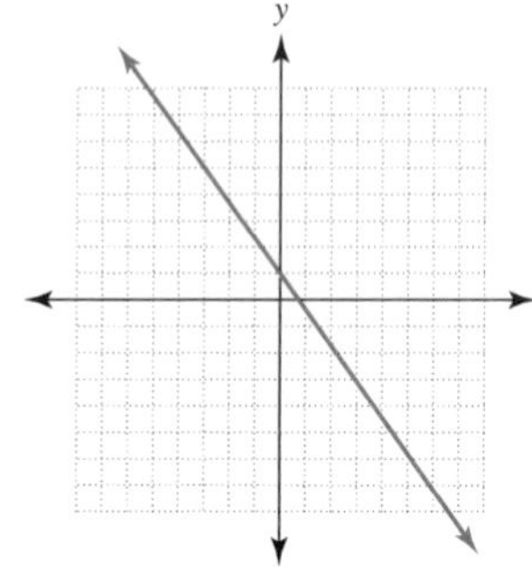

3.

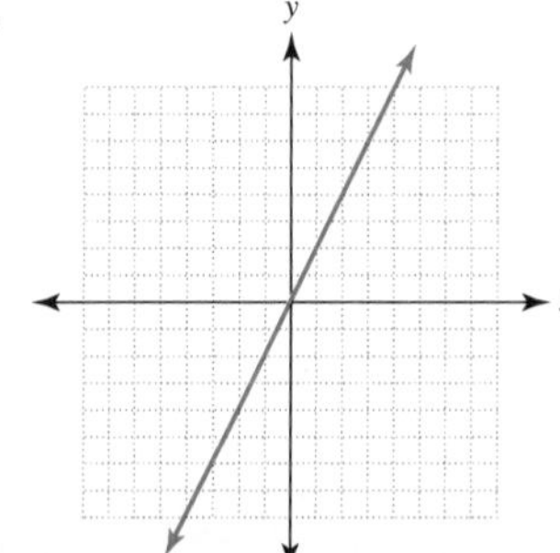

4.

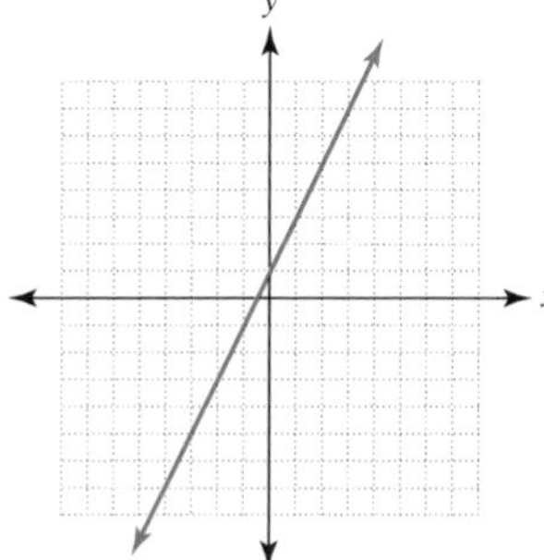

5.

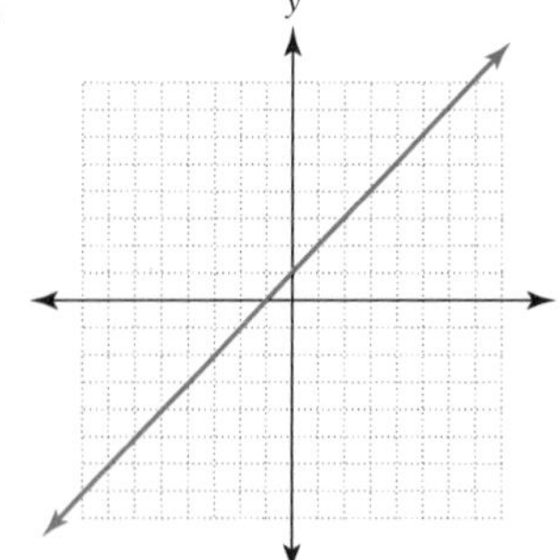

6.

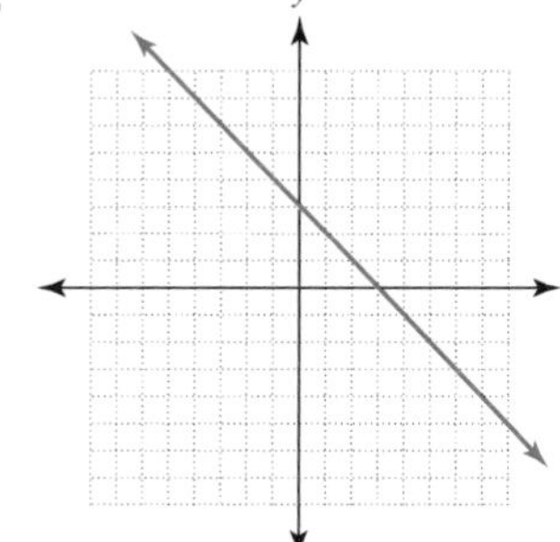

7.

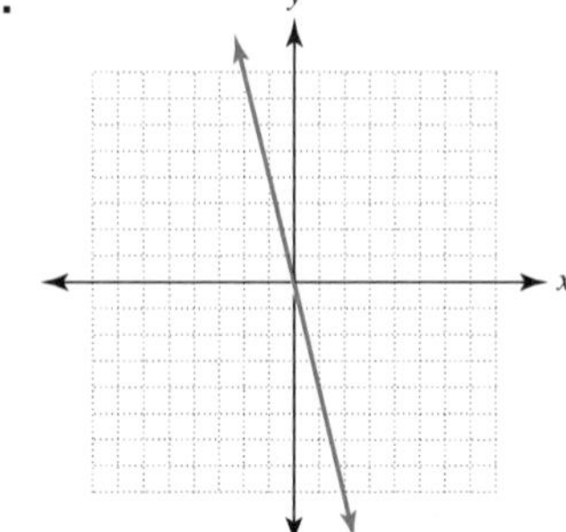

8.

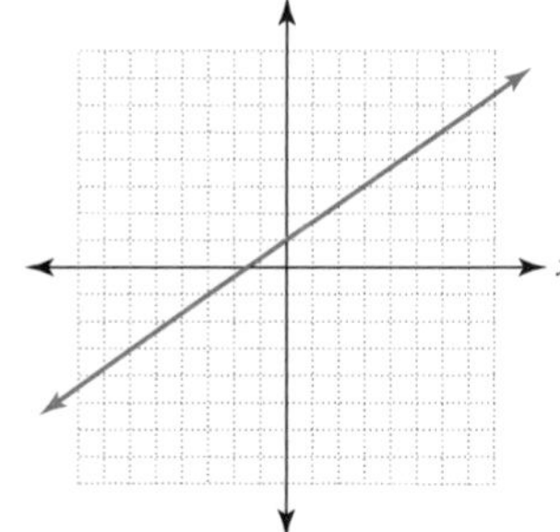

Answers

1. (e)
2. (g)
3. (a)
4. (d)
5. (b)
6. (c)
7. (h)
8. (f)

3.4 exercises

Write each equation in slope-intercept form. Give its slope and y-intercept.

9. $x + y = 5$

10. $2x - y = -2$

11. $x + 3y = 9$

12. $2x - 3y = 6$ > Videos

13. $2x - y = 0$

14. $y + 3 = 0$

< Objective 1 >

Write the equation of the line passing through each of the given points with the indicated slope. Give your results in slope-intercept form, when possible.

15. $(0, 2)$, $m = 3$

16. $(0, 2)$, $m = \frac{3}{2}$

17. $(0, 4)$, $m = 0$

18. $(1, 2)$, $m = 3$

19. $(-2, -3)$, $m = -3$

20. $(2, -3)$, m is undefined

21. $(5, 0)$, $m = -\frac{4}{5}$

Write the equation of the line passing through each of the given pairs of points. Write your result in slope-intercept form, when possible.

22. $(2, 3)$ and $(5, 6)$

23. $(-2, -3)$ and $(2, 0)$

24. $(-3, 2)$ and $(4, 2)$

25. $(2, -3)$ and $(2, 4)$

26. $(2, 0)$ and $(0, -3)$

27. $(0, 4)$ and $(-2, -1)$

Determine whether the statements are **true** *or* **false.**

28. (a) Given two points, there is exactly one line that will pass through them.

(b) Given a line, there is exactly one other line that is perpendicular to it.

Fill in the blanks with **always, sometimes,** *or* **never.**

29. (a) You can _________ write the equation of a line if you know two points that are on the line.

(b) The equation of a line can _________ be put into slope-intercept form.

Answers

9. $y = -x + 5$, $m = -1$, y-int: $(0, 5)$

10. $y = 2x + 2$, $m = 2$, y-int: $(0, 2)$

11. $y = -\frac{1}{3}x + 3$, $m = -\frac{1}{3}$, y-int: $(0, 3)$

12. $y = \frac{2}{3}x - 2$, $m = \frac{2}{3}$, y-int: $(0, -2)$

13. $y = 2x$, $m = 2$, y-int: $(0, 0)$

14. $y = -3$, $m = 0$, y-int: $(0, -3)$

15. $y = 3x + 2$

16. $y = \frac{3}{2}x + 2$

17. $y = 4$

18. $y = 3x - 1$

19. $y = -3x - 9$

20. $x = 2$

21. $y = -\frac{4}{5}x + 4$

22. $y = x + 1$

23. $y = \frac{3}{4}x - \frac{3}{2}$

24. $y = 2$

25. $x = 2$

26. $y = \frac{3}{2}x - 3$

27. $y = \frac{5}{2}x + 4$

28. (a) True; (b) False

29. (a) always; (b) sometimes

Answers

30. $y = -\frac{2}{3}x + 4$

31. $y = -\frac{1}{2}x + 2$

32. $y = \frac{3}{4}x + \frac{3}{2}$

33. $y = 4$

34. $x = -2$

35. $y = 5x - 13$

36. $y = -\frac{3}{2}x - 7$

37. $y = 3x + 3$

38. $y = \frac{2}{3}x - 3$

39. (a) $T = 35h + 75$; (b) See exercise

40. (a) $S = 0.10x + 200$; (b) See exercise

Write the equation of the line L satisfying the given geometric conditions.

30. L has slope $-\frac{2}{3}$ and y-intercept $(0, 4)$.

31. L has x-intercept $(4, 0)$ and y-intercept $(0, 2)$.

32. L has x-intercept $(-2, 0)$ and slope $\frac{3}{4}$.

33. L has y-intercept $(0, 4)$ and a 0 slope.

34. L has x-intercept $(-2, 0)$ and an undefined slope.

35. L passes through point $(3, 2)$ with a slope of 5.

36. L passes through point $(-2, -4)$ with a slope of $-\frac{3}{2}$.

37. L has y-intercept $(0, 3)$ and is parallel to the line with equation $y = 3x - 5$.

38. L has y-intercept $(0, -3)$ and is parallel to the line with equation $y = \frac{2}{3}x + 1$.

< Objective 2 >

39. Business and Finance A college has tuition charges based on the following pattern. Tuition is \$35 per credit-hour plus a fixed student fee of \$75.

(a) Write a linear equation that shows the relationship between the total tuition charge, T, and the number of credit-hours taken, h.

(b) Graph the relationship between T and h.

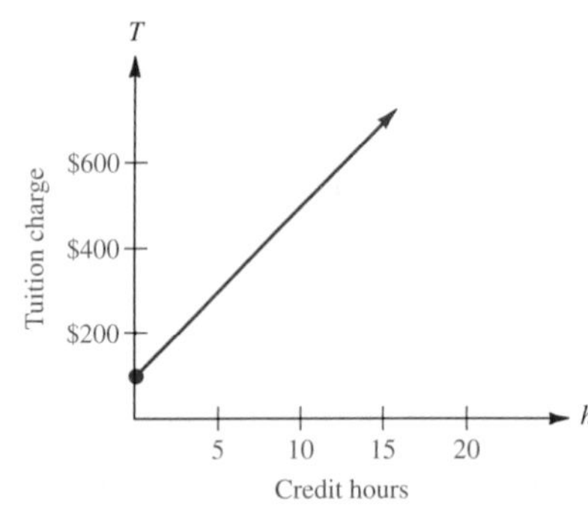

40. Business and Finance A salesperson's weekly salary is based on a fixed amount of \$200 plus 10% of the total amount of weekly sales.

(a) Write an equation that shows the relationship between the weekly salary, S, and the amount of weekly sales, x (in dollars).

(b) Graph the relationship between S and x.

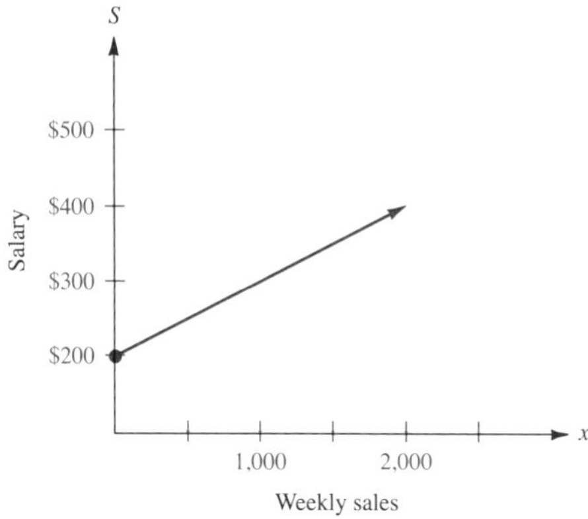

41. **Science and Medicine** A temperature of 10°C corresponds to a temperature of 50°F. Also 40°C corresponds to 104°F. Find the linear equation relating F and C.

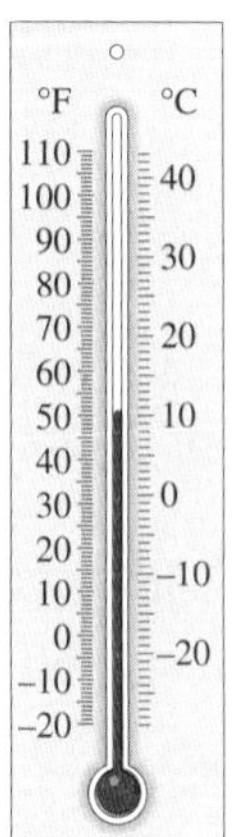
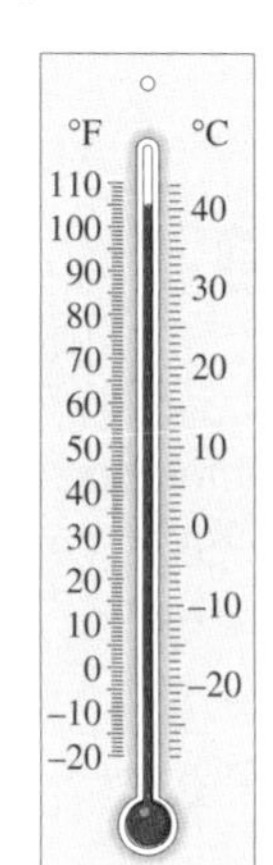

42. A realtor receives $500 a month plus 4% commission on sales. The equation that describes the total monthly income, I (in dollars), of the realtor is $I = 0.04s + 500$, in which s is the amount of sales.

(a) Graph this equation for $0 \le s \le 160$, in which s is measured in thousands of dollars. (**Hint:** This means if the amount of sales is $20,000, it would be graphed as 20 since the scale for sales is in thousands of dollars.)

(b) Plot the point whose coordinates are (90, 4,100) on the graph. Write a sentence to describe the meaning of this ordered pair.

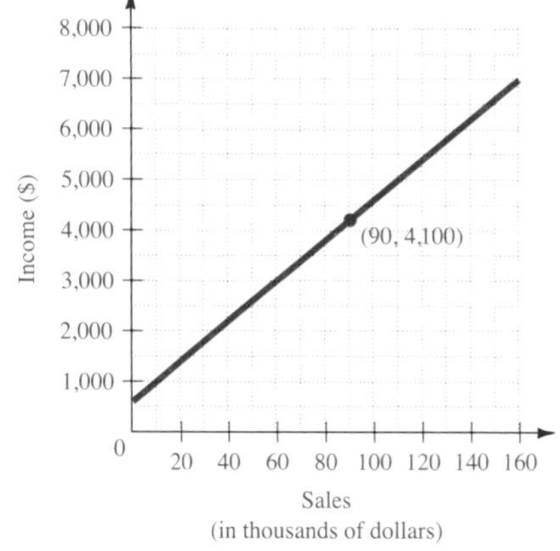

Answers

41. $F = \frac{9}{5}C + 32$

42. (a) See exercise; (b) $90,000 in sales produces $4,100 in income.

Answers

43. (a) See answers; (b) 180 mi

44. $C = 60x + 4{,}000$

45. (a) $C = 35x + 50$; (b) \$172.50; (c) 3.15 h

46. -3

47. 13

48. -7

49. -19

50. -1

51. $5a - 1$

52. $10r - 1$

53. $5x + 4$

54. $5a - 11$

55. $5x + 5h - 1$

56. 5

43. Trac Hunyh's weekly cost of operating a taxi is \$100 plus 15¢ a mile. The equation that describes Trac's cost is $C = 100 + 0.15m$, in which m is the number of miles driven in a week.

(a) Graph the equation for $0 \le m \le 200$.

(b) How many miles would Trac have to drive for the weekly cost to be \$127?

44. **Business and Finance** In planning for a new item, a manufacturer assumes that the number of items produced, x, and the cost in dollars, C, of producing these items are related by a linear equation. Projections are that 100 items will cost \$10,000 to produce and that 300 items will cost \$22,000 to produce. Find the equation that relates C and x.

45. **Business and Finance** Mike bills a customer at the rate of \$35 per hour plus a fixed service call charge of \$50.

(a) Write an equation that will allow you to compute the total bill for any number of hours, x, that it takes to complete a job.

(b) What will the total cost of a job be if it takes 3.5 h to complete?

(c) How many hours would a job have to take if the total bill were \$160.25?

< Objective 3 >

In exercises 46 to 50, if $f(x) = 4x - 3$, find the following.

46. $f(0)$

47. $f(4)$

48. $f(-1)$

49. $f(-4)$

50. $f\left(\frac{1}{2}\right)$

In exercises 51 to 56, if $f(x) = 5x - 1$, find the following.

51. $f(a)$

52. $f(2r)$

53. $f(x + 1)$

54. $f(a - 2)$

55. $f(x + h)$

56. $\dfrac{f(x + h) - f(x)}{h}$

In exercises 57 to 60, if $g(x) = -3x + 2$, find the following.

57. $g(m)$

58. $g(5n)$

59. $g(x + 2)$ 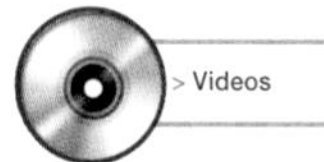

60. $g(s - 1)$

Basic Skills | **Advanced Skills** | Vocational-Technical Applications | Calculator/Computer | Above and Beyond

Use the graph to determine the slope and y-intercept of the line. Then write the equation of the line in slope-intercept form.

61.

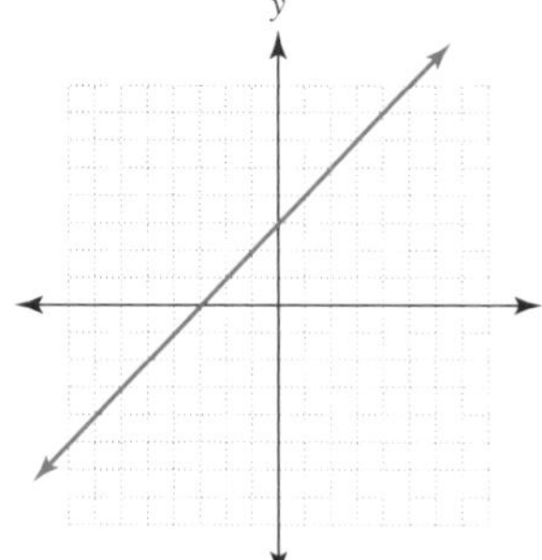

62.

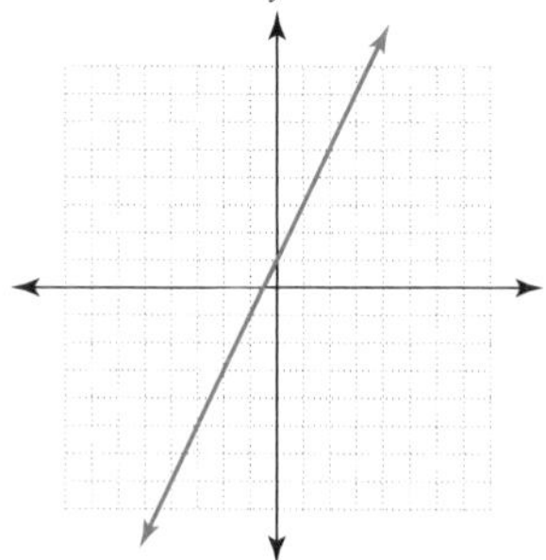

63.

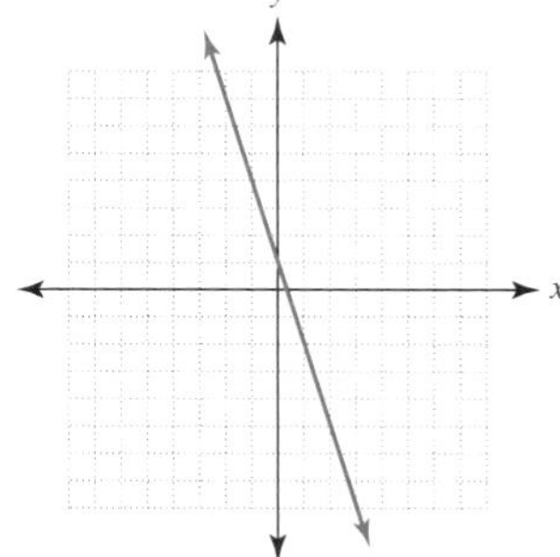

64.

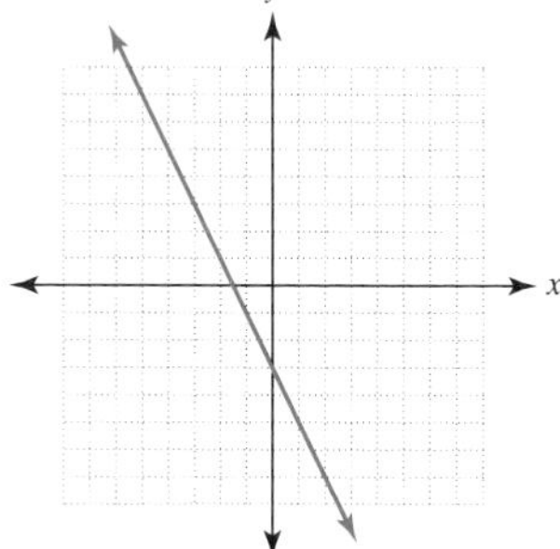

65.

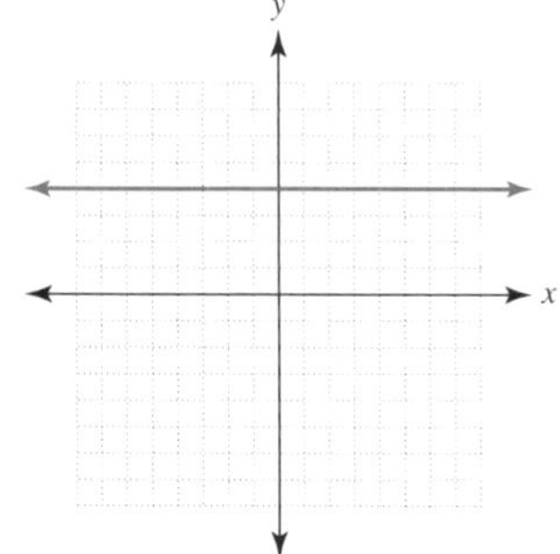

Answers

57. $-3m + 2$

58. $-15n + 2$

59. $-3x - 4$

60. $-3s + 5$

61. $m = 1$, y-int: $(0, 3)$, $y = x + 3$

62. $m = 2$, y-int: $(0, 1)$, $y = 2x + 1$

63. $m = -3$, y-int: $(0, 1)$, $y = -3x + 1$

64. $m = -2$, y-int: $(0, -3)$, $y = -2x - 3$

65. $m = 0$, y-int: $(0, 4)$, $y = 4$

Answers

66. $f(x) = -\frac{3}{2}x + 2$

67. $f(x) = 2x + 8$

68. $f(x) = \frac{4}{3}x - 2$

69. $f(x) = -\frac{1}{3}x - \frac{5}{3}$

70. $f(x) = \frac{5}{3}x - 1$

71. $f(x) = -\frac{1}{2}x$

72. $f(x) = 5$

73. Same slope but different y-int.

74. Different slopes but same y-int.

75. (a) and (b) have the same y-int. but (a) rises and (b) falls, both at the same rate. (a) and (c) have the same slope but different y-int.

76. (b) and (c) are perpendicular

77. 4.9 hp per cylinder

In exercises 66 to 72, find a function $f(x)$ whose graph is the line L satisfying the given geometric conditions.

66. L has y-intercept (0, 2) and is perpendicular to the line with equation $2x - 3y = 6$.

67. L passes through point $(-3, 2)$ and is parallel to the line with equation $y = 2x - 3$.

68. L passes through point (3, 2) and is parallel to the line with equation $y = \frac{4}{3}x + 4$.

69. L passes through point $(-2, -1)$ and is perpendicular to the line with equation $y = 3x + 1$.

> Videos

70. L passes through point (3, 4) and is perpendicular to the line with equation $y = -\frac{3}{5}x + 2$.

71. L passes through $(-2, 1)$ and is parallel to the line with equation $x + 2y = 4$.

72. L passes through $(-3, 5)$ and is parallel to the x-axis.

In exercises 73 to 76, without graphing, compare and contrast the slopes and y-intercepts of the equations.

73. **(a)** $y = 2x + 1$, **(b)** $y = 2x - 5$, **(c)** $y = 2x$

74. **(a)** $y = 3x + 2$, **(b)** $y = \frac{3}{4}x + 2$, **(c)** $y = -2x + 2$

75. **(a)** $y = 4x + 5$, **(b)** $y = -4x + 5$, **(c)** $y = 4x - 5$

76. **(a)** $y = 3x$, **(b)** $y = \frac{1}{3}x$, **(c)** $y = -3x$

Basic Skills | Advanced Skills | **Vocational-Technical Applications** | Calculator/Computer | Above and Beyond

77. **Automotive Technology** In a car where the diameter of the cylinder bore is 3.5 inches, the estimate of the horsepower (hp) is given by the formula

$$\text{hp} = 4.9N$$

where N is the number of cylinders in the engine. What is the slope of the graph of this relationship?

78. **Allied Health** The ideal body weight (IBW) (in pounds), for a man is a linear function of his height, H (in inches), given by the formula $IBW = 106 + 6(H - 60)$.

(a) Determine the slope of this function.

(b) Interpret this slope verbally.

79. **Allied Health** The ideal body weight (IBW), in pounds, for a woman is a linear function of her height, H (in inches), given by the formula $IBW = 105 + 5(H - 60)$.

(a) Determine the slope of this function.

(b) Interpret this slope verbally.

80. **Construction Technology** During a welder's shift, at the end of hour 3, she had completed 46 parts. At the end of 10 hours, she had finished 158 parts. Write an equation to describe the number of parts, n, compared to the time (in hours), h.

81. **Manufacturing Technology** The length of a piece of polymer at 27°C is 14.84 inches. After being heated to 93°C, the length is 15.06 inches. Write an equation to describe the length of the piece, L, compared to the temperature, x.

82. **Allied Health** The absorbance, A, of a solution, or the amount of light that is absorbed by the solution, is a linear function of the solution's concentration, C. A lab technician mixes two solutions of bilirubin: one with a concentration of 150 milligrams per liter (mg/L) and an absorbance value of 0.35, as determined by a spectrophotometer, and one with a concentration of 77 mg/L and an absorbance value of 0.18.

(a) Find the slope of the line.

(b) Write an equation for the absorbance, A, as a function of its concentration, C, in mg/L.

(c) Record a table of values for your function for $C = 80, 90, \ldots,$ 150 mg/L.

Concentration C (mg/L)	Absorbance A
80	0.1847
90	0.2077
100	0.2307
110	0.2537
120	0.2767
130	0.2997
140	0.3227
150	0.3457

(d) What concentration of bilirubin will yield an absorbance value of 0.25?

(e) Interpret the slope verbally.

Answers

78. (a) 6 lb/in.; (b) For every additional inch in a man's height, his ideal body weight increases by 6 lb.

79. (a) 5 lb/in.; (b) For every additional inch in a woman's height, her ideal body weight increases by 5 lb.

80. $n = 16h - 2$

81. $L = \frac{1}{300}x + \frac{59}{4}$

82. (a) 0.0023; (b) $A(C) = 0.0023C + 0.0007$; (c) See exercise; (d) 108.4 mg/L; (e) For every additional milligram per liter in concentration of the bilirubin solution, the absorbance value increases by 0.0023.

Answers

83.

84.
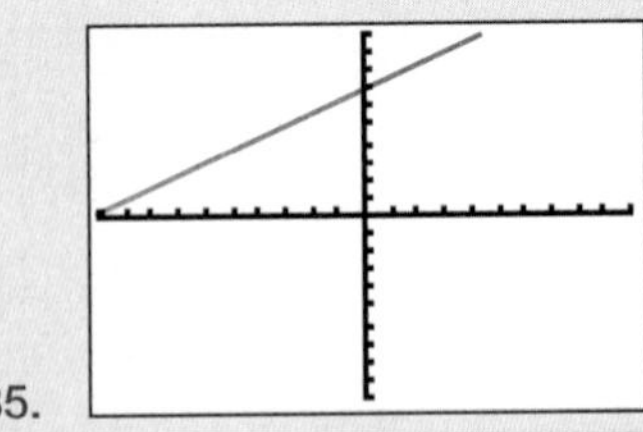

85.
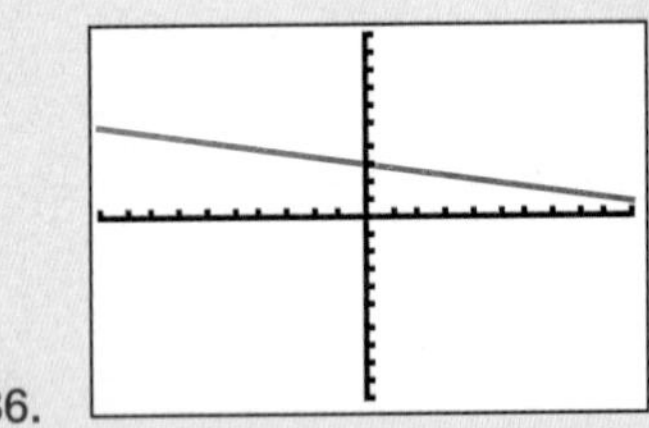

86.

87. $y = -\frac{4}{7}x + \frac{18}{7}$

88. $y = -5x + 19$

89. 5

90. 9

91. (1, 5), (3, 9)

92. $y = 2x + 3$

93. $y = 0.1097x - 217.682$, $y(2001) = 1.8275$, See exercise

Basic Skills | Advanced Skills | Vocational-Technical Applications | **Calculator/Computer** | Above and Beyond

Use your graphing utility to graph the following.

83. $3x - 5y = 30$

84. $2x + 7y = 14$

85. The line with slope $\frac{2}{3}$ and y-intercept at (0, 7).

86. The line with slope $-\frac{1}{5}$ and y-intercept at (0, 3).

Basic Skills | Advanced Skills | Vocational-Technical Applications | Calculator/Computer | **Above and Beyond**

87. GEOMETRY Find the equation of the perpendicular bisector of the segment joining $(-3, -5)$ and $(5, 9)$. [*Hint:* First determine the midpoint of the segment. The midpoint would be

$$\left(\frac{-3+5}{2}, \frac{-5+9}{2}\right) = (1, 2).$$

The perpendicular bisector passes through that point and is perpendicular to the line segment connecting the points.]

88. GEOMETRY Find the equation of the perpendicular bisector of the segment joining $(-2, 3)$ and $(8, 5)$.

In exercises 89 to 92, let $f(x) = 2x + 3$.

89. Find $f(1)$.

90. Find $f(3)$.

91. Form the ordered pairs $(1, f(1))$ and $(3, f(3))$.

92. Write the equation of the line passing through the points determined by the ordered pairs in exercise 91.

93. The average annual exchange rate for the years 1996–2000 between U.S. dollars and Australian dollars (AUS$) is provided in the given table.

Year	1996	1997	1998	1999	2000
Rate	1.278	1.347	1.592	1.550	1.725

Source: University of British Columbia

Plot the points given (Year, Rate) on the Cartesian coordinate system (scale the axes appropriately). Sketch a single line that *best fits* the data. Give the equation of this line. Use this line to predict the average annual exchange rate for the year 2001. How accurate is this prediction?

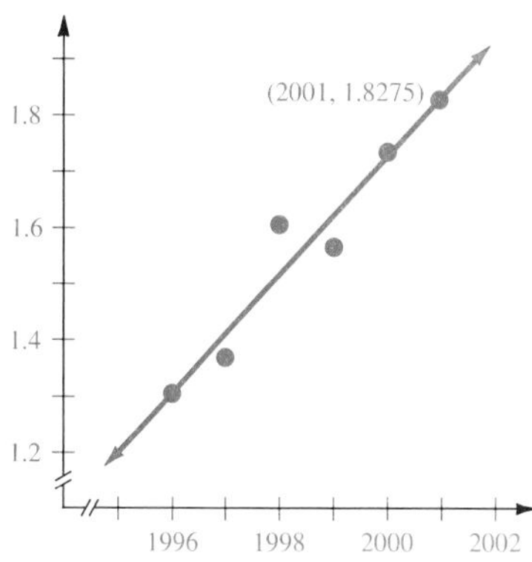

94. Use the line created in exercise 93 to predict the exchange rate (U.S. dollars to Australian dollars) in January 2002. Search the Internet to determine the accuracy of your prediction.

95. **Science and Medicine** Aerobic exercise requires that your heartbeat be at a certain rate for 12 min or more for full physical benefit. To determine the proper heart rate for a healthy person, start with the number 220 and subtract the person's age. Then multiply by 0.70. The result is the target aerobic heart rate, the rate to maintain during exercise.

(a) Write a formula for the relation between a person's age, A, and the person's target aerobic heart rate, R.

(b) Using at least 10 different ages, construct a table of target heart rates by age.

(c) Draw a graph of this table of values.

(d) What are reasonable limits for the person's age that you would use with your formula? Would it make sense to use $A = 2$? Or $A = 150$?

(e) What are the benefits of aerobic exercise over other types of exercise?

(f) List some different types of exercise that are nonaerobic. Describe the differences between the two different types of exercise.

Answers

94. 1.9372

95. Above and Beyond

Answers

1. (e) **3.** (a) **5.** (b) **7.** (h) **9.** $y = -x + 5, m = -1$, y-int: (0, 5)

11. $y = -\frac{1}{3}x + 3, m = -\frac{1}{3}$, y-int: (0, 3) **13.** $y = 2x, m = 2$, y-int: (0, 0)

15. $y = 3x + 2$ **17.** $y = 4$ **19.** $y = -3x - 9$ **21.** $y = -\frac{4}{5}x + 4$

23. $y = \frac{3}{4}x - \frac{3}{2}$ **25.** $x = 2$ **27.** $y = \frac{5}{2}x + 4$

29. **(a)** always; **(b)** sometimes **31.** $y = -\frac{1}{2}x + 2$ **33.** $y = 4$

35. $y = 5x - 13$ **37.** $y = 3x + 3$

39. (a) $T = 35h + 75$; **(b)**

41. $F = \frac{9}{5}C + 32$ **43. (a)**

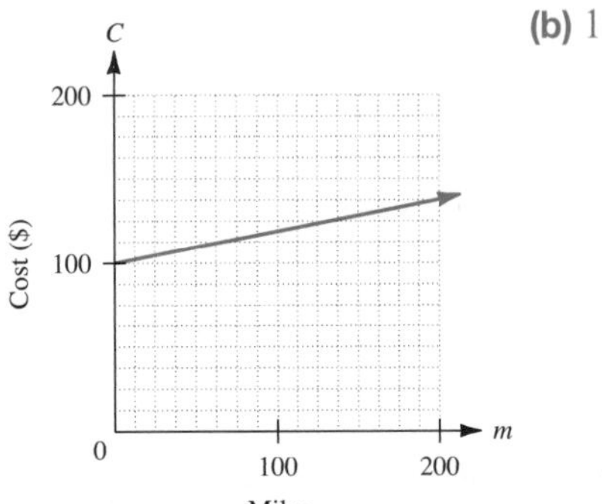

(b) 180 mi

45. (a) $C = 35x + 50$; **(b)** \$172.50; **(c)** 3.15 h **47.** 13 **49.** -19 **51.** $5a - 1$ **53.** $5x + 4$ **55.** $5x + 5h - 1$ **57.** $-3m + 2$ **59.** $-3x - 4$ **61.** $m = 1$, y-int: $(0, 3)$, $y = x + 3$ **63.** $m = -3$, y-int: $(0, 1)$, $y = -3x + 1$ **65.** $m = 0$, y-int: $(0, 4)$, $y = 4$

67. $f(x) = 2x + 8$ **69.** $f(x) = -\frac{1}{3}x - \frac{5}{3}$ **71.** $f(x) = -\frac{1}{2}x$

73. Same slope but different y-int. **75.** (a) and (b) have the same y-int but (a) rises and (b) falls, both at the same rate. (a) and (c) have the same slope but different y-int. **77.** 4.9 hp per cylinder **79. (a)** 5 lb/in.; **(b)** For every additional inch in a woman's height, her ideal body weight increases by 5 lb.

81. $L = \frac{1}{300}x + \frac{59}{4}$

83.

85.

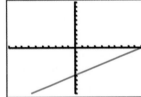

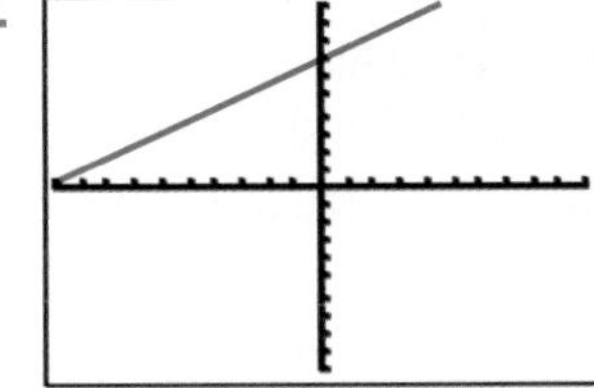

87. $y = -\frac{4}{7}x + \frac{18}{7}$ **89.** 5 **91.** $(1, 5)$, $(3, 9)$

93.

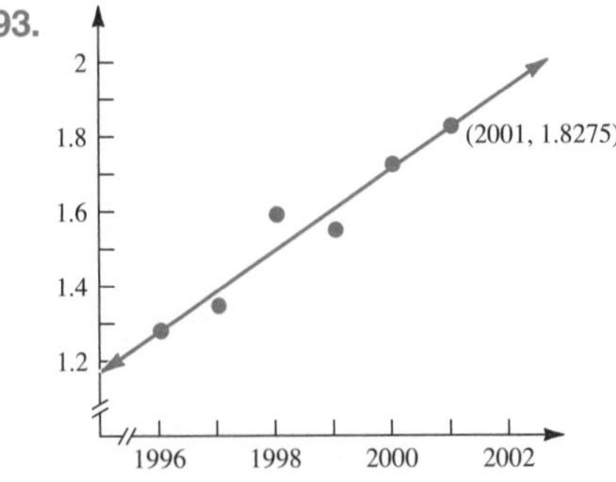

$y = 0.1097x - 217.682$, $y(2001) = 1.8275$ **95.** Above and Beyond

3.5 Graphing Absolute Value Functions and Linear Inequalities

< 3.5 Objectives >

1 > Graph an absolute value function

2 > Graph a linear inequality in two variables

Equations may contain absolute value notation in their statements. In this section, we will begin by looking at graphing absolute value functions.

We will start by looking at the graph of the function $f(x) = |x|$. All other graphs of linear absolute value functions are variations of this graph.

The graph can be found using a graphing calculator. We will develop the graph from a table of values.

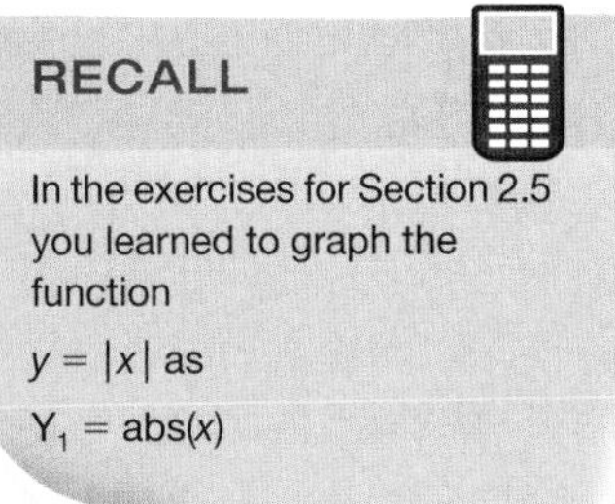
RECALL
In the exercises for Section 2.5 you learned to graph the function
y = |x| as
Y₁ = abs(x)

x	$f(x) = \|x\|$
-3	3
-2	2
-1	1
0	0
1	1
2	2

Plotting these ordered pairs, we see a pattern emerge. The graph is like a large V that has its vertex at the origin. The slope of the line to the right of 0 is 1, and the slope of the line to the left of 0 is -1.

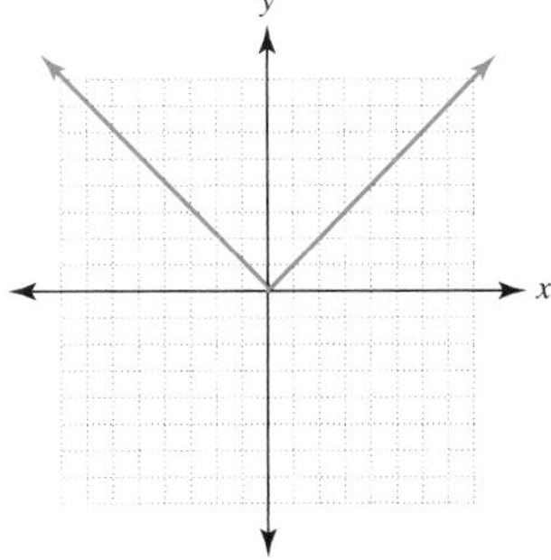
y
x

Let us now see what happens to the graph when we add or subtract some constant inside the absolute value bars.

Example 1 Graphing an Absolute Value Function

< Objective 1 >

Graph each function.

(a) $f(x) = |x - 3|$

Again, we start with a table of values.

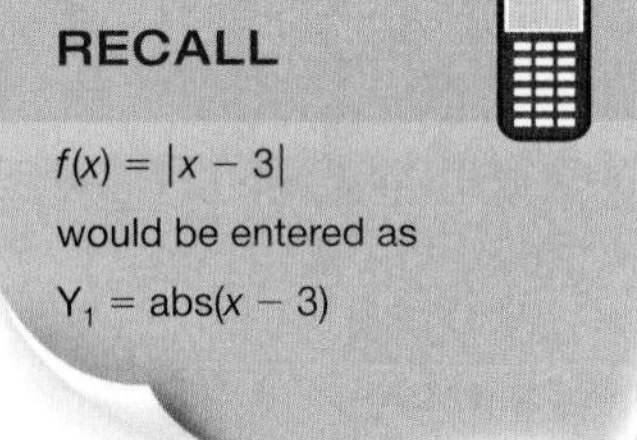

x	$f(x)$
−2	5
−1	4
0	3
1	2
2	1
3	0
4	1
5	2

Then, we plot the points associated with the set of ordered pairs.

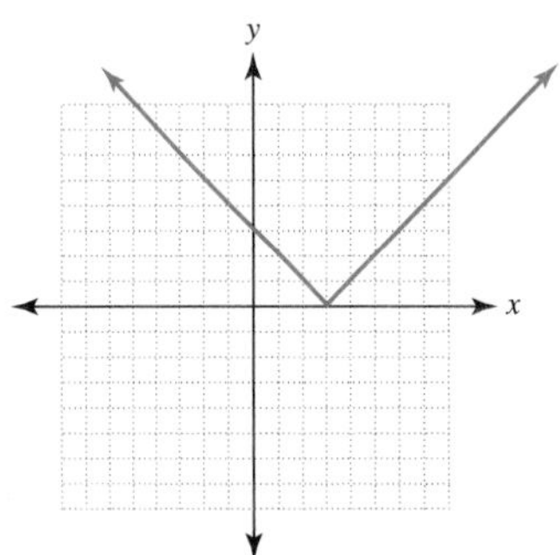

The graph of the function $f(x) = |x - 3|$ is the same shape as the graph of the function $f(x) = |x|$; it has just shifted to the right 3 units.

(b) $f(x) = |x + 1|$

We begin with a table of values.

x	$f(x)$
−2	1
−1	0
0	1
1	2
2	3
3	4

Then we graph.

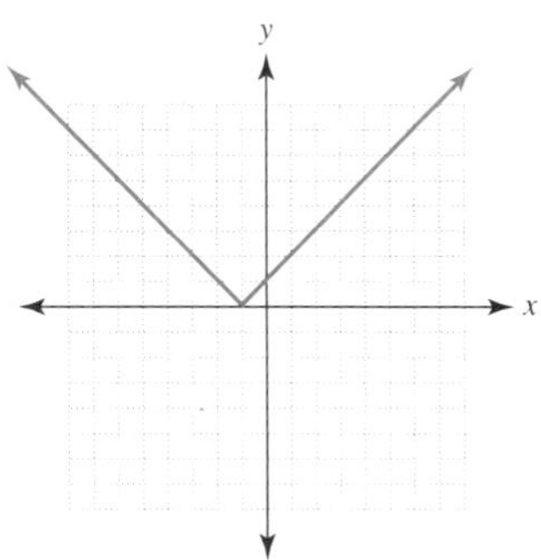

Note that the graph of $f(x) = |x + 1|$ is the same shape as the graph of the function $f(x) = |x|$, except that it is shifted 1 unit to the left.

NOTE

If a is negative, $x - a$ will be x plus some positive number. For example, if $a = -2$,

$x - a = x - (-2) = x + 2$

Check Yourself 1

Graph each function.

(a) $f(x) = |x - 2|$ **(b)** $f(x) = |x + 3|$

We can summarize what we have discovered about the horizontal shift of the graph of an absolute value function.

Property

Graphing Absolute Value Functions of the Form $f(x) = |x - a|$

The graph of the function $f(x) = |x - a|$ will be the same shape as the graph of $f(x) = |x|$ except that the graph will be shifted a units

To the right if a is positive
To the left if a is negative

Now we know what happens when we add or subtract some number inside the absolute value bars. What would happen if we added or subtracted some constant *outside* the absolute value bars? Consider Example 2.

Example 2 Graphing an Absolute Value Function

Graph each function.

(a) $f(x) = |x| - 2$

As before, start with a table of values.

x	$f(x)$
−2	0
−1	−1
0	−2
1	−1
2	0

Then, we plot the points to graph the function.

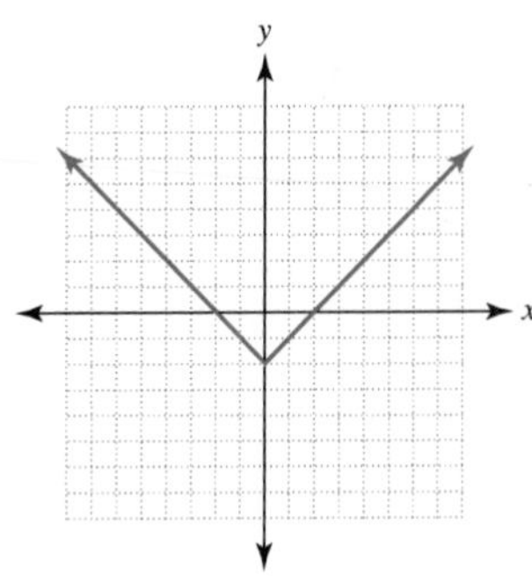

Notice the graph again has the shape of $f(x) = |x|$; it has just shifted down 2 units.

(b) $f(x) = |x| + 1$

As before, start with a table of values.

x	$f(x)$
−2	3
−1	2
0	1
1	2
2	3

Then we graph.

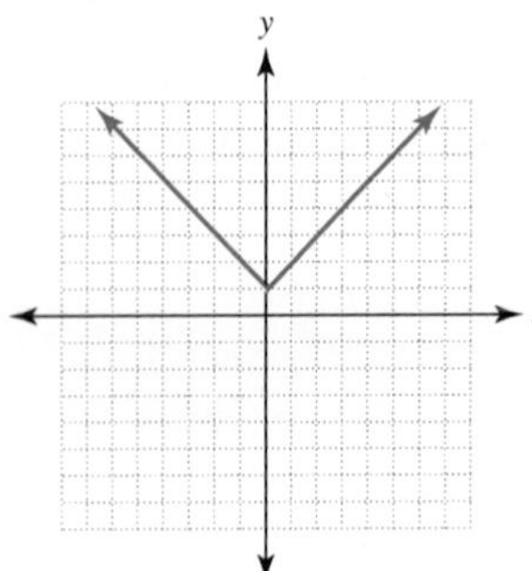

Check Yourself 2

Graph each function.

(a) $f(x) = |x| - 4$ **(b)** $f(x) = |x| + 2$

We can now summarize what we have discovered about vertical shift:

Property

Graphing Absolute Value Functions of the form $f(x) = |x| - a$

The graph of the function $f(x) = |x| - a$ will be the same shape as the graph of $f(x) = |x|$ except that the graph will be shifted a units

Up if a is positive
Down if a is negative

Combining the ideas from Examples 1 and 2 we can graph even more interesting absolute value functions.

Example 3 Graphing an Absolute Value Function

Graph $f(x) = |x - 5| + 3$.

Beginning as we did in earlier examples, we create a table of values.

x	$f(x)$
−10	18
−5	13
0	8
5	3
10	8
15	13

Now we graph.

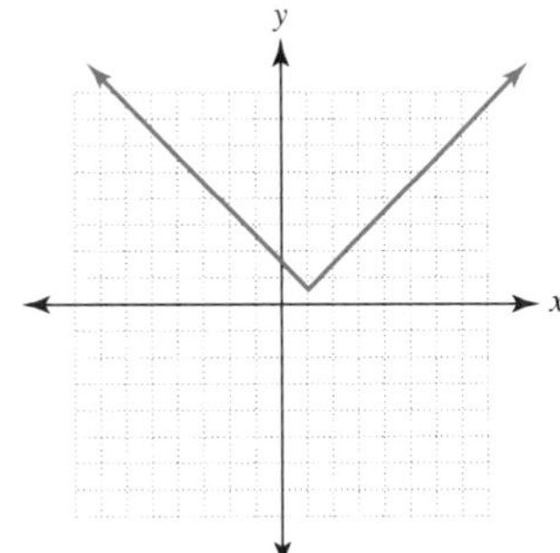

NOTE

The absolute value graph shifts *right* 5 units (since we are *subtracting* 5 *inside* the absolute value symbol) and *up* 3 units (since we are *adding* 3 *outside*).

Check Yourself 3

Graph the function $f(x) = |x + 5| - 3$.

In Section 2.5, we discussed solving absolute value equations and inequalities with one variable. We also learned how to graph inequalities on a number line. We have just learned how to graph absolute value functions in the plane. Now we will extend our work with graphing to include linear inequalities in two variables. We begin with a definition.

Definition

Linear Inequality in Two Variables

An inequality that can be written in the form

$Ax + By < C$

in which A and B are not both 0, is called a **linear inequality in two variables.**

NOTE

The inequality symbols $\leq$, $>$, and $\geq$ can also be used.

Some examples of linear inequalities in two variables are

$x + 3y > 6 \qquad y \leq 3x + 1 \qquad 2x - y \geq 3$

The *graph* of a linear inequality is always a region of the plane whose boundary is a straight line. We will look at an example of graphing such an inequality.

Example 4 Graphing a Linear Inequality

< Objective 2 >

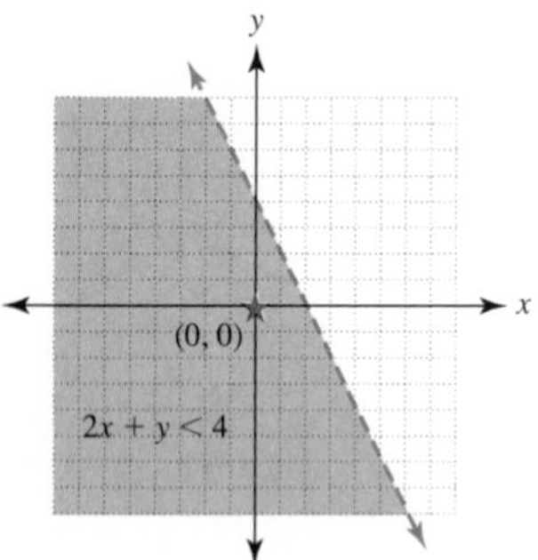

Graph $2x + y < 4$.

First, replace the inequality symbol ($<$) with an equal sign. We then have $2x + y = 4$. This equation forms the **boundary line** of the graph of the original inequality. You can graph the line by any of the methods discussed earlier.

The boundary line for our inequality is shown in the margin. The dashed line indicates that the points on the line $2x + y = 4$ are *not* part of the solutions for the inequality $2x + y < 4$. We see that the boundary line separates the plane into two regions, each of which is called a **half-plane.** The solution will include one of the half-planes.

We now need to choose the correct half-plane. Choose any convenient test point not on the boundary line. The origin (0, 0) is a good choice because it makes for easy calculations.

Substitute $x = 0$ and $y = 0$ into the inequality.

$$2 \cdot 0 + 0 \overset{?}{<} 4$$

$$0 + 0 \overset{?}{<} 4$$

$$0 < 4 \quad \text{A true statement}$$

NOTE

You can always use the origin for a test point unless the boundary line passes through the origin.

Because the inequality is *true* for the test point, the test point is a **solution** to the inequality. Therefore, we shade the half-plane containing that test point (here the origin). The origin and all other points *below* the boundary line then represent solutions for our original inequality.

Check Yourself 4

Graph the inequality $x + 3y < 3$.

The process is similar when the points on the boundary line are included in the solution set.

Example 5 Graphing a Linear Inequality

> **NOTES**
>
> Again, we replace the inequality symbol ($\geq$) with an equal sign to write the equation for our boundary line.
>
> Although any of our graphing methods can be used here, the intercept method is probably the most efficient.

Graph $4x - 3y \geq 12$.

First, graph the boundary line, $4x - 3y = 12$.

When equality *is included* ($\leq$ or $\geq$), use a *solid line* for the graph of the boundary line. This means that each point on the line is a solution of the inequality.

The graph of our boundary line (a solid line here) is shown in the figure.

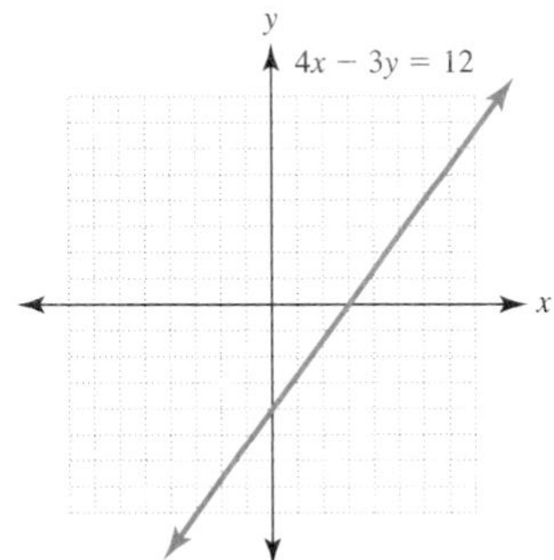

Again, we use (0, 0) as a convenient test point. Substituting 0 for both x and y in the original inequality, we have

$$4 \cdot 0 - 3 \cdot 0 \overset{?}{\geq} 12$$

$$0 \geq 12 \quad \text{A false statement}$$

Because the inequality is *false* for the test point, the test point is *not* part of the solution set. Therefore, we do not shade the side containing the test point—we shade the half-plane that does *not* contain that test point, here (0, 0).

> **NOTE**
>
> All points *on and below* the boundary line represent solutions for our original inequality.

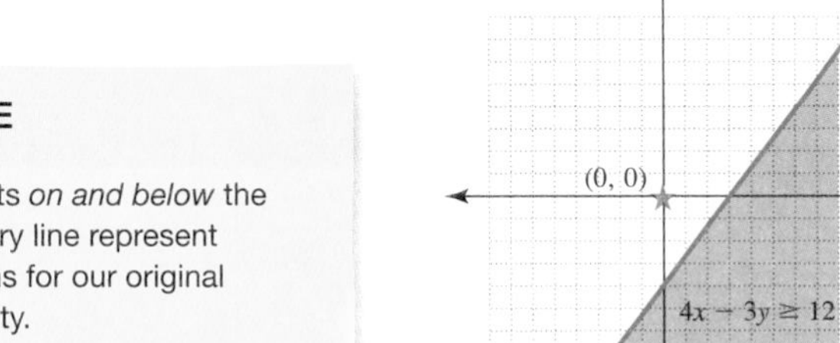

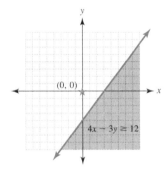

> **NOTE**
>
> If we have a strict inequality ($<$ or $>$), then choosing a point on the boundary line produces a false statement.

Check Yourself 5

Graph the inequality $3x + 2y \geq 6$.

Note that we do not choose a test point on the boundary line. In Example 5, $4x - 3y \geq 12$, if we choose a point on the boundary line, such as (3, 0), then we have $4(3) - 3(0) \geq 12$, which is a true statement. But this does not tell us which side of the boundary line to shade.

Example 6 Graphing a Linear Inequality

NOTES

The boundary line is a solid line because equality is included.

If the correct half-plane is obvious, you may not need to use a test point. Did you know without testing which half-plane to shade in this example?

Graph $x \le 5$.

The boundary line is $x = 5$. Using (0, 0) as a test point, we substitute 0 for x with the result

$0 \le 5$ A true statement

Because the inequality is *true* for the test point, we shade the half-plane containing the origin.

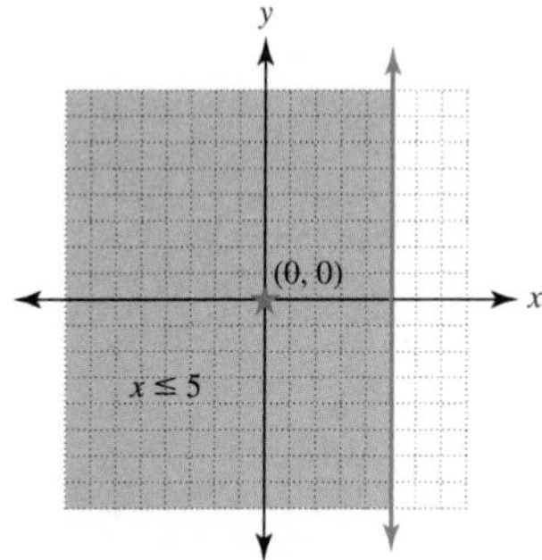

Check Yourself 6

Graph the inequality $y < 2$.

As we mentioned earlier, we may have to use a point other than the origin as our test point. Example 7 illustrates this approach.

Example 7 Graphing a Linear Inequality

Graph $2x + 3y < 0$.

The boundary line is $2x + 3y = 0$. Its graph is shown in the figure.

NOTE

We use a dashed line for our boundary line because equality is not included.

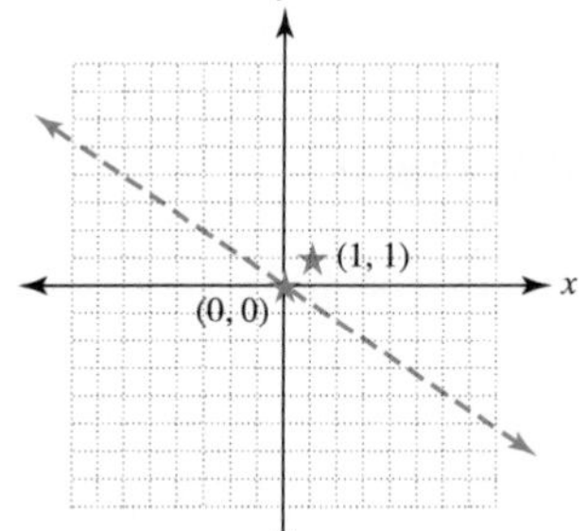

We cannot use (0, 0) as our test point in this case. Do you see why?

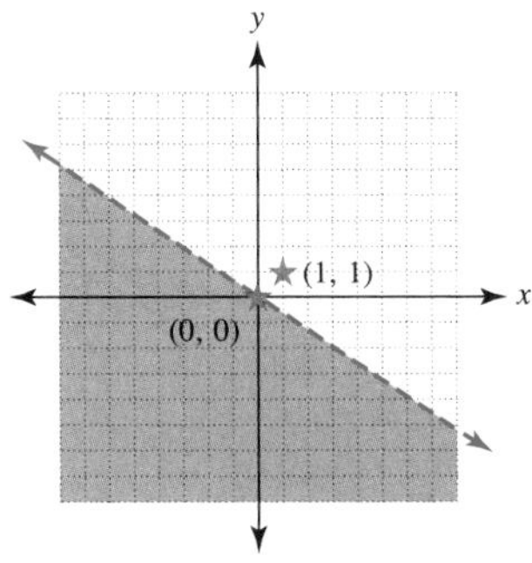

Choose any other point *not* on the line. For instance, we have picked (1, 1) as a test point. Substituting 1 for x and 1 for y gives

$$2 \cdot 1 + 3 \cdot 1 \stackrel{?}{<} 0$$
$$2 + 3 \stackrel{?}{<} 0$$
$$5 < 0 \quad \text{A false statement}$$

Because the inequality is *false* at our test point, we shade the half-plane *not* containing (1, 1). This is shown in the graph in the margin.

Check Yourself 7

Graph the inequality $x - 2y < 0$.

The solutions to an inequality in two variables are ordered pairs that, when graphed, always lie in a region (actually a half-plane). The following steps summarize our work in graphing linear inequalities in two variables.

Step by Step

To Graph a Linear Inequality

Step 1 Replace the inequality symbol with an equal sign to form the equation of the boundary line of the graph.

Step 2 Graph the boundary line. Use a dashed line if equality is not included ($<$ or $>$). Use a solid line if equality is included ($\le$ or $\ge$).

Step 3 Choose any convenient test point *not* on the line.

Step 4 If the inequality is *true* at the checkpoint, shade the half-plane containing the test point. If the inequality is *false* at the checkpoint, shade the half-plane not including the test point.

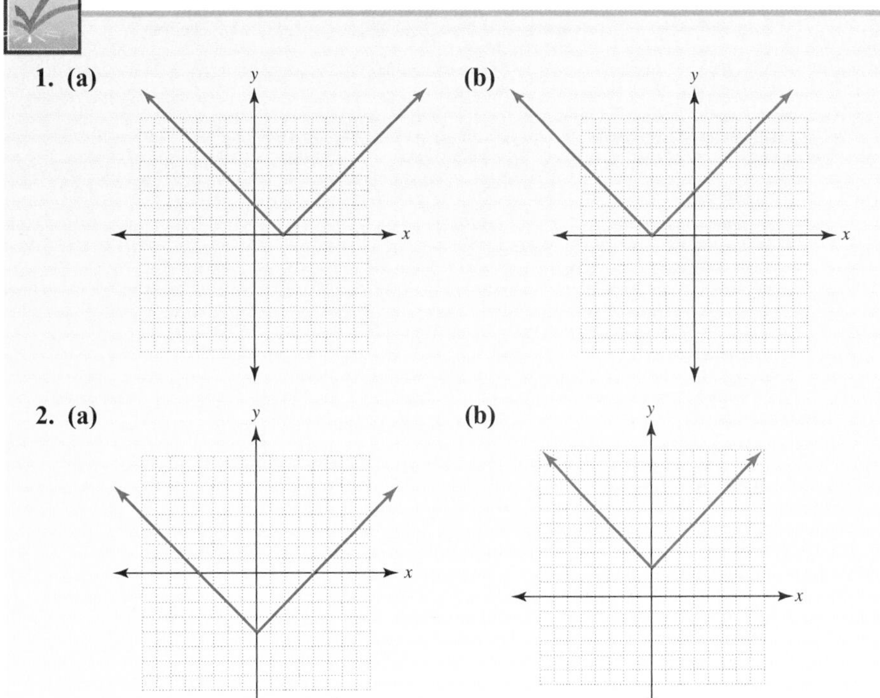

3.

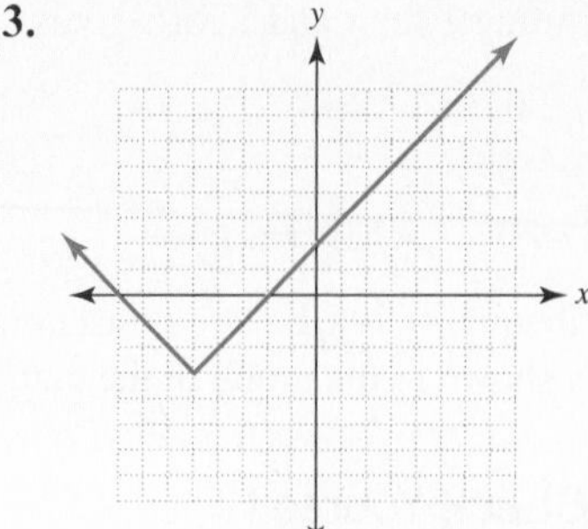

4.

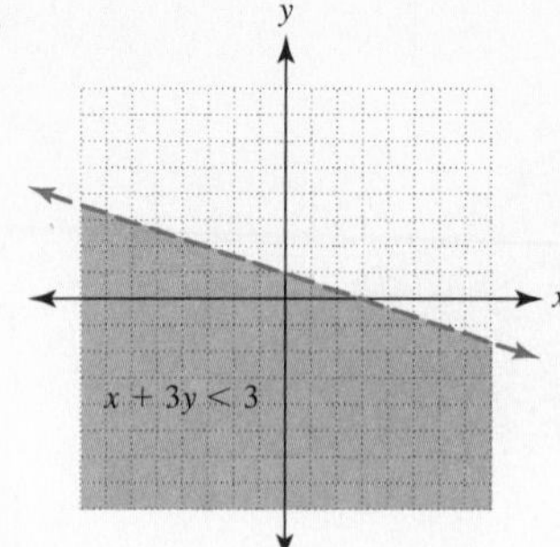

5.

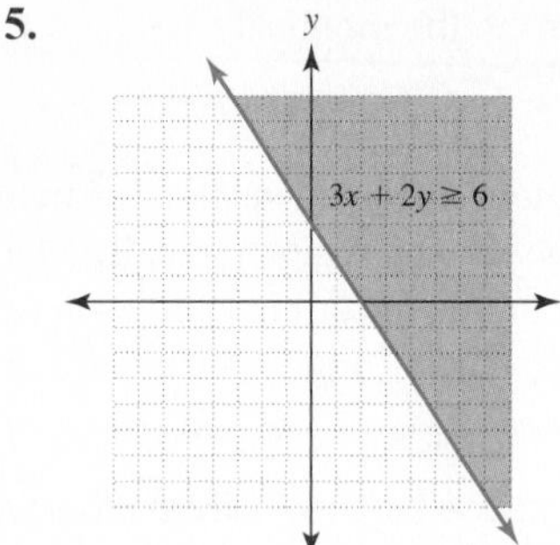

6.

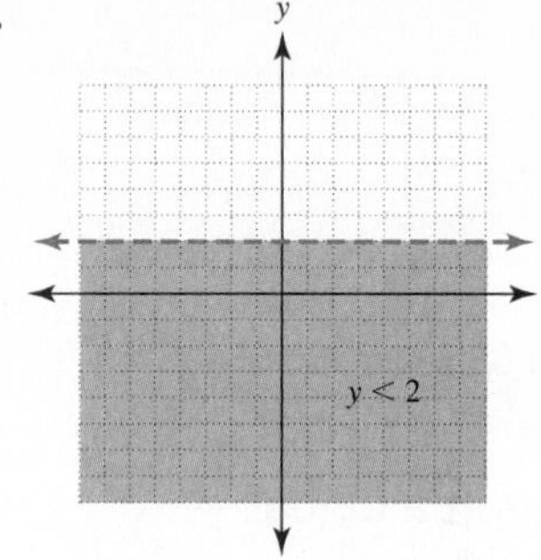

7.

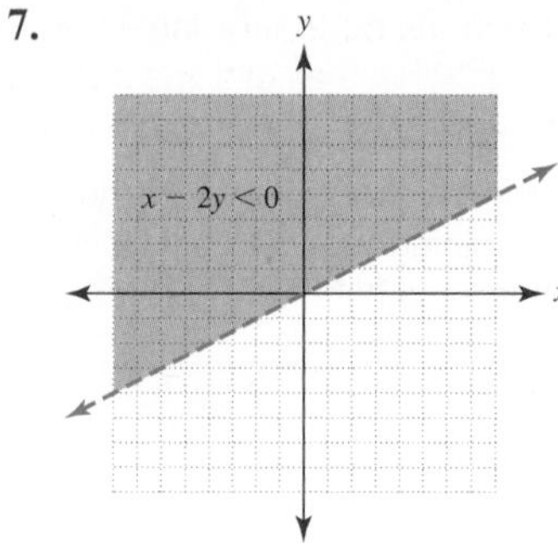

Reading Your Text

The following fill-in-the-blank exercises are designed to ensure that you understand some of the key vocabulary used in this section.

SECTION 3.5

(a) The graph of $f(x) =$ ______________, is like a large **V** that has its vertex at the origin.

(b) The graph of an equation forms the ______________ of the graph of a linear inequality in two variables.

(c) A ______________ boundary line indicates that the points on the line are *not* part of the solution to the inequality.

(d) The ______________ is usually a good choice for a convenient test point.

Basic Skills | Advanced Skills | Vocational-Technical Applications | Calculator/Computer | Above and Beyond

3.5 exercises

< Objective 1 >

Graph each function.

1. $f(x) = |x - 3|$

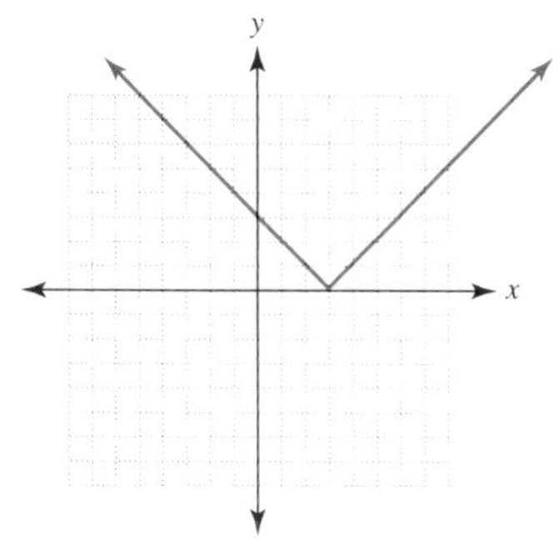

2. $f(x) = |x + 2|$

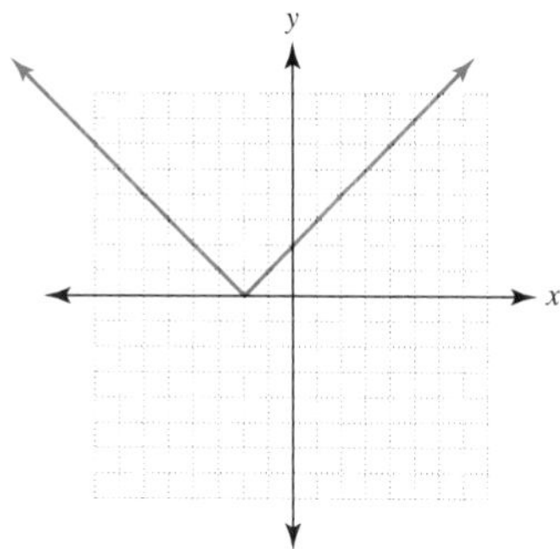

3. $f(x) = |x + 3|$

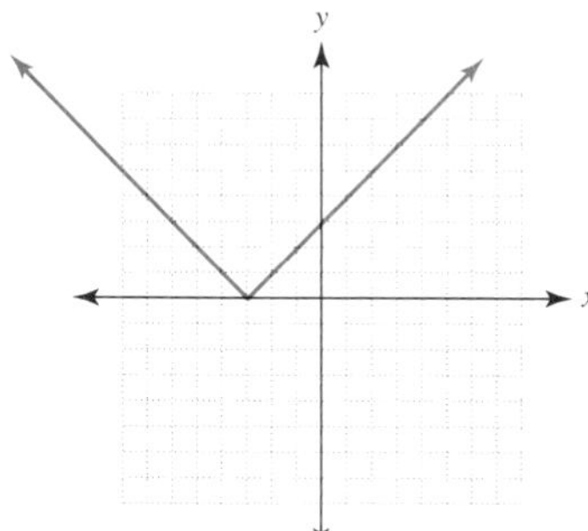

4. $f(x) = |x - 4|$

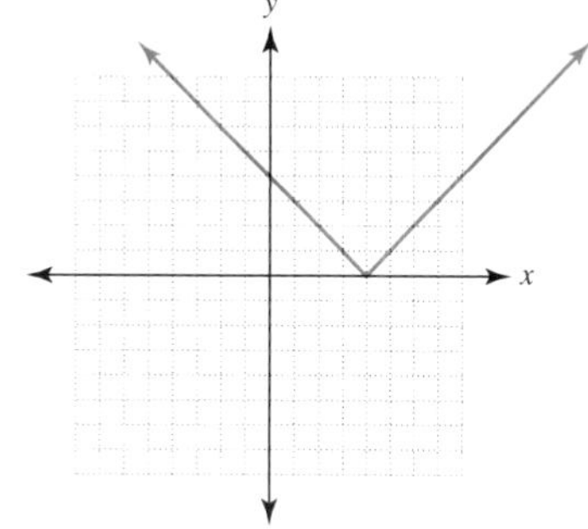

5. $f(x) = |x - (-3)|$

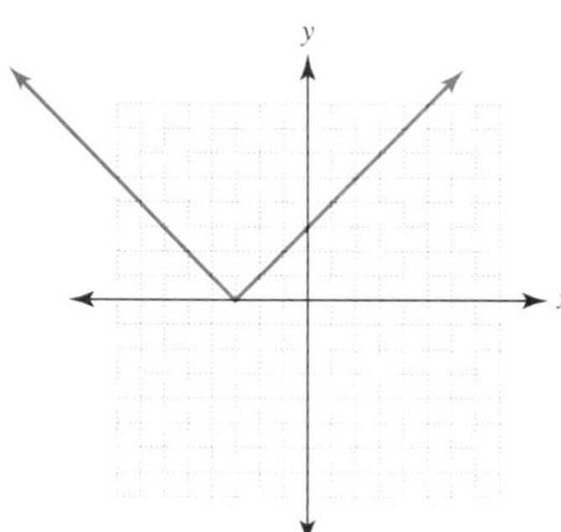

6. $f(x) = |x - (-5)|$

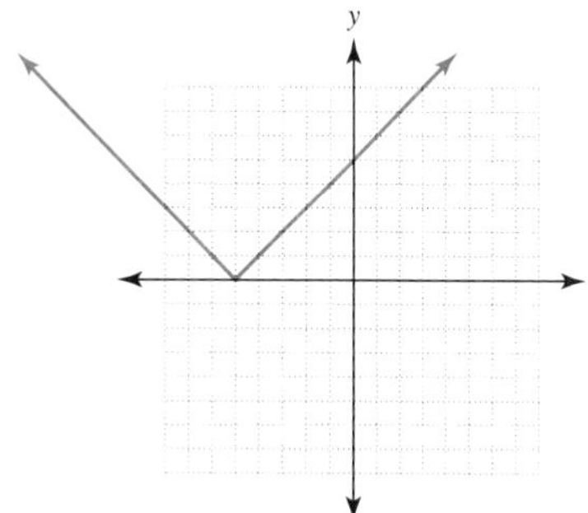

7. $f(x) = |x| + 4$

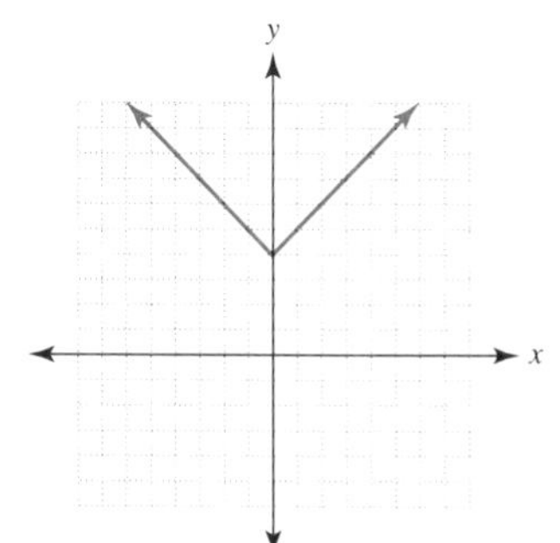

8. $f(x) = |x| - 1$

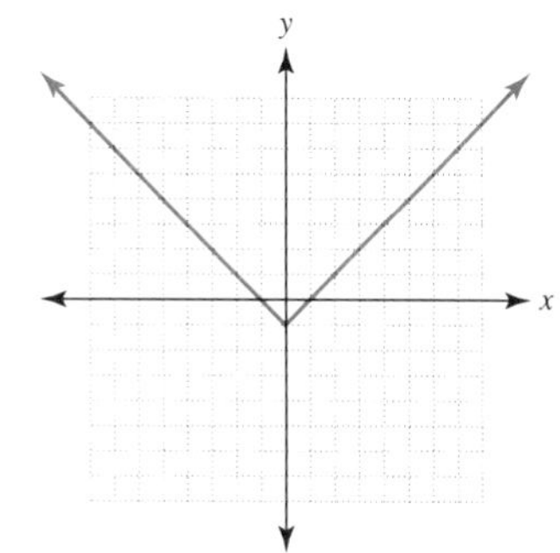

Name ____________

Section ______ Date ______

Answers

1. See exercise
2. See exercise
3. See exercise
4. See exercise
5. See exercise
6. See exercise
7. See exercise
8. See exercise

Answers

9. See exercise
10. See exercise
11. See exercise
12. See exercise
13. $f(x) = |x - 2|$
14. $f(x) = |x + 3|$
15. $f(x) = |x| - 7$
16. $f(x) = |x| + 6$

9. $f(x) = |x + 1| - 3$

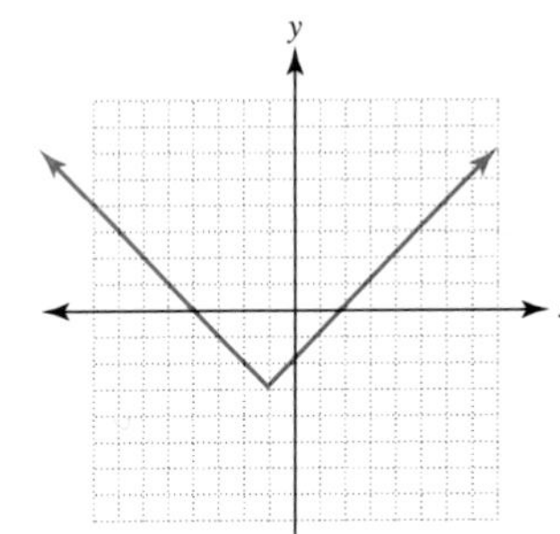

10. $f(x) = |x - 2| + 4$

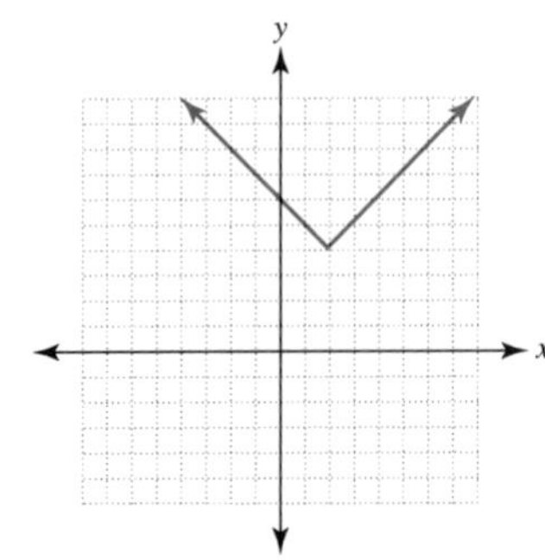

11. $f(x) = |x - 3| - 1$

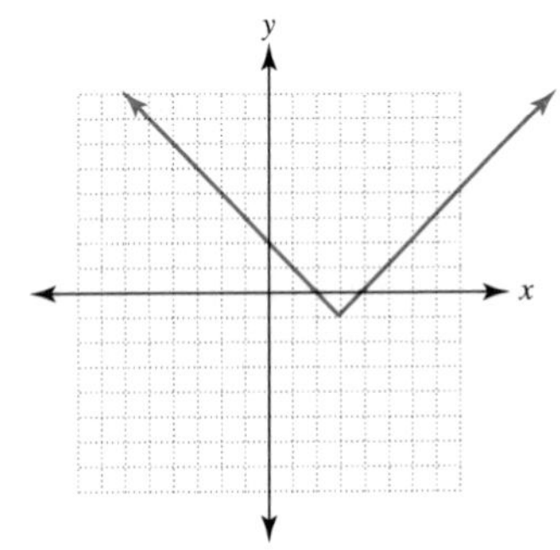

12. $f(x) = |x + 4| + 2$

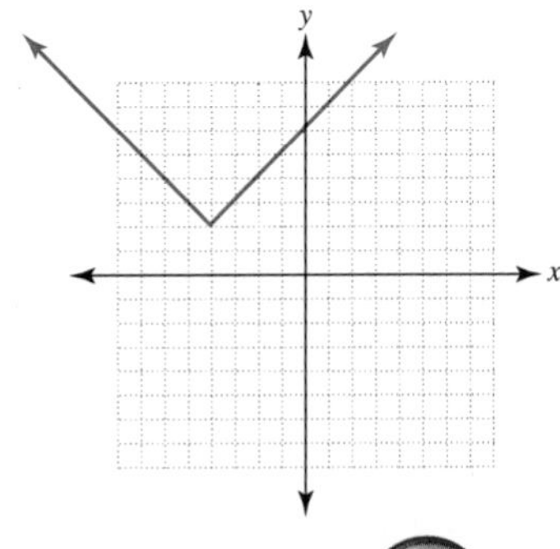

Determine the function represented by each graph.

13.

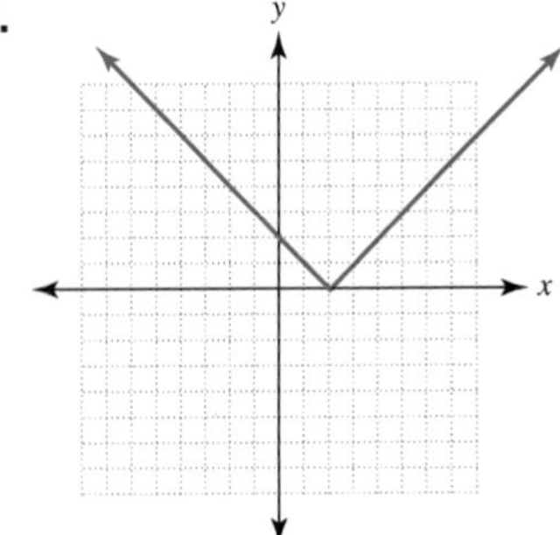

14.

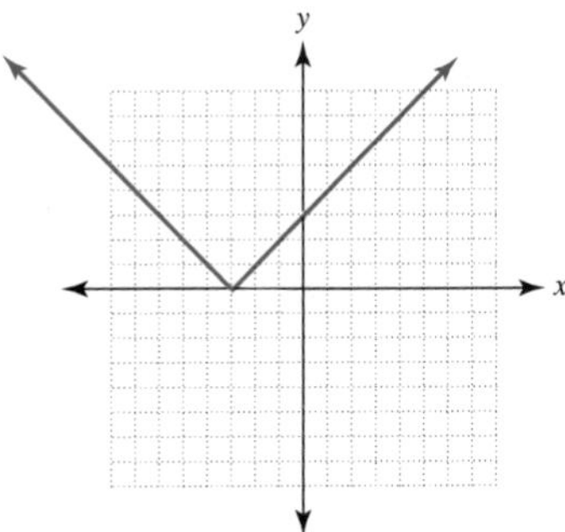

15.

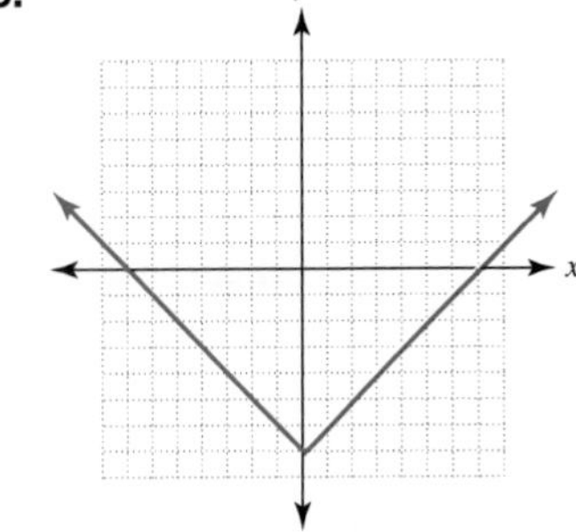

16.

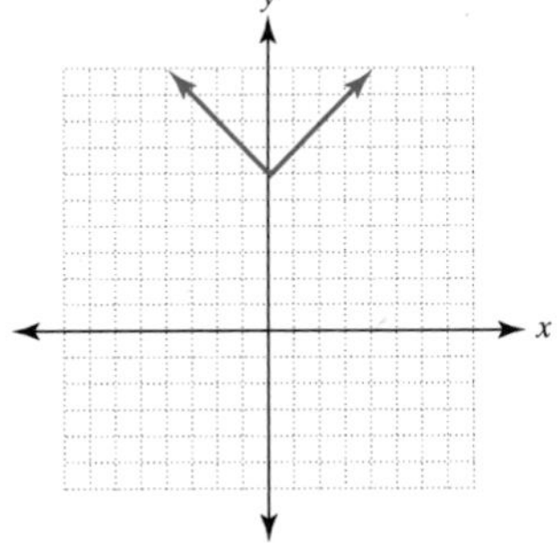

17.

18.

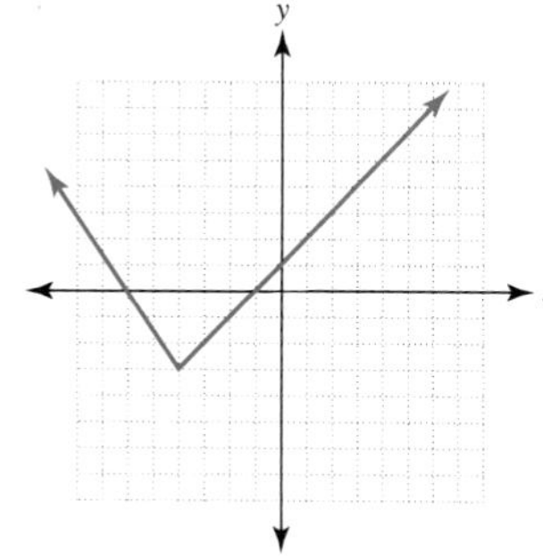

In each of the following statements, fill in the blank with **always, sometimes,** *or* **never.**

19. The graph of a linear absolute value function is _________ like a large **V**.

20. The boundary of a linear inequality is _________ a solid line.

21. The graph of a linear inequality is _________ a region of the plane.

22. A test point for knowing how to shade a linear inequality should _________ be on the boundary line.

We have graphed the boundary line for the linear inequality. Determine the correct half-plane in each case, and complete the graph.

23. $x + y < 5$

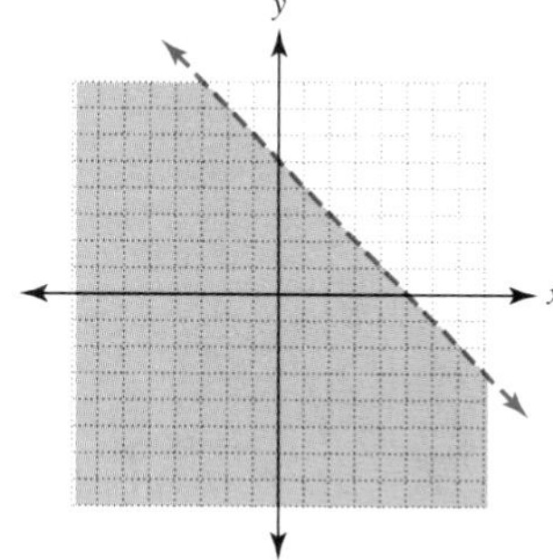

24. $x - y \geq 4$

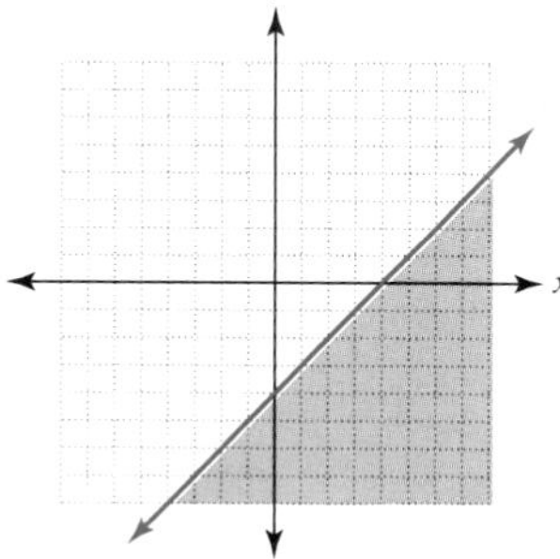

25. $x \leq -3$

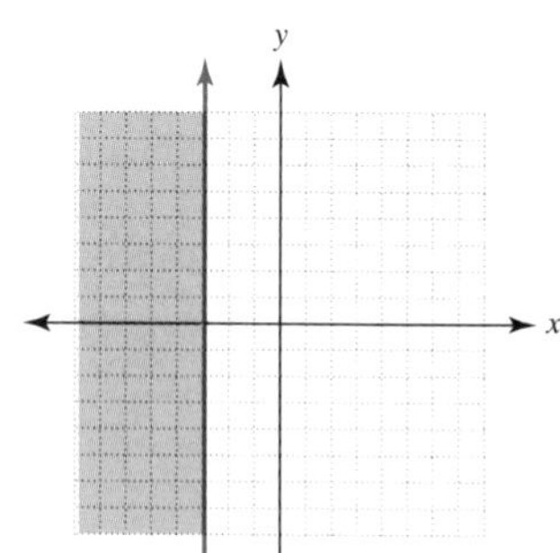

26. $y > 3$

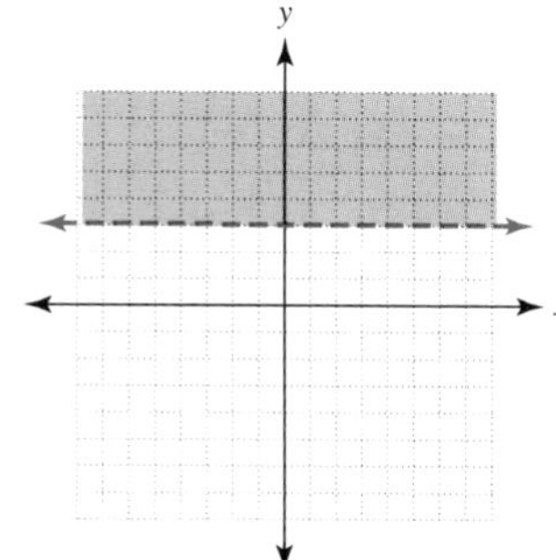

Answers

17. $f(x) = |x - 6| + 4$

18. $f(x) = |x + 4| - 3$

19. always

20. sometimes

21. always

22. never

23. See exercise

24. See exercise

25. See exercise

26. See exercise

Answers

27. See exercise

28. See exercise

29. See exercise

30. See exercise

31. See exercise

32. See exercise

< Objective 2 >

Graph each of the inequalities.

27. $x + y < 3$

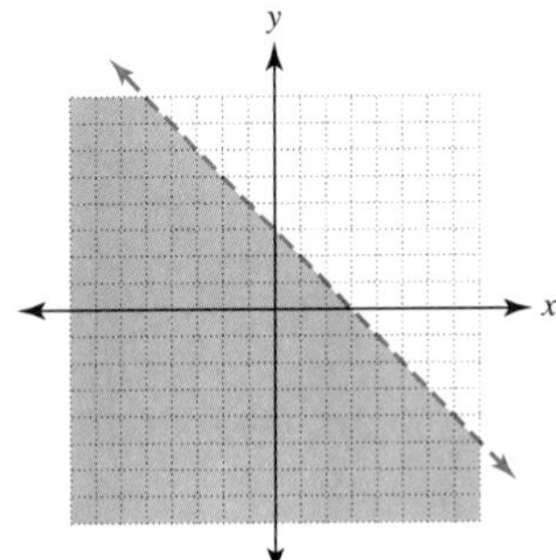

28. $x - y \geq 4$

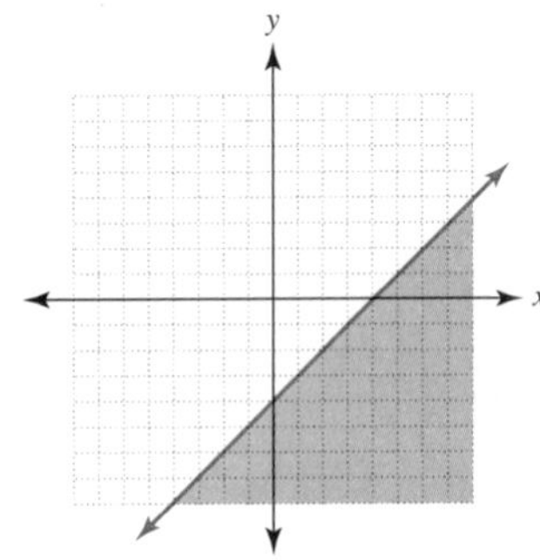

29. $2x + y < 6$

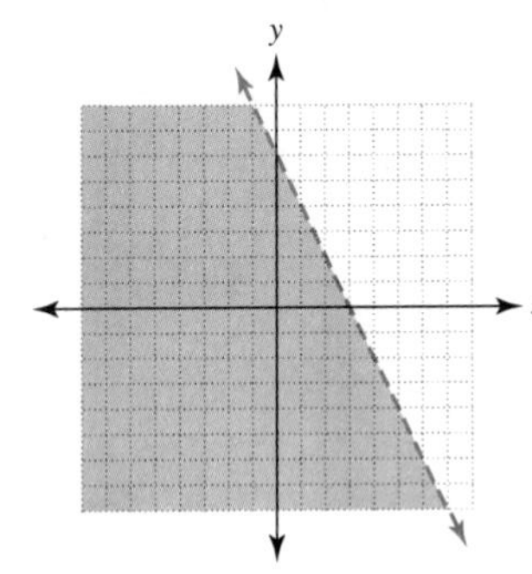

30. $3x + y \geq 6$

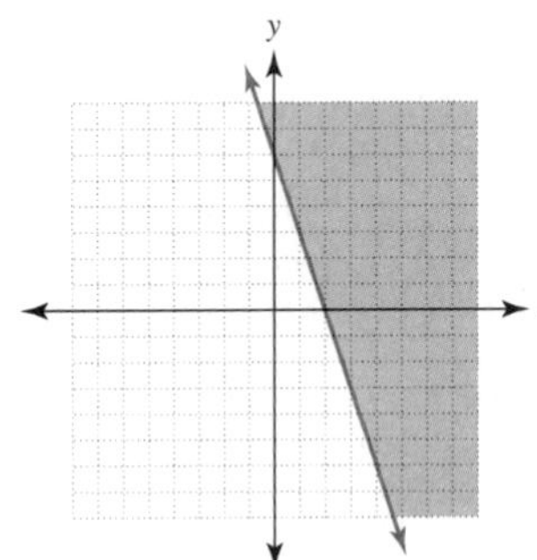

31. $x \leq 3$

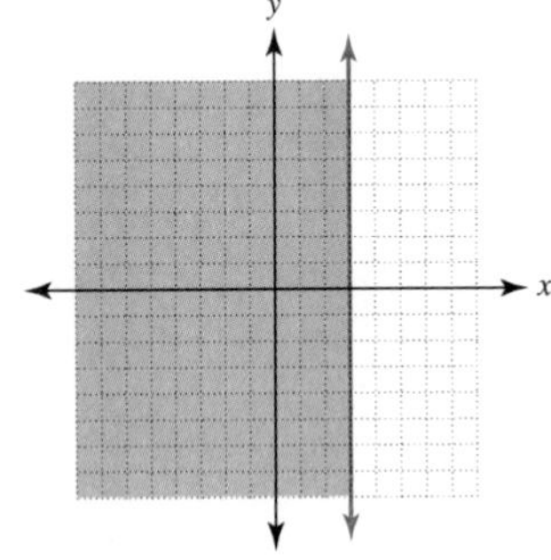

32. $x - 5y < 5$

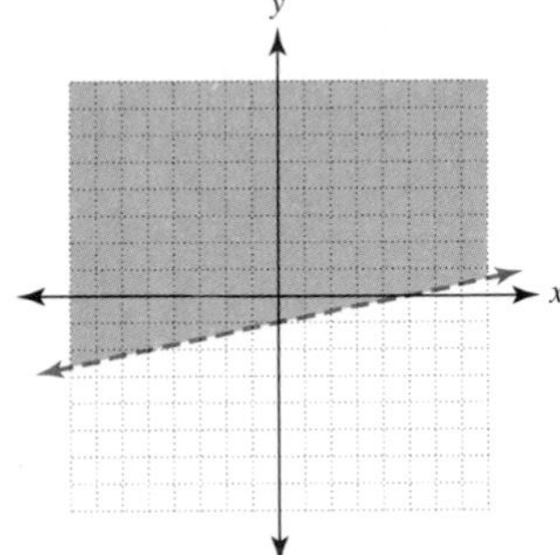

33. $y < -4$

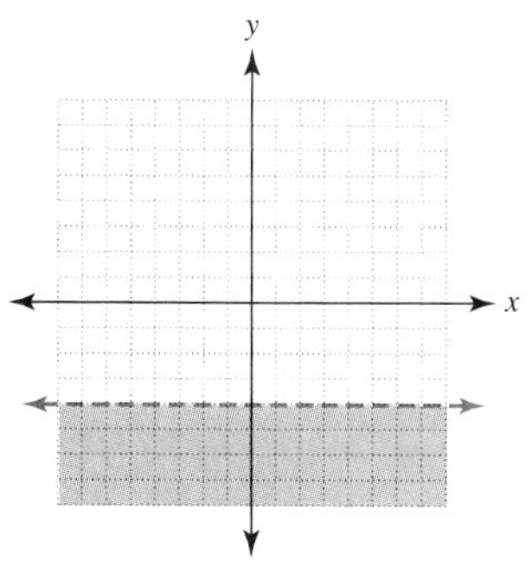

34. $4x + 3y > 12$

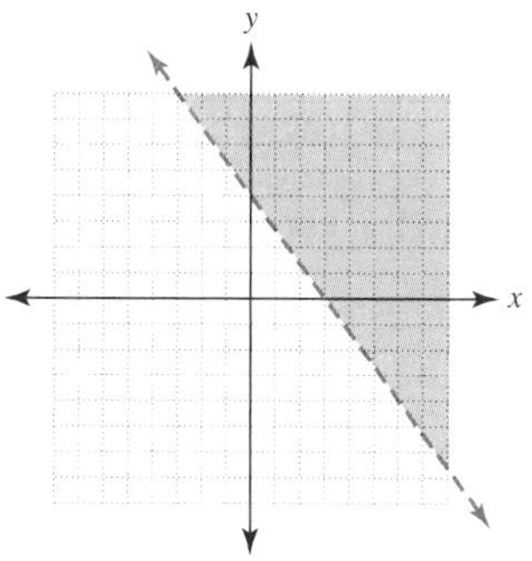

35. $2x - 3y \geq 6$

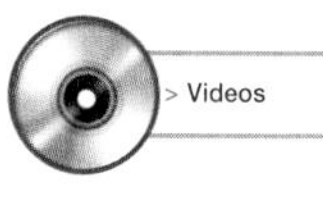

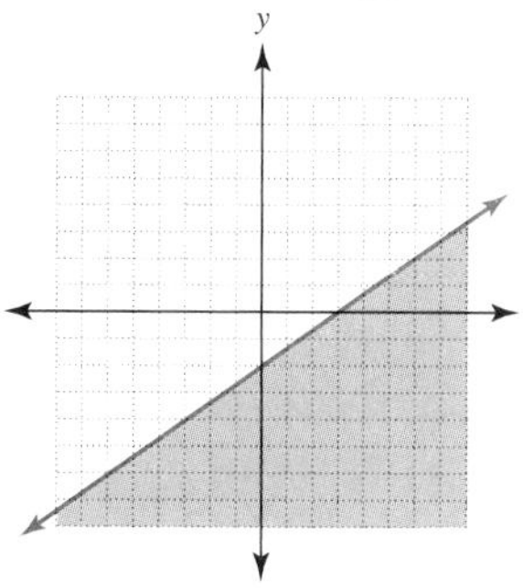

36. $3x + 2y \geq 0$

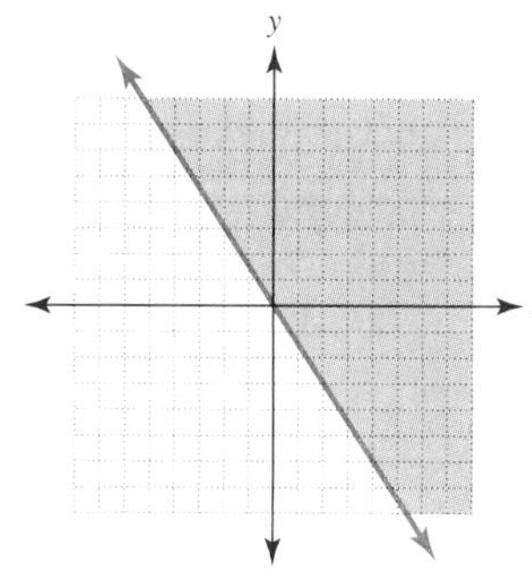

37. $5x + 2y > 10$

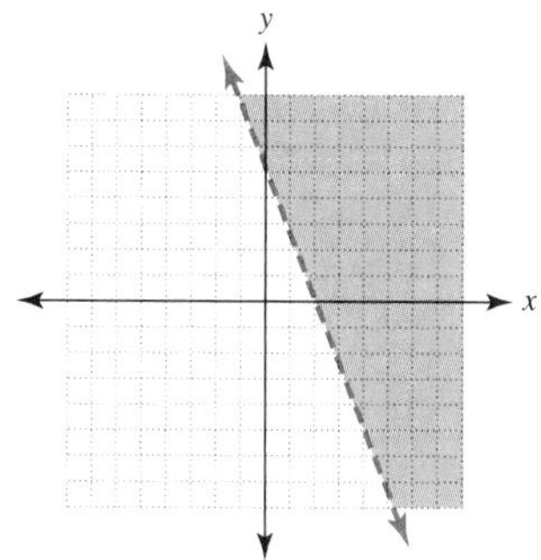

38. $x - 3y \geq 0$

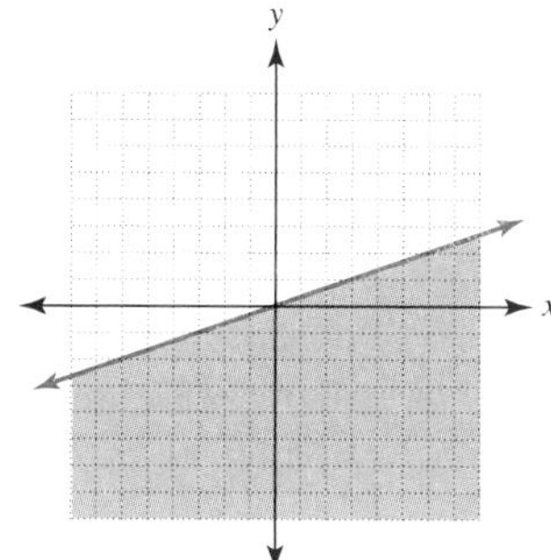

Answers

33. See exercise

34. See exercise

35. See exercise

36. See exercise

37. See exercise

38. See exercise

Answers

39. See exercise

40. See exercise

41. See exercise

42. See exercise

43. See exercise

44. See exercise

39. $y \le 2x$

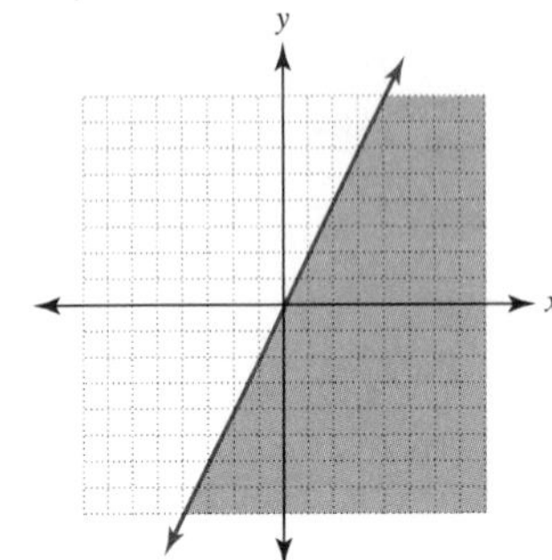

40. $3x - 4y < 12$

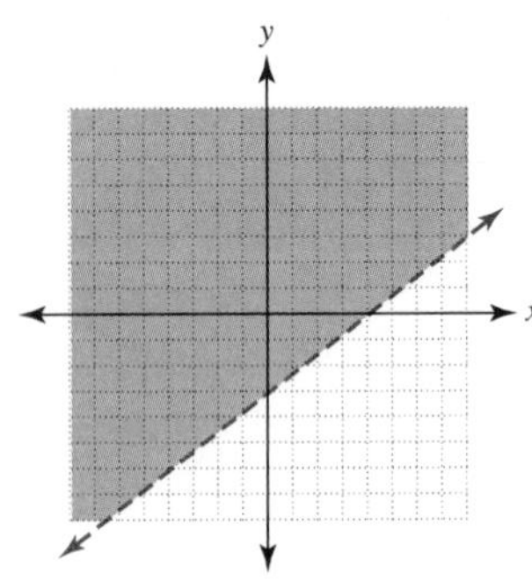

41. $y > 2x - 3$

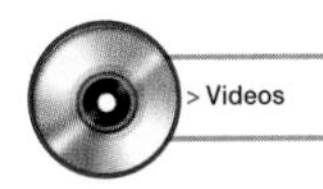

42. $y \le 3x + 4$

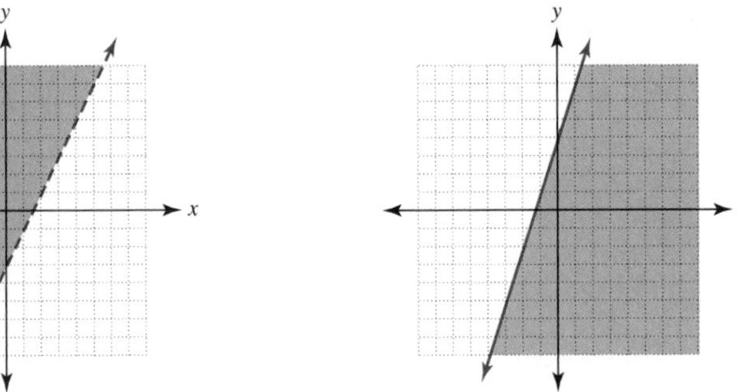

Basic Skills | **Advanced Skills** | Vocational-Technical Applications | Calculator/Computer | Above and Beyond

Simplify; then graph each of the inequalities.

43. $2(x + y) - x > 6$

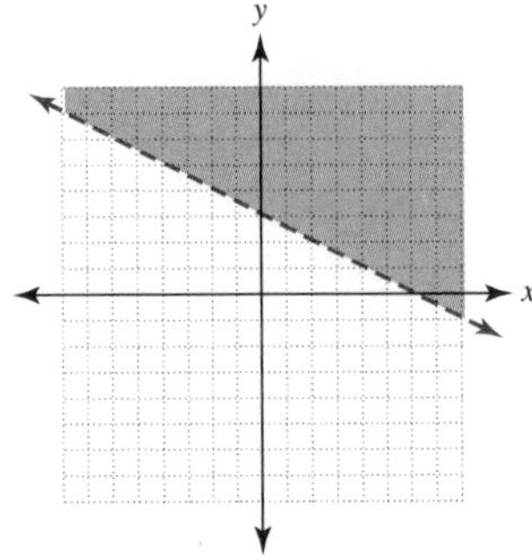

44. $3(x + y) - 2y < 3$

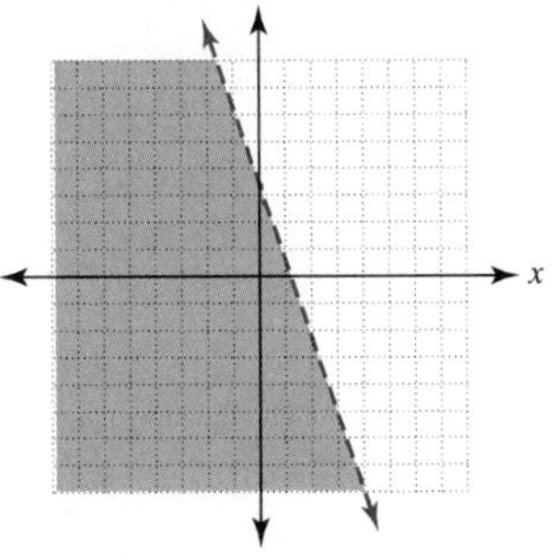

45. $4(x + y) - 3(x + y) \le 5$

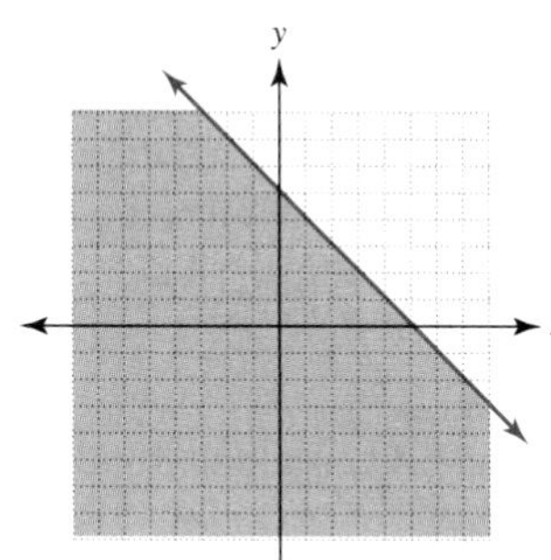

46. $5(2x + y) - 4(2x + y) \ge 4$

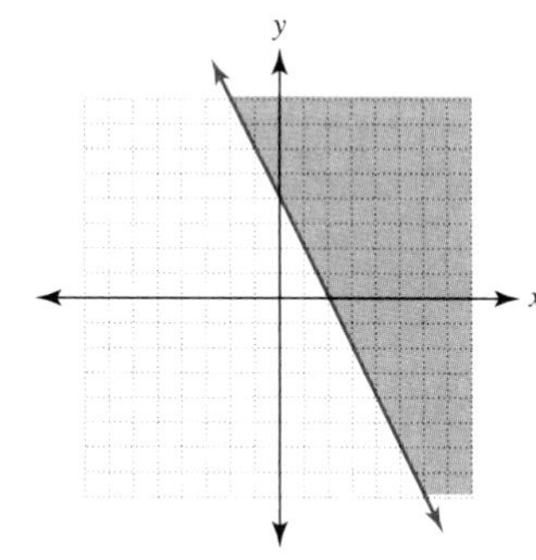

47. Write the inequality, and then sketch the graph that is equivalent to the statement, "The exchange rate to Japanese yen from U.S. dollars has always been at least 75 to 1."

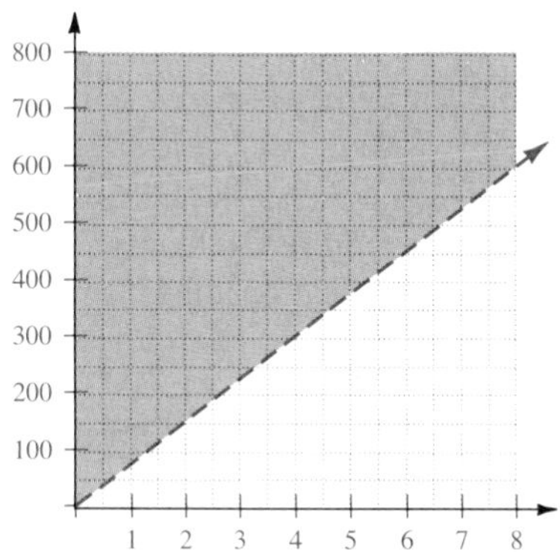

48. Write the inequality, and then sketch the graph that is equivalent to the statement, "The exchange rate to U.S. dollars from English pounds has always been no more than 3 to 1."

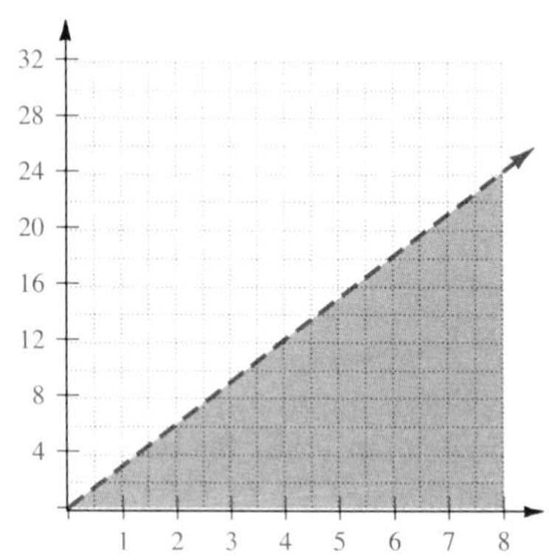

Answers

45. See exercise

46. See exercise

47. $y > 75x$; see exercise

48. $y < 3x$; see exercise

Answers

49. $10c + 5.50r \geq 500$
where c = number of hours at the major corporation and
r = number of hours at fast-food restaurant

50. See exercise

51. See exercise

52. Above and Beyond

49. Information Technology A computer technician works two part-time jobs as she is going to college. One is an internship with a major corporation for \$10/hour. The other is a major fast-food restaurant at \$5.50/hour. She needs to earn \$500 per week or more to support her family. Write an inequality that shows the various numbers of hours she can work per week.

50. Construction Technology The allowable load on a rectangular wooden beam is given by the inequality

Load $\leq$ 1,150A

Graph this inequality.

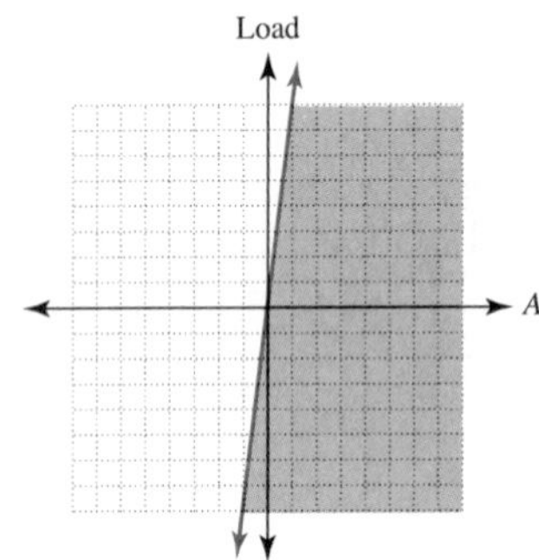

51. Agricultural Technology The amount of water required to feed an irrigation system for a 32-acre field is given by the relationship

$w \geq 15{,}488R$

where w is the water supply in gallons and R is the number of inches of rainfall we wish to simulate. Graph this relationship.

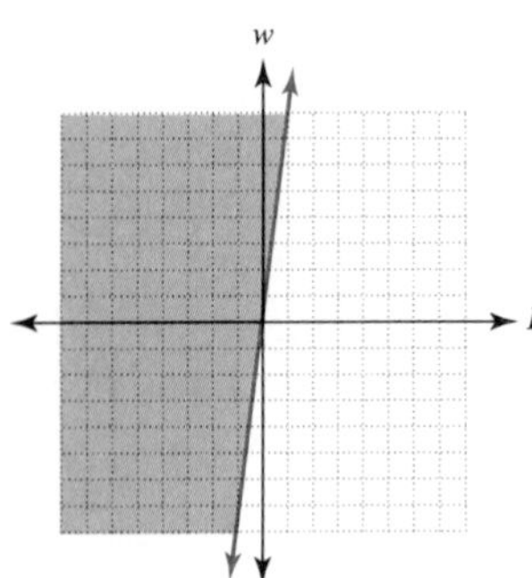

52. Linda Williams has just begun a nursery business and seeks your advice. She has limited funds to spend and wants to stock two kinds of fruit-bearing plants. She lives in the northeastern part of Texas and thinks that blueberry bushes and peach trees would sell well. Linda can buy blueberry bushes from a supplier for \$2.50 each and young peach trees for \$5.50 each. She wants to know what combination she should buy to keep her outlay to \$500 or less. Write an inequality and draw a graph to depict what combinations of blueberry bushes and peach trees she can buy for the amount of money she has. Explain the graph and her options.

53. After reading an article in *The New York Times* titled "You Have to be Good at Algebra to Figure Out the Best Deal for Long Distance," Rafaella decided to apply her skills in algebra to try to decide between two competing long-distance companies. It was difficult at first to get the companies to explain their charge policies. They both kept repeating that they were 25% cheaper than their competition. Finally, Rafaella found someone who explained that the charge depended on when she called, where she called, how long she talked, and how often she called. "Too many variables!" she exclaimed. So she decided to ask one company what they charged as a base amount, just for using the service.

LongdisCo said that they charged $5 for the privilege of using their long-distance service whether or not she made any phone calls, and that because of this fee they were able to allow her to call anywhere in the United States after 6 P.M. for only $0.15 a minute. Complete this table of charges based on this company's plan:

Total Minutes Long Distance in 1 Month (After 6 P.M.)	Total Charge
0 minutes	
10 minutes	
30 minutes	
60 minutes	
120 minutes	

Use this table to make a whole-page graph of the monthly charges from LongdisCo based on the number of minutes of long distance.

Rafaella wanted to compare this offer to Telerates, which she is currently using. She looked at her phone bill and saw that one month she had been charged $7.50 for 30 minutes and another month she had been charged $11.25 for 45 minutes of long-distance calling. These calls were made after 6 P.M. to her relatives in Indiana and in Arizona. Draw a graph on the same set of axes you made for LongdisCo's figures. Use your graph and what you know about linear inequalities to advise Rafaella about which company is best.

Answers

1.

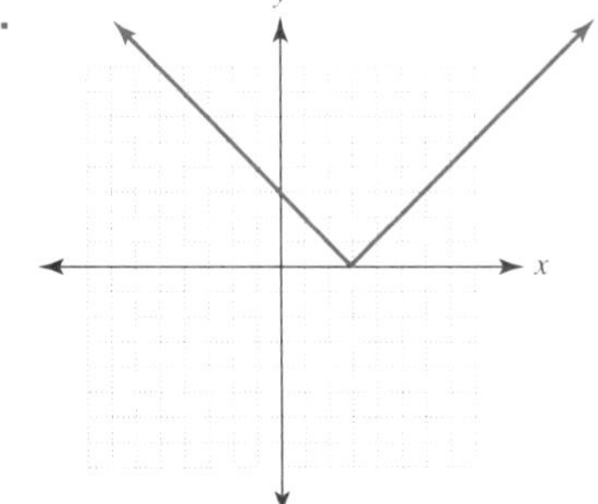

3.

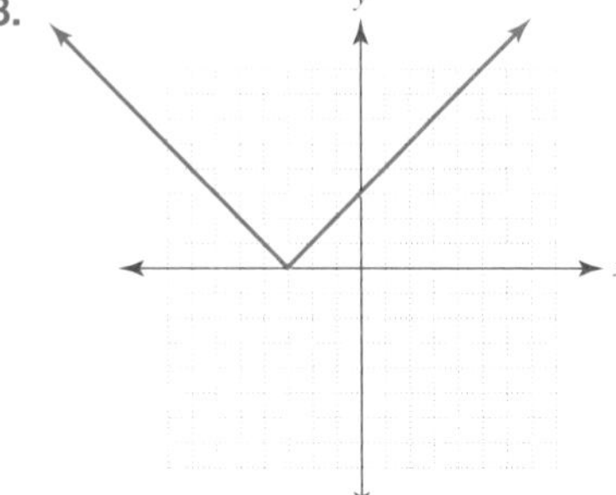

Answers

53. Above and Beyond

5.

7.

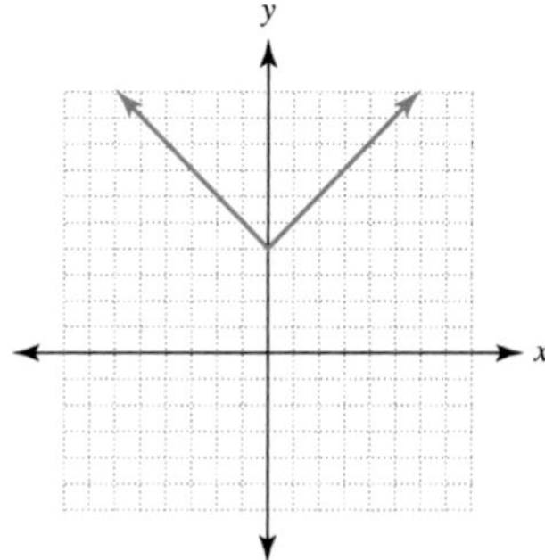

9.

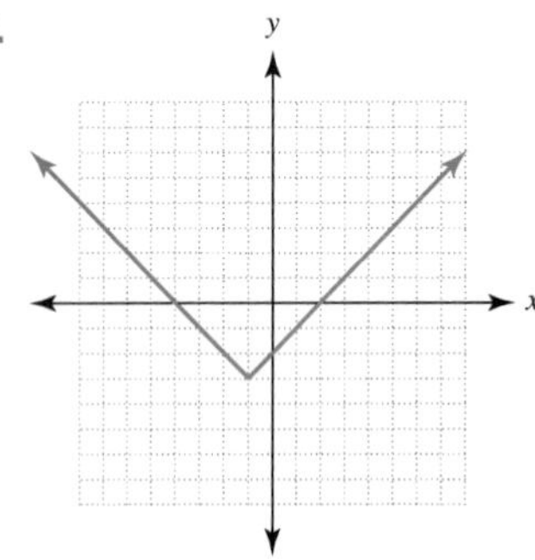

11.

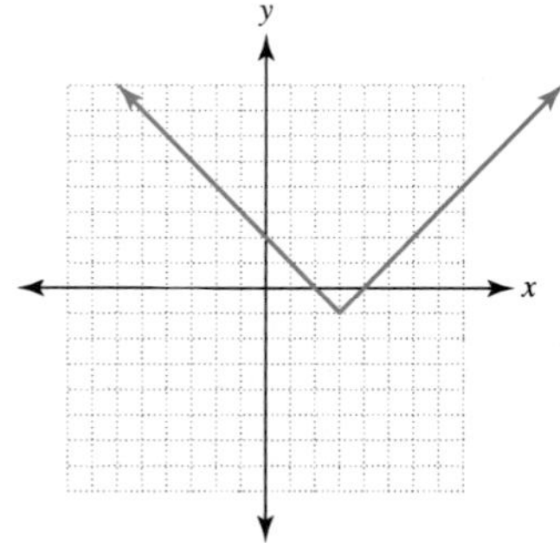

13. $f(x) = |x - 2|$ 15. $f(x) = |x| - 7$ 17. $f(x) = |x - 6| + 4$

19. always 21. always

23. $x + y < 5$

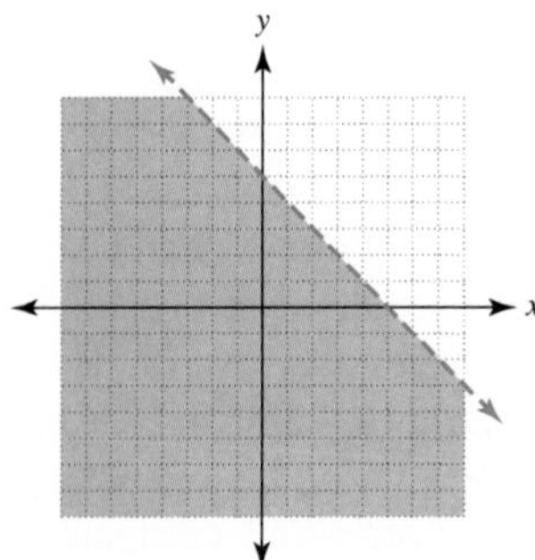

25. $x \leq -3$

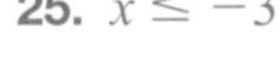

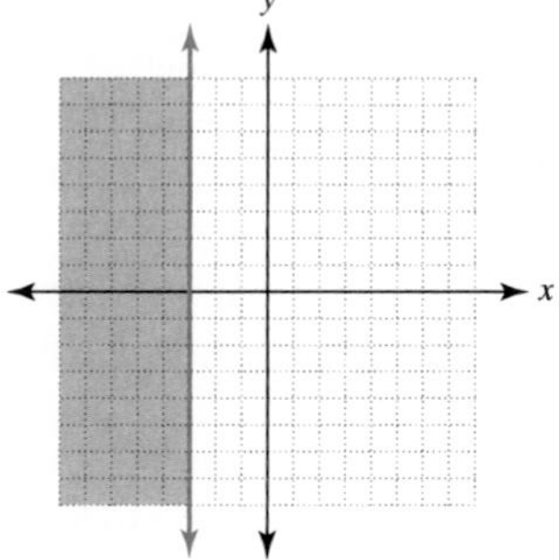

27. $x + y < 3$

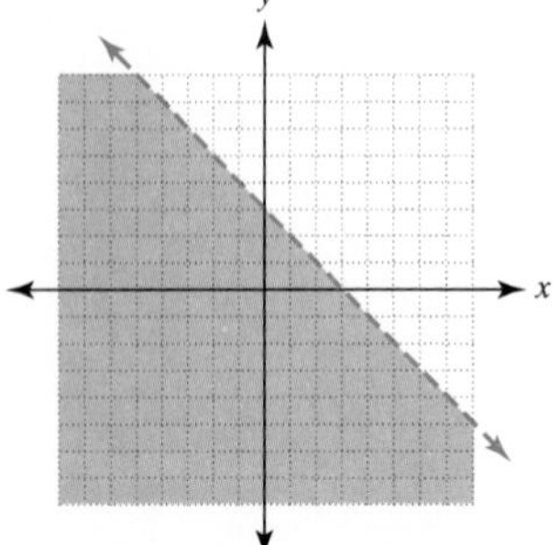

29. $2x + y < 6$

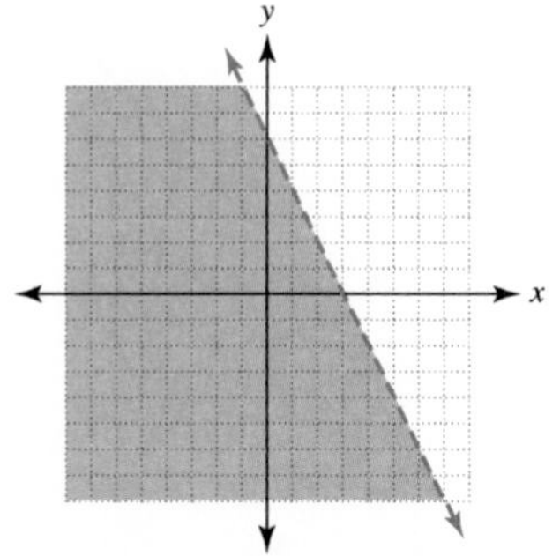

31. $x \leq 3$

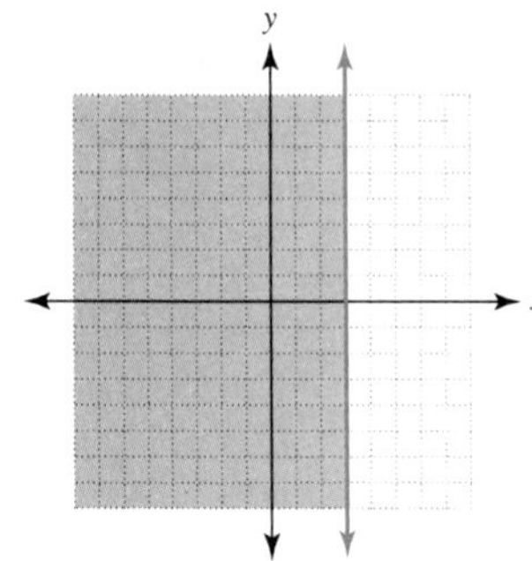

33. $y < -4$

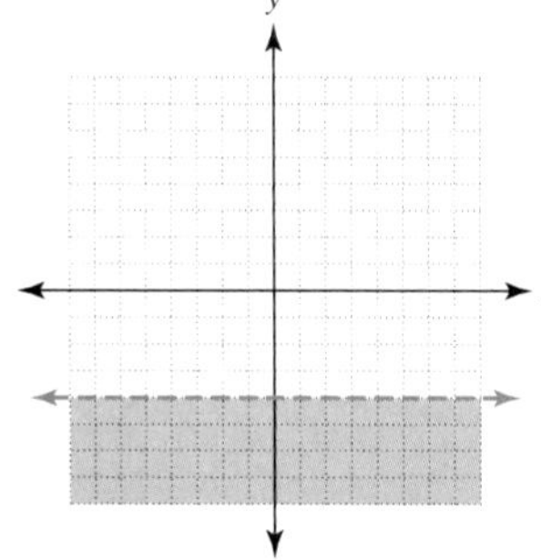

35. $2x - 3y \geq 6$

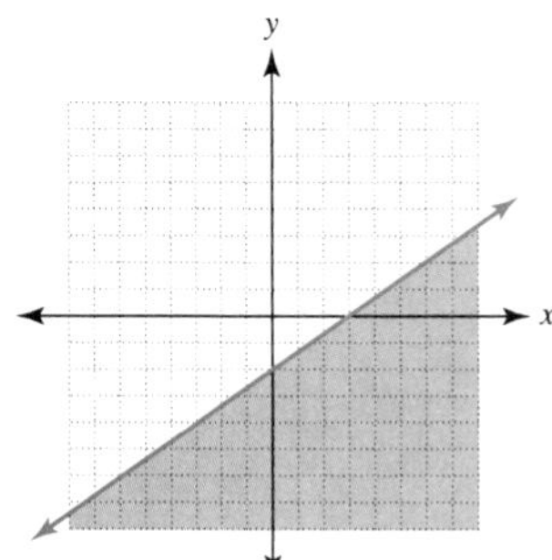

37. $5x + 2y > 10$

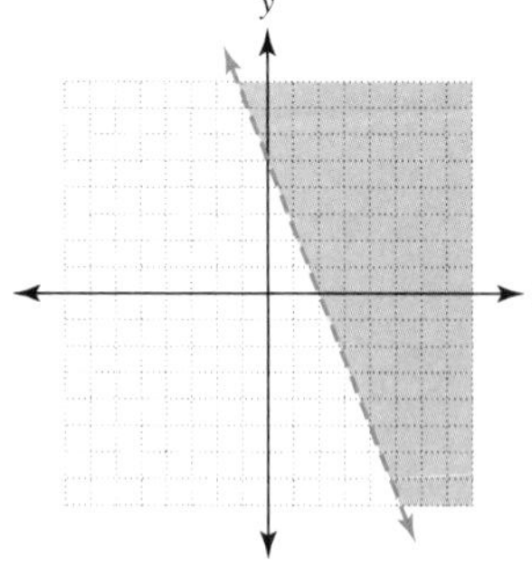

39. $y \leq 2x$

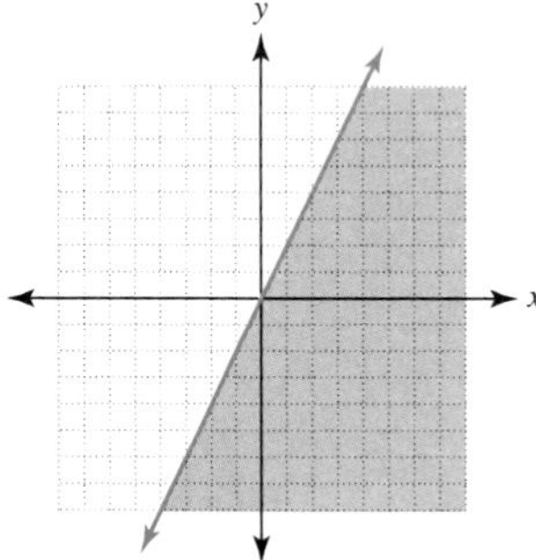

41. $y > 2x - 3$

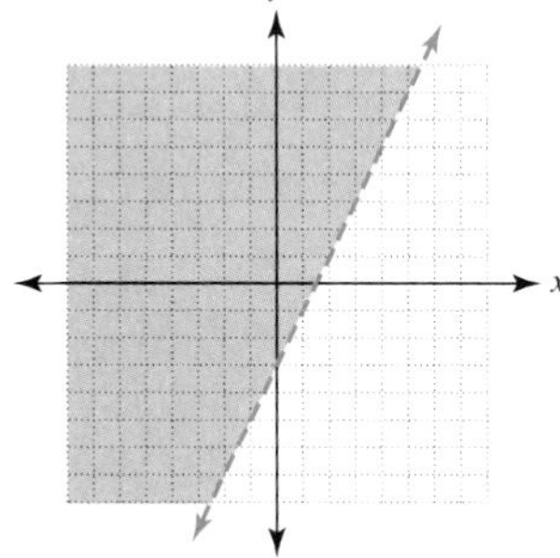

43. $x + 2y > 6$

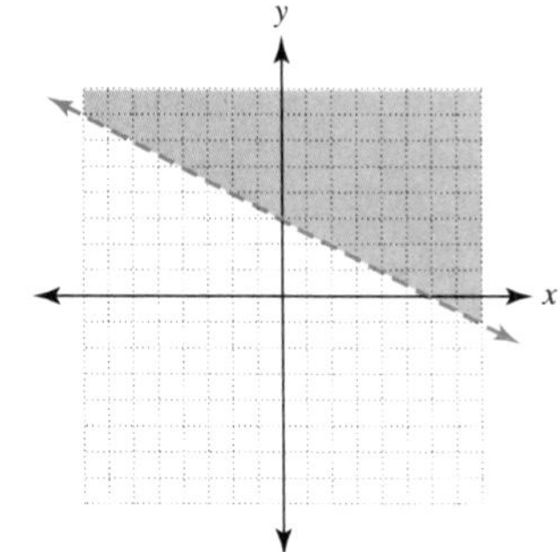

45. $x + y \leq 5$

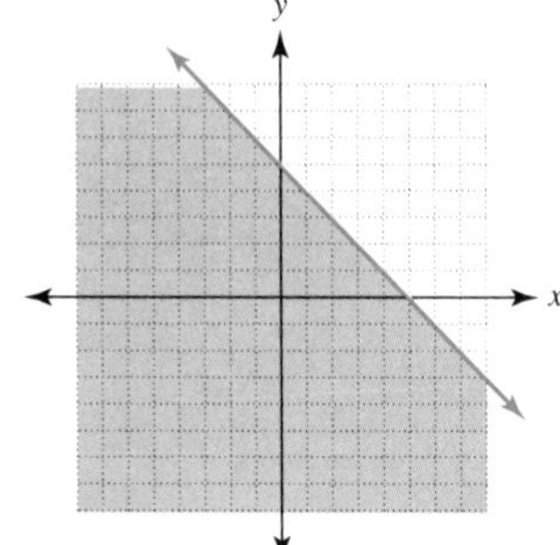

47. $y > 75x$

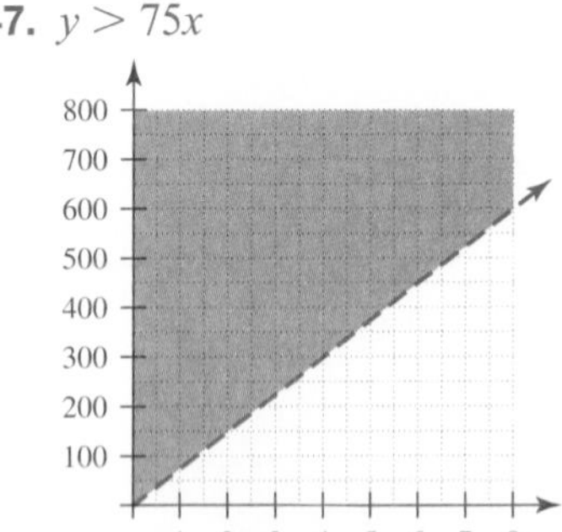

49. $10c + 5.50r \geq 500$ where c = number of hours at major corporation and r = number of hours at fast-food restaurant

51.

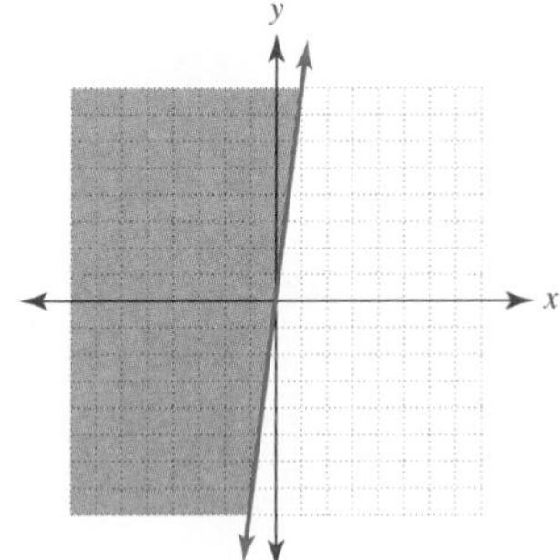

53. Above and Beyond

Definition/Procedure	Example	Reference

Graphing Linear Equations

Section 3.1

Ordered Pair

Given two related values, x and y, we write the pair of values as (x, y).

p. 179

The **rectangular coordinate system** allows us to establish a one-to-one correspondence between points in the plane and ordered pairs of real numbers.

(x, y)

x-coordinate y-coordinate

To **graph** (or **plot**) a point (x, y) in the plane:

1. Start at the origin.
2. Move to the right or left along the x-axis according to the value of the x-coordinate.
3. Move up or down and parallel to the y-axis according to the value of the y-coordinate.

It is not always desirable to use the same scale on both the x- and y-axes. In these situations, we use a different marked scale. This is called scaling the axes.

p. 180

Solutions for an equation in two variables are all ordered pairs of real numbers (x, y) that will make the equation a true statement.

An equation of the form

$Ax + By = C$

in which A and B cannot both be zero, is a linear equation in two variables. The graph of such an equation is always a *line*. An equation in this form is called the **standard form for a linear equation.**

$(1, 3)$ is a solution for

$3x + 2y = 9$

because

$3 \cdot 1 + 2 \cdot 3 = 9$

is a true statement.

p. 184

To graph a linear equation:

Step 1 Find at least three solutions for the equation, and write your results in a table of values.

Step 2 Graph the points associated with the ordered pairs found in step 1.

Step 3 Draw a line through the points plotted in step 1 to form the graph of the equation.

To graph

$y = 2x - 3$

$(0, -3)$, $(1, -1)$, and $(2, 1)$ are solutions.

p. 186

Continued

Definition/Procedure	Example	Reference
A second approach to graphing linear equations uses the x- and y-intercepts of the line. The x-intercept is the point at which the line intersects the x-axis. The y-intercept is the point at which the line intersects the y-axis. To graph by the intercept method: **Step 1** Find the x-intercept. Let $y = 0$ and solve for x. **Step 2** Find the y-intercept. Let $x = 0$ and solve for y. **Step 3** Plot the two intercepts determined in steps 1 and 2. **Step 4** Draw a line through the intercepts.	(2, 1) (1, −1) (0, −3)	p. 187
Vertical or Horizontal Lines		
1. A line with an equation of the form $y = k$ is horizontal (parallel to the x-axis). **2.** A line with an equation of the form $x = h$ is vertical (parallel to the y-axis).	$x = 3$ $y = -2$	p. 187
Introduction to Functions		**Section 3.2**
Relation		
A set of ordered pairs.	The set {(1, 4), (2, 5), (1, 6)} is a relation.	p. 207
Domain		
The set of all first elements of a relation.	The domain is {1, 2}.	p. 207
Range		
The set of all second elements of a relation.	The range is {4, 5, 6}.	p. 208
A **function** is set of ordered pairs (a relation) in which no two first coordinates are equal. A function can also be defined as a relation in which each element of the domain is paired with one and only one element of the range. The set of points in the plane that correspond to ordered pairs in a relation or function is called the *graph* of that relation or function.	{(1, 2), (2, 3), (3, 4)} is a function. {(1, 2), (2, 3), (2, 4)} is *not* a function.	p. 212

Definition/Procedure	Example	Reference
A useful means of determining whether a graph represents a function is called the **vertical line test.** If a vertical line meets the graph of a relation in more than one point, the relation is *not* a function.	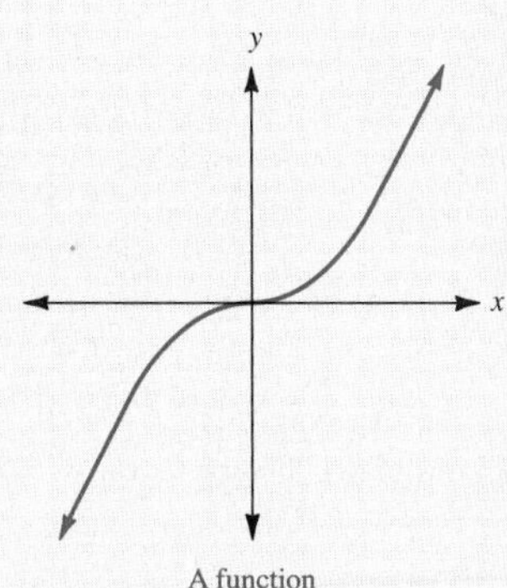 A function 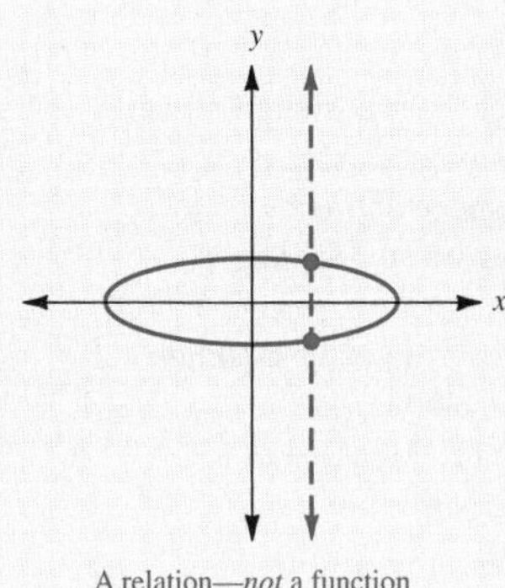 A relation—*not* a function	p. 214
Reading Values from a Graph		
For a specific value of x, let us call it a, we can find $f(a)$ with the following algorithm. **Step 1** Draw a vertical line through a on the x-axis. **Step 2** Find the point of intersection of that line with the graph. **Step 3** Draw a horizontal line through the graph at that point. **Step 4** Find the intersection of the horizontal line with the y-axis. **Step 5** $f(a)$ is that y-value. If given the function value, you find the x-values associated with it as follows. **Step 1** Find the given function value on the y-axis. **Step 2** Draw a horizontal line through that point. **Step 3** Find every point on the graph that intersects the horizontal line. **Step 4** Draw a vertical line through each of those points of intersection. **Step 5** Each point of intersection of the vertical lines and the x-axis gives an x-value.	Find $f(3)$. 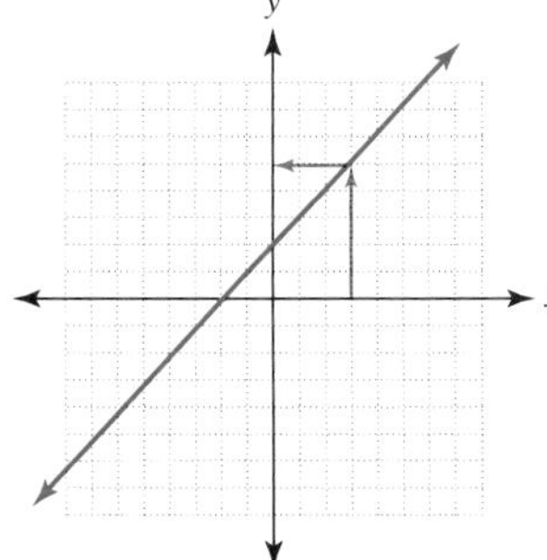 Draw a vertical line through $x = 3$. Draw a horizontal line through the intersection. The horizontal line passes through (0, 5). $f(3) = 5$	p. 217

Continued

Definition/Procedure	Example	Reference
The Slope of a Line		Section 3.3
The **slope** of a line gives a numerical measure of the direction and steepness, or inclination, of the line. The slope m of a line containing the distinct points in the plane (x_1, y_1) and (x_2, y_2) is given by $m = \dfrac{y_2 - y_1}{x_2 - x_1} \quad x_2 \neq x_1$ The slopes of two nonvertical parallel lines are equal. The slopes of two nonvertical perpendicular lines are the negative reciprocals of each other.	Given a line through $(2, -1)$ and $(-4, 5)$, the slope is $m = \dfrac{-1 - 5}{2 - (-4)} = \dfrac{-6}{6} = -1$	*pp.* 238, 242, 243
Forms of Linear Equations		Section 3.4
There are two useful special forms for the equation of a line. The **slope-intercept form** of the equation of a line is $y = mx + b$, in which the line has slope m and y-intercept $(0, b)$. The **point-slope form** of the equation of a line is $y - y_1 = m(x - x_1)$, in which the line has slope m and passes through the point (x_1, y_1). And $x = x_1$ is the equation of a line through (x, y) with undefined slope. The slope-intercept form can also be expressed as a function $f(x) = mx + b$.	$y = \frac{2}{3}x + 4$ is in slope-intercept form. The slope m is $\frac{2}{3}$, and the y-intercept is $(0, 4)$. If line l has slope $m = -2$ and passes through $(-2, 3)$, its equation is $y - 3 = -2[x - (-2)]$ $y - 3 = -2(x + 2)$ $y - 3 = -2x - 4$ $y = -2x - 1$	*pp.* 258, 261, 265
Graphing Absolute Value Functions and Linear Inequalities		Section 3.5
Graphing Absolute Value Functions		
The graph of the function $f(x) = \|x - a\|$ will be the same as the graph of $f(x) = \|x\|$ except that the graph will be shifted a units To the right if a is positive To the left if a is negative The graph of the function $f(x) = \|x\| + a$ will be the same as the graph of $f(x) = \|x\|$ except that the graph will be shifted a units Up if a is positive Down if a is negative		*pp.* 281, 283
An inequality that can be written in the form $Ax + By < C$, in which A and B are not both zero, is called **a linear inequality in two variables.**		*p.* 284

Definition/Procedure	Example	Reference
To graph a linear inequality: **Step 1** Replace the inequality symbol with an equal sign to form the equation of the boundary line of the graph. **Step 2** Graph the boundary line. Use a dashed line if equality is not included ($<$ or $>$). Use a solid line if equality is included ($\le$ or $\ge$). **Step 3** Choose any convenient test point not on the line. **Step 4** If the inequality is *true* at the checkpoint, shade the half-plane including the test point. If the inequality is *false* at the checkpoint, shade the half-plane that does not include the checkpoint.	To graph $x - 2y < 4$: $x - 2y = 4$ is the boundary line. Using (0, 0) as the checkpoint, we have $0 - 2 \cdot 0 \overset{?}{<} 4$ $0 < 4$ (True) Shade the half-plane that includes (0, 0).	*p.* 287

summary exercises :: chapter 3

This summary exercise set is provided to give you practice with each of the objectives of this chapter. Each exercise is keyed to the appropriate chapter section. When you are finished, you can check your answers to the odd-numbered exercises against those presented in the back of the text. If you have difficulty with any of these questions, go back and reread the examples from that section. The answers to the even-numbered exercises appear in the *Instructor's Solutions Manual.* Your instructor will give you guidelines on how best to use these exercises in your instructional setting.

3.1 *Identify which are ordered pairs.*

1. **(a)** $(2, 1)$ **(b)** $\{3, 4\}$ **(c)** $1, 4$ **(d)** $(-4, -3)$ **(e)** $((3, 2), 5)$ (a) and (d)

2. **(a)** $\{-1, 4\}$ **(b)** $6, 8$ **(c)** $(3, 4)$ **(d)** $\{(3, -1), 4\}$ **(e)** $(-2, 5)$ (c) and (e)

Graph the following points in the Cartesian coordinate system.

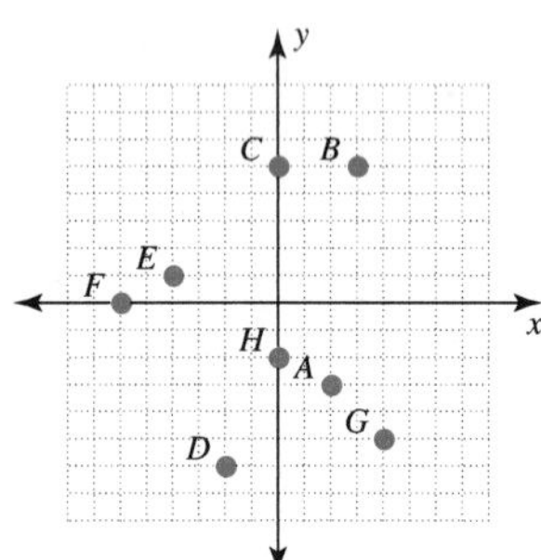

3. $A(2, -3)$ **4.** $B(3, 5)$ **5.** $C(0, 5)$

6. $D(-2, -6)$ **7.** $E(-4, 1)$ **8.** $F(-6, 0)$

9. $G(4, -5)$ **10.** $H(0, -2)$

Give the coordinates associated with the points indicated in the figure.

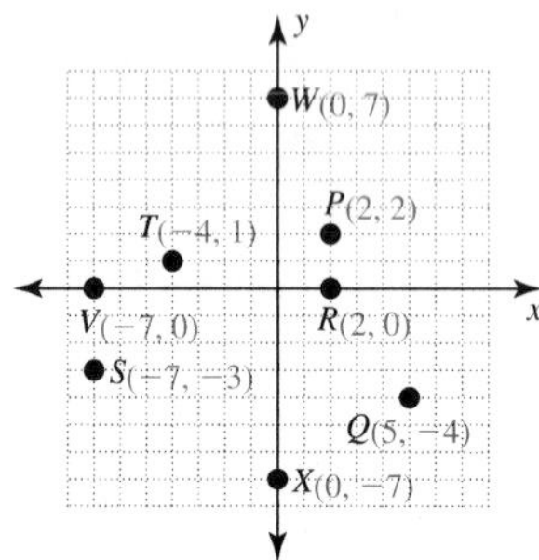

11. P **12.** Q **13.** R

14. S **15.** T **16.** V

17. W **18.** X

Find three ordered pairs that are solutions for the given equations.

19. $2x - y = 8$ Answers may vary; sample: (0, −8), (1, −6), (2, −4)

20. $3x + y = 7$ Answers may vary; sample: (0, 7), (1, 4), (2, 1)

21. $x + 2y = 5$ Answers may vary; sample: (1, 2), (3, 1), (5, 0)

Graph each equation.

22. $y = x + 1$

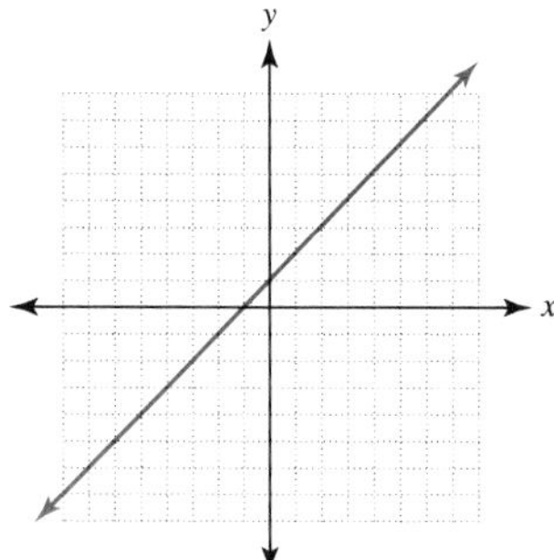

23. $y = 2x + 1$

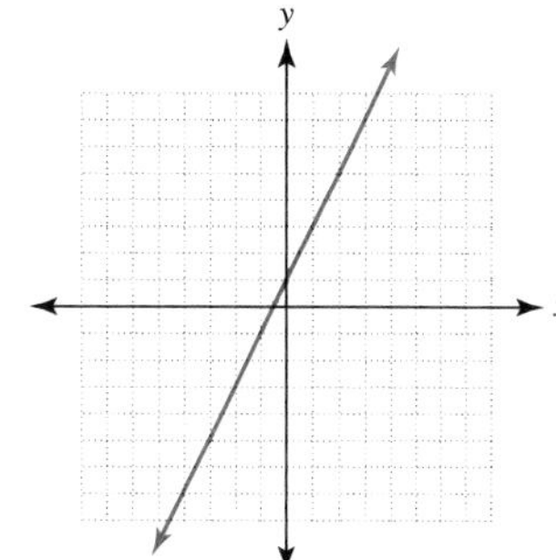

24. $y = -2x + 1$

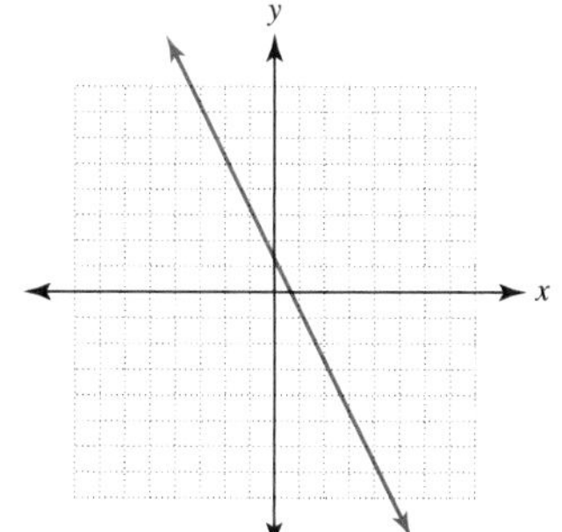

25. $y = -3x + 1$

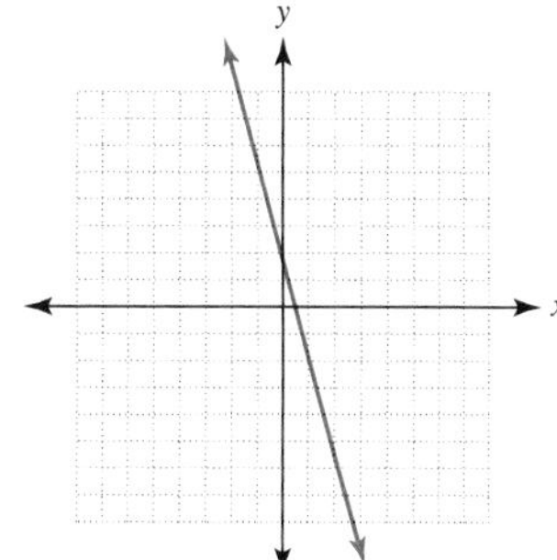

Find the x- and y-intercepts, and then graph each of the following equations.

26. $x - 2y = 4$

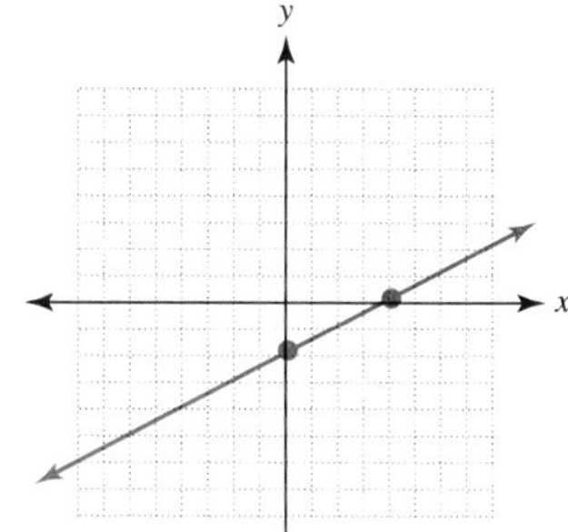

x-int: (4, 0), y-int: (0, −2)

27. $x + 3y = 6$

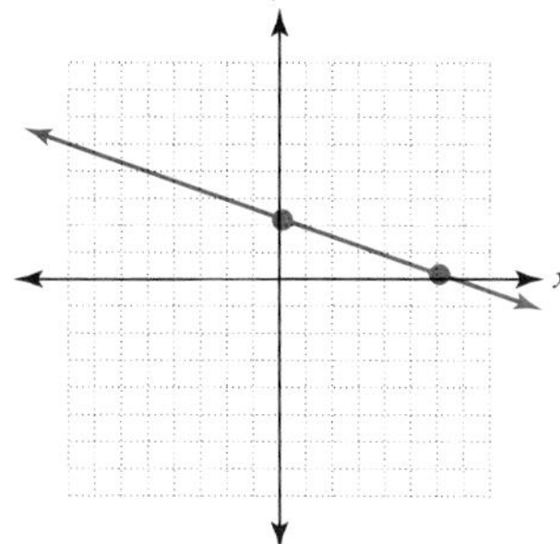

x-int: (6, 0), y-int: (0, 2)

28. $2x - y = 6$

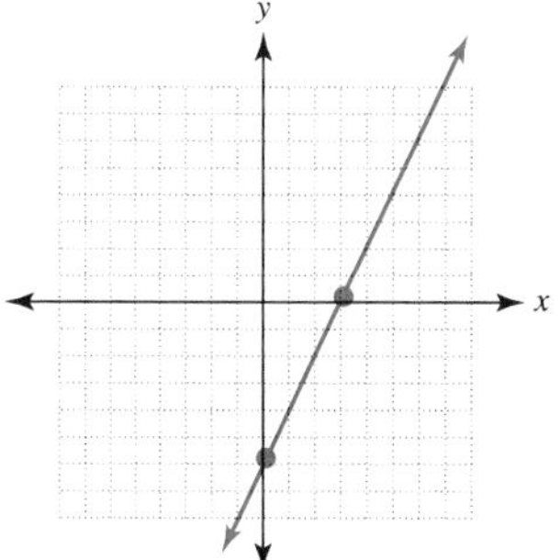

x-int: (3, 0), y-int: (0, −6)

29. $3x + 2y = 12$

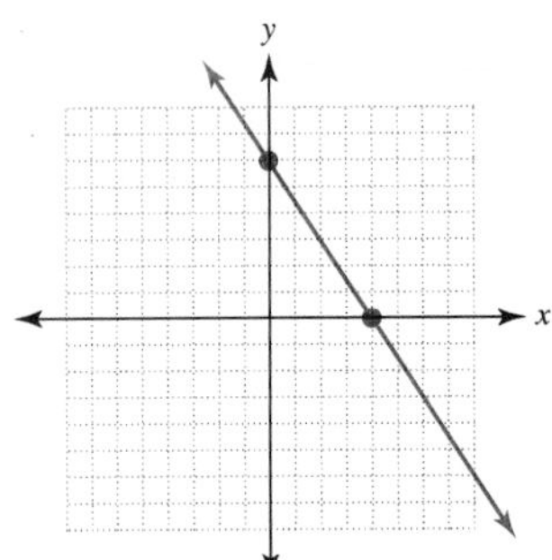

x-int: (4, 0), y-int: (0, 6)

30. $2x + 5y = 10$

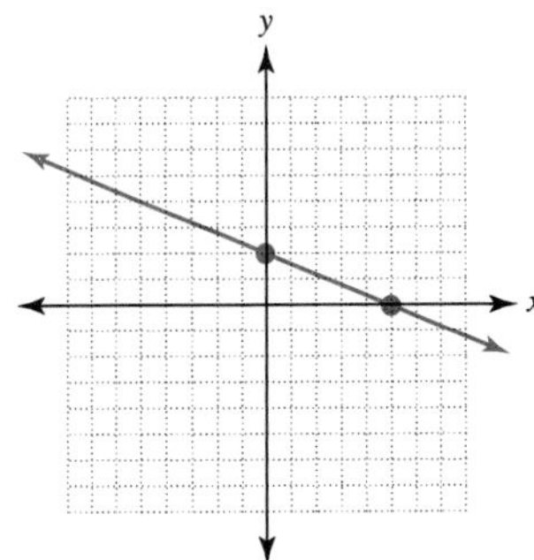

x-int: (5, 0), y-int: (0, 2)

31. $2x - 3y = 6$

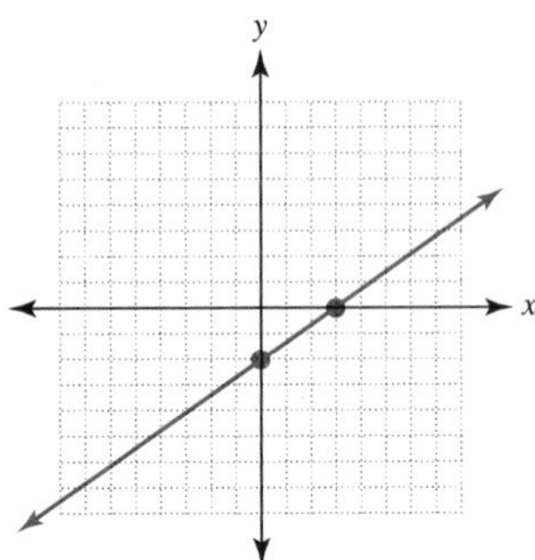

x-int: (3, 0), y-int: (0, −2)

32. $y = 4$

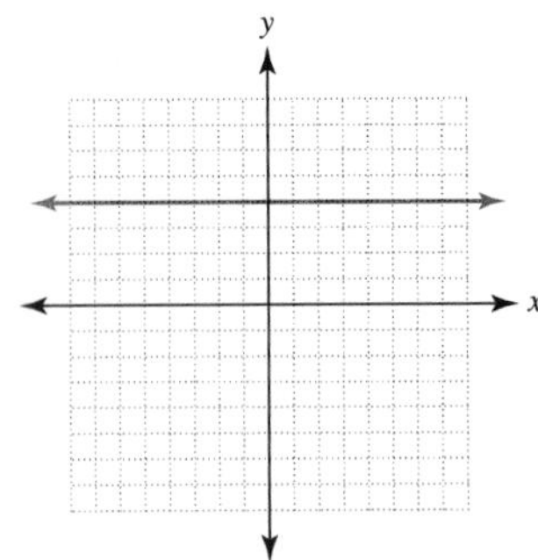

x-int: none, y-int: (0, 4)

33. $x = -3$

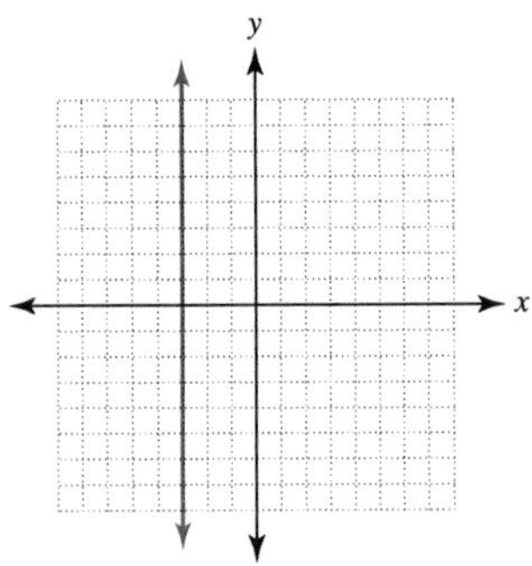

x-int: (−3, 0), y-int: none

3.2 *Find the domain and range of each relation.*

34. A = {(John Wayne, 1969), (Art Carney, 1974), (Peter Finch, 1976), (Marlon Brando, 1972)} D: {John Wayne, Art Carney, Peter Finch, Marlon Brando}, R: {1969, 1974, 1976, 1972}

35. B = {(Dean Smith, 65), (John Wooden, 47), (Denny Crum, 42), (Bob Knight, 41)} D: {Dean Smith, John Wooden, Denny Crum, Bob Knight}, R: {65, 47, 42, 41}

36. $C = \{$(Don Shula, 328), (George Halas, 318), (Tom Landry, 250), (Chuck Noll, 193)$\}$ D: {Don Shula, George Halas, Tom Landry, Chuck Noll}, R: {328, 318, 250, 193}

37. $\{(3, 5), (4, 6), (1, 2), (8, 1), (7, 3)\}$ D: $\{1, 3, 4, 7, 8\}$, R: $\{1, 2, 3, 5, 6\}$

38. $\{(-1, 3), (-2, 5), (3, 7), (1, 4), (2, -2)\}$ D: $\{-2, -1, 1, 2, 3\}$, R: $\{-2, 3, 4, 5, 7\}$

39. $\{(1, 3), (1, 5), (1, 7), (1, 9), (1, 10)\}$ D: $\{1\}$, R: $\{3, 5, 7, 9, 10\}$

40. $\{(2, 4), (-1, 4), (-3, 4), (1, 4), (6, 4)\}$ D: $\{-3, -1, 1, 2, 6\}$, R: $\{4\}$

Evaluate each function for the value specified.

41. $f(x) = x^2 - 3x + 5$; find **(a)** $f(0)$, **(b)** $f(-1)$, and **(c)** $f(0.5)$. (a) 5; (b) 9; (c) 3.75

42. $f(x) = -2x^2 + x - 7$; find **(a)** $f(0)$, **(b)** $f(2)$, and **(c)** $f(-2)$. (a) -7; (b) -13; (c) -17

43. $f(x) = x^3 - x^2 - 2x + 5$; find **(a)** $f(-1)$, **(b)** $f\left(-\frac{1}{2}\right)$, and **(c)** $f(0)$. (a) 5; (b) $\frac{45}{8}$; (c) 5

44. $f(x) = -x^2 + 7x - 9$; find **(a)** $f(-3)$, **(b)** $f(0)$, and **(c)** $f(1)$. (a) -39; (b) -9; (c) -3

45. $f(x) = 3x^2 - 5x + 1$; find **(a)** $f(-1)$, **(b)** $f(0)$, and **(c)** $f\left(\frac{1}{4}\right)$. (a) 9; (b) 1; (c) $-\frac{1}{16}$

46. $f(x) = -x^3 + 3x - 5$; find **(a)** $f(2)$, **(b)** $f(0)$, and **(c)** $f(1)$. (a) -7; (b) -5; (c) -3

Determine which relations are also functions.

47. $\{(1, 3), (2, 4), (5, -1), (-1, 3)\}$ Function

48. $\{(-2, 4), (3, 6), (1, 5), (0, 1)\}$ Function

49. $\{(1, 2), (0, 4), (1, 3), (2, 5)\}$ Not a function

50. $\{(1, 3), (2, 3), (3, 3), (4, 3)\}$ Function

Use the vertical line test to determine whether the given graph represents a function. Find the domain and range of the relation.

51.

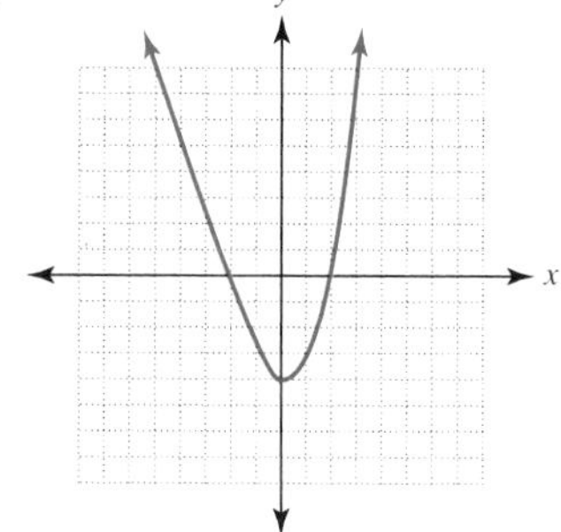

Function; D: $\mathbb{R}$; R: $\{y \mid y \geq -4\}$

52.

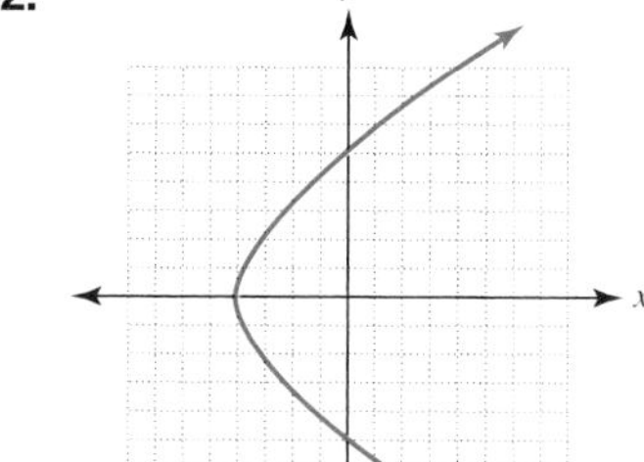

Not a function; D: $\{x \mid x \geq -4\}$; R: $\mathbb{R}$

53.

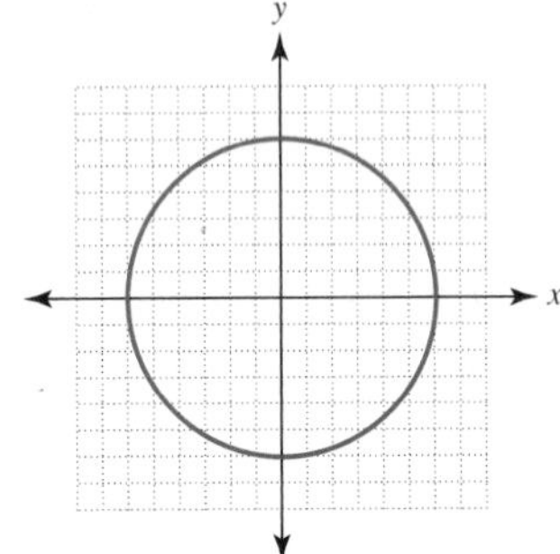

Not a function; D: $\{x \mid -6 \le x \le 6\}$; R: $\{y \mid -6 \le y \le 6\}$

54.

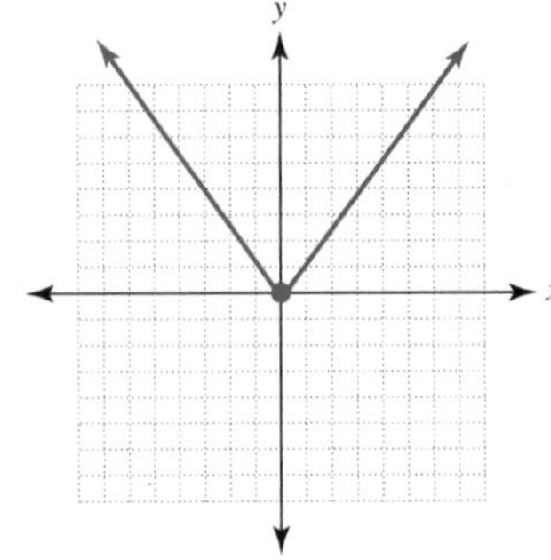

Function; D: $\mathbb{R}$; R: $\{y \mid y \ge 0\}$

Find the coordinates of the labeled points.

55.

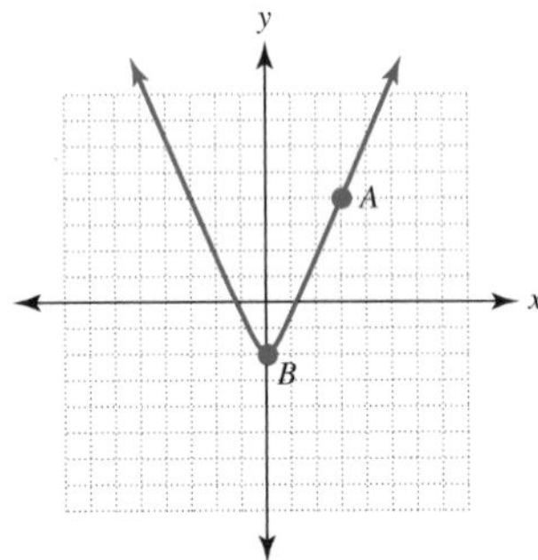

A: (3, 4); B: (0, −2)

56.

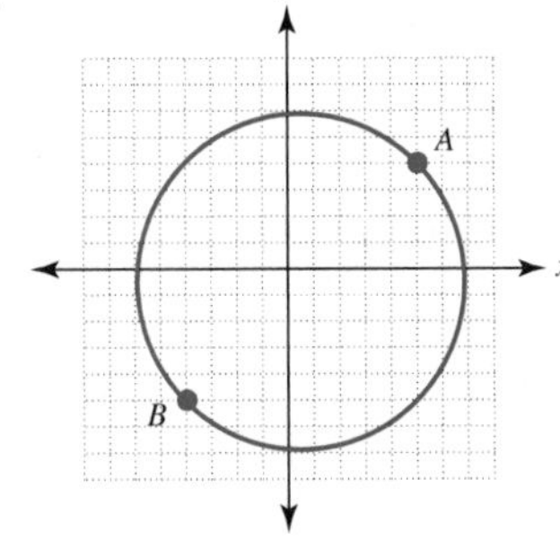

A: (5, 4); B: (−4, −5)

57.

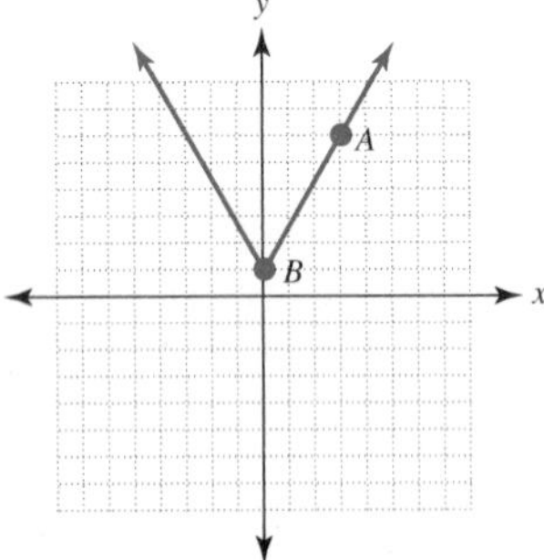

A: (3, 6); B: (0, 1)

58.

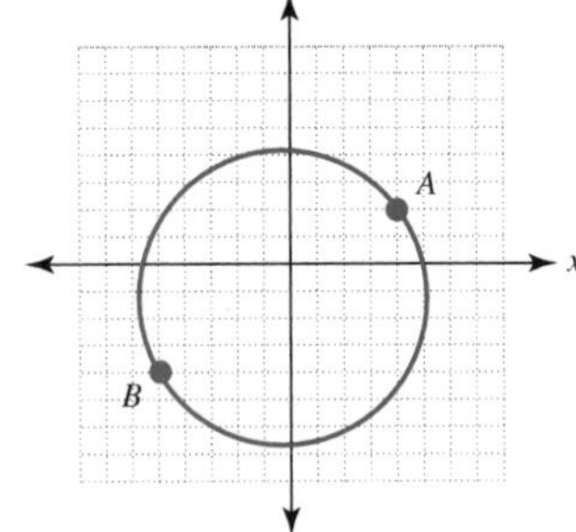

A: (4, 2); B: (−5, −4)

Use the graph to estimate **(a)** $f(-2)$, **(b)** $f(0)$, *and* **(c)** $f(2)$.

59.

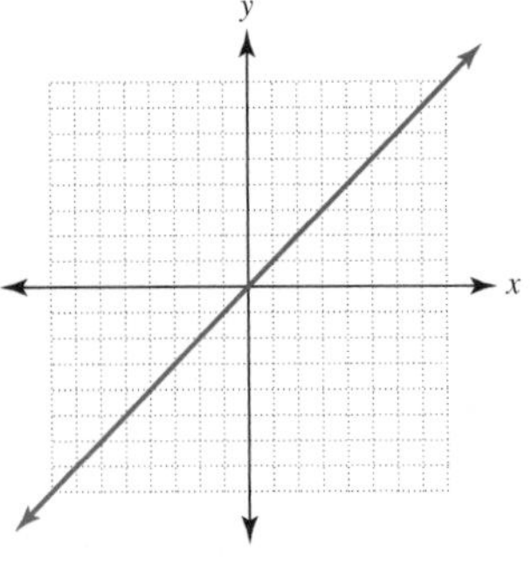

(a) −2; (b) 0; (c) 2

60.

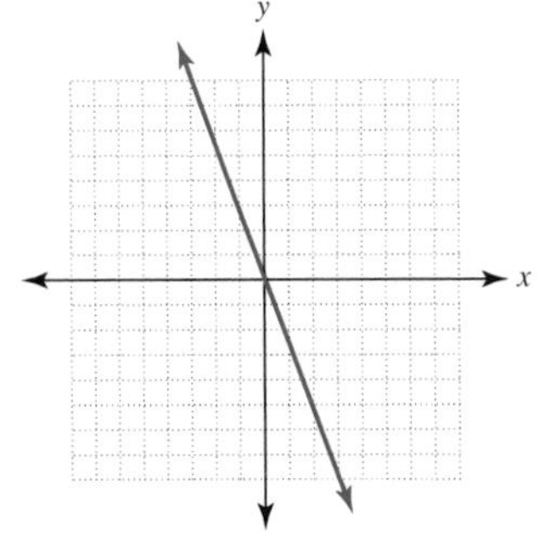

(a) 5; (b) 0; (c) −5

61.

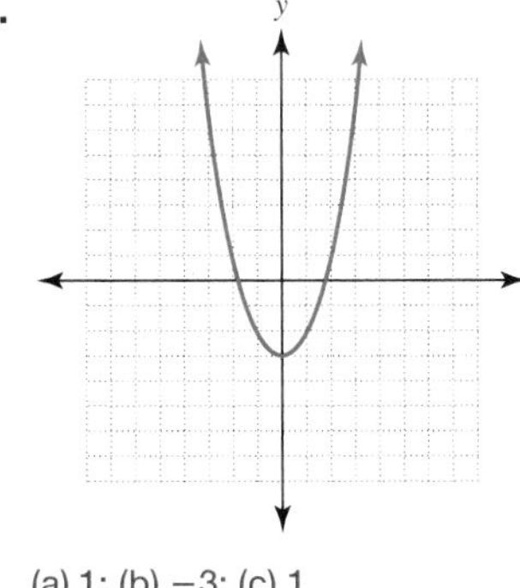

(a) 1; (b) −3; (c) 1

62.

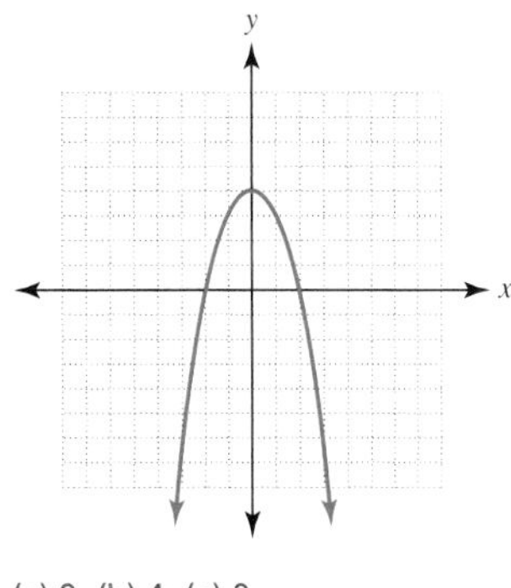

(a) 0; (b) 4; (c) 0

Use the graph of $f(x)$ to find all values of x such that **(a)** $f(x) = -1$, **(b)** $f(x) = 0$, *and* **(c)** $f(x) = 1$.

63.

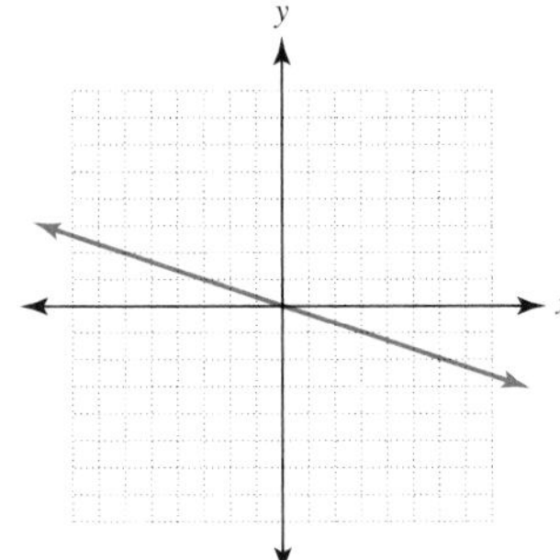

(a) 3; (b) 0; (c) −3

64.

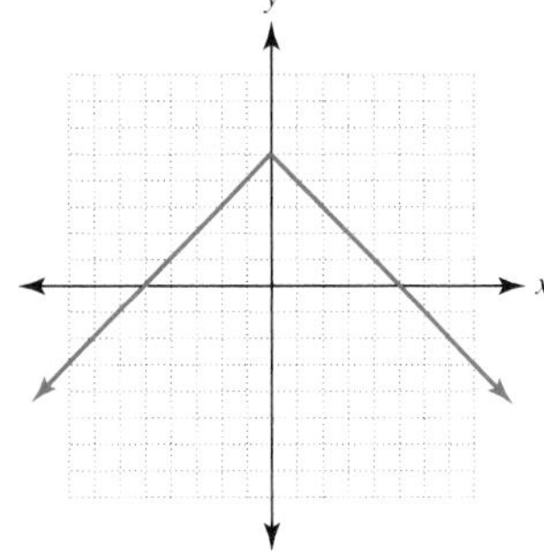

(a) −6, 6; (b) −5, 5; (c) −4, 4

65.

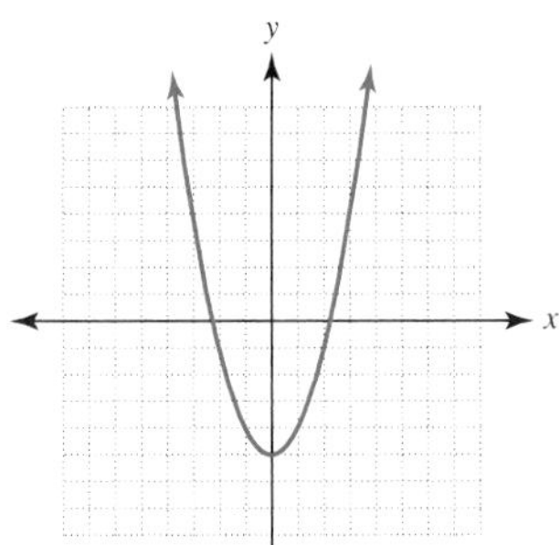

(a) −2, 2; (b) −2.2, 2.2; (c) −2.5, 2.5

66.

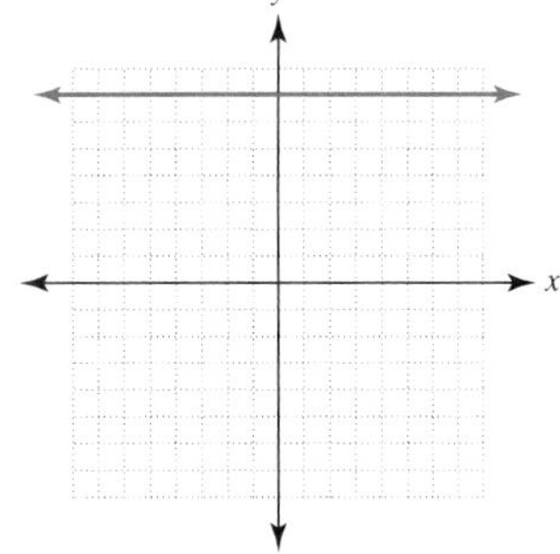

(a) No solutions; (b) no solutions; (c) no solutions

Find the x- and y-intercepts from the graph.

67.

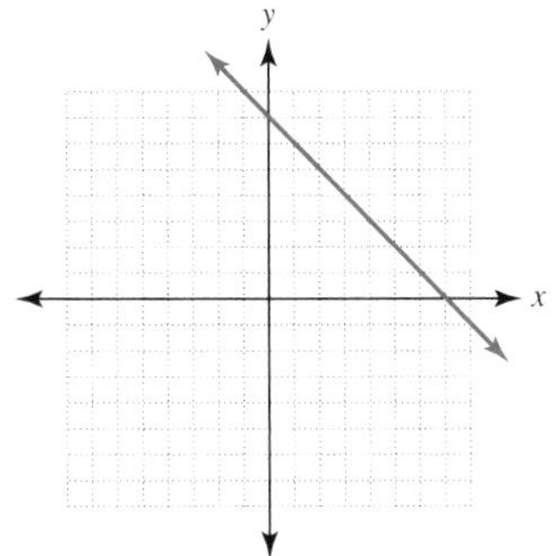

x-int: (7, 0), *y*-int: (0, 7)

68.

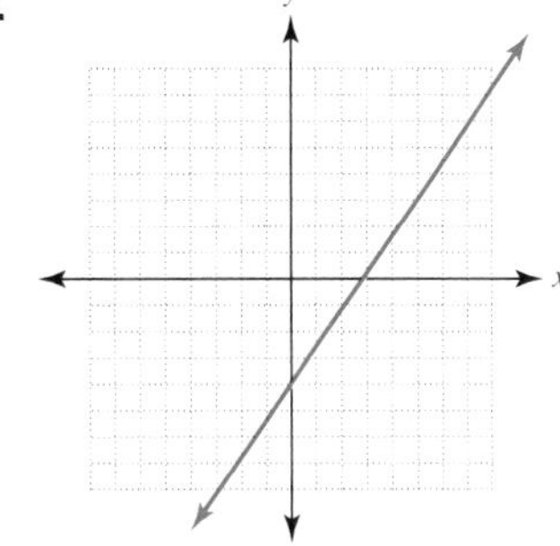

x-int: (3, 0), *y*-int: (0, −4)

69.

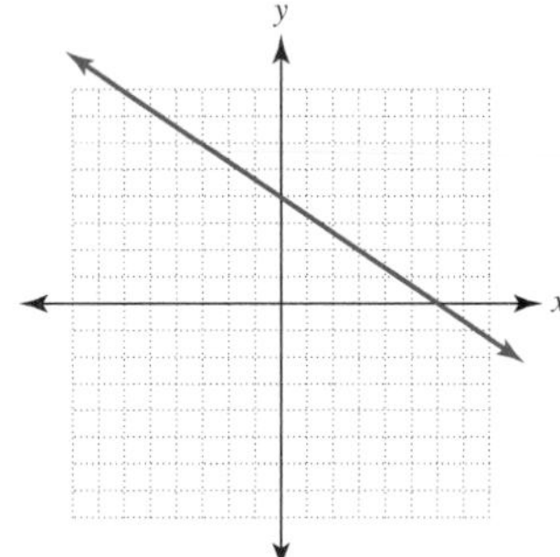

x-int: (6, 0), y-int: (0, 4)

70.

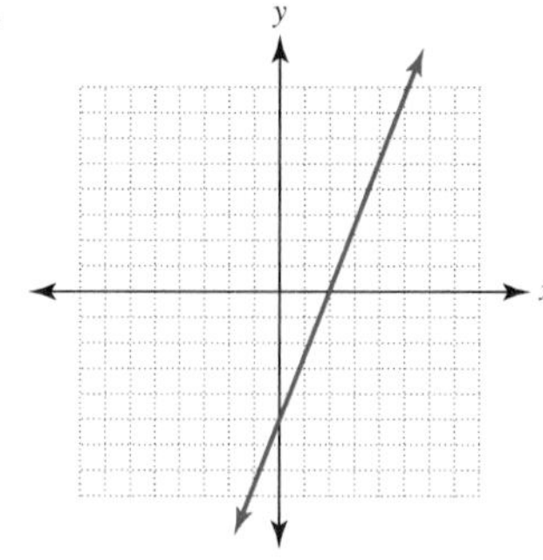

x-int: (2, 0), y-int: (0, −5)

71.

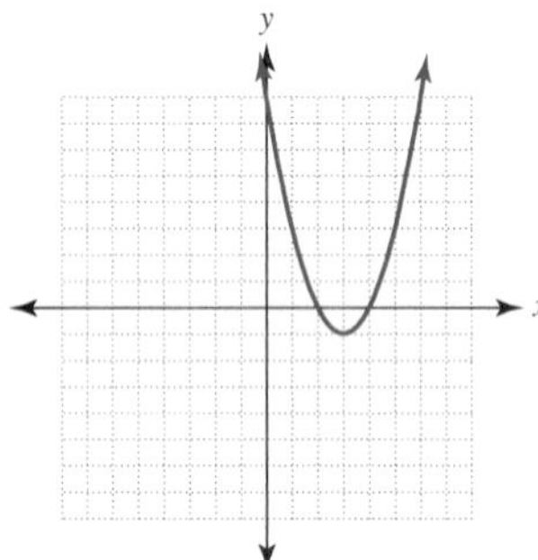

x-int: (2, 0) and (4, 0), y-int: (0, 8)

72.

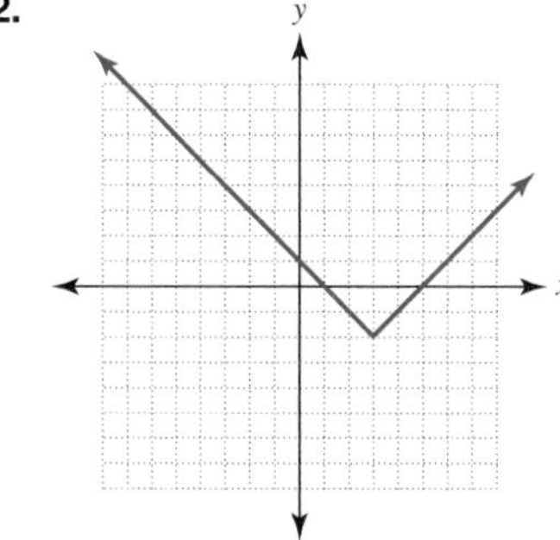

x-int: (1, 0) and (5, 0), y-int: (0, 1)

73.

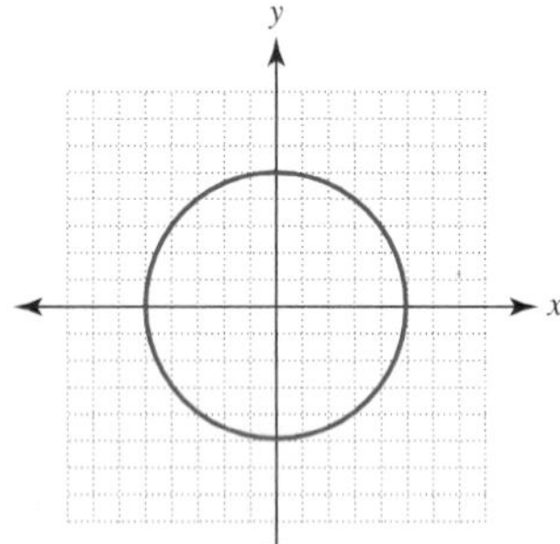

x-int: (−5, 0) and (5, 0), y-int: (0, −5) and (0, 5)

74.

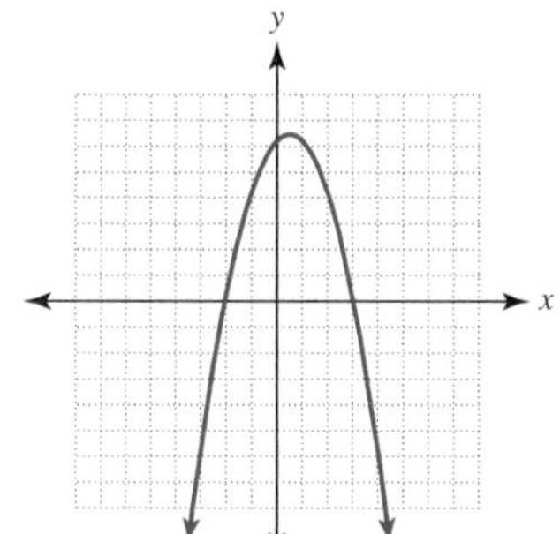

x-int: (−2, 0) and (3, 0), y-int: (0, 6)

3.3 *Find the slope (if it exists) of the line determined by the given pair of points.*

75. $(-2, 5)$ and $(1, -1)$ -2

76. $(2, -4)$ and $(3, 5)$ 9

77. $(-3, -4)$ and $(3, 0)$ $\frac{2}{3}$

78. $(4, -3)$ and $(4, 4)$ Undefined

79. $(4, -2)$ and $(-2, -2)$ 0

80. $(2, -4)$ and $(-1, -3)$ $-\frac{1}{3}$

81. $(5, -2)$ and $(5, 3)$ Undefined

Find the slope of the line determined by the given equation.

82. $3x + 2y = 6$ $-\frac{3}{2}$

83. $x - 4y = 8$ $\frac{1}{4}$

Without graphing, are the pairs of lines **parallel, perpendicular,** *or* **neither?**

84. L_1 through $(-3, -2)$ and $(1, 3)$
L_2 through $(0, 3)$ and $(4, 8)$ Parallel

85. L_1 through $(-4, 1)$ and $(2, -3)$
L_2 through $(0, -3)$ and $(2, 0)$ Perpendicular

86. L_1 with equation $x + 2y = 6$
L_2 with equation $x + 3y = 9$ Neither

87. L_1 with equation $4x - 6y = 18$
L_2 with equation $2x - 3y = 6$ Parallel

3.4 *Write the equation of the line passing through the given point with the indicated slope. Give your results in slope-intercept form, when possible.*

88. $(0, -5)$, $m = \frac{2}{3}$

$y = \frac{2}{3}x - 5$

89. $(0, -3)$, $m = 0$

$y = -3$

90. $(2, 3)$, $m = 3$

$y = 3x - 3$

91. $(4, 3)$, m is undefined

$x = 4$

92. $(3, -2)$, $m = \frac{5}{3}$

$y = \frac{5}{3}x - 7$

93. $(-2, -3)$, $m = 0$

$y = -3$

94. $(-2, -4)$, $m = -\frac{5}{2}$

$y = -\frac{5}{2}x - 9$

95. $(-3, 2)$, $m = -\frac{4}{3}$

$y = -\frac{4}{3}x - 2$

96. $\left(\frac{2}{3}, -5\right)$, $m = 0$

$y = -5$

97. $\left(-\frac{5}{2}, -1\right)$, m is undefined

$x = -\frac{5}{2}$

Use the graph to determine the slope and y-intercept of the line.

98.

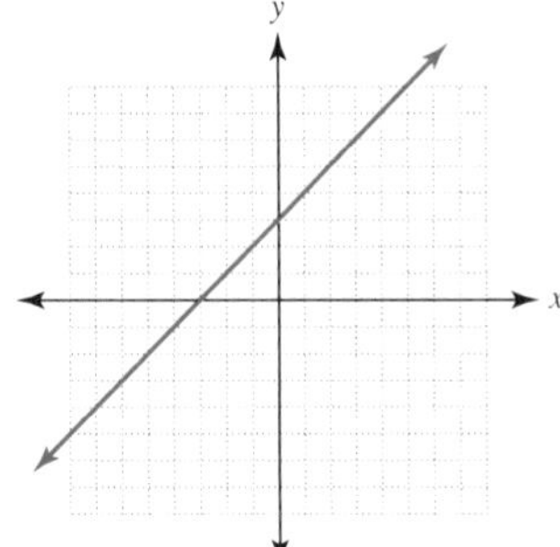

$m = 1$; y-int: $(0, 3)$

99.

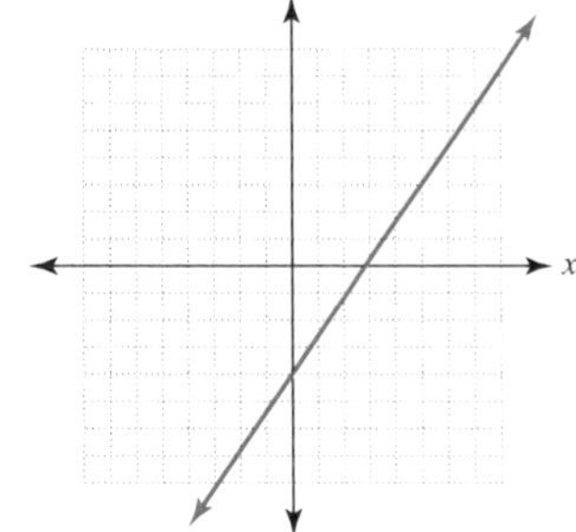

$m = \frac{4}{3}$; y-int: $(0, -4)$

 The Streeter/Hutchison Series in Mathematics Intermediate Algebra

100.

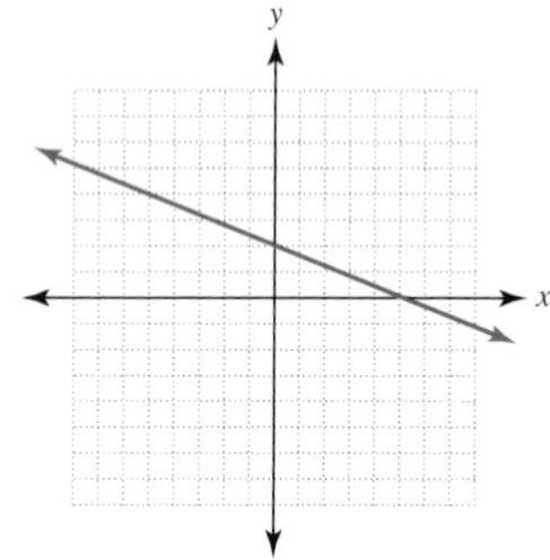

$m = -\frac{2}{5}$; y-int: (0, 2)

101.

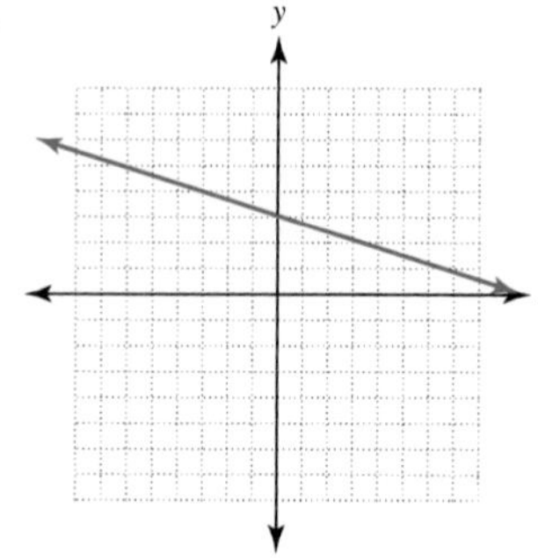

$m = -\frac{1}{3}$; y-int: (0, 3)

Write the equation of the line L satisfying the given set of geometric conditions.

102. L passes through $(-3, -1)$ and $(3, 3)$. $y = \frac{2}{3}x + 1$

103. L passes through $(0, 4)$ and $(5, 3)$. $y = -\frac{1}{5}x + 4$

104. L has slope $\frac{3}{4}$ and y-intercept $(0, 3)$. $y = \frac{3}{4}x + 3$

105. L passes through $(4, -3)$ with a slope of $-\frac{5}{4}$. $y = -\frac{5}{4}x + 2$

106. L has y-intercept $(0, -4)$ and is parallel to the line with equation $3x - y = 6$. $y = 3x - 4$

107. L passes through $(3, -2)$ and is perpendicular to the line with equation $3x - 5y = 15$. $y = -\frac{5}{3}x + 3$

108. L passes through $(2, -1)$ and is perpendicular to the line with equation $3x - 2y = 5$. $y = -\frac{2}{3}x + \frac{1}{3}$

109. L passes through the point $(-5, -2)$ and is parallel to the line with equation $4x - 3y = 9$. $y = \frac{4}{3}x + \frac{14}{3}$

110. Faheem purchases a professional four-color laser printer for his business for $1,800. If the printer is valued at $1,000 after 2 years, what is the equation that describes the value, V, of the printer after t years (assume the printer depreciates linearly)? $V = -400t + 1{,}800$

111. A local band charges a fixed fee of $250 plus $15 per hour for performing at a wedding. Write a linear equation that shows the relationship between the total cost, C, and the number of hours, h, played. $C = 250 + 15h$

3.5 *Graph each of the following absolute value functions.*

112. $f(x) = |x + 3|$

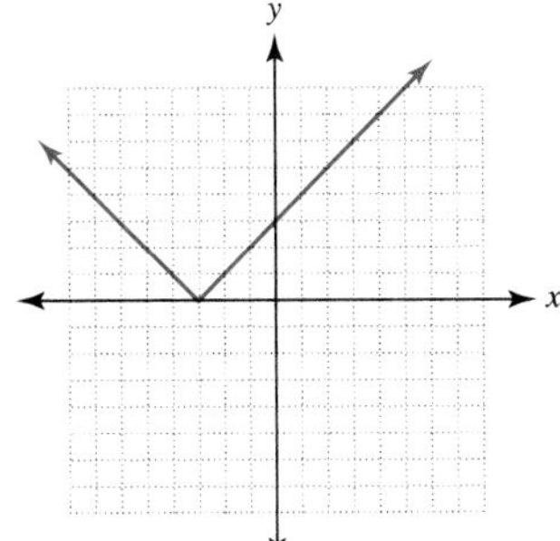

113. $f(x) = |x - 2|$

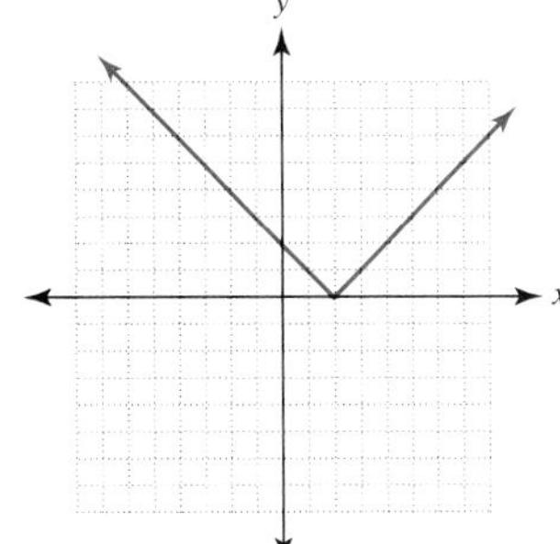

114. $f(x) = |x| - 9$

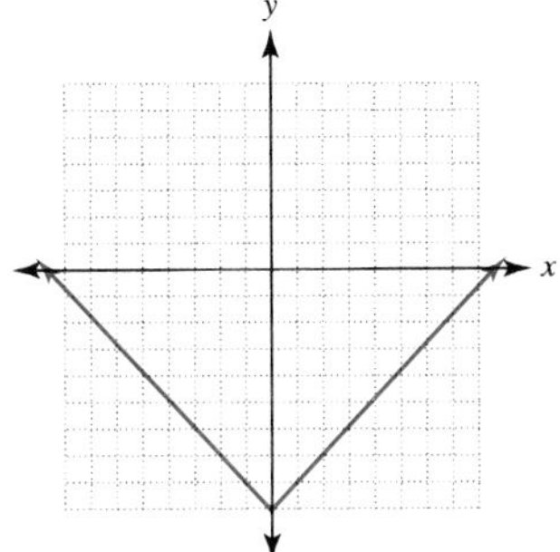

115. $f(x) = |x| + 7$

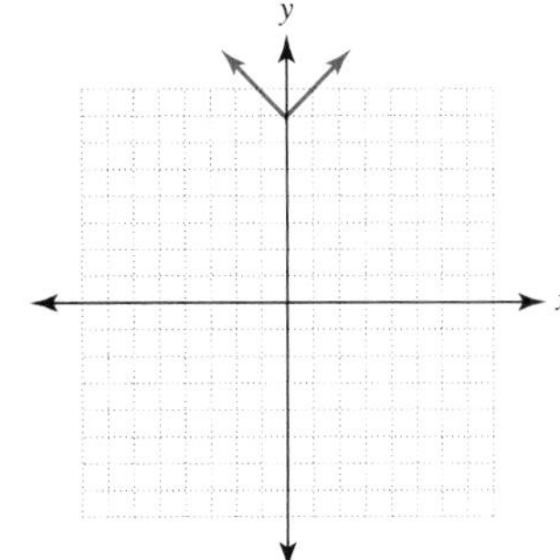

116. $f(x) = |x - 5| + 2$

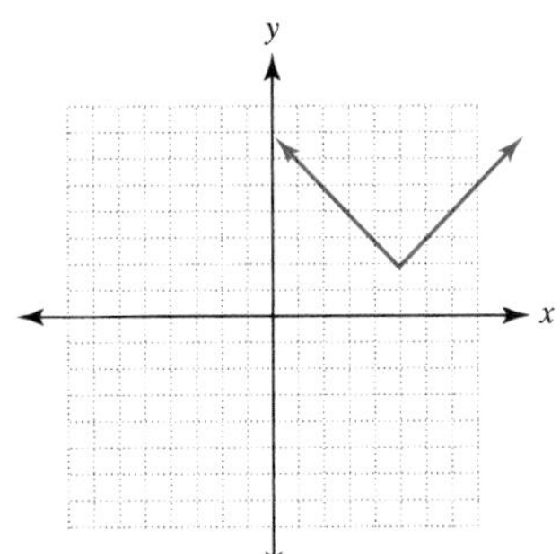

117. $f(x) = |x + 6| - 9$

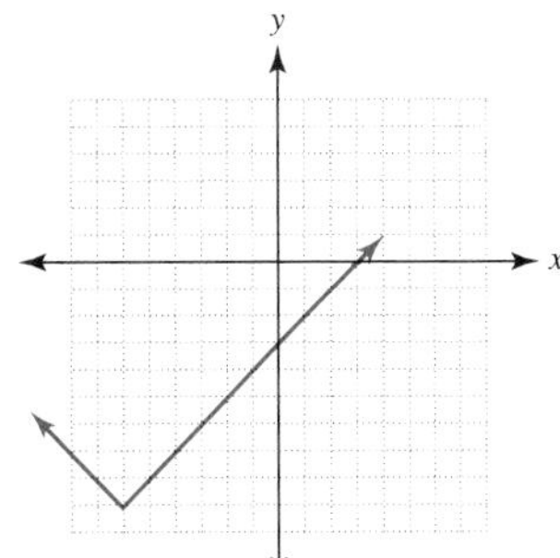

Graph each of the inequalities.

118. $x + y \leq 4$

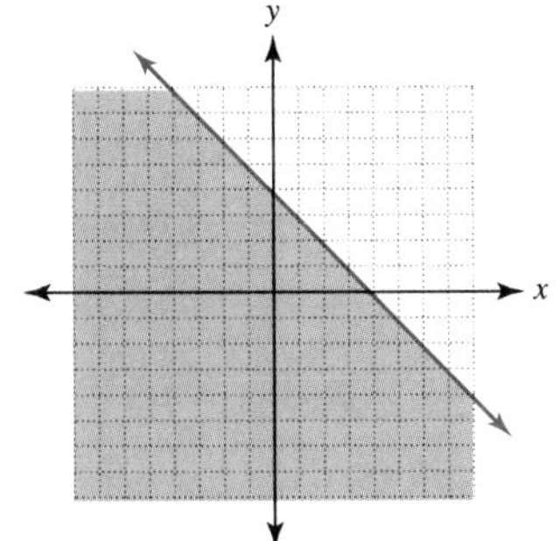

119. $x - y > 5$

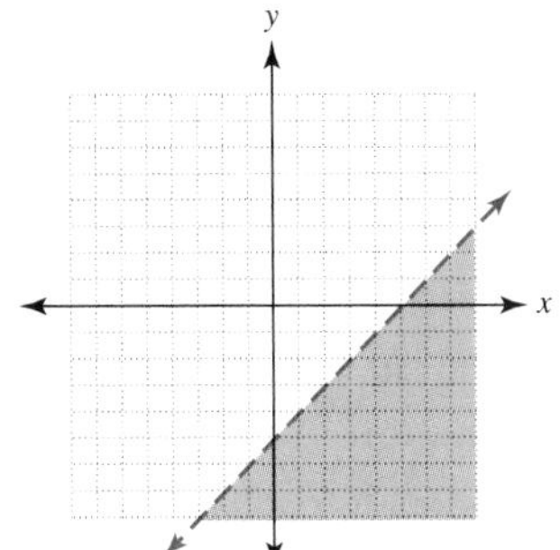

120. $2x + y < 6$

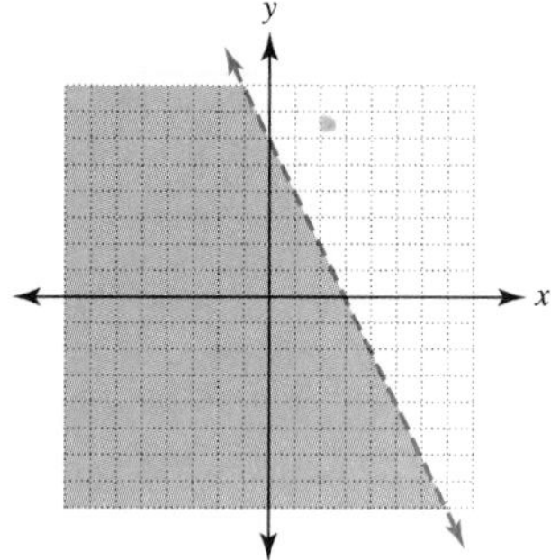

121. $2x - y \geq 6$

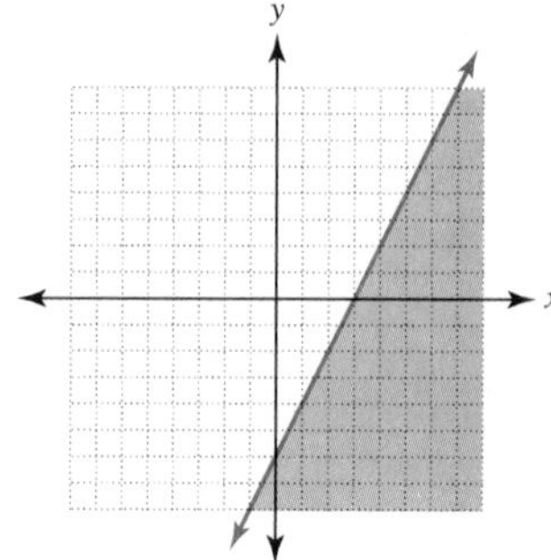

122. $x > 3$

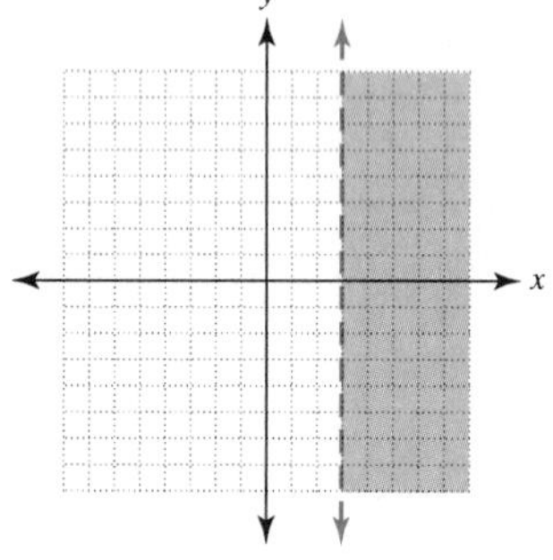

123. $y \leq 2$

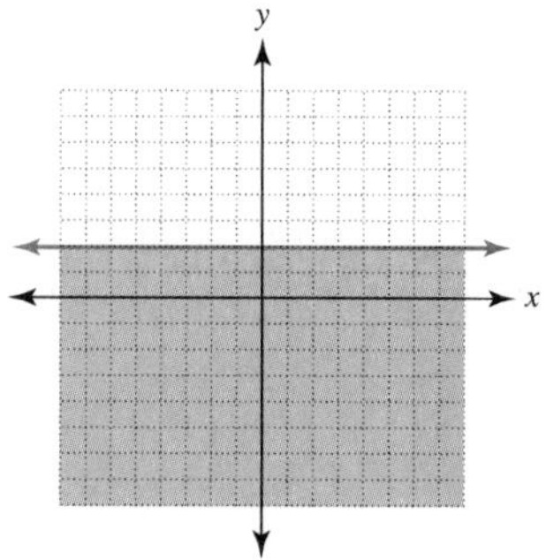

self-test 3

Name ____________

Section ________ Date ________

The purpose of this chapter test is to help you check your progress so that you can find sections and concepts that you need to review before the next exam. Allow yourself about an hour to take this test. At the end of that hour, check your answers against those given in the back of this text. If you missed any, note the section reference that accompanies the answer. Go back to that section and reread the examples until you have mastered that particular concept.

3.1

1. Identify which of the following are ordered pairs.

(a) $\{-1, 3\}$ **(b)** $(1, 4)$ **(c)** $[2, 4]$

(d) 5, 6 **(e)** $\{(2, 1), (4, 5)\}$

2. Give the coordinates associated with the indicated points in the figure.

(a) A **(b)** B **(c)** C **(d)** D

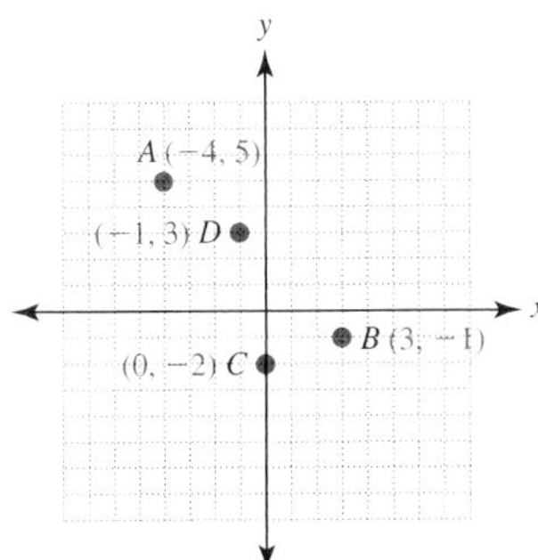

Identify the x- and y-intercepts and graph the equation.

3. $5x + 6y = 30$

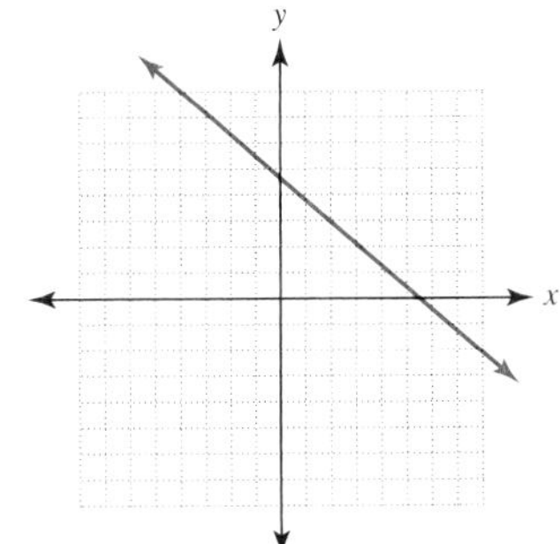

4. $48 - 16x = 0$

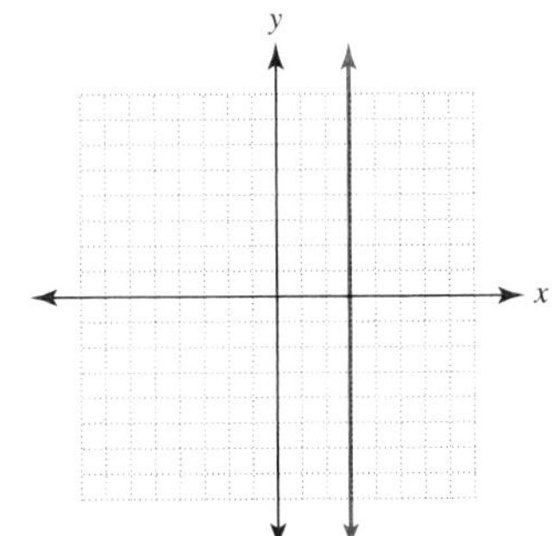

Answers

1. (b)

2. See exercise

3. x-int: (6, 0), y-int: (0, 5)

4. x-int: (3, 0), y-int: none

Answers

5. (a) D: $\{-3, 1, 2, 3, 4\}$, R: $\{-2, 0, 1, 5, 6\}$; (b) D: {United States, Germany, Russia, China}; R: $\{101, 65, 63, 50\}$

6. (a) 6; (b) 12; (c) 2

7. (a) 2; (b) -5

8. Function

9. Not a function

10. A: $(1, 0)$; B: $(-3, -4)$

11. A: $(-4, -2)$; B: $(1, 2)$

3.2

5. For each of the following sets of ordered pairs, identify the domain and range.

   (a) $\{(1, 6), (-3, 5), (2, 1), (4, -2), (3, 0)\}$

   (b) {(United States, 101), (Germany, 65), (Russia, 63), (China, 50)}

6. If $f(x) = x^2 - 5x + 6$, find **(a)** $f(0)$, **(b)** $f(-1)$, **(c)** $f(1)$.

7. If $f(x) = -3x^2 - 2x + 3$, find **(a)** $f(-1)$, **(b)** $f(-2)$.

Use the vertical line test to determine whether the following graphs represent functions.

8.

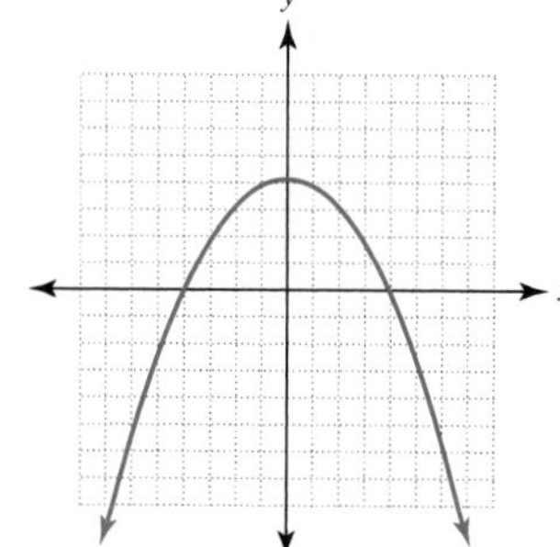

9.

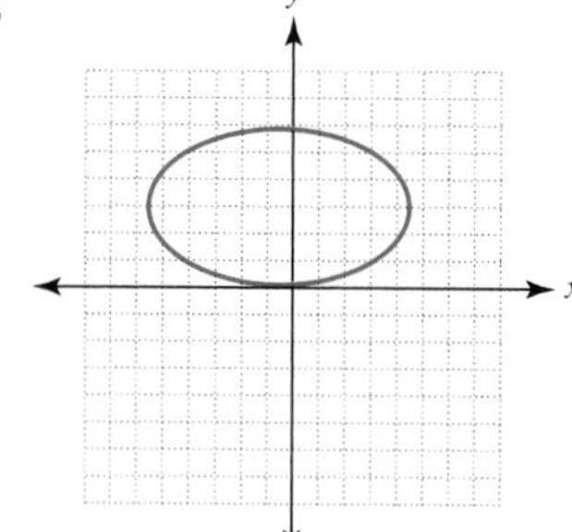

Find the coordinates of the labeled points.

10.

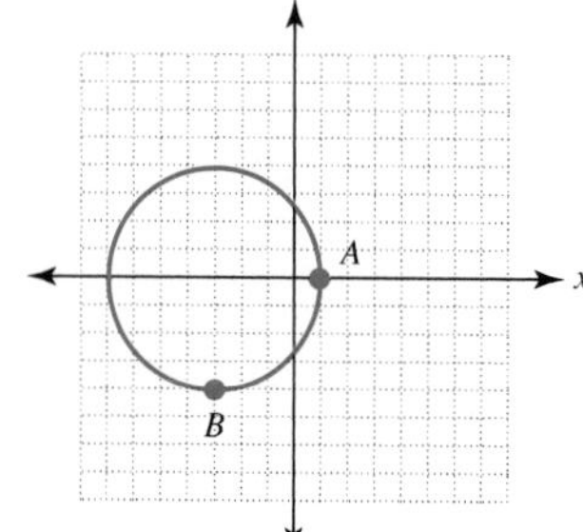

11.

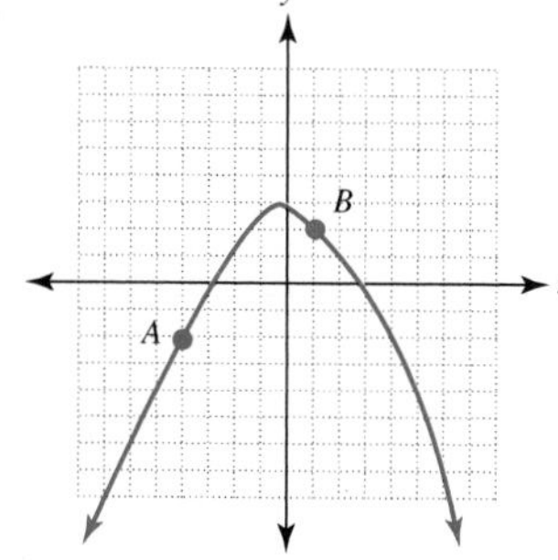

In the following, use the graph to find **(a)** $f(-1)$, **(b)** $f(0)$, *and* **(c)** $f(1)$.

12.

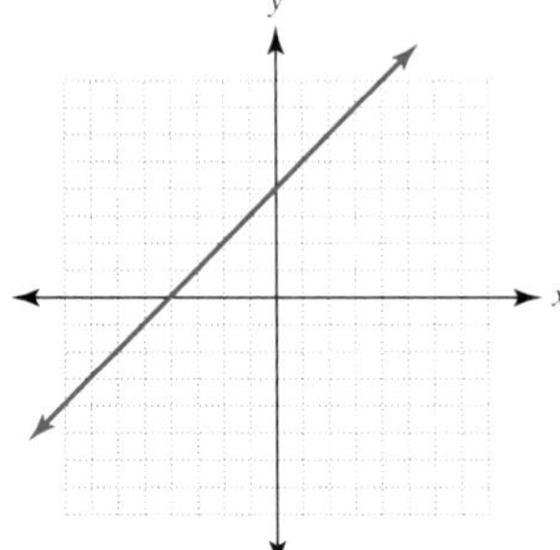

13.

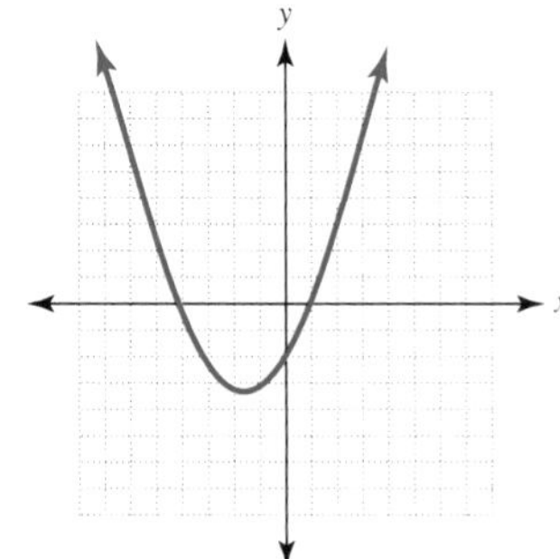

In the following, use the graph of $f(x)$ *to find all values of* x *such that* **(a)** $f(x) = -2$, **(b)** $f(x) = 0$, *and* **(c)** $f(x) = 2$.

14.

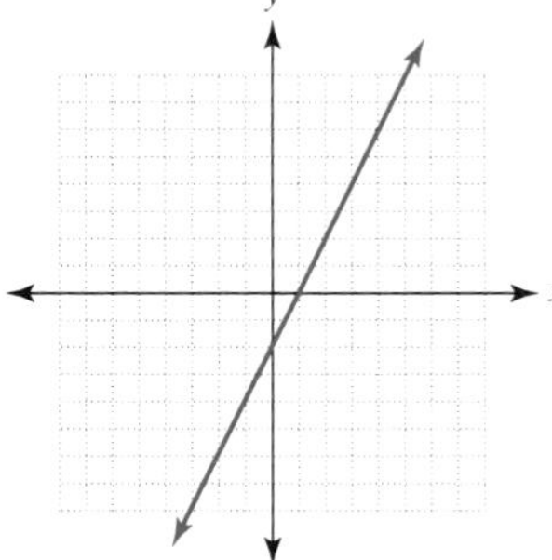

15.

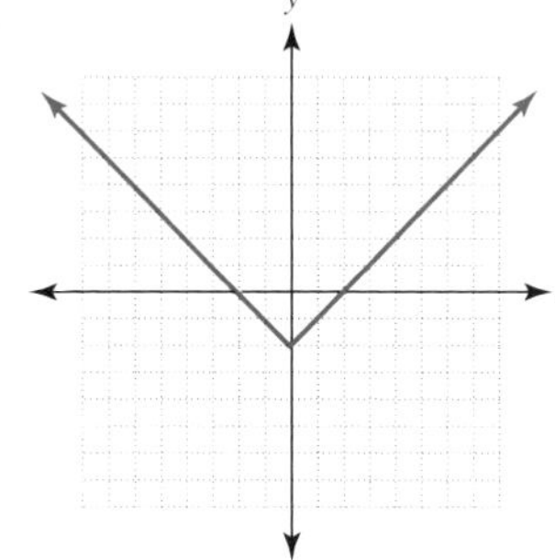

In exercises 16 and 17, find the x- and y-intercepts from the graph.

16.

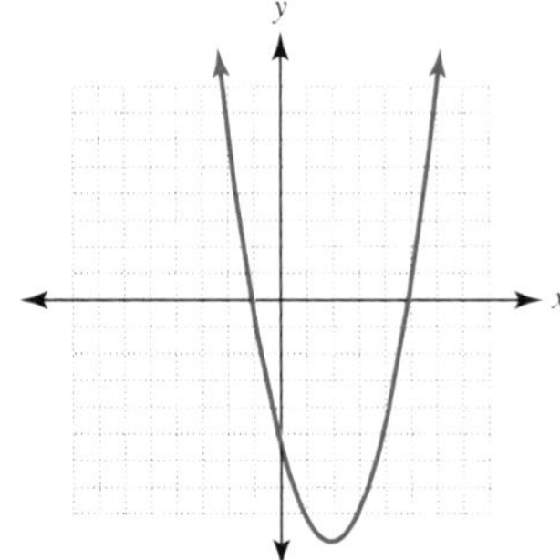

17.

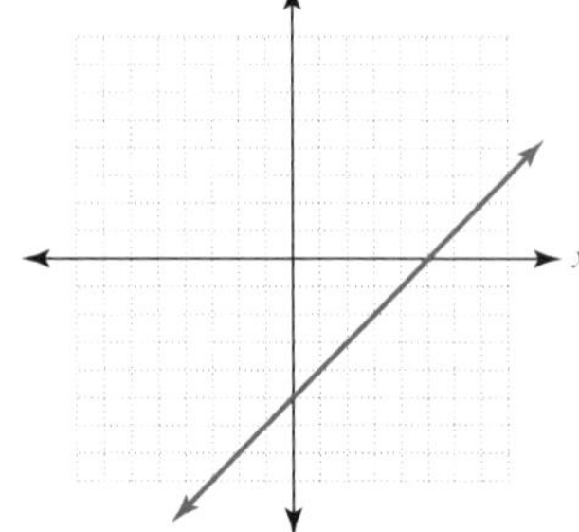

Answers

12. (a) 3; (b) 4; (c) 5

13. (a) −3; (b) −2; (c) 0

14. (a) 0; (b) 1; (c) 2

15. (a) 0; (b) −2, 2; (c) −4, 4

16. x-int: (−1, 0) and (5, 0), y-int: (0, −5)

17. x-int: (5, 0), y-int: (0, −5)

Answers

18. D: $\{x \mid -7 \le x \le 7\}$, R: $\{y \mid -7 \le y \le 7\}$

19. D: $\mathbb{R}$, R: $\{y \mid y \le 9\}$

20. 2

21. Undefined

22. 0

23. $-\frac{2}{5}$

24. Undefined

25. 0

26. Neither

27. Perpendicular

28. Parallel

29. $y = 2x - 1$

30. $y = \frac{2}{3}x - 4$

31. $y = -3x - 1$

32. $y = 4x - 2$

33. $y = \frac{2}{3}x + 3$

34. $C = 2.4m + 2.05$

In exercises 18 and 19, use the graph to determine the domain and range of the relation.

18.

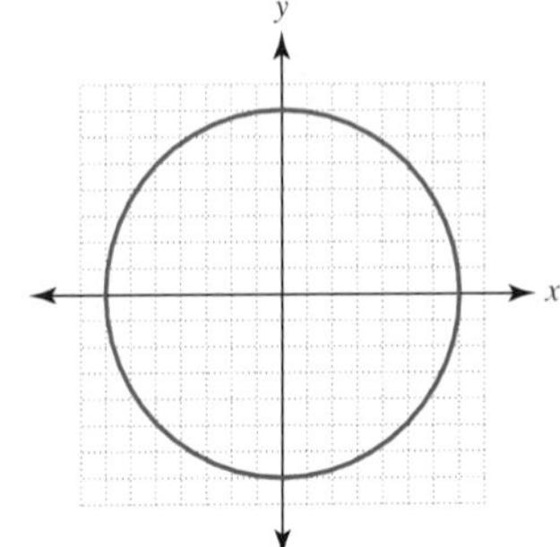

19.

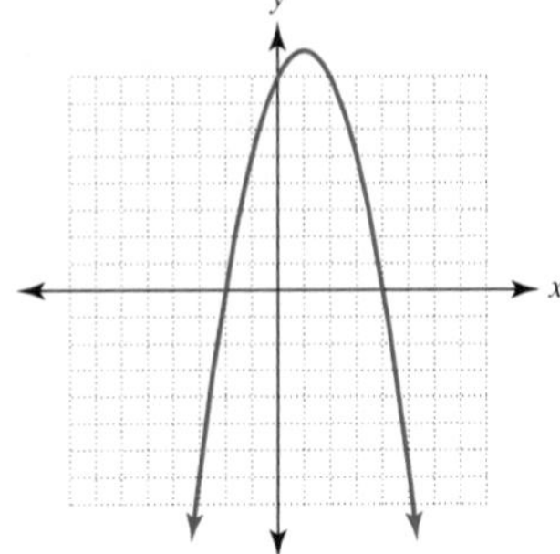

3.3

Find the slope of the line connecting the given points.

20. (5, 6) and (−3, −10)

21. (9, 5) and (9, −3)

22. (3, 6) and (−2, 6)

Find the slope of the line determined by the given equation.

23. $2x + 5y = 10$

24. $3x - 6 = 0$

25. $4y + 24 = 0$

Without graphing, determine if the given lines are **parallel, perpendicular,** *or* **neither.**

26. $3x + 5y = 10$
$5x + 3y = 10$

27. $2y - 3x = 12$
$3y + 2x = 15$

28. $5x + 6y = 2$
$15x + 18y = 2$

3.4

Write the equation of the line L that satisfies the given set of geometric conditions.

29. L passes through (2, 3) and (4, 7).

30. L has slope $\frac{2}{3}$ and y-intercept (0, −4).

31. L passes through (−1, 2) and has a slope of −3.

32. L has y-intercept (0, −2) and is parallel to $4x - y = 8$.

33. L passes through the point (3, 5) and is perpendicular to $3x + 2y = 4$.

34. A yellow cab charges \$2.25 for the first $\frac{1}{12}$ mi and 20¢ for each additional $\frac{1}{12}$ mi. Write a linear equation that gives the cost, C, of taking a taxi m mi $\left(m \ge \frac{1}{12}\right)$.

3.5

Graph the following absolute value function.

35. $f(x) = |x - 2| + 5$

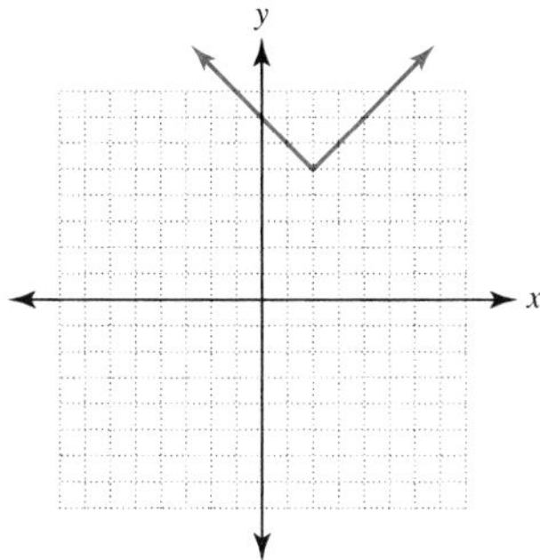

Graph the following inequality.

36. $x + y < 3$

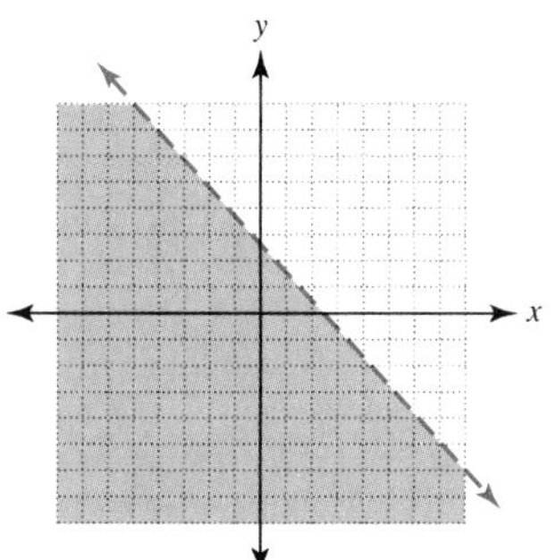

Answers

35. See exercise

36. See exercise

Activity 3 ::
Growth of Children—Fitting a Linear Model to Data

Each chapter in this text concludes with a chapter activity such as this one. These activities provide you with the opportunity to apply the math you studied in that chapter to a relevant topic. Your instructor will determine how best to use these activities in your instructional setting. You may find yourself working in class or outside of class; you may find yourself working alone or in small groups; you may even be asked to perform research in a library or on the Internet.

When you walk into a home that has had children, you will often find a wall with notches showing the heights of the children at various points in their lives. Nearly every time you bring a child to see the doctor, the child's height and weight are recorded, regardless of the reason for the office visit.

The National Institutes of Health (NIH) through the Centers for Disease Control and Prevention (CDC) publishes and updates data detailing heights and weights of children for the populace as a whole and for what they consider to be healthy children. These data were most recently updated in November 2000.

In this activity, we will explore the graphing of trend data and its predictive capability. We use a child's height and weight at various ages for our data.

I.

1. Locate the medical records of a child between 2 and 5 years old that you are familiar with.
2. Create a *table* with three columns and seven rows. Label the table "Height and Weight of [name]; Year 2."
3. Label the first column "Age (months)," the second column, "Height (in.)," and the third column, "Weight (lb)."
4. In the first column, write the numbers (one to each row): 14, 16, 18, 20, 22, 24.
5. In the second column, list the child's height at each of the months listed in the first column.
6. Do likewise in the third column with the child's weight.

II.

1. Create a scatter plot of the data in your table by plotting the coordinate pairs.
2. Describe the trend of the data. Fit a line to the data and give the equation of the line.
3. Use the equation of the line to predict the child's height and weight at 10 months of age.
4. Use the equation of the line to predict the child's height and weight at 28 months of age.
5. Use the equation of the line to predict the child's height and weight at 240 months (20 years) of age.
6. According to the model, how tall will the child be when he or she is 50 years old (600 months)?
7. Discuss the accuracy of the predictions made in steps 3 to 6. What can you discern about using scatter-plot data to make predictions in general?

Data Set

I.

Median Heights and Weights for Children: Year 2

Age (months)	Median Height for Girls (in.)	Median Weight for Boys (lb)
14	30	24
16	30.75	25
18	31.5	25.75
20	32.5	26.25
22	33	27.25
24	34	28

Source: Centers for Disease Control and Prevention.

II. 1.

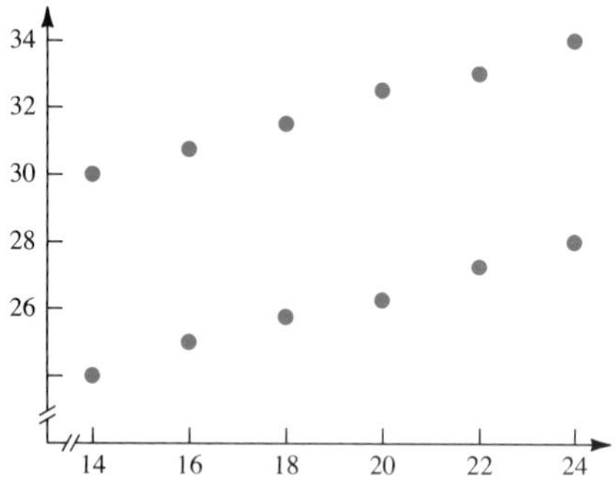

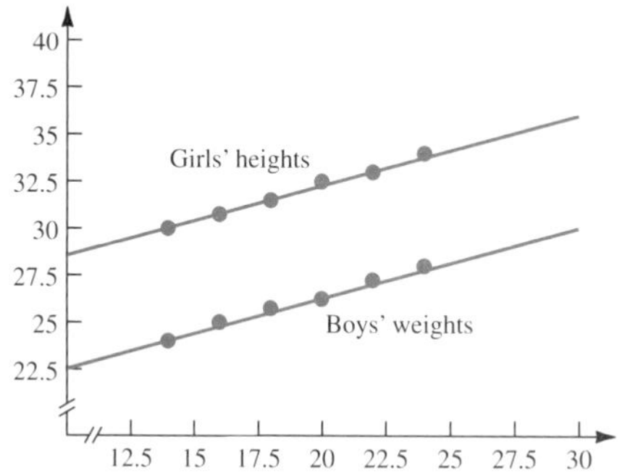

II. 2. Both sets of data appear linear. The lines shown have the following equations:

Girls' heights: $y = 0.4x + 24.4$

Boys' weights: $y = 0.39x + 18.6$

II. 3–6.

Predictions

Age (months)	10	28	240	600
Girls' heights (in.)	28.4	35.6	120.4	264.4
Boys' weights (lb)	22.5	29.52	111.2	252.6

While the predictions for 10 and 28 months are reasonably accurate, 20-year-old women tend to be shorter than the 10 ft given by the prediction and 20-year-old men tend to be heavier than the predicted 112 lb. Likewise, women do not grow to be 22 ft tall by the age of 50.

II. 7. We need to be careful when using data to predict that we stay close to the original data source. That is, we can reasonably predict a person's height at 10 months from the data of their second year of age, but we cannot extrapolate that to their height 50 years later.

cumulative review chapters 1-3

Name ____________________

Section ________ Date ________

Answers

1. Associative property of multiplication

2. Commutative property of addition

3. Distributive property

4. 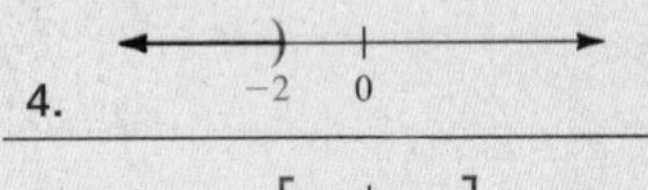

5. −3 0 4

6. $c = \frac{5}{2}$

7. $x = \frac{21}{2}$

8. $x = \frac{78}{7}$

9. $B = \frac{2A - hb}{h}$

10. $p = \frac{4y - 12}{7}$

11. $x < -7; (-\infty, -7)$

12. 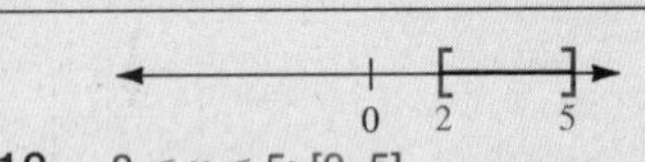
$2 \le x \le 5; [2, 5]$

13. $x < 0$ or $x > 5$; $(-\infty, 0) \cup (5, \infty)$

14. −7, −9

The following exercises are presented to help you review concepts from earlier chapters. This is meant as review material and not as a comprehensive exam. The answers are presented in the back of the text. Beside each answer is a section reference for the concept. If you have difficulty with any of these exercises, be certain to at least read through the summary related to that section.

1.2

Identify the property of real numbers that justifies each statement.

1. $(5x)y = 5(xy)$

2. $a + 3b = 3b + a$

3. $2c(x + d) = 2cx + 2cd$

1.3

Graph each of the following.

4. $x < -2$

5. $-3 \le x \le 4$

2.1

Solve each of the following equations and check the results.

6. $5c - 7 = 3c - 2$

7. $3x + 11 = 5(x - 2)$

8. $\frac{1}{3}x - 5 = 8 - \frac{5}{6}x$

2.2

Solve each of the following equations for the indicated variable.

9. $A = \frac{1}{2}h(B + b)$ for B

10. $7p - 4y + 12 = 0$ for p

2.5

Solve and graph the solution to each inequality, and then write the solution in interval notation.

11. $3x - 5 > 5x + 9$

12. $-11 \le -3x + 4 \le -2$

13. $|5 - 2x| > 5$

2.3

Solve each of the following applications. Be sure to show the equation used for the solution.

14. The sum of two consecutive odd integers is −16. What are the two integers?

15. Joshua received grades of 85 and 91 on his first two mathematics tests. What score does he need on the next test to have an average of 90 for the three tests?

16. Carla and Jake leave town at the same time, traveling in opposite directions. If Carla travels at 55 mi/h and Jake travels at 35 mi/h, how long will it take for them to be 330 mi apart?

17. At a school dance, admission was \$4 for tickets bought in advance and \$5 for those purchased at the door. If the 172 people attending paid a total of \$748, how many of each type of ticket were purchased?

3.1

Graph each of the following equations.

18. $x - y = 4$

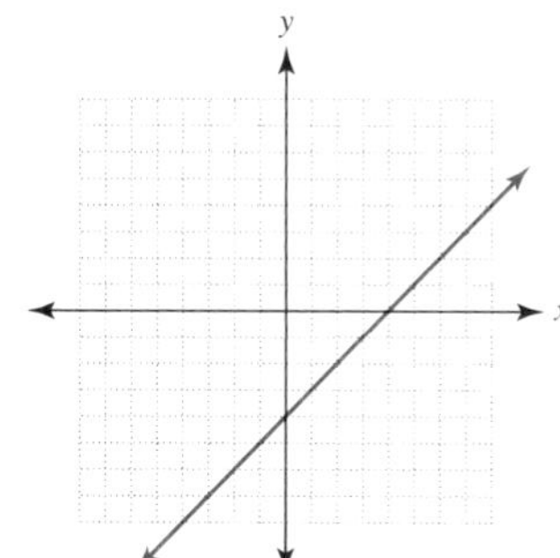

19. $y = 3x - 1$

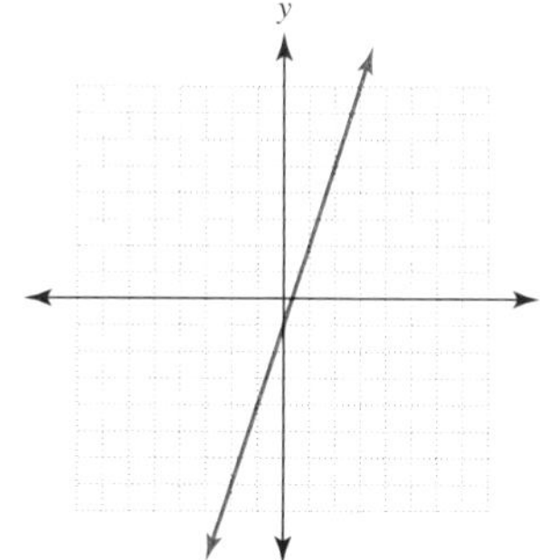

20. $3x + 2y = 12$

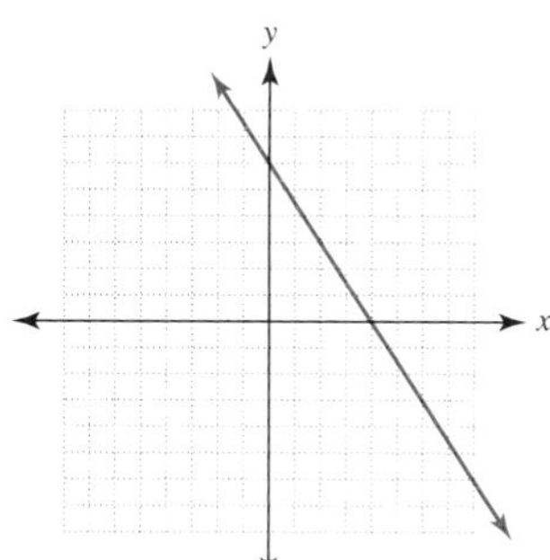

21. $x + 2y = 0$

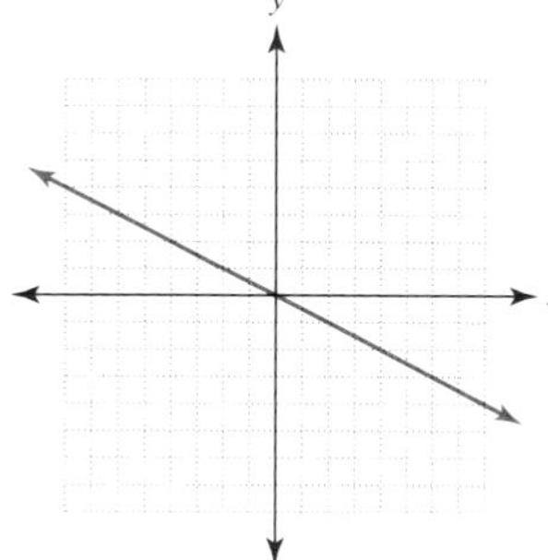

22. $x = -4$

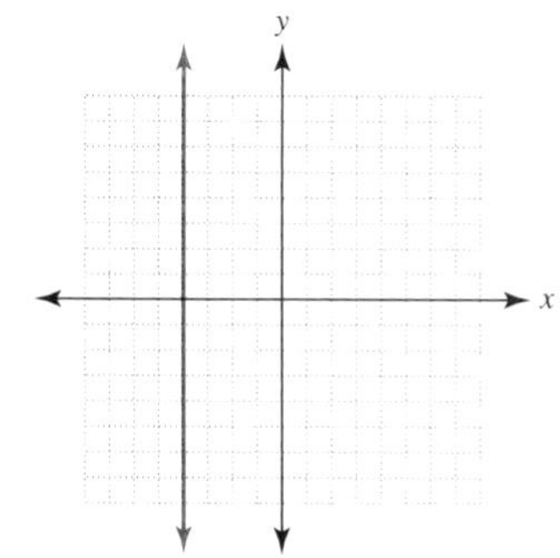

Answers

15. 94

16. $3\frac{2}{3}$ h

17. 112 \$4 tickets, 60 \$5 tickets

18. See exercise

19. See exercise

20. See exercise

21. See exercise

22. See exercise

Answers

23. −2

24. Undefined

25. $-\frac{3}{4}$

26. 0

27. Perpendicular

28. Neither

29. $y = 3$

30. $y = 5x - 2$

31. $y = \frac{1}{2}x + \frac{21}{2}$

32. $y = \frac{3}{4}x - 3$

33. $x = -3$

34. See exercise

3.3

Find the slope (if it exists) of the line determined by each of the following pairs of points.

23. $(3, -4)$ and $(-3, 8)$

24. $(-2, 4)$ and $(-2, 7)$

25. $(-4, 3)$ and $(4, -3)$

26. $(5, -3)$ and $(-2, -3)$

Are the following pairs of lines **parallel, perpendicular,** *or* **neither?**

27. L_1 through $(-3, 7)$ and $(1, -5)$
L_2 through $(2, 3)$ and $(-4, 1)$

28. L_1 with equation $x - 2y = 7$
L_2 with equation $2x + 4y = 3$

3.4

Write the equation of the line L satisfying each of the sets of geometric conditions.

29. L has a slope of 0 and y-intercept $(0, 3)$.

30. L has a slope of 5 and y-intercept $(0, -2)$.

31. L passes through $(-5, 8)$ and is perpendicular to the line $4x + 2y = 8$.

32. L has x-intercept $(4, 0)$ and y-intercept $(0, -3)$.

33. L passes through $(-3, 4)$ and has undefined slope.

3.5

Graph the inequality.

34. $3x + y \geq 9$

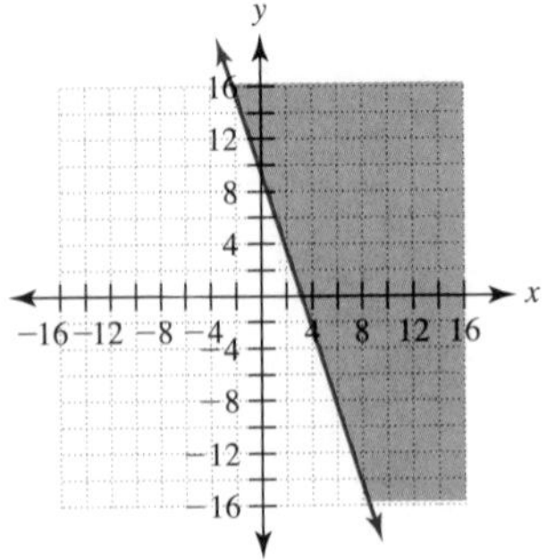

 The Streeter/Hutchison Series in Mathematics Intermediate Algebra

CHAPTER

4

Systems of Linear Relations

INTRODUCTION

The owner of a small bakery must decide how much of several kinds of bread to make based on the time it takes to produce each kind and the profit to be made on each one. The owner knows the bakery requires 0.8 h of oven time and 1.25 h of preparation time for every 8 loaves of bread, and that coffee cakes take 1 h of oven time and 1.25 h of preparation time for every 6 coffee cakes. In 1 day the bakery has 12 h of oven time and 16 h of preparation time available. The owner knows that she clears a profit of \$0.50 for every loaf of bread sold and \$1.75 for every coffee cake sold. But, she has found that on a regular day she sells no more than 12 coffee cakes.

Given these constraints, how many of each type of product can be made in a day? Which combination of products would give the highest profit if all the products are sold?

These questions can be answered by graphing a system of inequalities that model the constraints, in which b is the number of loaves of bread, and c is the number of coffee cakes. We begin by writing inequalities for baking and preparation times, and coffee cake sales.

The graph of these three inequalities on the following page shows where all these constraints overlap and indicate what is possible.

CHAPTER 4 OUTLINE

 The Streeter/Hutchison Series in Mathematics Intermediate Algebra

Oven time:

$$b\left(\frac{0.8}{8}\right) + c\left(\frac{1}{6}\right) \le 12$$

Preparation time:

$$b\left(\frac{1.25}{8}\right) + c\left(\frac{1.25}{6}\right) \le 16$$

Coffee cake sales:

$$c \le 12$$

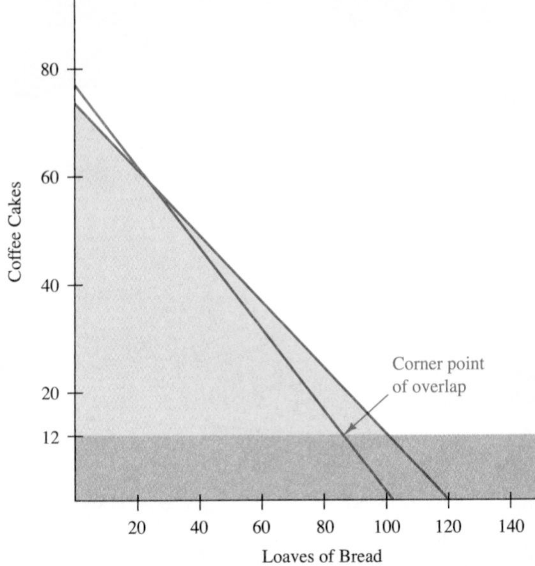

There is one point of particular interest; the point (86.4, 12) indicates that if no more than 12 coffee cakes can be sold, then 86 loaves of bread and 12 coffee cakes is the combination that fits the constraints and makes the most profit. In this case, the profit will be 86($0.50) + 12($1.75), or $64.00, for 1 day.

This graph not only tells the baker what combination gives the most profit but also indicates that she has room to market more of the coffee cakes. She might consider a sales promotion. To solve this problem, she would use a system of linear relations, which is the topic of this chapter.

In particular, Section 4.4 will deal with linear inequalities, such as the three discussed here. At the end of the chapter, you will find a more in-depth activity that looks closer at how to determine the maximum possible profit for a business.

pretest 4

Name ______________

Section ________ Date ________

This pretest will provide a preview of the types of exercises you will encounter in each section of this chapter. The answers for these exercises can be found in the back of the text. If you are working on your own, or ahead of the class, this pretest can help you identify the sections in which you should focus more of your time.

4.1 Solve each of the following systems. If a unique solution does not exist, state whether the given system is inconsistent or dependent.

1. $3x + y = 5$
$5x - 2y = 12$

2. $4x - 2y = 6$
$y = 2x - 3$

3. $5x + 3y = 3$
$-3x + y = 1$

4. $4x - 2y = 6$
$y = 2x + 7$

Solve each of the following problems by choosing a variable to represent each unknown quantity. Then write a system of equations that will allow you to solve for each variable.

5. One number is 3 less than 2 times another. If the sum of the two numbers is 15, find the two numbers.

6. A pharmacist mixes a 10% alcohol solution and a 60% alcohol solution to form 400 milliliters (mL) of a 50% solution. How much of each solution should she use in forming the mixture?

7. A jet flying east, with the wind, makes a trip of 2,000 miles in 4 hours. Returning, against the wind, the jet can travel only 1,600 miles in 4 hours. What is the plane's rate in still air? What is the rate of the wind?

4.2 Solve each of the following systems.

8. $x - y + z = 5$
$-2x + y + z = -11$
$x + 3z = 1$

9. $x + 3y - 2z = -6$
$3x - y + 2z = 6$
$-2x + 3y - 4z = -12$

Solve the following problem by choosing a variable to represent each unknown quantity. Then write a system of equations that will allow you to solve for each variable.

10. Ernesto decides to divide $16,000 into three investments: a savings account paying 3% annual interest, a bond paying 5%, and a mutual fund paying 7%. His annual interest from the three investments was $900, and he has as much in the mutual fund as in the savings account and bond combined. What amount did he invest in each type of account?

Answers

1. (2, −1)
2. Dependent
3. (0, 1)
4. Inconsistent
5. 6, 9
6. 80 mL of 10%, 320 mL of 60%
7. Jet: 450 mi/h, wind: 50 mi/h
8. (4, −2, −1)
9. (0, 0, 3)
10. Savings: $3,000, Bonds: $5,000, Funds: $8,000

Answers

11. (2, −1)

12. (4, −2, −1)

13. See exercise

14. See exercise

15. See exercise

4.3 **11.** Solve exercise 1 using elementary row operations.

12. Solve exercise 8 using elementary row operations.

4.4 Solve each of the following systems of linear inequalities by graphing.

13. $3x - y > 4$
$x + y < 4$

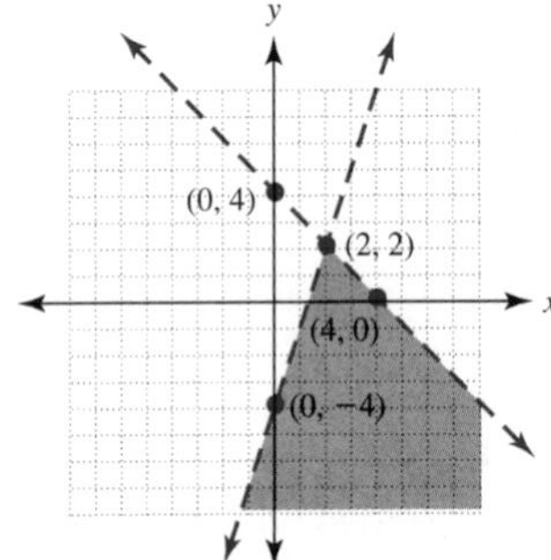

14. $x + 3y \le 9$
$2x - 3y \le 6$

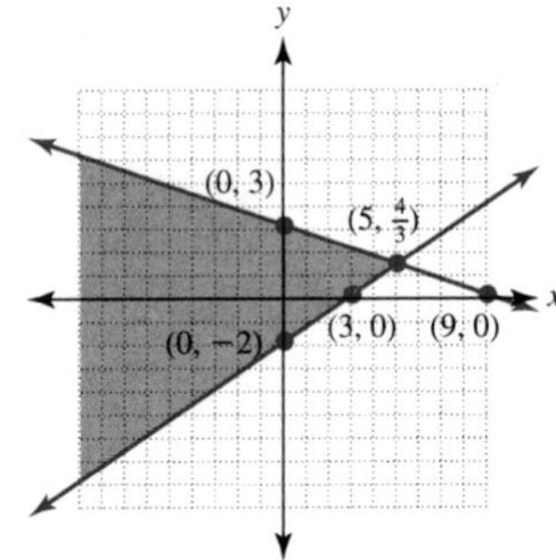

15. $3x - y \le 6$
$x \ge 1$
$y \le 3$

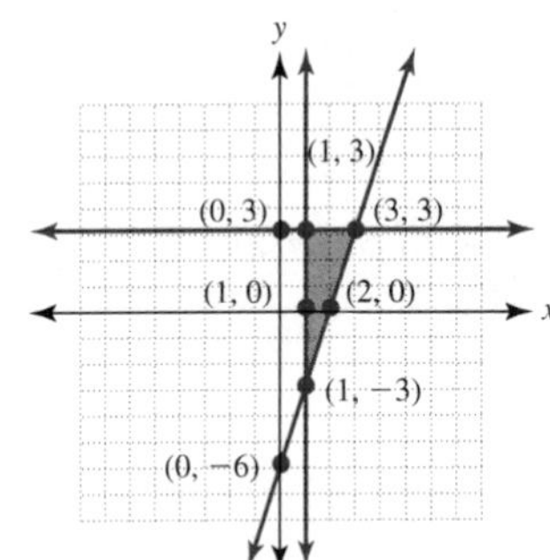

4.1 Systems of Linear Equations in Two Variables

< 4.1 Objectives >

1 > Find ordered pairs associated with two equations

2 > Solve a system by graphing

3 > Solve a system by the addition method

4 > Solve a system by the substitution method

5 > Use a system of two equations to solve an application

Our work in this chapter focuses on systems of equations and the various solution techniques available for your work with such systems. First, let us consider what we mean by a system of equations.

In many applications, you will find it helpful to use two variables when labeling the quantities involved. Often this leads to a **linear equation in two variables.** A typical equation might be

$$x - 2y = 6$$

A solution for such an equation is any ordered pair of real numbers (x, y) that satisfies the equation. For example, the ordered pair $(4, -1)$ is a solution for the equation because substituting 4 for x and -1 for y results in a true statement.

$$4 - 2(-1) \stackrel{?}{=} 6$$
$$4 + 2 \stackrel{?}{=} 6$$
$$6 \stackrel{?}{=} 6 \quad \text{True}$$

NOTE

Actually, there are an infinite number of solutions for an equation of this type. You might want to verify that $(2, -2)$ and $(6, 0)$ are also solutions.

Whenever two or more equations are considered together, they form a **system of equations.** If the equations of the system are linear, the system is called a **linear system.** Our work here involves finding solutions for such systems. We present three methods for solving such systems: the graphing method, the addition method, and the substitution method.

We begin our discussion with a definition.

Definition

Solution

A **solution** for a linear system of equations in two variables is an ordered pair of real numbers (x, y) that satisfies *both* equations in the system.

For instance, given the linear system

$$x - 2y = -1$$
$$2x + y = 8$$

NOTES

Both equations are satisfied by (3, 2).

It is helpful at this point to review Section 3.1 on graphing linear equations.

the pair (3, 2) is a solution because after substituting 3 for x and 2 for y in the two equations of the system, we have the *two* true statements

$$3 - 2(2) \stackrel{?}{=} -1 \quad \text{and} \quad 2(3) + 2 \stackrel{?}{=} 8$$
$$-1 = -1 \quad \text{and} \quad 8 = 8$$

The solution set for a linear equation in two variables may be graphed as a line. Because a solution to a system of equations represents a point on both lines, one approach to finding the solution for a system is to **graph** each equation on the same set of coordinate axes and then identify the point of intersection. This is shown in Example 1.

Example 1 Solving a System by Graphing

< Objectives 1 and 2 >

NOTE

Solve each equation for y and then graph.

$y = -2x + 4$

and

$y = x - 5$

We can *approximate* the solution by tracing the lines near their intersection.

Solve the system by graphing.

$$2x + y = 4$$
$$x - y = 5$$

We graph the lines corresponding to the two equations of the system.

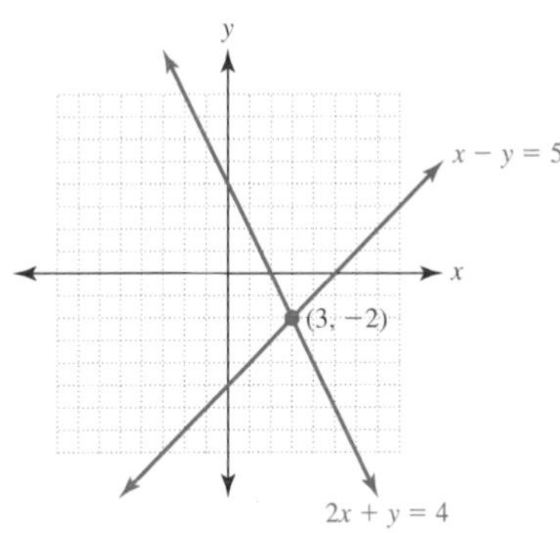

Each equation has an infinite number of solutions (ordered pairs) corresponding to points on a line. The point of intersection, here (3, −2), is the *only* point lying on both lines, and so (3, −2) is the only ordered pair satisfying both equations. Substituting 3 for x and −2 for y verifies that (3, −2) is the solution for the system.

Check Yourself 1

Solve the system by graphing.

$$3x - y = 2$$
$$x + y = 6$$

In Example 1, the two lines are nonparallel and intersect at only one point. They make up a consistent system.

Definition

Consistent System

A system of equations that has a unique solution is called a **consistent system.**

In Example 2, we examine a system representing two lines that have no point of intersection.

Example 2 Solving a System by Graphing

RECALL

Parallel lines have the same slope but different y-intercepts (Section 3.3). Solving each of these equations for y, $y = 2x - 4$ and $y = 2x - 6$, illustrates this.

Solve the system by graphing.

$$2x - y = 4$$
$$6x - 3y = 18$$

The lines corresponding to the two equations are shown in the following graph.

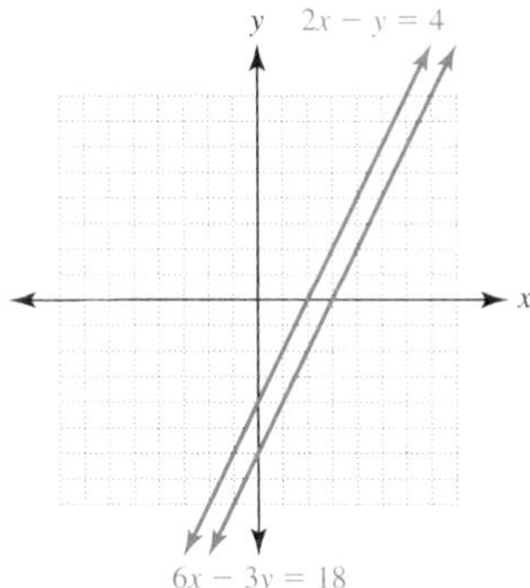

The lines are distinct and parallel and form an inconsistent system. There is no point at which they intersect, so the system has no solution.

Definition

Inconsistent System

A system of equations with no solution is called an **inconsistent system.**

Check Yourself 2

Solve the system by graphing.

$$3x - y = 1$$
$$6x - 2y = 3$$

Sometimes the equations in a system have the same graph.

Example 3 Solving a System by Graphing

Solve the system by graphing.

$$2x - y = 2$$
$$4x - 2y = 4$$

NOTE

Solving each equation for y gives us the same line, $y = 2x - 2$.

The equations are graphed as follows.

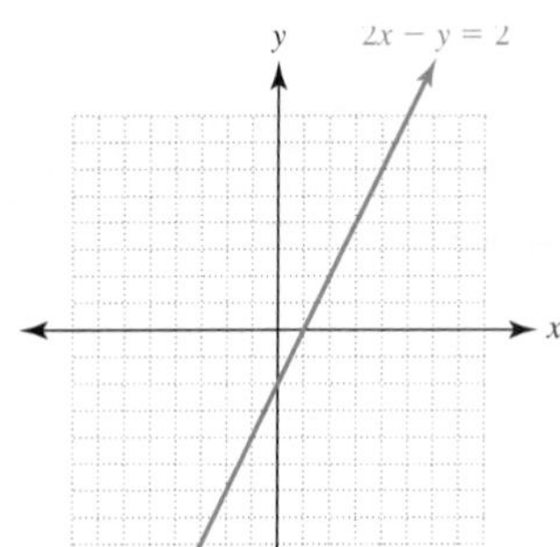

The lines have the same graph, so they have an infinite number of solutions in common. They represent a dependent system.

Definition

Dependent System A system with an infinite number of solutions is called a **dependent system.**

Check Yourself 3

Solve the system by graphing.

$$6x - 3y = 12$$
$$y = 2x - 4$$

The following summarizes our work in solving a system of two equations by graphing.

Step by Step

To Solve a System of Equations by Graphing

Step 1 Graph both equations on the same coordinate system.

Step 2 Determine the solution to the system as follows.

a. If the lines intersect at exactly one point, the solution is the ordered pair corresponding to that point. This is called a **consistent system.**

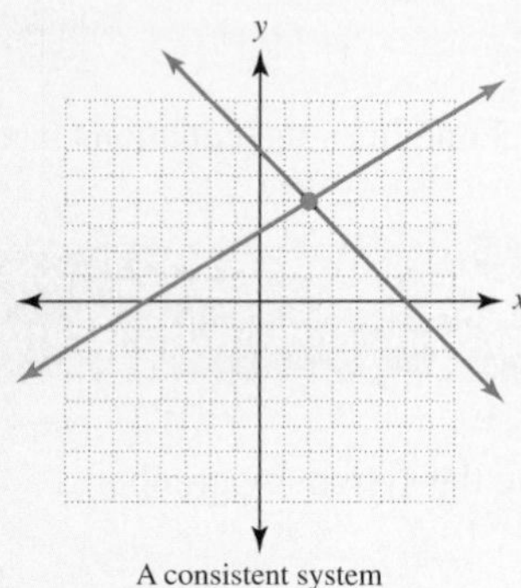

A consistent system

NOTES

There is no ordered pair that lies on both lines.

b. If the lines are parallel, there are no solutions. This is called an **inconsistent system.**

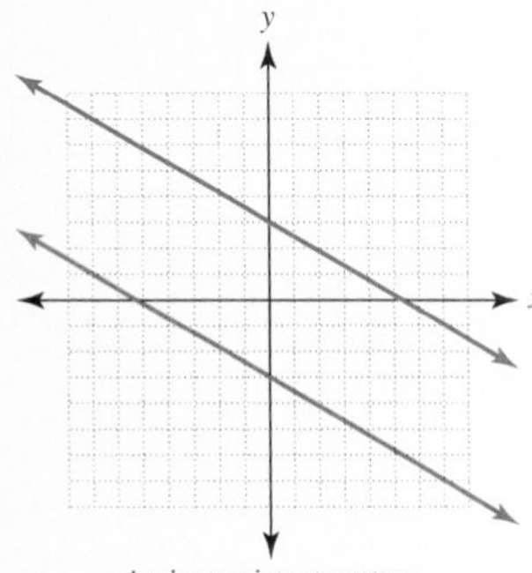

An inconsistent system

NOTES

Any ordered pair that corresponds to a point on the line is a solution.

c. If the two equations have the same graph, then the system has infinitely many solutions. This is called a **dependent system.**

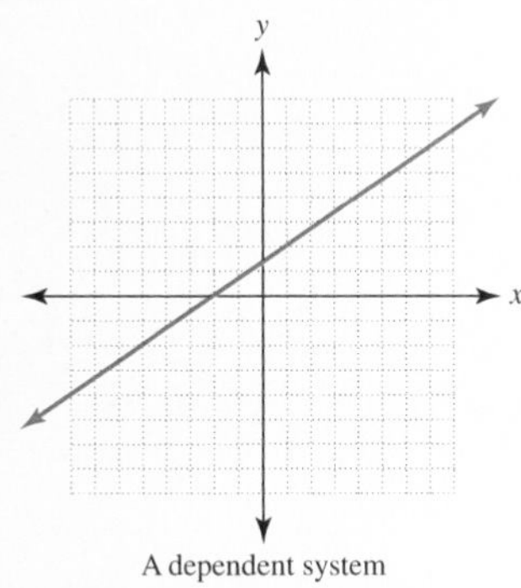

A dependent system

Step 3 Check the solution in both equations, if necessary.

The graphing method has two disadvantages. It is time consuming and is not always precise if the solution contains rational numbers such as $\left(\frac{5}{2}, -\frac{3}{4}\right)$. This type of solution is difficult to read from a graph and often provides only approximate solutions. A more precise method is the **addition method** or **solution by elimination.**

Given the system

$$x + y = 8$$
$$x - y = 2$$

we can eliminate the variable y by applying the addition property of equality, that is, by adding the two equations vertically. Note that the coefficients of the y-terms are "1" and "-1" although we usually do not write them out. They are additive opposites of one another, so in adding the two equations the y-terms are eliminated.

NOTE

The addition property states that if equals are added to equals the sums are equal.

$$\begin{array}{r} x + y = 8 \\ \underline{x - y = 2} \\ 2x + 0 = 10 \\ 2x = 10 \end{array}$$

Like variable terms with coefficients that are additive opposites are necessary in order to use the addition method in solving a system of equations. The resultant sum is one equation in one variable. We can then solve for x.

$x = 5$

Substituting the value for x in one of the original equations allows us to solve for y.

Example 4 illustrates the addition method of solution.

Example 4 Solving a System by the Addition Method

< Objective 3 >

Solve the system by the addition method.

$$5x - 2y = 12$$
$$3x + 2y = 12$$

In this case, adding the equations will eliminate the variable y, and we have

$$8x = 24$$
$$x = 3$$

Now we can substitute 3 in either of the original equations. We let $x = 3$ in the first equation.

$$5(3) - 2y = 12$$
$$15 - 2y = 12$$
$$-2y = -3$$
$$y = \frac{3}{2}$$

and $\left(3, \frac{3}{2}\right)$ is the solution for our system.

NOTE

The solution should be checked by substituting these values into the second equation. Here

$$3(3) + 2\left(\frac{3}{2}\right) \stackrel{?}{=} 12$$
$$9 + 3 \stackrel{?}{=} 12$$
$$12 = 12$$

is a true statement.

This ordered pair is the point of intersection of the two lines when graphed.

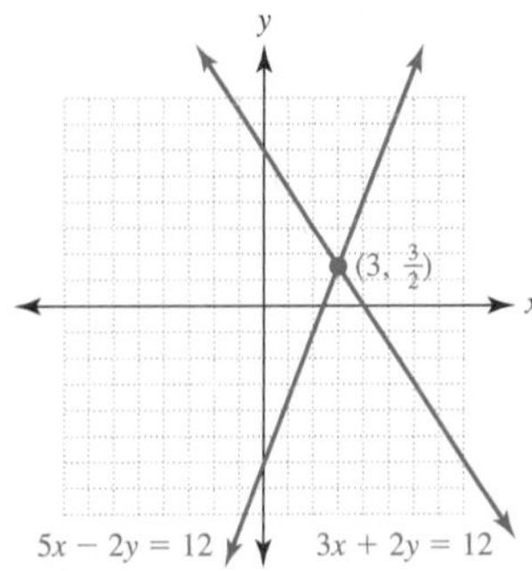

Check Yourself 4

Solve the system by the addition method.

$$4x - 3y = 19$$
$$-4x + 5y = -25$$

Example 4 and Check Yourself 4 were straightforward because adding the equations of the system immediately eliminated one of the variables. Example 5 illustrates a common situation in which we must multiply one or both of the equations by a nonzero constant before the addition method is applied. This multiplication results in a new system that is equivalent to the original system.

Procedure

Equivalent System

An **equivalent system** is formed whenever

1. One of the equations is multiplied by a nonzero number.
2. One of the equations is replaced by the sum of a constant multiple of another equation and that equation.

Example 5 — Solving a System by the Addition Method

Solve the system by the addition method.

$$3x - 5y = 19$$
$$5x + 2y = 11$$

NOTES

All these solutions can be approximated by graphing the lines and tracing near the intersection. This is particularly useful when the solutions are not integers.

The coefficients of y are now *opposites* of each other.

Again, the solution should be checked by substitution in the second equation since we used the first equation to solve for y.

It is clear that adding the equations of the given system will *not* eliminate one of the variables. Therefore, we must use multiplication to form an equivalent system. The choice of multipliers depends on which variable we decide to eliminate. Here we have decided to eliminate y. We multiply the first equation by 2 and the second equation by 5. We then have

$$6x - 10y = 38$$
$$25x + 10y = 55$$

Adding now eliminates y and yields

$$31x = 93$$
$$x = 3$$

Substituting 3 for x in the first equation, we have

$$3 \cdot 3 - 5y = 19$$
$$9 - 5y = 19$$
$$-5y = 10$$
$$y = -2$$

The solution for the system is $(3, -2)$.

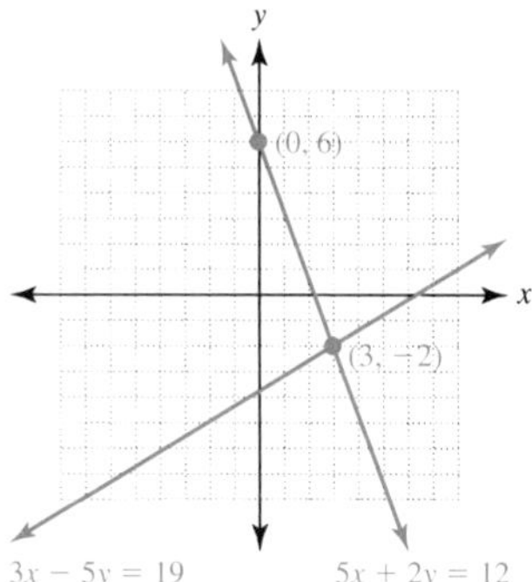

Check Yourself 5

Solve the system by the addition method.

$$2x + 3y = -18$$
$$6x - 10y = 22$$

The following algorithm summarizes the addition method of solving linear systems of two equations in two variables.

Step by Step

Solving by the Addition Method

Step 1 If necessary, multiply one or both of the equations by a constant so that one of the variables can be eliminated by addition.

Step 2 Add the equations of the equivalent system formed in step 1.

Step 3 Solve the equation found in step 2.

Step 4 Substitute the value found in step 3 into either of the equations of the original system to find the corresponding value of the remaining variable. The ordered pair formed is the solution to the system.

Step 5 Check the solution by substituting the pair of values found in step 4 into the other equation of the original system.

Example 6 illustrates two special situations you may encounter while applying the addition method.

Example 6 Solving a System by the Addition Method

Solve each system by the addition method.

(a) $4x + 5y = 20$
$8x + 10y = 19$

Multiply the first equation by -2. Then

$$\begin{aligned} -8x - 10y &= -40 \\ 8x + 10y &= 19 \\ \hline 0 &= -21 \end{aligned}$$

We add the two left sides to get 0 and the two right sides to get -21.

False

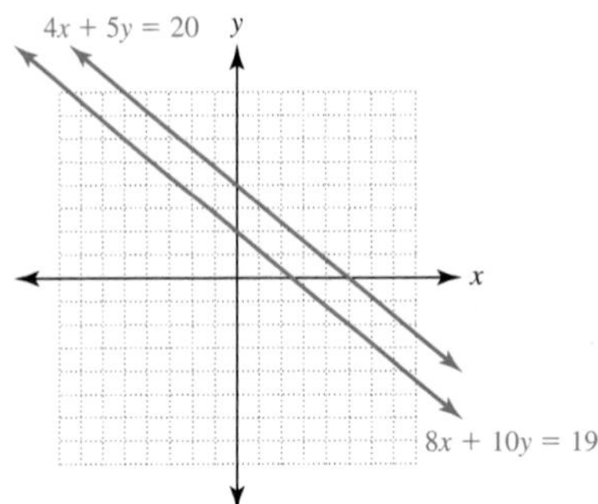

The result $0 = -21$ is a *false* statement, which means that there is no point of intersection. Therefore, the system is **inconsistent,** and there is no solution.

(b) $5x - 7y = 9$

$15x - 21y = 27$

Multiply the first equation by -3. We then have

$$\begin{aligned} -15x + 21y &= -27 \quad \text{We add the two equations.} \\ 15x - 21y &= 27 \\ \hline 0 &= 0 \quad \text{True} \end{aligned}$$

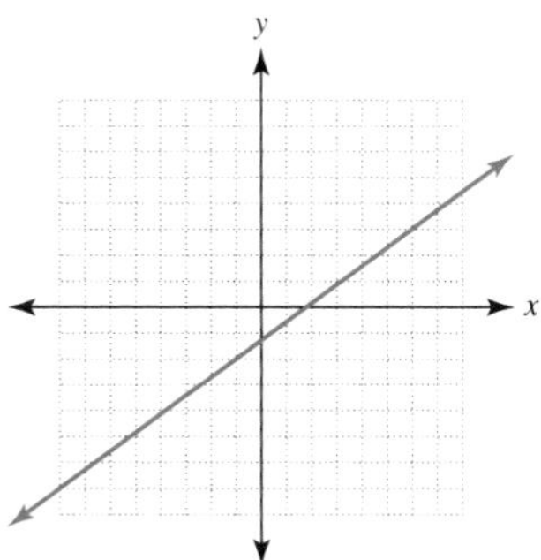

Both variables have been eliminated, and the result is a *true* statement. The two lines coincide, and there are an infinite number of solutions, one for each point on that line. We have a **dependent system.**

Check Yourself 6

Solve each system by the addition method.

(a) $3x + 2y = 8$

$9x + 6y = 11$

(b) $x - 2y = 8$

$3x - 6y = 24$

The results of Example 6 can be summarized as follows.

Property

Solving a System of Two Linear Equations

When a system of two linear equations is solved:

1. If a false statement such as $3 = 4$ is obtained, then the system is inconsistent and has no solution.
2. If a true statement such as $8 = 8$ is obtained, then the system is dependent and has an infinite number of solutions.

A third method for finding the solutions of linear systems in two variables is called the **substitution method.** You may very well find the substitution method more difficult to apply in solving certain systems than the addition method, particularly when the equations involved in the substitution lead to fractions. However, the substitution method does have important extensions to systems involving higher-degree equations, as you will see in later mathematics classes.

To outline this third technique, we solve one of the equations from the original system for one of the variables. That expression is then substituted into the *other* equation of the system to provide an equation in a single variable. The new equation is solved, and the corresponding value for the other variable is found as before, as Example 7 illustrates.

Example 7 Solving a System by the Substitution Method

< Objective 4 >

(a) Solve the system by the substitution method.

$$2x - 3y = -3$$
$$y = 2x - 1$$

Because the second equation is already solved for y, we substitute the expression $2x - 1$ for y in the first equation.

NOTE

We now have an equation in the single variable x.

$$2x - 3(2x - 1) = -3$$

Solving for x gives

$$2x - 6x + 3 = -3$$
$$-4x + 3 = -3$$
$$-4x = -6$$
$$x = \frac{3}{2}$$

We now substitute $\frac{3}{2}$ for x in the equation $y = 2x - 1$.

$$y = 2\left(\frac{3}{2}\right) - 1$$
$$= 3 - 1 = 2$$

The solution for our system is $\left(\frac{3}{2}, 2\right)$.

NOTE

To check this result, we substitute these values in the first equation and have

$$2\left(\frac{3}{2}\right) - 3 \cdot 2 \stackrel{?}{=} -3$$
$$3 - 6 \stackrel{?}{=} -3$$
$$-3 = -3$$

A true statement!

(b) Solve the system by the substitution method.

$$2x + 3y = 16$$
$$3x - y = 2$$

We start by solving the second equation for y.

$$3x - y = 2$$
$$-y = -3x + 2$$
$$y = 3x - 2$$

NOTE

Why did we choose to solve for y in the second equation? We could have solved for x, so that

$$x = \frac{y + 2}{3}$$

We simply chose the easier case (solving for the variable with a coefficient of 1 or -1) to avoid fractions.

Substituting in the first equation yields

$$2x + 3(3x - 2) = 16$$
$$2x + 9x - 6 = 16$$
$$11x - 6 = 16$$
$$11x = 22$$
$$x = 2$$

NOTE

The solution should be checked in *both* equations of the original system.

We now substitute 2 for x in the second equation.

$$3(2) - y = 2$$
$$6 - y = 2$$
$$-y = -4$$
$$y = 4$$

The solution for the system is (2, 4). We leave the check of this result to you.

Check Yourself 7

Solve each system by the substitution method.

(a) $2x + 3y = 6$
$x = 3y + 6$

(b) $3x + 4y = -3$
$x + 4y = 1$

The following algorithm summarizes the substitution method for solving linear systems of two equations in two variables.

Step by Step

Solving by the Substitution Method

Step 1 If necessary, solve one of the equations of the original system for one of the variables.

Step 2 Substitute the expression obtained in step 1 into the *other* equation of the system to write an equation in a single variable.

Step 3 Solve the equation found in step 2.

Step 4 Substitute the value found in step 3 into the equation derived in step 1 to find the corresponding value of the remaining variable. The ordered pair formed is the solution for the system.

Step 5 Check the solution by substituting the pair of values found in step 4 into *both* equations of the original system.

A natural question at this point is, How do you decide which solution method to use? First, the graphical method can generally provide only approximate solutions. When exact solutions are necessary, one of the algebraic methods must be applied.

The choice of which algebraic method (substitution or addition) to use is yours and depends largely on the given system. Here are some guidelines designed to help you choose an appropriate method for solving a linear system.

Property

Choosing an Appropriate Method for Solving a System

1. If one of the equations is already solved for x (or for y), then substitution is the preferred method.
2. If the coefficients of x (or of y) are the same, or opposites, in the two equations, then addition is the preferred method.
3. If solving for x (or for y) in either of the given equations will result in fractional coefficients, then addition is the preferred method.

Example 8 Choosing an Appropriate Method for Solving a System

Select the most appropriate method for solving each of the given systems.

(a) $8x - 9y = 11$
$4x + 9y = 15$

Addition is the most appropriate method because the coefficients of y are opposites.

(b) $5x + 3y = 9$
$2x - 7y = 8$

Addition is the most appropriate method because solving for a variable will result in fractional coefficients.

(c) $7x + 2y = 8$
$x = 3y - 5$

Substitution is the most appropriate method because the second equation is already solved for x.

Check Yourself 8

Select the most appropriate method for solving each of the given systems.

(a) $2x + 5y = 3$
$8x - 5y = -13$

(b) $4x - 3y = 2$
$y = 3x - 4$

(c) $3x - 5y = 2$
$x = 3y - 2$

(d) $5x - 2y = 19$
$4x + 6y = 38$

RECALL

In Chapter 2, all the unknowns in the problem had to be expressed in terms of that single variable.

In Chapter 2 we solved word problems by using equations in a single variable. Now that you have the background to use two equations in two variables to solve word problems, we will see how they can be applied. The five steps for solving word problems stay the same (in fact, we give them again for reference in each application example). Many students find that using two equations and two variables makes writing the necessary equations much easier, as Example 9 illustrates.

Example 9 Solving a Number Problem by Substitution

< Objective 5 >

The sum of two numbers is 25. If the second number is 5 less than twice the first number, what are the two numbers?

Step 1 You want to find the two unknown numbers.

Step 2 Let x = the first number and y = the second number.

Step 3

$$\underbrace{x + y}_{\text{The sum}} = \underbrace{25}_{\text{is 25.}}$$

NOTE

1. What do you want to find?
2. Assign variables. This time we use two letters, x and y.
3. Write equations for the solution. Here two equations are needed because we have introduced two variables.
4. Solve the system of equations.
5. Check the result.

$$y = \underbrace{2x - 5}$$

The second number — is 5 less than twice the first.

Step 4

$$x + y = 25$$
$$y = 2x - 5$$

Substitute $2x - 5$ for y in the first equation.

$$x + (2x - 5) = 25$$
$$3x - 5 = 25$$
$$3x = 30$$
$$x = 10$$

NOTE

We use the substitution method because the second equation is already solved for y.

From the first equation,

$$10 + y = 25$$
$$y = 15$$

The two numbers are 10 and 15.

Step 5 The sum of the numbers is 25. The second number, 15, is 5 less than twice the first number, 10. The solution checks.

Check Yourself 9

The sum of two numbers is 28. The second number is 4 more than twice the first number. What are the numbers?

Sketches are always helpful in solving applications from geometry. We will look at such an example.

Example 10 Solving an Application from Geometry

NOTE

We used x and y as our two variables in the previous examples. Use whatever letters you want. The process is the same, and sometimes choosing letters other than x or y helps you remember what letter stands for what. Here L = length and W = width.

The length of a rectangle is 3 m more than twice its width. If the perimeter of the rectangle is 42 m, find the dimensions of the rectangle.

Step 1 You want to find the dimensions (length and width) of the rectangle.

Step 2 Let L be the length of the rectangle and W the width. Now draw a sketch of the problem.

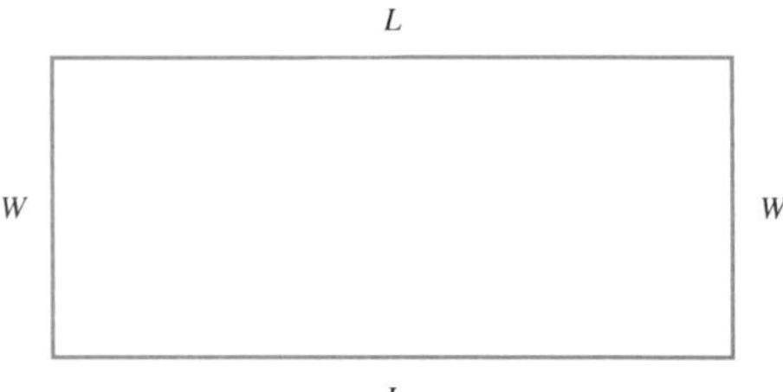

Step 3 Write the equations for the solution.

$L = \underbrace{2W + 3}$

3 more than twice the width

$\underbrace{2L + 2W} = 42$

The perimeter

Step 4 Solve the system.

$$L = 2W + 3$$
$$2L + 2W = 42$$

NOTE

Substitution is used because one equation is already solved for a variable.

From the first equation we can substitute $2W + 3$ for L in the second equation.

$$2(2W + 3) + 2W = 42$$
$$4W + 6 + 2W = 42$$
$$6W + 6 = 42$$
$$6W = 36$$
$$W = 6$$

Replace W with 6 in the first equation to find L.

$$L = 2 \cdot 6 + 3$$
$$= 12 + 3$$
$$= 15$$

NOTE

Also check that "the length is 3 m more than twice its width."

The length is 15 m, the width is 6 m.

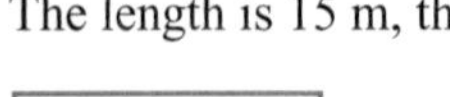

Step 5 Check these results. The perimeter is $2L + 2W$, which should give us 42 m.

$$2(15) + 2(6) \stackrel{?}{=} 42$$
$$30 + 12 = 42 \quad \text{True}$$

NOTE

You should always draw a sketch of the problem when it is appropriate.

Check Yourself 10

The length of each of the two equal legs of an isosceles triangle is 5 in. less than the length of the base. If the perimeter of the triangle is 50 in., find the lengths of the legs and the base.

Examples 9 and 10 were solved using the substitution method. We will now see that the addition method may also be used to solve application problems.

Example 11 Using a Sketch to Help Solve an Application

An 18-ft board is cut into two pieces, one of which is 4 ft longer than the other. How long is each piece?

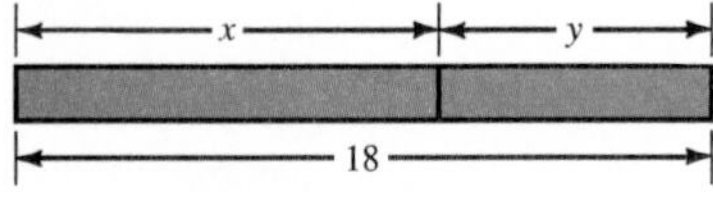

NOTE

Our second equation could also be written as

$x = y + 4$

Step 1 You want to find the two lengths.

Step 2 Let x be the length of the longer piece and y the length of the shorter piece.

Step 3 Write the equations for the solution.

$x + y = 18 \longleftarrow$ The total length is 18.
$x - y = 4 \longleftarrow$ The difference in lengths is 4.

Step 4 To solve the system, add:

$$\begin{aligned} x + y &= 18 \\ x - y &= 4 \\ \hline 2x \quad &= 22 \\ x &= 11 \end{aligned}$$

Replace x with 11 in the first equation.

$$\begin{aligned} 11 + y &= 18 \\ y &= 7 \end{aligned}$$

The longer piece has length 11 ft, the shorter piece 7 ft.

Step 5 We leave it to you to check this result in the original problem.

Check Yourself 11

A 20-ft board is cut into two pieces, one of which is 6 ft longer than the other. How long is each piece?

Using two equations in two variables also helps in solving **mixture problems.**

Example 12 Solving a Mixture Problem Involving Coins

Winnifred has collected \$4.50 in nickels and dimes. If she has 55 coins, how many of each kind of coin does she have?

NOTE

Again we choose appropriate variables—n for nickels, d for dimes.

Step 1 You want to find the number of nickels and the number of dimes.

Step 2 Let

n = number of nickels
d = number of dimes

RECALL

The value of a number of coins is the value per coin times the number of coins: $5n$, $10d$, and so on.

Step 3 Write the equations for the solution.

$n + d = 55$ ⟵ There are 55 coins in all.

$5n + 10d = 450$

(Labels: $5n$ — Value of nickels; $10d$ — Value of dimes; 450 — Total value (in cents))

Step 4 We now have the system

$$\begin{aligned} n + \quad d &= 55 \\ 5n + 10d &= 450 \end{aligned}$$

We will solve this system by addition. Multiply the first equation by -5. We then add the equations to eliminate the variable n.

$$\begin{aligned} -5n - \quad 5d &= -275 \\ 5n + 10d &= \quad 450 \\ \hline 5d &= \quad 175 \\ d &= \quad 35 \end{aligned}$$

We now substitute 35 for d in the first equation.

$$\begin{aligned} n + 35 &= 55 \\ n &= 20 \end{aligned}$$

There are 20 nickels and 35 dimes.

Step 5 We leave it to you to check this result. Just verify that the value of these coins is \$4.50.

Check Yourself 12

Tickets for a play cost \$8 or \$6. If 350 tickets were sold in all and receipts were \$2,500, how many of each price ticket were sold?

We can also solve mixture problems that involve percentages by using two equations in two unknowns, as illustrated in Example 13.

Example 13 Solving a Mixture Problem Involving Chemicals

In a chemistry lab are two solutions: a 20% acid solution and a 60% acid solution. How many milliliters of each should be mixed to produce 200 mL of a 44% acid solution?

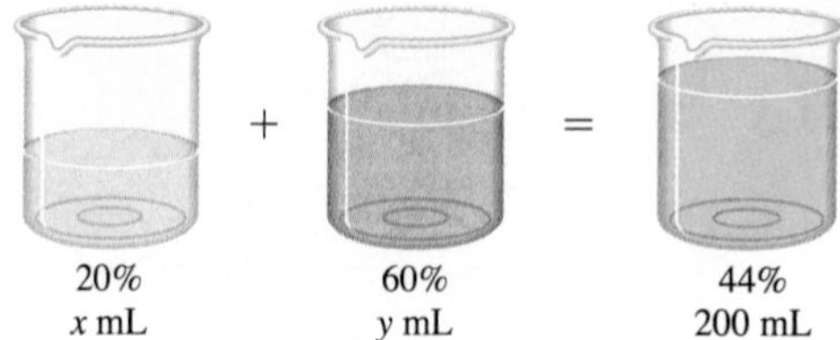

Step 1 You need to know the amount of each solution to use.

Step 2 Let

x = amount of 20% acid solution

y = amount of 60% acid solution

Step 3 Note that a 20% acid solution is 20% acid and 80% water.

We can write equations from the total amount of the solution, here 200 mL, and from the amount of acid in that solution. Many students find a table helpful in organizing the information at this point. Here, for example, we might have

			Totals
Amount of solution	x	y	200
% Acid	0.20	0.60	0.44
Amount of acid	$0.20x$	$0.60y$	(0.44)(200)

NOTES

The amount of acid is the amount of solution times the percentage of acid (as a decimal). That is the key to forming the third row of our table.

The first equation represents the total amount of the solution from the first row of our table.

The second equation represents the amount of acid from the third row of our table.

Now we are ready to form our system.

$$x + y = 200$$
$$0.20x + 0.60y = 0.44(200)$$

Acid in 20% solution ($0.20x$); Acid in 60% solution ($0.60y$); Acid in mixture ($0.44(200)$)

Step 4 If we multiply the second equation by 100 to clear it of decimals, we have

$$\begin{aligned} x + y &= 200 \xrightarrow[\text{by } -20]{\text{Multiply}} & -20x - 20y &= -4{,}000 \\ 20x + 60y &= 8{,}800 \longrightarrow & 20x + 60y &= 8{,}800 \\ & & 40y &= 4{,}800 \\ & & y &= 120 \end{aligned}$$

Substituting 120 for y in the first equation, we have

$$x + 120 = 200$$
$$x = 80$$

The amounts to be mixed are 80 mL (20% acid solution) and 120 mL (60% acid solution).

Step 5 You can check this solution by verifying that the amount of acid from the 20% solution added to the amount from the 60% solution is equal to the amount of acid in the mixture.

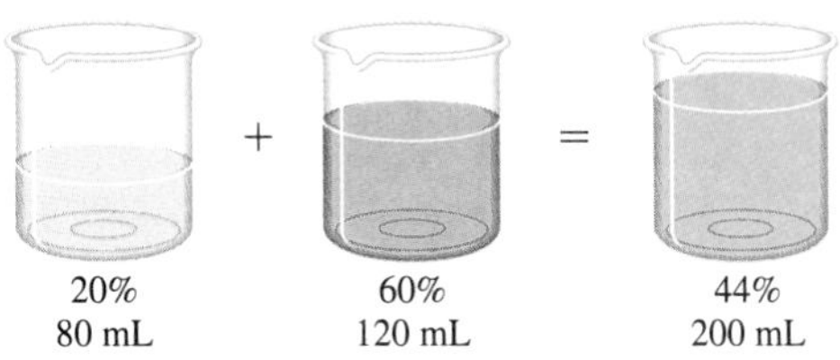

Check Yourself 13

You have a 30% alcohol solution and a 50% alcohol solution. How much of each solution should be combined to make 400 mL of a 45% alcohol solution?

A related kind of application involves simple interest. The key equation involves the *principal* (the amount invested), the annual *interest rate,* the *time* (in years) that the money is invested, and the amount of *interest* you receive.

$$I = P \cdot r \cdot t$$

Interest Principal Rate Time

For 1 year we have

$$I = P \cdot r \quad \text{because } t = 1$$

Example 14 Solving an Investment Application

Jeremy inherits \$20,000 and invests part of the money in bonds with an interest rate of 11%. The remainder of the money is invested in savings at a 9% rate. What amount has he invested at each rate if he receives \$2,040 in interest for 1 year?

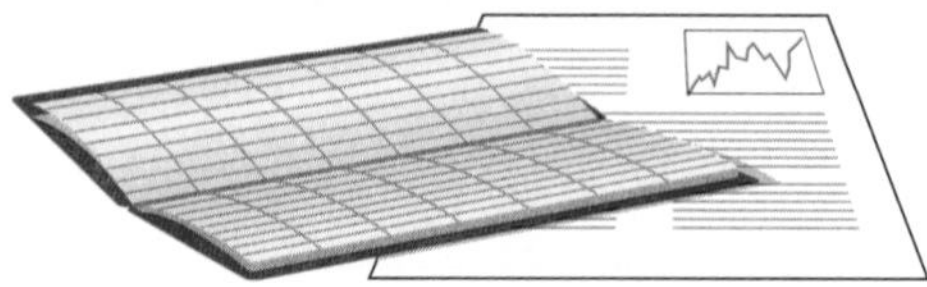

Step 1 You want to find the amounts invested at 11% and at 9%.

Step 2 Let x = the amount invested at 11% and y = the amount invested at 9%. Once again you may find a table helpful at this point.

	Principal	Rate	Interest
	x	11%	$0.11x$
	y	9%	$0.09y$
Totals	20,000		2,040

NOTES

The amount invested at 11% could have been represented by y and the amount invested at 9% by x.

The formula $I = P \cdot r$ (interest equals principal times rate) is the key to forming the third column of our table.

Notice the decimal form of 11% and 9% is used in the equation.

Step 3 Form the equations for the solution, using the first and third columns of the table.

$x + y = 20,000$ ⟵ He has \$20,000 invested in all.

$$0.11x + 0.09y = 2,040$$

The interest at 11% (rate · principal) — The interest at 9% — The total interest

Step 4 To solve the system, use addition.

$$\begin{aligned} x + \quad y &= 20,000 \\ 0.11x + 0.09y &= 2,040 \end{aligned}$$

To do this, multiply both sides of the first equation by −9. Multiplying both sides of the second equation by 100 will clear decimals. Adding the resulting equations will eliminate y.

$$\begin{aligned} -9x - 9y &= -180{,}000 \\ 11x + 9y &= 204{,}000 \\ \hline 2x \qquad &= 24{,}000 \\ x &= 12{,}000 \end{aligned}$$

NOTE

Be sure to answer the question asked in the problem.

Now, substitute 12,000 for x in the first equation and solve for y.

$$\begin{aligned} 12{,}000 + y &= 20{,}000 \\ y &= 8{,}000 \end{aligned}$$

Jeremy has \$12,000 invested at 11% and \$8,000 invested at 9%.

Step 5 To check, the interest at 11% is (\$12,000)(0.11), or \$1,320. The interest at 9% is (\$8,000)(0.09), or \$720. The total interest is \$2,040, and the solution is verified.

NOTE

Distance, rate, and time of travel are related by the equation

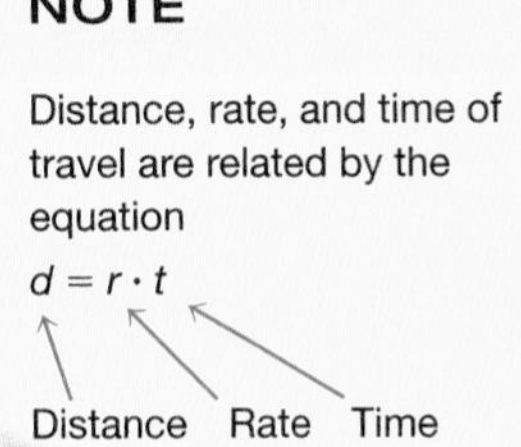

Check Yourself 14

Jan has \$2,000 more invested in a stock that pays 9% interest than in a savings account paying 8%. If her total interest for 1 year is \$860, how much does she have invested at each rate?

Another group of applications is called **motion problems;** they involve a distance traveled, the speed or rate of travel, and the time of travel. Example 15 shows the use of $d = r \cdot t$ in forming a system of equations to solve a motion problem.

Example 15 Solving a Motion Problem

A boat can travel 36 mi downstream in 2 h. Coming back upstream, the trip takes 3 h. Find the rate of the boat in still water and the rate of the current.

Step 1 You want to find the two rates (of the boat and the current).

Step 2 Let

x = rate of boat in still water

y = rate of current

Step 3 To write the equations, think about the following: What is the effect of the current? Suppose the boat's rate in still water is 10 mi/h and the current is 2 mi/h.

The current *increases* the rate *downstream* to 12 mi/h (10 + 2). The current *decreases* the rate *upstream* to 8 mi/h (10 − 2). So here the rate downstream will be $x + y$, and the rate upstream will be $x - y$. At this point a table of information is helpful.

	Distance	Rate	Time
Downstream	36	$x + y$	2
Upstream	36	$x - y$	3

From the relationship $d = r \cdot t$ we can now use our table to write the system

$36 = 2(x + y)$ (From line 1 of our table)

$36 = 3(x - y)$ (From line 2 of our table)

Step 4 Removing the parentheses by apply the distributive property in the equations of step 3, we have

$$2x + 2y = 36$$
$$3x - 3y = 36$$

By either of our earlier methods, this system gives values of 15 for x and 3 for y. The rate in still water is 15 mi/h, and the rate of the current is 3 mi/h.

Step 5 We leave the check to you.

Check Yourself 15

A plane flies 480 mi in an easterly direction, with the wind, in 4 h. Returning westerly along the same route, against the wind, the plane takes 6 h. What is the rate of the plane in still air? What is the rate of the wind?

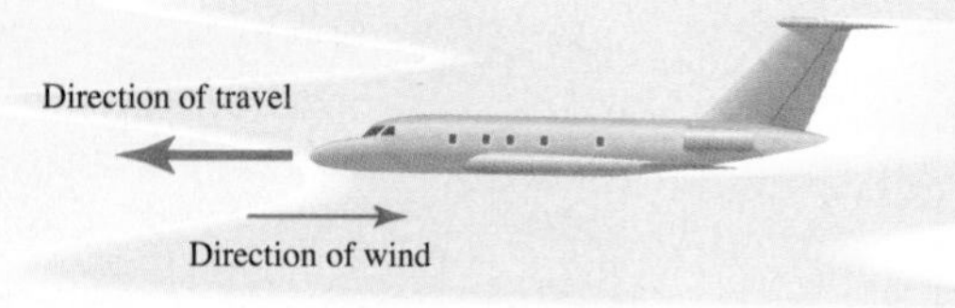

We will look at one final application that leads to a system of two equations.

Example 16 Solving a Business-Based Application

Two car rental agencies have the following rate structures for a subcompact car. Urent charges \$50 per day plus 15¢ per mile. Painz charges \$45 per day plus 20¢ per mile. If you rent a car for 1 day, for what number of miles driven will the two companies have the same total charge?

Step 1 We are looking for the number of miles.

Step 2 Letting c represent the total a company will charge and m the number of miles driven, we write the following equations.

Step 3 For Urent: $c = 50 + 0.15m$

For Painz: $c = 45 + 0.20m$

Step 4 The system can be solved most easily by substitution. Substituting $45 + 0.20m$ for c in the first equation gives

$$
\begin{aligned}
45 + 0.20m &= 50 + 0.15m \\
45 + 0.05m &= 50 \\
0.05m &= 5 \\
m &= 100 \text{ mi}
\end{aligned}
$$

Step 5 Show that the charges are the same at 100 miles.

The graph of the system is shown here.

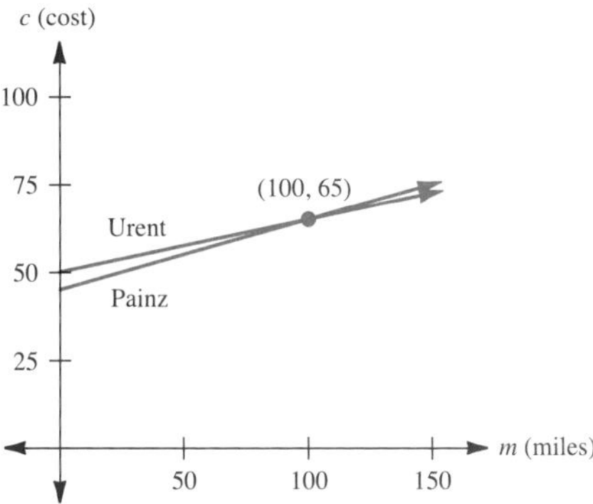

From the graph, how would you make a decision about which agency to use?

Check Yourself 16

For a luxury car, the same two companies charge \$54 per day plus 20¢ per mile and \$51 per day plus 22¢ per mile. For a 2-day rental, when will the charges be the same?

Check Yourself ANSWERS

1.

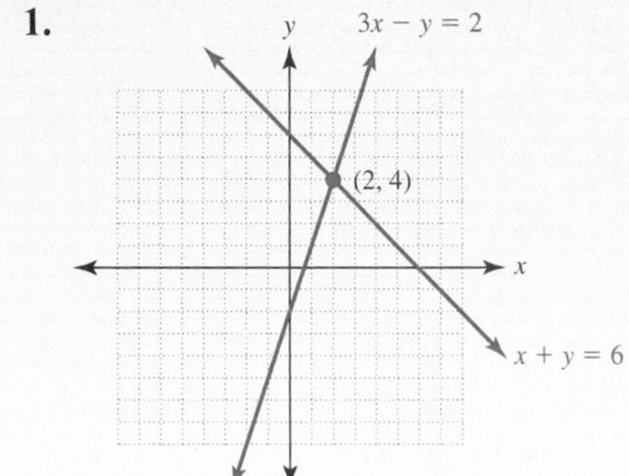

2. No solution

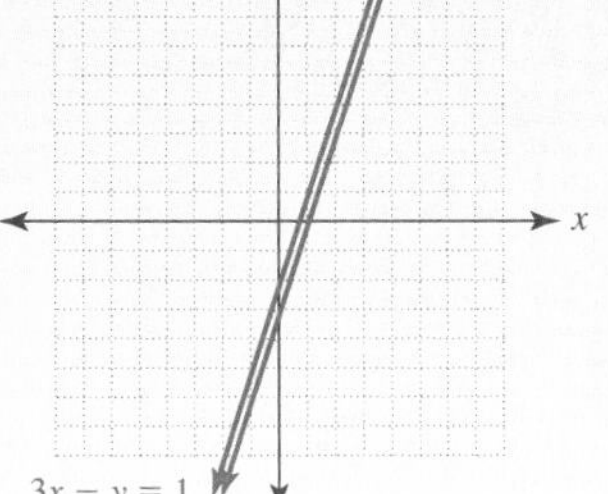

3. An infinite number of solutions **4.** $\left(\frac{5}{2}, -3\right)$ 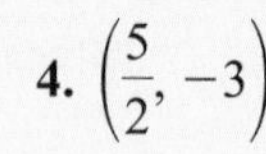 **5.** $(-3, -4)$

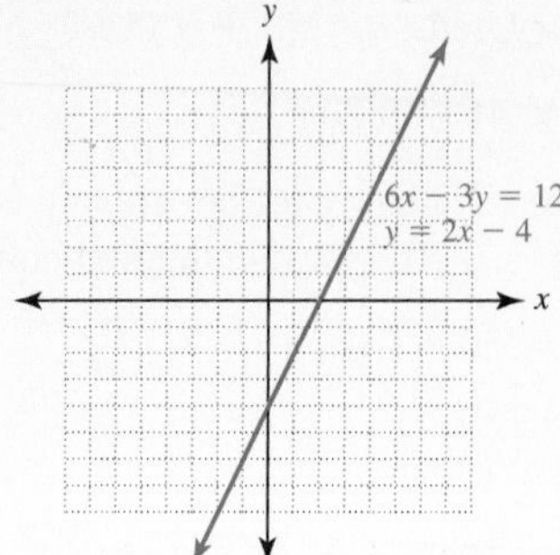

6. **(a)** Inconsistent system: no solution;
(b) dependent system: an infinite number of solutions

7. **(a)** $\left(4, -\frac{2}{3}\right)$; **(b)** $\left(-2, \frac{3}{4}\right)$

8. **(a)** Addition; **(b)** substitution; **(c)** substitution; **(d)** addition

9. The numbers are 8 and 20. **10.** The legs have length 15 in.; the base is 20 in.

11. 7 ft, 13 ft **12.** 150 $6 tickets, 200 $8 tickets

13. 100 mL (30%), 300 mL (50%) **14.** $4,000 at 8%, $6,000 at 9%

15. Plane's rate in still air, 100 mi/h; wind's rate, 20 mi/h

16. At 300 mi, $168 charge

Reading Your Text

The following fill-in-the-blank exercises are designed to ensure that you understand some of the key vocabulary used in this section.

SECTION 4.1

(a) When we consider two linear equations together, they form a ________ of linear equations.

(b) An ordered pair that satisfies both equations of a system is called a ________ for the system.

(c) A system with one solution is called a ________ system.

(d) If there are infinitely many solutions for a system, the system is called ________.

Basic Skills | Advanced Skills | Vocational-Technical Applications | Calculator/Computer | Above and Beyond

4.1 exercises

< Objectives 1 and 2 >

In exercises 1 to 8, solve each system by graphing. If a unique solution does not exist, state whether the system is dependent or inconsistent.

1. $x + y = 6$
$x - y = 4$

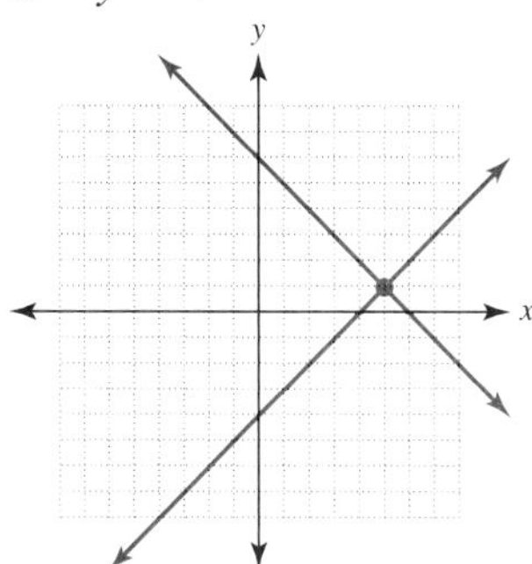

2. $x - y = 8$
$x + y = 2$

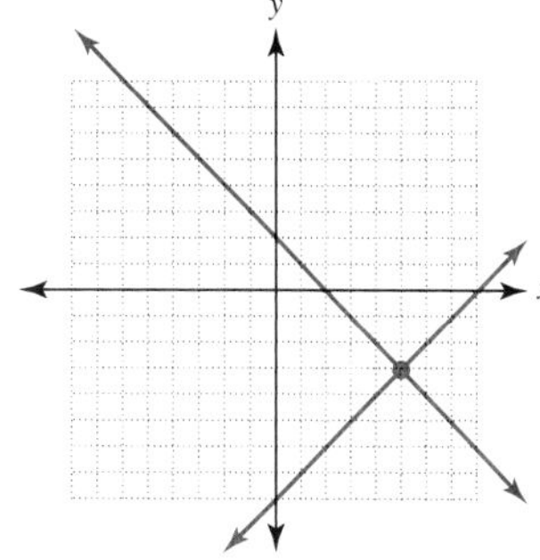

3. $x + 2y = 4$
$x - y = 1$

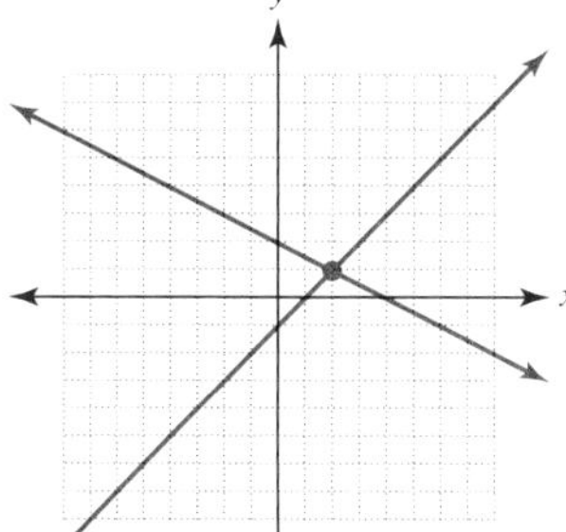

4. $x - 2y = 2$
$x + 2y = 6$

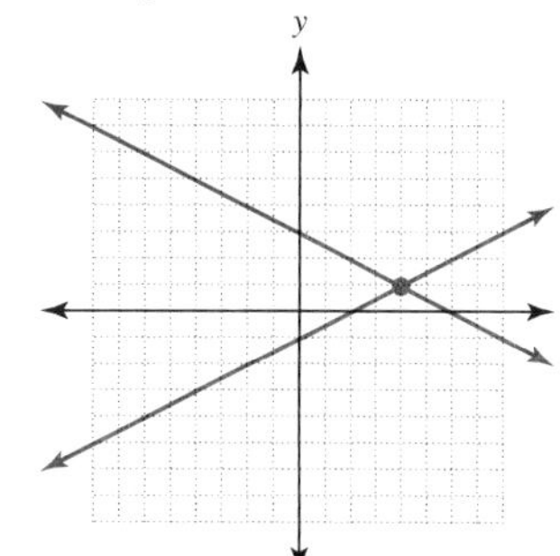

5. $3x - y = 3$
$3x - y = 6$

> Videos

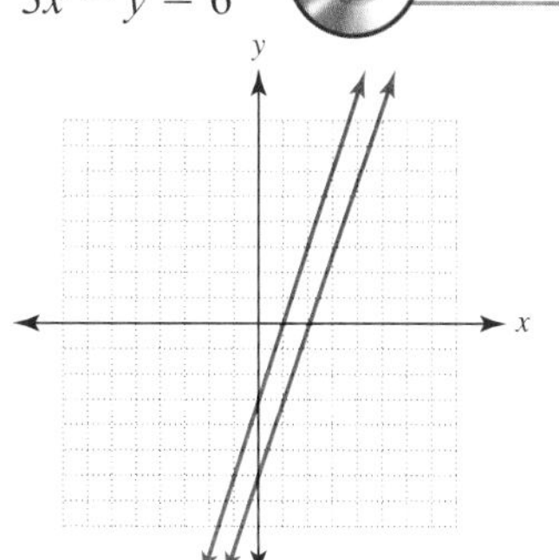

6. $3x + 2y = 12$
$y = 3$

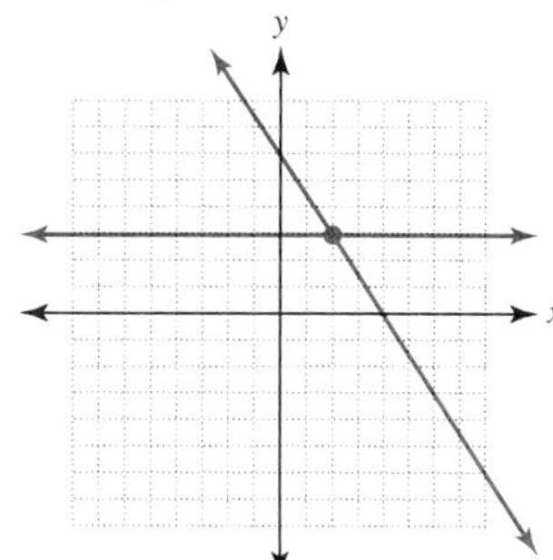

7. $x + 3y = 12$
$2x - 3y = 6$

8. $3x - 6y = 9$
$x - 2y = 3$

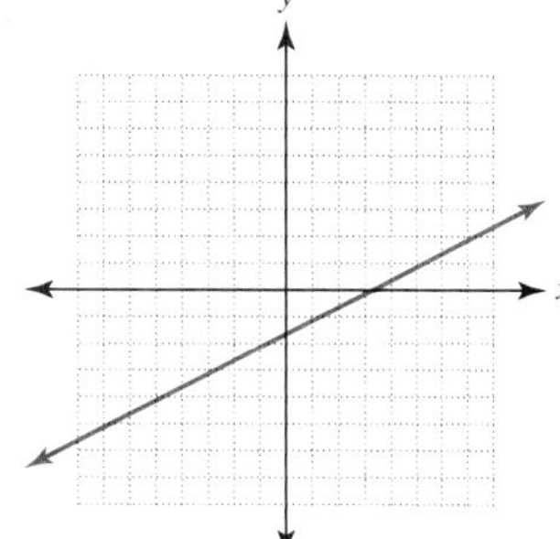

Name ______________

Section ________ Date ________

Answers

1. (5,1)
2. (5, −3)
3. (2, 1)
4. (4, 1)
5. Inconsistent system
6. (2, 3)
7. (6, 2)
8. Dependent system

Answers

9. (2, 3)
10. (6, 2)
11. $\left(-5, \frac{3}{2}\right)$
12. (5, −3)
13. (2, 1)
14. (3, 5)
15. Dependent system
16. (6, 4)
17. (5, −3)
18. Inconsistent system
19. Inconsistent system
20. (−4, 3)
21. (−8, −2)
22. Dependent system
23. (5, −2)
24. (10, 6)
25. (−4, −3)
26. Inconsistent system
27. Dependent system
28. (4, −2)
29. $\left(\frac{1}{3}, 2\right)$
30. $\left(5, \frac{3}{5}\right)$

< Objective 3 >

In exercises 9 to 22, solve each system by the addition method. If a unique solution does not exist, state whether the system is inconsistent or dependent.

9. $2x - y = 1$
$-2x + 3y = 5$

10. $x + 3y = 12$
$2x - 3y = 6$

11. $x + 2y = -2$
$3x + 2y = -12$

12. $2x + 3y = 1$
$5x + 3y = 16$

13. $x + y = 3$
$3x - 2y = 4$

14. $x - y = -2$
$2x + 3y = 21$

15. $2x + y = 8$
$-4x - 2y = -16$

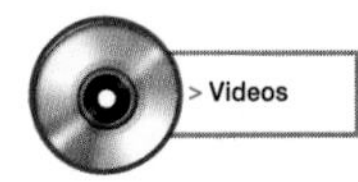

16. $3x - 4y = 2$
$4x - y = 20$

17. $5x - 2y = 31$
$4x + 3y = 11$

18. $2x - y = 4$
$6x - 3y = 10$

19. $3x - 2y = 7$
$-6x + 4y = -15$

20. $3x + 4y = 0$
$5x - 3y = -29$

21. $-2x + 7y = 2$
$3x - 5y = -14$

22. $5x - 2y = 3$
$10x - 4y = 6$

< Objective 4 >

In exercises 23 to 34, solve each system by the substitution method. If a unique solution does not exist, state whether the system is inconsistent or dependent.

23. $x - y = 7$
$y = 2x - 12$

24. $x - y = 4$
$x = 2y - 2$

25. $3x + 2y = -18$
$x = 3y + 5$

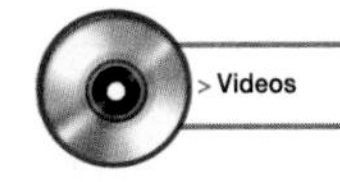

26. $3x - 18y = 4$
$x = 6y + 2$

27. $10x - 2y = 4$
$y = 5x - 2$

28. $4x + 5y = 6$
$y = 2x - 10$

29. $3x + 4y = 9$
$y = 3x + 1$

30. $6x - 5y = 27$
$x = 5y + 2$

31. $x - 7y = 3$
$2x - 5y = 15$

32. $4x + 3y = -11$
$5x + y = -11$

33. $4x - 12y = 5$
$-x + 3y = -1$

34. $5x - 6y = 21$
$x - 2y = 5$

In exercises 35 to 40, solve each system by any method discussed in this section.

35. $2x - 3y = 4$
$x = 3y + 6$

36. $5x + y = 2$
$5x - 3y = 6$

37. $4x - 3y = 0$
$5x + 2y = 23$

38. $7x - 2y = -17$
$x + 4y = 4$

39. $3x - y = 17$
$5x + 3y = 5$

40. $7x + 3y = -51$
$y = 2x + 9$

In exercises 41 to 44, solve each system by any method discussed in this section. (Hint: *You should multiply to clear fractions as your first step.*)

41. $\frac{1}{2}x - \frac{1}{3}y = 8$
$\frac{1}{3}x + y = -2$

42. $\frac{1}{5}x - \frac{1}{2}y = 0$
$x - \frac{3}{2}y = 4$

43. $\frac{2}{3}x + \frac{3}{5}y = -3$
$\frac{1}{3}x + \frac{2}{5}y = -3$

> Videos

44. $\frac{3}{8}x - \frac{1}{2}y = -5$
$\frac{1}{4}x + \frac{3}{2}y = 4$

< Objective 5 >

Each application in exercises 45 to 52 can be solved by the use of a system of linear equations. Match the application with the appropriate system given here.

(a) $12x + 5y = 116$
$8x + 12y = 112$

(b) $x + y = 8{,}000$
$0.06x + 0.09y = 600$

(c) $x + y = 200$
$0.20x + 0.60y = 90$

(d) $x + y = 36$
$y = 3x - 4$

(e) $2(x + y) = 36$
$3(x - y) = 36$

(f) $x + y = 200$
$6.50x + 4.50y = 980$

(g) $L = 2W + 3$
$2L + 2W = 36$

(h) $x + y = 120$
$2.20x + 5.40y = 360$

Answers

31. (10, 1)
32. (−2, −1)
33. Inconsistent system
34. (3, −1)
35. $\left(-2, -\frac{8}{3}\right)$
36. $\left(\frac{3}{5}, -1\right)$
37. (3, 4)
38. $\left(-2, \frac{3}{2}\right)$
39. (4, −5)
40. (−6, −3)
41. (12, −6)
42. (10, 4)
43. (9, −15)
44. (−8, 4)

Answers

45. (d)

46. (f)

47. (g)

48. (a)

49. (h)

50. (b)

51. (c)

52. (e)

53. 27 in. by 15 in.

45. NUMBER PROBLEM One number is 4 less than 3 times another. If the sum of the numbers is 36, what are the two numbers?

46. BUSINESS AND FINANCE Suppose a movie theater sold 200 adult and student tickets for a showing with a revenue of $980. If the adult tickets were $6.50 and the student tickets were $4.50, how many of each type of ticket were sold?

47. GEOMETRY The length of a rectangle is 3 cm more than twice its width. If the perimeter of the rectangle is 36 cm, find the dimensions of the rectangle.

48. BUSINESS AND FINANCE An order of 12 dozen roller-ball pens and 5 dozen ballpoint pens cost $116. A later order for 8 dozen roller-ball pens and 12 dozen ballpoint pens cost $112. What was the cost of 1 dozen of each type of pen?

49. BUSINESS AND FINANCE A candy merchant wants to mix peanuts selling at $2.20 per pound with cashews selling at $5.40 per pound to form 120 lb of a mixed-nut blend that will sell for $3 per pound. What amount of each type of nut should be used?

50. BUSINESS AND FINANCE Donald has investments totaling $8,000 in two accounts—one a savings account paying 6% interest, and the other a bond paying 9%. If the annual interest from the two investments was $600, how much did he have invested at each rate?

51. SCIENCE AND MEDICINE A chemist wants to combine a 20% alcohol solution with a 60% solution to form 200 mL of a 45% solution. How much of each solution should be used to form the mixture?

52. SCIENCE AND MEDICINE Xian was able to make a downstream trip of 36 mi in 2 h. Returning upstream, he took 3 h to make the trip. How fast can his boat travel in still water? What was the rate of the river's current?

In exercises 53 to 68, solve by choosing a variable to represent each unknown quantity and writing a system of equations.

53. GEOMETRY The length of a rectangle is 3 in. less than twice its width. If the perimeter of the rectangle is 84 in., find the dimensions of the rectangle.

54. **GEOMETRY** The length of a rectangle is 5 cm more than 3 times its width. If the perimeter of the rectangle is 74 cm, find the dimensions of the rectangle.

55. **BUSINESS AND FINANCE** Cheryl decided to divide $12,000 into two investments—one a time deposit that pays 8% annual interest and the other a bond that pays 9%. If her annual interest was $1,010, how much did she invest at each rate?

56. **BUSINESS AND FINANCE** Miguel has $3,000 more invested in a mutual fund paying 5% interest than in a savings account paying 3%. If he received $310 in interest for 1 year, how much did he have invested in the two accounts?

57. **SCIENCE AND MEDICINE** A chemist mixes a 10% acid solution with a 50% acid solution to form 400 mL of a 40% solution. How much of each solution should be used in the mixture?

> Videos

58. **SCIENCE AND MEDICINE** A laboratory technician wishes to mix a 70% saline solution and a 20% solution to prepare 500 mL of a 40% solution. What amount of each solution should be used?

59. **SCIENCE AND MEDICINE** A boat traveled 36 mi up a river in 3 h. Returning downstream, the boat took 2 h. What is the boat's rate in still water, and what is the rate of the river's current?

60. **SCIENCE AND MEDICINE** A jet flew east a distance of 1,800 mi with the jet stream in 3 h. Returning west, against the jet stream, the jet took 4 h. Find the jet's speed in still air and the rate of the jet stream.

61. **NUMBER PROBLEM** The sum of the digits of a two-digit number is 8. If the digits are reversed, the new number is 36 more than the original number. Find the original number. (*Hint:* If u represents the units digit of the number and t the tens digit, the original number can be represented by $10t + u$.)

62. **NUMBER PROBLEM** The sum of the digits of a two-digit number is 10. If the digits are reversed, the new number is 54 less than the original number. What was the original number?

63. **BUSINESS AND FINANCE** Two car rental agencies have the following rate structure for compact cars.

Company A: $30/day and 22¢/mi.

Company B: $28/day and 26¢/mi.

For a 2-day rental, at what number of miles will the charges be the same?

Answers

54. 8 cm by 29 cm
55. Time deposit: $7,000, bond: $5,000
56. Savings: $2,000, mutual: $5,000
57. 100 mL of 10%, 300 mL of 50%
58. 200 mL of 70%, 300 mL of 20%
59. Boat: 15 mi/h, current: 3 mi/h
60. Jet: 525 mi/h, jet stream: 75 mi/h
61. 26
62. 82
63. 100 mi

Answers

64. 800 ft^2

65. 533.3 mL of 40%, 266.7 mL of 25%

66. 21.4 mL of 9%, 53.6 mL of 2%

67. 12 gal

68. 76 drive assemblies, 42 relays

64. **Business and Finance** Two construction companies submit the following bid.

Company A: \$5,000 plus \$15 per square foot of building.

Company B: \$7,000 plus \$12.50 per square foot of building.

For what number of square feet of building will the bids of the two companies be the same?

Basic Skills | Advanced Skills | **Vocational-Technical Applications** | Calculator/Computer | Above and Beyond

65. **Allied Health** A medical lab technician needs to determine how much 40% alcohol solution, x, must be mixed with 25% alcohol solution, y, to produce 800 milliliters of a 35% solution. From this information, the technician derives two linear equations: $x + y = 800$ and $40x + 25y = 28{,}000$. Solve this system of equations by substitution, and report how much of each type of solution is needed to the nearest tenth of a milliliter.

66. **Allied Health** A medical lab technician needs to determine how much 9% sulfuric acid (H_2SO_4) solution, x, must be mixed with 2% H_2SO_4 solution, y, to produce 75 milliliters of a 4% solution. From this information, the technician derives two linear equations: $x + y = 75$ and $9x + 2y = 300$. Solve this system of equations by substitution, and report how much of each type of solution is needed to the nearest tenth of a milliliter.

67. **Manufacturing Technology** The antifreeze concentration in an industrial cooling system needs to be at 45%. If the system holds 32 gallons of coolant and is currently at a concentration of 30%, how much of the solution needs to be removed and replaced with pure antifreeze to bring the concentration up to the required level?

This can be solved with the system of equations:

$$0.30x + 0.70y = 14.4$$
$$x + y = 32$$

Solve this system of equations by substitution (x is the amount of coolant at 30% concentration and y is the amount removed and replaced).

68. **Manufacturing Technology** A manufacturer produces drive assemblies and relays. The drive assemblies sell for \$12 and the relays sell for \$3. On a given day, 118 items are produced with a total value of \$1,038. The production is described by the equations (x is the number of assemblies and y is the number of relays):

$$12x + 3y = 1{,}038$$
$$x + y = 118$$

Solve this system using the addition method. How many of each were produced?

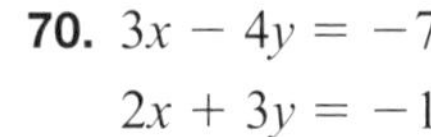

Basic Skills | Advanced Skills | Vocational-Technical Applications | **Calculator/Computer** | Above and Beyond

In exercises 69 and 70, use your calculator to approximate the solution to each system. Express your answer to the nearest tenth.

69. $y = 2x - 3$
$2x + 3y = 1$

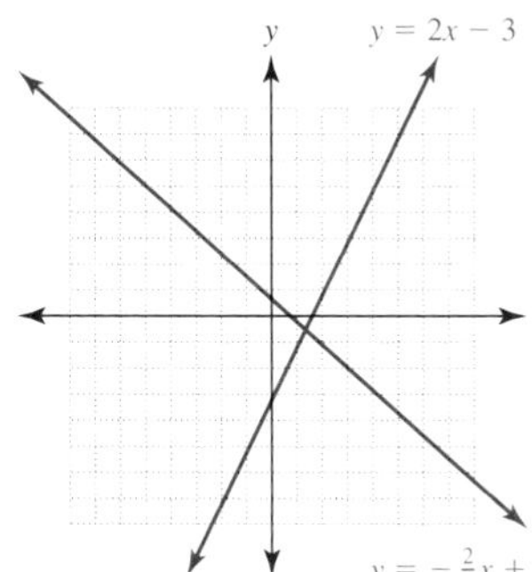

70. $3x - 4y = -7$
$2x + 3y = -1$

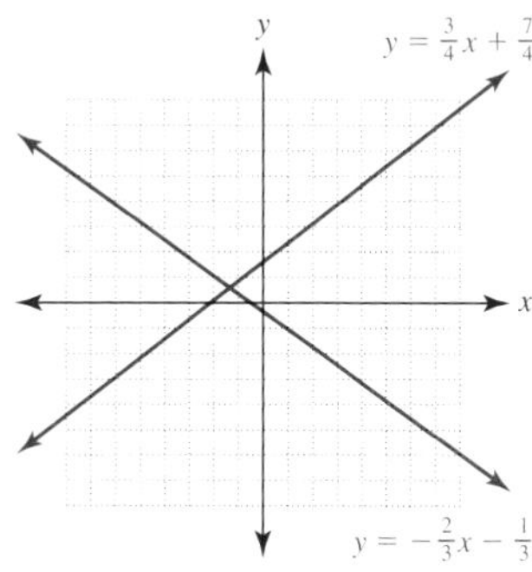

For exercises 71 and 72, adjust the viewing window on your calculator so that you can see the point of intersection for the two lines representing the equations in the system. Then approximate the solution to the nearest whole number.

71. $5x - 12y = 8$
$7x + 2y = 44$

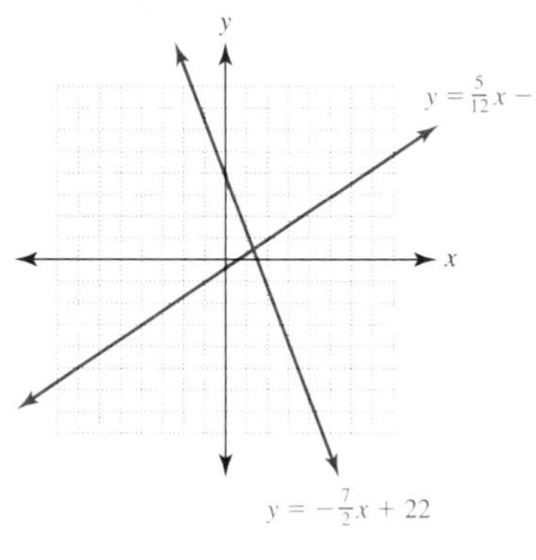

72. $9x - 3y = 10$
$x + 5y = 58$

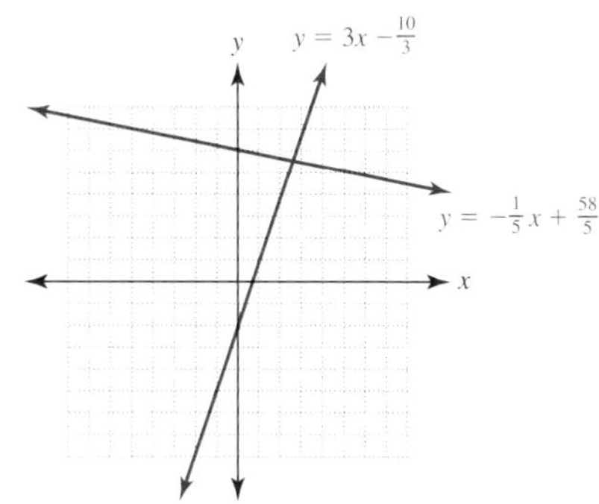

Basic Skills | Advanced Skills | Vocational-Technical Applications | Calculator/Computer | **Above and Beyond**

73. Find values for m and b in the following system so that the solution to the system is (1, 2).

$mx + 3y = 8$
$-3x + 4y = b$

Answers

69. (1.3, −0.5)

70. (−1.5, 0.6)

71. (6, 2)

72. (5, 11)

73. $m = 2, b = 5$

74. Find values for m and b in the following system so that the solution to the system is $(-3, 4)$.

$$5x + 7y = b$$
$$mx + y = 22$$

75. Complete the following statements in your own words:

"To solve an equation means to . . . ."

"To solve a system of equations means to . . . ."

76. A system of equations such as the following one is sometimes called a "2-by-2" system of linear equations.

$$3x + 4y = 1$$
$$x - 2y = 6$$

Explain this term.

77. Complete this statement in your own words: "All the points on the graph of the equation $2x + 3y = 6$ . . . ." Exchange statements with other students. Do you agree with other students' statements?

78. Does a system of linear equations always have a solution? How can you tell without graphing that a system of two equations will be graphed as two parallel lines? Give some examples to explain your reasoning.

79. Suppose we have the following linear system:

$$Ax + By = C$$
$$Dx + Ey = F$$

(a) Write the slope of the line determined by the first equation.

(b) Write the slope of the line determined by the second equation.

(c) What must be true about the given coefficients to guarantee that the system is consistent?

80. We have discussed three different methods of solving a system of two linear equations in two unknowns: the graphical method, the addition method, and the substitution method. Discuss the strengths and weaknesses of each method.

81. Determine a system of two linear equations for which the solution is (3, 4). Are there other systems that have the same solution? If so, determine at least one more and explain why this can be true.

Answers

74. $m = -6, b = 13$

75. Above and Beyond

76. Above and Beyond

77. Above and Beyond

78. Above and Beyond

79. (a) $-A/B$; (b) $-D/E$; (c) $AE - BD \neq 0$

80. Above and Beyond

81. Above and Beyond

82. Suppose we have the following linear system:

$$Ax + By = C$$
$$Dx + Ey = F$$

(a) Multiply the first equation by $-D$, multiply the second equation by A and add. This will allow you to eliminate x. Solve for y and indicate what must be true about the coefficients for a unique value of y to exist.

(b) Now return to the original system and eliminate y instead of x. (*Hint:* Try multiplying the first equation by E and the second equation (by $-B$.) Solve for x and again indicate what must be true about the coefficients for a unique value of x to exist.

Answers

82. (a) $y = \dfrac{AF - CD}{AE - BD}$, $AE - BD \neq 0$; (b) $x = \dfrac{CE - BF}{AE - BD}$, $AE - BD \neq 0$

Answers

1. Solution: (5, 1)

3. Solution: (2, 1)

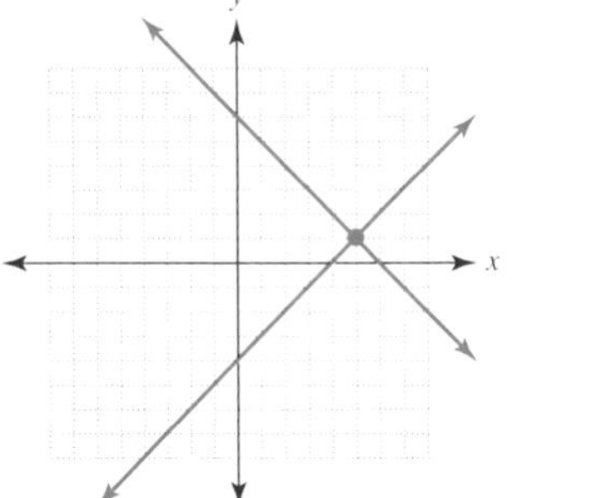

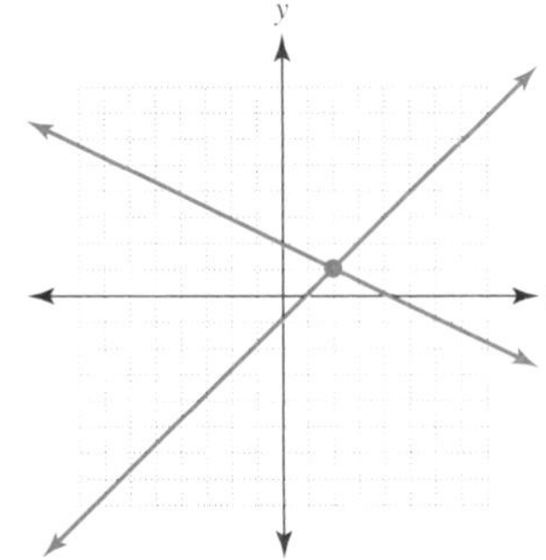

5. Inconsistent system

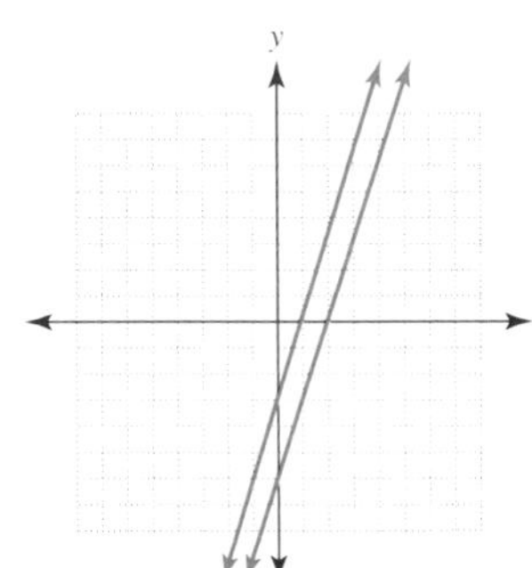

7. Solution: (6, 2)

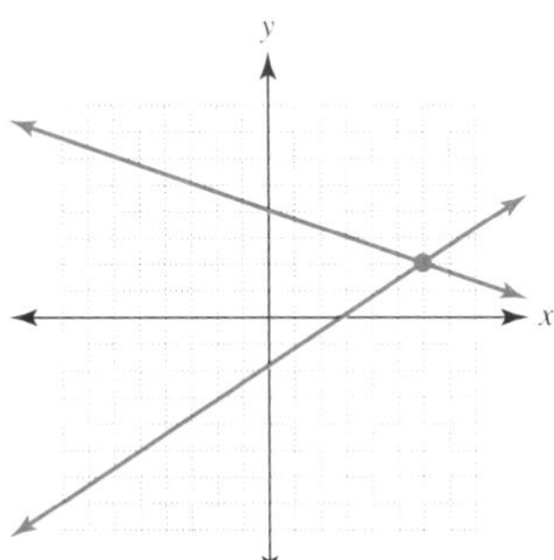

9. (2, 3) **11.** $\left(-5, \frac{3}{2}\right)$ **13.** (2, 1) **15.** Dependent system **17.** (5, −3) **19.** Inconsistent system **21.** (−8, −2) **23.** (5, −2) **25.** (−4, −3) **27.** Dependent system **29.** $\left(\frac{1}{3}, 2\right)$ **31.** (10, 1) **33.** Inconsistent system **35.** $\left(-2, -\frac{8}{3}\right)$ **37.** (3, 4) **39.** (4, −5) **41.** (12, −6) **43.** (9, −15) **45.** (d) **47.** (g) **49.** (h) **51.** (c) **53.** 27 in. by 15 in. **55.** Time deposit: \$7,000, bond: \$5,000 **57.** 100 mL of 10%, 300 mL of 50% **59.** Boat: 15 mi/h, current: 3 mi/h **61.** 26 **63.** 100 mi **65.** 533.3 mL of 40%, 266.7 mL of 25% **67.** 12 gal

69. (1.3, −0.5)

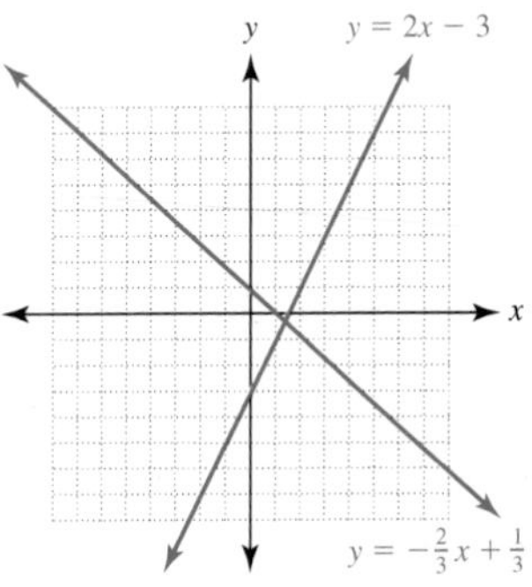

71. (6, 2)

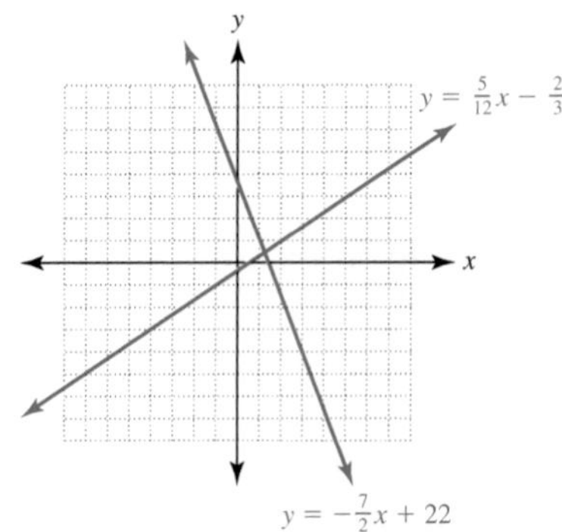

73. $m = 2, b = 5$ **75.** Above and Beyond **77.** Above and Beyond

79. **(a)** $-A/B$; **(b)** $-D/E$; **(c)** $AE - BD \neq 0$ **81.** Above and Beyond

4.2 Systems of Linear Equations in Three Variables

< 4.2 Objectives >

1 > Find ordered triples associated with three equations

2 > Solve a system by the addition method

3 > Use a system of three equations to solve an application

Suppose an application involves three quantities that we want to label x, y, and z. A typical equation used in solving the application might be

$$2x + 4y - z = 8$$

This is called a **linear equation in three variables.** The solution for such an equation is an **ordered triple** (x, y, z) of real numbers that satisfies the equation. For example, the ordered triple (2, 1, 0) is a solution for the preceding equation because substituting 2 for x, 1 for y, and 0 for z results in the following true statement.

$$2 \cdot 2 + 4 \cdot 1 - 0 \stackrel{?}{=} 8$$
$$4 + 4 \stackrel{?}{=} 8$$
$$8 = 8 \quad \text{True}$$

Of course, other solutions, in fact infinitely many, exist. You might want to verify that (1, 1, −2) and (3, 1, 2) are also solutions. To extend the concepts of Section 4.1, we want to consider systems of three linear equations in three variables such as

$$\begin{aligned} x + y + z &= 5 \\ 2x - y + z &= 9 \\ x - 2y + 3z &= 16 \end{aligned}$$

NOTES

For a unique solution to exist, when *three variables* are involved, we must have *three equations.*

The choice of which variable to eliminate is yours. Generally, you should pick the variable that allows the easiest computation.

The solution for such a system is the set of all ordered triples that satisfy each equation of the system. In this case, you can verify that (2, −1, 4) is a solution for the system because that ordered triple makes each equation a true statement.

Let us turn now to the process of solving such a system. In this section, we will consider the addition method. We will then apply what we have learned to solving applications.

The central idea is to choose *two pairs* of equations from the system and, by the addition method, to eliminate the *same variable* from each of those pairs. The method is best illustrated by example. So let's proceed to see how the solution for the previous system was determined.

Example 1 Solving a Linear System in Three Variables

< Objectives 1 and 2 >

Solve the system.

$$\begin{aligned} x + y + z &= 5 \\ 2x - y + z &= 9 \\ x - 2y + 3z &= 16 \end{aligned}$$

First we choose two of the equations and the variable to eliminate. Choosing the first two equations and the variable y seems convenient in this case. Pairing the first two equations and then adding, we have

NOTE

Any pair of equations could have been selected.

$$\begin{aligned} x + y + z &= 5 \\ 2x - y + z &= 9 \\ \hline 3x \quad + 2z &= 14 \end{aligned}$$

We now want to choose a different pair of equations to eliminate y. Using the first and third equations this time, we multiply the first equation by 2 and then add the result to the third equation.

$$\begin{aligned} 2x + 2y + 2z &= 10 \\ x - 2y + 3z &= 16 \\ \hline 3x \quad + 5z &= 26 \end{aligned}$$

We now have two equations in variables x and z.

$$\begin{aligned} 3x + 2z &= 14 \\ 3x + 5z &= 26 \end{aligned}$$

Because we are now dealing with a system of two equations in two variables, any of the methods of Section 4.1 apply. We have chosen to multiply the first resultant equation by -1 and then add that to the second resultant equation. This yields

$$\begin{aligned} -3x - 2z &= -14 \\ 3x + 5z &= 26 \\ \hline 3z &= 12 \\ z &= 4 \end{aligned}$$

Substituting $z = 4$ in the first equation in x and z gives

$$\begin{aligned} 3x + 2 \cdot 4 &= 14 \\ 3x + 8 &= 14 \\ 3x &= 6 \\ x &= 2 \end{aligned}$$

Finally, letting $x = 2$ and $z = 4$ in the first original equation in the system gives

$$\begin{aligned} 2 + y + 4 &= 5 \\ y + 6 &= 5 \\ y &= -1 \end{aligned}$$

and $(2, -1, 4)$ is shown to be the solution for the system.

NOTES

We could have substituted $z = 4$ in the second equation in x and z.

Any of the original equations could have been used for letting $x = 2$ and $z = 4$.

To check, substitute the three values of the solution ($x = 2, y = -1, z = 4$) into the other equations of the original system.

Check Yourself 1

Solve the system.

$$\begin{aligned} x - 2y + z &= 0 \\ 2x + 3y - z &= 16 \\ 3x - y - 3z &= 23 \end{aligned}$$

One or more of the equations of a system may already have a missing variable. The elimination process is simplified in that case, as Example 2 illustrates.

Example 2 Solving a Linear System in Three Variables

Solve the system.

$$\begin{aligned} 2x + y - z &= -3 \\ y + z &= 2 \\ 4x - y + z &= 12 \end{aligned}$$

Noting that the second equation involves only y and z, we can simplify our work by just finding another equation in those same two variables. Multiply the first equation by -2 and add the result to the third equation to eliminate x.

NOTE

We now have a *second* equation in y and z.

$$\begin{aligned} -4x - 2y + 2z &= 6 \\ 4x - y + z &= 12 \\ \hline -3y + 3z &= 18 \\ y - z &= -6 \end{aligned}$$

We now form a system consisting of the original second equation and the resultant equation in y and z and solve as before.

$$\begin{aligned} y + z &= 2 \\ y - z &= -6 \\ \hline 2y &= -4 \\ y &= -2 \end{aligned}$$

From the second original equation, if $y = -2$,

$$\begin{aligned} -2 + z &= 2 \\ z &= 4 \end{aligned}$$

and from the first original equation, if $y = -2$ and $z = 4$,

$$\begin{aligned} 2x - 2 - 4 &= -3 \\ 2x - 6 &= -3 \\ 2x &= 3 \\ x &= \frac{3}{2} \end{aligned}$$

The solution for the system is

$$\left(\frac{3}{2}, -2, 4\right)$$

Check Yourself 2

Solve the system.

$$x + 2y - z = -3$$
$$x - y + z = 2$$
$$x - z = 3$$

The following algorithm summarizes the procedure for finding the solutions for a linear system of three equations in three variables.

Step by Step

Solving a System of Three Equations in Three Unknowns

Step 1 Choose a pair of equations from the system, and use the addition method to eliminate one of the variables.

Step 2 Choose a *different* pair of equations, and eliminate the *same* variable.

Step 3 Solve the system of two equations in two variables determined in steps 1 and 2.

Step 4 Substitute the values found in step 3 into one of the original equations, and solve for the remaining variable.

Step 5 The solution is the ordered triple of values found in steps 3 and 4. It can be checked by substituting into the other equations of the original system.

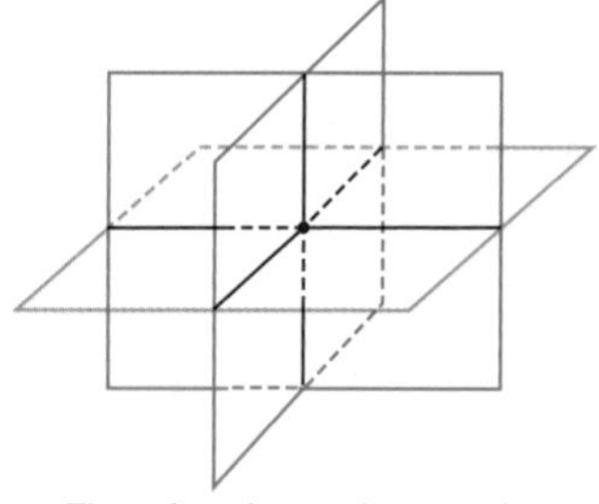

Three planes intersecting at a point

Systems of three equations in three variables may have (1) exactly one solution, (2) infinitely many solutions, or (3) no solution. Before we look at an algebraic approach in the second and third cases, let us discuss the geometry involved.

The graph of a linear equation in three variables is a plane (a flat surface) in three dimensions. Two distinct planes either will be parallel or will intersect in a line.

If three distinct planes intersect, that intersection will be either a single point (as in our first example) or a line (think of three pages in an open book—they intersect along the binding of the book).

Let us look at an example of how we might proceed in these cases.

Example 3 Solving a Dependent Linear System in Three Variables

Solve the system.

$$x + 2y - z = 5$$
$$x - y + z = -2$$
$$-5x - 4y + z = -11$$

We begin as before by choosing two pairs of equations from the system and eliminating the same variable z from each of the pairs. Adding the first and second equations gives

$$\begin{array}{r} x + 2y - z = 5 \\ x - y + z = -2 \\ \hline 2x + y \quad = 3 \end{array}$$

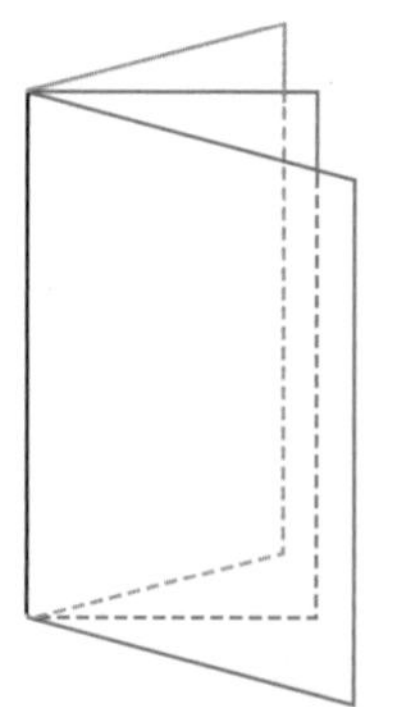

Three planes intersecting in a line

Adding the first and third equations gives

$$\begin{aligned} x + 2y - z &= 5 \\ -5x - 4y + z &= -11 \\ \hline -4x - 2y \quad &= -6 \end{aligned}$$

Now consider the system formed by the two resultant equations in x and y. We multiply the first resultant equation by 2 and add again:

NOTE

There are ways of representing the solutions, as you will see in later courses.

$$\begin{aligned} 4x + 2y &= 6 \\ -4x - 2y &= -6 \\ \hline 0 &= 0 \end{aligned}$$

This true statement tells us that the system has an infinite number of solutions (lying along a straight line). Again, such a system is dependent.

Check Yourself 3

Solve the system.

$$\begin{aligned} 2x - y + 3z &= 3 \\ -x + y - 2z &= 1 \\ y - z &= 5 \end{aligned}$$

There is a third possibility for the solutions of systems in three variables, as Example 4 illustrates.

Example 4 Solving an Inconsistent Linear System in Three Variables

Solve the system.

$$\begin{aligned} 3x + y - 3z &= 1 \\ -2x - y + 2z &= 1 \\ -x - y + z &= 2 \end{aligned}$$

This time we eliminate variable y. Adding the first two equations, we have

$$\begin{aligned} 3x + y - 3z &= 1 \\ -2x - y + 2z &= 1 \\ \hline x \quad - z &= 2 \end{aligned}$$

Adding the first and third equations gives

$$\begin{aligned} 3x + y - 3z &= 1 \\ -x - y + z &= 2 \\ \hline 2x \quad - 2z &= 3 \end{aligned}$$

Now, multiply the first equation in x and z by -2 and add the result to the second equation in x and z.

$$\begin{aligned} -2x + 2z &= -4 \\ 2x - 2z &= 3 \\ \hline 0 &= -1 \end{aligned}$$

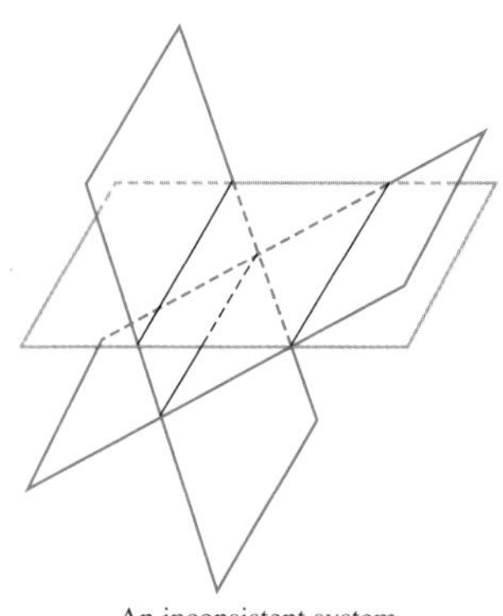

An inconsistent system

All the variables have been eliminated, and we have arrived at a contradiction, $0 = -1$. This means that the system is *inconsistent* and has no solutions. There is *no* point common to all three planes.

Check Yourself 4

Solve the system.

$$\begin{aligned} x - y - z &= 0 \\ -3x + 2y + z &= 1 \\ 3x - y + z &= -1 \end{aligned}$$

As a closing note, we have by no means illustrated all possible types of inconsistent and dependent systems. Other possibilities involve either distinct parallel planes or planes that coincide. The solution techniques in these additional cases are, however, similar to those that have been illustrated.

In many instances, if an application involves three unknown quantities, you will find it useful to assign three variables to those quantities and then build a system of three equations from the given relationships in the problem. The extension of our problem-solving strategy is natural, as Example 5 illustrates.

Example 5 Solving a Number Problem

< Objective 3 >

The sum of the digits of a three-digit number is 12. The tens digit is 2 less than the hundreds digit, and the units digit is 4 less than the sum of the other two digits. What is the number?

NOTES

Sometimes it helps to choose variable letters that relate to the words as is done here.

Take a moment now to go back to the original problem and pick out those conditions. That skill is a crucial part of the problem-solving strategy.

Step 1 The three unknowns are, of course, the three digits of the number.

Step 2 We now want to assign variables to each of the three digits. Let u be the units digit, t be the tens digit, and h be the hundreds digit.

Step 3 There are three conditions given in the problem that allow us to write the necessary three equations. From those conditions

$$\begin{aligned} h + t + u &= 12 \\ t &= h - 2 \\ u &= h + t - 4 \end{aligned}$$

Step 4 There are various ways to approach the solution. To use addition, write the system in the equivalent form

$$\begin{aligned} h + t + u &= 12 \\ -h + t \qquad &= -2 \\ -h - t + u &= -4 \end{aligned}$$

and solve by our earlier methods. The solution, which you can verify, is $h = 5$, $t = 3$, and $u = 4$. The desired number is 534.

Step 5 To check, you should show that the digits of 534 meet each of the conditions of the original problem.

Check Yourself 5

The sum of the measures of the angles of a triangle is 180°. In a given triangle, the measure of the second angle is twice the measure of the first. The measure of the third angle is 30° less than the sum of the measures of the first two. Find the measure of each angle.

Let us continue with a financial application that will lead to a system of three equations.

Example 6 Solving an Investment Application

Monica decided to divide a total of \$42,000 into three investments: a savings account paying 5% interest, a time deposit paying 7%, and a bond paying 9%. Her total annual interest from the three investments was \$2,600, and the interest from the savings account was \$200 less than the total interest from the other two investments. How much did she invest at each rate?

> **NOTES**
>
> Again, we choose letters that suggest the unknown quantities—*s* for savings, *t* for time deposit, and *b* for bond.
>
> For 1 year, the interest formula is
>
> $I = Pr$
>
> (interest equals principal times rate).

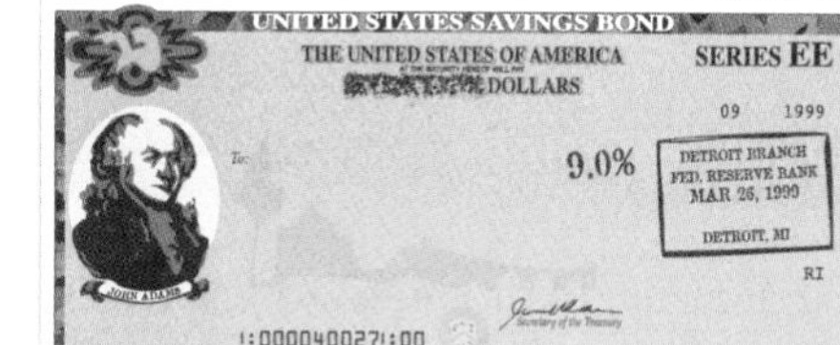

Step 1 The three amounts are the unknowns.

Step 2 We let s be the amount invested at 5%, t the amount at 7%, and b the amount at 9%. Note that the interest from the savings account is then $0.05s$, and so on.

A table will help with the next step.

	5%	7%	9%
Principal	s	t	b
Interest	$0.05s$	$0.07t$	$0.09b$

> **NOTES**
>
> The first equation represents the total money invested.
>
> The second equation represents the total interest earned.
>
> The third equation states the savings interest was \$200 *less than* that from the other two investments.
>
> We then solve this system to find the interest earned from each investment, and verify that the conditions of the problem are satisfied.

Step 3 Again there are three conditions in the given problem. By using the preceding table, they lead to the following equations.

$$s + t + b = 42{,}000$$
$$0.05s + 0.07t + 0.09b = 2{,}600$$
$$0.05s = 0.07t + 0.09b - 200$$

Step 4 We clear of decimals and solve as before, with the result

$s = \$24{,}000 \qquad t = \$11{,}000 \qquad b = \$7{,}000$

Step 5 We leave the check of these solutions to you.

Check Yourself 6

Glenn has a total of $11,600 invested in three accounts: a savings account paying 6% interest, a stock paying 8%, and a mutual fund paying 10%. The annual interest from the stock and mutual fund is twice that from the savings account, and the mutual fund returned $120 more than the stock. How much did Glenn invest in each account?

Check Yourself ANSWERS

1. (5, 1, −3) **2.** (1, −3, −2)
3. The system is dependent (there are an infinite number of solutions).
4. The system is inconsistent (there are no solutions).
5. The three angles are 35°, 70°, and 75°.
6. $5,000 in savings, $3,000 in stocks, and $3,600 in mutual funds.

Reading Your Text

The following fill-in-the-blank exercises are designed to ensure that you understand some of the key vocabulary used in this section.

SECTION 4.2

(a) To solve a system of three linear equations in three variables, choose two pairs of equations from the system and, by the addition method, eliminate the ____________ variable from each of those pairs.

(b) Systems of three equations in three variables may have a unique solution, infinitely many solutions, or ____________.

(c) The unique solution for a system of three equations in three variables is called an ordered ____________.

(d) The graph of a linear equation in three variables is a plane in three dimensions. If three distinct planes (representing a system of three linear equations in three variables) intersect in a line, then the system is ____________.

Basic Skills | Advanced Skills | Vocational-Technical Applications | Calculator/Computer | Above and Beyond

4.2 exercises

< Objectives 1 and 2 >

Solve each system of equations. If a unique solution does not exist, state whether the system is inconsistent or has an infinite number of solutions.

1. $x - y + z = 3$
$2x + y + z = 8$
$3x + y - z = 1$

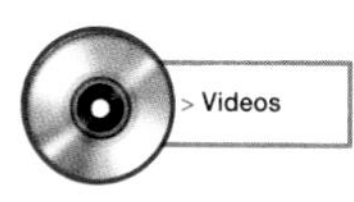

2. $x - y - z = 2$
$2x + y + z = 8$
$x + y + z = 6$

3. $x + y + z = 1$
$2x - y + 2z = -1$
$-x - 3y + z = 1$

4. $x - y - z = 6$
$-x + 3y + 2z = -11$
$3x + 2y + z = 1$

5. $x + y + z = 1$
$-2x + 2y + 3z = 20$
$2x - 2y - z = -16$

6. $x + y + z = -3$
$3x + y - z = 13$
$3x + y - 2z = 18$

7. $2x + y - z = 2$
$-x - 3y + z = -1$
$-4x + 3y + z = -4$

8. $x + 4y - 6z = 8$
$2x - y + 3z = -10$
$3x - 2y + 3z = -18$

9. $3x - y + z = 5$
$x + 3y + 3z = -6$
$x + 4y - 2z = 12$

10. $2x - y + 3z = 2$
$x - 2y + 3z = 1$
$4x - y + 5z = 5$

11. $x + 2y + z = 2$
$2x + 3y + 3z = -3$
$2x + 3y + 2z = 2$

12. $x - 4y - z = -3$
$x + 2y + z = 5$
$3x - 7y - 2z = -6$

13. $x + 3y - 2z = 8$
$3x + 2y - 3z = 15$
$4x + 2y + 3z = -1$

14. $x + y - z = 2$
$3x + 5y - 2z = -5$
$5x + 4y - 7z = -7$

15. $x + y - z = 2$
$x - 2z = 1$
$2x - 3y - z = 8$

16. $x + y + z = 6$
$x - 2y = -7$
$4x + 3y + z = 7$

17. $x - 3y + 2z = 1$
$16y - 9z = 5$
$4x + 4y - z = 8$

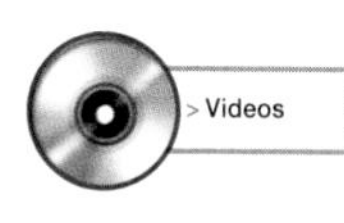

18. $x - 4y + 4z = -1$
$y - 3z = 5$
$3x - 4y + 6z = 1$

19. $x + 2y - 4z = 13$
$3x + 4y - 2z = 19$
$3x + 2z = 3$

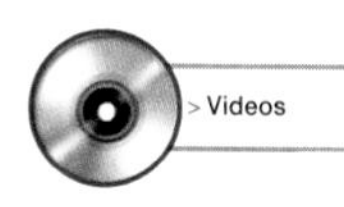

20. $x + 2y - z = 6$
$-3x - 2y + 5z = -12$
$x - 2z = 3$

Name ____________

Section ________ Date ________

Answers

1. (1, 2, 4)
2. Inconsistent system
3. (−2, 1, 2)
4. (2, −1, −3)
5. (−4, 3, 2)
6. (3, −1, −5)
7. Infinite number of solutions
8. $\left(-4, 4, \frac{2}{3}\right)$
9. $\left(3, \frac{1}{2}, -\frac{7}{2}\right)$
10. Inconsistent system
11. (3, 2, −5)
12. $\left(\frac{1}{2}, -\frac{1}{2}, \frac{11}{2}\right)$
13. (2, 0, −3)
14. (30, −13, 15)
15. $\left(4, -\frac{1}{2}, \frac{3}{2}\right)$
16. $\left(-\frac{3}{2}, \frac{11}{4}, \frac{19}{4}\right)$
17. Inconsistent system
18. (3, −1, −2)
19. $\left(2, \frac{5}{2}, -\frac{3}{2}\right)$
20. Infinite number of solutions

Answers

21. 3, 5, 8

22. 5, 7, 12

23. 3 nickels, 5 dimes, 17 quarters

24. Adult: 150, student: 80, children: 48

25. 4 cm, 7 cm, 8 cm

26. 35°, 50°, 95°

27. Savings: $3,000, bond: $9,000, money market: $5,000

28. Savings: $2,000, time deposit: $3,000, bond: $1,000

< Objective 3 >

Solve exercises 21 to 32 by choosing a variable to represent each unknown quantity and writing a system of equations.

21. NUMBER PROBLEM The sum of three numbers is 16. The largest number is equal to the sum of the other two, and 3 times the smallest number is 1 more than the largest. Find the three numbers.

22. NUMBER PROBLEM The sum of three numbers is 24. Twice the smallest number is 2 less than the largest number, and the largest number is equal to the sum of the other two. What are the three numbers?

23. BUSINESS AND FINANCE A cashier has 25 coins consisting of nickels, dimes, and quarters with a value of $4.90. If the number of dimes is 1 less than twice the number of nickels, how many of each type of coin does she have?

24. BUSINESS AND FINANCE A theater has tickets at $6 for adults, $3.50 for students, and $2.50 for children under 12 years old. A total of 278 tickets were sold for one showing with a total revenue of $1,300. If the number of adult tickets sold was 10 less than twice the number of student tickets, how many of each type of ticket were sold for the showing?

25. GEOMETRY The perimeter of a triangle is 19 cm. If the length of the longest side is twice that of the shortest side and 3 cm less than the sum of the lengths of the other two sides, find the lengths of the three sides.

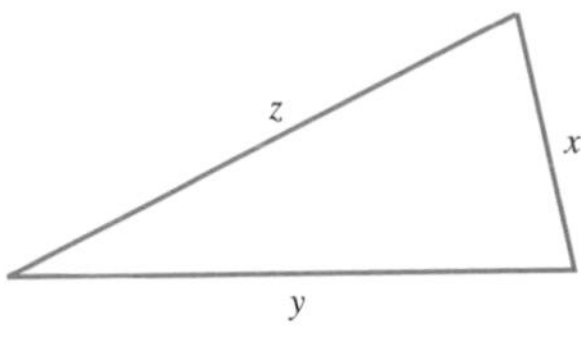

Perimeter = 19 cm

26. GEOMETRY The measure of the largest angle of a triangle is 10 degrees more than the sum of the measures of the other two angles and 10 degrees less than 3 times the measure of the smallest angle. Find the measures of the three angles of the triangle.

27. BUSINESS AND FINANCE Jovita divides $17,000 into three investments: a savings account paying 6% annual interest, a bond paying 9%, and a money market fund paying 11%. The annual interest from the three accounts is $1,540, and she has three times as much invested in the bond as in the savings account. What amount does she have invested in each account?

28. BUSINESS AND FINANCE Adrienne has $6,000 invested among a savings account paying 3%, a time deposit paying 4%, and a bond paying 8%. She has

$1,000 less invested in the bond than in her savings account, and she earned a total of $260 in annual interest. What has she invested in each account?

29. **Number Problem** The sum of the digits of a three-digit number is 9, and the tens digit of the number is twice the hundreds digit. If the digits are reversed in order, the new number is 99 more than the original number. What is the original number?

30. **Number Problem** The sum of the digits of a three-digit number is 9. The tens digit is 3 times the hundreds digit. If the digits are reversed in order, the new number is 99 less than the original number. Find the original three-digit number.

31. **Science and Medicine** Roy, Sally, and Jeff drive a total of 50 mi to work each day. Sally drives twice as far as Roy, and Jeff drives 10 mi farther than Sally. Use a system of three equations in three unknowns to find how far each person drives each day.

32. **Social Science** A parking lot has spaces reserved for motorcycles, cars, and vans. There are five more spaces reserved for vans than for motorcycles. There are three times as many car spaces as van and motorcycle spaces combined. If the parking lot has 180 total reserved spaces, how many of each type are there?

Basic Skills | Advanced Skills | Vocational-Technical Applications | Calculator/Computer | **Above and Beyond**

The solution process illustrated in this section can be extended to solving systems of more than three variables in a natural fashion. For instance, if four variables are involved, eliminate one variable in the system and then solve the resulting system in three variables as before. Substituting those three values into one of the original equations will provide the value for the remaining variable and the solution for the system.

In exercises 33 and 34, use this procedure to solve the system.

33.
$$\begin{aligned} x + 2y + 3z + w &= 0 \\ -x - y - 3z + w &= -2 \\ x - 3y + 2z + 2w &= -11 \\ -x + y - 2z + w &= 1 \end{aligned}$$

34.
$$\begin{aligned} x + y - 2z - w &= 4 \\ x - y + z + 2w &= 3 \\ 2x + y - z - w &= 7 \\ x - y + 2z + w &= 2 \end{aligned}$$

In some systems of equations there are more equations than variables. We can illustrate this situation with a system of three equations in two variables. To solve this type of system, pick any two of the equations and solve this system. Then substitute the solution obtained into the third equation. If a true statement results, the solution used is the solution to the entire system. If a false statement occurs, the system has no solution.

In exercises 35 and 36, use this procedure to solve each system.

35.
$$\begin{aligned} x - y &= 5 \\ 2x + 3y &= 20 \\ 4x + 5y &= 38 \end{aligned}$$

36.
$$\begin{aligned} 3x + 2y &= 6 \\ 5x + 7y &= 35 \\ 7x + 9y &= 8 \end{aligned}$$

Answers

29. 243
30. 261
31. Roy: 8 mi, Sally: 16 mi, Jeff: 26 mi
32. Motorcycles: 20, cars: 135, vans: 25
33. (1, 2, −1, −2)
34. (3, 2, 0, 1)
35. (7, 2)
36. No solution

Answers

37. Trucks: 20 mi, cars: 25 mi, buses: 40 mi

38. Trucks: 30 mi, cars: 16 mi, trains: 95 mi

39. (a) $y = 2x^2 - x + 4$; (b) $y = 3x^2 - 2x + 1$

37. Experiments have shown that cars (C), trucks (T), and buses (B) emit different amounts of air pollutants. In one such experiment, a truck emitted 1.5 pounds (lb) of carbon dioxide (CO_2) per passenger-mile and 2 grams (g) of nitrogen oxide (NO) per passenger-mile. A car emitted 1.1 lb of CO_2 per passenger-mile and 1.5 g of NO per passenger-mile. A bus emitted 0.4 lb of CO_2 per passenger-mile and 1.8 g of NO per passenger-mile. A total of 85 mi was driven by the three vehicles, and 73.5 lb of CO_2 and 149.5 g of NO were collected. Use the following system of equations to determine the miles driven by each vehicle.

$$\begin{aligned} T + \quad C + \quad B &= 85.0 \\ 1.5T + 1.1C + 0.4B &= 73.5 \\ 2T + 1.5C + 1.8B &= 149.5 \end{aligned}$$

38. Experiments have shown that cars (C), trucks (T), and trains (R) emit different amounts of air pollutants. In one such experiment, a truck emitted 0.8 lb of carbon dioxide per passenger-mile and 1 g of nitrogen oxide per passenger-mile. A car emitted 0.7 lb of CO_2 per passenger-mile and 0.9 g of NO per passenger-mile. A train emitted 0.5 lb of CO_2 per passenger-mile and 4 g of NO per passenger-mile. A total of 141 mi was driven by the three vehicles, and 82.7 lb of CO_2 and 424.4 g of NO were collected. Use the following system of equations to determine the miles driven by each vehicle.

$$\begin{aligned} T + \quad C + \quad R &= 141.0 \\ 0.8T + 0.7C + 0.5R &= 82.7 \\ T + 0.9C + \quad 4R &= 424.4 \end{aligned}$$

39. In Chapter 8 you will learn about quadratic functions and their graphs. A quadratic function has the form $y = ax^2 + bx + c$, in which a, b, and c are specific numbers and $a \neq 0$. Three distinct points on the graph are enough to determine the equation.

(a) Suppose that (1, 5), (2, 10), and (3, 19) are on the graph of $y = ax^2 + bx + c$. Substituting the pair (1, 5) into this equation (that is, let $x = 1$ and $y = 5$) yields $5 = a + b + c$. Substituting each of the other ordered pairs yields $10 = 4a + 2b + c$ and $19 = 9a + 3b + c$. Solve the resulting system of equations to determine the values of a, b, and c. Then write the equation of the function.

(b) Repeat the work of part **(a)** using the following three points: (1, 2), (2, 9), and (3, 22).

Answers

1. (1, 2, 4) **3.** (−2, 1, 2) **5.** (−4, 3, 2)
7. Infinite number of solutions **9.** $\left(3, \frac{1}{2}, -\frac{7}{2}\right)$ **11.** (3, 2, −5)
13. (2, 0, −3) **15.** $\left(4, -\frac{1}{2}, \frac{3}{2}\right)$ **17.** Inconsistent system
19. $\left(2, \frac{5}{2}, -\frac{3}{2}\right)$ **21.** 3, 5, 8 **23.** 3 nickels, 5 dimes, 17 quarters
25. 4 cm, 7 cm, 8 cm
27. Savings: \$3,000, bond: \$9,000, money market: \$5,000
29. 243 **31.** Roy: 8 mi, Sally: 16 mi, Jeff: 26 mi **33.** (1, 2, −1, −2)
35. (7, 2) **37.** Trucks: 20 mi, cars: 25 mi, buses: 40 mi
39. (a) $y = 2x^2 - x + 4$; **(b)** $y = 3x^2 - 2x + 1$

4.3 Solving Systems of Linear Equations Using Matrices

< 4.3 Objectives >

1 > Write an augmented matrix

2 > Solve a system of linear equations by using matrices

NOTE

The credit for inventing matrices is generally given to the English mathematician Arthur Cayley (1821–1895).

Your work in this section will provide experience with another technique for solving systems of equations. Thus far we have considered the solution of linear systems by the algebraic methods of addition, substitution, and graphing. In this section we consider yet another approach to the solution of linear systems—the use of matrices. This solution technique can be easily extended to larger systems and so has particular significance in the computer solution of such systems. It is an abbreviated method of solving a system using elimination by addition. First, some definitions.

A **matrix** is a rectangular array of numbers. Each number in the matrix is called an **element** of the matrix. For example,

NOTE

The plural of *matrix* is *matrices.*

$$\begin{bmatrix} 2 & 3 & 1 \\ -1 & 3 & 2 \end{bmatrix}$$

is a matrix with elements 2, 3, 1, -1, 3, and 2. This matrix has two rows and three columns. It is called a 2×3 (read "2 by 3") matrix. We always give the number of rows and *then* the number of columns.

Now we will see how a matrix of numbers is associated with a system of linear equations. For the system of equations

NOTE

Brackets [ ] are used to enclose the elements of a matrix. You may also encounter the use of large parentheses to designate a matrix. In that case, the matrix would look like this:

$$\begin{pmatrix} 2 & 3 & 1 \\ -1 & 3 & 2 \end{pmatrix}$$

$$\begin{aligned} x - 2y &= -1 \\ 2x + y &= 8 \end{aligned}$$

the **coefficient matrix** is

$$\begin{matrix} x & y \end{matrix}$$
$$\begin{bmatrix} 1 & -2 \\ 2 & 1 \end{bmatrix}$$

The coefficient of x in the first equation is understood to be 1.
The coefficient of y in the second equation is understood to be 1.

The first column contains the x-coefficients in the system and the second column contains the y-coefficients.

The **constant matrix** is

$$\begin{bmatrix} -1 \\ 8 \end{bmatrix}$$

NOTE

The dotted vertical line is just for convenience, to separate the coefficients and the constants.

These are the constants corresponding to the equations in the system.

The matrix

$$\left[\begin{array}{cc:c} 1 & -2 & -1 \\ 2 & 1 & 8 \end{array}\right]$$

is called the **augmented matrix** of the system, and it is formed by adjoining the constant matrix to the coefficient matrix so that the matrix contains both the coefficients of the variables and the constants from the system. Notice that pairing the x- and y-variables with the first and second column values, respectively, and setting them equal to the corresponding values in the third column brings you back to the given system of equations.

Example 1 Writing an Augmented Matrix

< Objective 1 >

Write the augmented matrix for the given systems.

(a) $5x - 2y = 7$
$3x + 4y = 8$

The augmented matrix for the system is

$$\left[\begin{array}{cc|c} 5 & -2 & 7 \\ 3 & 4 & 8 \end{array}\right]$$

NOTE

Zero is used for the x-coefficient in the second equation.

(b) $2x - 3y = 9$
$y = 6$

The augmented matrix for the system is

$$\left[\begin{array}{cc|c} 2 & -3 & 9 \\ 0 & 1 & 6 \end{array}\right]$$

Check Yourself 1

Write the augmented matrices for each of the given systems.

(a) $3x - 5y = -2$
$2x + 3y = 5$

(b) $x - 3y = 3$
$y = 2$

NOTE

This form of the coefficient matrix is important. We have 1's along the *main diagonal* (from the upper left to the lower right) and 0's below that diagonal. This is often referred to as **echelon form.**

Your work in the Check Yourself 1(b) exercise led to a particular form of augmented matrix. The matrix

$$\left[\begin{array}{cc|c} 1 & -3 & 3 \\ 0 & 1 & 2 \end{array}\right]$$

is associated with the system

$$x - 3y = 3$$
$$y = 2$$

Given a system in this form, it is particularly easy to solve for the desired variables by a process called **back substitution.**

From the second equation we know that $y = 2$. Substituting that value back into the first equation, we have

$$x - 3(2) = 3$$
$$x - 6 = 3$$
$$x = 9$$

and (9, 2) is the solution for our system.

Our goal in this section will be to transform the augmented matrix of a given system to the form just illustrated, so that the solutions can be found easily by back substitution.

How do we go about transforming the augmented matrix? The rules are based on our earlier work with linear systems.

NOTE

Recall that an equivalent system has the same solutions as the original system.

An equivalent system is formed when

1. Two equations are interchanged.
2. An equation is multiplied by a nonzero constant.
3. An equation is replaced by adding a constant multiple of another equation to that equation.

Now each of these properties produces a corresponding property that can be applied to the rows of the augmented matrix rather than to the actual equations of the system. These are called the **elementary row operations,** and they will always produce the augmented matrix of an equivalent system of equations.

Property

Elementary Row Operations

1. Two rows can be interchanged.
2. A row can be multiplied by a nonzero constant.
3. A row can be replaced by adding a nonzero multiple of another row to that row.

We will now apply these elementary row operations to the solution of a linear system.

Example 2 Solving a System of Two Equations

< Objective 2 >

Solve the system, using elementary row operations.

$$2x - 3y = 2$$
$$x + 2y = 8$$

First, we write the augmented matrix of the given system:

$$\left[\begin{array}{cc|c} 2 & -3 & 2 \\ 1 & 2 & 8 \end{array}\right]$$

NOTES

Compare this form to the augmented matrix in our discussion of back substitution. In the coefficient matrix we want 1's along the main diagonal and 0's below.

The notation $R_1 \leftrightarrow R_2$ is an abbreviation indicating that we have interchanged those rows.

Think about our objective. We want to use back substitution to solve an equivalent system whose augmented matrix has the form

$$\left[\begin{array}{cc|c} 1 & a & b \\ 0 & 1 & c \end{array}\right]$$

To arrive at this form, we start with the first column. Interchanging the rows of the augmented matrix will give a 1 in the top position, as desired:

$$\left[\begin{array}{cc|c} 2 & -3 & 2 \\ 1 & 2 & 8 \end{array}\right] \xrightarrow{R_1 \leftrightarrow R_2} \left[\begin{array}{cc|c} 1 & 2 & 8 \\ 2 & -3 & 2 \end{array}\right]$$

Now multiply row 1 by -2 and add the result to row 2. This will give a 0 in the lower position of column 1.

$$\left[\begin{array}{cc|c} 1 & 2 & 8 \\ 2 & -3 & 2 \end{array}\right] \xrightarrow{-2R_1 + R_2} \left[\begin{array}{cc|c} 1 & 2 & 8 \\ 0 & -7 & -14 \end{array}\right]$$

NOTES

The notation $-2R_1 + R_2$ means R_2 has been replaced by the sum of -2 times row 1 and row 2.

The notation $-\frac{1}{7}R_2$ means we have multiplied row 2 by $-\frac{1}{7}$.

We now multiply row 2 by the constant $-\frac{1}{7}$, to produce a 1 in the second position of the second row:

$$\left[\begin{array}{cc|c} 1 & 2 & 8 \\ 0 & -7 & -14 \end{array}\right] \xrightarrow{-\frac{1}{7}R_2} \left[\begin{array}{cc|c} 1 & 2 & 8 \\ 0 & 1 & 2 \end{array}\right]$$

The final matrix is in the desired form with 1's along the main diagonal and 0's below. It represents the equivalent system

$$\begin{aligned} x + 2y &= 8 \\ y &= 2 \end{aligned}$$

and we can apply back substitution for our solution. Since $y = 2$, in the first equation, we have

$$\begin{aligned} x + 2(2) &= 8 \\ x &= 4 \end{aligned}$$

The solution for our system is (4, 2).

Check Yourself 2

Use elementary row operations to solve the system.

$$\begin{aligned} -3x - 2y &= -1 \\ x + 3y &= -9 \end{aligned}$$

We will extend our matrix approach to consider a system of three linear equations in three unknowns. Again our procedure is to find the augmented matrix of an equivalent system with 1's along the main diagonal of the coefficient matrix and 0's below that diagonal.

Example 3 Solving a System of Three Equations

Use elementary row operations to solve the system.

$$\begin{aligned} x - 2y + z &= 10 \\ -3x + y + 2z &= 5 \\ 2x + 3y - z &= -9 \end{aligned}$$

The augmented matrix for the system is

$$\left[\begin{array}{ccc|c} 1 & -2 & 1 & 10 \\ -3 & 1 & 2 & 5 \\ 2 & 3 & -1 & -9 \end{array}\right]$$

Again we start with the first column. The top entry is already 1, and we want 0's below that entry.

$$\xrightarrow{3R_1 + R_2} \left[\begin{array}{ccc|c} 1 & -2 & 1 & 10 \\ 0 & -5 & 5 & 35 \\ 2 & 3 & -1 & -9 \end{array}\right]$$

$$\xrightarrow{-2R_1 + R_3} \left[\begin{array}{ccc|c} 1 & -2 & 1 & 10 \\ 0 & -5 & 5 & 35 \\ 0 & 7 & -3 & -29 \end{array}\right]$$

NOTE

The order of obtaining the 1's and 0's should be followed carefully.

We now want a 1 in the center position of column 2 and a 0 below that 1:

$$\xrightarrow{-\frac{1}{5}R_2} \left[\begin{array}{ccc|c} 1 & -2 & 1 & 10 \\ 0 & 1 & -1 & -7 \\ 0 & 7 & -3 & -29 \end{array}\right]$$

$$\xrightarrow{-7R_2 + R_3} \left[\begin{array}{ccc|c} 1 & -2 & 1 & 10 \\ 0 & 1 & -1 & -7 \\ 0 & 0 & 4 & 20 \end{array}\right]$$

Finally, we want a 1 in the third position of the third column.

$$\xrightarrow{\frac{1}{4}R_3} \left[\begin{array}{ccc|c} 1 & -2 & 1 & 10 \\ 0 & 1 & -1 & -7 \\ 0 & 0 & 1 & 5 \end{array}\right]$$

The augmented matrix is now in the desired form and corresponds to the system

$$\begin{aligned} x - 2y + z &= 10 \\ y - z &= -7 \\ z &= 5 \end{aligned}$$

Substituting $z = 5$ in the second equation produces

$$\begin{aligned} y - 5 &= -7 \\ y &= -2 \end{aligned}$$

Substituting $y = -2$ and $z = 5$ in the first equation gives

$$\begin{aligned} x - 2(-2) + 5 &= 10 \\ x + 4 + 5 &= 10 \\ x + 9 &= 10 \\ x &= 1 \end{aligned}$$

and $(1, -2, 5)$ is the solution set for our system.

Check Yourself 3

Use elementary row operations to solve the system.

$$\begin{aligned} x + 2y - 4z &= -9 \\ 2x + 5y - 10z &= -21 \\ -3x - 5y + 11z &= 28 \end{aligned}$$

Will our work with matrices provide solutions for all linear systems? From your previous work with inconsistent and dependent systems, you should realize that the answer is no. Examples 4 and 5 illustrate.

Example 4 Solving a System Using Elementary Row Operations

Use elementary row operations to solve the system, if possible.

$$\begin{aligned} x + 2y &= 2 \\ -3x - 6y &= -5 \end{aligned}$$

The augmented matrix for the system is

$$\left[\begin{array}{cc|c} 1 & 2 & 2 \\ -3 & -6 & -5 \end{array}\right]$$

NOTE

In general, if we have a row with all 0's as coefficients and a nonzero constant on the right, the system is inconsistent.

Adding 3 times row 1 to row 2, we have

$$\xrightarrow{3R_1 + R_2} \left[\begin{array}{cc|c} 1 & 2 & 2 \\ 0 & 0 & 1 \end{array}\right]$$

Note that row 2 now gives $0x + 0y = 1$, which implies that $0 = 1$, a contradiction. This means that the given system is inconsistent. There are *no* solutions.

Check Yourself 4

Use elementary row operations to solve the system, if possible.

$$\begin{aligned} 2x - 4y &= 6 \\ -x + 2y &= -2 \end{aligned}$$

Example 5 considers one final case.

Example 5 Using Elementary Row Operations

Use elementary row operations to solve the system, if possible.

$$\begin{aligned} x - 4y &= 4 \\ 2x - 8y &= 8 \end{aligned}$$

The augmented matrix for this system is

$$\left[\begin{array}{cc|c} 1 & -4 & 4 \\ 2 & -8 & 8 \end{array}\right]$$

In this case we multiply row 1 by -2 and add that result to row 2:

$$\xrightarrow{-2R_1 + R_2} \left[\begin{array}{cc|c} 1 & -4 & 4 \\ 0 & 0 & 0 \end{array}\right]$$

The bottom row of 0's represents the statement

$$\begin{aligned} 0x + 0y &= 0 \\ 0 + 0 &= 0 \\ 0 &= 0 \end{aligned}$$

which is, of course, true for any values of x and y. This means that the original system was dependent and has an infinite number of solutions, in this case all values (x, y) that satisfy the equation $x - 4y = 4$.

Check Yourself 5

Use elementary row operations to solve the system, if possible.

$$\begin{aligned} 3x - 6y &= -9 \\ -x + 2y &= 3 \end{aligned}$$

Check Yourself ANSWERS

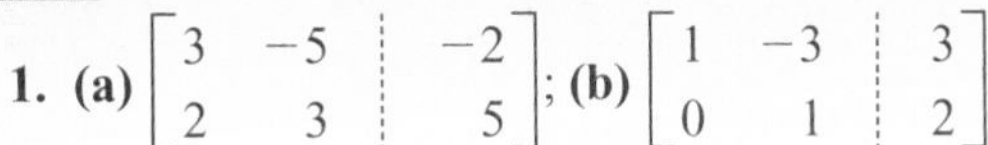

1. (a) $\left[\begin{array}{cc|c} 3 & -5 & -2 \\ 2 & 3 & 5 \end{array}\right]$; **(b)** $\left[\begin{array}{cc|c} 1 & -3 & 3 \\ 0 & 1 & 2 \end{array}\right]$

2. $(3, -4)$ **3.** $(-3, 5, 4)$ **4.** Inconsistent system; no solutions

5. Dependent system; infinite number of solutions

Reading Your Text

The following fill-in-the-blank exercises are designed to ensure that you understand some of the key vocabulary used in this section.

SECTION 4.3

(a) A matrix is a ____________________ array of numbers.

(b) Each number in the matrix is called an ______________ of the matrix.

(c) The matrix formed by adjoining the constant matrix to the coefficient matrix is called the ______________ matrix of the system.

(d) According to elementary row operations any two rows can be ______________.

4.3 exercises

Basic Skills | Advanced Skills | Vocational-Technical Applications | Calculator/Computer | Above and Beyond

MathZone

Boost your grade at mathzone.com!

- > Practice Problems
- > NetTutor
- > Self-Tests
- > e-Professors
- > Videos

Name ______________

Section ________ Date ________

Answers

1. See exercise
2. See exercise
3. See exercise
4. See exercise
5. See exercise
6. See exercise
7. $x + 2y = 3$; $x + 5y = -6$
8. $x + 2y = 3$; $-3x + y = -3$
9. $x + 3y = 5$; $y = 2$
10. $x - 2y = 4$; $y = 3$
11. $x + 2y = 4$; $y + 5z = 3$; $x + y + z = 1$
12. $x + 2y - z = 3$; $y + 4z = 1$; $z = -5$
13. (1, −2)
14. (−3, 2)
15. (5, −3)
16. (2, −6)
17. (2, −4)
18. (3, −4)

< Objective 1 >

Write the augmented matrix for each of the systems of equations.

1. $\begin{aligned} 2x - 3y &= 5 \\ x + 4y &= 2 \end{aligned}$ $\left[\begin{array}{cc|c} 2 & -3 & 5 \\ 1 & 4 & 2 \end{array}\right]$

2. $\begin{aligned} x + 5y &= 3 \\ -2x + y &= -1 \end{aligned}$ $\left[\begin{array}{cc|c} 1 & 5 & 3 \\ -2 & 1 & -1 \end{array}\right]$

3. $\begin{aligned} x - 5y &= 6 \\ y &= 2 \end{aligned}$ $\left[\begin{array}{cc|c} 1 & -5 & 6 \\ 0 & 1 & 2 \end{array}\right]$

4. $\begin{aligned} x + 3y &= 6 \\ y &= 3 \end{aligned}$ $\left[\begin{array}{cc|c} 1 & 3 & 6 \\ 0 & 1 & 3 \end{array}\right]$

5. $\begin{aligned} x + 2y - z &= 3 \\ x + 3z &= 1 \\ y - 2z &= 4 \end{aligned}$ $\left[\begin{array}{ccc|c} 1 & 2 & -1 & 3 \\ 1 & 0 & 3 & 1 \\ 0 & 1 & -2 & 4 \end{array}\right]$

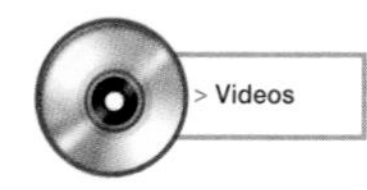

6. $\begin{aligned} x - 2y + 5z &= 3 \\ 3y - 2z &= 1 \\ z &= 4 \end{aligned}$ $\left[\begin{array}{ccc|c} 1 & -2 & 5 & 3 \\ 0 & 3 & -2 & 1 \\ 0 & 0 & 1 & 4 \end{array}\right]$

Write the systems of equations corresponding to each of the augmented matrices.

7. $\left[\begin{array}{cc|c} 1 & 2 & 3 \\ 1 & 5 & -6 \end{array}\right]$

8. $\left[\begin{array}{cc|c} 1 & 2 & 3 \\ -3 & 1 & -3 \end{array}\right]$

9. $\left[\begin{array}{cc|c} 1 & 3 & 5 \\ 0 & 1 & 2 \end{array}\right]$

10. $\left[\begin{array}{cc|c} 1 & -2 & 4 \\ 0 & 1 & 3 \end{array}\right]$

11. $\left[\begin{array}{ccc|c} 1 & 2 & 0 & 4 \\ 0 & 1 & 5 & 3 \\ 1 & 1 & 1 & 1 \end{array}\right]$

12. $\left[\begin{array}{ccc|c} 1 & 2 & -1 & 3 \\ 0 & 1 & 4 & 1 \\ 0 & 0 & 1 & -5 \end{array}\right]$

< Objective 2 >

Solve each of the systems, using elementary row operations.

13. $\begin{aligned} x + 3y &= -5 \\ 2x + y &= 0 \end{aligned}$

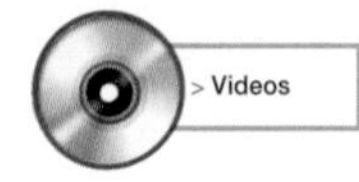

14. $\begin{aligned} x - 3y &= -9 \\ -3x + y &= 11 \end{aligned}$

15. $\begin{aligned} x - 5y &= 20 \\ -4x + 3y &= -29 \end{aligned}$

16. $\begin{aligned} x + 2y &= -10 \\ 5x - y &= 16 \end{aligned}$

17. $\begin{aligned} 3x - 2y &= 14 \\ x + 5y &= -18 \end{aligned}$

18. $\begin{aligned} 4x + 3y &= 0 \\ x + 5y &= -17 \end{aligned}$

19. $\begin{aligned} 5x + 3y &= 11 \\ -x - 2y &= 2 \end{aligned}$

20. $\begin{aligned} 6x - y &= 24 \\ -x + 3y &= 13 \end{aligned}$

21. $\begin{aligned} x - 3y &= 5 \\ -4x + 12y &= -18 \end{aligned}$

22. $\begin{aligned} -3x + 6y &= -15 \\ x - 2y &= 5 \end{aligned}$

Solve each of the systems, using elementary row operations.

23. $\begin{aligned} x + y - z &= -1 \\ -3y + 2z &= 6 \\ 2x + 3z &= 2 \end{aligned}$

24. $\begin{aligned} x + 2y &= -3 \\ x + 3y - 6z &= -9 \\ 2x - 3z &= 0 \end{aligned}$

25. $\begin{aligned} x - z &= 2 \\ 2x - y + z &= 3 \\ y - 2z &= -2 \end{aligned}$

26. $\begin{aligned} x - 2y + 5z &= 10 \\ -3x + 4y &= -12 \\ x + z &= 3 \end{aligned}$

27. $\begin{aligned} x - z &= 6 \\ x + 2y + z &= -7 \\ 2x - y + 2z &= 1 \end{aligned}$

28. $\begin{aligned} x + 2y + 3z &= 1 \\ -2x - 3y - 4z &= -1 \\ y + 3z &= 3 \end{aligned}$

29. $\begin{aligned} x + 2y + 3z &= 1 \\ x + 3y + z &= 2 \\ 3x + 2y + z &= -1 \end{aligned}$

30. $\begin{aligned} 2x + 2y + z &= 3 \\ 3x + 2y + 2z &= 7 \\ x + y + z &= 2 \end{aligned}$

Answers

1. $\left[\begin{array}{cc|c} 2 & -3 & 5 \\ 1 & 4 & 2 \end{array}\right]$
3. $\left[\begin{array}{cc|c} 1 & -5 & 6 \\ 0 & 1 & 2 \end{array}\right]$
5. $\left[\begin{array}{ccc|c} 1 & 2 & -1 & 3 \\ 1 & 0 & 3 & 1 \\ 0 & 1 & -2 & 4 \end{array}\right]$
7. $\begin{aligned} x + 2y &= 3 \\ x + 5y &= -6 \end{aligned}$
9. $\begin{aligned} x + 3y &= 5 \\ y &= 2 \end{aligned}$
11. $\begin{aligned} x + 2y &= 4 \\ y + 5z &= 3 \\ x + y + z &= 1 \end{aligned}$
13. $(1, -2)$
15. $(5, -3)$ 17. $(2, -4)$ 19. $(4, -3)$
21. Inconsistent system; no solutions 23. $(1, -2, 0)$ 25. $(-1, -8, -3)$
27. $\left(\frac{5}{2}, -3, -\frac{7}{2}\right)$ 29. $(-1, 1, 0)$

Answers

19. $(4, -3)$
20. $(5, 6)$
21. Inconsistent; no solutions
22. Dependent; infinite number of solutions
23. $(1, -2, 0)$
24. $\left(1, -2, \frac{2}{3}\right)$
25. $(-1, -8, -3)$
26. $\left(2, -\frac{3}{2}, 1\right)$
27. $\left(\frac{5}{2}, -3, -\frac{7}{2}\right)$
28. $(1, -3, 2)$
29. $(-1, 1, 0)$
30. $(3, -2, 1)$

4.4 Graphing Systems of Linear Inequalities in Two Variables

< 4.4 Objectives >

1 > Solve a system of linear inequalities in two variables

2 > Solve an application of a system of linear inequalities

In Section 4.1, we dealt with finding the solution set of a system of linear equations. That solution represented the points of intersection of the graphs of the equations in the system. In this section, we extend that idea to include systems of linear inequalities.

In this case, the solution is the set of all ordered pairs that satisfy each inequality. **The graph of the solution of a system of linear inequalities** is then the intersection of the graphs of the individual inequalities. Let us look at an example.

Example 1 Solving a System by Graphing

< Objective 1 >

NOTES

The boundary line is dashed to indicate that points on the line do *not* represent solutions.

Points on the lines are not included in the solution.

Solve the following system of linear inequalities by graphing

$x + y > 4$

$x - y < 2$

We start by graphing each inequality (as discussed in Section 3.5) separately. The boundary line is drawn, and using (0, 0) as a test point, we see that we should shade the half-plane above the line in both graphs.

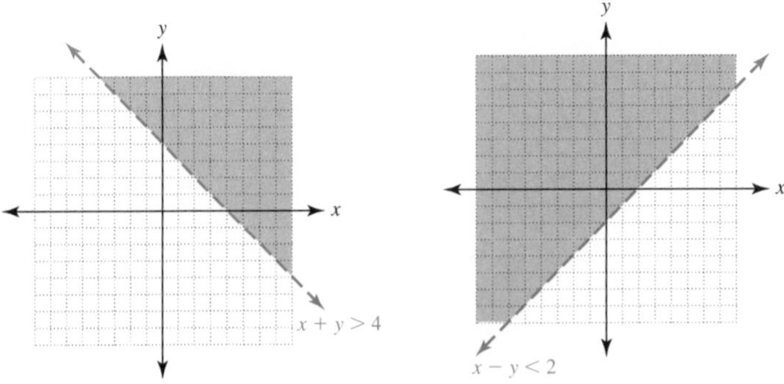

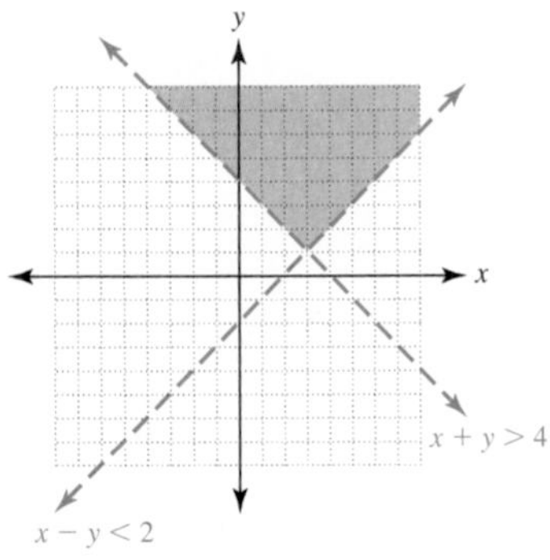

In practice, the graphs of the two inequalities are combined on the same set of axes, as is shown to the left. The graph of the solution of the original system is the intersection of the graphs of the two inequalities.

Check Yourself 1

Solve the following system of linear inequalities by graphing.

$2x - y < 4$
$x + y < 3$

Most applications of systems of linear inequalities lead to **bounded regions.** This requires a system of three or more inequalities, as shown in Example 2.

Example 2 Solving a System by Graphing

Solve the following system of linear inequalities by graphing.

$x + 2y \leq 6$
$x + y \leq 5$
$x \geq 2$
$y \geq 0$

NOTE

The vertices of the shaded region are given because they have particular significance in later applications of this concept. Can you see how the coordinates of the vertices were determined?

On the same set of axes, we graph the boundary line of each of the inequalities. We then choose the appropriate half-planes (indicated by the arrow that is perpendicular to the line) in each case, and we locate the intersection of these regions for our graph.

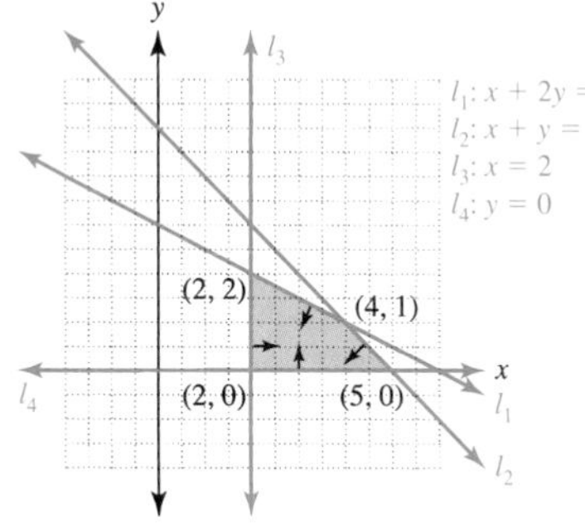

Check Yourself 2

Solve the following system of linear inequalities by graphing.

$2x - y \leq 8 \qquad x \geq 0$
$x + y \leq 7 \qquad y \geq 0$

Let us look at an application of our work with systems of linear inequalities. Consider Example 3.

Example 3 Solving a Business-Based Application

< Objective 2 >

A manufacturer produces a standard model and a deluxe model of a 25-in. television set. The standard model requires 12 h of labor to produce, and the deluxe model requires 18 h. The labor available is limited to 360 h per week. Also, the plant capacity is limited to producing a total of 25 sets per week. Draw a graph of the region representing the number of sets that can be produced, given these conditions.

As suggested earlier, we let x represent the number of standard-model sets produced and y the number of deluxe-model sets. Because the labor is limited to 360 h, we have

NOTE

The total labor is limited to (or less than or equal to) 360 h.

$$12x + 18y \le 360$$

12 h per standard set (for $12x$); 18 h per deluxe set (for $18y$)

The total production, here $x + y$ sets, is limited to 25, so we can write

$$x + y \le 25$$

For convenience in graphing, we divide both sides of the initial inequality by 6, to write the equivalent system

NOTE

We have $x \ge 0$ and $y \ge 0$ because the number of sets produced cannot be negative.

$$\begin{aligned} 2x + 3y &\le 60 \\ x + y &\le 25 \\ x &\ge 0 \\ y &\ge 0 \end{aligned}$$

We now graph the system of inequalities as before. The shaded area represents all possibilities in terms of the number of sets that can be produced.

NOTE

The shaded area is called the **feasible region.** All points in the region meet the given conditions of the problem and represent possible production options.

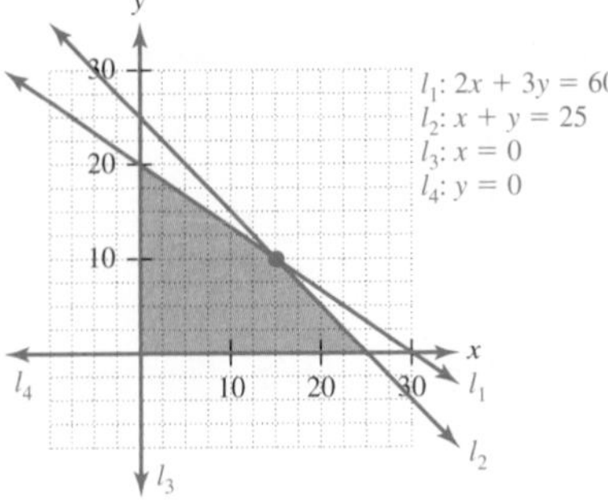

Check Yourself 3

A manufacturer produces TVs and CD players. The TVs require 10 h of labor to produce and the CD players require 20 h. The labor hours available are limited to 300 h per week. Existing orders require that at least 10 TVs and at least 5 CD players be produced per week. Draw a graph of the region representing the possible production options.

Check Yourself ANSWERS

1. $2x - y < 4$
   $x + y < 3$

2. $2x - y \leq 8$
   $x + y \leq 7$
   $x \geq 0$
   $y \geq 0$

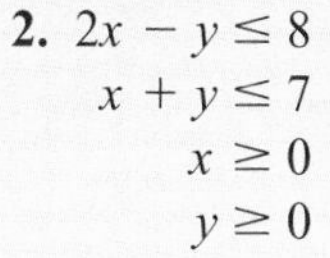

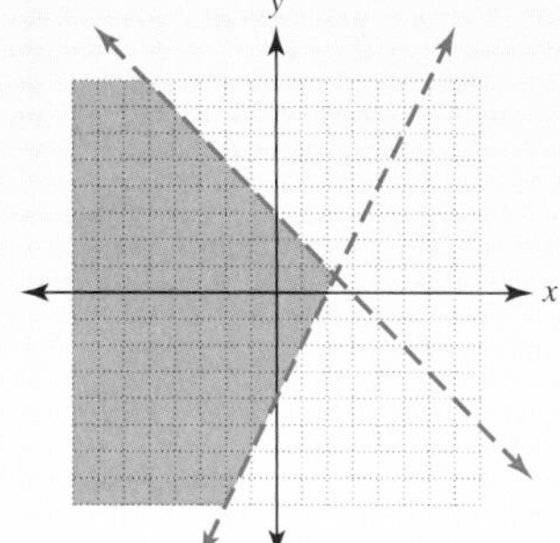

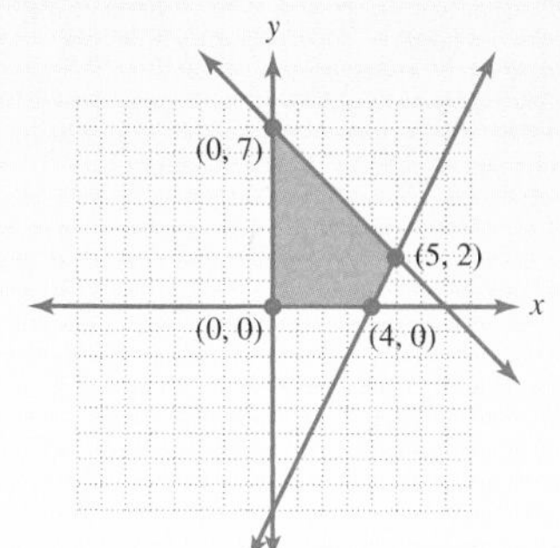

3. Let x be the number of TVs and y be the number of CD players. The system is

$$10x + 20y \leq 300$$
$$x \geq 10$$
$$y \geq 5$$

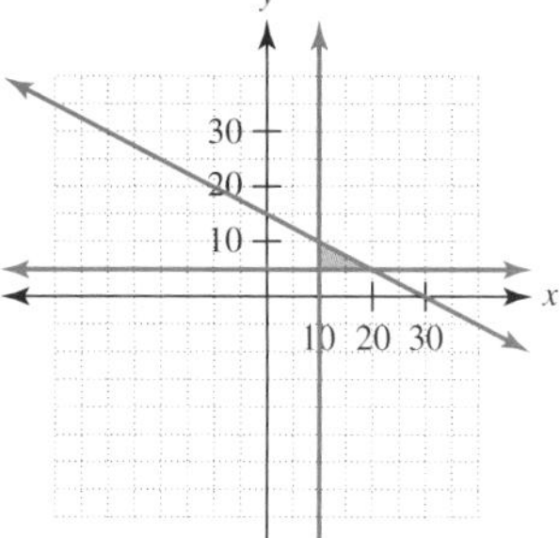

Reading Your Text

The following fill-in-the-blank exercises are designed to ensure that you understand some of the key vocabulary used in this section.

SECTION 4.4

(a) The graph of the solution of a system of linear inequalities is the ______________ of the graphs of the individual inequalities.

(b) The boundary line is ______________ to indicate it is not included in the graph.

(c) Most applications of systems of linear inequalities lead to ____________ regions.

(d) The shaded area in an application problem is called the ____________ region.

4.4 exercises

Basic Skills | Advanced Skills | Vocational-Technical Applications | Calculator/Computer | Above and Beyond

MathZone

Boost your grade at mathzone.com!
- > Practice Problems
- > NetTutor
- > Self-Tests
- > e-Professors
- > Videos

Name ____________

Section ________ Date ________

Answers

1. See exercise
2. See exercise
3. See exercise
4. See exercise
5. See exercise
6. See exercise
7. See exercise
8. See exercise

< Objective 1 >

In exercises 1 to 18, solve each system of linear inequalities by graphing.

1. $x + 2y \leq 4$
$x - y \geq 1$

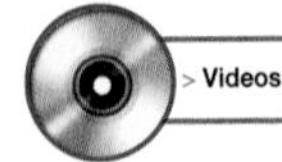

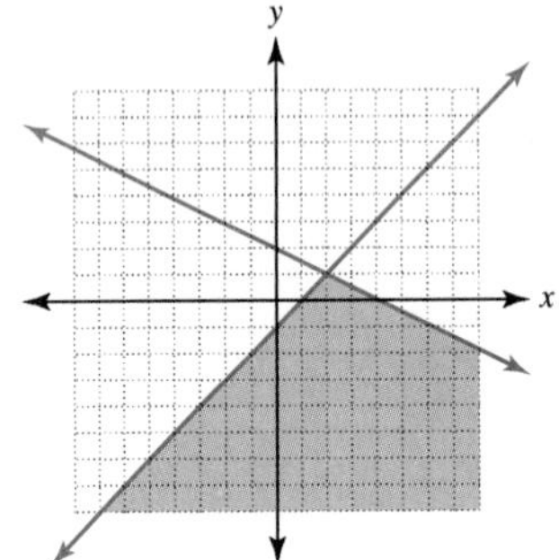

2. $3x - y > 6$
$x + y < 6$

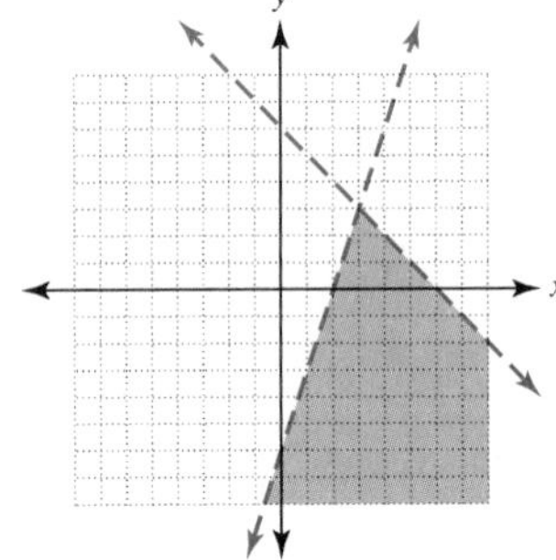

3. $3x + y < 6$
$x + y > 4$

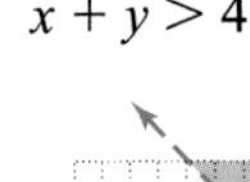

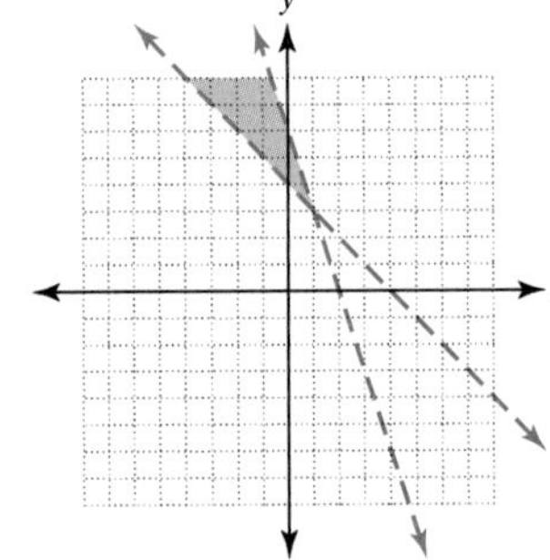

4. $2x + y \geq 8$
$x + y \geq 4$

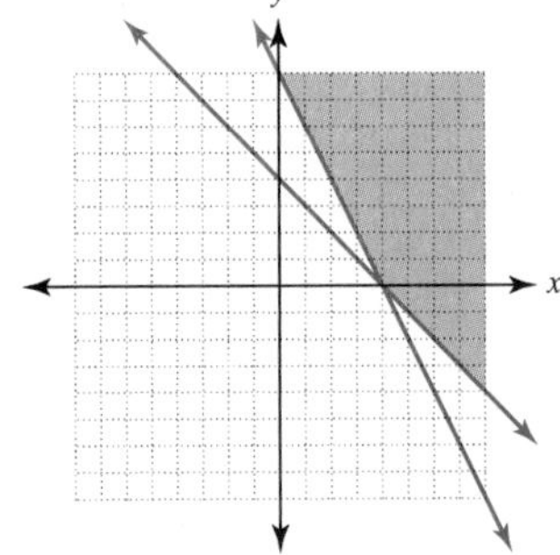

5. $x + 3y \leq 12$
$2x - 3y \leq 6$

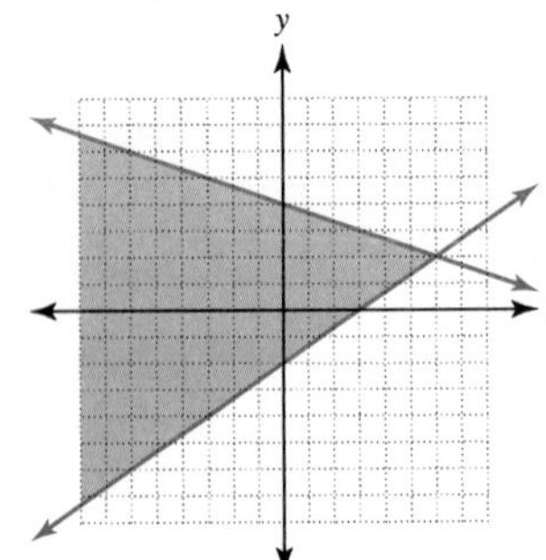

6. $x - 2y > 8$
$3x - 2y > 12$

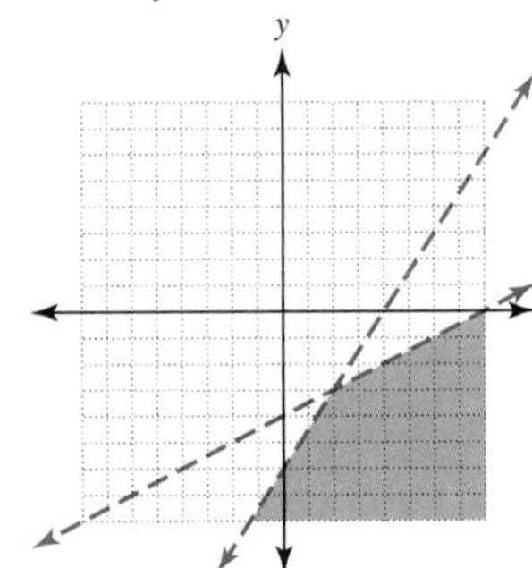

7. $3x + 2y \leq 12$
$x \geq 2$

> Videos

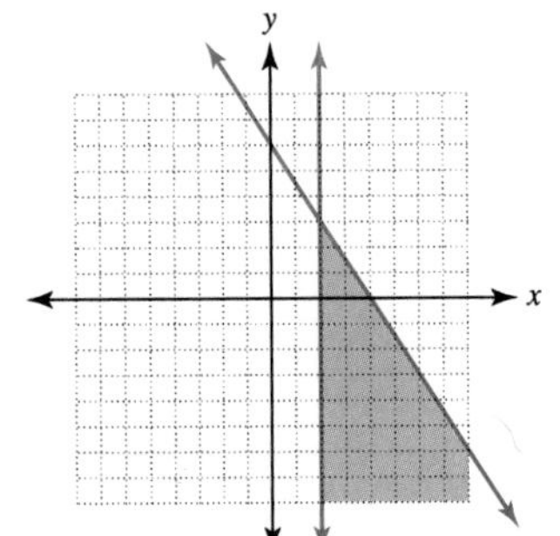

8. $2x + y \leq 6$
$y \geq 1$

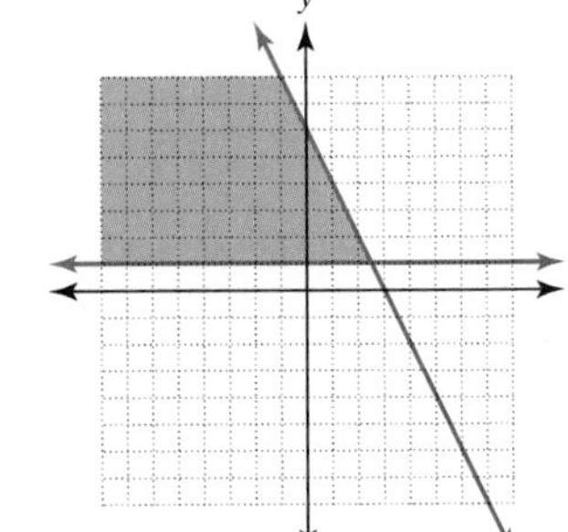

9. $2x + y < 8$
$x > 1$
$y > 2$

> Videos

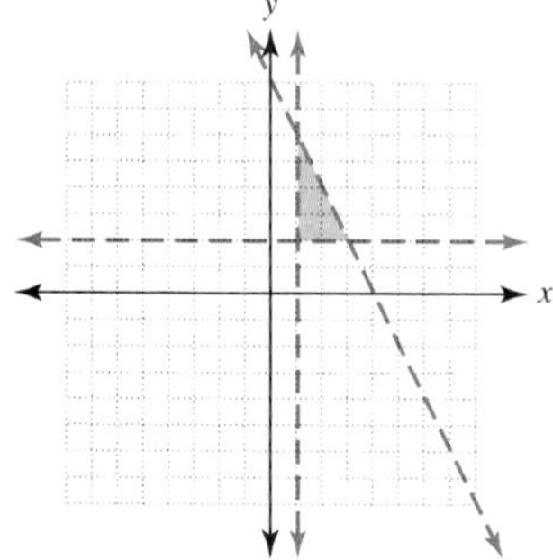

10. $3x - y \le 6$
$x \ge 1$
$y \le 3$

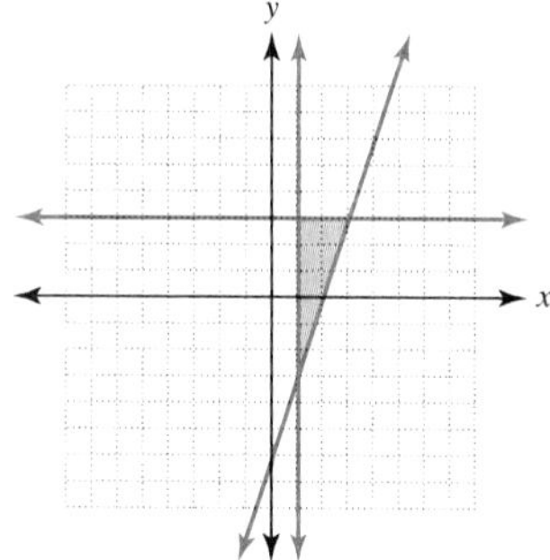

11. $x + 2y \le 8$
$2 \le x \le 6$
$y \ge 0$

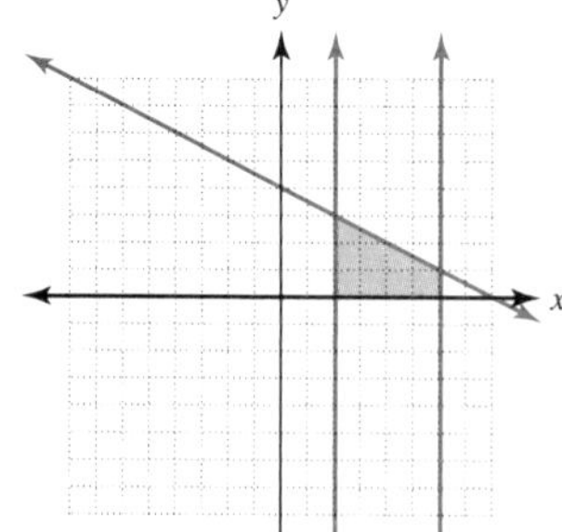

12. $x + y < 6$
$0 \le y \le 3$
$x \ge 1$

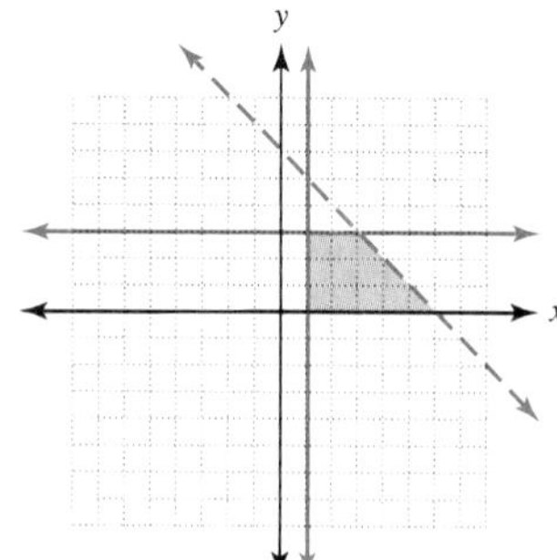

13. $3x + y \le 6$
$x + y \le 4$
$x \ge 0$
$y \ge 0$

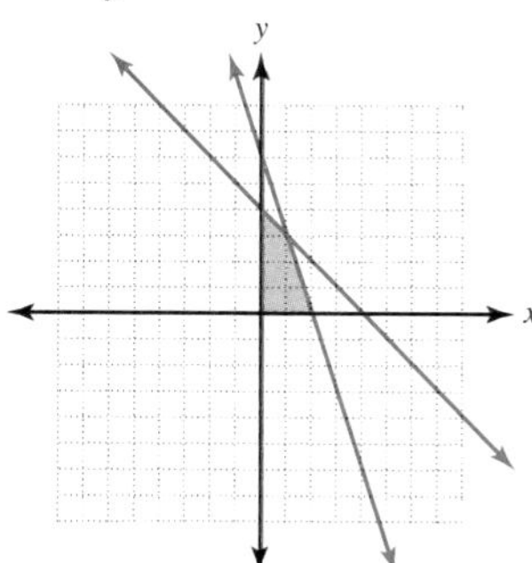

14. $x - 2y \ge -2$
$x + 2y \le 6$
$x \ge 0$
$y \ge 0$

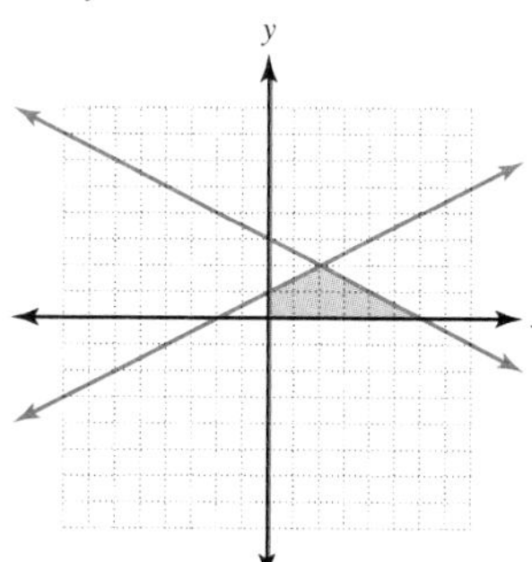

15. $4x + 3y \le 12$
$x + 4y \le 8$
$x \ge 0$
$y \ge 0$

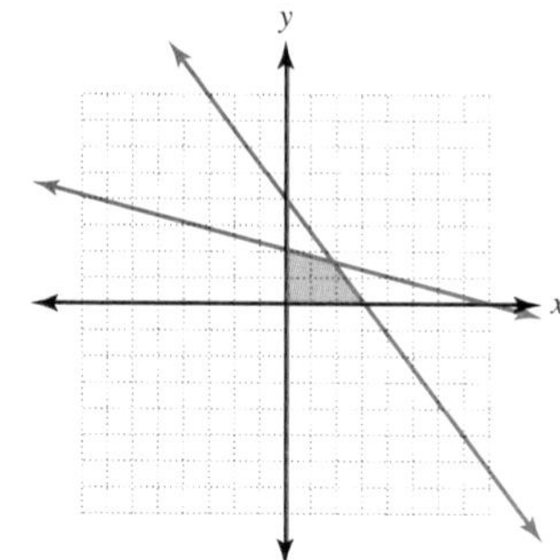

16. $2x + y \le 8$
$x + y \ge 3$
$x \ge 0$
$y \ge 0$

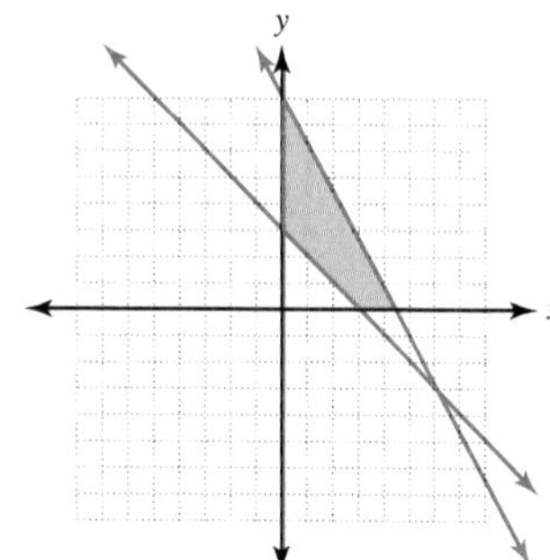

Answers

9. See exercise

10. See exercise

11. See exercise

12. See exercise

13. See exercise

14. See exercise

15. See exercise

16. See exercise

Answers

17. See exercise

18. See exercise

19. See exercise

20. See exercise

17. $x - 4y \leq -4$
$x + 2y \leq 8$
$x \geq 2$

> Videos

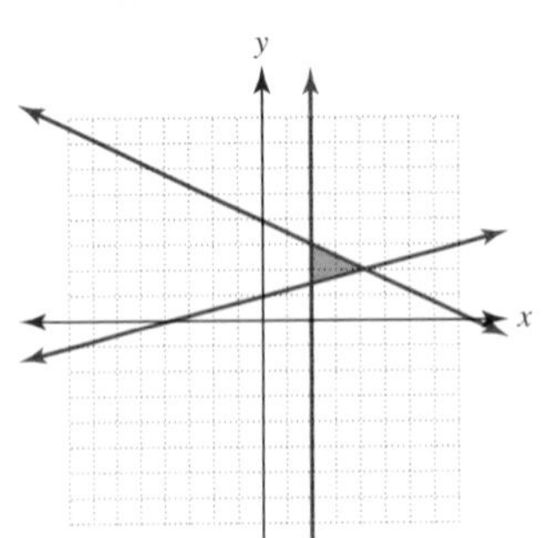

18. $x - 3y \geq -6$
$x + 2y \geq 4$
$x \leq 4$

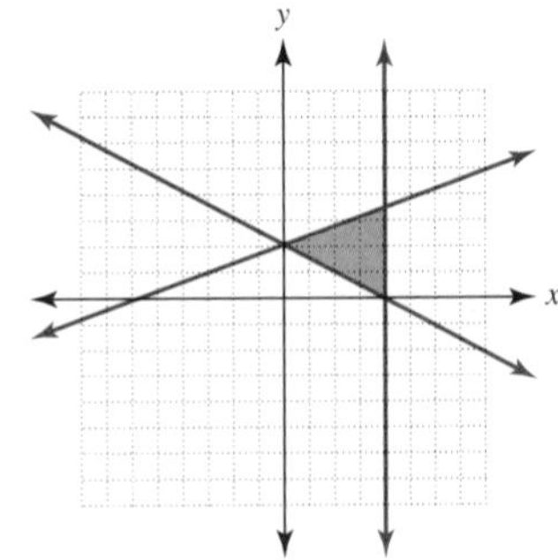

< Objective 2 >

In exercises 19 and 20, draw the appropriate graph.

19. **Business and Finance** A manufacturer produces both two-slice and four-slice toasters. The two-slice toaster takes 6 h of labor to produce and the four-slice toaster 10 h. The labor available is limited to 300 h per week, and the total production capacity is 40 toasters per week. Draw a graph of the feasible region, given these conditions, in which x is the number of two-slice toasters and y is the number of four-slice toasters.

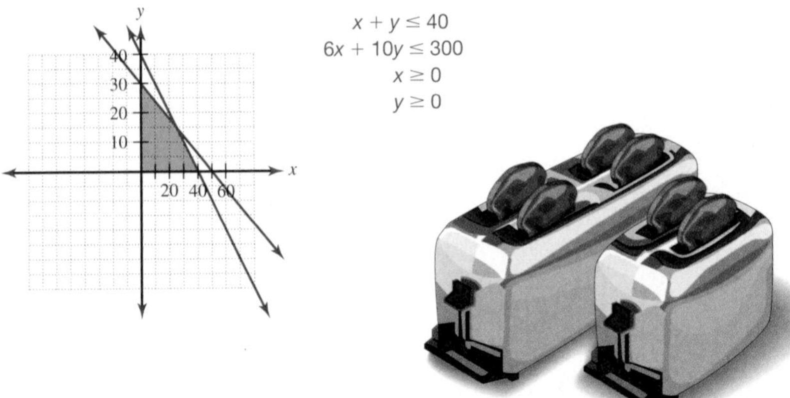

$x + y \leq 40$
$6x + 10y \leq 300$
$x \geq 0$
$y \geq 0$

20. **Business and Finance** A small firm produces both AM and AM/FM car radios. The AM radios take 15 h to produce, and the AM/FM radios take 20 h. The number of production hours is limited to 300 h per week. The plant's capacity is limited to a total of 18 radios per week, and existing orders require that at least 4 AM radios and at least 3 AM/FM radios be produced per week. Draw a graph of the feasible region, given these conditions, in which x is the number of AM radios and y the number of AM/FM radios.

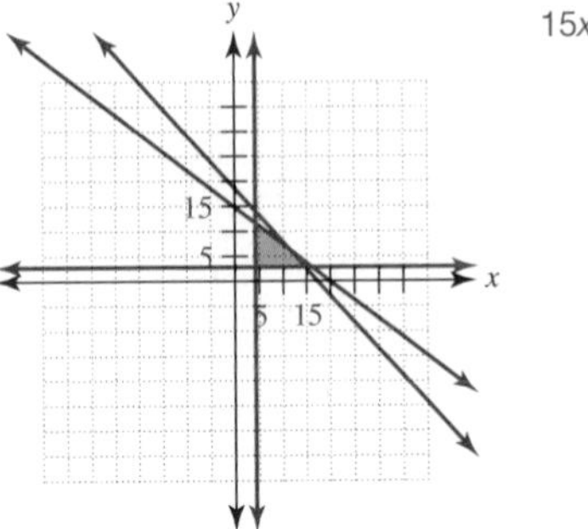

$15x + 20y \leq 300$
$x + y \leq 18$
$x \geq 4$
$y \geq 3$

Basic Skills | Advanced Skills | Vocational-Technical Applications | Calculator/Computer | **Above and Beyond**

21. When you solve a system of linear inequalities, it is often easier to shade the region that is not part of the solution, rather than the region that is. Try this method and then describe its benefits.

22. Describe a system of linear inequalities for which there is no solution.

23. Write the system of inequalities whose graph is the shaded region.

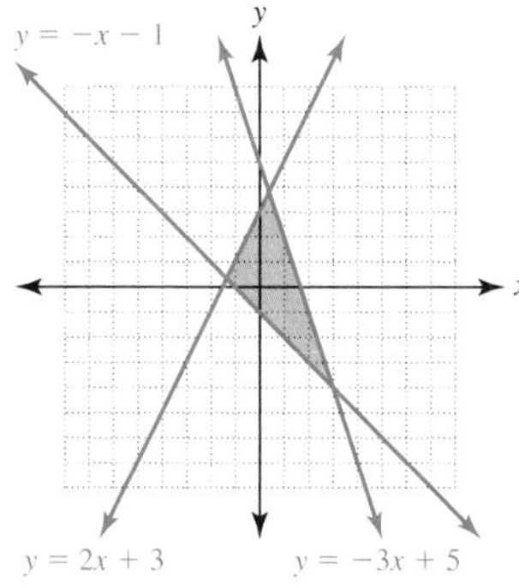

24. Write the system of inequalities whose graph is the shaded region.

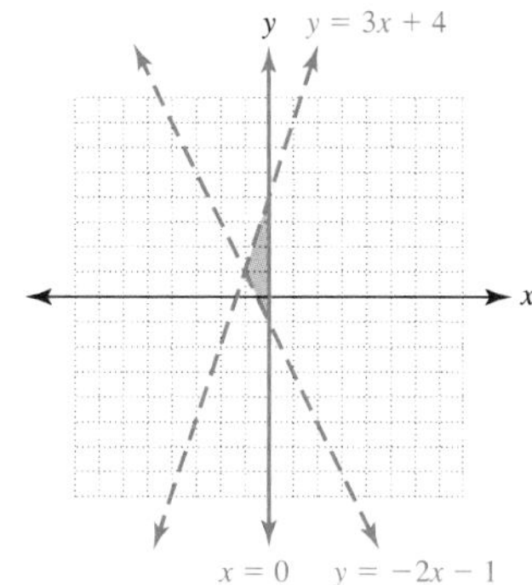

Answers

1.

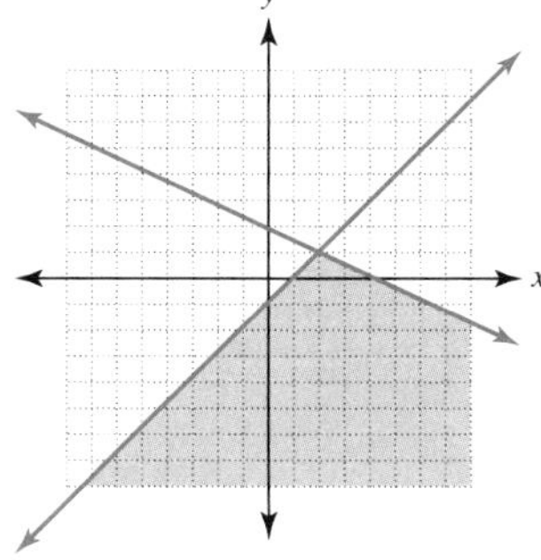

3.

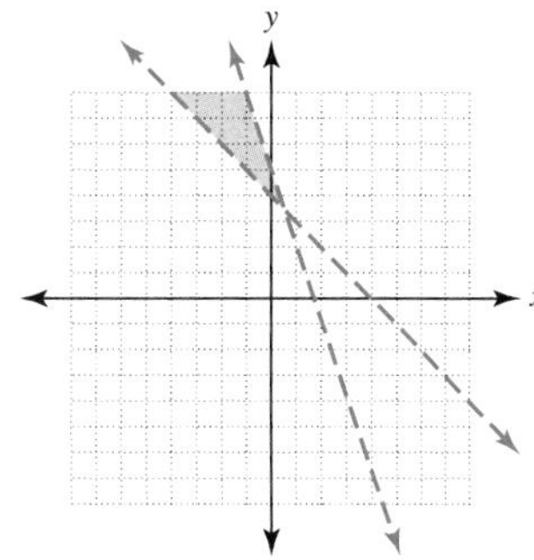

5.

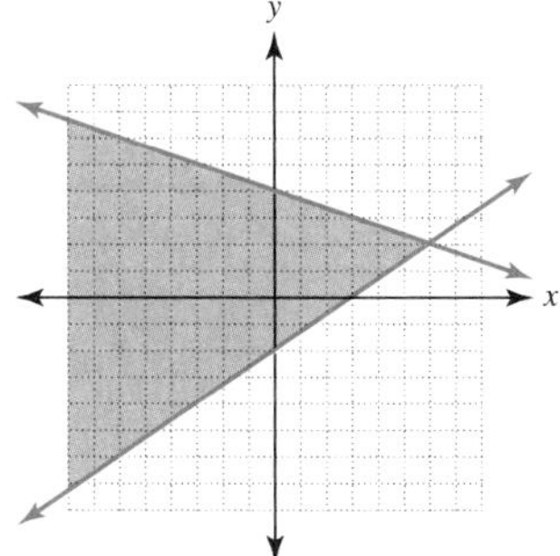

7.

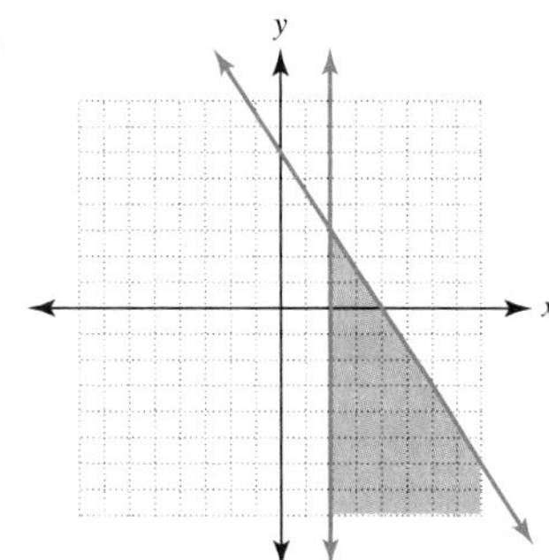

Answers

21. Above and Beyond

22. Above and Beyond

23. $y \le 2x + 3$
$y \le -3x + 5$
$y \ge -x - 1$

24. $x \le 0$
$y < 3x + 4$
$y > -2x - 1$

9.

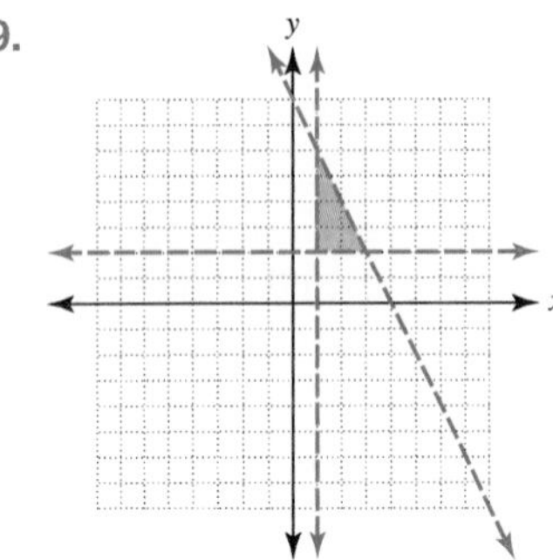

11.

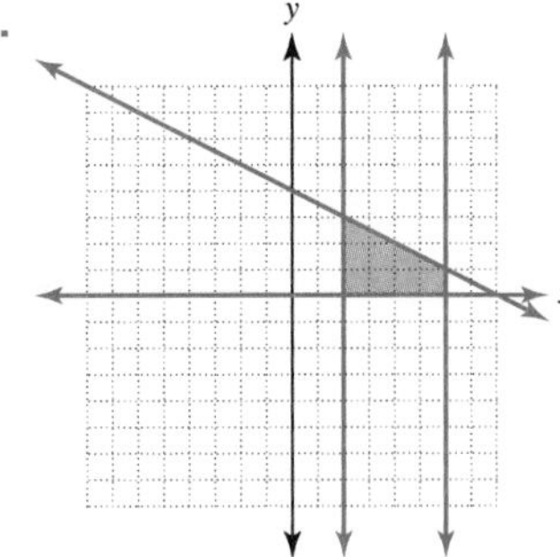

13.

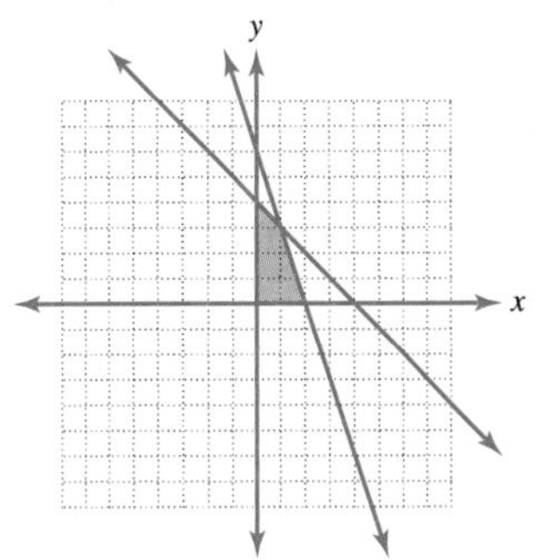

15.

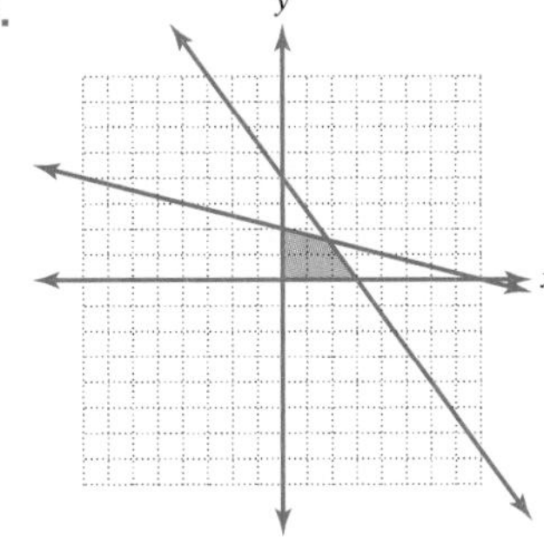

17.

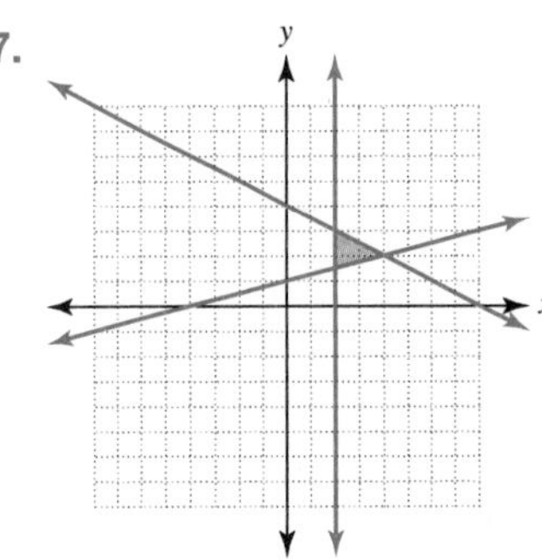

19.
$$x + y \le 40$$
$$6x + 10y \le 300$$
$$x \ge 0$$
$$y \ge 0$$

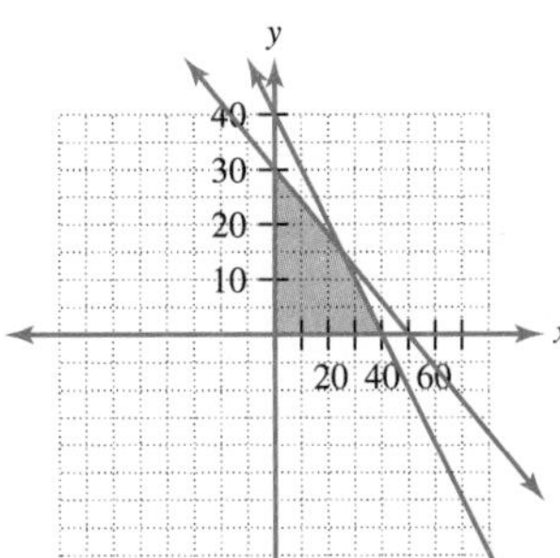

21. Above and Beyond

23.
$$y \le 2x + 3$$
$$y \le -3x + 5$$
$$y \ge -x - 1$$

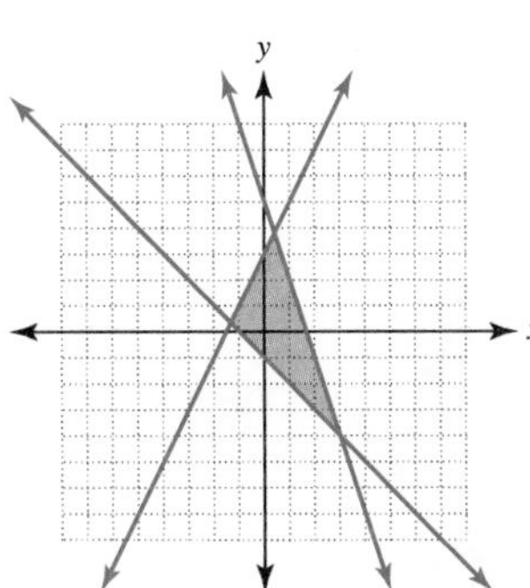

Definition/Procedure	Example	Reference

Systems of Linear Equations in Two Variables

Section 4.1

A **system of linear equations** is two or more linear equations considered together. A solution for a linear system in two variables is an ordered pair of real numbers (x, y) that satisfies both equations in the system.

There are three solution techniques: the graphing method, the addition method, and the substitution method.

The solution for the system

$$2x - y = 7$$
$$x + y = 2$$

is $(3, -1)$. It is the only ordered pair that will satisfy each equation.

p. 331

Solving by the Graphing Method

Graph each equation of the system on the same set of coordinate axes. If a solution exists, it will correspond to the point of intersection of the two lines. Such a system is called a **consistent system.** If a solution does not exist, there is no point at which the two lines intersect. Such lines are parallel, and the system is called an **inconsistent system.** If there are an infinite number of solutions, the lines coincide. Such a system is called a **dependent system.** You may or may not be able to determine exact solutions for the system of equations with this method.

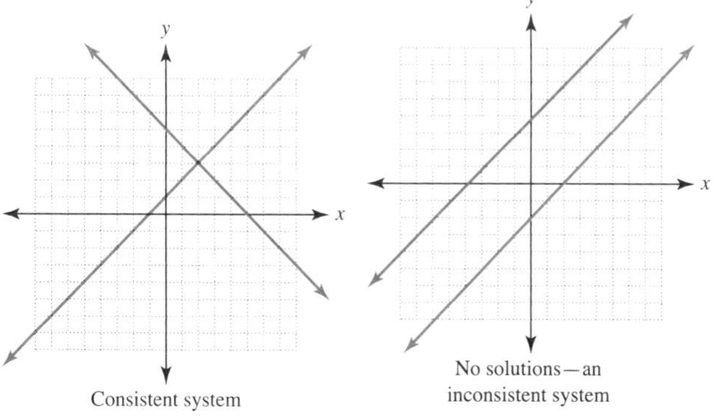

Consistent system

No solutions—an inconsistent system

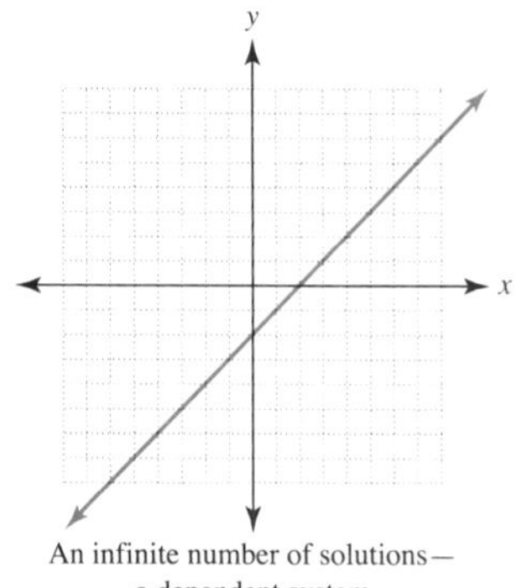

An infinite number of solutions—a dependent system

To solve

$$2x - y = 7$$
$$x + y = 2$$

by graphing

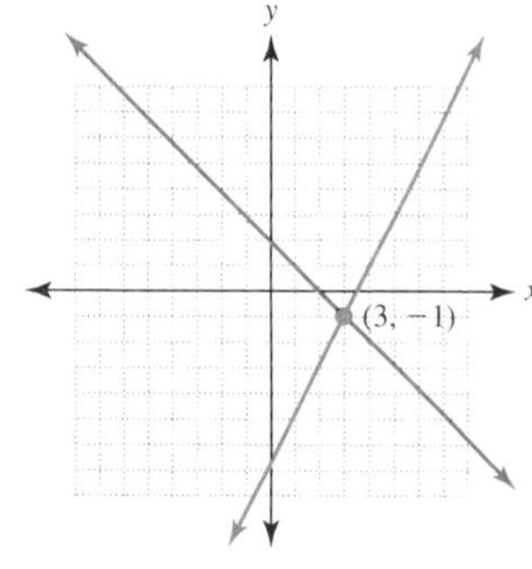

pp. 332–335

Continued

Definition/Procedure	Example	Reference
Solving by the Addition Method		
Step 1 If necessary, multiply one or both of the equations by a constant so that one of the variables can be eliminated by addition. **Step 2** Add the equations of the equivalent system formed in step 1. **Step 3** Solve the equation found in step 2. **Step 4** Substitute the value found in step 3 into either of the equations of the original system to find the corresponding value of the remaining variable. The ordered pair formed is the solution to the system. **Step 5** Check the solution by substituting the pair of values found in step 4 into the other equation of the original system.	To solve $5x - 2y = 11$ $2x + 3y = 12$ Multiply the first equation by 3 and the second equation by 2. Then add to eliminate y. $19x = 57$ $x = 3$ Substituting 3 for x in the first equation, we have $15 - 2y = 11$ $y = 2$ (3, 2) is the solution.	*p.* 338
Solving by the Substitution Method **Step 1** If necessary, solve one of the equations of the original system for one of the variables. **Step 2** Substitute the expression obtained in step 1 into the *other* equation of the system to write an equation in a single variable. **Step 3** Solve the equation found in step 2. **Step 4** Substitute the value found in step 3 into the equation derived in step 1 to find the corresponding value of the remaining variable. The ordered pair formed is the solution for the system. **Step 5** Check the solution by substituting the pair of values found in step 4 into *both* equations of the original system.	To solve $3x - 2y = 6$ $6x + y = 2$ by substitution, solve the second equation for y. $y = -6x + 2$ Substituting in the first equation gives $3x - 2(-6x + 2) = 6$ and $x = \frac{2}{3}$ Substituting $\frac{2}{3}$ for x in $y = -6x + 2$ gives $y = (-6)\left(\frac{2}{3}\right) + 2$ $= -4 + 2 = -2$ The solution is $\left(\frac{2}{3}, -2\right)$	*p.* 341

Definition/Procedure	Example	Reference
Applications of Systems of Linear Equations		
1. Read the problem carefully to determine the unknown quantities.	Also determine the condition that relates the unknown quantities.	p. 342
2. Choose a variable to represent any unknown. **3.** Translate the problem to the language of algebra to form a system of equations.	Use a different letter for each variable.	
4. Solve the system of equations by any of the methods discussed, and answer the question in the original problem. **5.** Verify your solution by returning to the original problem.	A table or a sketch often helps in writing the equations of the system.	
Systems of Linear Equations in Three Variables		**Section 4.2**
A solution for a linear system of three equations in three variables is an ordered triple of numbers (x, y, z) that satisfies each equation in the system. *Solving a System of Three Equations in Three Unknowns* **Step 1** Choose a pair of equations from the system, and use the addition method to eliminate one of the variables. **Step 2** Choose a different pair of equations, and eliminate the same variable. **Step 3** Solve the system of two equations in two variables determined in steps 1 and 2. **Step 4** Substitute the values found in step 3 into one of the original equations, and solve for the remaining variable. **Step 5** The solution is the ordered triple of values found in steps 3 and 4. It can be checked by substituting into the other equations of the original system.	To solve $x + y - z = 6$ $2x - 3y + z = -9$ $3x + y + 2z = 2$ Adding the first two equations gives $3x - 2y = -3$ Multiplying the first equation by 2 and adding the result to the third equation gives $5x + 3y = 14$ The system consisting of the two resultant equations is solved as before and $x = 1 \quad y = 3$ Substituting these values into the first given equation gives $z = -2$ The solution is $(1, 3, -2)$.	pp. 363, 366
Solving Systems of Linear Equations Using Matrices		**Section 4.3**
A **matrix** is a rectangular array of numbers. A system of linear equations can be translated to an augmented matrix. Using elementary row operations (see following section) on the augmented matrix results in an equivalent system that can be solved by back substitution yielding a solution to the original system.	To solve $3x - 4y = 8$ $x - 2y = 4$ Augmented matrix $\left[\begin{array}{cc\|c} 3 & -4 & 8 \\ 1 & -2 & 4 \end{array}\right]$ x-coefficients; y-coefficients; Constants	p. 375

Continued

Definition/Procedure	Example	Reference

Elementary Row Operations

1. Two rows can be interchanged.
2. A row can be multiplied by a nonzero constant.
3. A row can be replaced by adding a nonzero multiple of another row to that row.

Use elementary row operations.

$$\left[\begin{array}{cc|c} 1 & -2 & 4 \\ 3 & -4 & 8 \end{array}\right]$$ Exchange the two rows.

$$\left[\begin{array}{cc|c} -3 & 6 & -12 \\ 3 & -4 & 8 \end{array}\right]$$ Multiply first row by -3 then add to second row

$$\left[\begin{array}{cc|c} 1 & -2 & -4 \\ 0 & 2 & -4 \end{array}\right]$$ First row / New second row

$$\left[\begin{array}{cc|c} 1 & -2 & 4 \\ 0 & 1 & -2 \end{array}\right]$$ Multiply second row by $\frac{1}{2}$.

p. 377

We want 1 as the element in the first row, first column.

We want an equivalent to the first row to add to the second row to obtain a 0 below the 1.

We want a 1 as the second element in row 2. This yields a main diagonal made up of 1's with 0's below the 1's.

This form of the matrix produces a solution for one of the variables in the system and subsequently the remaining variable(s) by back substitution.

$$\left[\begin{array}{cc|c} 1 & a & b \\ 0 & 1 & c \end{array}\right]$$ A 2×2 system / Main diagonal is all 1's.

Rewrite the system with variables.

$$x - 2y = 4$$
$$y = -2$$

Back substitute the -2 for y and solve for x.

$$x - 2(-2) = 4$$
$$x + 4 = 4$$
$$x = 0$$

The solution to the system is $(0, -2)$.

p. 377

Graphing Systems of Linear Inequalities in Two Variables

Section 4.4

A **system of linear inequalities** is two or more linear inequalities considered together. The **graph of the solution** of a system of linear inequalities is the intersection of the graphs of the individual inequalities.

To solve

$$x + 2y \le 8$$
$$x + y \le 6$$
$$x \ge 0$$
$$y \ge 0$$

by graphing

p. 384

Solving Systems of Linear Inequalities by Graphing

1. Graph each inequality, shading the appropriate half-plane, on the same set of coordinate axes.
2. The graph of the system is the intersection of the regions shaded in step 1.

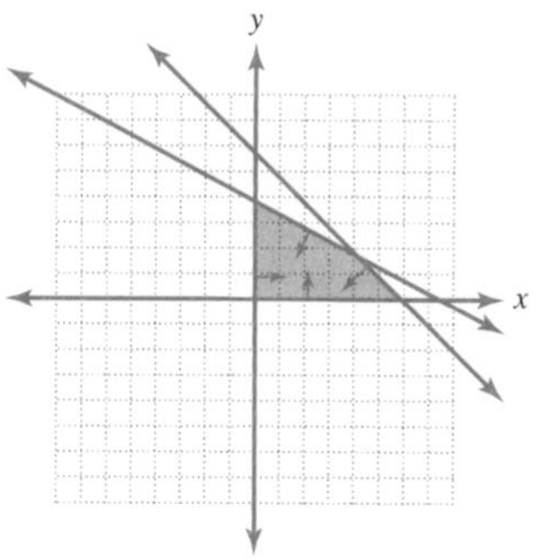

p. 385

This summary exercise set is provided to give you practice with each of the objectives of this chapter. Each exercise is keyed to the appropriate chapter section. When you are finished, you can check your answers to the odd-numbered exercises against those presented in the back of the text. If you have difficulty with any of these questions, go back and reread the examples from that section. The answers to the even-numbered exercises appear in the *Instructor's Solutions Manual.* Your instructor will give you guidelines on how best to use these exercises in your instructional setting.

4.1 *Solve each of the following systems by graphing.*

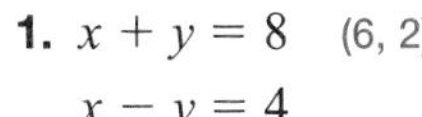

1. $x + y = 8$ (6, 2)
   $x - y = 4$

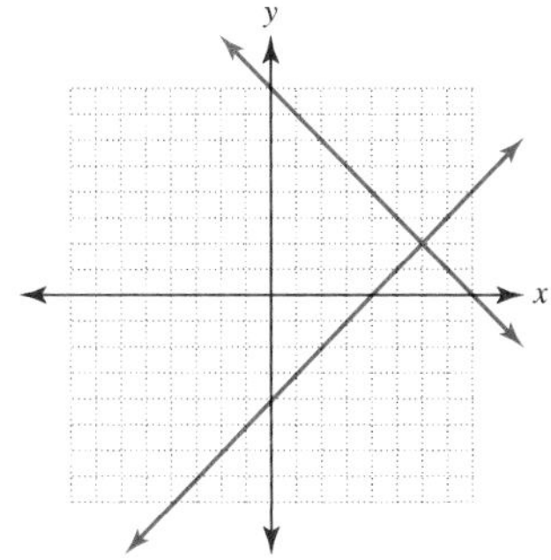

2. $x + 2y = 8$ (6, 1)
   $x - y = 5$

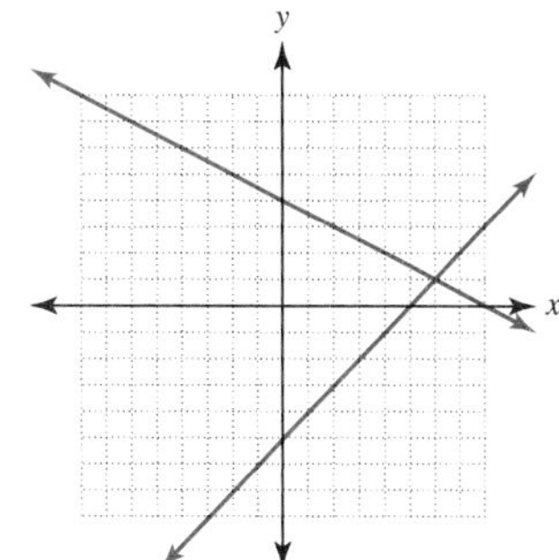

3. $2x + 3y = 12$ (3, 2)
   $2x + y = 8$

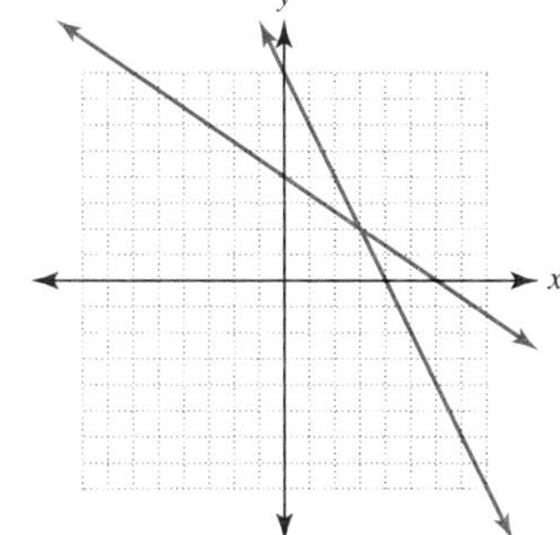

4. $x + 4y = 8$ (4, 1)
   $y = 1$

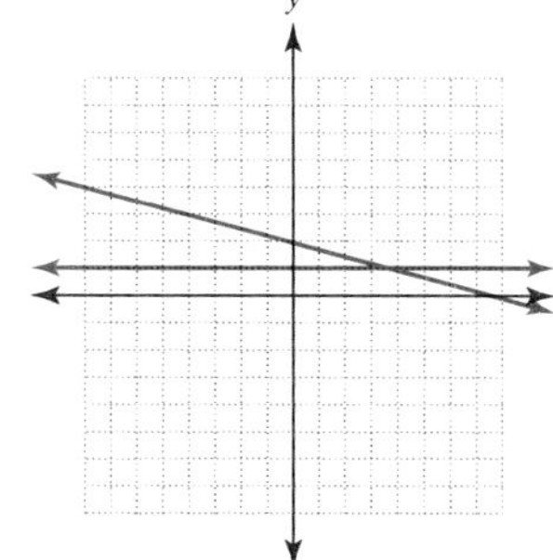

Solve each of the following systems by the addition method. If a unique solution does not exist, state whether the given system is inconsistent or dependent.

5. $x + 2y = 7$ (3, 2)
   $x - y = 1$

6. $x + 3y = 14$ (5, 3)
   $4x + 3y = 29$

7. $3x - 5y = 5$ (0, −1)
   $-x + y = -1$

8. $x - 4y = 12$ Dependent
   $2x - 8y = 24$

9. $6x + 5y = -9$ $\quad$ (−4, 3)
$-5x + 4y = 32$

10. $3x + y = -17$ $\quad$ (−5, −2)
$5x - 3y = -19$

11. $3x + y = 8$ $\quad$ Inconsistent
$-6x - 2y = -10$

12. $5x - y = -17$ $\quad$ (−3, 2)
$4x + 3y = -6$

13. $7x - 4y = 27$ $\quad$ $\left(3, -\frac{3}{2}\right)$
$5x + 6y = 6$

14. $4x - 3y = 1$ $\quad$ $\left(\frac{5}{2}, 3\right)$
$6x + 5y = 30$

15. $x - \frac{1}{2}y = 8$ $\quad$ (6, −4)
$\frac{2}{3}x + \frac{3}{2}y = -2$

16. $\frac{1}{5}x - 2y = 4$ $\quad$ (−10, −3)
$\frac{3}{5}x + \frac{2}{3}y = -8$

Solve each of the following systems by the substitution method. If a unique solution does not exist, state whether the given system is inconsistent or dependent.

17. $2x + y = 23$ $\quad$ (9, 5)
$x = y + 4$

18. $x - 5y = 26$ $\quad$ (6, −4)
$y = x - 10$

19. $3x + y = 7$ $\quad$ Inconsistent
$y = -3x + 5$

20. $2x - 3y = 13$ $\quad$ $\left(4, -\frac{5}{3}\right)$
$x = 3y + 9$

21. $5x - 3y = 13$ $\quad$ (2, −1)
$x - y = 3$

22. $4x - 3y = 6$ $\quad$ (6, 6)
$x + y = 12$

23. $3x - 2y = -12$ $\quad$ $\left(-\frac{2}{3}, 5\right)$
$6x + y = 1$

24. $x - 4y = 8$ $\quad$ Dependent
$-2x + 8y = -16$

Solve each of the following problems by choosing a variable to represent each unknown quantity. Then, write a system of equations that will allow you to solve for each variable.

25. **Number Problem** One number is 2 more than 3 times another. If the sum of the two numbers is 30, find the two numbers. 7, 23

26. **Business and Finance** Suppose that a cashier has 78 \$5 and \$10 bills with a value of \$640. How many of each type of bill does she have? 28 \$5 bills, 50 \$10 bills

27. **Business and Finance** Tickets for a basketball game sold at \$7 for an adult ticket and \$4.50 for a student ticket. If the revenue from 1,200 tickets was \$7,400, how many of each type of ticket were sold? Adult: 800, student: 400

28. **Business and Finance** A purchase of eight blank cassette tapes and four blank videotapes costs \$36. A second purchase of four cassette tapes and five videotapes costs \$30. What is the price of a single cassette tape and of a single videotape? Cassette: \$2.50, videotape: \$4

29. **Geometry** The length of a rectangle is 4 cm less than twice its width. If the perimeter of the rectangle is 64 cm, find the dimensions of the rectangle. Length: 20 cm, width: 12 cm

30. **Business and Finance** A grocer in charge of bulk foods wishes to combine peanuts selling for \$2.25 per pound and cashews selling for \$6 per pound. What amount of each nut should be used to form a 120-lb mixture selling for \$3 per pound? Peanuts: 96 lb, cashews: 24 lb

31. **Business and Finance** Reggie has two investments totaling \$17,000—one a savings account paying 6%, the other a time deposit paying 8%. If his annual interest is \$1,200, what does he have invested in each account? Savings: \$8,000, time deposit: \$9,000

32. **Science and Medicine** A pharmacist mixes a 20% alcohol solution and a 50% alcohol solution to form 600 mL of a 40% solution. How much of each solution should she use in forming the mixture? 200 mL of 20%, 400 mL of 50%

33. **Science and Medicine** A jet flying east, with the wind, makes a trip of 2,200 mi in 4 h. Returning, against the wind, the jet can travel only 1,800 mi in 4 h. What is the plane's rate in still air? What is the rate of the wind? Plane: 500 mi/h, wind: 50 mi/h

34. **Number Problem** The sum of the digits of a two-digit number is 9. If the digits are reversed, the new number is 45 more than the original number. What is the original number? 27

35. **Business and Finance** A manufacturer produces CD-ROM drives and $3\frac{1}{2}$-in. drives. The CD-ROMs require 20 min of component assembly time; the $3\frac{1}{2}$-in. drives, 25 min. The manufacturer has 500 min of component assembly time available per day. Each drive requires 30 min for packaging and testing, and 690 min of that time is available per day. How many of each of the drives should be produced daily to use all the available time? CD-ROM drives: 15, $3\frac{1}{2}$-in. drives: 8

36. **Geometry** One side of an isosceles triangle is one less than twice the base. If the perimeter of the triangle is 18 cm, find the dimensions of the triangle. Base: 4 cm, each side: 7 cm

37. Business and Finance Two car rental agencies have the following rates for the rental of a compact automobile:

Company A: $18 per day plus 22¢ per mile.

Company B: $22 per day plus 18¢ per mile.

For a 3-day rental, at what number of miles will the charges from the two companies be the same? 300 mi

4.2 *Solve each of the following systems by the addition method. If a unique solution does not exist, state whether the given system is inconsistent or dependent.*

38. $\begin{aligned} x - y + z &= 0 \\ x + 4y - z &= 14 \\ x + y - z &= 6 \end{aligned}$ $\left(3, \frac{8}{3}, -\frac{1}{3}\right)$

39. $\begin{aligned} x - y + z &= 3 \\ 3x + y + 2z &= 15 \\ 2x - y + 2z &= 7 \end{aligned}$ (6, 1, −2)

40. $\begin{aligned} x - y - z &= 2 \\ -2x + 2y + z &= -5 \\ -3x + 3y + z &= -10 \end{aligned}$ Inconsistent

41. $\begin{aligned} x - y \quad &= 3 \\ 2y + z &= 5 \\ x \quad + 2z &= 7 \end{aligned}$ (5, 2, 1)

42. $\begin{aligned} x + y + z &= 2 \\ x + 3y - 2z &= 13 \\ y - 2z &= 7 \end{aligned}$ (4, 1, −3)

43. $\begin{aligned} x + y - z &= -1 \\ x - y + 2z &= 2 \\ -5x - y - z &= -1 \end{aligned}$ Dependent

44. $\begin{aligned} 2x + 3y + z &= 7 \\ -2x - 9y + 2z &= 1 \\ 4x - 6y + 3z &= 10 \end{aligned}$ $\left(\frac{1}{2}, \frac{2}{3}, 4\right)$

Solve each of the following problems by choosing a variable to represent each unknown quantity. Then, write a system of equations that will allow you to solve for each variable.

45. Number Problem The sum of three numbers is 15. The largest number is 4 times the smallest number, and it is also 1 more than the sum of the other two numbers. Find the three numbers. 2, 5, 8

46. Number Problem The sum of the digits of a three-digit number is 16. The tens digit is 3 times the hundreds digit, and the units digit is 1 more than the hundreds digit. What is the number? 394

47. Business and Finance A theater has orchestra tickets at $10, box-seat tickets at $7, and balcony tickets at $5. For one performance, a total of 360 tickets were sold, and the total revenue was $3,040. If the number of orchestra tickets sold was 40 more than that of the other two types combined, how many of each type of ticket were sold for the performance? Orchestra: 200, box-seat: 120, balcony: 40

48. Geometry The measure of the largest angle of a triangle is 15 degrees less than 4 times the measure of the smallest angle and 30 degrees more than the sum of the measures of the other two angles. Find the measures of the three angles of the triangle. 30°, 45°, 105°

49. Business and Finance Rachel divided $12,000 into three investments: a savings account paying 5%, a stock paying 7%, and a mutual fund paying 9%. Her annual interest from the investments was $800, and the amount that she had invested at 5% was equal to the sum of the amounts invested in the other accounts. How much did she have invested in each type of account? Savings: $6,000, stock: $2,000, mutual fund: $4,000

50. Number Problem The difference of two positive numbers is 3, and the sum of those numbers is 41. Find the two numbers. 19, 22

51. Number Problem The sum of two integers is 144, and the difference 42. What are the two integers? 51, 93

52. Geometry A rectangular building lot is $1\frac{1}{2}$ times as wide as it is long. The perimeter of the lot is 400 ft. Find the length and width of the lot. 80 ft by 120 ft

53. Business and Finance A manufacturer's cost for producing x units of a product is given by

$$C = 10x + 3{,}600$$

The revenue from selling x units of that product is given by

$$R = 100x$$

Find the break-even point for this product. 40 units

4.3 *Find the augmented matrix for each system of equations.*

54. $\begin{aligned} x - 3y &= -9 \\ -3x + y &= 11 \end{aligned}$ $\left[\begin{array}{cc|c} 1 & -3 & -9 \\ -3 & 1 & 11 \end{array}\right]$

55. $\begin{aligned} 5x + 3y &= 11 \\ -x - 2y &= 2 \end{aligned}$ $\left[\begin{array}{cc|c} 5 & 3 & 11 \\ -1 & -2 & 2 \end{array}\right]$

56. $\begin{aligned} 5x + 2y - z &= 13 \\ 2x + y + z &= 3 \\ 3y + z &= 7 \end{aligned}$ $\left[\begin{array}{ccc|c} 5 & 2 & -1 & 13 \\ 2 & 1 & 1 & 3 \\ 0 & 3 & 1 & 7 \end{array}\right]$

57. $\begin{aligned} x + 3y + z &= 3 \\ x + y - z &= -3 \\ x - 2y - 4z &= -12 \end{aligned}$ $\left[\begin{array}{ccc|c} 1 & 3 & 1 & 3 \\ 1 & 1 & -1 & -3 \\ 1 & -2 & -4 & -12 \end{array}\right]$

Solve each system by using elementary row operations.

58. $\begin{aligned} x - 3y &= -9 \\ -3x + y &= 11 \end{aligned}$ (−3, 2)

59. $\begin{aligned} 5x + 3y &= 11 \\ -x - 2y &= 2 \end{aligned}$ (4, −3)

60. $\begin{aligned} 5x + 2y - z &= 13 \\ 2x + y + z &= 3 \\ 3y + z &= 7 \end{aligned}$ (1, 3, −2)

61. $\begin{aligned} x + 3y + z &= 3 \\ x + y - z &= -3 \\ x - 2y - 3z &= -8 \end{aligned}$ (2, −1, 4)

4.4 *Solve each of the following systems of linear inequalities graphically.*

62. $x - y < 7$
$x + y > 3$

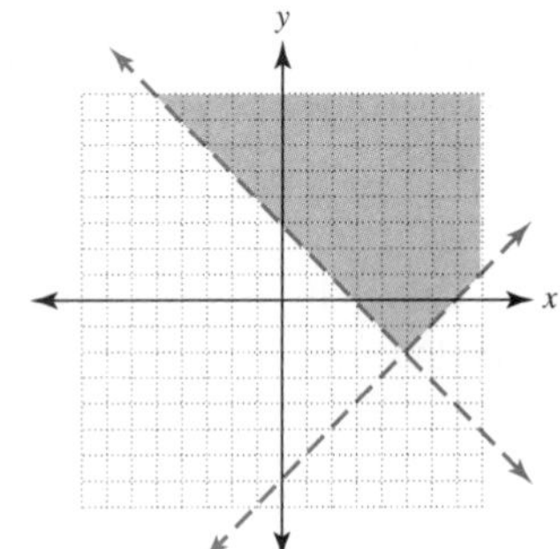

63. $x - 2y \le -2$
$x + 2y \le 6$

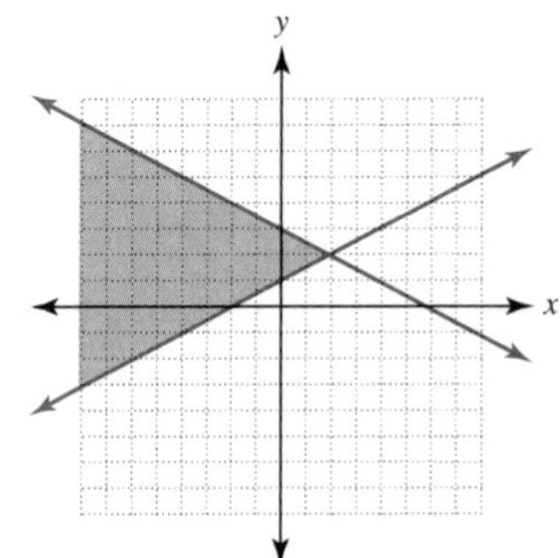

64. $x - 6y < 6$
$-x + y < 4$

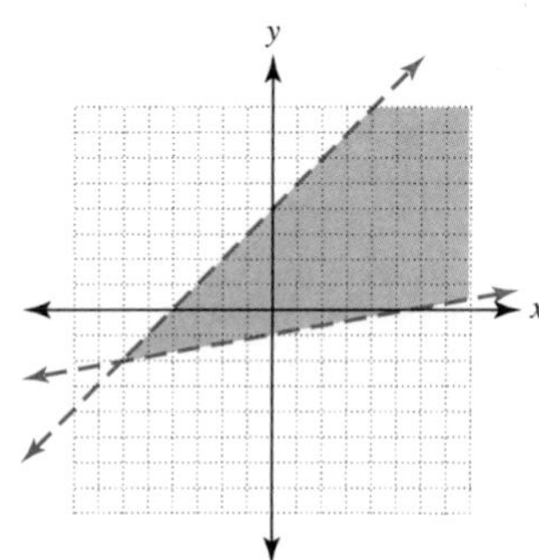

65. $2x + y \le 8$
$x \ge 1$
$y \ge 0$

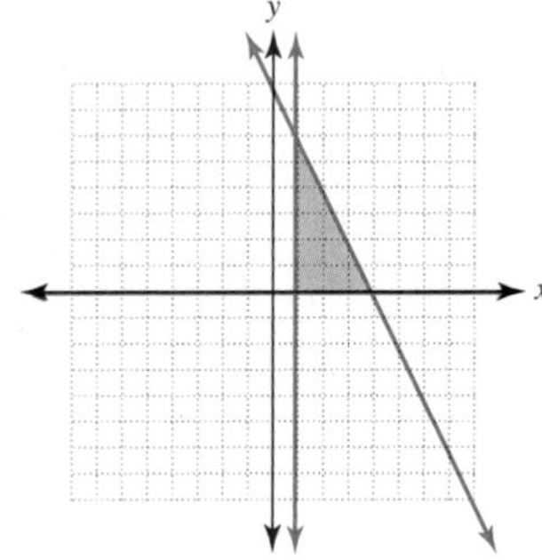

66. $2x + y \le 6$
$x \ge 1$
$y \ge 0$

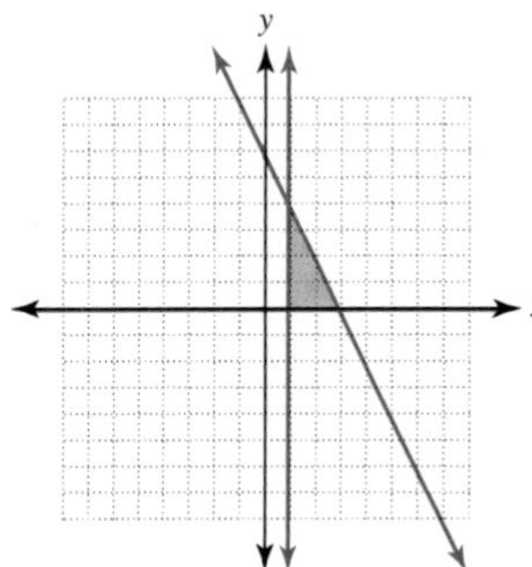

67. $4x + y \le 8$
$x \ge 0$
$y \ge 2$

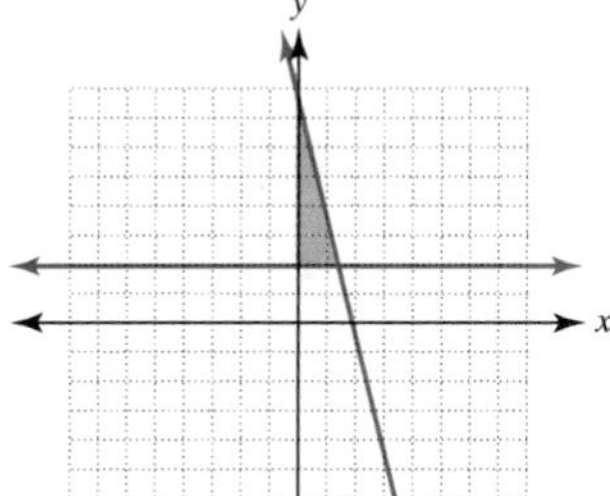

self-test 4

The purpose of this chapter test is to help you check your progress so that you can find sections and concepts that you need to review before the next exam. Allow yourself about an hour to take this test. At the end of that hour, check your answers against those given in the back of this text. If you missed any, note the section reference that accompanies the answer. Go back to that section and reread the examples until you have mastered that particular concept.

Name ____________________

Section __________ Date __________

4.1

Solve each of the following systems. If a unique solution does not exist, state whether the given system is inconsistent or dependent.

1. $3x + y = -5$
$5x - 2y = -23$

2. $4x - 2y = -10$
$y = 2x + 5$

3. $9x - 3y = 4$
$-3x + y = -1$

4. $5x - 3y = 5$
$3x + 2y = -16$

5. $x - 2y = 5$
$2x + 5y = 10$

6. $5x - 3y = 20$
$4x + 9y = -3$

Solve each of the following problems by choosing a variable to represent each unknown quantity. Then write a system of equations that will allow you to solve for each variable.

7. An order for 30 computer disks and 12 printer ribbons totaled \$147. A second order for 12 more disks and 6 additional ribbons cost \$66. What was the cost per individual disk and ribbon?

8. A candy dealer wants to combine jawbreakers selling for \$2.40 per pound and licorice selling for \$3.90 per pound to form a 100-lb mixture that will sell for \$3 per pound. What amount of each type of candy should be used?

9. A small electronics firm assembles 5-in. portable television sets and 12-in. models. The 5-in. set requires 9 h of assembly time; the 12-in. set, 6 h. Each unit requires 5 h for packaging and testing. If 72 h of assembly time and 50 h of packaging and testing time are available per week, how many of each type of set should be finished if the firm wishes to use all its available capacity?

10. To fence around a rectangular yard requires 260 ft of fencing. The length of the yard is 20 ft less than twice the width. Find the dimensions of the yard.

4.2

Solve each of the following systems.

11. $x - y + z = 1$
$-2x + y + z = 8$
$x + 5z = 19$

12. $x + 3y - 2z = -6$
$3x - y + 2z = 8$
$-2x + 3y - 4z = -11$

Answers

1. (−3, 4)
2. Dependent
3. Inconsistent
4. (−2, −5)
5. (5, 0)
6. $\left(3, -\frac{5}{3}\right)$
7. Disks: \$2.50, ribbons: \$6
8. Jawbreakers: 60 lb, licorice: 40 lb
9. Four 5-in. sets, six 12-in. sets
10. 50 ft by 80 ft
11. (−1, 2, 4)
12. $\left(2, -3, -\frac{1}{2}\right)$

Answers

13. Savings: \$8,000, bond: \$4,000, mutual fund: \$2,000

14. (2, 1)

15. (−1, 3, −2)

16. See exercise

17. See exercise

18. See exercise

Solve the following problem by choosing a variable to represent each unknown quantity. Then write a system of equations that will allow you to solve for each variable.

13. Hans decided to divide \$14,000 into three investments: a savings account paying 6% annual interest, a bond paying 9%, and a mutual fund paying 13%. His annual interest from the three investments was \$1,100, and he had twice as much invested in the bond as in the mutual fund. What amount did he invest in each type?

4.3

Solve each system by putting it into matrix form and using elementary row operations.

14. $2x + 3y = 7$
$x + 3y = 5$

15. $x + y + z = 0$
$2x - y + 2z = -9$
$y - 2z = 7$

4.4

Solve each of the following systems of linear inequalities by graphing.

16. $x - 2y < 6$
$x + y < 3$

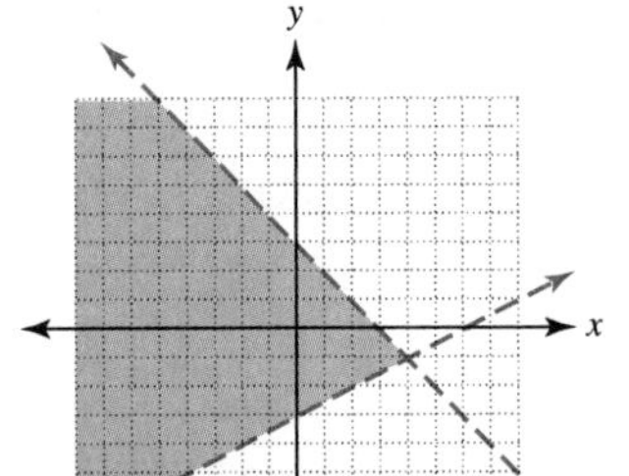

17. $3x + 4y \geq 12$
$x \geq 1$

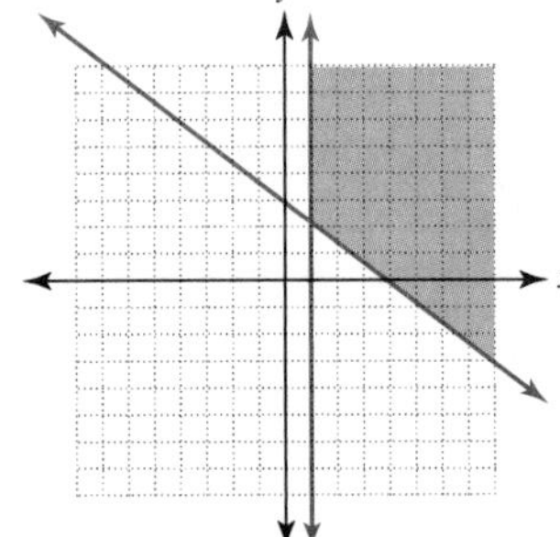

18. $x + 2y \leq 8$
$x + y \leq 6$
$x \geq 0$
$y \geq 0$

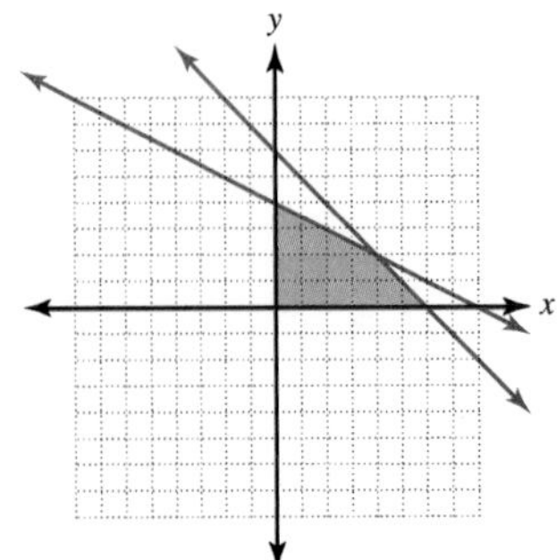

Activity 4 ::
Determining Maximum Possible Revenue

Each chapter in this text concludes with a chapter activity such as this one. These activities provide you with the opportunity to apply the math you studied in that chapter to a relevant topic. Your instructor will determine how best to use these activities in your instructional setting. You may find yourself working in class or outside of class; you may find yourself working alone or in small groups; you may even be asked to perform research in a library or on the Internet.

Everwear Park & Playground Equipment produces a Giraffe Climber and a Grasshopper Slide. Each climber requires 2 hours to assemble and 1 hour of finishing, while each slide requires 1 hour to assemble and 1 hour of finishing. There are 100 hours available for assembly and 70 hours for finishing. The profit on each climber is $40 and on each slide is $60. How many climbers and slides should the company produce to maximize profit?

The goal here is to determine the maximum possible profit based on the constraints in the production phase of the business.

To obtain a graphical solution:

1. Gather the information.

  (a) What are the items that are being manufactured?

  (b) What are the hours of assembly required for each item?

  (c) What are the hours of finishing required for each item?

  (d) What hours are available for assembly?

  (e) What hours are available for finishing?

  (f) What is the profit on each item?

2. Set up a mathematical model.

  (a) Select variables to represent each item.

  (b) Write the linear inequalities (constraints).

3. Graph the inequalities and find the feasible region.

  (a) Find the corner points (vertices) of the region.

  (b) Label the points.

4. From reading the graph determine the combination (corner point) that yields the most profit.

Solve the system of linear inequalities in two variables. Compare the solution with the corner point you determined maximized profit. How do they compare?

cumulative review chapters 1–4

Name ____________

Section ______ Date ______

The following exercises are presented to help you review concepts from earlier chapters. This is meant as review material and not as a comprehensive exam. The answers are presented in the back of the text. Beside each answer is a section reference for the concept. If you have difficulty with any of these exercises, be certain to at least read through the summary related to that section.

Answers

1. $x^{18}y^6$
2. 62
3. 39
4. $x = 15$
5. $x = 5, x = -\frac{5}{3}$
6. $R = \frac{R_1R_2}{R_1 + R_2}$
7. $x \le 1$
8. $x < -2$
9. $-3 < x < 6$
10. $x > 13$ or $x < -3$
11. $y = 2x - 3$
12. $y = \frac{2}{3}x + \frac{7}{3}$

1.5

1. Simplify the expression $(x^9y^3)^2$.

1.2

2. Perform the indicated operations: $56 \cdot 2 \div 4 - (-4^3 + 5 \cdot 6)$

3.2

3. If $f(x) = -4x^3 + 3x^2 - 5$, evaluate $f(-2)$.

Solve each equation.

2.1

4. $3x - 2(x - 5) + 8 = -3(4 - x)$

2.2

5. $|3x - 5| = 10$

6. $\frac{1}{R} = \frac{1}{R_1} + \frac{1}{R_2}$ for R

Solve the following inequalities.

2.3

7. $3x + 5 \le 8$

8. $2x - 9 > 4x - 5$

2.5

9. $|2x - 3| < 9$

10. $|x - 5| > 8$

Write the equation of the line L that satisfies the given conditions.

3.4

11. L has y-intercept $(0, -3)$ and slope of 2.

12. L passes through $(1, 3)$ and $(-2, 1)$.

13. L has y-intercept of $(0, -2)$ and is perpendicular to the line with equation $4x - 5y = 20$.

In each of the following, determine which relations are functions.

3.2

14. $\{(1, 2), (-1, 2), (3, 4), (5, 6)\}$

15.

x	y
−3	0
−2	1
−1	5
−1	3

Use the vertical line test to determine whether each of the following graphs represents a function.

16.

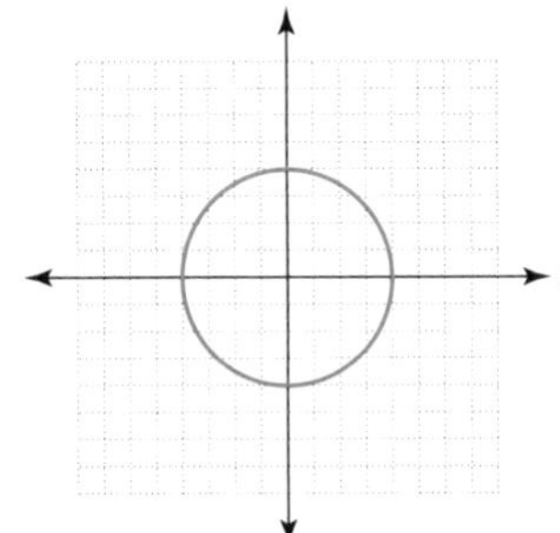

17.

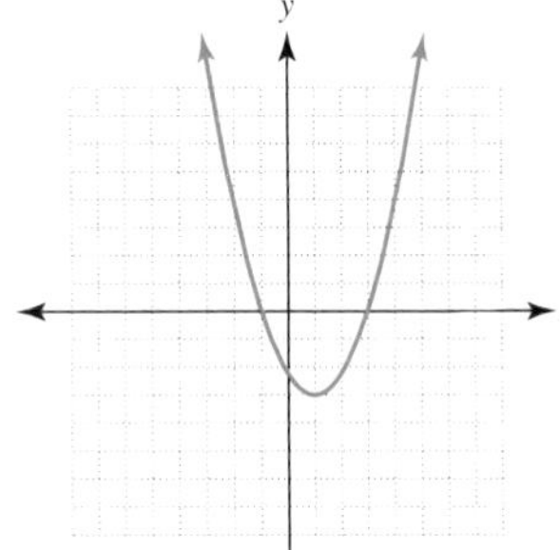

Solve each of the following systems. If a unique solution does not exist, state whether the given system is inconsistent or dependent.

4.1

18. $x + 3y = 12$
$2x - 3y = 6$

19. $7x + 3y = -51$
$y = 2x + 9$

20. $4x - 12y = 7$
$-x + 3y = 9$

21. $8x - 4y = 32$
$-2x + y = -8$

22. $7x - 2y = -17$
$x + 4y = 4$

4.2 **23.** $x + y + 2z = 9$
$-x - z = -1$
$2x - 3y = -17$

Answers

13. $y = -\frac{5}{4}x - 2$

14. Function

15. Not a function

16. Not a function

17. Function

18. (6, 2)

19. (−6, −3)

20. Inconsistent

21. Dependent

22. $\left(-2, \frac{3}{2}\right)$

23. (−4, 3, 5)

Answers

24. Binder: \$3, paper: \$2.50

25. Bond: \$7,000, time deposit: \$3,000

Solve each of the following problems by choosing a variable to represent each unknown quantity. Then write a system of equations that will allow you to solve for each variable.

4.1

24. An order for 3 three-ring binders and 10 packages of paper totaled \$34. A second order for 6 binders and 4 packages of paper cost \$28. What were the individual costs of a binder and a package of paper?

25. Josepha divided her \$10,000 inheritance into two investments: a bond paying 10% and a time deposit paying 7%. If her annual interest from the two investments was \$910, what amount did she have invested in each type?

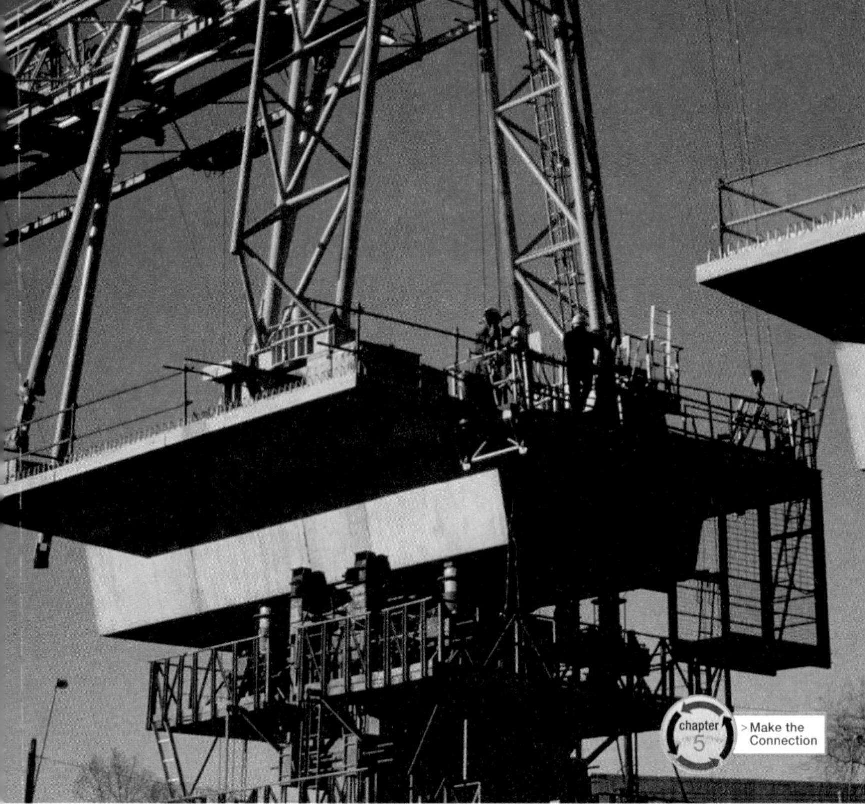

Polynomials and Polynomial Functions

INTRODUCTION

When developing aircraft, autos, and boats, engineers use computer design programs. To ensure that the smooth, curved shapes created by the design fit together when manufactured, engineers use "polynomial splines." These splines are also useful for civil engineers who design tunnels and highways. These splines help in the design of a roadway, ensuring that changes in direction and altitude occur smoothly and gradually. In some cases, roads make transitions from, say, a valley floor to a mountain pass while covering a distance of only a few kilometers. For example: a road passes through a valley at 50 meters altitude and then climbs through some hills, reaching an altitude of 350 meters before descending again. The graph on the next page shows the change in altitude for 19 km of the roadway.

The road seems very steep in this graph, but remember that the y-axis is the altitude measured in meters, and the x-axis is the horizontal distance measured in kilometers. To get a true feeling for the vertical change, the horizontal axis would have to be stretched by a factor of 1,070.

CHAPTER 5 OUTLINE

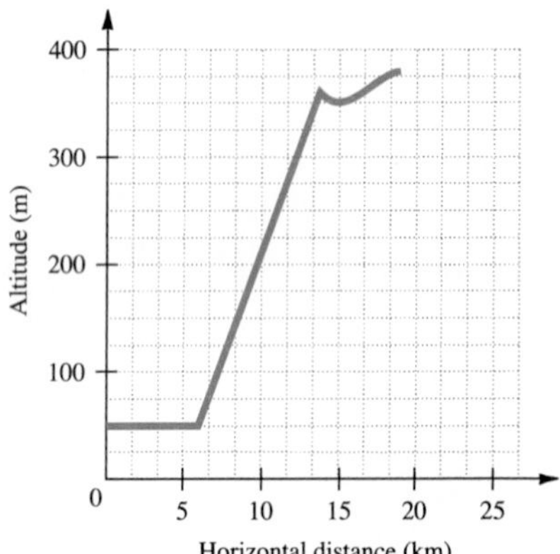

Based on measurements of the distance, altitude, and change in the slope taken at intervals along the planned path of the road, formulas are developed that model the roadway for short sections. The formulas are then pieced together to form a model of the road over several kilometers. Such formulas are found by using algebraic methods to solve systems of linear equations. The resulting splines can be linear, quadratic, or even cubic equations. Here are some of the splines that could be fit together to create the roadway needed in our graph; y is the altitude measured in meters and x is the horizontal distance, measured in kilometers.

First 6 km:	$y = 50$
Next 7.5 km:	$y = 40x - 190$
Final 5.5 km:	$y = -0.8x^3 + 41x^2 - 690x + 4{,}176$

By entering these equations in your calculator, you can see part of the design for the road. Be certain that you adjust your graphing window appropriately.

Polynomials are useful in many areas. In this chapter, you will learn how to solve problems involving polynomials. Then, at the end of the chapter, you will find a more in-depth activity to explore the features of a graphing calculator.

pretest 5

Name ____________________

Section __________ Date __________

This pretest provides a preview of the types of exercises you will encounter in each section of this chapter. The answers for these exercises can be found in the back of the text. If you are working on your own, or ahead of the class, this pretest can help you identify the sections in which you should focus more of your time.

5.1

1. Given $f(x) = -3x^2 - 5x + 8$, find $f(-2)$.

In exercises 2 and 3, $f(x) = 3x^2 - 7x + 2$ and $g(x) = 7x^2 - 5x - 9$.

2. Find $f(x) + g(x)$.

3. Find $f(x) - g(x)$.

5.2

Multiply.

4. $(4d + 3)(2d^2 - 5d - 2)$

5. $(3m + 2n)^2$

5.3

Perform the indicated division.

6. $\dfrac{8m^4n^5p}{2m^6n^2}$

7. $(2x^2 + x + 4) \div (2x - 3)$

5.4–5.8

Factor each polynomial completely.

8. $x^2 - 9$

9. $2z^2 - 32z$

10. $2y^4 + 2y$

11. $m^2 - 3mn + 5m - 15n$

12. $12w^2 - 7w - 10$

5.9

Solve each of the equations for x.

13. $x^2 - 8x + 15 = 0$

14. $3x^2 = 2 - x$

15. $(x - 3)(x - 2) = 30$

Answers

1. 6
2. $10x^2 - 12x - 7$
3. $-4x^2 - 2x + 11$
4. $8d^3 - 14d^2 - 23d - 6$
5. $9m^2 + 12mn + 4n^2$
6. $\dfrac{4n^3p}{m^2}$
7. $x + 2 + \dfrac{10}{2x - 3}$
8. $(x + 3)(x - 3)$
9. $2z(z - 16)$
10. $2y(y + 1)(y^2 - y + 1)$
11. $(m - 3n)(m + 5)$
12. $(3w + 2)(4w - 5)$
13. $3, 5$
14. $-1, \dfrac{2}{3}$
15. $-3, 8$

5.1 Addition and Subtraction of Polynomials

< 5.1 Objectives >

1 > Identify types of polynomials

2 > Determine the degree of a polynomial

3 > Find an ordered pair associated with a given polynomial function

4 > Find the sum of two polynomial functions

5 > Find the difference of two polynomial functions

NOTES

$7p^2$ is an example of a term because

$7p^2 = 7 \cdot p \cdot p$

The difference of terms is also a polynomial since

$2x^2 - 3x = 2x^2 + (-3x)$

In this chapter we work with the most common kind of algebraic expression, a *polynomial*. Recall, from Section 1.4, that a term was defined as a number or a product of a number and one or more variables. The idea of a term is an important part of the definition of a polynomial. Note that $\frac{m}{2}$ is a term but $\frac{2}{m}$ is not. Similarly, $\sqrt{2} \cdot n$ is a term but $2 \cdot \sqrt{n}$ is not.

When a term consists of both numeric and variable factors, we call the numeric part the **coefficient** of the term. Given the term $5z^3$, the most basic factors are 5 and z. The number 5 is the coefficient of the term.

Definition

Polynomial

A **polynomial** is a term or sum of terms in which the only allowable exponents are the whole numbers.

Example 1 Identifying Polynomials

(a) $r + 3$ is a polynomial. The terms are r and 3. The coefficients are 1 and 3.

(b) $3x^2 - 2x + 5$, or $3x^2 + (-2x) + 5$, is also a polynomial. Its terms are $3x^2$, $-2x$, and 5. The coefficients are 3, -2, and 5.

(c) $5t^3 + 2 - \frac{3}{t}$ is *not* a polynomial because of the division by t in the third term.

RECALL

Whole numbers include 0, 1, 2, 3, . . .

$\frac{1}{t} = t^{-1}$

and -1 is not a whole number.

Check Yourself 1

Which are polynomials?

(a) $5z^2$ (b) $3y^3 - 2y + \frac{5}{y}$ (c) $4x^2 - 2x + 3$

Certain polynomials are given special names because of the number of terms that they have.

Definition

Monomial, Binomial, and Trinomial

A polynomial with exactly one term is called a **monomial.**
A polynomial with exactly two terms is called a **binomial.**
A polynomial with exactly three terms is called a **trinomial.**

Example 2 Identifying Types of Polynomials

< Objective 1 >

NOTE

The prefix *mono-* means "one." The prefix *bi-* means "two." The prefix *tri-* means "three." We will not use special names to indicate polynomials with four or more terms.

(a) $3m^2n$ is a monomial. It has one term.

(b) $2p^3 + 5p$ is a binomial. It has two terms, $2p^3$ and $5p$.

(c) $5q^2 - 4q + 3$ is a trinomial. Its three terms are $5q^2$, $-4q$, and 3.

Check Yourself 2

Classify each as a monomial, binomial, or trinomial.

(a) $5z^4 - 2z^3$ **(b)** $4y^7$ **(c)** $2x^2 + 5x - 3$

We also classify polynomials by their *degree.*

Definition

Degree of Monomials

The **degree** of a monomial is the sum of the exponents of the variable factors.

Example 3 Determining the Degree of a Monomial

(a) $5x^2$ has degree 2.

(b) $7n^5$ has degree 5.

(c) $3a^2b^4$ has degree 6. (The sum of the exponents, 2 and 4, is 6.)

(d) 9 has degree 0 (because $9 = 9 \cdot 1 = 9x^0$).

RECALL

$x^0 = 1, x \neq 0$

Check Yourself 3

Give the degree of each monomial.

(a) $4x^2$ **(b)** $7x^3y^2$ **(c)** $8p^2s$ **(d)** 5

Definition

Degree of Polynomials

The **degree** of a polynomial is that of the term with the highest degree.

Example 4 Determining the Degree of a Polynomial

< Objective 2 >

(a) $7x^3 - 5x^2 + 5$ has degree 3.

(b) $5y^7 - 3y^2 + 5y - 7$ has degree 7.

(c) $4a^2b^3 - 5abc^2$ has degree 5 because the sum of the variable exponents in the term with highest degree $(4a^2b^3)$ is 5.

Polynomials such as those in parts (**a**) and (**b**) are called **polynomials in one variable,** and they are usually written in *descending form* so that the power of the variable decreases from left to right. In that case, the coefficient of the first term is called the **leading coefficient.**

Check Yourself 4

Give the degree of each polynomial. For those polynomials in one variable, write in descending form and give the leading coefficient.

(a) $7x^4 - 5xy + 2$ **(b)** 5 **(c)** $4x^2 - 7x^3 - 8x + 5$

NOTE

A linear function, such as $f(x) = 4x + 9$, is a polynomial function of degree 1.

A **polynomial function** is a function in which the expression on the right-hand side is a polynomial expression. For example,

$$f(x) = 3x^3 + 2x^2 - x + 5$$
$$g(x) = 2x^3 - 5x - 1$$
$$P(x) = 2x^7 + 2x^6 - x^3 + 2x^4 + 5x^2 - 6$$

are all polynomial functions. In fact, polynomial functions are sometimes referred to as *n*th-degree equations. Can you see why? Because they are functions, every *x*-value determines a unique ordered pair.

Example 5 Finding Ordered Pairs

< Objective 3 >

Given $f(x) = 3x^3 + 2x^2 - x + 5$ and $g(x) = 2x^3 - 5x - 1$, find the following ordered pairs.

(a) $(0, f(0))$

To find $f(0)$, we substitute 0 for x in the function $f(x) = 3x^3 + 2x^2 - x + 5$.

$$f(0) = 3(0)^3 + 2(0)^2 - (0) + 5$$
$$= 0 + 0 - 0 + 5$$
$$= 5$$

Therefore, $(0, f(0)) = (0, 5)$.

(b) $\left(\frac{1}{2}, f\left(\frac{1}{2}\right)\right)$

$$f\left(\frac{1}{2}\right) = 3\left(\frac{1}{2}\right)^3 + 2\left(\frac{1}{2}\right)^2 - \left(\frac{1}{2}\right) + 5$$
$$= 3 \cdot \frac{1}{8} + 2 \cdot \frac{1}{4} - \frac{1}{2} + 5$$
$$= \frac{3}{8} + \frac{2}{4} - \frac{1}{2} + 5$$
$$= \frac{3}{8} + \frac{4}{8} - \frac{4}{8} + \frac{40}{8}$$
$$= \frac{43}{8}$$

Therefore, $\left(\frac{1}{2}, f\left(\frac{1}{2}\right)\right) = \left(\frac{1}{2}, \frac{43}{8}\right)$.

(c) $(-0.2, f(-0.2))$

$$f(-0.2) = 3(-0.2)^3 + 2(-0.2)^2 - (-0.2) + 5$$
$$= 3(-0.008) + 2(0.04) - (-0.2) + 5$$
$$= -0.024 + 0.08 + 0.2 + 5$$
$$= 5.256$$

Therefore, $(-0.2, f(-0.2)) = (-0.2, 5.256)$.

(d) $(0, g(0))$

$$g(0) = 2(0)^3 - 5(0) - 1$$
$$= 2 \cdot 0 - 5 \cdot 0 - 1$$
$$= -1$$

Therefore, $(0, g(0)) = (0, -1)$.

(e) $\left(\frac{1}{2}, g\left(\frac{1}{2}\right)\right)$

$$g\left(\frac{1}{2}\right) = 2\left(\frac{1}{2}\right)^3 - 5\left(\frac{1}{2}\right) - 1$$
$$= 2 \cdot \frac{1}{8} - 5 \cdot \frac{1}{2} - 1$$
$$= \frac{2}{8} - \frac{5}{2} - 1$$
$$= \frac{2}{8} - \frac{20}{8} - \frac{8}{8}$$
$$= -\frac{26}{8} = -\frac{13}{4}$$

Therefore, $\left(\frac{1}{2}, g\left(\frac{1}{2}\right)\right) = \left(\frac{1}{2}, -\frac{13}{4}\right)$.

(f) $(-0.2, g(-0.2))$

$$g(-0.2) = 2(-0.2)^3 - 5(-0.2) - 1$$
$$= 2(-0.008) - 5(-0.2) - 1$$
$$= -0.016 + 1 - 1$$
$$= -0.016$$

Therefore, $(-0.2, g(-0.2)) = (-0.2, -0.016)$.

Check Yourself 5

Given $f(x) = x^3 - 7x + 1$ and $g(x) = x^3 + 2x^2 - 3x - 4$, find the following ordered pairs.

(a) $(0, f(0))$ **(b)** $\left(\frac{1}{2}, f\left(\frac{1}{2}\right)\right)$ **(c)** $(-0.2, f(-0.2))$

(d) $(0, g(0))$ **(e)** $\left(\frac{1}{2}, g\left(\frac{1}{2}\right)\right)$ **(f)** $(-0.2, g(-0.2))$

You may remember from previous math courses that to find the sum of two polynomials, we add the like terms. Given

$(3x^3 + 2x - 5) + (x^3 - x^2 + 5x - 1)$

we could use the associative and commutative properties of addition to rewrite the sum as

$(3x^3 + x^3) + (-x^2) + (2x + 5x) + (-5 - 1)$

This simplifies to

$4x^3 - x^2 + 7x - 6$

The process for adding polynomial functions is nearly identical, as Example 6 illustrates.

Example 6 Adding Two Polynomial Functions

< Objective 4 >

Given $f(x) = 3x^3 + 2x^2 - x + 5$ and $g(x) = 2x^3 - 5x - 1$, and letting $h(x) = f(x) + g(x)$, find $h(x)$.

$$\begin{aligned} h(x) &= f(x) + g(x) \\ &= (3x^3 + 2x^2 - x + 5) + (2x^3 - 5x - 1) && \text{Substitute the polynomial functions.} \\ &= (3x^3 + 2x^3) + 2x^2 + (-5x - x) + (5 - 1) && \text{Collect like terms.} \\ &= 5x^3 + 2x^2 - 6x + 4 \end{aligned}$$

Check Yourself 6

Given $f(x) = x^3 - 7x + 1$ and $g(x) = x^3 + 2x^2 - 3x - 4$, and letting $h(x) = f(x) + g(x)$, find $h(x)$.

Example 7 demonstrates a method by which we can check our results when we add two polynomials.

Example 7 Adding Two Polynomial Functions

Given $f(x) = 3x^3 + 2x^2 - x + 5$ and $g(x) = 2x^3 - 5x - 1$, and letting $h(x) = f(x) + g(x)$, find the following.

(a) $f(2) + g(2)$

$$\begin{aligned} f(2) &= 3(2)^3 + 2(2)^2 - (2) + 5 \\ &= 24 + 8 - 2 + 5 \\ &= 35 \end{aligned}$$

$$g(2) = 2(2)^3 - 5(2) - 1$$
$$= 16 - 10 - 1$$
$$= 5$$
$$f(2) + g(2) = 35 + 5$$
$$= 40$$

(b) Use the result from Example 6 to find $h(2)$

From Example 6, we have

$$h(x) = 5x^3 + 2x^2 - 6x + 4$$

Therefore,

$$h(2) = 5(2)^3 + 2(2)^2 - 6(2) + 4$$
$$= 40 + 8 - 12 + 4$$
$$= 40$$

Note that $h(2) = f(2) + g(2)$. This helps us confirm that we have correctly added the polynomials.

Check Yourself 7

Given $f(x) = x^3 - 7x + 1$ and $g(x) = x^3 + 2x^2 - 3x - 4$, and letting $h(x) = f(x) + g(x)$, complete the following.

(a) Find $f(2) + g(2)$.
(b) Use the result of Check Yourself 6 to find $h(2)$.
(c) Compare the results of parts (a) and (b).

Subtracting polynomials requires a bit more work since the associative and commutative properties do not apply for subtraction. Recall from Chapter 1 that we viewed subtraction of a quantity as adding its opposite, so that

$$a - b = a + (-b)$$

The opposite of a quantity with more than one term requires that we take the opposite of each term. For example,

$$-(a + b) = -a - b \quad \text{and} \quad -(a - b) = -a + b$$

Alternatively, the negative in front of a quantity can be understood as -1. Applying the distributive property we get the same results.

$$-(a + b) = -1(a + b) = -a - b \quad \text{and} \quad -(a - b) = -1(a - b) = -a + b$$

We can now go on to subtracting polynomials.

Example 8 Subtracting Polynomial Functions

< Objective 5 >

Given $f(x) = 7x^2 - 2x$ and $g(x) = 4x^2 + 5x$, and letting $h(x) = f(x) - g(x)$, find the following.

(a) $h(x)$

$$\begin{aligned} h(x) &= f(x) - g(x) \\ &= (7x^2 - 2x) - (4x^2 + 5x) \\ &= 7x^2 - 2x - 4x^2 - 5x \\ &= 7x^2 - 4x^2 - 2x - 5x \\ &= 3x^2 - 7x \end{aligned}$$

(b) $f(2) - g(2)$

$$\begin{aligned} f(2) - g(2) &= (7(2)^2 - 2(2)) - (4(2)^2 + 5(2)) \\ &= (28 - 4) - (16 + 10) \\ &= (24) - (26) \\ &= -2 \end{aligned}$$

(c) Use the results of part **(a)** to find $h(2)$.

$$\begin{aligned} h(2) &= 3(2)^2 - 7(2) \\ &= 12 - 14 \\ &= -2 \end{aligned}$$

As was the case with addition, we have found an easy way to check our work when we are subtracting polynomial functions. We have found that $(2, h(2)) = (2, -2) = (2, f(2) - g(2))$.

Check Yourself 8

Given $f(x) = 8x^2 - x$ and $g(x) = x^2 - 2x$, and letting $h(x) = f(x) - g(x)$, find the following.

(a) $h(x)$
(b) $f(2) - g(2)$
(c) Use the result of part **(a)** to find $h(2)$.

Example 9 Subtracting Polynomial Functions

Given $f(x) = 5x^2 + 2x$ and $g(x) = 3x^2 - 5x$, and letting $h(x) = f(x) - g(x)$, find the following.

(a) $h(x)$

$$\begin{aligned} h(x) &= f(x) - g(x) \\ &= (5x^2 + 2x) - (3x^2 - 5x) \\ &= 5x^2 + 2x - 3x^2 + 5x \\ &= 5x^2 - 3x^2 + 2x + 5x \\ &= 2x^2 + 7x \end{aligned}$$

(b) $f(1) - g(1)$

$$\begin{aligned} f(1) - g(1) &= (5(1)^2 + 2(1)) - (3(1)^2 - 5(1)) \\ &= (5 + 2) - (3 - 5) \\ &= (7) - (-2) \\ &= 9 \end{aligned}$$

(c) Use the result of part **(a)** to find $h(1)$.

$$h(1) = 2(1)^2 + 7(1)$$
$$= 2 + 7$$
$$= 9$$

We see that $(1, h(1)) = (1, 9) = (1, f(1) - g(1))$.

Check Yourself 9

Given $f(x) = 3x^2 - 4x$ and $g(x) = 6x^2 - x$, and letting $h(x) = f(x) - g(x)$, find the following.

(a) $h(x)$
(b) $f(1) - g(1)$
(c) Use the results of part (a) to find $h(1)$.

Check Yourself ANSWERS

1. (a) and (c) are polynomials. **2. (a)** binomial; **(b)** monomial; **(c)** trinomial **3. (a)** 2; **(b)** 5; **(c)** 3; **(d)** 0 **4. (a)** Degree is 4; **(b)** degree is 0; **(c)** degree is 3, $-7x^3 + 4x^2 - 8x + 5$, leading coefficient is -7. **5. (a)** (0, 1); **(b)** $\left(\frac{1}{2}, -\frac{19}{8}\right)$; **(c)** (−0.2, 2.392); **(d)** (0, −4); **(e)** $\left(\frac{1}{2}, -\frac{39}{8}\right)$; **(f)** (−0.2, −3.328) **6.** $2x^3 + 2x^2 - 10x - 3$ **7. (a)** 1; **(b)** 1; **(c)** $h(2) = f(2) + g(2)$ **8. (a)** $h(x) = 7x^2 + x$; **(b)** 30; **(c)** 30 **9. (a)** $h(x) = -3x^2 - 3x$; **(b)** −6; **(c)** −6

Reading Your Text

The following fill-in-the-blank exercises are designed to ensure that you understand some of the key vocabulary used in this section.

SECTION 5.1

(a) A ______________ consists of one or more terms in which the only allowable exponents are the whole numbers, 0, 1, 2, 3, and so on.

(b) A ______________ is a function in which the expression on the right-hand side is a polynomial expression.

(c) To find the sum of two polynomials, we add the ______________.

(d) $-(a + b) =$ ______________ and $-(a - b) =$ ______________.

5.1 exercises

MathZone

Boost your grade at mathzone.com!

- > Practice Problems
- > NetTutor
- > Self-Tests
- > e-Professors
- > Videos

Name ____________________

Section ________ Date ________

Answers

1. Binomial
2. Monomial
3. Trinomial
4. Trinomial
5. Not classified
6. Not a polynomial
7. Monomial
8. Not classified
9. Not a polynomial
10. Binomial
11. $4x^5 - 3x^2$; 5
12. $-3x^3 + 5x^2 + 4$; 3
13. $-5x^9 + 7x^7 + 4x^3$; 9
14. $x + 2$; 1
15. $4x^2y^4z$; 7
16. $8p^5s^2 - 7p^3s$; 7
17. $x^6 - 3x^5 + 5x^2 - 7$; 6
18. 5; 0
19. 7, −5
20. 4, −4
21. 62, 30
22. 0, 0

Basic Skills | Advanced Skills | Vocational-Technical Applications | Calculator/Computer | Above and Beyond

< Objective 1 >

Classify each of the following as a **monomial, binomial,** *or* **trinomial** *where possible.*

1. $7x^3 - 3x^2$

2. $4x^7$

3. $7y^2 + 4y + 5$

4. $2x^2 + 3xy + y^2$

5. $-2x^4 - 3x^2 + 5x - 2$

6. $x^4 + \frac{5}{x} + 7$

7. $6y^8$

8. $4x^4 - 2x^2 + 5x - 7$

9. $x^5 - \frac{3}{x^2}$

10. $4x^2 - 9$

< Objective 2 >

Arrange in descending-exponent form if necessary, and give the degree of each polynomial.

11. $4x^5 - 3x^2$

12. $5x^2 - 3x^3 + 4$

13. $7x^7 - 5x^9 + 4x^3$

14. $2 + x$

15. $4x^2y^4z$

16. $8p^5s^2 - 7p^3s$

17. $5x^2 - 3x^5 + x^6 - 7$

18. 5

Find the values of each of the following polynomials for the given values of the variable.

19. $6x + 1$; $x = 1$ and $x = -1$

20. $x^3 - 2x$; $x = 2$ and $x = -2$

21. $3x^2 + 4x - 2$; $x = 4$ and $x = -4$

22. $-x^2 - 2x + 3$; $x = 1$ and $x = -3$

< Objective 3 >

In exercises 23 to 26, the polynomial functions $f(x)$ and $g(x)$ are given. Find the ordered pairs **(a)** $(0, f(0))$, **(b)** $\left(\frac{1}{2}, f\left(\frac{1}{2}\right)\right)$, **(c)** $(-0.2, f(-0.2))$, **(d)** $(0, g(0))$, **(e)** $\left(\frac{1}{2}, g\left(\frac{1}{2}\right)\right)$, *and* **(f)** $(-0.2, g(-0.2))$.

23. $f(x) = 2x^2 + 3x - 5$ and $g(x) = 4x^2 - 5x - 7$

24. $f(x) = x^3 + 8x^2 - 4x + 10$ and $g(x) = 3x^3 + 4x^2 - 5x - 3$

25. $f(x) = -4x^3 - 5x^2 + 8x - 12$ and $g(x) = -x^3 + 5x^2 + 7x - 14$

26. $f(x) = 10x^3 + 5x^2 - 3x$ and $g(x) = 8x^3 + 4x^2 + 9$

< Objective 4 >

In exercises 27 to 30, $f(x)$ and $g(x)$ are given. Let $h(x) = f(x) + g(x)$. Find **(a)** $h(x)$, **(b)** $f(1) + g(1)$, *and* **(c)** *use the results of part* **(a)** *to find* $h(1)$.

27. $f(x) = 5x - 3$ and $g(x) = 4x + 7$

28. $f(x) = 5x^2 + 3x$ and $g(x) = 4x + 2x^2$

29. $f(x) = -3x^2 - 5x - 7$ and $g(x) = 2x^2 + 3x + 5$

30. $f(x) = -5x^2 - 3x - 15$ and $g(x) = 5x^3 - 8x - 10$

< Objective 5 >

In exercises 31 to 34, $f(x)$ and $g(x)$ are given. Let $h(x) = f(x) - g(x)$. Find **(a)** $h(x)$, **(b)** $f(1) - g(1)$, *and* **(c)** *use the results of part* **(a)** *to find* $h(1)$.

31. $f(x) = 7x + 10$ and $g(x) = 5x - 3$

32. $f(x) = 7x^2 - 3x$ and $g(x) = -5x^2 - 2x$

33. $f(x) = 8x^2 - 5x - 7$ and $g(x) = 5x^2 - 3x$

34. $f(x) = 5x^2 - 5$ and $g(x) = 8x^2 - 7x$

Answers

23. (a) $(0, -5)$; (b) $\left(\frac{1}{2}, -3\right)$; (c) $(-0.2, -5.52)$; (d) $(0, -7)$; (e) $\left(\frac{1}{2}, -\frac{17}{2}\right)$; (f) $(-0.2, -5.84)$

24. (a) $(0, 10)$; (b) $\left(\frac{1}{2}, \frac{81}{8}\right)$; (c) $(-0.2, 11.112)$; (d) $(0, -3)$; (e) $\left(\frac{1}{2}, -\frac{33}{8}\right)$; (f) $(-2, -1)$ $(-0.2, -1.864)$

25. (a) $(0, -12)$; (b) $\left(\frac{1}{2}, -\frac{39}{4}\right)$; (c) $(-0.2, -13.768)$; (d) $(0, -14)$; (e) $\left(\frac{1}{2}, -\frac{75}{8}\right)$; (f) $(-0.2, 15.192)$

26. (a) $(0, 0)$; (b) $\left(\frac{1}{2}, 1\right)$; (c) $(-0.2, 0.72)$; (d) $(0, 9)$; (e) $\left(\frac{1}{2}, 11\right)$; (f) $(-0.2, 9.096)$

27. (a) $h(x) = 9x + 4$; (b) 13; (c) 13

28. (a) $h(x) = 7x^2 + 7x$; (b) 14; (c) 14

29. (a) $h(x) = -x^2 - 2x - 2$; (b) -5; (c) -5

30. (a) $h(x) = 5x^3 - 5x^2 - 11x - 25$; (b) -36; (c) -36

31. (a) $h(x) = 2x + 13$; (b) 15; (c) 15

32. (a) $h(x) = 12x^2 - x$; (b) 11; (c) 11

33. (a) $h(x) = 3x^2 - 2x - 7$; (b) -6; (c) -6

34. (a) $h(x) = -3x^2 + 7x - 5$; (b) -1; (c) -1

Answers

35. always

36. never

37. sometimes

38. always

39. sometimes

40. always

41. sometimes

42. sometimes

43. $C(x) = 3x + 20$; \$170

44. $C(x) = 20x + 150$; \$290

45. $4x + 7$

46. $-x^2 - 8x + 3$

47. $13x^2 + 5$

48. $-3x - 3$

49. $3x + 4$

50. $4x^2 + 2x$

51. $x - 12$

52. $-6x - 24$

Indicate whether each of the following statements is **always true, sometimes true,** *or* **never true.**

35. A monomial is a polynomial.

36. A binomial is a trinomial.

37. The degree of a trinomial is 3.

38. A trinomial has three terms.

39. A polynomial has four or more terms.

40. A binomial must have two coefficients.

41. If x equals 0, the value of the polynomial in x equals 0.

42. The coefficient of the leading term in a polynomial is the largest coefficient of the polynomial.

Basic Skills | **Advanced Skills** | Vocational-Technical Applications | Calculator/Computer | Above and Beyond

43. **Business and Finance** The cost, in dollars, of typing a term paper is given as three times the number of pages plus 20. Use x as the number of pages to be typed, and write a polynomial function to describe this cost. Then find the cost of typing a 50-page paper.

44. **Business and Finance** The cost, in dollars, of making suits is described as 20 times the number of suits plus 150. Use x as the number of suits, and write a polynomial function to describe this cost. Then find the cost of making seven suits.

Simplify each polynomial function.

45. $f(x) = (2x - 3) + (4x + 7) - (2x - 3)$

46. $f(x) = (5x^2 - 2x + 7) - (2x^2 + 3x + 1) - (4x^2 + 3x + 3)$

47. $f(x) = (8x^2 - 3) + (5x^2 + 7x) - (7x - 8)$

48. $f(x) = x - [5x - (x - 3)]$

49. $f(x) = (2x - 3) - [x - (2x + 7)]$

50. $f(x) = (3x^2 + 5x) - [x^2 - (2x^2 - 3x)]$

51. $f(x) = 2x - (3x + 2[x - 2(x - 3)])$

52. $f(x) = 3x - (5x - 2[x - 3(x + 4)])$

Suppose that revenue is given by the polynomial $R(x)$ and cost is given by the polynomial $C(x)$. Profit $P(x)$ can then be found with the formula

$P(x) = R(x) - C(x)$

In exercises 53 and 54, find the polynomial representing profit in each expression.

53. $R(x) = 100x$
$C(x) = 2{,}000 + 50x$

54. $R(x) = 100x + 2x^2$
$C(x) = 2{,}000 + 50x + 5x^2$

55. If $P(x) = -2x + 1$, find $P(a + h) - P(a)$.

56. If $P(x) = 5x$, find $\dfrac{P(a + h) - P(a)}{h}$.

57. Find the difference when $4x^2 + 2x + 1$ is subtracted from the sum of $x^2 - 2x - 3$ and $3x^2 + 5x - 7$.

58. Subtract $7x^2 + 5x - 3$ from the sum of $2x^2 - 5x + 7$ and $-9x^2 - 2x + 5$.

59. Subtract $8x^2 - 2x$ from the sum of $x^2 - 5x$ and $7x^2 + 5$.

Basic Skills | Advanced Skills | **Vocational-Technical Applications** | Calculator/Computer | Above and Beyond

60. Allied Health The concentration, C, of a sedative, in micrograms per milliliter (mcg/mL), in a patient's bloodstream t hours after injection is given by the polynomial function $C(t) = -1.35t^2 + 10.81t + 7.38$. Determine the concentration of digoxin in a patient's bloodstream 3.5 hours after injection.

61. Construction Technology The height (in feet) of a beam above the foundation of a house is described by the polynomial function $h(x) = 0.001(x^2 - 16x) + 8$, where x is the distance (in feet) from the left end of the beam. What is the height of the beam 4 feet from the left end?

62. Agricultural Technology The crown of the grain in a bin (in feet) is given by the polynomial function $c(x) = -0.032(x^2 - 24x) + 12.4$, where x is the distance from the wall of the bin (in feet). What is the height of the crown 14 feet from the outside wall?

63. Allied Health A diabetic patient's morning, m, and evening, n, blood glucose levels are a function of the number of days, t, since the patient was diagnosed and can be approximated by the formulas $m(t) = 0.472t^3 - 5.298t^2 + 11.802t + 93.143$ and $n(t) = -1.083t^3 - 11.464t^2 - 29.524t + 117.429$. Write a polynomial function approximating the difference, d, in morning and evening blood glucose levels as a function of the number of days since diagnosis.

Answers

53. $P(x) = 50x - 2{,}000$
54. $P(x) = -3x^2 + 50x - 2{,}000$
55. $-2h$
56. 5
57. $x - 11$
58. $-14x^2 - 12x + 15$
59. $-3x + 5$
60. 28.7 mcg/mL
61. 7.952 ft
62. 16.88 ft
63. $d(t) = 1.555t^3 - 16.762t^2 + 41.326t - 24.286$

Answers

64. (a) $T(d) + I(d) = 0.6d^3 + \frac{\pi}{4}d^2 + 1.57d$; (b) 40.84 ft-lb

65. −15

66. −5

67. $a = 3, b = 5, c = 0, d = -1$

68. $a = 1, b = -4, c = -2, d = 6$

69. $28x + 4$

70. $12x + 4$

71. $10x - 2$

72. $5x - 6$

64. Automotive Technology The torque, measured in foot-pounds (ft-lb), generated by a piston can be found using the polynomial function

$T(d) = 0.4d^3 + \frac{\pi}{4}d^2 + 1.25d$. Adding a turbo will add to this torque.

The increase in torque is described by $I(d) = 0.2d^3 + 0.32d$.

(a) Write the polynomial function to describe the torque of the piston with the turbo.

(b) What is the torque generated by a 3.5-inch-diameter cylinder with a turbo?

Basic Skills | Advanced Skills | Vocational-Technical Applications | Calculator/Computer | **Above and Beyond**

Let $P(x) = 2x^3 - 3x^2 + 5x - 5$ *and* $Q(x) = -x^2 + 2x - 2$. *Find each of the following.*

65. $P[Q(1)]$

66. $Q[P(1)]$

Find values for a, b, c, and d so that the following equations are true.

67. $3ax^4 - 5x^3 + x^2 - cx + 2 = 9x^4 - bx^3 + x^2 - 2d$

68. $(4ax^3 - 3bx^2 - 10) - 3(x^3 + 4x^2 - cx - d) = x^3 - 6x + 8$

69. Geometry A rectangle has sides of $8x + 9$ and $6x - 7$. Find the polynomial that represents its perimeter.

70. Geometry A triangle has sides $3x + 7$, $4x - 9$, and $5x + 6$. Find the polynomial that represents its perimeter.

71. For the given figure, write the polynomial that represents the perimeter.

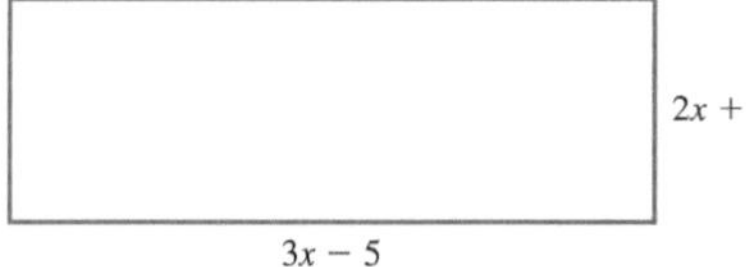

72. For the given figure, the perimeter is given by $14x + 5$. Write the polynomial that represents the missing side.

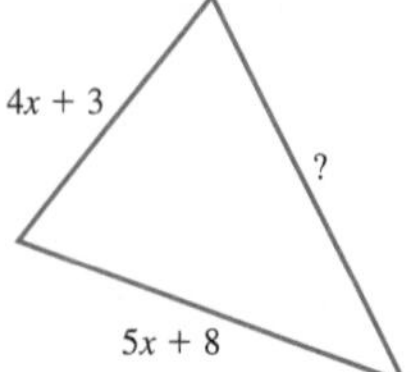

73. The length of a rectangle is 1 cm more than twice its width. Represent the width of the rectangle by w, and write a polynomial to express the perimeter of the rectangle in terms of w. Be sure to simplify your result.

74. One integer is 2 more than twice the first. Another is 3 less than 3 times the first. Represent the first integer by x, and then write a polynomial to express the sum of the three integers in terms of x. Be sure to simplify your result.

Polynomials are sometimes thought of as "numbers" in base x rather than base 10. Exercises 75 and 76 explore this idea further.

75. The number 3078 can be written as the polynomial

$3(10)^3 + 0(10)^2 + 7(10)^1 + 8(10)^0$

because 10 is the *base* of the number system we commonly use. All numbers can be written as a polynomial if we allow integer exponents. Interpret the following polynomials by writing them the way they would normally appear.

(a) $7(10)^4 + 5(10)^3 + 0(10)^2 + 2(10) + 0(10)^0 =$ __________

(b) $4(10)^2 + 2(10) + 3(10)^{-1} + 2(10)^{-2} + 5(10)^{-3} =$ __________

Write these numbers as polynomials:

(c) $6525 =$ __________

(d) $99.95 =$ __________

76. In exercise 75, the first number in the list could be written with a variable in place of the 10: $7(n)^4 + 5(n)^3 + 0(n)^2 + 2(n) + 0(n)^0$. Notice this gives a polynomial "number" in base n. The number could still be written as 75020, but the value of the number would be very different from 75 thousand 20 if the *base* were different. Try $n = 8$ and calculate the value of 75020_8. This is read "75020 base 8." Did you get 31248?

The number 11011 in base 10 is eleven thousand eleven. Written as a polynomial:

$1(n)^4 + 1(n)^3 + 0(n)^2 + 1(n) + 1(n)^0$

If $n = 2$, we have another value for 11011 but this time in *base 2,* another very widely used number system because it is used by computers. Evaluate 11011_2 in base 10.

Write the following as polynomials and then evaluate the numbers in base 10:

(a) $546302_7 =$ __________ = __________ in base 10

(b) $111100111_2 =$ __________ = __________ in base 10

(c) $21112_3 =$ __________ = __________ in base 10

(d) $21112_5 =$ __________ = __________ in base 10

You may want to find out more about base 2 numbers or the binary number system because versions of it are widely used in computers, bar code scanners, and other electronic devices.

Answers

73. $6w + 2$

74. $6x - 1$

75. (a) 75,020; (b) 420.325; (c) $6(10)^3 + 5(10)^2 + 2(10)^1 + 5(10)^0$; (d) $9(10)^1 + 9(10)^0 + 9(10)^{-1} + 5(10)^{-2}$

76. (a) 95,846; (b) 487; (c) 203; (d) 1,407

Answers

1. Binomial **3.** Trinomial **5.** Not classified **7.** Monomial
9. Not a polynomial **11.** $4x^5 - 3x^2$; 5 **13.** $-5x^9 + 7x^7 + 4x^3$; 9
15. $4x^2y^4z$; 7 **17.** $x^6 - 3x^5 + 5x^2 - 7$; 6 **19.** 7, -5 **21.** 62, 30
23. (a) $(0, -5)$; **(b)** $\left(\frac{1}{2}, -3\right)$; **(c)** $(-0.2, -5.52)$; **(d)** $(0, -7)$; **(e)** $\left(\frac{1}{2}, -\frac{17}{2}\right)$;
(f) $(-0.2, -5.84)$ **25. (a)** $(0, -12)$; **(b)** $\left(\frac{1}{2}, -\frac{39}{4}\right)$; **(c)** $(-0.2, -13.768)$;
(d) $(0, -14)$; **(e)** $\left(\frac{1}{2}, -\frac{75}{8}\right)$; **(f)** $(-0.2, -15.192)$ **27. (a)** $h(x) = 9x + 4$;
(b) 13; **(c)** 13 **29. (a)** $h(x) = -x^2 - 2x - 2$; **(b)** -5; **(c)** -5
31. (a) $h(x) = 2x + 13$; **(b)** 15; **(c)** 15 **33. (a)** $h(x) = 3x^2 - 2x - 7$; **(b)** -6;
(c) -6 **35.** always **37.** sometimes **39.** sometimes
41. sometimes **43.** $C(x) = 3x + 20$; \$170 **45.** $4x + 7$
47. $13x^2 + 5$ **49.** $3x + 4$ **51.** $x - 12$ **53.** $P(x) = 50x - 2{,}000$
55. $-2h$ **57.** $x - 11$ **59.** $-3x + 5$ **61.** 7.952 ft
63. $d(t) = 1.555t^3 - 16.762t^2 + 41.326t - 24.286$ **65.** -15
67. $a = 3, b = 5, c = 0, d = -1$ **69.** $28x + 4$ **71.** $10x - 2$
73. $6w + 2$ **75. (a)** 75,020; **(b)** 420.325;
(c) $6(10)^3 + 5(10)^2 + 2(10)^1 + 5(10)^0$;
(d) $9(10)^1 + 9(10)^0 + 9(10)^{-1} + 5(10)^{-2}$

5.2 Multiplication of Polynomials

< 5.2 Objectives >

1 > Evaluate $f(x) \cdot g(x)$ for a given x

2 > Multiply two polynomial functions

3 > Multiply using the special product formulas

RECALL

$a^m \cdot a^n = a^{m+n}$

You have already had some experience multiplying polynomials. In Section 1.5, we stated the product property of exponents and used that property to find the product of two monomials. We will review briefly.

Step by Step

To Find the Product of Monomials

Step 1 Multiply the coefficients.
Step 2 Use the product property of exponents to combine the variables.

Example 1 Multiplying Monomials

RECALL

The associative and commutative properties are used to "regroup" and "reorder" the factors.

Multiply.

$$(8x^2y)(4x^3y^4) = (8 \cdot 4)(x^{2+3})(y^{1+4})$$

Add exponents.

Multiply coefficients.

$$= 32x^5y^5$$

Check Yourself 1

Multiply.

(a) $(4a^3b)(9a^3b^2)$ **(b)** $(-5m^3n)(7mn^5)$

RECALL

The distributive property is $a(b + c) = ab + ac$

We now want to extend this process to multiplying polynomial functions. To do this we will need to find the product of a monomial and a polynomial.

Property

To Multiply a Polynomial by a Monomial

Use the distributive property to multiply each term of the polynomial by the monomial.

Example 2 Multiplying a Monomial and a Binomial Function

Given $f(x) = 5x^2$ and $g(x) = 3x^2 - 5x$, and letting $h(x) = f(x) \cdot g(x)$, find $h(x)$.

$$\begin{aligned} h(x) &= f(x) \cdot g(x) \\ &= 5x^2 \cdot (3x^2 - 5x) \qquad \text{Apply the distributive property.} \\ &= 5x^2 \cdot 3x^2 - 5x^2 \cdot 5x \\ &= 15x^4 - 25x^3 \end{aligned}$$

Check Yourself 2

Given $f(x) = 3x^2$ and $g(x) = 4x^2 + x$, and letting $h(x) = f(x) \cdot g(x)$, find $h(x)$.

We can check this result by comparing the values of $h(x)$ and of $f(x) \cdot g(x)$ for a specific value of x. This is illustrated in Example 3.

Example 3 Evaluating $f(x) \cdot g(x)$ for a Given x

< Objective 1 >

Given $f(x) = 5x^2$ and $g(x) = 3x^2 - 5x$, and letting $h(x) = f(x) \cdot g(x)$, compare $f(1) \cdot g(1)$ with $h(1)$.

$$\begin{aligned} f(1) \cdot g(1) &= 5(1)^2 \cdot (3(1)^2 - 5(1)) \\ &= 5(3 - 5) \\ &= 5(-2) \\ &= -10 \end{aligned}$$

From Example 2, we know that

$$h(x) = 15x^4 - 25x^3$$

So

$$\begin{aligned} h(1) &= 15(1)^4 - 25(1)^3 \\ &= 15 - 25 \\ &= -10 \end{aligned}$$

Therefore, $h(1) = f(1) \cdot g(1)$.

Check Yourself 3

Given $f(x) = 3x^2$ and $g(x) = 4x^2 + x$, and letting $h(x) = f(x) \cdot g(x)$, compare $f(1) \cdot g(1)$ with $h(1)$.

The distributive property is also used to multiply two polynomial functions. To consider the pattern, let us start with the product of two binomial functions.

Example 4 Multiplying Binomial Functions

< Objective 2 >

Given $f(x) = x + 3$ and $g(x) = 2x + 5$, and letting $h(x) = f(x) \cdot g(x)$, find the following.

(a) $h(x)$

$h(x) = f(x) \cdot g(x)$

$= (x + 3)(2x + 5)$ Apply the distributive property.

$= (x + 3)(2x) + (x + 3)(5)$ Apply the distributive property again.

$= (x)(2x) + (3)(2x) + (x)(5) + (3)(5)$

$= 2x^2 + 6x + 5x + 15$

$= 2x^2 + 11x + 15$

Notice that this ensures that each term in the first polynomial is multiplied by each term in the second polynomial.

(b) $f(1) \cdot g(1)$

$f(1) \cdot g(1) = (1 + 3)(2(1) + 5)$

$= 4(7)$

$= 28$

(c) $h(1)$

From part **(a)**, we have $h(x) = 2x^2 + 11x + 15$, so

$h(1) = 2(1)^2 + 11(1) + 15$

$= 2 + 11 + 15$

$= 28$

Again, we see that $h(1) = f(1) \cdot g(1)$.

Check Yourself 4

Given $f(x) = 3x - 2$ and $g(x) = x + 3$, and letting $h(x) = f(x) \cdot g(x)$, find the following.

(a) $h(x)$ **(b)** $f(1) \cdot g(1)$ **(c)** $h(1)$

You may remember a pattern that allows you to write the product of two binomials without going through all the preceding steps. It is called the **FOIL method** of multiplying. Consider $(x + 3)(2x + 5)$ again. To multiply:

NOTES

Remember this by F.

Remember this by O.

1. $(x + 3)(2x + 5)$

$x \cdot 2x$ Find the product of the *first* terms of the factors.

2. $(x + 3)(2x + 5)$

$x \cdot 5$ Find the product of the *outer* terms.

NOTES

Remember this by I.

Remember this by L.

3. $(x + 3)(2x + 5)$

$3 \cdot 2x$ Find the product of the *inner* terms.

4. $(x + 3)(2x + 5)$

$3 \cdot 5$ Find the product of the *last* terms.

Combining the four steps, we have

$(x + 3)(2x + 5)$

$= 2x^2 + 5x + 6x + 15$ Same four terms as in Example 4(a)

$= 2x^2 + 11x + 15$

RECALL

When polynomials are multiplied, each term of one polynomial must multiply each term of the other polynomial.

As can be seen, this method produces the same four products as distributing. It is called FOIL to give you an easy way of remembering the steps: *F*irst, *O*uter, *I*nner, *L*ast. With practice, you can use the FOIL method to write products quickly and easily. However, FOIL can only be used when multiplying two binomials since it involves four products: *F*irst, *O*uter, *I*nner, *L*ast. When multiplying larger polynomials, we need more products, so FOIL cannot be used. We will look at such multiplying shortly. But first, let us consider some common problem types that occur when multiplying two binomials.

Certain products occur frequently enough in algebra that it is worth learning special formulas for dealing with them. Consider these products of two equal binomial factors.

NOTE

$a^2 + 2ab + b^2$

and

$a^2 - 2ab + b^2$

are called **perfect-square trinomials.**

$$(a + b)^2 = (a + b)(a + b)$$
$$= a^2 + 2ab + b^2$$
$$(a - b)^2 = (a - b)(a - b)$$
$$= a^2 - 2ab + b^2$$

We can summarize these statements as follows.

Property

Squaring a Binomial

The square of a binomial has three terms: (1) the square of the first term, (2) twice the product of the two terms, and (3) the square of the last term.

$(a + b)^2 = a^2 + 2ab + b^2$

and

$(a - b)^2 = a^2 - 2ab + b^2$

Example 5 **Squaring a Binomial**

< Objective 3 >

NOTE

Be sure to write out the expansion in detail.

Find each of the following binomial squares.

(a) $(x + 5)^2 = x^2 + 2(x)(5) + 5^2$

Square of first term | Twice the product of the two terms | Square of last term

$= x^2 + 10x + 25$

> CAUTION

Be Careful! A very common mistake in squaring binomials is to forget *the middle* term!
$(y + 7)^2$
is not equal to
$y^2 + (7)^2$
The correct square is
$y^2 + 14y + 49$
The square of a binomial is *always* a trinomial.

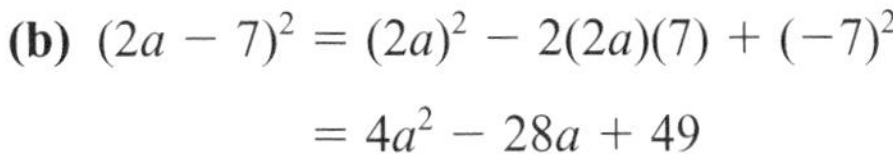

(b) $(2a - 7)^2 = (2a)^2 - 2(2a)(7) + (-7)^2$

$= 4a^2 - 28a + 49$

Check Yourself 5

Find each of the following binomial squares.

(a) $(x + 8)^2$ **(b)** $(3x - 5)^2$

NOTE

We will call this final expression the **difference of two squares.**

Another special product involves binomials that differ only in sign. It will be extremely important in your work on factoring later in this chapter. Consider the following:

$$(a + b)(a - b) = a^2 - ab + ab + b^2$$
$$= a^2 - b^2$$

Property

Product of Binomials Differing in Sign

$(a + b)(a - b) = a^2 - b^2$

In words, the product of two binomials that differ only in the signs of their second terms is the difference of the squares of the two terms of the binomials.

Example 6 Finding a Special Product

NOTE

Two binomials that differ only in the signs of their second terms are called **conjugates.** We will see these again in later chapters.

Multiply.

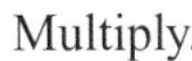

(a) $(x - 3)(x + 3) = x^2 - (3)^2$

$= x^2 - 9$

(b) $(2x - 3y)(2x + 3y) = (2x)^2 - (3y)^2$

$= 4x^2 - 9y^2$

(c) $(5a + 4b^2)(5a - 4b^2) = (5a)^2 - (4b^2)^2$

$= 25a^2 - 16b^4$

> CAUTION

In part **(b),** the entire term $2x$ is squared, not just the x.

Check Yourself 6

Find each of the following products.

(a) $(y + 5)(y - 5)$ **(b)** $(2x - 3)(2x + 3)$ **(c)** $(4r + 5s^2)(4r - 5s^2)$

When multiplying two polynomials that do not fit one of the special product patterns, there are two different ways to set up the multiplication. Example 7 will illustrate the vertical approach.

Example 7 Multiplying Polynomials

NOTE

This format ensures that each term of one polynomial multiplies each term of the other.

Multiply $3x^3 - 2x^2 + 5$ and $3x + 2$.

Step 1

$$\begin{array}{r} 3x^3 - 2x^2 + 5 \\ 3x + 2 \\ \hline 6x^3 - 4x^2 + 10 \end{array}$$

Multiply by 2.

Step 2

$$\begin{array}{r} 3x^3 - 2x^2 + 5 \\ 3x + 2 \\ \hline 6x^3 - 4x^2 + 10 \\ 9x^4 - 6x^3 + 15x \\ \hline \end{array}$$

Multiply by $3x$. Note that we align the terms in the partial product.

Step 3

$$\begin{array}{r} 3x^3 - 2x^2 + 5 \\ 3x + 2 \\ \hline 6x^3 - 4x^2 + 10 \\ 9x^4 - 6x^3 + 15x \\ \hline 9x^4 - 4x^2 + 15x + 10 \end{array}$$

Add the partial products.

Check Yourself 7

Find the following product, using the vertical method.

$(4x^3 - 6x - 7)(3x - 2)$

A horizontal approach to the multiplication in Example 7 is also possible by the distributive property. As we see in Example 8, we first distribute $3x$ over the trinomial and then we distribute 2 over the trinomial.

Example 8 Multiplying Polynomials

NOTE

Again, this ensures that each term of one polynomial multiplies each term of the other.

Multiply $(3x + 2)(3x^3 - 2x^2 + 5)$, using a horizontal format.

Step 1

$(3x + 2)(3x^3 - 2x^2 + 5)$

Step 2

$= \underbrace{9x^4 - 6x^3 + 15x}_{\text{Step 1}} + \underbrace{6x^3 - 4x^2 + 10}_{\text{Step 2}}$ Combine like terms.

$= 9x^4 - 4x^2 + 15x + 10$ Write the product in descending form.

> CAUTION

We are not multiplying two binomials, so FOIL cannot be used here. This problem requires six product terms.

Check Yourself 8

Find the product of Check Yourself 7, using a horizontal format.

Multiplication sometimes involves the product of more than two polynomials. In such cases, the associative property of multiplication allows us to regroup the factors to make the multiplication easier. Generally, we choose to start with the product of binomials. Example 9 illustrates this approach.

Example 9 Multiplying Polynomials

Find the products.

(a) $x(x + 3)(x - 3) = x(x^2 - 9)$ — Find the product $(x + 3)(x - 3)$.

$= x^3 - 9x$ — Then distribute x as the last step.

(b) $2x(x + 3)(2x - 1) = 2x(2x^2 + 5x - 3)$ — Find the product of the binomials.

$= 4x^3 + 10x^2 - 6x$ — Then distribute $2x$.

Check Yourself 9

Find each of the following products.

(a) $m(2m + 3)(2m - 3)$ **(b)** $3a(2a + 5)(a - 3)$

Check Yourself ANSWERS

1. **(a)** $36a^6b^3$; **(b)** $-35m^4n^6$ **2.** $h(x) = 12x^4 + 3x^3$ **3.** $f(1) \cdot g(1) = 15 = h(1)$ **4.** **(a)** $h(x) = 3x^2 + 7x - 6$; **(b)** $f(1) \cdot g(1) = 4$; **(c)** $h(1) = 4$ **5.** **(a)** $x^2 + 16x + 64$; **(b)** $9x^2 - 30x + 25$ **6.** **(a)** $y^2 - 25$; **(b)** $4x^2 - 9$; **(c)** $16r^2 - 25s^4$ **7.** $12x^4 - 8x^3 - 18x^2 - 9x + 14$ **8.** $12x^4 - 8x^3 - 18x^2 - 9x + 14$ **9.** **(a)** $4m^3 - 9m$; **(b)** $6a^3 - 3a^2 - 45a$

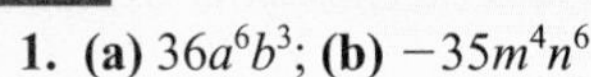

Reading Your Text

The following fill-in-the-blank exercises are designed to ensure that you understand some of the key vocabulary used in this section.

SECTION 5.2

(a) We use the ____________ property to multiply two polynomial functions.

(b) $a^2 - 2ab + b^2$ is called a ____________.

(c) The square of a binomial has ____________ terms.

(d) The FOIL method of multiplying can only be used to multiply two ____________.

5.2 exercises

Basic Skills | Advanced Skills | Vocational-Technical Applications | Calculator/Computer | Above and Beyond

Name ____________

Section ________ Date ________

Find each product.

1. $(4x)(5y)$

2. $(-3m)(5n)$

3. $(6x^2)(-3x^3)$

4. $(5y^4)(3y^2)$

5. $(5r^2s)(6r^3s^4)$

6. $(-8a^2b^5)(-3a^3b^2)$

< Objective 1 >

In exercises 7 to 14, $f(x)$ and $g(x)$ are given. Let $h(x) = f(x) \cdot g(x)$. Find **(a)** *$h(x)$,* **(b)** *$f(1) \cdot g(1)$, and* **(c)** *use the result of part* **(a)** *to find $h(1)$.*

7. $f(x) = 3x$ and $g(x) = 2x^2 - 3x$

8. $f(x) = 4x$ and $g(x) = 2x^2 - 7x$

9. $f(x) = -5x$ and $g(x) = -3x^2 - 5x + 8$

10. $f(x) = 2x^2$ and $g(x) = -7x^2 + 2x$

11. $f(x) = 4x^3$ and $g(x) = 9x^2 + 3x - 5$

12. $f(x) = 2x^3$ and $g(x) = 2x^3 - 4x$

13. $f(x) = 3x^3$ and $g(x) = 5x^2 - 4x$

14. $f(x) = -x^2$ and $g(x) = -7x^3 - 5x^2$

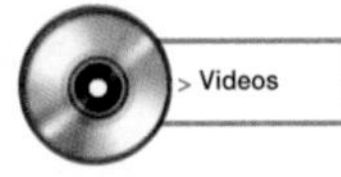

< Objective 2 >

Find each product.

15. $(x + y)(x + 3y)$

16. $(x - 3y)(x + 5y)$

17. $(x - 2y)(x + 7y)$

18. $(x + 7y)(x - 3y)$

Answers

1. $20xy$
2. $-15mn$
3. $-18x^5$
4. $15y^6$
5. $30r^5s^5$
6. $24a^5b^7$
7. (a) $6x^3 - 9x^2$; (b) -3; (c) -3
8. (a) $8x^3 - 28x^2$; (b) -20; (c) -20
9. (a) $15x^3 + 25x^2 - 40x$; (b) 0; (c) 0
10. (a) $-14x^4 + 4x^3$; (b) -10; (c) -10
11. (a) $36x^5 + 12x^4 - 20x^3$; (b) 28; (c) 28
12. (a) $4x^6 - 8x^4$; (b) -4; (c) -4
13. (a) $15x^5 - 12x^4$; (b) 3; (c) 3
14. (a) $7x^5 + 5x^4$; (b) 12; (c) 12
15. $x^2 + 4xy + 3y^2$
16. $x^2 + 2xy - 15y^2$
17. $x^2 + 5xy - 14y^2$
18. $x^2 + 4xy - 21y^2$

19. $(5x - 7y)(5x - 9y)$

20. $(3x - 5y)(7x + 2y)$

21. $(7x - 5y)(7x - 4y)$

22. $(9x + 7y)(3x - 2y)$

23. $(5x^2 - 2y)(3x + 2y^2)$

24. $(6x^2 - 5y^2)(3x^2 - 2y)$

< Objective 3 >

Multiply the polynomial expressions using the special product formulas.

25. $(x + 5)^2$

26. $(x - 7)^2$

27. $(2x - 3)^2$

28. $(5x + 3)^2$

29. $(4x - 3y)^2$

30. $(7x - 5y)^2$

31. $(4x + 3y^2)^2$

32. $(3x^3 - 7y)^2$

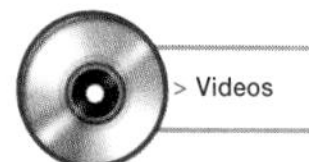

33. $(x - 3y)(x + 3y)$

34. $(x + 5y)(x - 5y)$

35. $(2x - 3y)(2x + 3y)$

36. $(5x + 3y)(5x - 3y)$

37. $(4x^2 + 3y)(4x^2 - 3y)$

38. $(7x - 6y^2)(7x + 6y^2)$

In exercises 39 and 40, multiply using the horizontal format.

39. $(3x - y)(x^2 + 3xy - y^2)$

40. $(5x + y)(x^2 - 3xy + y^2)$

In exercises 41 and 42, multiply using the vertical format.

41. $(x - 2y)(x^2 + 2xy + 4y^2)$

42. $(x + 3y)(x^2 - 3xy + 9y^2)$

Answers

19. $25x^2 - 80xy + 63y^2$
20. $21x^2 - 29xy - 10y^2$
21. $49x^2 - 63xy + 20y^2$
22. $27x^2 + 3xy - 14y^2$
23. $15x^3 + 10x^2y^2 - 6xy - 4y^3$
24. $18x^4 - 15x^2y^2 - 12x^2y + 10y^3$
25. $x^2 + 10x + 25$
26. $x^2 - 14x + 49$
27. $4x^2 - 12x + 9$
28. $25x^2 + 30x + 9$
29. $16x^2 - 24xy + 9y^2$
30. $49x^2 - 70xy + 25y^2$
31. $16x^2 + 24xy^2 + 9y^4$
32. $9x^6 - 42x^3y + 49y^2$
33. $x^2 - 9y^2$
34. $x^2 - 25y^2$
35. $4x^2 - 9y^2$
36. $25x^2 - 9y^2$
37. $16x^4 - 9y^2$
38. $49x^2 - 36y^4$
39. $3x^3 + 8x^2y - 6xy^2 + y^3$
40. $5x^3 - 14x^2y + 2xy^2 + y^3$
41. $x^3 - 8y^3$
42. $x^3 + 27y^3$

Answers

43. $x^3 - 2x^2 - 3x$
44. $x^3 + 2x^2 - 8x$
45. $2x^3 - 2x^2 - 40x$
46. $x^5 - 4x^4 + 5x^3 - 20x^2$
47. False
48. False
49. True
50. True
51. $x^2 - 36$
52. $x^2 + 10x + 25$
53. $x^2 - 8x + 16$
54. $x^2 - 25$
55. $\frac{x^2}{3} + \frac{11x}{45} - \frac{4}{15}$
56. $\frac{x^2}{4} + \frac{29x}{80} - \frac{9}{20}$
57. $x^2 - y^2 + 4y - 4$
58. $x^2 - y^2 + 6y - 9$
59. $R(x) = 100x - 2x^3$
60. $R(x) = 100x - 0.2x^2$; $4,500

Simplify each function.

43. $f(x) = x(x - 3)(x + 1)$

44. $f(x) = x(x + 4)(x - 2)$

45. $f(x) = 2x(x - 5)(x + 4)$

46. $f(x) = x^2(x - 4)(x^2 + 5)$

Determine whether the following statements are **true** *or* **false.**

47. $(x + y)^2 = x^2 + y^2$

48. $(x - y)^2 = x^2 - y^2$

49. $(x + y)^2 = x^2 + 2xy + y^2$

50. $(x - y)^2 = x^2 - 2xy + y^2$

Basic Skills | **Advanced Skills** | Vocational-Technical Applications | Calculator/Computer | Above and Beyond

For each of the following problems, let x represent the number; then write an expression for the product.

51. The product of 6 more than a number and 6 less than that same number

52. The square of 5 more than a number

53. The square of 4 less than a number

54. The product of 5 less than a number and 5 more than that same number

Multiply the following.

55. $\left(\frac{x}{2} + \frac{2}{3}\right)\left(\frac{2x}{3} - \frac{2}{5}\right)$

56. $\left(\frac{x}{3} + \frac{3}{4}\right)\left(\frac{3x}{4} - \frac{3}{5}\right)$

57. $[x + (y - 2)][x - (y - 2)]$

58. $[x + (3 - y)][x - (3 - y)]$

If the polynomial p(x) represents the selling price of an object, then the polynomial R(x), in which $R(x) = x \cdot p(x)$, is the revenue produced by selling x objects. Use this information for exercises 59 and 60.

59. If $p(x) = 100 - 2x^2$, find $R(x)$.

60. If $p(x) = 100 - 0.2x$, find $R(x)$. Then find $R(50)$.

61. **GEOMETRY** The length of a rectangle is given by $3x + 5$ centimeters (cm) and the width is given by $2x - 7$ cm. Express the area of the rectangle in terms of x.

62. **GEOMETRY** The base of a triangle measures $3y + 7$ inches (in.) and the height is $2y - 3$ in. Express the area of the triangle as a polynomial.

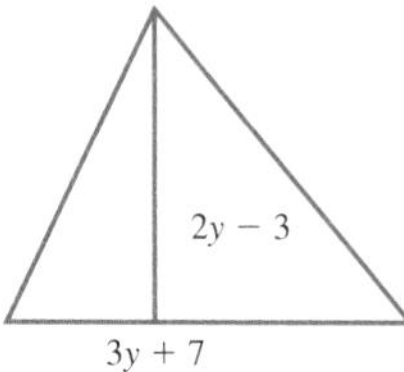

63. **GEOMETRY** A square has sides of length $3a - 2$ centimeters (cm). Express the area of the square as a polynomial.

64. **GEOMETRY** The length and width of a rectangle are given by two consecutive odd integers. Write an expression for the area of the rectangle.

65. **GEOMETRY** The length of a rectangle is 6 less than three times the width. Write an expression for the area of the rectangle.

Basic Skills | Advanced Skills | **Vocational-Technical Applications** | Calculator/Computer | Above and Beyond

66. **ALLIED HEALTH** One proposed rule for estimating the body surface area (BSA) of young children is based entirely on the child's weight, w (in pounds): BSA $= 0.75526w + 1321$. One rule for estimating a child's dose, d, of a medication based on the recommended adult dose, A, is given by the formula $d = 0.5621(\text{BSA})(A)$. Write a simplified formula for estimating a child's dose based only on the child's weight, w, and the recommended adult dose, A.

67. **MANUFACTURING TECHNOLOGY** The maximum stress for a given allowable strain (deformation) for a certain material is given by the polynomial: Stress $= 82.6x - 0.4x^2 + 322$, where x is the weight percent of nickel. After heat treating, the strength polynomial is found by multiplying by $(0.08x + 0.9)$. Find the strength after heat treating.

Basic Skills | Advanced Skills | Vocational-Technical Applications | Calculator/Computer | **Above and Beyond**

68. Complete the following statement: $(a + b)^2$ is not equal to $a^2 + b^2$ because . . . But, wait! Isn't $(a + b)^2$ *sometimes* equal to $a^2 + b^2$? What do you think?

69. Is $(a + b)^3$ ever equal to $a^3 + b^3$? Explain.

Answers

61. $6x^2 - 11x - 35$ cm^2

62. $3y^2 + \frac{5}{2}y - \frac{21}{2}$ in.^{2}

63. $9a^2 - 12a + 4$ cm^2

64. $x(x + 2)$ or $x^2 + 2x$

65. $x(3x - 6)$ or $3x^2 - 6x$

66. $d = 0.4245Aw + 742.5341A$

67. $-0.032x^3 + 6.248x^2 + 100.1x + 289.8$

68. Above and Beyond

69. Above and Beyond

Answers

70. 2,499

71. 884

72. 3,575

73. $a + b, a + b, a^2 + 2ab + b^2; x + 2, x + 2, x^2 + 4x + 4$

74. $x^2; 4x^2; 9x^2; 16x^2; n^2x^2; 6x + 9; 4x - 4; 2xn + n^2; 2xn - n^2$

75. Above and Beyond

Note that $(28)(32) = (30 - 2)(30 + 2) = 900 - 4 = 896$. *Use this pattern for exercises 70–72 to find each of the following products.*

70. $(49)(51)$

71. $(34)(26)$

72. $(55)(65)$

73. In the following figures, identify the length and the width of the square, and then find the area.

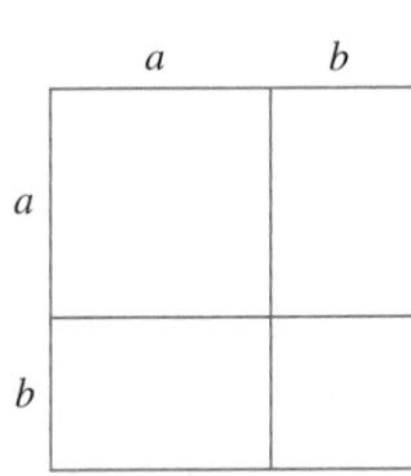

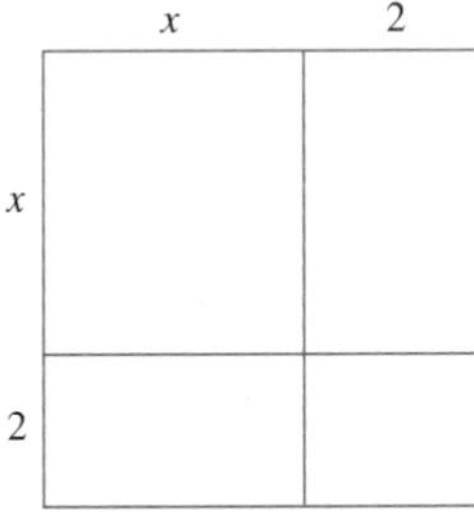

Length = ________ Length = ________

Width = ________ Width = ________

Area = ________ Area = ________

74. The square shown is x units on a side. The area is ________.

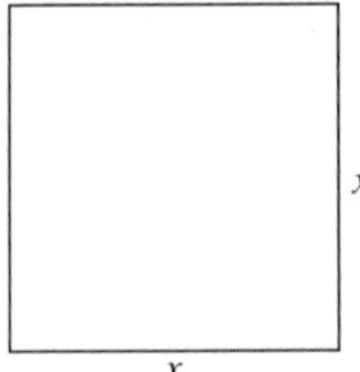

Draw a picture of what happens when the sides are doubled. The area is ________.

Continue the picture to show what happens when the sides are tripled. The area is ________.

If the sides are quadrupled, the area is ________.

In general, if the sides are multiplied by n, the area is ________.

If each side is increased by 3, the area is increased by ________.

If each side is decreased by 2, the area is decreased by ________.

In general, if each side is increased by n, the area is increased by ________, and if each side is decreased by n, the area is decreased by ________.

75. Work with another student to complete this table and write the polynomial. A paper box is to be made from a piece of cardboard 20 inches (in.) wide and 30 in. long. The box will be formed by cutting squares out of each of the four corners and folding up the sides to make a box.

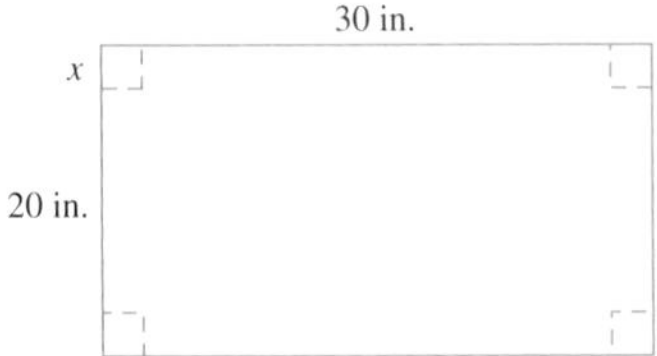

If x is the dimension of the side of the square cut out of the corner, when the sides are folded up, the box will be x inches tall. You should use a piece of paper to try this to see how the box will be made. Complete the following chart.

Length of Side of Corner Square	Length of Box	Width of Box	Depth of Box	Volume of Box
1 in.				
2 in.				
3 in.				
x in.				

Write general formulas for the width, length, and height of the box and a general formula for the *volume* of the box, and simplify it by multiplying. The variable will be the height, the side of the square cut out of the corners. What is the highest power of the variable in the polynomial you have written for the volume? Extend the table to decide what the dimensions are for a box with maximum volume. Draw a sketch of this box and write in the dimensions.

Answers

1. $20xy$ **3.** $-18x^5$ **5.** $30r^5s^5$ **7.** (a) $6x^3 - 9x^2$; (b) -3; (c) -3
9. (a) $15x^3 + 25x^2 - 40x$; (b) 0; (c) 0 **11.** (a) $36x^5 + 12x^4 - 20x^3$; (b) 28; (c) 28
13. (a) $15x^5 - 12x^4$; (b) 3; (c) 3 **15.** $x^2 + 4xy + 3y^2$
17. $x^2 + 5xy - 14y^2$ **19.** $25x^2 - 80xy + 63y^2$ **21.** $49x^2 - 63xy + 20y^2$
23. $15x^3 + 10x^2y^2 - 6xy - 4y^3$ **25.** $x^2 + 10x + 25$ **27.** $4x^2 - 12x + 9$
29. $16x^2 - 24xy + 9y^2$ **31.** $16x^2 + 24xy^2 + 9y^4$ **33.** $x^2 - 9y^2$
35. $4x^2 - 9y^2$ **37.** $16x^4 - 9y^2$ **39.** $3x^3 + 8x^2y - 6xy^2 + y^3$
41. $x^3 - 8y^3$ **43.** $x^3 - 2x^2 - 3x$ **45.** $2x^3 - 2x^2 - 40x$
47. False **49.** True **51.** $x^2 - 36$ **53.** $x^2 - 8x + 16$
55. $\frac{x^2}{3} + \frac{11x}{45} - \frac{4}{15}$ **57.** $x^2 - y^2 + 4y - 4$ **59.** $R(x) = 100x - 2x^3$
61. $6x^2 - 11x - 35$ cm^2 **63.** $9a^2 - 12a + 4$ cm^2
65. $x(3x - 6)$ or $3x^2 - 6x$ **67.** $-0.032x^3 + 6.248x^2 + 100.1x + 289.8$
69. Above and Beyond **71.** 884
73. $a + b, a + b, a^2 + 2ab + b^2; x + 2, x + 2, x^2 + 4x + 4$
75. Above and Beyond

5.3 Division of Polynomials

< 5.3 Objectives >

1 > Find the quotient when a polynomial is divided by a monomial

2 > Find the quotient of two polynomials

3 > Use synthetic division to divide polynomials

In Section 1.5, we introduced the quotient property of exponents, which was used to divide one monomial by another monomial. We will now review that process.

Step by Step

To Divide a Monomial by a Monomial

Step 1 Divide the coefficients.

Step 2 Use the quotient property of exponents to combine the variables.

Example 1 Dividing Monomials

RECALL

The quotient property of exponents says: If a is not zero,

$$\frac{a^m}{a^n} = a^{m-n}$$

Divide: $\frac{8}{2} = 4$

(a) $\frac{8x^4}{2x^2} = 4x^{4-2}$

Subtract the exponents.

$= 4x^2$

(b) $\frac{45a^5b^3}{9a^2b} = 5a^3b^2$

Check Yourself 1

Divide.

(a) $\frac{16a^5}{8a^3}$ (b) $\frac{28m^4n^3}{7m^3n}$

NOTE

This step depends on the distributive property and the definition of division.

Now we will look at how this can be extended to divide any polynomial by a monomial. For example, to divide $12a^3 + 8a^2$ by 4, proceed as follows:

$$\frac{12a^3 + 8a^2}{4} = \frac{12a^3}{4} + \frac{8a^2}{4}$$

Divide each term in the numerator by the denominator, 4.

Now do each division.

$$= 3a^3 + 2a^2$$

This work leads us to the following rule.

Step by Step

To Divide a Polynomial by a Monomial

Step 1 Divide each term of the polynomial by the monomial.
Step 2 Simplify the results.

Example 2 Dividing by Monomials

< Objective 1 >

Divide each term by 2.

(a) $$\frac{4a^2 + 8}{2} = \frac{4a^2}{2} + \frac{8}{2}$$
$$= 2a^2 + 4$$

Divide each term by $6y$.

(b) $$\frac{24y^3 + (-18y^2)}{6y} = \frac{24y^3}{6y} + \frac{-18y^2}{6y}$$
$$= 4y^2 - 3y$$

Remember the rules for signs in division.

(c) $$\frac{15x^2 + 10x}{-5x} = \frac{15x^2}{-5x} + \frac{10x}{-5x}$$
$$= -3x - 2$$

NOTE

With practice you can write just the quotient.

(d) $$\frac{14x^4 + 28x^3 - 21x^2}{7x^2} = \frac{14x^4}{7x^2} + \frac{28x^3}{7x^2} - \frac{21x^2}{7x^2}$$
$$= 2x^2 + 4x - 3$$

(e) $$\frac{9a^3b^4 - 6a^2b^3 + 12ab^4}{3ab} = \frac{9a^3b^4}{3ab} - \frac{6a^2b^3}{3ab} + \frac{12ab^4}{3ab}$$
$$= 3a^2b^3 - 2ab^2 + 4b^3$$

Check Yourself 2

Divide.

(a) $\dfrac{20y^3 - 15y^2}{5y}$ (b) $\dfrac{8a^3 - 12a^2 + 4a}{-4a}$

(c) $\dfrac{16m^4n^3 - 12m^3n^2 + 8mn}{4mn}$

We are now ready to look at dividing one polynomial by another polynomial (with more than one term). The process is very much like long division in arithmetic, as Example 3 illustrates.

Example 3 Dividing by a Binomial

< Objective 2 >

Compare the steps in these two divisions.

Divide $x^2 + 7x + 10$ *by* $x + 2$. *Divide* 2,176 *by* 32.

NOTE

The first term in the dividend, x^2, is divided by the first term in the divisor, x.

Step 1 $$\begin{array}{r} x \\ x + 2\overline{)x^2 + 7x + 10} \end{array}$$ Divide x^2 by x to get x. $$\begin{array}{r} 6 \\ 32\overline{)2176} \end{array}$$

Step 2 $$\begin{array}{r} x \\ x + 2\overline{)x^2 + 7x + 10} \\ \underline{x^2 + 2x} \end{array}$$ Multiply the divisor, $x + 2$, by x. $$\begin{array}{r} 6 \\ 32\overline{)2176} \\ \underline{192} \end{array}$$

RECALL

To subtract $x^2 + 2x$, mentally change each sign to $-x^2 - 2x$, and add. Take your time and be careful here. This is where most errors are made.

Step 3 $$\begin{array}{r} x \\ x + 2\overline{)x^2 + 7x + 10} \\ \underline{x^2 + 2x} \\ 5x + 10 \end{array}$$ Subtract and bring down 10. $$\begin{array}{r} 6 \\ 32\overline{)2176} \\ \underline{192} \\ 256 \end{array}$$

Step 4 $$\begin{array}{r} x + 5 \\ x + 2\overline{)x^2 + 7x + 10} \\ \underline{x^2 + 2x} \\ 5x + 10 \end{array}$$ Divide $5x$ by x to get 5. $$\begin{array}{r} 68 \\ 32\overline{)2176} \\ \underline{192} \\ 256 \end{array}$$

NOTES

We repeat the process until the degree of the remainder is less than that of the divisor or until there is no remainder.

To check this result, we multiply the divisor $(x + 2)$ by the quotient $(x + 5)$:

$(x + 2)(x + 5) = x^2 + 7x + 10$

Step 5 $$\begin{array}{r} x + 5 \\ x + 2\overline{)x^2 + 7x + 10} \\ \underline{x^2 + 2x} \\ 5x + 10 \\ \underline{5x + 10} \\ 0 \end{array}$$ Multiply $x + 2$ by 5 and then subtract. $$\begin{array}{r} 68 \\ 32\overline{)2176} \\ \underline{192} \\ 256 \\ \underline{256} \\ 0 \end{array}$$

The quotient is $x + 5$.

Check Yourself 3

Divide $x^2 + 9x + 20$ by $x + 4$.

In Example 3, we showed all the steps separately to help you see the process. In practice, the work can be shortened.

Example 4 Dividing by Binomials

NOTE

You might want to write out a problem like $408 \div 17$, to compare the steps.

Divide $x^2 + x - 12$ by $x - 3$.

$$
\begin{array}{r}
x + 4 \\
x - 3\overline{)x^2 + x - 12} \\
\underline{x^2 - 3x} \\
4x - 12 \\
\underline{4x - 12} \\
0
\end{array}
$$

Step 1 Divide x^2 by x to get x, the first term of the quotient.
Step 2 Multiply $x - 3$ by x.
Step 3 Subtract and bring down -12. Remember to mentally change the signs to $-x^2 + 3x$ and add.
Step 4 Divide $4x$ by x to get 4, the second term of the quotient.
Step 5 Multiply $x - 3$ by 4 and subtract.

The quotient is $x + 4$.

Check Yourself 4

Divide.

$(x^2 + 2x - 24) \div (x - 4)$

You may have a remainder in algebraic long division just as in arithmetic. Consider Example 5.

Example 5 Dividing by Binomials

Divide $4x^2 - 8x + 11$ by $2x - 3$.

$$
\begin{array}{r}
2x - 1 \quad \text{Quotient} \\
2x - 3\overline{)4x^2 - 8x + 11} \leftarrow \text{Dividend} \\
\underline{4x^2 - 6x} \\
-2x + 11 \\
\underline{-2x + 3} \\
8 \leftarrow \text{Remainder}
\end{array}
$$

Divisor ($2x - 3$)

NOTE

The divisor is always a denominator. This is similar to

$\frac{7}{5} = 1\frac{2}{5}$

This result can be written as

$$\frac{4x^2 - 8x + 11}{2x - 3}$$

$$= \underbrace{2x - 1}_{\text{Quotient}} + \frac{8 \leftarrow \text{Remainder}}{2x - 3 \leftarrow \text{Divisor}}$$

Check Yourself 5

Divide.

$(6x^2 - 7x + 15) \div (3x - 5)$

The division process shown in our previous examples can be extended to dividends of a higher degree. The steps involved in the division process are exactly the same, as Example 6 illustrates.

Example 6 Dividing by Binomials

Divide $6x^3 + x^2 - 4x - 5$ by $3x - 1$.

$$
\begin{array}{r@{}l}
 & 2x^2 + x - 1 \\
3x - 1 & \overline{)6x^3 + x^2 - 4x - 5} \\
 & \underline{6x^3 - 2x^2} \\
 & \phantom{6x^3 -{}} 3x^2 - 4x \\
 & \phantom{6x^3 -{}} \underline{3x^2 - x} \\
 & -3x - 5 \\
 & \underline{-3x + 1} \\
 & -6
\end{array}
$$

The result can be written as

$$\frac{6x^3 + x^2 - 4x - 5}{3x - 1} = 2x^2 + x - 1 + \frac{-6}{3x - 1}$$

Check Yourself 6

Divide $4x^3 - 2x^2 + 2x + 15$ by $2x + 3$.

NOTE

The term with zero becomes a place holder, just like in arithmetic.

Suppose that the dividend is "missing" a term in some power of the variable. You can use 0 as the coefficient for the missing term. Consider Example 7.

Example 7 Dividing by Binomials

Divide $x^3 - 2x^2 + 5$ by $x + 3$.

$$
\begin{array}{r@{}l}
 & x^2 - 5x + 15 \\
x + 3 & \overline{)x^3 - 2x^2 + 0x + 5} \\
 & \underline{x^3 + 3x^2} \\
 & -5x^2 + 0x \\
 & \underline{-5x^2 - 15x} \\
 & \phantom{x^3 - 5x^2 -{}} 15x + 5 \\
 & \phantom{x^3 - 5x^2 -{}} \underline{15x + 45} \\
 & -40
\end{array}
$$

Write $0x$ for the "missing" term in x.

This result can be written as

$$\frac{x^3 - 2x^2 + 5}{x + 3} = x^2 - 5x + 15 + \frac{-40}{x + 3}$$

Check Yourself 7

Divide.

$(4x^3 + x + 10) \div (2x - 1)$

You should always arrange the terms of the divisor and dividend in descending order before starting the long-division process, as illustrated in Example 8.

Example 8 Dividing by Binomials

Divide $5x^2 - x + x^3 - 5$ by $-1 + x^2$.

Write the divisor as $x^2 - 1$ and the dividend as $x^3 + 5x^2 - x - 5$.

$$\begin{array}{r|rrrr} & & & x & +\,5 \\ \cline{2-5} x^2 - 1 & x^3 & +\,5x^2 & -\,x & -\,5 \\ & x^3 & & -\,x & \\ \cline{2-4} & & 5x^2 & & -\,5 \\ & & 5x^2 & & -\,5 \\ \cline{3-5} & & & & 0 \end{array}$$

Write $x^3 - x$, the product of x and $x^2 - 1$, so that like terms fall in the same columns.

Check Yourself 8

Divide.

$(5x^2 + 10 + 2x^3 + 4x) \div (2 + x^2)$

So far we have been dividing polynomials using long division. Now we will examine an abbreviated method called *synthetic division.*

Consider Example 3 again, but this time without writing the variables: Divide $x^2 + 7x + 10$ by $x + 2$.

$$\begin{array}{rr|rrr} & & & 1 & 5 \\ \cline{3-5} 1 & 2 & 1 & 7 & 10 \\ & & 1 & 2 & \\ \cline{3-4} & & & 5 & 10 \\ & & & 5 & 10 \\ \cline{4-5} & & & & 0 \end{array}$$

This can be abbreviated even more using the process of synthetic division. Since we are dividing by $x + 2$, we begin by writing the opposite of 2 (separated as shown) and the coefficients of the polynomial. The leading coefficient is rewritten below the line.

$$\begin{array}{r|rrr} -2 & 1 & 7 & 10 \\ & & & \\ \hline & 1 & & \end{array}$$

We then multiply the number separated (in this case -2) by the leading coefficient (in this case 1). The result is added to the second coefficient.

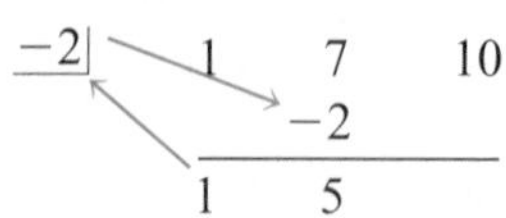

The process is repeated until we have used all the coefficients.

$$\begin{array}{r|rrr} -2 & 1 & 7 & 10 \\ & & -2 & -10 \\ \hline & 1 & 5 & 0 \end{array}$$

You will notice several similarities between long division and synthetic division. The most interesting is along the bottom row. Compare this last row with the results in Example 3. Note that the first two numbers are the coefficients of the quotient, and the last number is the remainder. This will always be the case in synthetic division. Also the exponent of the first term of the quotient will always be one less than the highest degree of the polynomial we are dividing. Therefore, our synthetic division work for this problem matches what we did in Example 3 showing that the quotient is $x + 5$ and the remainder is 0.

Example 9 Using Synthetic Division

< Objective 3 >

NOTE

The divisor is $x - 3$, and the opposite of -3 is 3, which is the separated number.

Use synthetic division to divide $2x^3 - 4x^2 - 7x + 5$ by $x - 3$.

$$\begin{array}{r|rrrr} 3 & 2 & -4 & -7 & 5 \\ & & 6 & 6 & -3 \\ \hline & 2 & 2 & -1 & 2 \end{array} \longleftarrow \text{Remainder}$$

Coefficients of the quotient

So $2x^3 - 4x^2 - 7x + 5 = (x - 3)(2x^2 + 2x - 1) + 2$.

Check Yourself 9

Use synthetic division to find the quotient and remainder when $2x^3 + 7x^2 + 12x - 8$ is divided by $x - 1$.

It is important to remember that to use synthetic division, the divisor must be of the form $x - a$, where the coefficient of x is 1. Just as in long division, we must also be careful when one of the coefficients of the dividend polynomial is 0. We will again use a place holder of 0 when this occurs. Consider Example 10.

Example 10 Dividing a Polynomial

NOTE

Zero represents the coefficient of the x^3 term.

Use synthetic division to find the quotient and remainder when $4x^4 - 3x^2 + 2x - 7$ is divided by $x + 1$.

$$\begin{array}{r|rrrrr} -1 & 4 & 0 & -3 & 2 & -7 \\ & & -4 & 4 & -1 & -1 \\ \hline & 4 & -4 & 1 & 1 & -8 \end{array}$$

Coefficients of the quotient Remainder

So $4x^4 - 3x^2 + 2x - 7 = (x + 1)(4x^3 - 4x^2 + x + 1) + (-8)$.

Check Yourself 10

Use synthetic division to find the quotient and remainder when $3x^4 - 3x^3 + 2$ is divided by $x + 1$.

Now that you have learned synthetic division as a faster way to divide polynomials, you may be wondering why we began this section by discussing long division. One reason is so that you will see why synthetic division works. It really is just an abbreviated form of doing long division. More importantly, however, is to remember that synthetic division only works for problems that have a divisor of the form $x - a$. Therefore, it is helpful to know two different ways of dividing polynomials.

Check Yourself ANSWERS

1. **(a)** $2a^2$; **(b)** $4mn^2$ **2.** **(a)** $4y^2 - 3y$; **(b)** $-2a^2 + 3a - 1$; **(c)** $4m^3n^2 - 3m^2n + 2$ **3.** $x + 5$ **4.** $x + 6$ **5.** $2x + 1 + \dfrac{20}{3x - 5}$ **6.** $2x^2 - 4x + 7 + \dfrac{-6}{2x + 3}$ **7.** $2x^2 + x + 1 + \dfrac{11}{2x - 1}$ **8.** $2x + 5$ **9.** $(x - 1)(2x^2 + 9x + 21) + 13$ **10.** $(x + 1)(3x^3 - 6x^2 + 6x - 6) + 8$

Reading Your Text

The following fill-in-the-blank exercises are designed to ensure that you understand some of the key vocabulary used in this section.

SECTION 5.3

(a) When dividing two monomials, we use the quotient property of exponents to combine the ______________.

(b) Our final step when dividing a polynomial by a monomial is to ______________ the result.

(c) When the dividend is missing a term in some power of the variable, we use ______________ as a coefficient for that missing term.

(d) Synthetic division can only be used for dividing polynomials when the divisor is of the form ______________.

5.3 exercises

Basic Skills | Advanced Skills | Vocational-Technical Applications | Calculator/Computer | Above and Beyond

Boost your grade at mathzone.com!
> Practice Problems
> NetTutor
> Self-Tests
> e-Professors
> Videos

Name ________________

Section ________ Date ________

Answers

1. $2x^4$
2. $4a^2$
3. $5m^2$
4. $7x^2y$
5. $a + 2$
6. $x - 2$
7. $3b^2 - 4$
8. $2m^2 + m$
9. $4a^2 - 6a$
10. $3x^2 + 4x$
11. $-4m - 2$
12. $-4b^2 + 5b$
13. $3a^3 + 2a^2 - a$
14. $3x^4 - 4x^3 + 2x^2$
15. $4x^2y - 3y^2 + 2x$
16. $2m^2n + 3m - 5n$
17. $x + 3$
18. $x + 5$
19. $x - 5$
20. $x - 7$
21. $x + 3$
22. $x + 8$

< Objective 1 >

Divide.

1. $\dfrac{18x^6}{9x^2}$

2. $\dfrac{20a^7}{5a^5}$

3. $\dfrac{35m^3n^2}{7mn^2}$

4. $\dfrac{42x^5y^2}{6x^3y}$

5. $\dfrac{3a + 6}{3}$

6. $\dfrac{4x - 8}{4}$

7. $\dfrac{9b^2 - 12}{3}$

8. $\dfrac{10m^2 + 5m}{5}$

9. $\dfrac{16a^3 - 24a^2}{4a}$

10. $\dfrac{9x^3 + 12x^2}{3x}$

11. $\dfrac{12m^2 + 6m}{-3m}$

12. $\dfrac{20b^3 - 25b^2}{-5b}$

13. $\dfrac{18a^4 + 12a^3 - 6a^2}{6a}$

14. $\dfrac{21x^5 - 28x^4 + 14x^3}{7x}$

15. $\dfrac{20x^4y^2 - 15x^2y^3 + 10x^3y}{5x^2y}$

16. $\dfrac{16m^3n^3 + 24m^2n^2 - 40mn^3}{8mn^2}$

< Objective 2 >

Find the quotient and remainder (if one exists).

17. $\dfrac{x^2 + 5x + 6}{x + 2}$

18. $\dfrac{x^2 + 8x + 15}{x + 3}$

19. $\dfrac{x^2 - x - 20}{x + 4}$

20. $\dfrac{x^2 - 2x - 35}{x + 5}$

21. $\dfrac{2x^2 + 5x - 3}{2x - 1}$

22. $\dfrac{3x^2 + 20x - 32}{3x - 4}$

23. $\frac{2x^2 - 3x - 5}{x - 3}$

24. $\frac{3x^2 + 17x - 12}{x + 6}$

25. $\frac{4x^2 - 18x - 15}{x - 5}$

26. $\frac{3x^2 - 18x - 32}{x - 8}$

27. $\frac{6x^2 - x - 10}{3x - 5}$

28. $\frac{4x^2 + 6x - 25}{2x + 7}$

29. $\frac{x^3 + x^2 - 4x - 4}{x + 2}$

30. $\frac{x^3 - 2x^2 + 4x - 21}{x - 3}$

31. $\frac{4x^3 + 7x^2 + 10x + 5}{4x - 1}$

32. $\frac{2x^3 - 3x^2 + 4x + 4}{2x + 1}$

33. $\frac{x^3 - x^2 + 5}{x - 2}$

34. $\frac{x^3 + 4x - 3}{x + 3}$

35. $\frac{25x^3 + x}{5x - 2}$

36. $\frac{8x^3 - 6x^2 + 2x}{4x + 1}$

37. $\frac{2x^2 - 8 - 3x + x^3}{x - 2}$

38. $\frac{x^2 - 18x + 2x^3 + 32}{x + 4}$

39. $\frac{x^4 - 1}{x - 1}$

40. $\frac{x^4 + x^2 - 16}{x + 2}$

41. $\frac{x^3 - 3x^2 - x + 3}{x^2 - 1}$

42. $\frac{x^3 + 2x^2 + 3x + 6}{x^2 + 3}$

43. $\frac{x^4 + 2x^2 - 2}{x^2 + 3}$

44. $\frac{x^4 + x^2 - 5}{x^2 - 2}$

Answers

23. $2x + 3 + \frac{4}{x - 3}$

24. $3x - 1 + \frac{-6}{x + 6}$

25. $4x + 2 + \frac{-5}{x - 5}$

26. $3x + 6 + \frac{16}{x - 8}$

27. $2x + 3 + \frac{5}{3x - 5}$

28. $2x - 4 + \frac{3}{2x + 7}$

29. $x^2 - x - 2$

30. $x^2 + x + 7$

31. $x^2 + 2x + 3 + \frac{8}{4x - 1}$

32. $x^2 - 2x + 3 + \frac{1}{2x + 1}$

33. $x^2 + x + 2 + \frac{9}{x - 2}$

34. $x^2 - 3x + 13 + \frac{-42}{x + 3}$

35. $5x^2 + 2x + 1 + \frac{2}{5x - 2}$

36. $2x^2 - 2x + 1 + \frac{-1}{4x + 1}$

37. $x^2 + 4x + 5 + \frac{2}{x - 2}$

38. $2x^2 - 7x + 10 + \frac{-8}{x + 4}$

39. $x^3 + x^2 + x + 1$

40. $x^3 - 2x^2 + 5x - 10 + \frac{4}{x + 2}$

41. $x - 3$

42. $x + 2$

43. $x^2 - 1 + \frac{1}{x^2 + 3}$

44. $x^2 + 3 + \frac{1}{x^2 - 2}$

The Streeter/Hutchison Series in Mathematics Intermediate Algebra

Answers

45. $y^2 - y + 1$

46. $y^2 + 2y + 4$

47. $x^2 + 1$

48. $x^3 + 1$

49. Quotient: $x + 5$, remainder: 10

50. Quotient: x, remainder: 4

51. Quotient: $3x^2 - x - 4$, remainder: 6

52. Quotient: $2x^2 - 9x + 20$, remainder: -42

53. Quotient: $4x^2 + 12x + 33$, remainder: 101

54. Quotient: $3x^2 + 12x + 42$, remainder: 170

55. True

56. True

57. $c = -2$

58. $c = 1$

59. Above and Beyond

60. Above and Beyond

45. $\dfrac{y^3 + 1}{y + 1}$

46. $\dfrac{y^3 - 8}{y - 2}$

47. $\dfrac{x^4 - 1}{x^2 - 1}$

48. $\dfrac{x^6 - 1}{x^3 - 1}$

< Objective 3 >

Using synthetic division, find the quotient and remainder for each division.

49. $(x^2 + 4x + 5) \div (x - 1)$

50. $(x^2 - 3x + 4) \div (x - 3)$

51. $(3x^3 + 2x^2 - 5x + 2) \div (x + 1)$

52. $(2x^3 - 5x^2 + 2x - 2) \div (x + 2)$

53. $(4x^3 - 3x + 2) \div (x - 3)$

54. $(3x^3 - 6x + 2) \div (x - 4)$

Determine if the following statements are **true** *or* **false.**

55. When dividing a polynomial by a monomial, the number of terms in the answer will always equal the number of terms in the polynomial.

56. The quotient $\dfrac{x^2 - 7x + 10}{x - 5}$ can be found by synthetic division.

Basic Skills | Advanced Skills | Vocational-Technical Applications | Calculator/Computer | **Above and Beyond**

57. Find the value of c so that $\dfrac{y^2 - y + c}{y + 1} = y - 2$.

58. Find the value of c so that $\dfrac{x^3 + x^2 + x + c}{x^2 + 1} = x + 1$.

59. Write a summary of your work with polynomials. Explain how a polynomial is recognized, and explain the rules for the arithmetic of polynomials—how to add, subtract, multiply, and divide. What parts of this chapter do you feel you understand very well, and what part(s) do you still have questions about, or feel unsure of? Exchange papers with another student and compare your answers.

60. An interesting (and useful) thing about division of polynomials: To find out about this interesting thing, do this division. Compare your answer with another student.

$x - 2\overline{)\,2x^2 + 3x - 5}$ Is there a remainder?

Now, evaluate the polynomial $2x^2 + 3x - 5$ when $x = 2$. Is this value the same as the remainder?

Try $x + 3\overline{)5x^2 - 2x + 1}$. Is there a remainder?

Evaluate the polynomial $5x^2 - 2x + 1$ when $x = -3$. Is this value the same as the remainder?

What happens when there is no remainder?

Try $x - 6\overline{)3x^3 - 14x^2 - 23x - 6}$. Is the remainder zero?

Evaluate the polynomial $3x^3 - 14x^2 - 23x + 6$ when $x = 6$. Is this value zero? Write a description of the patterns you see. When does the pattern hold? Make up several more examples, and test your conjecture.

61. **(a)** Divide $\dfrac{x^2 - 1}{x - 1}$. **(b)** Divide $\dfrac{x^3 - 1}{x - 1}$. **(c)** Divide $\dfrac{x^4 - 1}{x - 1}$.

(d) Based on your results to parts **(a)**, **(b)**, and **(c)**, predict $\dfrac{x^{50} - 1}{x - 1}$.

62. **(a)** Divide $\dfrac{x^2 + x + 1}{x - 1}$. **(b)** Divide $\dfrac{x^3 + x^2 + x + 1}{x - 1}$.

(c) Divide $\dfrac{x^4 + x^3 + x^2 + x + 1}{x - 1}$.

(d) Based on your results to parts **(a)**, **(b)**, and **(c)**,

predict $\dfrac{x^{10} + x^9 + x^8 + \cdots + x + 1}{x - 1}$.

Answers

1. $2x^4$ **3.** $5m^2$ **5.** $a + 2$ **7.** $3b^2 - 4$ **9.** $4a^2 - 6a$
11. $-4m - 2$ **13.** $3a^3 + 2a^2 - a$ **15.** $4x^2y - 3y^2 + 2x$ **17.** $x + 3$
19. $x - 5$ **21.** $x + 3$ **23.** $2x + 3 + \dfrac{4}{x - 3}$ **25.** $4x + 2 + \dfrac{-5}{x - 5}$
27. $2x + 3 + \dfrac{5}{3x - 5}$ **29.** $x^2 - x - 2$ **31.** $x^2 + 2x + 3 + \dfrac{8}{4x - 1}$
33. $x^2 + x + 2 + \dfrac{9}{x - 2}$ **35.** $5x^2 + 2x + 1 + \dfrac{2}{5x - 2}$
37. $x^2 + 4x + 5 + \dfrac{2}{x - 2}$ **39.** $x^3 + x^2 + x + 1$ **41.** $x - 3$
43. $x^2 - 1 + \dfrac{1}{x^2 + 3}$ **45.** $y^2 - y + 1$ **47.** $x^2 + 1$
49. Quotient: $x + 5$, remainder: 10 **51.** Quotient: $3x^2 - x - 4$, remainder: 6
53. Quotient: $4x^2 + 12x + 33$, remainder: 101 **55.** True **57.** $c = -2$
59. Above and Beyond **61.** **(a)** $x + 1$; **(b)** $x^2 + x + 1$; **(c)** $x^3 + x^2 + x + 1$; **(d)** $x^{49} + x^{48} + \cdots + x + 1$

Answers

61. (a) $x + 1$;
(b) $x^2 + x + 1$;
(c) $x^3 + x^2 + x + 1$;
(d) $x^{49} + x^{48} + \cdots + x + 1$

62. (a) $x + 2 + \dfrac{3}{x - 1}$;
(b) $x^2 + 2x + 3 + \dfrac{4}{x - 1}$;
(c) $x^3 + 2x^2 + 3x + 4 + \dfrac{5}{x - 1}$;
(d) $x^9 + 2x^8 + 3x^7 + \cdots + 9x + 10 + \dfrac{11}{x - 1}$

5.4 Common Factors and Factoring by Grouping

< 5.4 Objectives >

1 > Find the greatest common factor (GCF)

2 > Factor out the GCF

3 > Factor by grouping

In Section 5.2 you were given polynomial factors and asked to find the product. We are now going to reverse the process. You will be given a polynomial and asked to find its factors. This is called **factoring.** We will see that a polynomial in factored form is often more useful than a polynomial in standard form.

You have probably had some experience with factoring in previous math courses. You may remember that the concept of greatest common factor plays a central role in factoring. Since it is so important to what we will be doing, after a brief reminder of what factoring means, we will begin our discussion of factoring with a detailed review of the greatest common factor.

Let us start with an example from arithmetic. To *multiply* $5 \cdot 7$, you write

$$5 \cdot 7 = 35$$

To *factor* 35, you would write

$$35 = 5 \cdot 7$$

Factoring is the *reverse* of multiplication.

Now let us look at factoring in algebra. You have used the distributive property as

$$a(b + c) = ab + ac$$

For instance,

$$3(x + 5) = 3x + 15$$

NOTE

3 and $x + 5$ are the factors of $3x + 15$.

To use the distributive property in factoring, we reverse that property as

$$ab + ac = a(b + c)$$

The property lets us remove the common factor a from the terms of $ab + ac$. To use this in factoring, the first step is to see whether each term of the polynomial has a common monomial factor. In our earlier example,

$$3x + 15 = 3 \cdot x + 3 \cdot 5$$

Common factor

NOTE

Again, factoring is the reverse of multiplication.

So, by the distributive property,

$$3x + 15 = 3(x + 5)$$

The original terms are each divided by the greatest common factor to determine the terms in parentheses.

NOTE

Factoring out the GCF is the *first* method to try in any of the factoring problems we will discuss.

To check this, multiply $3(x + 5)$.

Multiplying →

$$3(x + 5) = 3x + 15$$

← Factoring

The first step in factoring is to identify the *greatest common factor* (GCF) of a set of terms. This factor is the product of the largest common numerical coefficient and the highest common power of each variable.

Definition

Greatest Common Factor

The **greatest common factor (GCF)** of a polynomial is the factor that is a product of the largest numerical coefficient factor of the polynomial and each common variable with the smallest exponent in any term.

Example 1 Finding the GCF

< Objective 1 >

Find the GCF for each set of terms.

(a) 9 and 12 The largest number that is a factor of both is 3.

(b) 10, 25, 150 The GCF is 5.

(c) x^4 and x^7

$$x^4 = (x) \cdot (x) \cdot (x) \cdot (x)$$

$$x^7 = (x) \cdot (x) \cdot (x) \cdot (x) \cdot x \cdot x \cdot x$$

NOTE

If a variable is not in a term, its exponent is zero.

The largest power that divides both terms is x^4. (Notice that in the original two terms 4 is the smallest exponent of the two terms.)

(d) $12a^3$ and $18a^2$

$$12a^3 = 2 \cdot (2) \cdot (3) \cdot (a) \cdot (a) \cdot a$$

$$18a^2 = (2) \cdot (3) \cdot 3 \cdot (a) \cdot (a)$$

The GCF is $6a^2$.

NOTE

Checking your factoring by multiplying the factors together is always important.

Check Yourself 1

Find the GCF for each set of terms.

(a) 14, 24 **(b)** 9, 27, 81 **(c)** a^9, a^5 **(d)** $10x^5, 35x^4$

Step by Step

To Factor a Monomial from a Polynomial

Step 1 Find the GCF for all the terms.

Step 2 Use the GCF to factor each term and then apply the distributive property.

Step 3 Mentally check your factoring by multiplication.

Example 2 Factoring Out the GCF

< Objective 2 >

(a) Factor $4x^3 - 12x$.

The largest common numerical factor of 4 and 12 is 4 and x is the common variable with the smallest exponent. So $4x$ is the GCF. Write

$$4x^3 - 12x = 4x \cdot x^2 - 4x \cdot 3$$
$$= 4x(x^2 - 3)$$

NOTE

In part (b), 6 is the GCF of the numerical coefficients, the highest power of a common to all terms is 2, and the highest power of b common to all terms is 2.

(b) Factor $6a^3b^2 - 12a^2b^3 + 24a^4b^4$.

The GCF in this case is $6a^2b^2$. Write

$$6a^3b^2 - 12a^2b^3 + 24a^4b^4$$
$$= 6a^2b^2 \cdot a - 6a^2b^2 \cdot 2b + 6a^2b^2 \cdot 4a^2b^2$$
$$= 6a^2b^2(a - 2b + 4a^2b^2)$$

(c) Factor $8m^4n^2 - 16m^2n^2 + 24mn^3 - 32mn^4$.

Here the GCF is $8mn^2$, and we have

$$8m^4n^2 - 16m^2n^2 + 24mn^3 - 32mn^4$$
$$= 8mn^2 \cdot m^3 - 8mn^2 \cdot 2m + 8mn^2 \cdot 3n - 8mn^2 \cdot 4n^2$$
$$= 8mn^2(m^3 - 2m + 3n - 4n^2)$$

Notice that in part **(b)** it is also true that

$$6a^3b^2 - 12a^2b^3 + 24a^4b^4 = 3ab(2a^2b - 4ab^2 + 8a^3b^3)$$

However, this is not in *completely factored form* because we have not factored out the GCF (that monomial with the largest possible coefficient and degree). In this case, we must remove $6a^2b^2$.

Check Yourself 2

Write each of the following in completely factored form.

(a) $7x^3y - 21x^2y^2 + 28xy^3$ (b) $15m^4n^4 - 5mn^3 + 20mn^2 - 25m^2n^2$

We can have terms with a binomial factor in common, as is the case in Example 3.

Example 3 Finding a Common Factor

RECALL

Because of the commutative property, the factors can be written in either order.

(a) Factor $3x(x + y) + 2(x + y)$.

We see that *the binomial* $x + y$ is a common factor and can be removed.

$$3x(x + y) + 2(x + y)$$
$$= (x + y) \cdot 3x + (x + y) \cdot 2$$
$$= (x + y)(3x + 2)$$

(b) Factor $3x^2(x - y) + 6x(x - y) + 9(x - y)$.
We note that here the GCF is $3(x - y)$. Factoring as before, we have

$$3(x - y)(x^2 + 2x + 3)$$

Check Yourself 3

Completely factor each of the polynomials.

(a) $7a(a - 2b) + 3(a - 2b)$ **(b)** $4x^2(x + y) - 8x(x + y) - 16(x + y)$

Some polynomials can be factored by grouping the terms and finding common factors within each group. Such a process is called **factoring by grouping.**

In Example 3, we looked at the expression $3x(x + y) + 2(x + y)$ and found that we could factor out the common binomial, $(x + y)$, giving us

$$(3x + 2)(x + y)$$

This technique will be used in the first example of factoring by grouping.

Example 4 Factoring by Grouping

< Objective 3 >

Suppose we want to factor the polynomial

$$ax - ay + bx - by$$

As you can see, the polynomial has no common factors. However, look at what happens if we separate the polynomial into *two groups of two terms.*

$$ax - ay + bx - by$$
$$= \underbrace{ax - ay}_{(1)} + \underbrace{bx - by}_{(2)}$$

NOTE

Our example has *four* terms. This is a clue to try the factoring by grouping method.

Now *each* group has a common factor, and we can write the polynomial as

$$a(x - y) + b(x - y)$$

In this form, we can see that $x - y$ is the GCF. Factoring out $x - y$, we get

$$a(x - y) + b(x - y) = (a + b)(x - y)$$

Check Yourself 4

Use the factoring by grouping method to factor the polynomial.

$x^2 - 2xy + 3x - 6y$

Be particularly careful of your treatment of algebraic signs when applying the factoring by grouping method. Consider Example 5.

Example 5 Factoring by Grouping Terms

RECALL

$9 = (-3)(-3)$

Factor $2x^3 - 3x^2 - 6x + 9$.

We group the polynomial as follows.

$$\underbrace{2x^3 - 3x^2}_{(1)} \underbrace{- 6x + 9}_{(2)}$$ Remove the common factor of -3 from the second two terms.

$$= x^2(2x - 3) - 3(2x - 3)$$
$$= (2x - 3)(x^2 - 3)$$

Check Yourself 5

Factor by grouping.

$3y^3 + 2y^2 - 6y - 4$

It may also be necessary to change the order of the terms as they are grouped. Look at Example 6.

Example 6 Factoring by Grouping

NOTE

It is often true that the grouping can be done in more than one way. The factored form will be the same.

Factor $x^2 - 6yz + 2xy - 3xz$.

Grouping the terms as before, we have

$$\underbrace{x^2 - 6yz}_{(1)} + \underbrace{2xy - 3xz}_{(2)}$$

Do you see that we have accomplished nothing because there are no common factors in the first group?

We can, however, rearrange the terms to write the original polynomial as

$$\underbrace{x^2 + 2xy}_{(1)} \underbrace{- 3xz - 6yz}_{(2)}$$

$$= x(x + 2y) - 3z(x + 2y)$$
$$= (x + 2y)(x - 3z)$$

We can now remove the common factor of $x + 2y$ from each group.

Check Yourself 6

We can write the polynomial of Example 6 as

$x^2 - 3xz + 2xy - 6yz$

Factor, and verify that the factored form is the same in either case.

Check Yourself ANSWERS

1. (a) 2; **(b)** 9; **(c)** a^5; **(d)** $5x^4$ **2. (a)** $7xy(x^2 - 3xy + 4y^2)$; **(b)** $5mn^2(3m^3n^2 - n + 4 - 5m)$ **3. (a)** $(a - 2b)(7a + 3)$; **(b)** $4(x + y)(x^2 - 2x - 4)$ **4.** $(x - 2y)(x + 3)$ **5.** $(3y + 2)(y^2 - 2)$ **6.** $(x - 3z)(x + 2y)$

Reading Your Text

The following fill-in-the-blank exercises are designed to ensure that you understand some of the key vocabulary used in this section.

SECTION 5.4

(a) When the integers 5 and 7 are multiplied, the product is 35 and the two numbers 5 and 7 are called ______________.

(b) The ______________ of a polynomial is the factor that is a product of the largest numerical coefficient factor of the polynomial and each common variable with the smallest exponent in any term.

(c) Because of the ______________ property, factors can be written in any order.

(d) When a polynomial has four terms, this is a clue to try factoring by using the ______________ method.

5.4 exercises

Basic Skills | Advanced Skills | Vocational-Technical Applications | Calculator/Computer | Above and Beyond

MathZone

Boost your grade at mathzone.com!
> Practice Problems
> NetTutor
> Self-Tests
> e-Professors
> Videos

Name ______

Section ______ Date ______

< Objective 1 >

Find the greatest common factor for each of the following sets of terms.

1. 10, 12

2. 16, 32, 88 

3. x^2, x^5

4. a^3, a^6, a^9

5. $5x^4, 10x^5$

6. $8a^4, 6a^6, 10a^{10}$

7. $9x^2y, 12xy^2, 15x^2y^2$

8. $15ab^3, 10a^2bc, 25b^2c^3$

9. $15a^2bc^2, 9ab^2c^2, 6a^2b^2c^2$ 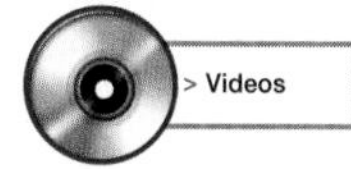

10. $(x + y)^2, (x + y)^3$

< Objective 2 >

Completely factor each polynomial.

11. $6x + 9y$

12. $4x^2 - 12x$

13. $18m^2n + 27mn^2$

14. $5x^3 - 15x^2 + 25x$ 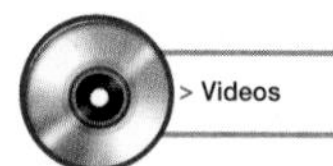

15. $12p^3q - 6pq + 18pq^2$

16. $12a^3b^2 + 18a^2b^3 + 6a^4b^4$

17. $9x^2 - 3xy^3 - 6y^3$

18. $18x^3y^2z^3 - 27x^4y^2z^3 + 81xy^2z$

19. $4r^3s^2 - 8r^2s + 12rs^2 - 4rs$

20. $x(y - z) + 3(y - z)$

Answers

1. 2
2. 8
3. x^2
4. a^3
5. $5x^4$
6. $2a^4$
7. $3xy$
8. $5b$
9. $3abc^2$
10. $(x + y)^2$
11. $3(2x + 3y)$
12. $4x(x - 3)$
13. $9mn(2m + 3n)$
14. $5x(x^2 - 3x + 5)$
15. $6pq(2p^2 - 1 + 3q)$
16. $6a^2b^2(2a + 3b + a^2b^2)$
17. $3(3x^2 - xy^3 - 2y^3)$
18. $9xy^2z(2x^2z^2 - 3x^3z^2 + 9)$
19. $4rs(r^2s - 2r + 3s - 1)$
20. $(y - z)(x + 3)$

21. $3(m - n) + 5(m - n)^2$

22. $5x^2(x - y) - 10x(x - y) + 15(x - y)$

23. $7a^2(a + 2b) + 21a(a + 2b) - 14(a + 2b)$

24. $12(p + q)^4 + 4(p + q)^3$

< Objective 3 >

Factor each polynomial by grouping.

25. $ab - ac + b^2 - bc$

26. $2x^2 - 4x + xz - 2z$

27. $6r^2 + 12rs - r - 2s$

28. $4x + 8x^2 + 1 + 2x$

29. $2mn - 4m^2 + 3n - 6m$

30. $ab^2 - 2b^2 + 3a - 6$

31. $6y^2 - 3y + 2py - p$

32. $r^2s^2 - 3s^2 - 2r^2 + 6$

33. $n^3 - n^2 - nq + q$

34. $n^2m + 2nm + 2n + n^2$

Factor each polynomial by grouping. (Hint: *Consider a rearrangement of terms.*)

35. $x^2 - 10y - 5xy + 2x$

36. $a^2 - 12b + 3ab - 4a$

37. $m^2 - 6n^3 + 2mn^2 - 3mn$

38. $r^2 - 3rs^2 - 12s^3 + 4rs$

Complete each of the following with **never, sometimes,** *or* **always.**

39. The GCF for two numbers is __________ a prime number.

40. The GCF of a polynomial __________ includes variables.

Answers

21. $(m - n)(3 + 5m - 5n)$
22. $5(x - y)(x^2 - 2x + 3)$
23. $7(a + 2b)(a^2 + 3a - 2)$
24. $4(p + q)^3(3p + 3q + 1)$
25. $(b - c)(a + b)$
26. $(x - 2)(2x + z)$
27. $(r + 2s)(6r - 1)$
28. $(1 + 2x)(4x + 1)$
29. $(n - 2m)(2m + 3)$
30. $(a - 2)(b^2 + 3)$
31. $(2y - 1)(3y + p)$
32. $(r^2 - 3)(s^2 - 2)$
33. $(n - 1)(n^2 - q)$
34. $n(n + 2)(m + 1)$
35. $(x + 2)(x - 5y)$
36. $(a + 3b)(a - 4)$
37. $(m - 3n)(m + 2n^2)$
38. $(r - 3s^2)(r + 4s)$
39. sometimes
40. sometimes

Answers

41. always

42. never

43. Correct

44. Correct

45. Incorrect

46. Incorrect

47. Correct

48. Correct

49. $(x + y)(x^2 - x + 3)$

50. $(m + 2n)(m^2 - m - 4)$

51. $(a - b)(a^2 - 3a + 3)$

52. $(r + 2s)(r^2 + r - 3)$

53. $100x(32 - 3x)$

54. $\text{hp} = d\left(2d + \frac{1}{3}\right)$

41. Multiplying the result of factoring will ________ result in the original polynomial.

42. Factoring a negative number from a negative term will ________ result in a negative term.

Basic Skills | **Advanced Skills** | Vocational-Technical Applications | Calculator/Computer | Above and Beyond

Determine if the factoring in each of the following is correct.

43. $x^2 - x - 6 = (x - 3)(x + 2)$

44. $x^2 + x - 12 = (x + 4)(x - 3)$

45. $x^2 + x - 12 = (x + 6)(x - 2)$

46. $x^2 + 2x - 8 = (x + 8)(x - 1)$

47. $2x^2 - 5x - 3 = (2x + 1)(x - 3)$

48. $6x^2 - 13x + 6 = (3x - 2)(2x - 3)$

Factor. (Hint: *Consider* three *groups of* two *terms.*)

49. $x^3 - x^2 + 3x + x^2y - xy + 3y$

50. $m^3 - m^2 - 4m + 2m^2n - 2mn - 8n$

51. $a^3 - a^2b - 3a^2 + 3ab + 3a - 3b$

52. $r^3 + 2r^2s + r^2 + 2rs - 3r - 6s$

Basic Skills | Advanced Skills | **Vocational-Technical Applications** | Calculator/Computer | Above and Beyond

53. **Manufacturing Technology** The bending moment on a beam is given by the expression $3{,}200x - 300x^2$. Factor this expression.

54. **Automotive Technology** The estimated horsepower of an engine is given by

$$\text{hp} = 2d^2 + \frac{1}{3}d$$

Factor the right side of the equation.

55. **Construction Technology** The amount of heat energy required to cut a piece of steel is given by the expression

$812mt + 128m$

Factor this expression.

56. **Agricultural Technology** The increase in yield of a corn crop due to the use of irrigation is estimated by the expression

$4.1r - 0.0018r^2$

Factor this expression.

57. **Allied Health** The concentration, C [in micrograms per milliliter (mcg/mL)] of chloramphenicol, a strong antibiotic, is given by the function $C(t) = 8t^2 - 2t^3$ where t is the number of hours since the drug was taken orally. Write this function in factored form.

58. **Allied Health** A patient's protein secretion amounts, p (in milligrams per day), are tested for several days. From the test results, lab technicians have determined that the function $p(t) = -t^3 - 6t^2 + 11t + 66$ is a good approximation of the patient's protein secretion amounts t days after testing began. Write this function in factored form.

Basic Skills | Advanced Skills | Vocational-Technical Applications | Calculator/Computer | **Above and Beyond**

59. The GCF of $2x - 6$ is 2. The GCF of $5x + 10$ is 5. Find the greatest common factor of the product $(2x - 6)(5x + 10)$.

60. The GCF of $3z + 12$ is 3. The GCF of $4z + 8$ is 4. Find the GCF of the product $(3z + 12)(4z + 8)$.

61. The GCF of $2x^3 - 4x$ is $2x$. The GCF of $3x + 6$ is 3. Find the GCF of the product $(2x^3 - 4x)(3x + 6)$.

62. State, in a sentence, the rule that exercises 59 to 61 illustrated.

63. For the monomials x^4y^2, x^8y^6, and x^9y^4, explain how you can determine the GCF by inspecting exponents.

64. It is not possible to use the grouping method to factor $2x^3 + 6x^2 + 8x + 4$. Is it correct to conclude that the polynomial is prime? Justify your answer.

65. **Geometry** The area of a rectangle with width t is given by $33t - t^2$. Factor the expression and determine the length of the rectangle in terms of t.

66. **Geometry** The area of a rectangle of length x is given by $3x^2 + 5x$. Find the width of the rectangle.

Answers

55. $4m(203t + 32)$
56. $r(4.1 - 0.0018r)$
57. $C(t) = 2t^2(4 - t)$
58. $p(t) = (t + 6)(-t^2 + 11)$
59. 10
60. 12
61. $6x$
62. Above and Beyond
63. Above and Beyond
64. Above and Beyond
65. $33 - t$
66. $3x + 5$

Answers

67. Above and Beyond

68. Above and Beyond

69. Above and Beyond

67. For centuries, mathematicians have found factoring numbers into prime factors a fascinating subject. A prime number is a number that cannot be written as a product of any whole numbers but 1 and itself. The list of positive primes begins with 2 because 1 is not considered a prime number and then goes on: 3, 5, 7, 11, ... What are the first 10 primes? What are the primes less than 100? If you list the numbers from 1 to 100 and then cross out all numbers that are multiples of 2, 3, 5, and 7, what is left? Are all the numbers not crossed out prime? Write a paragraph to explain why this might be so. You might want to investigate the sieve of Eratosthenes, a system from 230 B.C. for finding prime numbers.

68. If we could make a list of all the prime numbers, what number would be at the end of the list? Because there are an infinite number of prime numbers, there is no "largest prime number." But is there some formula that will give us all the primes? Here are some formulas proposed over the centuries:

$n^2 + n + 17 \qquad 2n^2 + 29 \qquad n^2 - n + 11$

In all these expressions, $n = 1, 2, 3, 4, \ldots$, that is, a positive integer beginning with 1. Investigate these expressions with a partner. Do the expressions give prime numbers when they are evaluated for these values of n? Do the expressions give *every* prime in the range of resulting numbers? Can you put in *any* positive number for n?

69. How are primes used in coding messages and for security? Work together to decode the messages. The messages are coded using this code: After the numbers are factored into prime factors, the power of 2 gives the number of the letter in the alphabet. This code would be easy for a code breaker to figure out, but you might make up a code that would be more difficult to break.

(a) 1310720, 229376, 1572864, 1760, 460, 2097152, 336

(b) 786432, 143, 4608, 278528, 1344, 98304, 1835008, 352, 4718592, 5242880

(c) Code a message using this rule. Exchange your message with a partner to decode it.

Answers

1. 2 **3.** x^2 **5.** $5x^4$ **7.** $3xy$ **9.** $3abc^2$ **11.** $3(2x + 3y)$
13. $9mn(2m + 3n)$ **15.** $6pq(2p^2 - 1 + 3q)$ **17.** $3(3x^2 - xy^3 - 2y^3)$
19. $4rs(r^2s - 2r + 3s - 1)$ **21.** $(m - n)(3 + 5m - 5n)$
23. $7(a + 2b)(a^2 + 3a - 2)$ **25.** $(b - c)(a + b)$ **27.** $(r + 2s)(6r - 1)$
29. $(n - 2m)(2m + 3)$ **31.** $(2y - 1)(3y + p)$ **33.** $(n - 1)(n^2 - q)$
35. $(x + 2)(x - 5y)$ **37.** $(m - 3n)(m + 2n^2)$ **39.** sometimes
41. always **43.** Correct **45.** Incorrect **47.** Correct
49. $(x + y)(x^2 - x + 3)$ **51.** $(a - b)(a^2 - 3a + 3)$ **53.** $100x(32 - 3x)$
55. $4m(203t + 32)$ **57.** $C(t) = 2t^2(4 - t)$ **59.** 10 **61.** $6x$
63. Above and Beyond **65.** $33 - t$ **67.** Above and Beyond
69. Above and Beyond

5.5 Factoring Special Binomials

< 5.5 Objectives >

1 > Factor the difference of two squares

2 > Factor the sum or difference of two cubes

> CAUTION

What about the sum of two squares, such as

$x^2 + 25$

In general, it is *not possible* to factor (using real numbers) a sum of two squares. So

$(x^2 + 25) \neq (x + 5)(x + 5)$

In this section, we will look at several special binomials. These binomials are special because they fit a recognizable pattern. Pattern recognition is an important element of mathematics. Many mathematical discoveries were made because somebody recognized a pattern.

The first pattern, which we saw in Section 5.2, is called the **difference of two squares.**

Property

The Difference of Two Squares

$a^2 - b^2 = (a + b)(a - b)$

In words: The *difference of two squares* factors into the product of two binomials, the sum and difference of the same two terms.

This equation is easy to apply in factoring. It is just a matter of recognizing a binomial as the difference of two squares.

To confirm this identity, use the FOIL method to multiply

$(a + b)(a - b)$

Example 1 Factoring the Difference of Two Squares

< Objective 1 >

(a) Factor $x^2 - 25$.

Note that our example has two terms—a clue to try factoring as the difference of two squares.

$$x^2 - 25 = (x)^2 - (5)^2$$
$$= (x + 5)(x - 5)$$

(b) Factor $9a^2 - 16$.

$$9a^2 - 16 = (3a)^2 - (4)^2$$
$$= (3a + 4)(3a - 4)$$

(c) Factor $25m^4 - 49n^2$.

$$25m^4 - 49n^2 = (5m^2)^2 - (7n)^2$$
$$= (5m^2 + 7n)(5m^2 - 7n)$$

NOTE

We are looking for perfect squares—the exponents must be multiples of 2 and the coefficients perfect squares—1, 4, 9, 16, and so on. Don't forget that we also need subtraction.

Check Yourself 1

Factor each of the following binomials.

(a) $y^2 - 36$ **(b)** $25m^2 - n^2$ **(c)** $16a^4 - 9b^2$

We mentioned earlier that factoring out the greatest common factor should always be considered your first step. In some polynomials, you will need to factor out the GCF and then use other factoring techniques. Consider Example 2.

Example 2 Factoring the Difference of Two Squares

Factor $a^3 - 16ab^2$.

First note the GCF of a. Removing that factor, we have

$$a^3 - 16ab^2 = a(a^2 - 16b^2)$$

We now see that the binomial factor is a difference of squares, and we can continue to factor as before. So

$$a^3 - 16ab^2 = a(a + 4b)(a - 4b)$$

Check Yourself 2

Factor $2x^3 - 18xy^2$.

You may also have to apply the difference of two squares method *more than once* to completely factor a polynomial.

Example 3 Factoring the Difference of Two Squares

Factor $m^4 - 81n^4$.

$$m^4 - 81n^4 = (m^2 + 9n^2)(m^2 - 9n^2)$$

Do you see that we are not done in this case? Because $m^2 - 9n^2$ is still factorable, we can continue to factor as follows.

$$m^4 - 81n^4 = (m^2 + 9n^2)(m + 3n)(m - 3n)$$

NOTES

The other binomial factor, $m^2 + 9n^2$, is a *sum of two squares,* which cannot be factored further.

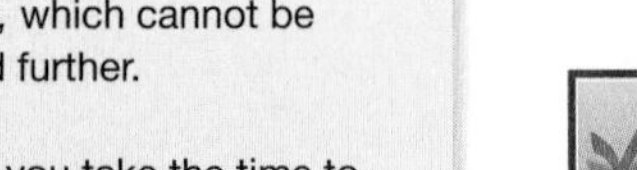

Be sure you take the time to expand the product on the right-hand side to confirm the identity.

Check Yourself 3

Factor $x^4 - 16y^4$.

Two additional patterns for factoring certain binomials include the **sum or difference of two cubes.**

Property

The Sum or Difference of Two Cubes

$$a^3 + b^3 = (a + b)(a^2 - ab + b^2)$$

$$a^3 - b^3 = (a - b)(a^2 + ab + b^2)$$

Example 4 Factoring the Sum or Difference of Two Cubes

< Objective 2 >

NOTE

We are now looking for perfect cubes—the exponents must be multiples of 3 and the coefficients perfect cubes—1, 8, 27, 64, and so on.

(a) Factor $x^3 + 27$.

The first term is the cube of x, and the second is the cube of 3, so we can apply the sum of two cubes formula. Letting $a = x$ and $b = 3$, we have

$$x^3 + 27 = (x + 3)(x^2 - 3x + 9)$$

(b) Factor $8w^3 - 27z^3$.

This is a difference of cubes, so use the difference of two cubes formula.

$$8w^3 - 27z^3 = (2w - 3z)[(2w)^2 + (2w)(3z) + (3z)^2]$$
$$= (2w - 3z)(4w^2 + 6wz + 9z^2)$$

(c) Factor $5a^3b - 40b^4$.

First note the GCF of $5b$. After factoring out $5b$, the remaining binomial is the difference of cubes, so use the difference of two cubes formula.

NOTES

Unlike factoring two squares, which generally must be subtracted, the terms may be added *or* subtracted when factoring two cubes.

Again, looking for the GCF should be your first step.

Remember to write the GCF as a part of the final factored form.

$$5a^3b - 40b^4 = 5b(a^3 - 8b^3)$$
$$= 5b(a - 2b)(a^2 + 2ab + 4b^2)$$

Check Yourself 4

Factor completely.

(a) $27x^3 + 8y^3$ **(b)** $3a^4 - 24ab^3$

In each example in this section, we factored a polynomial expression. Since an unfactored polynomial is equivalent to a factored polynomial, to evaluate a polynomial function for a given value we can use either the factored or unfactored version of the polynomial.

Example 5 Factoring a Polynomial Function

Given the function $f(x) = 4x^2 - 16$, complete the following.

(a) Find $f(1)$.

$$f(1) = 4(1)^2 - 16$$
$$= 4 - 16$$
$$= -12$$

NOTE

As in Section 5.1, this gives us another way to check our work.

(b) Factor $f(x)$.

$$f(x) = 4x^2 - 16$$
$$= 4(x^2 - 4)$$
$$= 4(x + 2)(x - 2)$$

(c) Find $f(1)$ from the factored form of $f(x)$.

$$f(1) = 4((1) + 2)((1) - 2)$$
$$= 4(3)(-1)$$
$$= -12$$

Check Yourself 5

Given the function $f(x) = 4x^3 - 32$, complete the following.

(a) Find $f(1)$. **(b)** Factor $f(x)$.
(c) Find $f(1)$ from the factored form of $f(x)$.

Check Yourself ANSWERS

1. **(a)** $(y + 6)(y - 6)$; **(b)** $(5m + n)(5m - n)$; **(c)** $(4a^2 + 3b)(4a^2 - 3b)$
2. $2x(x + 3y)(x - 3y)$ **3.** $(x^2 + 4y^2)(x + 2y)(x - 2y)$
4. **(a)** $(3x + 2y)(9x^2 - 6xy + 4y^2)$; **(b)** $3a(a - 2b)(a^2 + 2ab + 4b^2)$
5. **(a)** -28; **(b)** $4(x - 2)(x^2 + 2x + 4)$; **(c)** -28

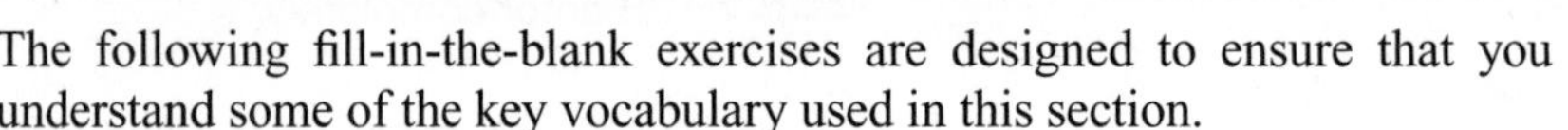

Reading Your Text

The following fill-in-the-blank exercises are designed to ensure that you understand some of the key vocabulary used in this section.

SECTION 5.5

(a) The ______________ factors into the product of two binomials, the sum and the difference of the same two terms.

(b) In general, it is ______________ to factor (using real numbers) a sum of two squares.

(c) When factoring, looking for the ______________ should be your first step.

(d) We can factor the sum and the difference of two ______________.

Basic Skills | Advanced Skills | Vocational-Technical Applications | Calculator/Computer | Above and Beyond

5.5 exercises

Tell which special binomial formula (if any) each of the following represents. Then tell if the binomial can be factored or not.

1. $3x^2 + 2y^2$

2. $16g^2 - 25h^2$

3. $z^3 + 8$

4. $t^2 + 100$

5. $4a^3 - b^3$

6. $k^2 - 45$

7. $8p^6 - 27q^3$

8. $5w^3 + 7z^3$

9. $121m^2 + 144n^2$

10. $125r^3 + 64s^6$

11. $c^2d^2 - 25$

12. $27u^3 - 1{,}000v^3$

< Objective 1 >

Factor the binomials.

13. $x^2 - 49$

14. $a^2 + 81$

15. $9p^2 + 1$

16. $25a^2 - 16$

Name ______________

Section ________ Date ________

Answers

1. Not a special binomial; cannot be factored
2. Difference of two squares; can be factored
3. Sum of two cubes; can be factored
4. Sum of two squares; cannot be factored
5. Not a special binomial; cannot be factored
6. Not a special binomial; cannot be factored
7. Difference of two cubes; can be factored
8. Not a special binomial; cannot be factored
9. Sum of two squares; cannot be factored
10. Sum of two cubes; can be factored
11. Difference of two squares; can be factored
12. Difference of two cubes; can be factored
13. $(x + 7)(x - 7)$
14. Prime, does not factor
15. Prime, does not factor
16. $(5a + 4)(5a - 4)$

17. $x^2y^2 - 25$

18. $4c^2 + 25d^2$

19. $49p^2 + 64q^2$

20. $x^4 - 36y^2$

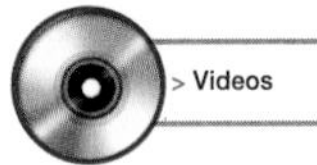

21. $a^3 - 4ab^2$

22. $9p^2q - q^3$

23. $a^4 - 16b^4$

24. $81x^4 - y^4$

< Objective 2 >

Factor the binomials.

25. $x^3 + 64$

26. $m^3 - 125$

27. $a^3b^3 - 27$

28. $8w^3 + z^3$

29. $8x^3 - 27y^3$

30. $8x^3 + y^6$

31. $4x^3 - 32y^3$

32. $3a^3 + 81b^3$

For each of the functions in exercises 33 to 38, **(a)** *find $f(1)$,* **(b)** *factor $f(x)$, and* **(c)** *find $f(1)$ from the factored form of $f(x)$.*

33. $f(m) = 3m^2 - 3$

34. $f(t) = 36t^2 - 16$

35. $f(a) = 5a^3 + 5$

36. $f(m) = 2m^3 + 16$

37. $f(t) = 125t^3 - 8$

38. $f(z) = 216z^3 - 1$

Answers

17. $(xy + 5)(xy - 5)$

18. Prime, does not factor

19. Prime, does not factor

20. $(x^2 + 6y)(x^2 - 6y)$

21. $a(a + 2b)(a - 2b)$

22. $q(3p + q)(3p - q)$

23. $(a^2 + 4b^2)(a + 2b)(a - 2b)$

24. $(9x^2 + y^2)(3x + y)(3x - y)$

25. $(x + 4)(x^2 - 4x + 16)$

26. $(m - 5)(m^2 + 5m + 25)$

27. $(ab - 3)(a^2b^2 + 3ab + 9)$

28. $(2w + z)(4w^2 - 2wz + z^2)$

29. $(2x - 3y)(4x^2 + 6xy + 9y^2)$

30. $(2x + y^2)(4x^2 - 2xy^2 + y^4)$

31. $4(x - 2y)(x^2 + 2xy + 4y^2)$

32. $3(a + 3b)(a^2 - 3ab + 9b^2)$

33. (a) 0; (b) $3(m + 1)(m - 1)$; (c) 0

34. (a) 20; (b) $4(3t + 2)(3t - 2)$; (c) 20

35. (a) 10; (b) $5(a + 1)(a^2 - a + 1)$; (c) 10

36. (a) 18; (b) $2(m + 2)(m^2 - 2m + 4)$; (c) 18

37. (a) 117; (b) $(5t - 2)(25t^2 + 10t + 4)$; (c) 117

38. (a) 215; (b) $(6z - 1)(36z^2 + 6z + 1)$; (c) 215

Determine whether the following statements are **true** *or* **false.**

39. A perfect-square term has a coefficient that is a square and has variables with exponents that are factors of 2.

40. Any time an expression is the sum of two cubes, it can be factored.

41. Although the difference of two squares can be factored, the sum of two squares cannot.

42. When factoring, the middle factor is always factored out as the first step.

Basic Skills | **Advanced Skills** | Vocational-Technical Applications | Calculator/Computer | Above and Beyond

Factor completely.

43. $18x^3 - 2xy^2$

44. $50c^4d^2 - 8c^2d^4$

45. $375t^3 + 24s^3$

46. $3a^5y + 12ay^5$

47. $8k^6 - 27q^3$

48. $2x^4y - 512y^5$

49. $2x^9y + 2xy^9$

50. $12m^3n - 75mn^3$

51. $27a^3 - 64b^3$

52. $125z^3 + 64r^6$

53. $a^5 - ab^4$

54. $50c^2d + 2d^3$

55. $16x^3y^4z - x^3y^4z^5$

56. $54r^3 + 2{,}000s^3$

57. $2p^{10}q - 32p^2q^5$

Basic Skills | Advanced Skills | **Vocational-Technical Applications** | Calculator/Computer | Above and Beyond

58. **Allied Health** A toxic chemical is introduced into a protozoan culture. The number of deaths per hour, N, is given by the function $N(t) = 338 - 2t^2$, where t is the number of hours after the chemical's introduction. Write this function in factored form.

Answers

39. False
40. True
41. True
42. False
43. $2x(3x + y)(3x - y)$
44. $2c^2d^2(5c - 2d)(5c + 2d)$
45. $3(5t + 2s)(25t^2 - 10st + 4s^2)$
46. $3ay(a^4 + 4y^4)$
47. $(2k^2 - 3q)(4k^4 + 6k^2q + 9q^2)$
48. $2y(x - 4y)(x + 4y)(x^2 + 16y^2)$
49. $2xy(x^8 + y^8)$
50. $3mn(2m + 5n)(2m - 5n)$
51. $(3a - 4b)(9a^2 + 12ab + 16b^2)$
52. $(5z + 4r^2)(25z^2 - 20r^2z + 16r^4)$
53. $a(a + b)(a - b)(a^2 + b^2)$
54. $2d(25c^2 + d^2)$
55. $x^3y^4z(2 - z)(2 + z)(4 + z^2)$
56. $2(3r + 10s)(9r^2 - 30rs + 100s^2)$
57. $2p^2q(p^2 - 2q)(p^2 + 2q)(p^4 + 4q^2)$
58. $N(t) = 2(13 - t)(13 + t)$

Answers

59. $N(t) = 4(6 - t)(6 + t)$

60. $W = \frac{1}{2}m(\omega_1 + \omega_2)(\omega_1 - \omega_2)$

61. $s = \frac{(x + 9)(x - 9)}{40}$

62. $p = 0.1(3h + 14)(3h - 14)$

63. $(x + y)^2(x - y)$

64. $(b - c)(a + 4b)(a - 4b)$

65. $2(m - 2n)(m + 3n)(m - 3n)$

66. $3a(2a + b)(a + 3b)(a - 3b)$

67. 4

68. 49

69. 18

70. 45

71. Above and Beyond

72. Above and Beyond

59. **Allied Health** One technique of controlling cancer is to use radiation therapy. After such a treatment, the total number of cancerous cells, N, in thousands, can be estimated by the function $N(t) = 144 - 4t^2$, where t is the number of days of treatment. Write this function in factored form.

60. **Automotive Technology** The work done by an engine measured at the fly wheel is given by the formula $W = \frac{1}{2}m(\omega_1^2 - \omega_2^2)$. Factor this expression.

61. **Construction Technology** The shape of a sagging floor joist is given by the equation $s = \frac{x^2 - 81}{40}$

Factor the numerator of this equation.

62. **Agricultural Technology** The pressure generated by the corn piled in a bin is described by the equation $p = 0.9h^2 - 19.6$. Factor the right side of this equation.

Basic Skills | Advanced Skills | Vocational-Technical Applications | Calculator/Computer | **Above and Beyond**

For exercises 63 to 66, factor completely.

63. $x^2(x + y) - y^2(x + y)$

64. $a^2(b - c) - 16b^2(b - c)$

65. $2m^2(m - 2n) - 18n^2(m - 2n)$

66. $3a^3(2a + b) - 27ab^2(2a + b)$

67. Find a value for k so that $kx^2 - 25$ will have the factors $2x + 5$ and $2x - 5$.

68. Find a value for k so that $9m^2 - kn^2$ will have the factors $3m + 7n$ and $3m - 7n$.

69. Find a value for k so that $2x^3 - kxy^2$ will have the factors $2x$, $x - 3y$, and $x + 3y$.

70. Find a value for k so that $20a^3b - kab^3$ will have the factors $5ab$, $2a - 3b$, and $2a + 3b$.

71. Complete the following statement in complete sentences: "To factor a number you . . . ".

72. Complete this statement: "To factor an algebraic expression into prime factors means . . . ".

73. Verify the formula for factoring the sum of two cubes by finding the product $(a + b)(a^2 - ab + b^2)$.

74. Verify the formula for factoring the difference of two cubes by finding the product $(a - b)(a^2 + ab + b^2)$.

75. What are the characteristics of a monomial that is a perfect cube?

76. Suppose you factored the polynomial $4x^2 - 16$ as follows:

$4x^2 - 16 = (2x + 4)(2x - 4)$

Would this be in completely factored form? If not, what would be the final form?

Answers

73. Above and Beyond

74. Above and Beyond

75. Above and Beyond

76. Above and Beyond

Answers

1. Not a special binomial; cannot be factored 3. Sum of two cubes; can be factored 5. Not a special binomial; cannot be factored 7. Difference of two cubes; can be factored 9. Sum of two squares; cannot be factored 11. Difference of two squares; can be factored 13. $(x + 7)(x - 7)$ 15. Prime, does not factor 17. $(xy + 5)(xy - 5)$ 19. Prime, does not factor 21. $a(a + 2b)(a - 2b)$ 23. $(a^2 + 4b^2)(a + 2b)(a - 2b)$ 25. $(x + 4)(x^2 - 4x + 16)$ 27. $(ab - 3)(a^2b^2 + 3ab + 9)$ 29. $(2x - 3y)(4x^2 + 6xy + 9y^2)$ 31. $4(x - 2y)(x^2 + 2xy + 4y^2)$ 33. **(a)** 0; **(b)** $3(m + 1)(m - 1)$; **(c)** 0 35. **(a)** 10; **(b)** $5(a + 1)(a^2 - a + 1)$; **(c)** 10 37. **(a)** 117; **(b)** $(5t - 2)(25t^2 + 10t + 4)$; **(c)** 117 39. False 41. True 43. $2x(3x + y)(3x - y)$ 45. $3(5t + 2s)(25t^2 - 10st + 4s^2)$ 47. $(2k^2 - 3q)(4k^4 + 6k^2q + 9q^2)$ 49. $2xy(x^8 + y^8)$ 51. $(3a - 4b)(9a^2 + 12ab + 16b^2)$ 53. $a(a + b)(a - b)(a^2 + b^2)$ 55. $x^3y^4z(2 - z)(2 + z)(4 + z^2)$ 57. $2p^2q(p^2 - 2q)(p^2 + 2q)(p^4 + 4q^2)$ 59. $N(t) = 4(6 - t)(6 + t)$ 61. $s = \dfrac{(x + 9)(x - 9)}{40}$ 63. $(x + y)^2(x - y)$ 65. $2(m - 2n)(m + 3n)(m - 3n)$ 67. 4 69. 18 71. Above and Beyond 73. Above and Beyond 75. Above and Beyond

5.6 Factoring Trinomials: Trial and Error

< 5.6 Objectives >

1 > Factor a trinomial of the form $x^2 + bx + c$ using the trial-and-error method

2 > Factor a trinomial containing a common factor

NOTE

The process used to factor here is frequently called the *trial-and-error method.* You will see the reason for the name as you work through this section.

You learned how to find the product of any two binomials by using the FOIL method in Section 5.2. Because factoring is the reverse of multiplication, we now want to use that pattern to find the factors of certain trinomials.

Recall that to multiply two binomials, we have

$$(x + 2)(x + 3) = x^2 + 5x + 6$$

The product of the first terms $(x \cdot x)$ — The sum of the products of the outer and inner terms ($3x$ and $2x$) — The product of the last terms $(2 \cdot 3)$

> CAUTION

Not every trinomial can be written as the product of two binomials.

Suppose now that you are given $x^2 + 5x + 6$ and want to find its factors. First, you know that the factors of a trinomial may be two binomials. So write

$$x^2 + 5x + 6 = (\qquad)(\qquad)$$

Because the first term of the trinomial is x^2, the first terms of the binomial factors must be x and x. We now have

$$x^2 + 5x + 6 = (x \qquad)(x \qquad)$$

The product of the last terms must be 6. Because 6 is positive, the factors must have *like* signs. Here are the possibilities:

$$6 = 1 \cdot 6$$
$$= 2 \cdot 3$$
$$= (-1)(-6)$$
$$= (-2)(-3)$$

This means that the possible factors of the trinomial are

$$(x + 1)(x + 6)$$
$$(x + 2)(x + 3)$$
$$(x - 1)(x - 6)$$
$$(x - 2)(x - 3)$$

How do we tell which is the correct pair? From the FOIL pattern we know that the sum of the outer and inner products must equal the middle term of the trinomial, in this case $5x$. This is the crucial step!

Possible Factors	Middle Term
$(x + 1)(x + 6)$	$7x$
$(x + 2)(x + 3)$	$5x$
$(x - 1)(x - 6)$	$-7x$
$(x - 2)(x - 3)$	$-5x$

The correct middle term!

So we know that the correct factorization is

$$x^2 + 5x + 6 = (x + 2)(x + 3)$$

Are there any clues so far that will make this process quicker? Yes, there is an important one that you may have spotted. We started with a trinomial that had a positive middle term and a positive last term. The negative pairs of factors for 6 led to negative middle terms. So you do not need to bother with the negative factors if the middle term and the last term of the trinomial are both positive.

Example 1 Factoring a Trinomial

< Objective 1 >

(a) Factor $x^2 + 9x + 8$.

Because the middle term and the last term of the trinomial are both positive, consider only the positive factor-pairs of 8, that is, $8 = 1 \cdot 8$ or $8 = 2 \cdot 4$.

NOTE

If you are wondering why we did not list $(x + 8)(x + 1)$ as a possibility, remember that multiplication is commutative. The order does not matter!

Possible Factors	Middle Term
$(x + 1)(x + 8)$	$9x$
$(x + 2)(x + 4)$	$6x$

Because the first pair gives the correct middle term,

$$x^2 + 9x + 8 = (x + 1)(x + 8)$$

(b) Factor $x^2 + 12x + 20$.

NOTE

The factors for 20 are
$20 = 1 \cdot 20$
$= 2 \cdot 10$
$= 4 \cdot 5$

Possible Factors	Middle Term
$(x + 1)(x + 20)$	$21x$
$(x + 2)(x + 10)$	$12x$
$(x + 4)(x + 5)$	$9x$

So

$$x^2 + 12x + 20 = (x + 2)(x + 10)$$

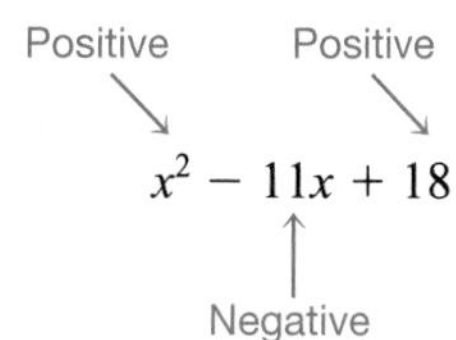

Check Yourself 1

Factor.

(a) $x^2 + 6x + 5$ (b) $x^2 + 10x + 16$

We will look at some examples in which the middle term of the trinomial is negative but the first and last terms are still positive. Consider

RECALL

The product of two negative numbers is positive, while their sum is negative.

Positive ↘ x^2 (Positive ↘ $+18$)

$$x^2 - 11x + 18$$

↑ Negative ($-11x$)

Because we want a negative middle term $(-11x)$, we use *two negative factors* for 18.

Example 2 Factoring a Trinomial

(a) Factor $x^2 - 11x + 18$.

NOTE

The negative factors of 18 are

$18 = (-1)(-18)$
$= (-2)(-9)$
$= (-3)(-6)$

Possible Factors	Middle Term
$(x - 1)(x - 18)$	$-19x$
$(x - 2)(x - 9)$	$-11x$
$(x - 3)(x - 6)$	$-9x$

So

$$x^2 - 11x + 18 = (x - 2)(x - 9)$$

(b) Factor $x^2 - 13x + 12$.

NOTE

The negative factors of 12 are

$12 = (-1)(-12)$
$= (-2)(-6)$
$= (-3)(-4)$

Possible Factors	Middle Term
$(x - 1)(x - 12)$	$-13x$
$(x - 2)(x - 6)$	$-8x$
$(x - 3)(x - 4)$	$-7x$

So

$$x^2 - 13x + 12 = (x - 1)(x - 12)$$

A few more clues: We have listed all the possible factors in these examples. It really is not necessary. Just work until you find the right pair. Also, with practice much of this work can be done mentally.

Check Yourself 2

Factor.

(a) $x^2 - 10x + 9$

(b) $x^2 - 10x + 21$

We will look now at the process of factoring a trinomial whose last term is negative. For instance, to factor $x^2 + 2x - 15$, we can start as before:

$$x^2 + 2x - 15 = (x \quad ?)(x \quad ?)$$

Note that the product of the last terms must be negative (−15 here). So we must choose factors that have different signs.

What are our choices for the factors of −15?

$$\begin{aligned} -15 &= (1)(-15) \\ &= (-1)(15) \\ &= (3)(-5) \\ &= (-3)(5) \end{aligned}$$

This means that the possible factors and the resulting middle terms are

NOTE

Another clue: Some students prefer to look at the list of numerical factors rather than looking at the actual algebraic factors. Here you want the pair whose sum is 2, the coefficient of the middle term of the trinomial. That pair is −3 and 5, which leads us to the correct factors.

Possible Factors	Middle Term
$(x + 1)(x - 15)$	$-14x$
$(x - 1)(x + 15)$	$14x$
$(x + 3)(x - 5)$	$-2x$
$(x - 3)(x + 5)$	$2x$

So $x^2 + 2x - 15 = (x - 3)(x + 5)$.

We will work through some examples in which the constant term is negative.

Example 3 Factoring a Trinomial

NOTE

You may be able to pick the factors directly from this list. You want the pair whose sum is −5 (the coefficient of the middle term).

(a) Factor $x^2 - 5x - 6$.

First, list the factors of −6. Of course, one factor will be positive, and one will be negative.

$$\begin{aligned} -6 &= (1)(-6) \\ &= (-1)(6) \\ &= (2)(-3) \\ &= (-2)(3) \end{aligned}$$

For the trinomial, then, we have

Possible Factors	Middle Term
$(x + 1)(x - 6)$	$-5x$
$(x - 1)(x + 6)$	$5x$
$(x + 2)(x - 3)$	$-x$
$(x - 2)(x + 3)$	x

So $x^2 - 5x - 6 = (x + 1)(x - 6)$.

(b) Factor $x^2 + 8xy - 9y^2$.

The process is similar if two variables are involved in the trinomial you are to factor. Start with

$$x^2 + 8xy - 9y^2 = (x \quad ?)(x \quad ?).$$

The product of the last terms must be $-9y^2$.

$$-9y^2 = (-y)(9y)$$
$$= (y)(-9y)$$
$$= (3y)(-3y)$$

Possible Factors	Middle Term
$(x - y)(x + 9y)$	$8xy$
$(x + y)(x - 9y)$	$-8xy$
$(x + 3y)(x - 3y)$	0

So $x^2 + 8xy - 9y^2 = (x - y)(x + 9y)$.

Check Yourself 3

Factor.

(a) $x^2 + 7x - 30$ **(b)** $x^2 - 3xy - 10y^2$

Recall from Section 5.4, any time we have a common factor, that factor should be removed *before* trying any other factoring technique. Consider Example 4.

Example 4 Factoring a Trinomial

< Objective 2 >

(a) Factor $3x^2 - 21x + 18$.

$3x^2 - 21x + 18 = 3(x^2 - 7x + 6)$ Remove the common factor 3.

We now factor the remaining trinomial. For $x^2 - 7x + 6$:

Possible Factors	Middle Term
$(x - 2)(x - 3)$	$-5x$
$(x - 1)(x - 6)$	$-7x$

The correct middle term

> CAUTION

A common mistake is to forget to include the 3 that was factored out as the first step.

So $3x^2 - 21x + 18 = 3(x - 1)(x - 6)$.

(b) Factor $2x^3 + 16x^2 - 40x$.

$2x^3 + 16x^2 - 40x = 2x(x^2 + 8x - 20)$ Remove the common factor $2x$.

To factor the remaining trinomial, which is $x^2 + 8x - 20$, we have

NOTE

Once we have found the desired middle term, there is no need to continue.

Possible Factors	Middle Term
$(x - 4)(x + 5)$	x
$(x - 5)(x + 4)$	$-x$
$(x - 10)(x + 2)$	$-8x$
$(x - 2)(x + 10)$	$8x$

The correct middle term

So $2x^3 + 16x^2 - 40x = 2x(x - 2)(x + 10)$.

Check Yourself 4

Factor.

(a) $3x^2 - 3x - 36$ **(b)** $4x^3 + 24x^2 + 32x$

One further comment: Have you wondered if all trinomials are factorable? Look at the trinomial

$x^2 + 2x + 6$

The only possible factors are $(x + 1)(x + 6)$ and $(x + 2)(x + 3)$. Neither pair is correct (you should check the middle terms), and so this trinomial does not have factors with integer coefficients. In fact, there are many trinomials that do not factor.

Check Yourself ANSWERS

1. (a) $(x + 1)(x + 5)$; **(b)** $(x + 2)(x + 8)$ **2. (a)** $(x - 9)(x - 1)$; **(b)** $(x - 3)(x - 7)$ **3. (a)** $(x + 10)(x - 3)$; **(b)** $(x + 2y)(x - 5y)$ **4. (a)** $3(x - 4)(x + 3)$; **(b)** $4x(x + 2)(x + 4)$

Reading Your Text

The following fill-in-the-blank exercises are designed to ensure that you understand some of the key vocabulary used in this section.

SECTION 5.6

(a) The factors of a trinomial may be two ____________.

(b) The product of the first terms of two binomials must equal the ____________ term of the trinomial, and the product of the last terms of two binomials must equal the ____________ term of the trinomial.

(c) The sum of the outer and inner products must equal the ____________ term of the trinomial.

(d) There are ____________ trinomials that do not factor.

5.6 exercises

MathZone

Boost your grade at mathzone.com!
> Practice Problems
> NetTutor
> Self-Tests
> e-Professors
> Videos

Name ______________

Section ________ Date ________

Complete each of the statements.

1. $x^2 - 8x + 15 = (x - 3)(\quad)$

2. $m^2 + 8m + 12 = (m + 2)(\quad)$

3. $p^2 - 8p - 20 = (p + 2)(\quad)$

4. $a^2 + 9a - 36 = (a + 12)(\quad)$

5. $x^2 - 7xy + 10y^2 = (x - 2y)(\quad)$

6. $a^2 + 18ab + 81b^2 = (a + 9b)(\quad)$

< Objective 1 >

Factor each of the trinomials completely.

7. $x^2 + 8x + 15$

8. $x^2 - 11x + 28$

9. $x^2 + x + 3$

10. $a^2 - 2a - 48$

11. $m^2 + 3m - 28$

12. $x^2 + 7xy + 10y^2$

13. $a^2 - ab - 42b^2$

14. $m^2 - 8mn + 16n^2$

15. $x^2 - 13xy + 40y^2$

16. $r^2 - 12r - 35$

17. $b^2 + 6ab + 9a^2$

Answers

1. $x - 5$
2. $m + 6$
3. $p - 10$
4. $a - 3$
5. $x - 5y$
6. $a + 9b$
7. $(x + 3)(x + 5)$
8. $(x - 4)(x - 7)$
9. Prime, does not factor
10. $(a - 8)(a + 6)$
11. $(m + 7)(m - 4)$
12. $(x + 2y)(x + 5y)$
13. $(a + 6b)(a - 7b)$
14. $(m - 4n)(m - 4n)$ or $(m - 4n)^2$
15. $(x - 5y)(x - 8y)$
16. Prime, does not factor
17. $(b + 3a)(b + 3a)$ or $(b + 3a)^2$

Answers

18. $3(a + 6)(a - 7)$
19. $r(r - 2)(r + 9)$
20. $h(h^2 + 11h + 12)$
21. $2x(x - 12)(x + 2)$
22. $3p(p - 2)(p + 18)$
23. $y(x + 3y)(x - 12y)$
24. $4s^2(s + 3t)(s - 8t)$
25. $m(m - 5n)(m - 24n)$
26. $2a(a - 2b)(a - 24b)$
27. True
28. False
29. False
30. True
31. $5(z - 2)(z - 2)$ or $5(z - 2)^2$
32. $3(x + 5)(x + 5)$ or $3(x + 5)^2$
33. $k^5(k - 7)(k + 2)$
34. Prime, does not factor
35. $(5m + n)(5m + n)$ or $(5m + n)^2$
36. $(8x - y)(8x - y)$ or $(8x - y)^2$
37. $3r(r - 6)(r - 4)$
38. $4(n^2 + 4n + 12)$
39. $xy(x + 3y)(x + 3y)$ or $xy(x + 3y)^2$
40. $(c + 2d)(c + 2d)$ or $(c + 2d)^2$

< Objective 2 >

Factor each of the trinomials completely. (Hint: *Try to factor out the greatest common factor first.*)

18. $3a^2 - 3a - 126$

19. $r^3 + 7r^2 - 18r$

20. $h^3 + 11h^2 + 12h$

21. $2x^3 - 20x^2 - 48x$

22. $3p^3 + 48p^2 - 108p$

23. $x^2y - 9xy^2 - 36y^3$

24. $4s^4 - 20s^3t - 96s^2t^2$

25. $m^3 - 29m^2n + 120mn^2$

26. $2a^3 - 52a^2b + 96ab^2$

In exercises 27 to 30, determine whether each statement is **true** *or* **false.**

27. $x^2 + 6x + 9 = (x + 3)(x + 3)$

28. $x^2 - 2x - 8 = (x - 2)(x + 4)$

29. $x^2 + x - 6 = (x - 5)(x + 1)$

30. $x^2 - 7x + 10 = (x - 5)(x - 2)$

Basic Skills | **Advanced Skills** | Vocational-Technical Applications | Calculator/Computer | Above and Beyond

Factor completely.

31. $5z^2 - 20z + 20$

32. $3x^2 + 30x + 75$

33. $k^7 - 5k^6 - 14k^5$

34. $p^2 + 4p + 5$

35. $25m^2 + 10mn + n^2$

36. $64x^2 - 16xy + y^2$

37. $3r^3 - 30r^2 + 72r$

38. $4n^2 + 16n + 48$

39. $x^3y + 6x^2y^2 + 9xy^3$

40. $c^2 + 4cd + 4d^2$

41. $5z^2 - 35z - 60$

42. $3m^4 - 3m^3 - 90m^2$

43. $3y^5 - 18y^4 + 15y^3$

44. $k^3w + 10k^2w^2 + 25kw^3$

45. $100 - 20m + m^2$

46. $a^2 - 14ab + 49b^2$

47. $f^2 + f + 2$

48. $2x^6 - 8x^5 - 42x^4$

Basic Skills | Advanced Skills | **Vocational-Technical Applications** | Calculator/Computer | Above and Beyond

49. **Construction Technology** The bending stress on an overhanging beam is given by the expression $310(x^2 - 36x + 128)$. Factor this expression. (*Hint:* You only need to factor the trinomial.)

50. **Automotive Technology** The acceleration curve for low gear in a car is described by the equation: $a = \frac{1}{20}(x^2 - 16x - 80)$. Factor the right side of this equation.

51. **Construction Technology** The stress-strain curve of a weld is given by the formula $-s = l^2 - 60l - 325$. Factor the right side of this equation.

52. **Manufacturing Technology** The maximum stress for a given allowable strain (deformation) for a certain material is given by the polynomial: Stress $= 85.8x - 0.6x^2 - 1{,}537.2$, where x is the allowable strain in micrometers. Factor this expression. (*Hint:* Rearrange the polynomial and factor out a common factor of -0.6 first.)

Basic Skills | Advanced Skills | Vocational-Technical Applications | **Calculator/Computer** | Above and Beyond

In exercises 53 to 56, **(a)** *divide the polynomial $f(x)$ by the given linear factor and* **(b)** *factor the quotient obtained in part* **(a)**. *Then,* **(c)** *using your graphing calculator, graph the polynomial $f(x)$ and determine where the graph passes through the x-axis and* **(d)** *compare the results of parts* **(b)** *and* **(c)**.

53. $f(x) = x^3 + 5x^2 + 2x - 8;\ x + 2$

54. $f(x) = x^3 - 2x^2 - 11x + 12;\ x + 3$

55. $f(x) = x^3 + x^2 - 4x - 4;\ x + 1$

56. $f(x) = x^3 - 3x^2 - 16x + 48;\ x - 3$

Answers

41. $5(z^2 - 7z - 12)$

42. $3m^2(m - 6)(m + 5)$

43. $3y^3(y - 5)(y - 1)$

44. $kw(k + 5w)(k + 5w)$ or $kw(k + 5w)^2$

45. $(10 - m)(10 - m)$ or $(10 - m)^2$

46. $(a - 7b)(a - 7b)$ or $(a - 7b)^2$

47. Prime, does not factor

48. $2x^4(x - 7)(x + 3)$

49. $310(x - 4)(x - 32)$

50. $a = \frac{1}{20}(x - 20)(x + 4)$

51. $-s = (l + 5)(l - 65)$

52. $-0.6(x - 21)(x - 122)$

53. (a) $x^2 + 3x - 4$; (b) $(x + 4)(x - 1)$; (c) $-2, -4, 1$

54. (a) $x^2 - 5x + 4$; (b) $(x - 4)(x - 1)$; (c) $-3, 4, 1$

55. (a) $x^2 - 4$; (b) $(x + 2)(x - 2)$; (c) $-1, 2, -2$

56. (a) $x^2 - 16$; (b) $(x + 4)(x - 4)$; (c) $3, 4, -4$

Answers

57. 6 or 9

58. 8, 10, or 17

59. 4

60. 2

61. 3, 8, 15, 24, . . .

Basic Skills | Advanced Skills | Vocational-Technical Applications | Calculator/Computer | **Above and Beyond**

Find a positive value for k for which each of the trinomials can be factored.

57. $x^2 + kx + 8$

58. $x^2 - kx + 16$

59. $x^2 - kx - 5$

60. $x^2 + 3x + k$

61. $x^2 + 2x - k$

Answers

1. $x - 5$ **3.** $p - 10$ **5.** $x - 5y$ **7.** $(x + 3)(x + 5)$
9. Prime, does not factor **11.** $(m + 7)(m - 4)$ **13.** $(a + 6b)(a - 7b)$
15. $(x - 5y)(x - 8y)$ **17.** $(b + 3a)(b + 3a)$ or $(b + 3a)^2$
19. $r(r - 2)(r + 9)$ **21.** $2x(x - 12)(x + 2)$ **23.** $y(x + 3y)(x - 12y)$
25. $m(m - 5n)(m - 24n)$ **27.** True **29.** False
31. $5(z - 2)(z - 2)$ or $5(z - 2)^2$ **33.** $k^5(k - 7)(k + 2)$
35. $(5m + n)(5m + n)$ or $(5m + n)^2$ **37.** $3r(r - 6)(r - 4)$
39. $xy(x + 3y)(x + 3y)$ or $xy(x + 3y)^2$ **41.** $5(z^2 - 7z - 12)$
43. $3y^3(y - 5)(y - 1)$ **45.** $(10 - m)(10 - m)$ or $(10 - m)^2$
47. Prime, does not factor **49.** $310(x - 4)(x - 32)$
51. $-s = (1 + 5)(1 - 65)$
53. **(a)** $x^2 + 3x - 4$; **(b)** $(x + 4)(x - 1)$; **(c)** $-2, -4, 1$
55. **(a)** $x^2 - 4$; **(b)** $(x + 2)(x - 2)$; **(c)** $-1, 2, -2$ **57.** 6 or 9
59. 4 **61.** 3, 8, 15, 24, . . .

5.7 Factoring Trinomials: The *ac* Method

< 5.7 Objectives >

1 > Use the *ac* test to determine factorability

2 > Factor a trinomial using the *ac* method

3 > Completely factor a trinomial

Factoring trinomials is more time-consuming when the coefficient of the first term is not 1. Consider the following product:

$$(5x + 2)(2x + 3) = 10x^2 + 19x + 6$$

Factors of $10x^2$ Factors of 6

Do you see the additional difficulty? If we were to factor the polynomial on the right, we would need to consider all possible factors of the first coefficient (10 in the example) as well as those of the third term (6 in the example).

In Section 5.6, we used the trial-and-error method to factor trinomials whose first term had a coefficient of 1. We also learned that not all trinomials can be factored. In this section we will look at trinomials again, but in a slightly different context. We will first learn a way to determine whether any trinomial is factorable. We will then use the results of that analysis to factor the trinomial, without having to use guessing and checking.

Some students prefer the trial-and-error method for factoring because it is generally faster and more intuitive. Other students prefer the method of this section (called the ***ac* method**) because it yields the answer in a systematic way. It does not matter which method you choose. Either method will work to factor a trinomial. We are introducing you to both so you can determine which method you prefer.

To introduce the new *ac* method, we will first factor trinomials of the form $x^2 + bx + c$, like those from Section 5.6. Then we will apply the *ac* method to factor trinomials whose leading coefficient is not 1 (usually written as $ax^2 + bx + c$).

First, let us consider some trinomials that are already factored.

Example 1 Matching Trinomials and Their Factors

Determine which of these are true statements.

(a) $x^2 - 2x - 8 = (x - 4)(x + 2)$

This is a true statement. Using the FOIL method, we see that

$$\begin{aligned}(x - 4)(x + 2) &= x^2 + 2x - 4x - 8\\ &= x^2 - 2x - 8\end{aligned}$$

(b) $x^2 + 6x + 5 = (x + 2)(x + 3)$

This is not a true statement.

$(x + 2)(x + 3) = x^2 + 3x + 2x + 6 = x^2 + 5x + 6$

(c) $3x^2 + 11x - 4 = (3x - 1)(x + 4)$

This is true: $(3x - 1)(x + 4) = 3x^2 + 12x - x - 4 = 3x^2 + 11x - 4$

(d) $x^2 - 8x - 15 = (x - 5)(x - 3)$

This is false: $(x - 5)(x - 3) = x^2 - 3x - 5x + 15 = x^2 - 8x + 15$

Check Yourself 1

Determine which are true statements.

(a) $2x^2 - 2x - 3 = (2x - 3)(x + 1)$
(b) $x^2 + 5x - 14 = (x - 2)(x + 7)$
(c) $2x^2 - 7x + 3 = (x - 3)(2x - 1)$

As we saw when using the trial-and-error method, the coefficients of a trinomial are very important to factoring. This is also the case when using the *ac* method. So that we are consistent, we first write the trinomial in standard $ax^2 + bx + c$ form, and then label the three coefficients as *a*, *b*, and *c*.

Example 2 Identifying the Coefficients of $ax^2 + bx + c$

First, when necessary, rewrite the trinomial in $ax^2 + bx + c$ form. Then give the values for *a*, *b*, and *c*, in which *a* is the coefficient of the x^2-term, *b* is the coefficient of the *x*-term, and *c* is the constant.

(a) $x^2 - 3x - 18$

$a = 1 \qquad b = -3 \qquad c = -18$

(b) $x^2 - 24x + 23$

$a = 1 \qquad b = -24 \qquad c = 23$

NOTE

The negative sign is attached to the coefficient.

(c) $x^2 + 8 - 11x$

First rewrite the trinomial in descending order:

$x^2 - 11x + 8$

$a = 1 \qquad b = -11 \qquad c = 8$

Check Yourself 2

First, when necessary, rewrite the trinomials in $ax^2 + bx + c$ form. Then label *a*, *b*, and *c*, in which *a* is the coefficient of the x^2-term, *b* is the coefficient of the *x*-term, and *c* is the constant.

(a) $x^2 + 5x - 14$ **(b)** $x^2 - 18x + 17$ **(c)** $x - 6 + 2x^2$

As we saw in Section 5.6, not all trinomials can be factored. To discover if a trinomial is factorable, we use the ***ac* test.**

Definition

The *ac* Test

A trinomial of the form $ax^2 + bx + c$ is factorable if (and only if) there are two integers, m and n, such that

$ac = mn \quad \text{and} \quad b = m + n$

In Example 3 we will look for m and n to determine whether each trinomial is factorable.

Example 3 Using the *ac* Test

< Objective 1 >

Use the ac test to determine which of these trinomials can be factored. Find the values of m and n for each trinomial that can be factored.

(a) $x^2 - 3x - 18$

First, we find the values of a, b, and c, so that we can find ac.

$a = 1 \qquad b = -3 \qquad c = -18$

$ac = 1(-18) = -18 \qquad \text{and} \qquad b = -3$

NOTES

We want two integers whose product is the same as $a \cdot c$ and whose sum is the same as b.

In words, we need two numbers whose product is -18 and whose sum is -3.

Then, we look for two numbers, m and n, such that $mn = ac$, and $m + n = b$. In this case, that means

$mn = -18 \qquad \text{and} \qquad m + n = -3$

We now look at all pairs of integers with a product of -18. We then look at the sum of each pair of integers, looking for a sum of -3.

mn	$m + n$
$1(-18) = -18$	$1 + (-18) = -17$
$2(-9) = -18$	$2 + (-9) = -7$
$3(-6) = -18$	$3 + (-6) = -3$
$6(-3) = -18$	
$9(-2) = -18$	
$18(-1) = -18$	

We need look no further than 3 and -6.

NOTE

We could have chosen $m = -6$ and $n = 3$ as well.

3 and -6 are the two integers with a product of ac and a sum of b. We can say that

$m = 3 \quad \text{and} \quad n = -6$

Because we found values for m and n, we know that $x^2 - 3x - 18$ is factorable.

(b) $x^2 - 24x + 23$

We find that

$a = 1 \qquad b = -24 \qquad c = 23$

$ac = 1(23) = 23 \quad \text{and} \quad b = -24$

So

$mn = 23$ and $m + n = -24$

We now calculate integer pairs, looking for two numbers with a product of 23 and a sum of -24.

mn	$m + n$
$1(23) = 23$	$1 + 23 = 24$
$-1(-23) = 23$	$-1 + (-23) = -24$

$m = -1$ and $n = -23$

So, $x^2 - 24x + 23$ is factorable.

(c) $x^2 - 11x + 8$

We find that $a = 1$, $b = -11$, and $c = 8$. Therefore, $ac = 8$ and $b = -11$. Thus $mn = 8$ and $m + n = -11$. We calculate integer pairs:

mn	$m + n$
$1(8) = 8$	$1 + 8 = 9$
$2(4) = 8$	$2 + 4 = 6$
$-1(-8) = 8$	$-1 + (-8) = -9$
$-2(-4) = 8$	$-2 + (-4) = -6$

There are no other pairs of integers with a product of 8, and none of these pairs has a sum of -11. The trinomial $x^2 - 11x + 8$ is not factorable.

(d) $2x^2 + 7x - 15$

We find that $a = 2$, $b = 7$, and $c = -15$. Therefore, $ac = 2(-15) = -30$ and $b = 7$. Thus $mn = -30$ and $m + n = 7$. We calculate integer pairs:

mn	$m + n$
$1(-30) = -30$	$1 + (-30) = -29$
$2(-15) = -30$	$2 + (-15) = -13$
$3(-10) = -30$	$3 + (-10) = -7$
$5(-6) = -30$	$5 + (-6) = -1$
$6(-5) = -30$	$6 + (-5) = 1$
$10(-3) = -30$	$10 + (-3) = 7$

There is no need to go any further. We see that 10 and -3 have a product of -30 and a sum of 7, so

$m = 10$ and $n = -3$

Therefore, $2x^2 + 7x - 15$ is factorable.

It is not always necessary to evaluate all the products and sums to determine whether a trinomial is factorable. You may have noticed patterns and shortcuts that make it easier to find m and n. By all means, use them to help you find m and n. This is essential in mathematical thinking. You are taught a mathematical process that will always work for solving a problem. Recall that such a process is called an *algorithm*. It is very easy to teach a computer to use an algorithm. It is very difficult (some would say impossible) for a computer to have insight. Shortcuts that you discover are *insights*. They may be the most important part of your mathematical development.

Check Yourself 3

Use the *ac* test to determine which of the trinomials can be factored. Find the values of *m* and *n* for each trinomial that can be factored.

(a) $x^2 - 7x + 12$ **(b)** $x^2 + 5x - 14$
(c) $3x^2 - 6x + 7$ **(d)** $2x^2 + x - 6$

So far we have used the results of the *ac* test only to determine whether a trinomial is factorable. The results can also be used to help factor the trinomial. We will now factor the polynomials from Example 3 using the results we found.

Example 4 Using the Results of the *ac* Test to Factor

< Objective 2 >

Rewrite the middle term as the sum of two terms, and then factor by grouping.

(a) $x^2 - 3x - 18$

We find that $a = 1$, $b = -3$, and $c = -18$, so $ac = -18$ and $b = -3$. We are looking for two numbers, m and n, where $mn = -18$ and $m + n = -3$. In Example 3, part **(a)**, we found the two integers to be 3 and -6, because $3(-6) = -18$ and $3 + (-6) = -3$, so $m = 3$ and $n = -6$. We now use that result to rewrite the middle term as the sum of $3x$ and $-6x$.

$$x^2 + 3x - 6x - 18$$

Since we now have four terms, we factor by grouping:

$$\begin{aligned} x^2 + 3x - 6x - 18 &= x(x + 3) - 6(x + 3) \\ &= (x - 6)(x + 3) \end{aligned}$$

> **NOTE**
>
> *m* and *n* become coefficients of *x* as we "split" the middle term:
>
> $x^2 - 3x - 18$
>
> $x^2 + 3x - 6x - 18$

(b) $x^2 - 24x + 23$

We use the results from Example 3, part **(b)**, in which we found $m = -1$ and $n = -23$, to rewrite the middle term of the equation.

$$x^2 - 24x + 23 = x^2 - x - 23x + 23$$

Then we factor by grouping:

$$\begin{aligned} x^2 - x - 23x + 23 &= (x^2 - x) - (23x - 23) \\ &= x(x - 1) - 23(x - 1) \\ &= (x - 23)(x - 1) \end{aligned}$$

> **NOTE**
>
> In part **(a)**, we factor out -6 from the second pair so that both terms include an $(x + 3)$ factor. We do something similar in part **(b)**.
>
> *Hint:* You may want to try factoring out a negative number if the first term of the second pair is negative.

(c) $x^2 - 11x + 8$

In Example 3, part **(c)**, we found there were not two numbers whose product was 8 and whose sum was -11, therefore, we found this trinomial was not factorable.

(d) $2x^2 + 7x - 15$

From Example 3, part **(d)**, we know that this trinomial is factorable, and $m = 10$ and $n = -3$. We use that result to rewrite the middle term of the trinomial.

$$\begin{aligned} 2x^2 + 7x - 15 &= 2x^2 + 10x - 3x - 15 \\ &= (2x^2 + 10x) - (3x + 15) \\ &= 2x(x + 5) - 3(x + 5) \\ &= (2x - 3)(x + 5) \end{aligned}$$

Check Yourself 4

Use the results of Check Yourself 3 to rewrite the middle term as the sum of two terms, and then factor by grouping.

(a) $x^2 - 7x + 12$ **(b)** $x^2 + 5x - 14$ **(c)** $2x^2 + x - 6$

We will now consider an example in its entirety. We will need to first find m and n, and then factor the trinomial.

Example 5 Rewriting Middle Terms to Factor

Rewrite the middle term as the sum of two terms, and then factor by grouping.

(a) $2x^2 - 13x - 7$

Since $a = 2$, $b = -13$, and $c = -7$, it can be found that $mn = ac = -14$ and $m + n = b = -13$. Therefore,

mn	$m + n$
$1(-14) = -14$	$1 + (-14) = -13$

So, $m = 1$ and $n = -14$. We rewrite the middle term of the trinomial:

$$\begin{aligned} 2x^2 - 13x - 7 &= 2x^2 + x - 14x - 7 \\ &= (2x^2 + x) - (14x + 7) \\ &= x(2x + 1) - 7(2x + 1) \\ &= (x - 7)(2x + 1) \end{aligned}$$

(b) $6x^2 - 5x - 6$

We find that $a = 6$, $b = -5$, and $c = -6$, so $mn = ac = -36$ and $m + n = b = -5$.

mn	$m + n$
$1(-36) = -36$	$1 + (-36) = -35$
$2(-18) = -36$	$2 + (-18) = -16$
$3(-12) = -36$	$3 + (-12) = -9$
$4(-9) = -36$	$4 + (-9) = -5$

So, $m = 4$ and $n = -9$. We rewrite the middle term of the trinomial:

$$\begin{aligned} 6x^2 - 5x - 6 &= 6x^2 + 4x - 9x - 6 \\ &= (6x^2 + 4x) - (9x + 6) \\ &= 2x(3x + 2) - 3(3x + 2) \\ &= (2x - 3)(3x + 2) \end{aligned}$$

Check Yourself 5

Rewrite the middle term as the sum of two terms, and then factor by grouping.

(a) $2x^2 - 7x - 15$ **(b)** $6x^2 - 5x - 4$

Remember that our first step is always to try to factor out the GCF. To make sure you have not missed the GCF, be sure to check the factors of your answer to make sure each is factored completely.

Example 6 Removing Common Factors

< Objective 3 >

NOTE

If we had not removed the GCF in the first step, we would have gotten either $(3x + 15)(x - 1)$ or $(x + 5)(3x - 3)$ after factoring. Neither of these would be factored completely since there still is a binomial containing a GCF of 3. If we then factor out the GCF of 3, we will get the same answer:

$3(x + 5)(x - 1)$

Completely factor the trinomial.

$3x^2 + 12x - 15$

We first remove the common factor of 3:

$3x^2 + 12x - 15 = 3(x^2 + 4x - 5)$

Finding m and n for the trinomial $x^2 + 4x - 5$ yields $mn = -5$ and $m + n = 4$.

mn	$m + n$
$1(-5) = -5$	$1 + (-5) = -4$
$5(-1) = -5$	$-1 + (5) = 4$

So, $m = 5$ and $n = -1$. This gives us

$$\begin{aligned} 3x^2 + 12x - 15 &= 3(x^2 + 4x - 5) \\ &= 3(x^2 + 5x - x - 5) \\ &= 3[(x^2 + 5x) - (x + 5)] \\ &= 3[x(x + 5) - (x + 5)] \\ &= 3[(x + 5)(x - 1)] \\ &= 3(x + 5)(x - 1) \end{aligned}$$

NOTE

If the leading coefficient is not positive, factor out a GCF of -1 and then consider, the remaining polynomial—whose leading coefficient is now positive.

Check Yourself 6

Completely factor the trinomial.

$6x^3 + 3x^2 - 18x$

Not all possible product pairs need to be tried to find m and n. A look at the sign pattern of the trinomial will eliminate many of the possibilities. Assuming the leading coefficient is positive, there are four possible sign patterns.

Pattern	Example	Conclusion
1. b and c are both positive.	$2x^2 + 13x + 15$	m and n must both be positive.
2. b is negative and c is positive.	$x^2 - 7x + 12$	m and n must both be negative.
3. b is positive and c is negative.	$x^2 + 3x - 10$	m and n have opposite signs. (The value with the larger absolute value is positive.)
4. b is negative and c is negative.	$x^2 - 3x - 10$	m and n have opposite signs. (The value with the larger absolute value is negative.)

Sometimes the factors of a trinomial seem obvious. At other times you might be certain that there are only a couple of possible sets of factors for a trinomial. It is perfectly acceptable to check these proposed factors to see if they work. If you find the factors in this manner, we say that you have used the *trial-and-error method* as was discussed in Section 5.6. The trial-and-error method will also work when the leading coefficient is not 1. As we mentioned at the beginning of this section, either the *ac* method or the trial-and-error method can be used to factor a trinomial. It is up to you to determine which you prefer.

To this point we have been factoring trinomial expressions. As we saw in Section 5.5, when a function is defined by a polynomial expression, we can factor that expression without affecting any of the order pairs associated with the function. Actually, factoring the expression often makes it easier to find some of the ordered pairs.

Reviewing our work from Section 5.5 and previewing the work we will do in Section 5.9, we are especially interested in looking for values of x that cause $f(x)$ to be zero. We do this by using the **zero-product principle.**

NOTE

In the property below, $a = b = 0$ means that a and b are both zero.

Property

Zero-Product Principle If $a \cdot b = 0$, then $a = 0$, or $b = 0$, or $a = b = 0$.

Another way to say this is: if the product of two numbers is zero, then at least one of those numbers must be zero.

Example 7 Factoring Polynomial Functions

Given the function $f(x) = 2x^2 + 7x - 15$, complete the following.

(a) Rewrite the function in factored form.
From Example 4(d) we have

$f(x) = (x + 5)(2x - 3)$

(b) Find the ordered pair associated with $f(0)$.

$f(0) = (0 + 5)(0 - 3) = -15$

The ordered pair is $(0, -15)$.

(c) Find all ordered pairs $(x, 0)$.

We are looking for the x-value for which $f(x) = 0$, so

$(x + 5)(2x - 3) = 0$

By the zero-product principle, we know that either

$x + 5 = 0$ or $2x - 3 = 0$

which means that

$$x = -5 \quad \text{or} \quad 2x = 3$$
$$x = \frac{3}{2}$$

The ordered pairs are $(-5, 0)$ and $\left(\frac{3}{2}, 0\right)$. Check the original function to see that these ordered pairs are associated with that function.

Check Yourself 7

Given the function $f(x) = 2x^2 - x - 6$, complete the following.

(a) Rewrite the function in factored form.
(b) Find the ordered pair associated with $f(0)$.
(c) Find all ordered pairs $(x, 0)$.

Check Yourself ANSWERS

1. (a) False; **(b)** true; **(c)** true **2. (a)** $a = 1, b = 5, c = -14$; **(b)** $a = 1, b = -18, c = 17$; **(c)** $a = 2, b = 1, c = -6$
3. (a) Factorable, $m = -3, n = -4$; **(b)** factorable, $m = 7, n = -2$; **(c)** not factorable; **(d)** factorable, $m = 4, n = -3$
4. (a) $x^2 - 3x - 4x + 12 = (x - 3)(x - 4)$; **(b)** $x^2 + 7x - 2x - 14 = (x + 7)(x - 2)$; **(c)** $2x^2 + 4x - 3x - 6 = (2x - 3)(x + 2)$
5. (a) $2x^2 - 10x + 3x - 15 = (2x + 3)(x - 5)$; **(b)** $6x^2 - 8x + 3x - 4 = (3x - 4)(2x + 1)$ **6.** $3x(2x - 3)(x + 2)$
7. (a) $f(x) = (2x + 3)(x - 2)$; **(b)** $(0, -6)$; **(c)** $(-\frac{3}{2}, 0)$ and $(2, 0)$

Reading Your Text

The following fill-in-the-blank exercises are designed to ensure that you understand some of the key vocabulary used in this section.

SECTION 5.7

(a) To discover if a trinomial is factorable, we try the ______________.

(b) Either the *ac* method or ______________ can be used to try to factor a trinomial.

(c) The first step in factoring a polynomial is to factor out the ______________.

(d) The ______________ says that if the product of two numbers is zero, then at least one of those numbers must be zero.

5.7 exercises

Basic Skills | Advanced Skills | Vocational-Technical Applications | Calculator/Computer | Above and Beyond

MathZone

Boost your grade at mathzone.com!
> Practice Problems
> NetTutor
> Self-Tests
> e-Professors
> Videos

Name ____________

Section ________ Date ________

Determine which are true statements.

1. $x^2 - 2x - 8 = (x - 2)(x + 4)$

2. $2x^2 - 5x + 4 = (2x - 1)(x - 4)$

3. $3x^2 - 13x - 10 = (3x + 2)(x - 5)$

4. $6x^2 + 7x - 3 = (3x - 1)(2x + 3)$

5. $-2x^2 + 11x - 5 = (-x + 5)(2x + 1)$

6. $-6x^2 + 13x - 6 = (2x - 3)(-3x + 2)$

When necessary, rewrite the trinomial in $ax^2 + bx + c$ form, and then label a, b, and c.

7. $2x^2 + 5x + 3$

8. $-3x^2 - x + 2$

9. $x - 1 + 2x^2$

10. $4 - 5x - 3x^2$

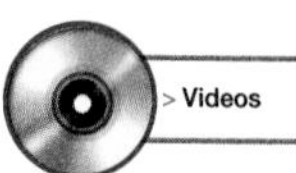

< Objective 1 >

Use the ac test to determine which trinomials can be factored. Find the values of m and n for each trinomial that can be factored.

11. $x^2 + 3x - 10$

12. $x^2 - 2x + 3$

13. $2x^2 - 3x + 2$

14. $3x^2 - 10x - 8$

15. $2x^2 + 5x + 2$

16. $3x^2 + x - 2$

< Objective 2 >

Factor each trinomial.

17. $x^2 + 8xy + 15y^2$

18. $3x^2 + 11x - 20$

19. $5x^2 + 18x - 8$

20. $12x^2 + 23x + 5$

Answers

1. False
2. False
3. True
4. True
5. False
6. True
7. $a = 2, b = 5, c = 3$
8. $a = -3, b = -1, c = 2$
9. $a = 2, b = 1, c = -1$
10. $a = -3, b = -5, c = 4$
11. Factorable, $m = 5$, $n = -2$
12. Not factorable
13. Not factorable
14. Factorable, $m = -12$, $n = 2$
15. Factorable, $m = 4$, $n = 1$
16. Factorable, $m = 3$, $n = -2$
17. $(x + 3y)(x + 5y)$
18. $(3x - 4)(x + 5)$
19. $(5x - 2)(x + 4)$
20. $(3x + 5)(4x + 1)$

21. $4x^2 + 20x + 25$

22. $7x^2 - 6x + 3$

23. $5x^2 + 24x - 36$

24. $10x^2 - 7x - 12$

25. $16x^2 + 40x + 25$ > Videos

26. $7x^2 - 17xy + 6y^2$

27. $8x^2 - 30xy + 7y^2$

< Objective 3 >

Factor completely.

28. $3x^2 - 24x + 45$

29. $2x^2 - 26x + 72$

30. $4x^2 - 11x + 4$

31. $5x^3 + 14x^2 - 24x$

32. $3x^4 + 17x^3 - 28x^2$

33. $3x^3 - 15x^2y - 18xy^2$

34. $2x^3 - 10x^2y - 72xy^2$

35. $49c^2 + 28cd + 4d^2$

36. $11n + 12n^2 - 5$

37. $6z^2 - 42z - 72$ > Videos

38. $100r^2 - 140rs + 49s^2$

39. $16k^3 + 4k^2 - 30k$

40. $6m^2 + 23mn + 21n^2$

41. $4k^3w + 20k^2w^2 + 25kw^3$

42. $12x^4y - 2x^3y - 24x^2y$

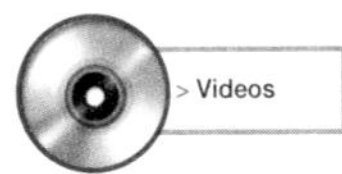

43. $2 + 7b + 6b^2$

Answers

21. $(2x + 5)^2$
22. Prime, not factorable
23. $(5x - 6)(x + 6)$
24. $(2x - 3)(5x + 4)$
25. $(4x + 5)^2$
26. $(7x - 3y)(x - 2y)$
27. $(4x - y)(2x - 7y)$
28. $3(x - 5)(x - 3)$
29. $2(x - 4)(x - 9)$
30. Prime, not factorable
31. $x(x + 4)(5x - 6)$
32. $x^2(x + 7)(3x - 4)$
33. $3x(x - 6y)(x + y)$
34. $2x(x + 4y)(x - 9y)$
35. $(7c + 2d)(7c + 2d)$ or $(7c + 2d)^2$
36. $(4n + 5)(3n - 1)$
37. $6(z^2 - 7z - 12)$
38. $(10r - 7s)(10r - 7s)$ or $(10r - 7s)^2$
39. $2k(4k - 5)(2k + 3)$
40. $(3m + 7n)(2m + 3n)$
41. $kw(2k + 5w)(2k + 5w)$ or $kw(2k + 5w)^2$
42. $2x^2y(3x + 4)(2x - 3)$
43. $(3b + 2)(2b + 1)$

Answers

44. $3a^2(5a + 3)(3a - 2)$

45. $(4p - 9q)(3p - 2q)$

46. Prime, not factorable

47. (a) $(x - 3)(x + 1)$; (b) $(0, -3)$; (c) $(3, 0)$ and $(-1, 0)$

48. (a) $(x - 5)(x + 2)$; (b) $(0, -10)$; (c) $(5, 0)$ and $(-2, 0)$

49. (a) $(2x - 1)(x + 2)$; (b) $(0, -2)$; (c) $\left(\frac{1}{2}, 0\right)$ and $(-2, 0)$

50. (a) $(3x - 2)(x - 3)$; (b) $(0, 6)$; (c) $\left(\frac{2}{3}, 0\right)$ and $(3, 0)$

51. (a) $(x + 4)(3x - 7)$; (b) $(0, -28)$; (c) $(-4, 0)$ and $\left(\frac{7}{3}, 0\right)$

52. (a) $(5x - 1)(2x + 3)$; (b) $(0, -3)$; (c) $\left(\frac{1}{5}, 0\right)$ and $\left(-\frac{3}{2}, 0\right)$

53. $(x^2 + 1)(x^2 + 2)$

54. $(x^2 - 5)(x^2 - 2)$

55. $(x^2 - 11)(x^2 + 3)$

56. $(x^2 + 7)(x^2 - 2)$

57. $(y^3 - 5)(y^3 + 3)$

58. $(x^3 + 7)(x^3 + 3)$

59. $x(x^2 + 2)(x^2 - 8)$

60. $x^2(x^2 - 3)(x^2 - 5)$

44. $45a^4 - 3a^3 - 18a^2$

45. $12p^2 - 35pq + 18q^2$

46. $3t^2 - 4t - 3$

In exercises 47 to 52, for each function, **(a)** *rewrite the function in factored form,* **(b)** *find the ordered pair associated with $f(0)$, and* **(c)** *find all ordered pairs $(x, 0)$.*

47. $f(x) = x^2 - 2x - 3$

48. $f(x) = x^2 - 3x - 10$

49. $f(x) = 2x^2 + 3x - 2$

50. $f(x) = 3x^2 - 11x + 6$

51. $f(x) = 3x^2 + 5x - 28$

52. $f(x) = 10x^2 + 13x - 3$

Basic Skills | **Advanced Skills** | Vocational-Technical Applications | Calculator/Computer | Above and Beyond

Certain trinomials in quadratic form can be factored with similar techniques. For instance, we can factor $x^4 - 5x^2 - 6$ as $(x^2 - 6)(x^2 + 1)$. In exercises 53 to 64, apply a similar method to completely factor each polynomial.

53. $x^4 + 3x^2 + 2$

54. $x^4 - 7x^2 + 10$

55. $x^4 - 8x^2 - 33$

56. $x^4 + 5x^2 - 14$

57. $y^6 - 2y^3 - 15$

58. $x^6 + 10x^3 + 21$

59. $x^5 - 6x^3 - 16x$

60. $x^6 - 8x^4 + 15x^2$

61. $x^4 - 5x^2 - 36$

62. $x^4 - 5x^2 + 4$

63. $x^6 - 6x^3 - 16$

64. $x^6 - 2x^3 - 3$

Basic Skills | Advanced Skills | **Vocational-Technical Applications** | Calculator/Computer | Above and Beyond

65. **ALLIED HEALTH** One technique of controlling cancer is to use radiation therapy. After such a treatment, the total number of cancerous cells, N, in thousands, can be estimated by the function $N(t) = 9 + 25t - 6t^2$, where t is the number of days of treatment. Write this function in factored form.

66. **ALLIED HEALTH** The number of people who are sick t days after the outbreak of a flu epidemic is given by the function $P(t) = 50 + 25t - 3t^2$. Write this function in factored form.

67. **MECHANICAL ENGINEERING** The flow rate through a hydraulic hose can be found from the equation $2Q^2 + Q - 21 = 0$. Factor the left side of this equation.

68. **MANUFACTURING TECHNOLOGY** The bending moment in an overhanging beam is described by the expression $204x^2 - 4{,}476x + 7{,}920$. Factor this expression.

69. **CONSTRUCTION TECHNOLOGY** The profit curve for a welding shop is given by the function $P(x) = 2x^2 - 143x - 1{,}360$. Write this function in factored form.

70. **AGRICULTURAL TECHNOLOGY** The yield of a crop is given by the function $f(x) = -0.05x^2 + 1.5x + 140$. Write this function in factored form.

Basic Skills | Advanced Skills | Vocational-Technical Applications | **Calculator/Computer** | Above and Beyond

In each of the following, **(a)** *factor the given function,* **(b)** *identify the values of x for which f(x) = 0,* **(c)** *graph f(x) using the graphing calculator and determine where the graph crosses the x-axis, and* **(d)** *compare the results of* **(b)** *and* **(c)**.

71. $f(x) = x^2 - 2x - 8$

72. $f(x) = x^2 - 3x - 10$

73. $f(x) = 2x^2 - x - 3$

74. $f(x) = 3x^2 - x - 2$

Basic Skills | Advanced Skills | Vocational-Technical Applications | Calculator/Computer | **Above and Beyond**

In exercises 75 to 78, determine a value k so that the polynomial can be factored.

75. $x^2 + 5x + k$

76. $4x^2 - x + k$

77. $x^2 + kx - 6$

78. $6x^2 + kx - 3$

Answers

61. $(x + 3)(x - 3)(x^2 + 4)$
62. $(x + 1)(x - 1)(x + 2)(x - 2)$
63. $(x - 2)(x^2 + 2x + 4)(x^3 + 2)$
64. $(x^3 - 3)(x + 1)(x^2 - x + 1)$
65. $N(t) = (-2t + 9)(3t + 1)$
66. $P(t) = (3t + 5)(-t + 10)$
67. $(2Q + 7)(Q - 3) = 0$
68. $12(x - 20)(17x - 33)$
69. $P(x) = (2x + 17)(x - 80)$
70. $f(x) = -0.05(x + 40)(x - 70)$
71. (a) $(x - 4)(x + 2)$; (b) $4, -2$
72. (a) $(x - 5)(x + 2)$; (b) $5, -2$
73. (a) $(2x - 3)(x + 1)$; (b) $\frac{3}{2}, -1$
74. (a) $(3x + 2)(x - 1)$; (b) $-\frac{2}{3}, 1$
75. 0, 4, 6, −6, −14, −24, −36,...
76. 0, −5 or −3
77. −5, 5, −1, or 1
78. 0, 7, −7, 17, −17, 3, or −3

Answers

79. $x(x + 2)(x + 4)$

80. $x(x + 1)(x + 2)$

81. $(2x - 3)$ and $(x + 5)$

82. $(3x + 5)$ and $(x + 2)$

79. The product of three numbers is $x^3 + 6x^2 + 8x$. Show that the numbers are consecutive even or consecutive odd integers. (*Hint:* Factor the expression.)

80. The product of three numbers is $x^3 + 3x^2 + 2x$. Show that the numbers are consecutive integers.

In exercises 81 and 82, determine the binomials that represent the dimensions of the given figure.

81. Area $= 2x^2 + 7x - 15$? ?

82. Area $= 3x^2 + 11x + 10$? ?

Answers

1. False **3.** True **5.** False **7.** $a = 2, b = 5, c = 3$
9. $a = 2, b = 1, c = -1$ **11.** Factorable, $m = 5, n = -2$
13. Not factorable **15.** Factorable; $m = 4, n = 1$ **17.** $(x + 3y)(x + 5y)$
19. $(5x - 2)(x + 4)$ **21.** $(2x + 5)^2$ **23.** $(5x - 6)(x + 6)$
25. $(4x + 5)^2$ **27.** $(4x - y)(2x - 7y)$ **29.** $2(x - 4)(x - 9)$
31. $x(x + 4)(5x - 6)$ **33.** $3x(x - 6y)(x + y)$
35. $(7c + 2d)(7c + 2d)$ or $(7c + 2d)^2$ **37.** $6(z^2 - 7z - 12)$
39. $2k(4k - 5)(2k + 3)$ **41.** $kw(2k + 5w)(2k + 5w)$ or $kw(2k + 5w)^2$
43. $(3b + 2)(2b + 1)$ **45.** $(4p - 9q)(3p - 2q)$
47. **(a)** $(x - 3)(x + 1)$; **(b)** $(0, -3)$; **(c)** $(3, 0)$ and $(-1, 0)$
49. **(a)** $(2x - 1)(x + 2)$; **(b)** $(0, -2)$; **(c)** $\left(\frac{1}{2}, 0\right)$ and $(-2, 0)$
51. **(a)** $(x + 4)(3x - 7)$; **(b)** $(0, -28)$; **(c)** $(-4, 0)$ and $\left(\frac{7}{3}, 0\right)$
53. $(x^2 + 1)(x^2 + 2)$ **55.** $(x^2 - 11)(x^2 + 3)$ **57.** $(y^3 - 5)(y^3 + 3)$
59. $x(x^2 + 2)(x^2 - 8)$ **61.** $(x + 3)(x - 3)(x^2 + 4)$
63. $(x - 2)(x^2 + 2x + 4)(x^3 + 2)$ **65.** $N(t) = (-2t + 9)(3t + 1)$
67. $(2Q + 7)(Q - 3) = 0$ **69.** $P(x) = (2x + 17)(x - 80)$
71. **(a)** $(x - 4)(x + 2)$; **(b)** $4, -2$ **73.** **(a)** $(2x - 3)(x + 1)$; **(b)** $\frac{3}{2}, -1$
75. $0, 4, 6, -6, -14, -24, -36, \ldots$ **77.** $-5, 5, -1$, or 1
79. $x(x + 2)(x + 4)$
81. $(2x - 3)$ and $(x + 5)$

5.8 Strategies in Factoring

< 5.8 Objectives >

1 > Recognize factoring patterns

2 > Apply appropriate factoring strategies

In Sections 5.4 to 5.7 you saw a variety of techniques for factoring polynomials. This section reviews those techniques and presents some guidelines for choosing an appropriate strategy or a combination of strategies.

1. Always look for a greatest common factor. If you find a GCF (other than 1), factor out the GCF as your first step.

To factor $5x^2y - 10xy + 25xy^2$, the GCF is $5xy$, so

$$5x^2y - 10xy + 25xy^2 = 5xy\,(x - 2 + 5y)$$

2. Now look at the number of terms in the polynomial you are trying to factor.

(a) If the polynomial is a *binomial,* consider the special binomial formulas.

(i) To factor $x^2 - 49y^2$, recognize the difference of squares, so

$$x^2 - 49y^2 = (x + 7y)(x - 7y)$$

(ii) The binomial

$$x^2 + 121$$

is the sum of two squares and cannot be further factored.

(iii) To factor $t^3 - 64$, recognize the difference of two cubes, so

$$t^3 - 64 = (t - 4)(t^2 + 4t + 16)$$

(iv) The binomial $z^3 + 1$ is the sum of two cubes, so

$$z^3 + 1 = (z + 1)(z^2 - z + 1)$$

(b) If the polynomial is a *trinomial,* try to factor it as a product of two binomials. You can use either the trial-and-error method or the *ac* method.

To factor $2x^2 - x - 6$, a consideration of possible factors will lead to

$$2x^2 - x - 6 = (2x + 3)(x - 2)$$

(c) If the polynomial has *more than three terms,* try factoring by grouping.

To factor $2x^2 - 3xy + 10x - 15y$, group the first two terms, and then the last two, and factor out common factors.

$$2x^2 - 3xy + 10x - 15y = x(2x - 3y) + 5(2x - 3y)$$

RECALL

$a^2 - b^2 = (a + b)(a - b)$

The sum of two squares $a^2 + b^2$ cannot usually be factored.

$a^3 - b^3 = (a - b)(a^2 + ab + b^2)$

$a^3 + b^3 = (a + b)(a^2 - ab + b^2)$

Now factor out the common binomial factor $(2x - 3y)$.

$$2x^2 - 3xy + 10x - 15y = (2x - 3y)(x + 5)$$

3. You should always factor the polynomial completely. So after you apply one of the techniques given in part 2, another one may be necessary.

(a) To factor $6x^3 + 22x - 40x$ first factor out the common factor of $2x$. So

$$6x^3 + 22x - 40x = 2x(3x^2 + 11x - 20)$$

Now continue to factor the trinomial as before to obtain

$$6x^3 + 22x - 40x = 2x(3x - 4)(x + 5)$$

(b) To factor $x^3 - x^2y - 4x + 4y$ first proceed by grouping:

$$x^3 - x^2y - 4x + 4y = x^2(x - y) - 4(x - y)$$
$$= (x - y)(x^2 - 4)$$

Now because $x^2 - 4$ is a difference of two squares, continue to factor and obtain

$$x^3 - x^2y - 4x + 4y = (x - y)(x + 2)(x - 2)$$

4. You can always check your answer by multiplying.

Example 1 Recognizing Factoring Patterns

< Objective 1 >

For each of the following expressions, state the appropriate first step for factoring the polynomial.

(a) $9x^2 - 18x - 72$

Find the GCF.

(b) $x^2 - 3x + 2xy - 6y$

Group the terms.

(c) $x^4 - 81y^4$

Factor the difference of squares.

(d) $3x^2 + 7x + 2$

Use the *ac* method (or trial and error).

Check Yourself 1

For each of the following expressions, state the appropriate first step for factoring the polynomial.

(a) $5x^2 + 2x - 3$ **(b)** $a^4b^4 - 16$
(c) $3x^2 + 3x - 60$ **(d)** $2a^2 - 5a + 4ab - 10b$

Example 2 Factoring Polynomials

< Objective 2 >

For each of the following expressions, completely factor the polynomial.

(a) $9x^2 - 18x - 72$

The GCF is 9.

$$\begin{aligned} 9x^2 - 18x - 72 &= 9(x^2 - 2x - 8) \\ &= 9(x - 4)(x + 2) \end{aligned}$$

(b) $x^2 - 3x + 2xy - 6y$

Grouping the terms, we have

$$\begin{aligned} x^2 - 3x + 2xy - 6y &= (x^2 - 3x) + (2xy - 6y) \\ &= x(x - 3) + 2y(x - 3) \\ &= (x - 3)(x + 2y) \end{aligned}$$

(c) $x^4 - 81y^4$

Factoring the difference of squares, we find

$$\begin{aligned} x^4 - 81y^4 &= (x^2 + 9y^2)(x^2 - 9y^2) \\ &= (x^2 + 9y^2)(x - 3y)(x + 3y) \end{aligned}$$

(d) $3x^2 + 7x + 2$

Using the *ac* method, we find $m = 1$ and $n = 6$.

$$\begin{aligned} 3x^2 + 7x + 2 &= 3x^2 + x + 6x + 2 \\ &= (3x^2 + x) + (6x + 2) \\ &= x(3x + 1) + 2(3x + 1) \\ &= (3x + 1)(x + 2) \end{aligned}$$

Check Yourself 2

For each of the following expressions, completely factor the polynomial.

(a) $5x^2 + 2x - 3$ **(b)** $a^4b^4 - 16$
(c) $3x^2 + 3x - 60$ **(d)** $2a^2 - 5a + 4ab - 10b$

Check Yourself ANSWERS

1. **(a)** Use the *ac* method (or trial and error); **(b)** factor the difference of squares; **(c)** find the GCF; **(d)** group the terms

2. **(a)** $(5x - 3)(x + 1)$; **(b)** $(a^2b^2 + 4)(ab - 2)(ab + 2)$; **(c)** $3(x + 5)(x - 4)$; **(d)** $(2a - 5)(a + 2b)$

Reading Your Text

The following fill-in-the-blank exercises are designed to ensure that you understand some of the key vocabulary used in this section.

SECTION 5.8

(a) Step one in factoring requires that we find the ______________ of all the terms.

(b) Step ______________ in factoring is to consider the number of terms in the polynomial.

(c) You should always factor a given polynomial ______________.

(d) It is a good idea to ______________ in order to make sure your answer is correct.

Basic Skills | Advanced Skills | Vocational-Technical Applications | Calculator/Computer | Above and Beyond

5.8 exercises

< Objectives 1 and 2 >

Factor each polynomial completely. To begin, state which method should be applied as the first step, given the guidelines of this section. Then continue the exercise and factor each polynomial completely.

1. $x^2 - 3x$

2. $4y^2 - 9$

3. $x^2 - 5x - 24$

4. $8x^3 + 27$

5. $x(x - y) + 2(x - y)$

6. $5a^2 - 10a + 25$

7. $2x^2y - 6xy + 8y^2$

8. $2p - 6q + pq - 3q^2$

9. $y^2 - 13y + 40$

10. $m^3 + 27m^2n$

11. $3b^2 + 17b - 28$

12. $3x^2 + 6x - 5xy - 10y$

13. $3x^2 - 14xy - 24y^2$

14. $c^3 - 64$

15. $2a^2 + 11a + 12$

16. $m^3n^3 - mn$

Name ____________

Section ________ Date ________

Answers

1. GCF, $x(x - 3)$
2. Difference of squares, $(2y + 3)(2y - 3)$
3. Trial and error, $(x - 8)(x + 3)$
4. Sum of cubes, $(2x + 3)(4x^2 - 6x + 9)$
5. GCF, $(x + 2)(x - y)$
6. GCF, $5(a^2 - 2a + 5)$
7. GCF, $2y(x^2 - 3x + 4y)$
8. Grouping, $(p - 3q)(2 + q)$
9. Trial and error, $(y - 5)(y - 8)$
10. GCF, $m^2(m + 27n)$
11. Trial and error, $(b + 7)(3b - 4)$
12. Grouping, $(x + 2)(3x - 5y)$
13. Trial and error, $(3x + 4y)(x - 6y)$
14. Difference of cubes, $(c - 4)(c^2 + 4c + 16)$
15. Trial and error, $(2a + 3)(a + 4)$
16. GCF, then difference of squares, $mn(mn + 1)(mn - 1)$

Answers

17. GCF, $r^2(125r + 1)$

18. Difference of squares, $(x - y + 4)(x - y - 4)$

19. GCF, then trial and error, $3(x - 3)(x - 7)$

20. GCF, then difference of squares, $3(a + 6)(a - 6)$

21. GCF, $5(8a^2 + 1)$

22. GCF, then trial and error, $4(p + 3)(p - 5)$

23. GCF, then trial and error, $2(w - 9)(w + 2)$

24. GCF, then sum of cubes, $xy(y + 1)(y^2 - y + 1)$

25. GCF, then difference of squares, $3b(a + 4b)(a - 4b)$

26. GCF, then trial and error, $2b(6b - 1)(b - 7)$

27. Trial and error, $(x^2 - 5)(x^2 + 2)$

28. Difference of squares, $(m^2 + 3n^2)(m^2 - 3n^2)$

29. Prime, not factorable

30. $2k^2(2k - 3w)(k + w)$

31. $(r^4 + s^4)(r^2 + s^2)(r + s)(r - s)$

32. $n(n + 2)(m + 1)$

33. $(5b - 8c)^2$

34. $3(p^2q^2 + 4)$

35. $5(3a - b)(a + b)$

36. $(x^2 + 2)(x^2 + 3)$

37. $m^4n\,(3m + 2n)\,(2m + n)$

38. $-(8b + 1)(3b - 5)$

17. $125r^3 + r^2$

18. $(x - y)^2 - 16$

19. $3x^2 - 30x + 63$

20. $3a^2 - 108$

21. $40a^2 + 5$

22. $4p^2 - 8p - 60$

23. $2w^2 - 14w - 36$

24. $xy^4 + xy$

25. $3a^2b - 48b^3$

26. $12b^3 - 86b^2 + 14b$

27. $x^4 - 3x^2 - 10$

28. $m^4 - 9n^4$

Factor completely.

29. $3w^2 + 2wz + 5z^2$ 

30. $4k^4 - 2k^3w - 6k^2w^2$ 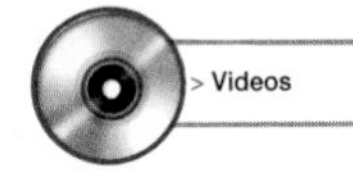

31. $r^8 - s^8$ 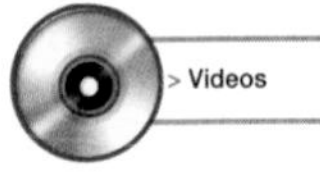

32. $n^2 + 2n + 2nm + n^2m$

33. $25b^2 - 80bc + 64c^2$

34. $3p^2q^2 + 12$ 

35. $15ab - 5b^2 + 15a^2 - 5ab$

36. $x^4 + 5x^2 + 6$

37. $6m^6n + 7m^5n^2 + 2m^4n^3$

38. $37b - 24b^2 + 5$ 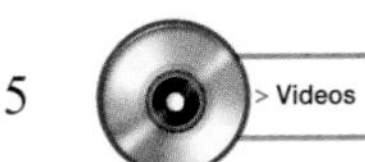

39. $121x^8y^3 + 77x^6y^3$

40. $w^2z + 4wz - 32z$

41. $18m^2n^2 - 27m^2n + 18m^2n^3$

42. $(a - b)^3 - (a + b)^3$

43. $-40k^2 - k + 6$

44. $8x^3 - 36x^2 - 20x$

45. $3h^3 - 6h^2 + 15h$

46. $12p^2 + 2pq - 24q^2$

47. $64t^6 + 1$

48. $4y^2 + 7xy^2 - 15x^2y^2$

Basic Skills | **Advanced Skills** | Vocational-Technical Applications | Calculator/Computer | Above and Beyond

Factor completely.

49. $(a - 5)^2 - 169$

50. $(b - 7)^2 - 81$

51. $18c^2(d - 3)^2 + 15c(d - 3)^2 - 75(d - 3)^2$

52. $25g^2(h + 1)^3 - 5g(h + 1)^3 - 2(h + 1)^3$

53. $j^2 + 4jk + 4k^2 - 16$

54. $9m^2 + 12mn + 4n^2 - 25$

55. $10(a - b)^2 - 11(a - b) - 6$

56. $8(r + s)^2 + 14(r + s) - 15$

57. $6(t - 2)^2 + 7(t - 2) - 5$

58. $12(v + 1)^2 - 17(v + 1) + 6$

59. $24(x - 1)^2 - 14(x - 1) - 3$

60. $14(2 - y)^2 - 15(2 - y) - 11$

Answers

1. GCF, $x(x - 3)$ 3. Trial and error, $(x - 8)(x + 3)$
5. GCF, $(x + 2)(x - y)$ 7. GCF, $2y(x^2 - 3x + 4y)$
9. Trial and error, $(y - 5)(y - 8)$ 11. Trial and error, $(b + 7)(3b - 4)$

Answers

39. $11x^6y^3(11x^2 + 7)$
40. $z(w + 8)(w - 4)$
41. $9m^2n(2n - 3 + 2n^2)$
42. $-2b(3a^2 + b^2)$
43. $-(8k - 3)(5k + 2)$
44. $4x(2x + 1)(x - 5)$
45. $3h(h^2 - 2h + 5)$
46. $2(2p + 3q)(3p - 4q)$
47. $(4t^2 + 1)(16t^4 - 4t^2 + 1)$
48. $-y^2(5x - 4)(3x + 1)$
49. $(a + 8)(a - 18)$
50. $(b + 2)(b - 16)$
51. $3(d - 3)^2(3c - 5)(2c + 5)$
52. $(h + 1)^3(5g + 1)(5g - 2)$
53. $(j + 2k + 4)(j + 2k - 4)$
54. $(3m + 2n + 5)(3m + 2n - 5)$
55. $(5a - 5b + 2)(2a - 2b - 3)$
56. $(4r + 4s - 3)(2r + 2s + 5)$
57. $(2t - 5)(3t - 1)$
58. $(4v + 1)(3v + 1)$
59. $(6x - 5)(4x - 7)$
60. $(3 - 7y)(5 - 2y)$

13. Trial and error, $(3x + 4y)(x - 6y)$ **15.** Trial and error, $(2a + 3)(a + 4)$
17. GCF, $r^2(125r + 1)$ **19.** GCF, then trial and error, $3(x - 3)(x - 7)$
21. GCF, $5(8a^2 + 1)$ **23.** GCF, then trial and error, $2(w - 9)(w + 2)$
25. GCF, then difference of squares, $3b(a + 4b)(a - 4b)$
27. Trial and error, $(x^2 - 5)(x^2 + 2)$ **29.** Prime, not factorable
31. $(r^4 + s^4)(r^2 + s^2)(r + s)(r - s)$ **33.** $(5b - 8c)^2$
35. $5(3a - b)(a + b)$ **37.** $m^4n(3m + 2n)(2m + n)$
39. $11x^6y^3(11x^2 + 7)$ **41.** $9m^2n(2n - 3 + 2n^2)$
43. $-(8k - 3)(5k + 2)$ **45.** $3h(h^2 - 2h + 5)$
47. $(4t^2 + 1)(16t^4 - 4t^2 + 1)$ **49.** $(a + 8)(a - 18)$
51. $3(d - 3)^2(3c - 5)(2c + 5)$ **53.** $(j + 2k + 4)(j + 2k - 4)$
55. $(5a - 5b + 2)(2a - 2b - 3)$ **57.** $(2t - 5)(3t - 1)$
59. $(6x - 5)(4x - 7)$

5.9 Solving Quadratic Equations by Factoring

< 5.9 Objectives >

1 > Solve a quadratic equation by factoring

2 > Find the zeros of a quadratic function

3 > Solve applications of quadratic equations

The factoring techniques you have learned provide us with tools for solving equations that can be written in the form

$$ax^2 + bx + c = 0 \qquad a \neq 0$$

This is a quadratic equation in one variable, here x. You can recognize such a quadratic equation by the fact that the highest power of the variable x is the second power.

in which a, b, and c are constants.

An equation written in the form $ax^2 + bx + c = 0$ is called a **quadratic equation in standard form.** Using factoring to solve quadratic equations requires the *zero-product principle.* As we saw in Section 5.7, this says that if the product of two factors is 0, then one or both of the factors must be equal to 0.

We can now apply this principle to solve quadratic equations.

Example 1 — **Solving Equations by Factoring**

< Objective 1 >

Solve.

$$x^2 - 3x - 18 = 0$$

Factoring on the left, we have

$$(x - 6)(x + 3) = 0$$

By the zero-product principle, we know that one or both of the factors must be zero. We can then write

$$x - 6 = 0 \quad \text{or} \quad x + 3 = 0$$

Solving each equation gives

$$x = 6 \quad \text{or} \quad x = -3$$

The two solutions are 6 and -3.

The solutions are sometimes called the **zeros,** or **roots,** of the equation. They represent the x-coordinates of the points where the graph of the equation $y = x^2 - 3x - 18$ crosses the x-axis. As we learned in Section 3.2, these are the x-intercepts. In this case, the x-intercepts are at $(-3, 0)$ and $(6, 0)$.

NOTE

To use the zero-product principle, 0 must be on one side of the equation.

NOTE

Graph the function
$y = x^2 - 3x - 18$
on your graphing calculator. The solutions to the equation $0 = x^2 - 3x - 18$ will be the *x*-coordinates of the points on the curve at which $y = 0$. Those are the points at which the graph intercepts the *x*-axis. In other words, the solutions are the *x*-intercepts of the graph.

Quadratic equations can be checked in the same way as linear equations were checked: by substitution. For instance, if $x = 6$, we have

$$6^2 - 3 \cdot 6 - 18 \stackrel{?}{=} 0$$
$$36 - 18 - 18 \stackrel{?}{=} 0$$
$$0 = 0$$

which is a true statement. We leave it to you to check the solution -3.

Check Yourself 1

Solve $x^2 - 9x + 20 = 0$.

Other factoring techniques are also used in solving quadratic equations. Example 2 illustrates this concept.

Example 2 Solving Equations by Factoring

(a) Solve $x^2 - 5x = 0$.

Again, factor the left side of the equation and apply the zero-product principle.

$$x(x - 5) = 0$$

Now

$$x = 0 \quad \text{or} \quad x - 5 = 0$$
$$x = 5$$

The two solutions are 0 and 5.

> CAUTION

A *common mistake* is to forget the statement $x = 0$ when you are solving equations of this type. Be sure to include both solutions in the solution set.

(b) Solve $4x^2 - 1 = 0$.

Factoring yields

$$(2x + 1)(2x - 1) = 0$$
$$2x + 1 = 0 \quad \text{or} \quad 2x - 1 = 0$$
$$2x = -1 \qquad 2x = 1$$
$$x = -\frac{1}{2} \qquad x = \frac{1}{2}$$

The solutions may be written as $x = \pm\frac{1}{2}$.

NOTE

The symbol $\pm$ is read "plus or minus."

Check Yourself 2

Solve by factoring.

(a) $x^2 + 8x = 0$ **(b)** $16x^2 - 25 = 0$

Example 3 illustrates a crucial point. Our solution technique depends on the zero-product principle, which means that the product of factors *must be equal to* 0. The importance of this is shown now.

Example 3 Solving Equations by Factoring

Solve $2x^2 - x = 3$.

The first step in the solution is to write the equation in standard form (that is, when one side of the equation is 0). So start by adding -3 to both sides of the equation. Then,

$$2x^2 - x - 3 = 0$$

Make sure all terms are on one side of the equation. The other side will be 0.

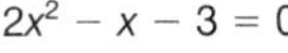

> CAUTION

Consider the equation

$x(2x - 1) = 3$

Students are sometimes tempted to write

$x = 3$ or $2x - 1 = 3$

This is *not correct.* Instead, subtract 3 from both sides of the equation as *the first step* to write

$2x^2 - x - 3 = 0$

in standard form. Only *now* can you factor and proceed as before.

You can now factor and solve by using the zero-product principle.

$$(2x - 3)(x + 1) = 0$$

$$2x - 3 = 0 \quad \text{or} \quad x + 1 = 0$$

$$2x = 3 \qquad\qquad x = -1$$

$$x = \frac{3}{2}$$

The solutions are $\frac{3}{2}$ and -1.

Check Yourself 3

Solve $3x^2 = 5x + 2$.

In all previous examples, the quadratic equations had two distinct real-number solutions. That may not always be the case, as we shall see.

Example 4 Solving Equations by Factoring

Solve $9x^2 - 30x + 25 = 0$.

Factoring, we have

$$(3x - 5)(3x - 5) = 0$$

and

$$3x - 5 = 0 \quad \text{or} \quad 3x - 5 = 0$$

$$x = \frac{5}{3} \qquad\qquad x = \frac{5}{3}$$

The solution is $\frac{5}{3}$.

A quadratic (or second-degree) equation always has *two* solutions. When an equation such as this one has two solutions that are the same number, we call $\frac{5}{3}$ the **repeated** (or **double**) **solution** of the equation.

Although a quadratic equation will always have two solutions, they may not always be real numbers. You will learn more about this in Chapter 8.

Check Yourself 4

Solve $16x^2 + 24x + 9 = 0$.

Always examine the quadratic expression of an equation for common factors. It will make your work much easier, as Example 5 illustrates.

Example 5 Solving Equations by Factoring

Solve $3x^2 - 3x - 60 = 0$.

First, note the common factor 3 in the quadratic expression on the left side of the equation. Factoring out the 3, we have

$$3(x^2 - x - 20) = 0$$

NOTE

The advantage of dividing both sides by 3 is that the coefficients in the quadratic expression become smaller, and that expression is much easier to factor.

Now because the GCF has no variables, we can divide both sides of the equation by 3.

$$\frac{3(x^2 - x - 20)}{3} = \frac{0}{3}$$

or

$$x^2 - x - 20 = 0$$

We can now factor and solve as before.

$$(x - 5)(x + 4) = 0$$

$$x - 5 = 0 \quad \text{or} \quad x + 4 = 0$$

$$x = 5 \qquad\qquad x = -4$$

RECALL

A *linear function* is a function that can be written in the form

$f(x) = ax + b$

in which a and b are real numbers.

Check Yourself 5

Solve $2x^2 - 10x - 48 = 0$.

In Chapter 3, we introduced the concept of a function and discussed the relationship between linear polynomials and linear functions. Since we have been learning about quadratic polynomials, you may be wondering if these are related to functions as well. In fact there is another type of function called a quadratic function.

Definition

Quadratic Function

A **quadratic function** is a function that can be written in the form

$f(x) = ax^2 + bx + c$

in which a, b, and c are real numbers and $a \neq 0$.

For example, $f(x) = 3x^2 - 2x - 1$ and $g(x) = x^2 - 2$ are quadratic functions. In working with functions, we often want to find the values of x for which $f(x) = 0$. As in quadratic equations, these values are called the **zeros of the function.** They represent the x-intercepts of the function. To find the zeros of a quadratic function, a quadratic equation must be solved.

Example 6 Finding the Zeros of a Function

< Objective 2 >

Find the zeros of $f(x) = x^2 - x - 2$.

To find the zeros of $f(x) = x^2 - x - 2$, we must solve the quadratic equation $f(x) = 0$.

$$f(x) = 0$$
$$x^2 - x - 2 = 0$$
$$(x - 2)(x + 1) = 0$$
$$x - 2 = 0 \quad \text{or} \quad x + 1 = 0$$
$$x = 2 \qquad\qquad x = -1$$

The zeros of the function are -1 and 2.

NOTE

The graph of

$f(x) = x^2 - x - 2$

intercepts the x-axis at the points (2, 0) and $(-1, 0)$, so 2 and -1 are the *zeros* of the function.

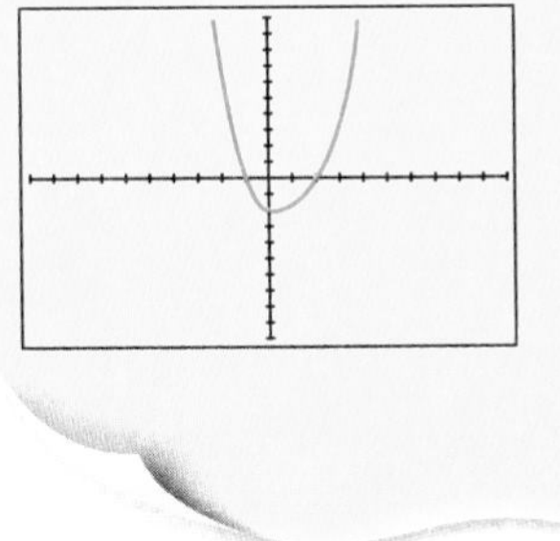

Check Yourself 6

Find the zeros of $f(x) = 2x^2 - x - 3$.

With the techniques introduced in this section for solving equations by factoring, we can now examine a new group of applications. Recall that the key to problem solving lies in a step-by-step, organized approach to the process. You might want to take time now to review the five-step process introduced in Section 2.3. All of the examples in the remainder of this section make use of that model.

You will find that these applications typically lead to quadratic equations that may be solved by factoring. Remember that such quadratic equations will have two, one, or no distinct real-number solutions. Step 5, the process of verifying or checking your solutions, is particularly important here. By checking solutions, you may find that both, only one, or none of the derived solutions satisfy the physical conditions stated in the original problem.

We begin with a numerical application.

Example 7 Solving a Number Application

< Objective 3 >

One integer is 3 less than twice another. If their product is 35, find the two integers.

Step 1 The unknowns are the two integers.

Step 2 Let x represent the first integer. Then

$$2x - 3$$

Twice 3 less than

represents the second.

Step 3 Form an equation:

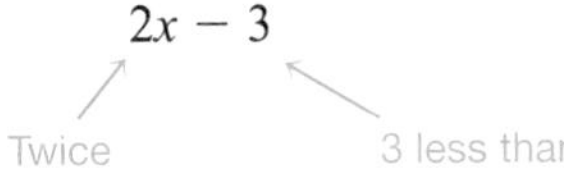

$$x(2x - 3) = 35$$

Product of the two integers

Step 4 Remove the parentheses and solve as before.

$$2x^2 - 3x = 35$$
$$2x^2 - 3x - 35 = 0$$

Factor the left side of the equation:

NOTE

These represent solutions to the equation, but may not be answers to the original problem.

$$(2x + 7)(x - 5) = 0$$

$$2x + 7 = 0 \quad \text{or} \quad x - 5 = 0$$

$$2x = -7 \qquad x = 5$$

$$x = -\frac{7}{2}$$

Step 5 From step 4, we have the two solutions $-\frac{7}{2}$ and 5. Since the original problem asks for *integers,* we must consider only 5 as a solution.

Using 5 for x, we see that the other integer is $2x - 3 = 2(5) - 3 = 7$. So the desired integers are 5 and 7.

To verify, note that **(a)** 7 is 3 less than 2 times 5, and **(b)** the product of 5 and 7 is 35.

Check Yourself 7

One integer is 2 more than 3 times another. If their product is 56, what are the two integers?

Problems involving consecutive integers may also lead to quadratic equations. Recall that consecutive integers can be represented by x, $x + 1$, $x + 2$, and so on. Consecutive even (or odd) integers are represented by x, $x + 2$, $x + 4$, and so on.

Example 8 Solving a Number Application

NOTE

You may be tempted to just use guessing and checking for problems of this type. However, this often causes you to miss one of the solutions.

The sum of the squares of two consecutive integers is 85. What are the two integers?

Step 1 The unknowns are the two consecutive integers.

Step 2 Let x be the first integer and $x + 1$ the second integer.

Step 3 Form the equation.

$$\underbrace{x^2 + (x + 1)^2}_{\text{Sum of squares}} = 85$$

Step 4 Solve.

$$x^2 + (x + 1)^2 = 85 \quad \text{Remove parentheses.}$$

$$x^2 + x^2 + 2x + 1 = 85 \quad \text{Write in standard form.}$$

$$2x^2 + 2x - 84 = 0 \quad \text{Note the common factor 2, and divide both sides of the equation by 2.}$$

$$x^2 + x - 42 = 0$$

$$(x + 7)(x - 6) = 0$$

$$x + 7 = 0 \quad \text{or} \quad x - 6 = 0$$

$$x = -7 \qquad x = 6$$

Step 5 The solution in step 4 leads to two possibilities, -7 or 6. Since *both numbers are integers,* both meet the conditions of the original problem. There are then two pairs of consecutive integers that work:

If x is -7, then $x + 1$ is -6, so the consecutive integers are -7 and -6.

If x is 6, then $x + 1$ is 7, so the consecutive integers are 6 and 7.

You should confirm that in both cases, the sum of the squares is 85.

Check Yourself 8

The sum of the squares of two consecutive even integers is 100. Find the two integers.

We proceed now to applications involving geometry.

Example 9 Solving a Geometric Application

The length of a rectangle is 3 cm greater than its width. If the area of the rectangle is 108 cm^2, what are the dimensions of the rectangle?

Step 1 You are asked to find the dimensions (the length and the width) of the rectangle.

Step 2 Whenever geometric figures are involved in an application, start by drawing, and *then labeling,* a sketch of the problem. Let x represent the width and $x + 3$ the length.

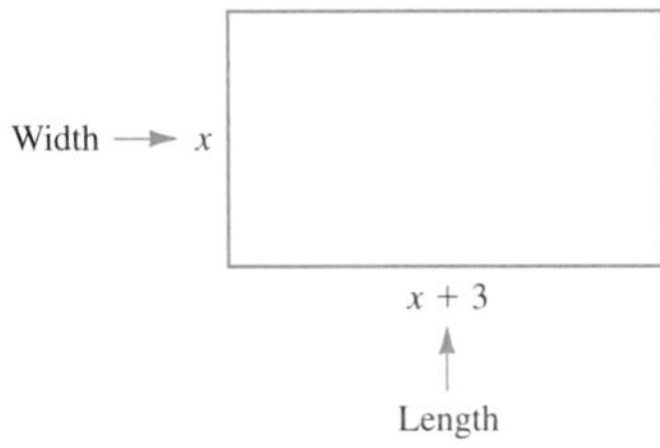

Step 3 Once the drawing is correctly labeled, this step should be easy. The area of a rectangle is the product of its length and width, so

$$x(x + 3) = 108$$

Step 4

$$x(x + 3) = 108$$ Multiply and rearrange to write in standard form.

$$x^2 + 3x - 108 = 0$$ Factor and then use the zero-factor principle as before.

$$(x + 12)(x - 9) = 0$$

$$x + 12 = 0 \quad \text{or} \quad x - 9 = 0$$

$$x = -12 \qquad\qquad x = 9$$

Step 5 We reject -12 (cm) as a solution. A length cannot be negative, and so we must consider only 9 (cm) in finding the required dimensions.

The width x is 9 cm, and the length $x + 3$ is 12 cm. Since this gives a rectangle of area 108 cm^2, the solution is verified.

Check Yourself 9

In a triangle, the base is 4 in. less than its height. If its area is 30 $in.^2$, find the length of the base and the height of the triangle.

(Note: The formula for the area of a triangle is $A = \frac{1}{2}bh$.)

We look at another geometric application.

Example 10 Solving a Rectangular Box Application

An open box is formed from a rectangular piece of cardboard, whose length is 2 in. more than its width, by cutting 2-in. squares from each corner and folding up the sides. If the volume of the box is to be 96 in.^{3}, what must be the size of the original piece of cardboard?

Step 1 We are asked for the dimensions of the sheet of cardboard.

Step 2 Again, sketch the problem.

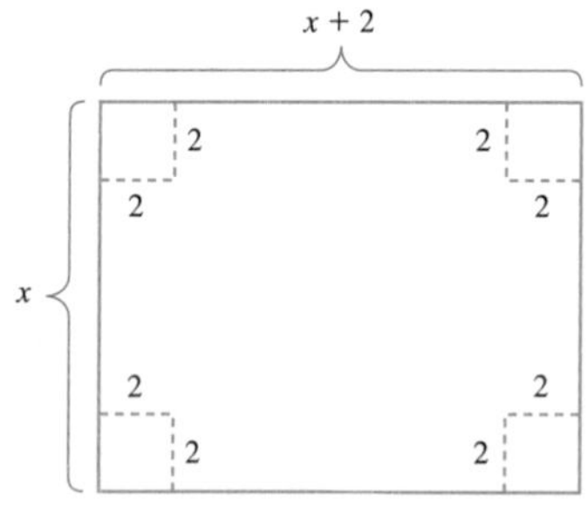

Step 3 To form an equation for volume, we sketch the completed box.

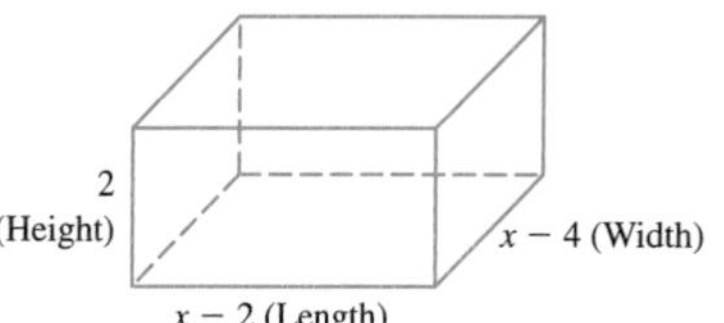

NOTE

The original width of the cardboard was x. Removing two 2-in. squares leaves $x - 4$ for the width of the box. Similarly, the length of the box is $x - 2$. Do you see why?

Since volume is the product of height, length, and width,

$$2(x - 2)(x - 4) = 96$$

Step 4

$2(x - 2)(x - 4) = 96$ Divide both sides by 2.

$(x - 2)(x - 4) = 48$ Multiply on the left.

$x^2 - 6x + 8 = 48$ Write in standard form.

$x^2 - 6x - 40 = 0$ Solve as before.

$(x - 10)(x + 4) = 0$

$x = 10$ or $x = -4$

Step 5 Again, we need consider only the positive solution. The width x of the original piece of cardboard is 10 in., and its length $x + 2$ is 12 in. The dimensions of the completed box will be 6 in. by 8 in. by 2 in., which gives the required volume of 96 in.^{3}

Check Yourself 10

A similar box is to be made by cutting 3-in. squares from a piece of cardboard that is 4 in. longer than it is wide. If the required volume is 180 in.^{3}, find the dimensions of the original piece of cardboard.

We now turn to another field for an application that leads to solving a quadratic equation. Many equations of motion in physics involve quadratic equations.

Example 11 Solving a Thrown Ball Application

Suppose that a person throws a ball directly upward, releasing the ball at a height of 5 feet above the ground. If the ball is thrown with an initial velocity of 80 feet per second, the height of the ball, in feet, above the ground after t seconds is given by

$h = -16t^2 + 80t + 5$

When is the ball at a height of 69 feet?

Step 1 The height h of the ball, and the time t since the ball was released are the unknowns.

Step 2 We want to know the value(s) of t for which $h = 69$.

Step 3 Write $69 = -16t^2 + 80t + 5$.

Step 4 Solve for t:

$69 = -16t^2 + 80t + 5$ Write in standard form.

$0 = -16t^2 + 80t - 64$ Divide both sides of the equation by -16.

$0 = t^2 - 5t + 4$ Factor.

$0 = (t - 1)(t - 4)$

$t - 1 = 0$ or $t - 4 = 0$

$t = 1$ $t = 4$

Step 5 By substituting 1 for t, we confirm that $h = 69$:

$h = -16(1)^2 + 80(1) + 5 = -16 + 80 + 5 = 69$

You should also check that $h = 69$ when $t = 4$.

The ball is at a height of 69 feet at $t = 1$ second (on the way up) and at $t = 4$ seconds (on the way down).

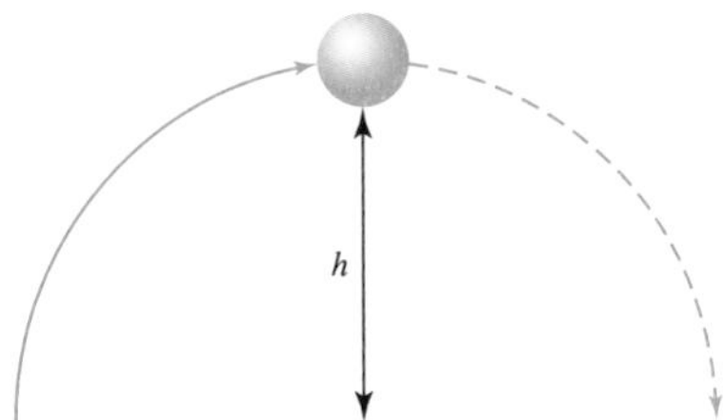

Check Yourself 11

A ball is thrown vertically upward from the top of a building 100 meters high with an initial velocity of 25 meters per second. After t seconds, the height h, in meters, is given by

$h = -5t^2 + 25t + 100$

When is the ball at a height of 130 meters?

In applications we must pay particular attention to the solutions that satisfy the given physical conditions. Consider Example 12.

Example 12 Solving a Thrown Ball Application

A ball is thrown vertically upward from the top of a building 60 meters high with an initial velocity of 20 meters per second. After t seconds, the height h is given by

$$h = -5t^2 + 20t + 60$$

(a) When is the ball at a height of 35 meters?

Steps 1 and 2 We want to know the value(s) of t for which $h = 35$.

Step 3 Write $35 = -5t^2 + 20t + 60$.

Step 4 Solve for t:

$35 = -5t^2 + 20t + 60$ Rearrange to write in standard form.

$0 = -5t^2 + 20t + 25$ Divide both sides of the equation by -5.

$0 = t^2 - 4t - 5$ Factor.

$0 = (t - 5)(t + 1)$

$t - 5 = 0$ or $t + 1 = 0$

$t = 5$ $t = -1$

Step 5 Note that $t = -1$ does not make sense in the context of this problem. (It represents 1 second *before* the ball is released!) You should check that when $t = 5, h = 35$. The ball is at a height of 35 meters at 5 seconds after release.

(b) When does the ball hit the ground?

Steps 1 and 2 When the ball hits the ground, the height of the ball is at 0 meters.

Step 3 Write $0 = -5t^2 + 20t + 60$.

Step 4 Solve for t:

$0 = -5t^2 + 20t + 60$ Divide both sides of the equation by -5.

$0 = t^2 - 4t - 12$ Factor.

$0 = (t - 6)(t + 2)$

$t - 6 = 0$ or $t + 2 = 0$

$t = 6$ $t = -2$

Step 5 As before, we reject the negative solution $t = -2$. The ball hits the ground after 6 seconds. You should verify that when $t = 6, h = 0$.

Check Yourself 12

A ball is thrown vertically upward from the top of a building 150 feet high with an initial velocity of 64 feet per second. After t seconds, the height h is given by

$$h = -16t^2 + 64t + 150$$

When is the ball at a height of 70 feet?

An important application that leads to a quadratic equation involves the stopping distance of a car and its relation to the speed of the car. This is illustrated in Example 13.

Example 13 Solving a Stopping Distance Application

The stopping distance d, in feet, of a car that is traveling at x miles per hour is approximated by the following equation:

$$d = \frac{x^2}{20} + x$$

If the stopping distance of a car is 240 feet, at what speed is the car traveling?

Step 1 The stopping distance d, in feet, and the car's speed x, in miles per hour, are the unknowns.

Step 2 We want to know the value of x such that $d = 240$.

Step 3 Write $240 = \frac{x^2}{20} + x$.

Step 4 Solve for x:

$$240 = \frac{x^2}{20} + x \quad \text{Multiply both sides of the equation by 20.}$$

$$4{,}800 = x^2 + 20x \quad \text{Write in standard form.}$$

$$0 = x^2 + 20x - 4{,}800 \quad \text{Factor.}$$

$$0 = (x + 80)(x - 60)$$

$$x + 80 = 0 \quad \text{or} \quad x - 60 = 0$$

$$x = -80 \qquad\qquad x = 60$$

Step 5 Because x represents the speed of the car, we reject the value $x = -80$. You should verify that if $x = 60$, $d = 240$. The speed of the car is 60 miles per hour.

Check Yourself 13

If the stopping distance of a car is 175 feet, at what speed is the car traveling? Use the equation

$$d = \frac{x^2}{20} + x$$

Check Yourself ANSWERS

1. 4, 5 **2.** **(a)** 0, −8; **(b)** $\frac{5}{4}, -\frac{5}{4}$ **3.** $-\frac{1}{3}, 2$ **4.** $-\frac{3}{4}$ **5.** −3, 8 **6.** $-1, \frac{3}{2}$ **7.** 4, 14 **8.** −8, −6 or 6, 8 **9.** Base: 6 in., or height: 10 in. **10.** 12 in. by 16 in. **11.** 2 sec and 3 sec **12.** 5 sec **13.** 50 mi/h

Reading Your Text

The following fill-in-the-blank exercises are designed to ensure that you understand some of the key vocabulary used in this section.

SECTION 5.9

(a) An equation written in the form $ax^2 + bx + c = 0$ is called a ______________ equation in standard form.

(b) Using factoring to solve quadratic equations requires the ______________ principle.

(c) The solutions to a quadratic equation are sometimes called the ______________ of the equation.

(d) Using the principle mentioned above, it is important that the product of factors must be equal to ______________.

Basic Skills | Advanced Skills | Vocational-Technical Applications | Calculator/Computer | Above and Beyond

5.9 exercises

< Objective 1 >

Solve the quadratic equations by factoring.

1. $x^2 + 4x + 3 = 0$

2. $x^2 - 5x = 50$

3. $x^2 = 2x + 35$

4. $x^2 - 8x = 0$

5. $x^2 = 5x$

6. $x^2 - 25 = 0$

7. $x^2 = 64$

8. $4x^2 + 12x + 9 = 0$

9. $3w^2 - w = 4$

10. $5t^2 = 15t$

11. $4z^2 - 24z = 0$

12. $2m^2 = 12m + 54$

13. $b(b - 2) = 15$

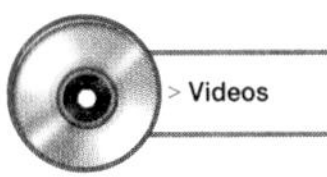

14. $5k^2 = 45$

15. $n(2n - 3) = 9$

16. $2p(3p + 1) = 28$

17. $9r(2r - 1) = 90$

18. $(c + 4)(c + 1) = 18$

19. $5(x - 1)(x - 3) = 75$

20. $(2w + 1)(w - 4) = 11$

21. $12s^2 - s + 1 = 7$

22. $(3h - 5)(h + 2) = 14$

Name ______________

Section ________ Date ________

Answers

1. $-3, -1$
2. $-5, 10$
3. $-5, 7$
4. $0, 8$
5. $0, 5$
6. $-5, 5$
7. $-8, 8$
8. $-\frac{3}{2}$
9. $-1, \frac{4}{3}$
10. $0, 3$
11. $0, 6$
12. $-3, 9$
13. $-3, 5$
14. $3, -3$
15. $-\frac{3}{2}, 3$
16. $-\frac{7}{3}, 2$
17. $-2, \frac{5}{2}$
18. $-7, 2$
19. $-2, 6$
20. $-\frac{3}{2}, 5$
21. $-\frac{2}{3}, \frac{3}{4}$
22. $-3, \frac{8}{3}$

Answers

23. 2, 6

24. −4, 7

25. −5, 1

26. 2, 9

27. $\frac{5}{3}$

28. $-4, \frac{3}{5}$

29. 5, 13

30. 4, 6

31. −9, −8 or 8, 9

32. 5, 6

33. −5, −4, −3 or 3, 4, 5

34. 4

35. 7 ft by 10 ft

36. Base: 6 in., height: 8 in.

37. 30 cm by 60 cm

< Objective 2 >

In exercises 23 to 28, find the zeros of the functions.

23. $f(x) = 3x^2 - 24x + 36$

24. $f(x) = 2x^2 - 6x - 56$

25. $f(x) = 4x^2 + 16x - 20$

26. $f(x) = 3x^2 - 33x + 54$

27. $f(x) = 9x^2 - 30x + 25$

28. $f(x) = 5x^2 + 17x - 12$

< Objective 3 >

Solve each of the applications.

29. **NUMBER PROBLEM** One integer is 3 more than twice another. If the product of those integers is 65, find the two integers.

30. **NUMBER PROBLEM** The sum of two integers is 10, and their product is 24. Find the two integers.

31. **NUMBER PROBLEM** The product of two consecutive integers is 72. What are the two integers?

32. **NUMBER PROBLEM** The sum of the squares of two consecutive whole numbers is 61. Find the two whole numbers.

33. **NUMBER PROBLEM** The sum of the squares of three consecutive integers is 50. Find the three integers.

34. **NUMBER PROBLEM** Twice the square of a positive integer is 12 more than 5 times that integer. What is the integer?

35. **GEOMETRY** The width of a rectangle is 3 ft less than its length. If the area of the rectangle is 70 ft^2, what are the dimensions of the rectangle?

36. **GEOMETRY** The height of a triangle is 2 in. more than the length of the base. If the base is tripled in length, the area of the new triangle is 48 in.^{2} more than the original. Find the height and base of the original triangle.

37. **CRAFTS** A box is to be made from a rectangular piece of tin that is twice as long as it is wide. To accomplish this, a 10-cm square is cut from each corner, and the sides are folded up. The volume of the finished box is to be 4,000 cm^3. Find the dimensions of the original piece of tin.

Hint 1: To solve this equation, you will want to use the given sketch of the piece of tin. Note that the original dimensions are represented by x and $2x$. Do you see why? Also recall that the volume of the resulting box will be the product of the length, width, and height.

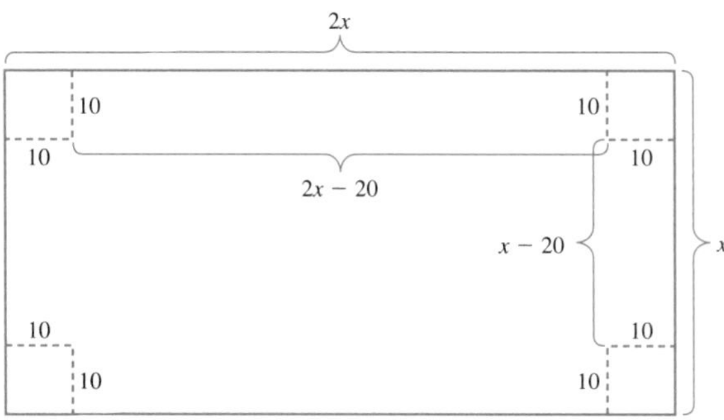

Hint 2: From this sketch, you can see that the equation that results from $V = LWH$ will be

$$(2x - 20)(x - 10)10 = 4{,}000$$

38. **Crafts** A square piece of cardboard is to be formed into a box. After 5-cm squares are cut from each corner and the sides are folded up, the resulting box will have a volume of 4,500 cm^3. Find the length of a side of the original piece of cardboard.

39. **Science and Medicine** If a ball is thrown vertically upward from the ground, with an initial velocity of 64 feet per second, its height h after t seconds is given by

$$h = -16t^2 + 64t$$

How long does it take the ball to return to the ground?

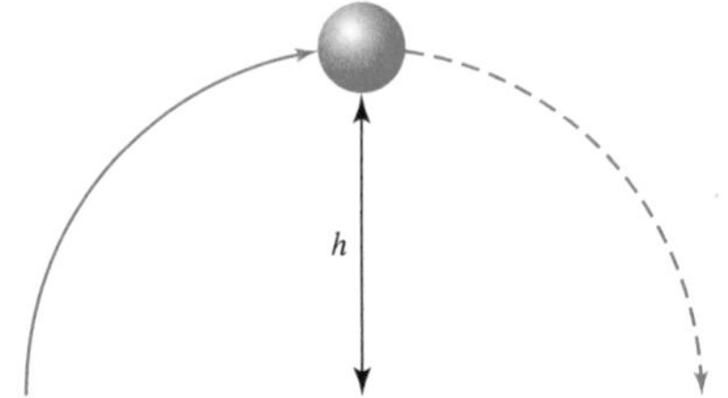

40. **Science and Medicine** If a ball is thrown vertically upward from the ground, with an initial velocity of 64 feet per second, its height h after t seconds is given by

$$h = -16t^2 + 64t$$

How long does it take the ball to reach a height of 48 feet on the way up?

Answers

38. 40 cm

39. 4 sec

40. 1 sec

Answers

41. 7 sec

42. 5 sec

43. 40 mi/h

44. 30 mi/h

45. 70 mi/h

46. 80 mi/h

47. 50 chairs

48. 20 items or 70 items

41. If a ball is thrown upward from the roof of a 105-meter building with an initial velocity of 20 meters per second, its approximate height h after t seconds is given by

$$h = -5t^2 + 20t + 105$$

How long will it take the ball to fall to the ground?

42. If a ball is thrown upward from the roof of a 105-meter building with an initial velocity of 20 meters per second, its approximate height h after t seconds is given by

$$h = -5t^2 + 20t + 105$$

When will the ball reach a height of 80 meters?

In exercises 43 to 46, use the equation $d = x^2/20 + x$, which relates the speed of a car x, in miles per hour, to the stopping distance d, in feet.

43. If the stopping distance of a car is 120 ft, how fast is the car traveling?

44. How fast is a car going if it requires 75 ft to stop?

45. Marcus is driving at high speed on the freeway when he spots a vehicle stopped ahead of him. If Marcus's car is 315 ft from the vehicle, what is the maximum speed that Marcus can be traveling and still stop in time?

46. Juliana is driving at high speed on a country highway when she sees a deer in the road ahead. If Juliana's car is 400 ft from the deer, what is the maximum speed that Juliana can be traveling and still stop in time?

47. **Business and Finance** Suppose that the cost C, in dollars, of producing x chairs is given by

$$C = 2x^2 - 40x + 2{,}400$$

How many chairs can be produced for $5,400?

48. **Business and Finance** A small manufacturer's weekly profit in dollars is given by

$$P = -3x^2 + 270x$$

Find the number of items x that must be produced to realize a profit of $4,200.

Basic Skills | **Advanced Skills** | Vocational-Technical Applications | Calculator/Computer | Above and Beyond

Write an equation that has the following solutions. (Hint: *Write the binomial factors and then the quadratic member of the equation.*)

49. 2, −3

50. 0, 5

51. 6, 2

52. −4, 4

The zero-product principle can be extended to three or more factors. If $a \cdot b \cdot c = 0$, then at least one of these factors is 0. Use this information to solve the equations.

53. $x^3 - 3x^2 - 10x = 0$

54. $x^3 + 8x^2 + 15x = 0$

55. $x^3 - 9x = 0$

56. $x^3 = 16x$

Extend the ideas in the previous exercises to find solutions for the following equations.

57. $x^3 + x^2 - 4x - 4 = 0$

58. $x^3 - 5x^2 - x + 5 = 0$

59. $x^4 - 10x^2 + 9 = 0$

60. $x^4 - 5x^2 + 4 = 0$

61. **Business and Finance** The manager of a bicycle shop knows that the cost of selling x bicycles is $C = 20x + 60$ and the revenue from selling x bicycles is $R = x^2 - 8x$. Find the break-even value of x.

62. **Business and Finance** A company that produces computer games has found that its operating cost in dollars is $C = 40x + 150$ and its revenue in dollars is $R = 65x - x^2$. For what value(s) of x will the company break even?

Basic Skills | Advanced Skills | **Vocational-Technical Applications** | Calculator/Computer | Above and Beyond

63. **Allied Health** A patient's body temperature, T (in degrees Fahrenheit), t hours after taking acetaminophen, a commonly prescribed analgesic, can be approximated by the function $T(t) = 0.4t^2 - 2.6t + 103$. Determine how long it takes for the patient's temperature to rise back up to 100°F. (*Hint:* After setting up the equation, multiply through by 10 to eliminate the decimals. Then solve by factoring.)

Answers

49. $x^2 + x - 6 = 0$
50. $x^2 - 5x = 0$
51. $x^2 - 8x + 12 = 0$
52. $x^2 - 16 = 0$
53. −2, 0, 5
54. −5, −3, 0
55. −3, 0, 3
56. −4, 0, 4
57. −2, −1, 2
58. −1, 1, 5
59. −3, −1, 1, 3
60. −2, −1, 1, 2
61. 30 bicycles
62. 10, 15
63. 5 h

Answers

64. 1 h

65. $x = 19$

66. 9 or −9

67. $a = 4$ or $a = -4$

68. $t = 1.25$ or $t = 3.75$

69. 2, 6 are the zeros of Exercise 23

70. −4, 7 are the zeros of Exercise 24

64. **Allied Health** A healthy person's blood glucose levels, g (in milligrams per 100 milliliters), t hours after eating a meal can be well approximated by the function $g(t) = -480t^2 + 400t + 80$. How long will it take for the blood glucose level to return to 0?

65. **Mechanical Engineering** The rotational moment in a shaft is given by the function $f(x) = -30x + 2x^2$. Find the value of x when the moment is equal to 152.

66. **Construction Technology** The sag in a floor joist is described by the equation

$$s = \frac{x^2 - 81}{40}$$

At what points does the sag in the floor equal 0?

67. **Construction Technology** A piece of stainless steel warps due to the heat created during welding. The shape of the warping approximately follows the curve

$$w = \frac{a^2 - 16}{64}$$

At what values of a is the value of $w = 0$?

68. **Agricultural Technology** The height of water above an irrigation nozzle in relation to the time since it left the nozzle is given by the formula $h(t) = v_0t - 16t^2$. If $v_0 = 80$, at what time, t, is the height equal to 75?

Basic Skills | Advanced Skills | Vocational-Technical Applications | **Calculator/Computer** | Above and Beyond

Use your calculator to graph $f(x)$.

69. $f(x) = 3x^2 - 24x + 36$. Note the x-values at which the graph crosses the x-axis. Compare your answer to the solution for Exercise 23.

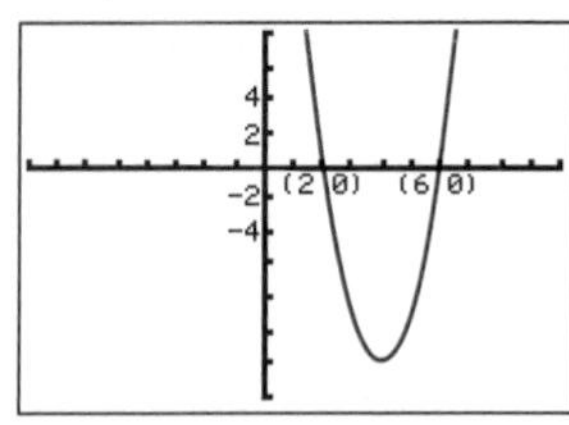

70. $f(x) = 2x^2 - 6x - 56$. Note the x-values at which the graph crosses the x-axis. Compare your answer to the solution for exercise 24.

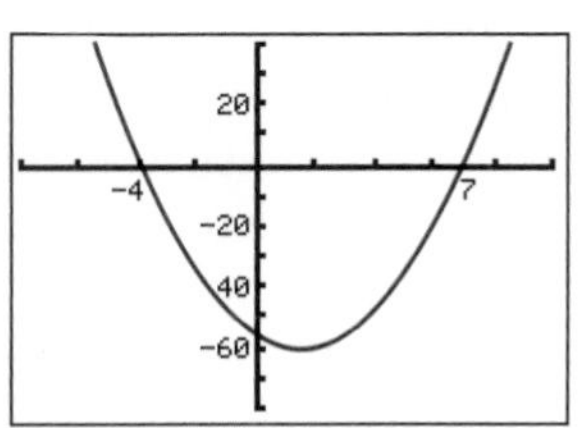

71. Work with another student and use your calculator to solve this exercise. Find an equation for each graph given. There could be more than one equation for some of the graphs. Remember the connection between the x-intercepts and the zeros.

chapter 5 > Make the Connection

(a)
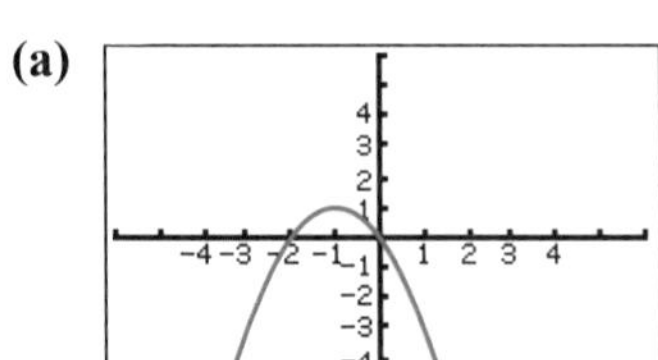

(b)
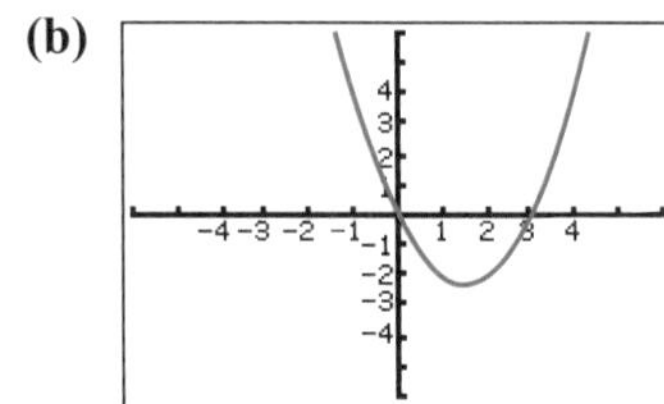

(c)
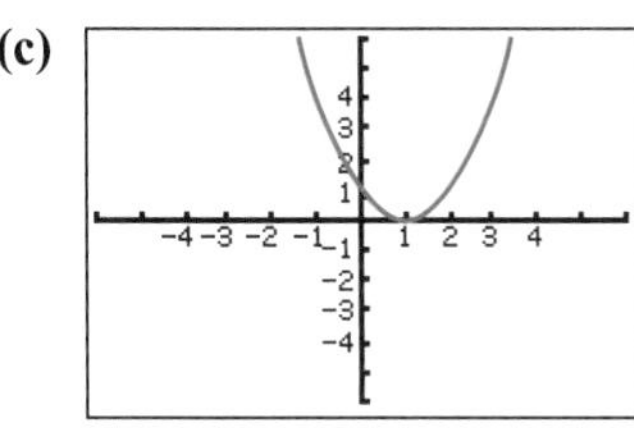

(d)
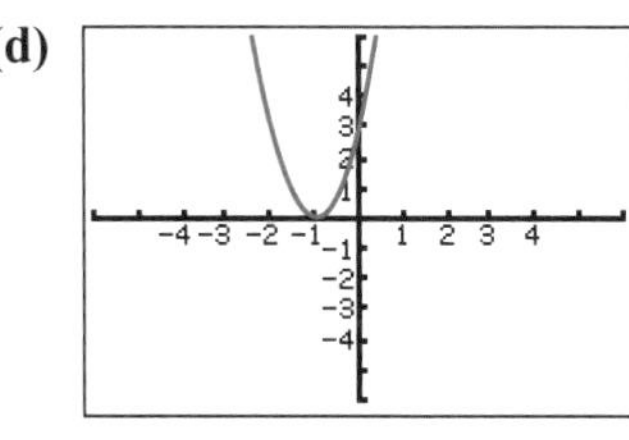

(e)
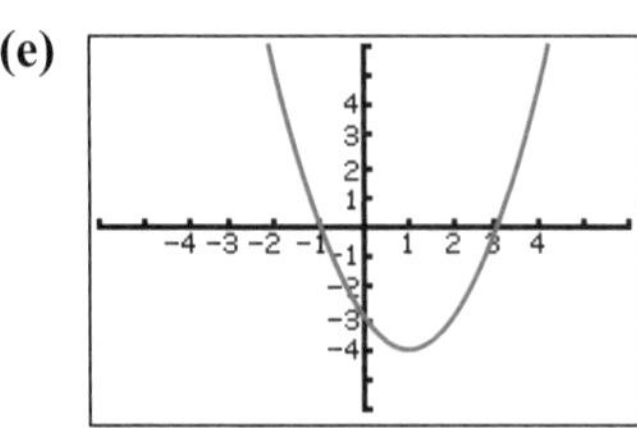

(f)
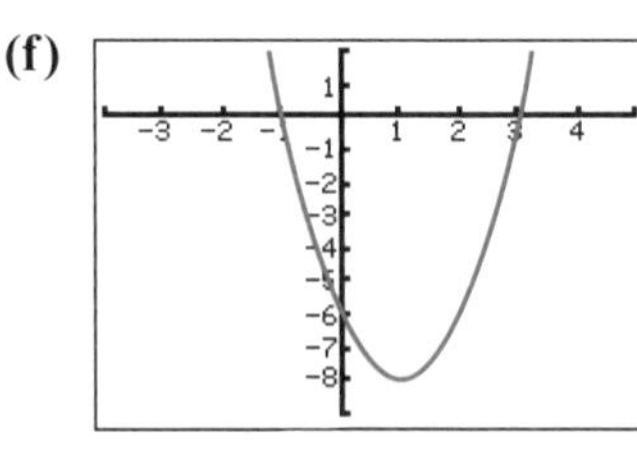

(g)
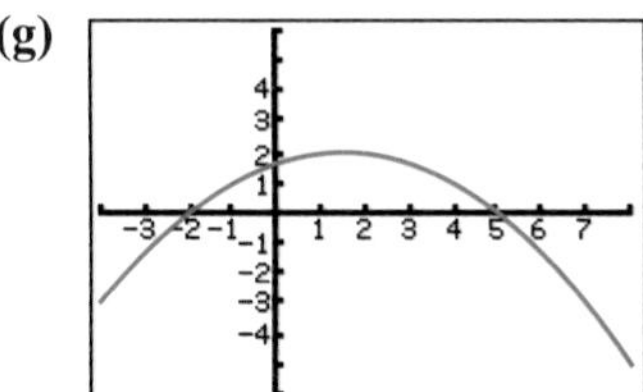

(h)
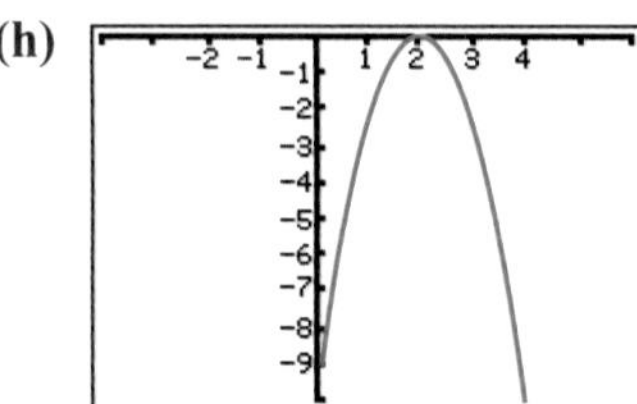

Basic Skills | Advanced Skills | Vocational-Technical Applications | Calculator/Computer | **Above and Beyond**

72. When solving quadratic equations, some people try to solve an equation in the manner shown here, but this doesn't work! Write a paragraph to explain what is wrong with this approach.

$$2x^2 + 7x + 3 = 52$$
$$(2x + 1)(x + 3) = 52$$
$$2x + 1 = 52 \quad \text{or} \quad x + 3 = 52$$
$$x = \frac{51}{2} \qquad\qquad x = 49$$

73. Write a short comparison that explains the difference between $ax^2 + bx + c$ and $ax^2 + bx + c = 0$.

Answers

71. (a) $-x(x + 2) = 0$; (b) $x(x - 3) = 0$; (c) $(x - 1)^2 = 0$; (d) $3(x + 1)^2 = 0$; (e) $(x + 1)(x - 3) = 0$; (f) $2(x + 1)(x - 3) = 0$; (g) $-\frac{1}{5}(x + 2)(x - 5) = 0$; (h) $-\frac{5}{2}(x - 2)^2 = 0$

72. Above and Beyond

73. Above and Beyond

Answers

74. Above and Beyond

75. Above and Beyond

76. Above and Beyond

77. Above and Beyond

74. Compare and contrast the methods for solving a quadratic equation and a linear equation.

75. Explain the difference between solving the equations $3(x-2)(x+5)=0$ and $3x(x-2)(x+5)=0$.

76. Explain the difference between solving the equations $x^2-4x=0$ and $x^2-4=0$.

77. How can a graphing calculator be used to determine the zeros of a quadratic function?

chapter 5 >Make the Connection

Answers

1. $-3, -1$ 3. $-5, 7$ 5. $0, 5$ 7. $-8, 8$ 9. $-1, \frac{4}{3}$ 11. $0, 6$
13. $-3, 5$ 15. $-\frac{3}{2}, 3$ 17. $-2, \frac{5}{2}$ 19. $-2, 6$ 21. $-\frac{2}{3}, \frac{3}{4}$
23. $2, 6$ 25. $-5, 1$ 27. $\frac{5}{3}$ 29. $5, 13$ 31. $-9, -8$ or $8, 9$
33. $-5, -4, -3$ or $3, 4, 5$ 35. 7 ft by 10 ft 37. 30 cm by 60 cm
39. 4 sec 41. 7 sec 43. 40 mi/h 45. 70 mi/h 47. 50 chairs
49. $x^2+x-6=0$ 51. $x^2-8x+12=0$ 53. $-2, 0, 5$
55. $-3, 0, 3$ 57. $-2, -1, 2$ 59. $-3, -1, 1, 3$ 61. 30 bicycles
63. 5 h 65. $x=19$ 67. $a=4$ or $a=-4$
69. 2, 6 are the zeros of Exercise 23;

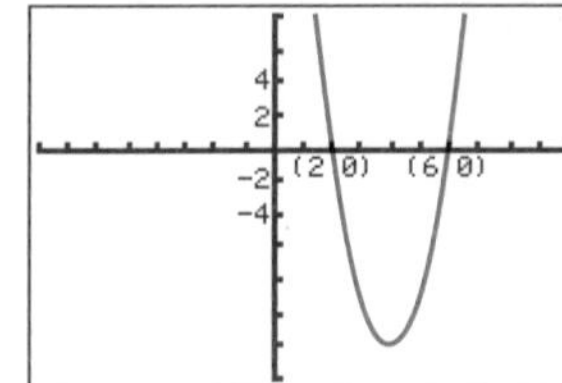

71. **(a)** $-x(x+2)=0$; **(b)** $x(x-3)=0$; **(c)** $(x-1)^2=0$; **(d)** $3(x+1)^2=0$; **(e)** $(x+1)(x-3)=0$; **(f)** $2(x+1)(x-3)=0$; **(g)** $-\frac{1}{5}(x+2)(x-5)=0$; **(h)** $-\frac{5}{2}(x-2)^2=0$
73. Above and Beyond 75. Above and Beyond 77. Above and Beyond

Definition/Procedure	Example	Reference
Addition and Subtraction of Polynomials		Section 5.1
Adding Polynomials		
To add polynomials, simply combine any like terms by using the distributive property.		pp. 416–417
Subtracting Polynomials		
To subtract polynomials, enclose the polynomial being subtracted in parentheses, preceded by a subtraction symbol. Then remove the parentheses and combine like terms.	$(4x^2 - 6x + 2) - (3x^2 - 2x - 5)$ $= 4x^2 - 6x + 2 - 3x^2 + 2x + 5$ $= x^2 - 4x + 7$	
Multiplication of Polynomials		Section 5.2
Multiplying Polynomials		
To multiply two polynomials, multiply each term of the first polynomial by each term of the second polynomial.	To multiply: $\begin{array}{r} 3x^2 - 2x + 5 \\ 5x - 2 \\ \hline -6x^2 + 4x - 10 \\ 15x^3 - 10x^2 + 25x \\ \hline 15x^3 - 16x^2 + 29x - 10 \end{array}$	pp. 430–432
Special Products Certain special products can be found by applying the following formulas. $(a + b)(a - b) = a^2 - b^2$ Product of binomials differing in sign $(a + b)^2 = a^2 + 2ab + b^2$ Squaring a binomial $(a - b)^2 = a^2 - 2ab + b^2$ Squaring a binomial	$(2x - 3)(2x + 3) = 4x^2 - 9$ $(2x + 5)^2 = 4x^2 + 20x + 25$ $(3a - b)^2 = 9a^2 - 6ab + b^2$	
Division of Polynomials		Section 5.3
To Divide a Polynomial by a Monomial		
Divide each term of the polynomial by the monomial. Then simplify the results.	$\frac{14x^2y - 21xy^2 + 7xy}{7xy}$ $= \frac{14x^2y}{7xy} + \frac{-21xy^2}{7xy} + \frac{7xy}{7xy}$ $= 2x - 3y + 1$	p. 441
To Divide a Polynomial by a Binomial		
Dividing a polynomial by a binomial can be done using long division or **synthetic division.**	Divide $x^2 + x - 1$ by $x - 1$ by using synthetic division: $\begin{array}{r\|rrr} 1 & 1 & 1 & -1 \\ & & 1 & 2 \\ \hline & 1 & 2 & 1 \end{array}$ This tells us the quotient is $x + 2$ and the remainder is 1.	pp. 445–446

Continued

Definition/Procedure	Example	Reference
Common Factors and Factoring by Grouping		Section 5.4
The **greatest common factor (GCF)** of a polynomial is the factor that is a product of the largest numerical coefficient factor of the polynomial and each common variable with the smallest exponent in any term.	$5x^2y^2 - 10xy^2 + 35x^2y$ has a GCF of $5xy$.	p. 453
Factoring a Monomial from a Polynomial		
1. Find the GCF for all terms. **2.** Use the GCF to factor each term and then apply the distributive property. **3.** Mentally check your factoring by multiplication.	$8x^4 - 12x^3 + 16x^2$ $= 4x^2(2x^2 - 3x + 4)$	p. 453
Factoring by Grouping		
When there are four terms of a polynomial, factor the first pair and factor the last pair. If these two pairs have a common binomial factor, factor that out. The result will be the product of two binomials.	$4x^2 - 6x + 10x - 15$ $= 2x(2x - 3) + 5(2x - 3)$ $= (2x - 3)(2x + 5)$	p. 455
Factoring Special Binomials		Section 5.5
To Factor a Binomial		
If a polynomial is a binomial, try factoring it as a **difference of two squares** or as a **sum or difference of two cubes.** $a^2 - b^2 = (a + b)(a - b)$ $a^2 + b^2$ usually doesn't factor. $a^3 + b^3 = (a + b)(a^2 - ab + b^2)$ $a^3 - b^3 = (a - b)(a^2 + ab + b^2)$	Factor: $16x^2 - 9y^2$ $= (4x + 3y)(4x - 3y)$ Factor: $x^3 + 8y^3$ $= (x + 2y)(x^2 - 2xy + 4y^2)$	pp. 463, 465
Factoring Trinomials: Trial and Error		Section 5.6
The Trial-and-Error Method		
To factor a trinomial, find the appropriate sign pattern, and then find integer values that yield the appropriate coefficients for the trinomial.	$x^2 - 5x - 24$ $= (x -\quad)(x +\quad)$ $= (x - 8)(x + 3)$	pp. 472–473
Factoring Trinomials: The *ac* Method		Section 5.7
The ac Test A trinomial of the form $ax^2 + bx + c$ is factorable if (and only if) there are two integers, m and n, such that $ac = mn \qquad b = m + n$	Given $2x^2 - 5x - 3$: $a = 2, \quad b = -5, \quad c = -3$ $ac = -6, \quad b = -5$ $m = -6 \quad n = 1$ $mn = -6 \quad m + n = -5$	p. 485

Definition/Procedure	Example	Reference
To Factor a Trinomial		
In general, you can apply the following steps. **1.** Write the trinomial in standard $ax^2 + bx + c$ form. **2.** Then, label the three coefficients a, b, and c. **3.** Find two integers, m and n, such that $ac = mn$ and $b = m + n$ **4.** Rewrite the trinomial as $ax^2 + mx + nx + c$ **5.** Factor by grouping. Not all trinomials are factorable. To discover if a trinomial is factorable, try the ***ac* test.**	$2x^2 - 6x + x - 3$ $2x(x - 3) + 1(x - 3)$ $(x - 3)(2x + 1)$	*pp.* 487–488
Strategies in Factoring		**Section 5.8**
1. Always look for a **greatest common factor.** If you find a GCF (other than 1), factor out the GCF as your first step. **2.** Now look at the **number of terms** in the polynomial you are trying to factor. **(a)** If the polynomial is a *binomial,* consider the special binomial formulas. **(b)** If the polynomial is a *trinomial,* try to factor it as a product of two binomials. You can use either the trial-and-error method or the *ac* method. **(c)** If the polynomial has *more than three terms,* try factoring by grouping. **3.** You should always **factor the polynomial completely.** So after you apply one of the techniques given in part 2, another one may be necessary. **4.** You can always **check your answer by multiplying.**	Factor completely. $2x^4 - 32$ $= 2(x^4 - 16)$ $= 2(x^2 + 4)(x^2 - 4)$ $= 2(x^2 + 4)(x + 2)(x - 2)$	*pp.* 497–498
Solving Quadratic Equations by Factoring		**Section 5.9**
1. Add or subtract the necessary terms on both sides of the equation so that the equation is in standard form (set equal to 0). **2.** Factor the quadratic expression. **3.** Set each factor equal to 0. **4.** Solve the resulting equations to find the solutions. **5.** Check each solution by substituting in the original equation.	To solve: $x^2 + 7x = 30$ $x^2 + 7x - 30 = 0$ $(x + 10)(x - 3) = 0$ $x + 10 = 0$ or $x - 3 = 0$ $x = -10$ and $x = 3$ are solutions.	*pp.* 505–506

summary exercises :: chapter 5

This summary exercise set is provided to give you practice with each of the objectives of this chapter. Each exercise is keyed to the appropriate chapter section. When you are finished, you can check your answers to the odd-numbered exercises against those presented in the back of the text. If you have difficulty with any of these questions, go back and reread the examples from that section. The answers to the even-numbered exercises appear in the *Instructor's Solutions Manual.* Your instructor will give you guidelines on how to best use these exercises in your instructional setting.

5.1 *Classify each of the following as a monomial, binomial, or trinomial, if possible.*

1. $5x^3 - 2x^2$ Binomial

2. $7x^5$ Monomial

3. $4x^5 - 8x^3 + 5$ Trinomial

4. $x^3 + 2x^2 - 5x + 3$ Not classified

5. $9a^2 - 18a$ Binomial

6. $4x^2 + \frac{2}{x}$ Not a polynomial

Arrange in descending-exponent form, and give the degree of each polynomial.

7. $5x^5 + 3x^2$ $5x^5 + 3x^2$, 5

8. $9x$ $9x$, 1

9. $6x^2 + 4x^4 + 6$ $4x^4 + 6x^2 + 6$, 4

10. $5 + x$ $x + 5$, 1

11. -8 -8, 0

12. $9x^4 - 3x + 7x^6$ $7x^6 + 9x^4 - 3x$, 6

13. Given $f(x) = 4x^2 + 5x - 6$, find $f(-2)$. 0

14. Given $f(x) = 5x^2 - 4x + 8$, find $f(3)$. 41

15. Given $f(x) = -2x^3 + 4x^2 - 5x + 8$, find $f(3)$. -25

16. Given $f(x) = 3x^3 + 5x^2 - 2x + 6$, find $f(-1)$. 10

17. Given $f(x) = -2x^4 - 5x^2 + 3x - 6$, find $f(2)$. -52

18. Given $f(x) = -x^5 - 3x^4 + 5x^3 - x - 4$, find $f(-2)$. -58

In each of the following, the polynomial functions f(x) and g(x) are given. Find the following ordered pairs: **(a)** $(0, f(0))$, **(b)** $(2, f(2))$, **(c)** $(0, g(0))$, and **(d)** $(2, g(2))$.

19. $f(x) = 5x^2 - 3x - 4$ and $g(x) = 3x^2 + 6x - 5$ (a) (0, −4); (b) (2, 10); (c) (0, −5); (d) (2, 19)

20. $f(x) = 2x^2 + 4x + 6$ and $g(x) = 3x^2 - 4x + 3$ (a) (0, 6); (b) (2, 22); (c) (0, 3); (d) (2, 7)

21. $f(x) = x^3 - 3x^2 + 7x$ and $g(x) = -2x^3 - x^2 + 3x + 1$ (a) (0, 0); (b) (2, 10); (c) (0, 1); (d) (2, −13)

22. $f(x) = -x^4 - 3x^2 + 2x$ and $g(x) = -2x^4 + 3x^3 - 2x^2 + 2$ (a) (0, 0); (b) (2, −24); (c) (0, 2); (d) (2, −14)

In each of the following, $f(x)$ and $g(x)$ are given. Let $h(x) = f(x) + g(x)$. Find **(a)** $h(x)$, **(b)** $f(1) + g(1)$, *and* **(c)** $h(1)$.

23. $f(x) = 4x^2 + 5x - 3$ and $g(x) = -2x^2 + x - 5$ (a) $h(x) = 2x^2 + 6x - 8$; (b) 0; (c) 0

24. $f(x) = -3x^3 + 2x^2 - 5$ and $g(x) = 4x^3 - 4x^2 + 5x + 6$ (a) $h(x) = x^3 - 2x^2 + 5x + 1$; (b) 5; (c) 5

25. $f(x) = 2x^4 + 4x^2 + 5$ and $g(x) = x^3 - 5x^2 + 6x$ (a) $h(x) = 2x^4 + x^3 - x^2 + 6x + 5$; (b) 13; (c) 13

26. $f(x) = 3x^3 + 5x - 5$ and $g(x) = -2x^3 + 2x^2 + 5x$ (a) $h(x) = x^3 + 2x^2 + 10x - 5$; (b) 8; (c) 8

In each of the following, $f(x)$ and $g(x)$ are given. Let $h(x) = f(x) - g(x)$. Find **(a)** $h(x)$, **(b)** $f(1) - g(1)$, *and* **(c)** $h(1)$.

27. $f(x) = 7x^2 - 2x + 3$ and $g(x) = 2x^2 - 5x - 7$ (a) $h(x) = 5x^2 + 3x + 10$; (b) 18; (c) 18

28. $f(x) = 9x^2 - 4x$ and $g(x) = 5x^2 + 3$ (a) $h(x) = 4x^2 - 4x - 3$; (b) -3; (c) -3

29. $f(x) = 8x^2 + 5x$ and $g(x) = 4x^2 - 3x$ (a) $h(x) = 4x^2 + 8x$; (b) 12; (c) 12

30. $f(x) = -2x^2 - 3x$ and $g(x) = -3x^2 + 4x - 5$ (a) $h(x) = x^2 - 7x + 5$; (b) -1; (c) -1

Simplify each of the following polynomial functions.

31. $f(x) = [(3x^2 + 4x) - 3] - (2x^2 - 6x - 2)$ $x^2 + 10x - 1$

32. $f(x) = (2x^3 + 4x) + (-3x^3 - 2x^2 + 5) - (4x^2 - 6x - 7)$ $-x^3 - 6x^2 + 10x + 12$

33. $f(x) = (3x - 7) - [5x^2 - (8x + 6)] + (-6x^2 - 9)$ $-11x^2 + 11x - 10$

34. $f(x) = (-3x^2 + 6x + 9) - (7x^2 + 5x - 8) + [2 - (-3x^2 + 7x + 9)]$ $-7x^2 - 6x + 10$

35. $f(x) = -4x^2(-6x + 5) - [(3x^3 - 5x^2 + 6) - (x^3 + 6x^2 + 4x - 2)]$ $22x^3 - 9x^2 + 4x - 8$

36. $f(x) = -5x^2(3x^2 + 6x - 2) + [-2x(-4x + 5) + (-3x^2 - x - 1)]$ $-15x^4 - 30x^3 + 15x^2 - 11x - 1$

5.2 *In each of the following, $f(x)$ and $g(x)$ are given. Let $h(x) = f(x) \cdot g(x)$. Find* **(a)** $h(x)$, **(b)** $f(1) \cdot g(1)$, *and* **(c)** $h(1)$.

37. $f(x) = 4x$ and $g(x) = 3x^2 - 5x$ (a) $h(x) = 12x^3 - 20x^2$; (b) -8; (c) -8

38. $f(x) = -6x$ and $g(x) = -4x^2 - 5x + 7$ (a) $h(x) = 24x^3 + 30x^2 - 42x$; (b) 12; (c) 12

39. $f(x) = 3x^3$ and $g(x) = -2x^2 - 8x + 1$ (a) $h(x) = -6x^5 - 24x^4 + 3x^3$; (b) -27; (c) -27

40. $f(x) = -7x^3$ and $g(x) = 5x^2 - 4x + 10$ (a) $h(x) = -35x^5 + 28x^4 - 70x^3$; (b) -77; (c) -77

Multiply each polynomial expression.

41. $5x(3x^2 - 4x)$ $15x^3 - 20x^2$

42. $5y^2(2y^3 - 3y^2 + 5y)$ $10y^5 - 15y^4 + 25y^3$

43. $(x - 2y)(x + 3y)$ $x^2 + xy - 6y^2$

44. $(a - 5b)(a - 6b)$ $a^2 - 11ab + 30b^2$

45. $(3c - 5d)(5c + 2d)$ $15c^2 - 19cd - 10d^2$

46. $(4x^2 - y)(2x + 3y^2)$ $8x^3 - 2xy + 12x^2y^2 - 3y^3$

47. $x(x - 3)(x + 2)$ $x^3 - x^2 - 6x$

48. $2y(2y + 3)(3y + 2)$ $12y^3 + 26y^2 + 12y$

Multiply the following polynomial expressions using the special product formulas.

49. $(x + 8)^2$ $x^2 + 16x + 64$

50. $(y - 5)^2$ $y^2 - 10y + 25$

51. $(2a - 3b)^2$ $4a^2 - 12ab + 9b^2$

52. $(5x + 2y)^2$ $25x^2 + 20xy + 4y^2$

53. $(x - 4y)(x + 4y)$ $x^2 - 16y^2$

54. $(2c - 3d)(2c + 3d)$ $4c^2 - 9d^2$

Multiply each polynomial expression using the vertical method.

55. $(2x - 3)(x^2 - 5x + 2)$ $2x^3 - 13x^2 + 19x - 6$

56. $(5a - b)(2a^2 - 3ab - 2b^2)$ $10a^3 - 17a^2b - 7ab^2 + 2b^3$

5.3 *Divide.*

57. $\frac{9a^5}{3a^2}$ $3a^3$

58. $\frac{24m^4n^2}{6m^2n}$ $4m^2n$

59. $\frac{15a - 10}{5}$ $3a - 2$

60. $\frac{32a^3 + 24a}{8a}$ $4a^2 + 3$

61. $\frac{9r^2s^3 - 18r^3s^2}{-3rs^2}$ $-3rs + 6r^2$

62. $\frac{35x^3y^2 - 21x^2y^3 + 14x^3y}{7x^2y}$ $5xy - 3y^2 + 2x$

Perform the indicated long division. Use synthetic division when it is appropriate.

63. $\frac{x^2 - 2x - 15}{x + 3}$ $x - 5$

64. $\frac{2x^2 + 9x - 35}{2x - 5}$ $x + 7$

65. $\frac{x^2 - 8x + 17}{x - 5}$ $x - 3 + \frac{2}{x - 5}$

66. $\frac{6x^2 - x - 10}{3x + 4}$ $2x - 3 + \frac{2}{3x + 4}$

67. $\frac{6x^3 + 14x^2 - 2x - 6}{6x + 2}$ $x^2 + 2x - 1 + \frac{-4}{6x + 2}$

68. $\frac{4x^3 + x + 3}{2x - 1}$ $2x^2 + x + 1 + \frac{4}{2x - 1}$

69. $\frac{3x^2 + x^3 + 5 + 4x}{x + 2}$ $x^2 + x + 2 + \frac{1}{x + 2}$

70. $\frac{2x^4 - 2x^2 - 10}{x^2 - 3}$ $2x^2 + 4 + \frac{2}{x^2 - 3}$

5.4 *Factor each of the following polynomials completely.*

71. $18x^2y + 24xy^2$ $6xy(3x + 4y)$

72. $35a^3 - 28a^2 + 7a$ $7a(5a^2 - 4a + 1)$

73. $18m^2n^2 - 27m^2n + 45m^2n^3$ $9m^2n(5n - 3)(n + 1)$

74. $x(2x - y) + y(2x - y)$ $(x + y)(2x - y)$

75. $5(w - 3z) - 10(w - 3z)^2$ $5(w - 3z)(1 - 2w + 6z)$

76. $x^2 - 4x + 5x - 20$ $(x - 4)(x + 5)$

77. $x^2 + 7x - 2x - 14$ $(x + 7)(x - 2)$

78. $6x^2 + 4x - 15x - 10$ $(2x - 5)(3x + 2)$

79. $12x^2 - 9x - 28x + 21$ $(4x - 3)(3x - 7)$

5.5 *Factor each of the following binomials completely.*

80. $x^2 - 64$ $(x + 8)(x - 8)$

81. $25a^2 - 16$ $(5a + 4)(5a - 4)$

82. $16m^2 - 49n^2$ $(4m + 7n)(4m - 7n)$

83. $3w^3 - 12wz^2$ $3w(w + 2z)(w - 2z)$

84. $a^4 - 16b^4$ $(a^2 + 4b^2)(a + 2b)(a - 2b)$

85. $m^3 - 64$ $(m - 4)(m^2 + 4m + 16)$

86. $8x^3 + 1$ $(2x + 1)(4x^2 - 2x + 1)$

87. $8c^3 - 27d^3$ $(2c - 3d)(4c^2 + 6cd + 9d^2)$

88. $125m^3 + 64n^3$ $(5m + 4n)(25m^2 - 20mn + 16n^2)$

89. $2x^4 + 54x$ $2x(x + 3)(x^2 - 3x + 9)$

For each of the following functions, **(a)** *find* $f(1)$, **(b)** *factor* $f(x)$, *and* **(c)** *find* $f(1)$ *from the factored form.*

90. $f(x) = 3x^3 + 15x^2$ (a) 18; (b) $3x^2(x + 5)$; (c) 18

91. $f(x) = -6x^3 - 2x^2$ (a) -8; (b) $-2x^2(3x + 1)$; (c) -8

92. $f(x) = 12x^6 - 8x^4$ (a) 4; (b) $4x^4(3x^2 - 2)$; (c) 4

93. $f(x) = 2x^5 - 2x$
(a) 0; (b) $2x(x^4 - 1) = 2x(x^2 + 1)(x + 1)(x - 1)$; (c) 0

5.6–5.8 *Completely factor each of the following polynomial expressions.*

94. $x^2 + 12x + 20$ $(x + 10)(x + 2)$

95. $a^2 - a - 12$ $(a - 4)(a + 3)$

96. $w^2 - 13w + 40$ $(w - 8)(w - 5)$

97. $r^2 - 9r - 36$ $(r - 12)(r + 3)$

98. $x^2 - 8xy - 48y^2$ $(x - 12y)(x + 4y)$

99. $a^2 + 17ab + 30b^2$ $(a + 15b)(a + 2b)$

100. $5x^2 + 13x - 6$ $(5x - 2)(x + 3)$

101. $2a^2 + 3a - 35$ $(2a - 7)(a + 5)$

102. $4r^2 + 20r + 21$ $(2r + 3)(2r + 7)$

103. $6c^2 - 19c + 10$ $(2c - 5)(3c - 2)$

104. $6m^2 - 19mn + 10n^2$ $(2m - 5n)(3m - 2n)$

105. $8x^2 + 14xy - 15y^2$ $(2x + 5y)(4x - 3y)$

106. $9x^2 - 15x - 6$ 3(3x + 1)(x − 2)

107. $5w^2 - 25wz + 30z^2$ 5(w − 2z)(w − 3z)

108. $3c^3 + 18c^2 + 15c$ 3c(c + 5)(c + 1)

109. $2a^3 + 4a^2b - 6ab^2$ 2a(a + 3b)(a − b)

110. $x^4 + 6x^2 + 5$ $(x^2 + 5)(x^2 + 1)$

111. $a^4 - 3a^2b^2 - 4b^4$ $(a^2 + b^2)(a + 2b)(a - 2b)$

5.9 *Solve each of the following equations by factoring.*

112. $x^2 + 5x - 6 = 0$ −6, 1

113. $x^2 - 2x - 8 = 0$ −2, 4

114. $x^2 + 7x = 30$ −10, 3

115. $x^2 - 6x = 40$ −4, 10

116. $x^2 = 11x - 24$ 3, 8

117. $x^2 = 28 - 3x$ −7, 4

118. $x^2 - 10x = 0$ 0, 10

119. $x^2 = 12x$ 0, 12

120. $x^2 - 25 = 0$ −5, 5

121. $x^2 = 144$ −12, 12

122. $2x^2 - x - 3 = 0$ $-1, \frac{3}{2}$

123. $3x^2 - 4x = 15$ $-\frac{5}{3}, 3$

124. $3x^2 + 9x - 30 = 0$ −5, 2

125. $4x^2 + 24x = -32$ −4, −2

126. $x(x - 3) = 18$ −3, 6

127. $(x - 2)(2x + 1) = 33$ $-\frac{7}{2}, 5$

128. $x^3 - 2x^2 - 15x = 0$ 0, −3, 5

129. $x^3 + x^2 - 4x - 4 = 0$ −2, −1, 2

130. Suppose that the cost, in dollars, of producing x stereo systems is given by

$C(x) = 3{,}000 - 60x + 3x^2$

How many systems can be produced for $7,500? 50 systems

131. The demand equation for a certain type of computer paper is predicted to be

$D = -4p + 72$

The supply equation is predicted to be

$S = -p^2 + 24p - 3$

Find the equilibrium price. $3 or $25

self-test 5

Name ______

Section ______ Date ______

The purpose of this chapter test is to help you check your progress so that you can find sections and concepts that you need to review before the next exam. Allow yourself about an hour to take this test. At the end of that hour, check your answers against those given in the back of this text. If you missed any, note the section reference that accompanies the answer. Go back to that section and reread the examples until you have mastered that particular concept.

5.1

Classify each of the following as a monomial, binomial, or trinomial, if possible.

1. $6x^2 + 7x$ **2.** $5x^2 + 8x - 8$ **3.** $-3x + \frac{1}{x}$

4. Arrange in descending-exponent form, and give the coefficients and degree.
$-3x^2 + 8x^4 - 7$

5. Given $f(x) = 3x^2 - 4x + 5$, find $f(-2)$.

In the following, $f(x)$ and $g(x)$ are given. Find **(a)** $h(x) = f(x) + g(x)$, **(b)** $p(x) = f(x) - g(x)$, **(c)** $f(1) + g(1)$, **(d)** $f(1) - g(1)$, **(e)** $h(1)$, **(f)** $p(1)$.

6. $f(x) = 4x^2 - 3x + 7$ and $g(x) = 2x^2$

7. $f(x) = -3x^3 + 5x^2 - 2x - 7$ and $g(x) = -2x^2 + 7x - 2$

Simplify the following polynomial function.

8. $f(x) = 5x - (4x + 2[x - 3(x + 2)])$

5.2

Multiply each of the following polynomials.

9. $(2a - 5b)(3a + 7b)$ **10.** $(5m - 3n)(5m + 3n)$

11. $(2a + 3b)^2$ **12.** $(2x - 5)(x^2 - 4x + 3)$

5.3

Perform the indicated long division. Use synthetic division when it is appropriate.

13. $\dfrac{3x^2 - 2x - 4}{3x + 1}$ **14.** $\dfrac{4x^3 - 5x^2 + 7x - 9}{x - 2}$

15. $\dfrac{3x^4 - 2x^2 - 5}{x^2 + 1}$

Answers

1. Binomial
2. Trinomial
3. Not a polynomial
4. $8x^4 - 3x^2 - 7$; 8, −3, −7; 4
5. 25
6. (a) $h(x) = 6x^2 - 3x + 7$; (b) $p(x) = 2x^2 - 3x + 7$; (c) 10; (d) 6; (e) 10; (f) 6
7. (a) $h(x) = -3x^3 + 3x^2 + 5x - 9$; (b) $p(x) = -3x^3 + 7x^2 - 9x - 5$; (c) −4; (d) −10; (e) −4; (f) −10
8. $5x + 12$
9. $6a^2 - ab - 35b^2$
10. $25m^2 - 9n^2$
11. $4a^2 + 12ab + 9b^2$
12. $2x^3 - 13x^2 + 26x - 15$
13. $x - 1 + \frac{-3}{3x + 1}$
14. $4x^2 + 3x + 13 + \frac{17}{x - 2}$
15. $3x^2 - 5$

Answers

16. $7ab(2ab - 3a + 5b)$

17. $(x - 3y)(x + 5)$

18. $(5c - 8d)(5c + 8d)$

19. $(3x - 1)(9x^2 + 3x + 1)$

20. $2a(2a + b)(4a^2 - 2ab + b^2)$

21. $(x - 8)(x + 6)$

22. $(5x - 2)(2x - 7)$

23. $3x(x + 3)(2x - 5)$

24. $-3, -\frac{1}{2}$

25. $-\frac{5}{2}, \frac{2}{3}$

5.4–5.8

Factor each of the following polynomials completely.

16. $14a^2b^2 - 21a^2b + 35ab^2$

17. $x^2 - 3xy + 5x - 15y$

18. $25c^2 - 64d^2$

19. $27x^3 - 1$

20. $16a^4 + 2ab^3$

21. $x^2 - 2x - 48$

22. $10x^2 - 39x + 14$

23. $6x^3 + 3x^2 - 45x$

5.9

Solve each of the following equations by factoring.

24. $2x^2 + 7x + 3 = 0$

25. $6x^2 = 10 - 11x$

Activity 5 :: Graphing Equations Using the TI-84 Plus

Each chapter in this text concludes with a chapter activity such as this one. These activities provide you with the opportunity to apply the math you studied in that chapter to a relevant topic. Your instructor will determine how best to use these activities in your instructional setting. You may find yourself working in class or outside of class; you may find yourself working alone or in small groups; you may even be asked to perform research in a library or on the Internet.

The graphing calculator is a tool that can be used to help you solve many different kinds of problems. This activity will walk you through several features of the TI-84 Plus. By the time you complete this activity, you will be able to graph equations, change the viewing window to better accommodate a graph, or look at a table of values that represent some of the solutions for an equation. The first portion of this activity will demonstrate how you can create the graph of an equation. The features described here can be found on most graphing calculators. See your calculator manual to see how to get your particular calculator model to perform this activity.

Menus and Graphing

1. GRAPH To graph the function $y = 2x + 3$ on a graphing calculator, follow these steps.

   (a) Press the Y = key.

   Plot1 Plot2 Plot3
   \Y1 =
   \Y2 =
   \Y3 =
   \Y4 =
   \Y5 =
   \Y6 =
   \Y7 =

   (b) Type $2x + 3$ at the Y_1 prompt. (This represents the first equation. You can type up to 10 separate equations.) Use the X, T, θ, *n* key for the variable.

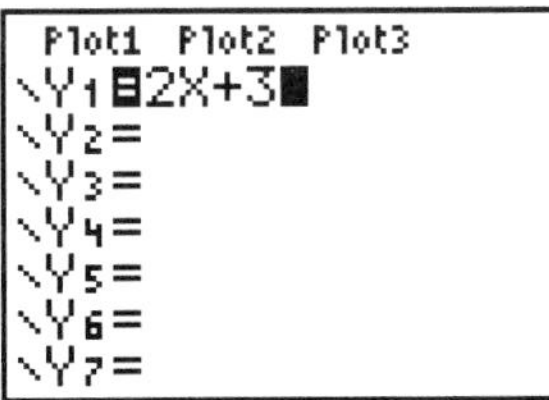

   (c) Press the GRAPH key to see the graph.

   (d) Press the TRACE key to display the equation of the function. Once you have selected the TRACE key, you can use the left and right arrows of the calculator to move the cursor along the line. Experiment with this movement. Look at the coordinates at the bottom of the display screen as you move along the line.

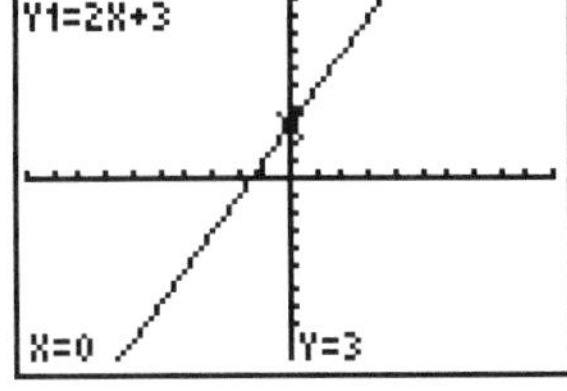

Frequently, we can learn more about an equation if we look at a different section of the graph than the one offered on the display screen. The portion of the graph displayed is called the **window.** The second portion of the activity explains how this window can be changed.

2. WINDOW. Press the WINDOW key. The **standard** graphing screen is shown.

   Xmin = left edge of screen
   Xmax = right edge of screen

Xscl = scale given by each tick on x-axis
Ymin = bottom edge of screen
Ymax = top edge of screen
Yscl = scale given by each tick on y-axis
Xres = resolution (do not alter this)

```
WINDOW
 Xmin=-10
 Xmax=10
 Xscl=1
 Ymin=-10
 Ymax=10
 Yscl=1
 Xres=1
```

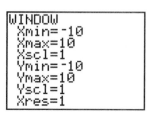

Note: To turn the scales off, enter a 0 for Xscl or Yscl. Do this when the intervals used are very large.

By changing the values for Xmin, Xmax, Ymin, and Ymax, you can adjust the viewing window. Change the viewing window so that Xmin = 0, Xmax = 40, Ymin = 0, and Ymax = 10. Notice that the tick marks along the x-axis are now much closer together. Changing Xscl from 1 to 5 will improve the display. Try it.

Sometimes we can learn something important about a graph by zooming in or zooming out. The third portion of this activity discusses this feature of the TI-84 Plus.

3. ZOOM

(a) Press the ZOOM key. There are 10 options. Use the ▼ key to scroll down.

```
ZOOM MEMORY
4↑ZDecimal
5:ZSquare
6:ZStandard
7:ZTrig
8:ZInteger
9:ZoomStat
0:ZoomFit
```

(b) Selecting the first option, ZBox, allows the user to enlarge the graph within a specified rectangle.

(i) Graph the function $y = x^2 + x - 1$ in the standard window. *Note:* To type in the exponent, use the x^2 key or the ∧ key.

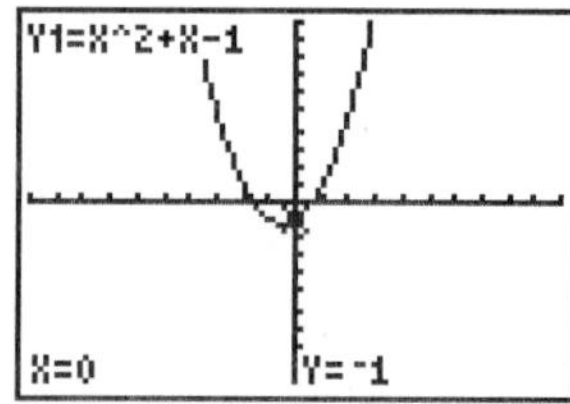

(ii) When ZBox is selected, a blinking "+" cursor will appear in the graph window. Use the arrow keys to move the cursor to where you would like a corner of the screen to be; then press the ENTER key.

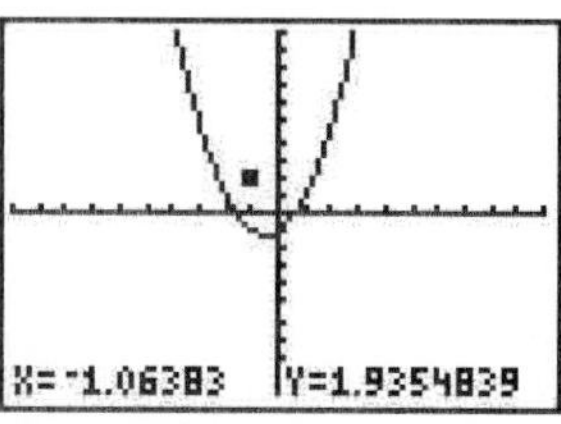

(iii) Use the arrow keys to trace out the box containing the desired portion of the graph. Do not press the [ENTER] key until you have reached the diagonal corner and a full box is on your screen.

After using the down arrow

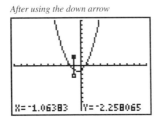

X=⁻1.06383 Y=⁻2.258065

After using the right arrow

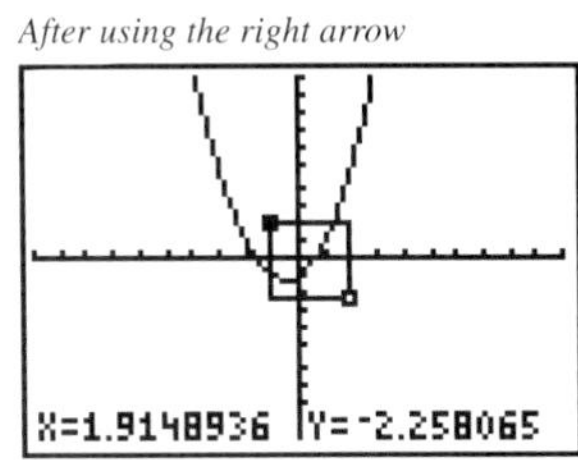

After pressing the [ENTER] key a second time

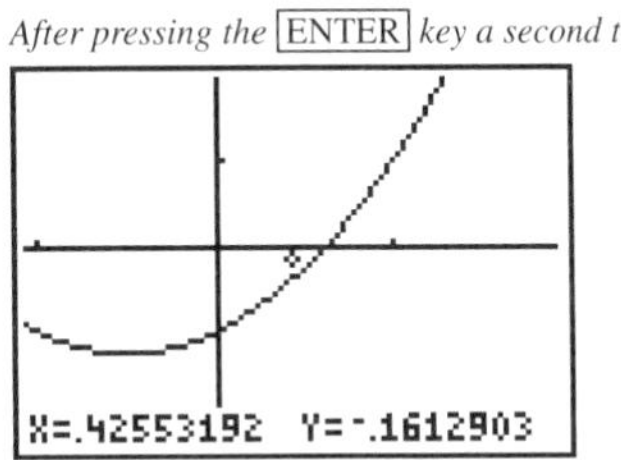

Now the desired portion of a graph can be seen more clearly.

The ZBox feature is especially useful when analyzing the roots (x-intercepts) of a function.

(c) Another feature that allows us to focus is ZoomIn. Press the ZoomIn button in the Zoom menu. Place the cursor in the center of the portion of the graph you are interested in and press the [ENTER] key. The window will reset with the cursor at the center of a zoomed-in view.

(d) ZoomOut works like ZoomIn, except that it sets the view larger (that is, it zooms out) to enable you to see a larger portion of the graph.

(e) ZStandard sets the window to the standard window. This is a quick and convenient way to reset the viewing window.

(f) ZSquare recalculates the view so that one horizontal unit is the same length as one vertical unit. This is sometimes necessary to get an accurate view of a graph since the width of the calculator screen is greater than its height.

Home Screen

This is where all the basic computations take place. To get to the home screen from any other screen, press [2nd], [Mode]. This accesses the QUIT feature. To clear the home screen of calculations, press the [CLEAR] key (once or twice).

Tables

The final feature that we will look at here is Table. Enter the function $y = 2x + 3$ into the Y= menu.

Then press [2nd], [WINDOW] to access the TBLSET menu. Set the table as shown here and press [2nd], [GRAPH] to access the TABLE feature. You will see the screen shown here.

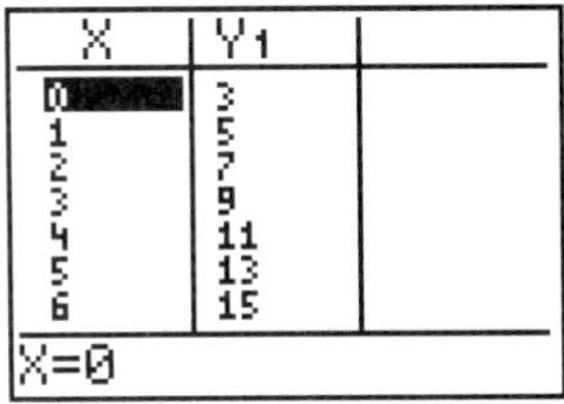

cumulative review chapters 1-5

Name ____________________

Section ________ Date ________

Answers

1. 2

2. −77

3. x-int: (6, 0), y-int: (0, 4)

4. $y = \frac{5}{4}x - \frac{3}{4}$

5. $256x^{13}y^{12}$

6. 25

7. Domain: all real numbers, range: all real numbers

The following exercises are presented to help you review concepts from earlier chapters. This is meant as review material and not as a comprehensive exam. The answers are presented in the back of the text. Beside each answer is a section reference for the concept. If you have difficulty with any of these exercises, be certain to at least read through the summary related to that section.

2.1

1. Solve the equation $4x - 2(x + 1) = 3(5 - x) - 7$.

3.2

2. If $f(x) = 4x^3 - 5x^2 + 7x - 11$, find $f(-2)$.

3.3

3. Find the x- and y-intercepts and graph the equation $2x + 3y = 12$.

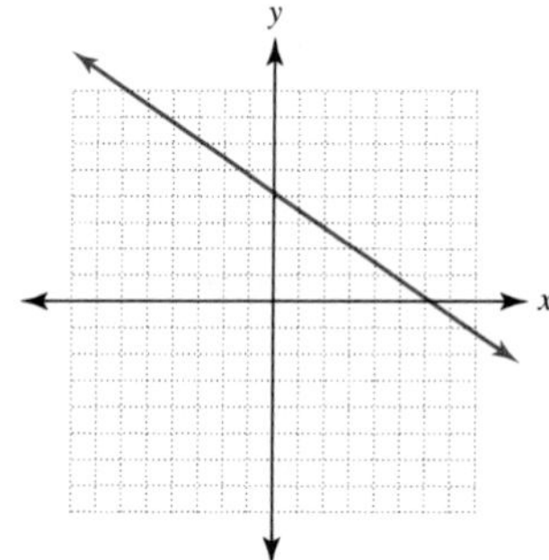

3.5

4. Find the equation of the line that passes through the point $(-1, -2)$ and is perpendicular to the line $4x + 5y = 15$.

1.5

5. Simplify the expression $(4x^3y^2)^3(-2x^2y^3)^2$.

1.2

6. Evaluate the expression $18 \div 3 \cdot 2 - (3 - 4^2)$.

3.1

7. Find the domain and range of the relation $4x - 3y = 15$.

3.2

8. Use the given graph to estimate **(a)** $f(-2)$, **(b)** $f(0)$, and **(c)** $f(3)$.

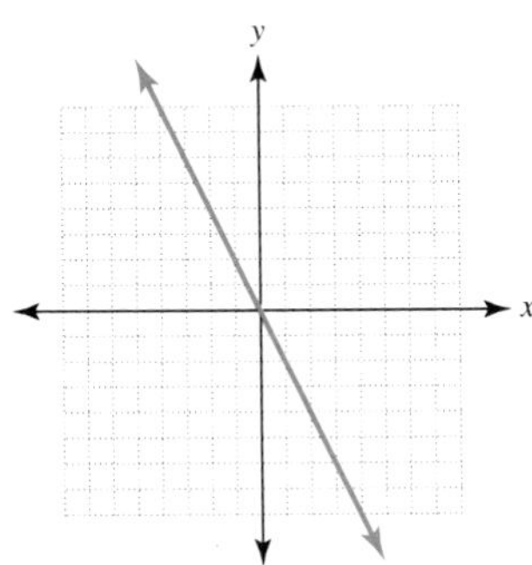

Simplify each of the following polynomial functions.

5.1

9. $f(x) = (2x^2 - 3x + 4) - (3x^2 + 2x - 5)$

5.2

10. $f(x) = (2x + 3)(5x - 4)$.

Factor each of the following completely.

5.7

11. $3x^3 - x^2 - 2x$

5.5

12. $16x^2 - 25y^2$

5.4

13. $3x^2 - 3xy + x - y$

5.1 and 5.2

14. If $f(x) = -5x + 1$ and $g(x) = 8x + 6$, find **(a)** $f(x) + g(x)$, **(b)** $f(x) - g(x)$, and **(c)** $f(x) \cdot g(x)$.

Solve the following equations.

2.1

15. $-6x - 6(2x - 9) = -3(x + 7)$

2.5

16. $|2x + 46| = 10$

2.1

17. $4(3x - 6) = -(8x - 2)$

Answers

8. (a) 4; (b) 0; (c) −6

9. $-x^2 - 5x + 9$

10. $10x^2 + 7x - 12$

11. $x(3x + 2)(x - 1)$

12. $(4x + 5y)(4x - 5y)$

13. $(x - y)(3x + 1)$

14. (a) $3x + 7$; (b) $-13x - 5$; (c) $-40x^2 - 22x + 6$

15. 5

16. −18, −28

17. $\frac{13}{10}$

Answers

18. $x \geq -1$

19. $-13 \leq x \leq -5$

20. $-6 < x < -4$

21. $\left(-10, \frac{26}{3}\right)$

22. $R = \frac{P - P_0}{IT}$

23. $3, -\frac{1}{2}$

24. 8 cm by 19 cm

25. 16, 14

Solve the following inequalities.

2.4

18. $4(3 + x) \geq 8$

2.5

19. $|x + 9| \leq 4$

20. $-3|x + 5| > -3$

4.1

21. Solve the following system of equations

$$2x + 3y = 6$$
$$5x + 3y = -24$$

2.2

22. Solve the equation $P = P_0 + IRT$ for R.

5.9

23. Solve the equation $2x^2 - 5x - 3 = 0$.

Solve the following applications.

2.3

24. The length of a rectangle is 3 cm more than twice its width. If the perimeter of the rectangle is 54 cm, find the dimensions of the rectangle.

25. The sum of two integers is 30 and the difference is 2. What are the two integers?

CHAPTER

6

Rational Expressions and Functions

INTRODUCTION

The House of Representatives is made up of officials elected from congressional districts within each state. The number of representatives a state sends to the U.S. House of Representatives depends on the state's population. The total number of representatives to the House has grown from 106 in 1790 to 435, the maximum number established in 1930. These 435 representatives are apportioned to the 50 states on the basis of population. This apportionment is revised after every decennial (10-year) census.

If a particular state has a population, A, and its number of representatives is equal to a, then $\frac{A}{a}$ represents the ratio of people in the state to their total number of representatives in the U.S. House. It follows that the total population of the country, P, and its total number of representatives, r, is represented by the ratio $\frac{P}{r}$. If another state, with population, E, has e number of representatives, then $\frac{E}{e}$ should also be equal to $\frac{P}{r}$ and to $\frac{A}{a}$, if the apportionment is fair.

A comparison of these ratios for states in 1990 finds Pennsylvania with 546,880 people per representative and Arizona with 610,800—Arizona was above the

CHAPTER 6 OUTLINE

national average of 571,750 people per representative for 1990, and Pennsylvania below. This is not so much a result of political backroom bargaining as it is a result of ratios that do not divide out evenly—there are remainders when the proportions are solved. Should the numbers be rounded up or down? If they are all rounded down, the total is too small, if rounded up, the total number of representatives would be more than the 435 seats in the House. So, because all the states cannot be treated equally, the question of what is fair and how to decide who gets the additional representatives has been debated in Congress since its inception.

In this chapter, we will develop many of the skills needed in handling rational expressions, which are frequently used to answer questions related to this apportionment issue. In Section 6.4, you will find exercises that deal with this topic. In addition, at the end of the chapter, you will find a more in-depth activity to explore the apportionment for your own state and compare it to that of other states.

pretest 6

Name ____________

Section ________ Date ________

This pretest will provide a preview of the types of exercises you will encounter in each section of this chapter. The answers for these exercises can be found in the back of the text. If you are working on your own, or ahead of the class, this pretest can help you identify the sections in which you should focus more of your time.

6.1 Simplify each of the following rational expressions.

1. $\dfrac{-12x^4y^3}{18x^2y^2}$

2. $\dfrac{3x^2 + 11x - 4}{2x^2 + 11x + 12}$

6.2 Multiply or divide as indicated.

3. $\dfrac{-2a^2}{ab^3} \cdot \dfrac{3ab^2}{-4ab}$

4. $\dfrac{x^2 + 7x + 10}{x^2 + 5x} \div \dfrac{x^2 - 4}{2x^2 - 7x + 6}$

6.3 Add or subtract as indicated.

5. $\dfrac{4}{x - 3} - \dfrac{1}{x}$

6. $\dfrac{3}{a^2 + 5a + 4} + \dfrac{2}{a^2 - 1}$

6.4 Simplify the complex fractions.

7. $\dfrac{\frac{x^2}{12}}{\frac{x^3}{8}}$

8. $\dfrac{1 + \frac{a}{b}}{1 - \frac{a}{b}}$

9. $\dfrac{1 - \frac{2}{x - 1}}{1 + \frac{3}{x - 4}}$

10. $\dfrac{\frac{1}{r} - \frac{1}{s}}{\frac{1}{r^2} - \frac{1}{s^2}}$

6.5 Solve the following equations.

11. $\dfrac{1}{2x} + \dfrac{1}{3x} = \dfrac{1}{6}$

12. $\dfrac{x}{x - 2} + 1 = \dfrac{x + 4}{x - 2}$

13. $\dfrac{2}{x - 4} = \dfrac{x}{x - 2} - \dfrac{x + 4}{x^2 - 6x + 8}$

6.6 Solve the following problems.

14. If y varies directly as x, and $y = 4$ when $x = 12$, find y when $x = 18$.

15. If r varies jointly as x and y, and $r = 12$ when $x = 4$ and $y = 6$, find r when $x = 8$ and $y = 5$.

16. If s varies inversely as r, and $s = 5$ when $r = 6$, find s when $r = 4$.

Answers

1. $\dfrac{-2x^2y}{3}$
2. $\dfrac{3x - 1}{2x + 3}$
3. $\dfrac{3a}{2b^2}$
4. $\dfrac{2x - 3}{x}$
5. $\dfrac{3x + 3}{x(x - 3)}$
6. $\dfrac{5}{(a - 1)(a + 4)}$
7. $\dfrac{2}{3x}$
8. $\dfrac{b + a}{b - a}$
9. $\dfrac{(x - 3)(x - 4)}{(x - 1)^2}$
10. $\dfrac{rs}{s + r}$
11. 5
12. 6
13. 0, 7
14. $y = 6$
15. $r = 20$
16. $s = 7.5$

6.1 Simplification of Rational Expressions and Functions

< 6.1 Objectives >

1 > Simplify a rational expression

2 > Identify a rational function

3 > Simplify a rational function

4 > Graph a rational function

NOTE

The word *rational* comes from "ratio."

Our work in this chapter will expand your experience with algebraic expressions to include algebraic fractions or **rational expressions.** We consider the four basic operations of addition, subtraction, multiplication, and division in the next sections. Fortunately, you will observe many parallels to your previous work with arithmetic fractions.

First, let us define what we mean by a rational expression. Recall that a rational number is the ratio of two integers. Similarly, a rational expression can be written as the ratio of two polynomials, in which the denominator cannot have the value 0.

Definition

Rational Expression

A **rational expression** is the ratio of two polynomials. It can be written as

$$\frac{P}{Q}$$

in which P and Q are polynomials and Q cannot have the value 0.

The expressions

$$\frac{x-3}{x+1}, \quad \frac{x^2+5}{x-3}, \quad \text{and} \quad \frac{x^2-2x}{x^2+3x+1}$$

are all rational expressions. The restriction that the denominator of the expressions not be 0 means that certain values for the variable may have to be excluded because division by 0 is undefined.

Example 1 **Precluding Division by Zero**

(a) For what values of x is the following expression undefined?

$$\frac{x}{x-5}$$

NOTE

A fraction is undefined when its denominator is equal to 0.

To answer this question, we must find where the denominator is 0. Set

$x - 5 = 0$

or

$x = 5$

The expression $\frac{x}{x - 5}$ is undefined for $x = 5$.

NOTE

When $x = 5$, $\frac{x}{x - 5}$ becomes $\frac{5}{5 - 5}$, or $\frac{5}{0}$.

(b) For what values of x is the following expression undefined?

$$\frac{3}{x + 5}$$

Again, set the denominator equal to 0:

$x + 5 = 0$

or

$x = -5$

The expression $\frac{3}{x + 5}$ is undefined for $x = -5$.

Check Yourself 1

For what values of the variable are the following expressions undefined?

(a) $\frac{1}{r + 7}$ **(b)** $\frac{5}{2x - 9}$

Generally, we want to write rational expressions in the simplest possible form. To begin our discussion of simplifying rational expressions, let us review for a moment. As we pointed out previously, there are many parallels to your work with arithmetic fractions. Recall that

$$\frac{3}{5} = \frac{3 \cdot 2}{5 \cdot 2} = \frac{6}{10}$$

so

$$\frac{3}{5} \text{ and } \frac{6}{10}$$

name equivalent fractions. In a similar fashion,

$$\frac{10}{15} = \frac{5 \cdot 2}{5 \cdot 3} = \frac{2}{3}$$

so

$$\frac{10}{15} \text{ and } \frac{2}{3}$$

name equivalent fractions.

We can always multiply or divide the numerator and denominator of a fraction by the same nonzero number. The same pattern is true in algebra.

Property

Fundamental Principle of Rational Expressions

For polynomials P, Q, and R,

$$\frac{P}{Q} = \frac{PR}{QR} \quad \text{when } Q \neq 0 \text{ and } R \neq 0$$

NOTE

In fact, you will see that most of the methods in this chapter depend on factoring polynomials.

This principle can be used in two ways. We can multiply or divide the numerator and denominator of a rational expression by the same nonzero polynomial. The result will always be an expression that is equivalent to the original one.

In simplifying arithmetic fractions, we used this principle to divide the numerator and denominator by all common factors. With arithmetic fractions, those common factors are generally easy to recognize. Given rational expressions in which the numerator and denominator are polynomials, we must determine those factors as our first step. The most important tools for simplifying expressions are the factoring techniques in Chapter 5.

Example 2 Simplifying Rational Expressions

< Objective 1 >

Simplify each rational expression. Assume denominators are not 0.

(a) $$\frac{4x^2y}{12xy^2} = \frac{4xy \cdot x}{4xy \cdot 3y} = \frac{x}{3y}$$

NOTES

We find the common factors 4, x, and y in the numerator and denominator. We divide the numerator and denominator by the common factor $4xy$. Note that

$$\frac{4xy}{4xy} = 1$$

(b) $$\frac{3x - 6}{x^2 - 4} = \frac{3(x - 2)}{(x + 2)(x - 2)}$$ Factor the numerator and the denominator.

We can now divide the numerator and denominator by the common factor $x - 2$:

$$\frac{3(x - 2)}{(x + 2)(x - 2)} = \frac{3}{x + 2}$$

and the rational expression is in simplest form.

We have *divided* the numerator and denominator by the common factor $x - 2$. Again note that

$$\frac{x - 2}{x - 2} = 1$$

Be Careful! Given the expression

$$\frac{x + 2}{x + 3}$$

students are often tempted to divide by variable x, as in

$$\frac{x + 2}{x + 3} \stackrel{?}{=} \frac{2}{3}$$

This is not a valid operation. We can only divide by common *factors,* and in the preceding expression, the variable x is a *term* in both the numerator and the denominator. The numerator and denominator of a rational expression must be factored *before* common factors are divided out. Therefore,

$$\frac{x + 2}{x + 3}$$

is in its simplest possible form.

> CAUTION

Pick any value other than 0 for the variable x, and substitute. You will quickly see that

$$\frac{x + 2}{x + 3} \neq \frac{2}{3}$$

Check Yourself 2

Simplify each expression.

(a) $\frac{36a^3b}{9ab^2}$ **(b)** $\frac{x^2 - 25}{4x + 20}$

The same techniques are used when trinomials need to be factored. Example 3 further illustrates the simplification of rational expressions.

Example 3 Simplifying Rational Expressions

Simplify each rational expression.

(a) $\frac{5x^2 - 5}{x^2 - 4x - 5} = \frac{5(x^2 - 1)}{x^2 - 4x - 5} = \frac{5(x - 1)(x + 1)}{(x - 5)(x + 1)}$

$= \frac{5(x - 1)}{x - 5}$

(b) $\frac{2x^2 + x - 6}{2x^2 - x - 3} = \frac{(x + 2)(2x - 3)}{(x + 1)(2x - 3)}$

$= \frac{x + 2}{x + 1}$

(c) $\frac{x^3 + 2x^2 - 3x - 6}{x^3 + 8} = \frac{(x + 2)(x^2 - 3)}{(x + 2)(x^2 - 2x + 4)} = \frac{x^2 - 3}{x^2 - 2x + 4}$

NOTES

Divide by the common factor $x + 1$, using the fact that

$\frac{x + 1}{x + 1} = 1$

when $x \neq -1$.

In part **(c)** we factor by grouping in the numerator and use the sum of cubes in the denominator. Note that

$x^3 + 2x^2 - 3x - 6$

$= x^2(x + 2) - 3(x + 2)$

$= (x + 2)(x^2 - 3)$

Check Yourself 3

Simplify each rational expression.

(a) $\frac{x^2 - 5x + 6}{3x^2 - 6x}$ **(b)** $\frac{3x^2 + 14x - 5}{3x^2 + 2x - 1}$

Simplifying certain algebraic expressions involves recognizing a particular pattern. Verify for yourself that

$3 - 9 = -(9 - 3)$

In general, it is true that

$a - b = a + (-b) = -b + a = -1(b - a)$

or, by dividing the left and right sides of the equation by $b - a$,

$$\frac{a - b}{b - a} = \frac{-(b - a)}{b - a} = -1$$

Example 4 makes use of this result.

NOTE

Notice that

$\frac{a - b}{a - b} = 1$

but

$\frac{a - b}{b - a} = -1$

when $a \neq b$.

Example 4 Simplifying Rational Expressions

Simplify each rational expression.

NOTE

From the preceding margin note, we get

$\frac{x-2}{2-x} = -1$

(a) $\frac{2x-4}{4-x^2} = \frac{2\overset{-1}{\cancel{(x-2)}}}{(2+x)\cancel{(2-x)}}$

$= \frac{2(-1)}{2+x} = \frac{-2}{2+x}$

(b) $\frac{9-x^2}{x^2+2x-15} = \frac{(3+x)\overset{-1}{\cancel{(3-x)}}}{(x+5)\cancel{(x-3)}}$

$= \frac{(3+x)(-1)}{x+5}$

$= \frac{-x-3}{x+5}$

Check Yourself 4

Simplify each rational expression.

(a) $\frac{5x-20}{16-x^2}$ (b) $\frac{x^2-6x-27}{81-x^2}$

The following algorithm summarizes our work with simplifying rational expressions.

Step by Step

Simplifying Rational Expressions

Step 1 Completely factor both the numerator and denominator of the expression.

Step 2 Divide the numerator and denominator by *all* common factors.

Step 3 The resulting expression will be in simplest form (or in lowest terms).

To identify rational functions, we begin with a definition.

Definition

Rational Function

A **rational function** is a function that is defined by a rational expression. It can be written as

$$f(x) = \frac{P}{Q}$$

in which P and Q are polynomials and $Q(x) \neq 0$ for all x.

Example 5 Identifying Rational Functions

< Objective 2 >

RECALL

From Chapter 5, there are no square roots of variables in a polynomial.

Which of the following are rational functions?

(a) $f(x) = 3x^3 - 2x + 5$ This is a rational function; it could be written over the denominator 1, and 1 is a polynomial.

(b) $f(x) = \dfrac{3x^2 - 5x + 2}{2x - 1}$ This is a rational function; it is the ratio of two polynomials.

(c) $f(x) = 3x^3 + 3\sqrt{x}$ This is not a rational function; it is not the ratio of two polynomials.

Check Yourself 5

Which of the following are rational functions?

(a) $f(x) = x^5 - 2x^4 + 3x - 1$ **(b)** $f(x) = \dfrac{x^2 - x + 7}{\sqrt{x} - 1}$

(c) $f(x) = \dfrac{3x^3 + 3x}{2x + 1}$

When we simplify a rational function, it is important that we note the x-values that need to be excluded, particularly when we are trying to draw the graph of a function. The set of ordered pairs of the simplified function will be exactly the same as the set of ordered pairs of the original function. If an excluded value for x yields ordered pair $(x, f(x))$, that ordered pair represents a "hole" in the graph. These holes are breaks in the curve. We use an open circle to designate them on a graph.

Example 6 Simplifying a Rational Function

< Objective 3 >

NOTE

$f(-1)$ is undefined.

Given the function

$$f(x) = \frac{x^2 + 2x + 1}{x + 1}$$

complete the following.

(a) Simplify the rational expression on the right.

$$\frac{x^2 + 2x + 1}{x + 1} = \frac{(x + 1)\overset{1}{\cancel{(x + 1)}}}{\underset{1}{\cancel{(x + 1)}}}$$

$$= (x + 1) \qquad x \neq -1$$

(b) Rewrite the function in simplified form.

$f(x) = x + 1 \qquad x \neq -1$

(c) Find the ordered pair associated with the hole in the graph of the original function.

Plugging -1 into the simplified function yields the ordered pair $(-1, 0)$. This represents the hole in the graph of the function

$$f(x) = \frac{x^2 + 2x + 1}{x + 1}$$

Check Yourself 6

Given the function

$$f(x) = \frac{5x^2 - 10x}{5x}$$

complete the following.

(a) Rewrite the function in simplified form.
(b) Find the ordered pair associated with the hole in the graph of the original function.

Certain rational functions can be graphed as a line with a hole in it. One such function is examined in Example 7.

Example 7 Graphing a Rational Function

< Objective 4 >

Graph the following function.

$$f(x) = \frac{x^2 + 2x + 1}{x + 1}$$

From Example 6, we know that

$$\frac{x^2 + 2x + 1}{x + 1} = x + 1 \qquad x \neq -1$$

Therefore,

$$f(x) = x + 1 \qquad x \neq -1$$

Because an x-value of -1 results in division by 0, there can be no point on the graph with an x-value of -1. The graph will be the graph of the line $f(x) = x + 1$, with an open circle at the point $(-1, 0)$.

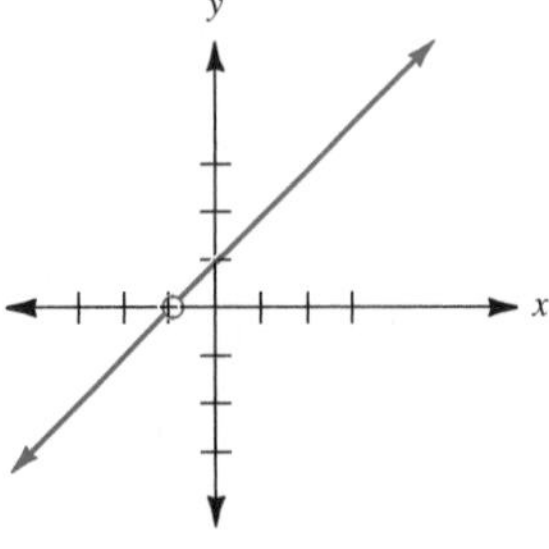

Check Yourself 7

Graph the function $f(x) = \dfrac{5x^2 - 10x}{5x}$.

Check Yourself ANSWERS

1. **(a)** $r = -7$; **(b)** $x = \frac{9}{2}$ **2.** **(a)** $\frac{4a^2}{b}$; **(b)** $\frac{x-5}{4}$

3. **(a)** $\frac{x-3}{3x}$; **(b)** $\frac{x+5}{x+1}$ **4.** **(a)** $\frac{-5}{x+4}$; **(b)** $\frac{-x-3}{x+9}$

5. **(a)** A rational function; **(b)** not a rational function; **(c)** a rational function

6. **(a)** $f(x) = x - 2, x \neq 0$; **(b)** $(0, -2)$ **7.**

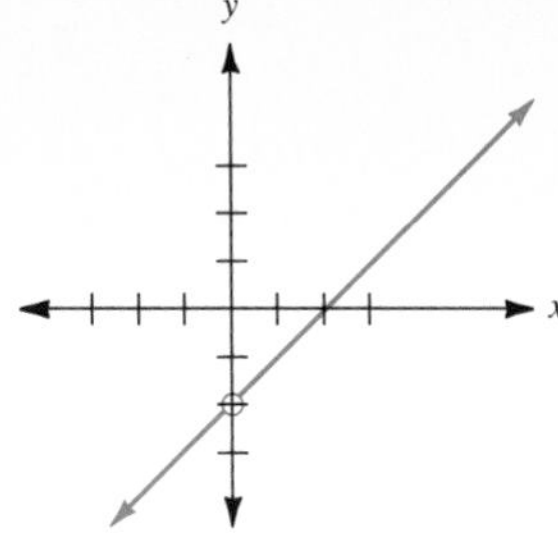

Reading Your Text

The following fill-in-the-blank exercises are designed to ensure that you understand some of the key vocabulary used in this section.

SECTION 6.1

(a) Rational expressions can be simplified if the numerator and denominator have a common ____________.

(b) We can multiply or divide the numerator and denominator of a rational expression by the same nonzero ____________.

(c) A rational function is a function that is defined by a ____________ expression.

(d) Certain rational functions can be graphed as a line with a ____________ in it.

6.1 exercises

Basic Skills | Advanced Skills | Vocational-Technical Applications | Calculator/Computer | Above and Beyond

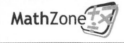

Name ______________

Section ________ Date ________

For what values of the variable is each rational expression undefined?

1. $\dfrac{x}{x - 5}$

2. $\dfrac{y}{y + 7}$

3. $\dfrac{x + 5}{3}$

4. $\dfrac{x - 6}{4}$

5. $\dfrac{2x - 3}{2x - 1}$

6. $\dfrac{3x - 2}{3x + 1}$

7. $\dfrac{2x + 5}{x}$

8. $\dfrac{3x - 7}{x}$

9. $\dfrac{x(x + 1)}{x + 2}$

10. $\dfrac{x + 2}{3x - 7}$

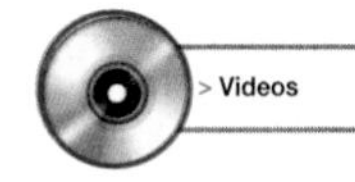

11. $\dfrac{4 - x}{x}$

12. $\dfrac{2x + 7}{3x + \frac{1}{3}}$

< Objective 1 >

Simplify each expression. Assume the denominators are not 0.

13. $\dfrac{14}{21}$

14. $\dfrac{45}{75}$

15. $\dfrac{4x^5}{6x^2}$

16. $\dfrac{25x^6}{20x^2}$

17. $\dfrac{10x^2y^5}{25xy^2}$

18. $\dfrac{18a^2b^3}{24a^4b^3}$

19. $\dfrac{-42x^3y}{14xy^3}$

> Videos

20. $\dfrac{-15x^3y^3}{-20xy^2}$

21. $\dfrac{28a^5b^3c^2}{84a^2bc^4}$

22. $\dfrac{-52p^5q^3r^2}{39p^3q^5r^2}$

23. $\dfrac{6x - 24}{x^2 - 16}$

24. $\dfrac{x^2 - 25}{3x - 15}$

Answers

1. 5
2. −7
3. Never undefined
4. Never undefined
5. $\frac{1}{2}$
6. $-\frac{1}{3}$
7. 0
8. 0
9. −2
10. $\frac{7}{3}$
11. 0
12. $-\frac{1}{9}$
13. $\frac{2}{3}$
14. $\frac{3}{5}$
15. $\frac{2x^3}{3}$
16. $\frac{5x^4}{4}$
17. $\frac{2xy^3}{5}$
18. $\frac{3}{4a^2}$
19. $\frac{-3x^2}{y^2}$
20. $\frac{3x^2y}{4}$
21. $\frac{a^3b^2}{3c^2}$
22. $\frac{-4p^2}{3q^2}$
23. $\frac{6}{x + 4}$
24. $\frac{x + 5}{3}$

25. $\dfrac{x^2 + 2x + 1}{6x + 6}$

26. $\dfrac{5y^2 - 10y}{y^2 + y - 6}$

27. $\dfrac{x^2 - 5x - 14}{x^2 - 49}$

28. $\dfrac{2m^2 + 11m - 21}{4m^2 - 9}$

29. $\dfrac{3b^2 - 14b - 5}{b - 5}$

30. $\dfrac{a^2 - 9b^2}{a^2 + 8ab + 15b^2}$

31. $\dfrac{2y^2 + 3yz - 5z^2}{2y^2 + 11yz + 15z^2}$

32. $\dfrac{6x^2 - x - 2}{3x^2 - 5x + 2}$

33. $\dfrac{x^3 - 64}{x^2 - 16}$

34. $\dfrac{r^2 - rs - 6s^2}{r^3 + 8s^3}$

35. $\dfrac{a^4 - 81}{a^2 + 5a + 6}$

36. $\dfrac{c^4 - 16}{c^2 - 3c - 10}$

37. $\dfrac{xy - 2x + 3y - 6}{x^2 + 8x + 15}$

38. $\dfrac{cd - 3c + 5d - 15}{d^2 - 7d + 12}$

39. $\dfrac{x^2 + 3x - 18}{x^3 - 3x^2 - 2x + 6}$

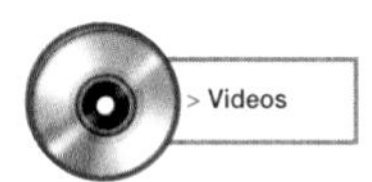

40. $\dfrac{y^2 + 2y - 35}{y^2 - 5y - 3y + 15}$

41. $\dfrac{2m - 10}{25 - m^2}$

42. $\dfrac{5x - 20}{16 - x^2}$

43. $\dfrac{49 - x^2}{2x^2 - 13x - 7}$

44. $\dfrac{2x^2 - 7x + 3}{9 - x^2}$

< Objective 2 >

Identify which functions are rational functions.

45. $f(x) = 4x^2 - 5x + 6$

46. $f(x) = \dfrac{x^3 - 2x^2 + 7}{\sqrt{x} + 2}$

47. $f(x) = \dfrac{x^2 - x - 1}{x + 2}$

48. $f(x) = \dfrac{\sqrt{x} - x + 3}{x - 2}$

49. $f(x) = 5x^2 - \sqrt[3]{x}$

50. $f(x) = \dfrac{x^2 - x + 5}{x}$

Answers

25. $\dfrac{x + 1}{6}$

26. $\dfrac{5y}{y + 3}$

27. $\dfrac{x + 2}{x + 7}$

28. $\dfrac{m + 7}{2m + 3}$

29. $3b + 1$

30. $\dfrac{a - 3b}{a + 5b}$

31. $\dfrac{y - z}{y + 3z}$

32. $\dfrac{2x + 1}{x - 1}$

33. $\dfrac{x^2 + 4x + 16}{x + 4}$

34. $\dfrac{r - 3s}{r^2 - 2rs + 4s^2}$

35. $\dfrac{(a^2 + 9)(a - 3)}{a + 2}$

36. $\dfrac{(c^2 + 4)(c - 2)}{c - 5}$

37. $\dfrac{y - 2}{x + 5}$

38. $\dfrac{c + 5}{d - 4}$

39. $\dfrac{x + 6}{x^2 - 2}$

40. $\dfrac{y + 7}{y - 3}$

41. $\dfrac{-2}{m + 5}$

42. $\dfrac{-5}{x + 4}$

43. $\dfrac{-x - 7}{2x + 1}$ or $-\dfrac{x + 7}{2x + 1}$

44. $\dfrac{-2x + 1}{x + 3}$ or $-\dfrac{2x - 1}{x + 3}$

45. Rational

46. Not rational

47. Rational

48. Not rational

49. Not rational

50. Rational

Answers

51. (a) $f(x) = x - 2$; (b) $(-1, -3)$

52. (a) $f(x) = x - 3$; (b) $(-4, -7)$

53. (a) $f(x) = 3x - 1$; (b) $(-2, -7)$

54. (a) $f(x) = x - 1$; (b) $\left(\frac{5}{2}, \frac{3}{2}\right)$

55. (a) $f(x) = \frac{x+2}{5}$; (b) $(-2, 0)$

56. (a) $f(x) = \frac{x-3}{7}$; (b) $(3, 0)$

57. See exercise

58. See exercise

59. See exercise

60. See exercise

< Objective 3 >

For the given functions in exercises 51 to 56, **(a)** *rewrite the function in simplified form, and* **(b)** *find the ordered pair associated with the hole in the graph of the original function.*

51. $f(x) = \dfrac{x^2 - x - 2}{x + 1}$

52. $f(x) = \dfrac{x^2 + x - 12}{x + 4}$

53. $f(x) = \dfrac{3x^2 + 5x - 2}{x + 2}$

54. $f(x) = \dfrac{2x^2 - 7x + 5}{2x - 5}$

55. $f(x) = \dfrac{x^2 + 4x + 4}{5(x + 2)}$

56. $f(x) = \dfrac{x^2 - 6x + 9}{7(x - 3)}$

< Objective 4 >

Graph the rational functions. Indicate the coordinates of the hole in the graph.

57. $f(x) = \dfrac{x^2 - 2x - 8}{x + 2}$

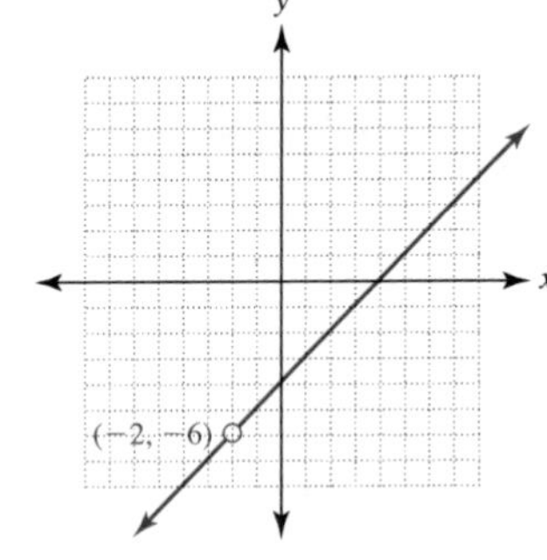

58. $f(x) = \dfrac{x^2 + 4x - 5}{x + 5}$

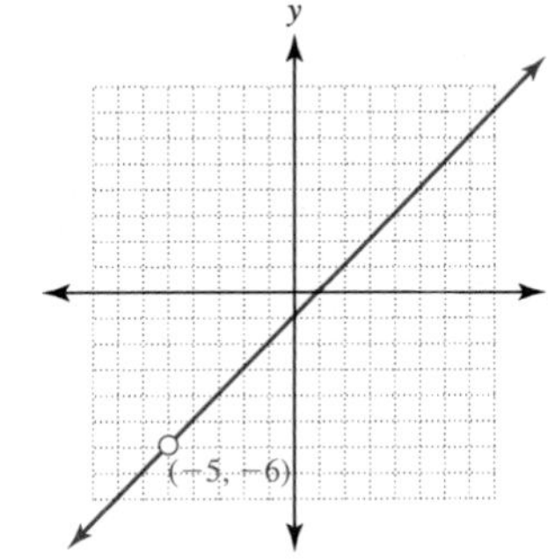

59. $f(x) = \dfrac{x^2 + 4x + 3}{x + 1}$

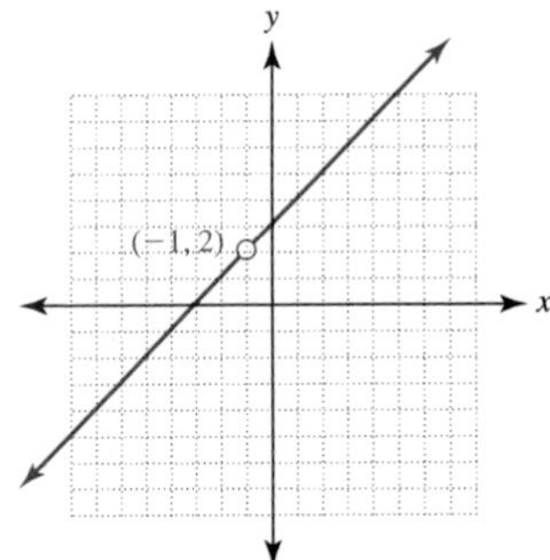

60. $f(x) = \dfrac{x^2 + 7x + 10}{x + 2}$

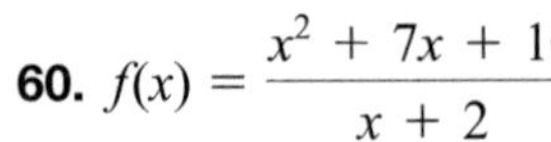

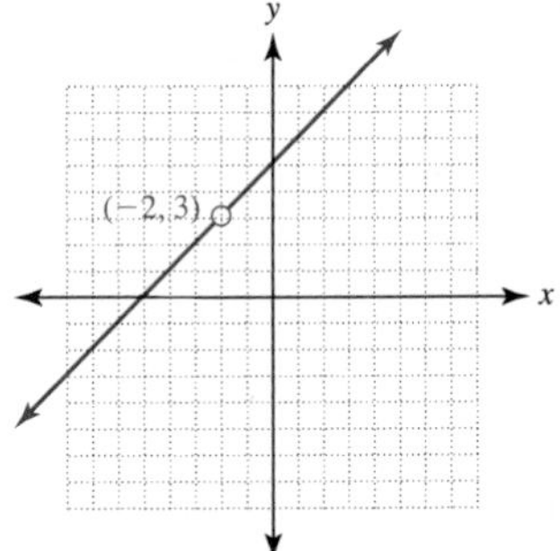

61. $f(x) = \dfrac{x^2 - 4x + 3}{x - 1}$ > Videos

62. $f(x) = \dfrac{x^2 - 6x + 8}{x - 4}$

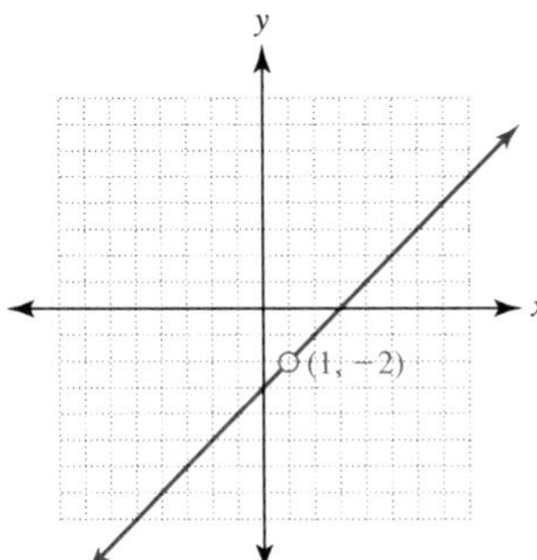

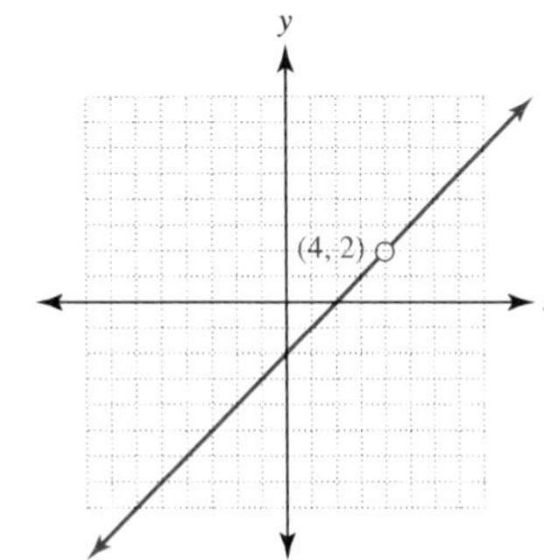

Basic Skills | **Advanced Skills** | Vocational-Technical Applications | Calculator/Computer | Above and Beyond

Simplify.

63. $\dfrac{2(x + h) - 2x}{(x + h) - x}$

64. $\dfrac{-3(x + h) - (-3x)}{(x + h) - x}$

65. $\dfrac{3(x + h) - 3 - (3x - 3)}{(x + h) - x}$

66. $\dfrac{2(x + h) + 5 - (2x + 5)}{(x + h) - x}$

67. $\dfrac{(x + h)^2 - x^2}{(x + h) - x}$

68. $\dfrac{(x + h)^3 - x^3}{(x + h) - x}$

Basic Skills | Advanced Skills | Vocational-Technical Applications | **Calculator/Computer** | Above and Beyond

Evaluate each expression, using a calculator.

69. $\dfrac{3x}{2x - 1}$ for $x = 2$

70. $\dfrac{5x}{4x - 3}$ for $x = 2$

71. $\dfrac{2x + 3}{x + 3}$ for $x = -6$

72. $\dfrac{4x - 7}{2x - 1}$ for $x = -2$

Answers

61. See exercise

62. See exercise

63. 2

64. −3

65. 3

66. 2

67. $2x + h$

68. $3x^2 + 3xh + h^2$

69. 2

70. 2

71. 3

72. 3

Answers

73. $x + 5$

74. $x + 7$

75. Above and Beyond

76. Above and Beyond

77. Above and Beyond

78. Above and Beyond

79. (a) \$3,000; (b) \$9,231; (c) \$15,000; (d) \$6,231

Given $f(x) = \dfrac{P(x)}{Q(x)}$, if the graphs of $P(x)$ and $Q(x)$ intersect at $(a, 0)$, then $x - a$ is a factor of both $P(x)$ and $Q(x)$. Use a graphing calculator to find the common factor for the expressions in exercises 73 and 74.

73. $f(x) = \dfrac{x^2 + 4x - 5}{x^2 + 3x - 10}$

74. $f(x) = \dfrac{2x^2 + 11x - 21}{2x^2 + 15x + 7}$

Basic Skills | Advanced Skills | Vocational-Technical Applications | Calculator/Computer | **Above and Beyond**

75. Explain why the following statement is false.

$$\frac{6m^2 + 2m}{2m} = 6m^2 + 1$$

76. State and explain the Fundamental Principle of Rational Expressions.

77. The rational expression $\dfrac{x^2 - 4}{x + 2}$ can be simplified to $x - 2$. Is this reduction true for all values of x? Explain.

78. What is meant by a rational expression in lowest terms?

79. **Business and Finance** The total revenue from the sale of a popular video is approximated by the rational function

$$R(x) = \frac{300x^2}{x^2 + 9}$$

in which x is the number of months since the video has been released and $R(x)$ is the total revenue in hundreds of dollars.

(a) Find the total revenue generated by the end of the first month.

(b) Find the total revenue generated by the end of the second month.

(c) Find the total revenue generated by the end of the third month.

(d) Find the revenue in the second month only.

80. **Business and Finance** A company has a setup cost of $3,500 for the production of a new product. The cost to produce a single unit is $8.75.

(a) Define a rational function that gives the average cost per unit when x units are produced.

(b) Find the average cost when 50 units are produced.

81. Besides holes, we sometimes encounter a different sort of "break" in the graph of a rational function. Consider the rational function

$$f(x) = \frac{1}{x - 3}$$

(a) For what value(s) of x is the function undefined?

(b) Complete the following table.

x	$f(x)$
4	1
3.1	10
3.01	100
3.001	1,000
3.0001	10,000

(c) What do you observe concerning $f(x)$ if x is chosen close to 3 (but slightly larger than 3)?

(d) Complete the table.

x	$f(x)$
2	−1
2.9	−10
2.99	−100
2.999	−1,000
2.9999	−10,000

(e) What do you observe concerning $f(x)$ if x is chosen close to 3 (but slightly smaller than 3)?

(f) Graph the function on your graphing calculator. Describe the behavior of the graph of $f(x)$ near $x = 3$.

82. Consider the rational function

$$f(x) = \frac{1}{x + 2}$$

(a) For what value(s) of x is the function undefined?

Answers

80. (a) $C(x) = \frac{3,500 + 8.75x}{x}$; (b) $78.75

81. (a) 3; (b) See exercise; (c) Above and Beyond; (d) See exercise; (e) Above and Beyond; (f) It is descending almost vertically.

Answers

82. (a) −2;
(b) See exercise;
(c) Above and Beyond;
(d) See exercise;
(e) Above and Beyond;
(f) It is ascending almost vertically.

83. Above and Beyond

(b) Complete the following table.

x	$f(x)$
−3	−1
−2.1	−10
−2.01	−100
−2.001	−1,000
−2.0001	−10,000

(c) What do you observe concerning $f(x)$ if x is chosen close to -2 (but slightly smaller than -2)?

(d) Complete the following table.

x	$f(x)$
−1	1
−1.9	10
−1.99	100
−1.999	1,000
−1.9999	10,000

(e) What do you observe concerning $f(x)$ if x is chosen close to -2 (but slightly larger than -2)?

(f) Graph the function on your graphing calculator. Describe the behavior of the graph near $x = -2$.

83. Science and Medicine Your friend has a 4-year-old cousin, Amy, who has a 9-year-old brother. The younger child is upset because not only does her brother refuse to let her play with him and his friends, he teases her because she can never catch up in age! You explain to the child that as she gets older, this age difference will not seem like such a big deal.

Write an expression for the ratio of the younger child's age to her brother's age.

1. What happens to the ratio as the children grow older?
2. Draw a graph of the ratio as a function of Amy's age to show how this ratio changes.
3. Assume that Amy and her brother live to be 100 and 105 years old, respectively. What will the ratio between their ages be?
4. Draw a graph of the ratio of Amy's brother's age to Amy's age. Does this graph have anything in common with the first graph? Explain.
5. Write a short explanation for Amy (who is only 4, remember!) of your conclusions about how their age ratios change over time.

Answers

1. 5 **3.** Never undefined **5.** $\frac{1}{2}$ **7.** 0 **9.** −2 **11.** 0

13. $\frac{2}{3}$ **15.** $\frac{2x^3}{3}$ **17.** $\frac{2xy^3}{5}$ **19.** $\frac{-3x^2}{y^2}$ **21.** $\frac{a^3b^2}{3c^2}$ **23.** $\frac{6}{x+4}$

25. $\frac{x+1}{6}$ **27.** $\frac{x+2}{x+7}$ **29.** $3b+1$ **31.** $\frac{y-z}{y+3z}$
33. $\frac{x^2+4x+16}{x+4}$ **35.** $\frac{(a^2+9)(a-3)}{a+2}$ **37.** $\frac{y-2}{x+5}$ **39.** $\frac{x+6}{x^2-2}$
41. $\frac{-2}{m+5}$ **43.** $\frac{-x-7}{2x+1}$ or $-\frac{x+7}{2x+1}$ **45.** Rational **47.** Rational
49. Not rational **51.** **(a)** $f(x) = x - 2$; **(b)** $(-1, -3)$
53. **(a)** $f(x) = 3x - 1$; **(b)** $(-2, -7)$ **55.** **(a)** $f(x) = \frac{x+2}{5}$; **(b)** $(-2, 0)$

57.

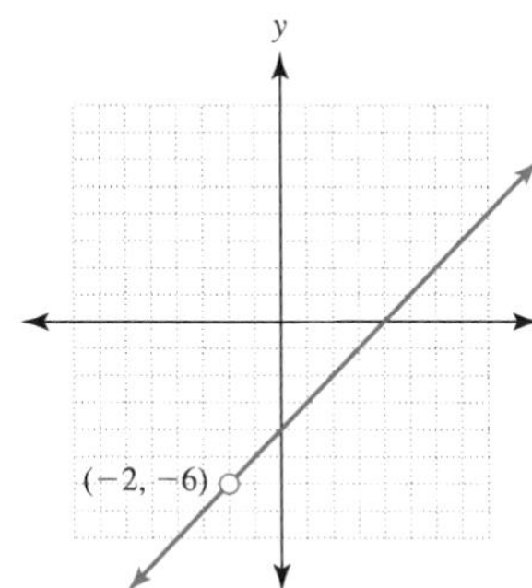

59.

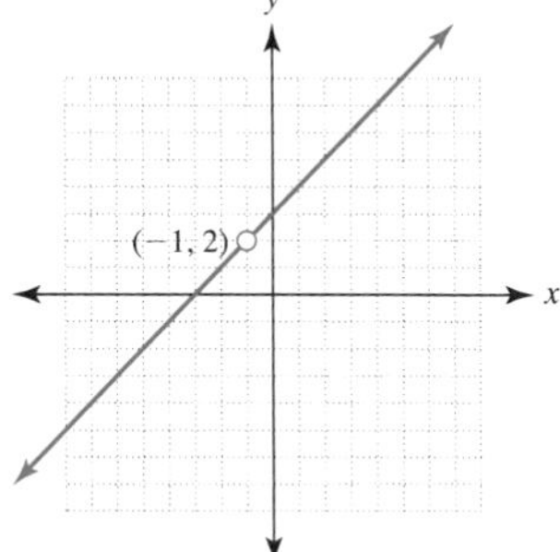

61.

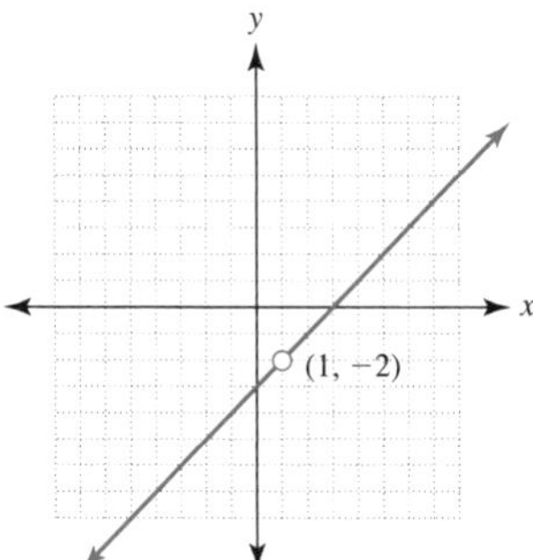

63. 2 **65.** 3 **67.** $2x + h$ **69.** 2 **71.** 3 **73.** $x + 5$
75. Above and Beyond **77.** Above and Beyond **79.** **(a)** \$3,000;
(b) \$9,231; **(c)** \$15,000; **(d)** \$6,231 **81.** **(a)** 3; **(b)** 1, 10, 100, 1,000, 10,000;
(c) Above and Beyond; **(d)** −1, −10, −100, −1,000, −10,000;
(e) Above and Beyond; **(f)** It is descending almost vertically.
83. Above and Beyond

6.2 Multiplication and Division of Rational Expressions and Functions

< 6.2 Objectives >

1 > Multiply two rational expressions

2 > Divide two rational expressions

3 > Multiply two rational functions

4 > Divide two rational functions

NOTE

For all problems with rational expressions, assume denominators are not 0.

Once again, let us turn to an example from arithmetic to begin our discussion of multiplying rational expressions. Recall that to multiply two fractions, we multiply the numerators and multiply the denominators. For instance,

$$\frac{2}{5} \cdot \frac{3}{7} = \frac{2 \cdot 3}{5 \cdot 7} = \frac{6}{35}$$

In algebra, the pattern is exactly the same.

Property

Multiplying Rational Expressions

For polynomials P, Q, R, and S,

$$\frac{P}{Q} \cdot \frac{R}{S} = \frac{PR}{QS} \quad \text{when } Q \neq 0 \quad \text{and} \quad S \neq 0$$

Example 1 Multiplying Rational Expressions

< Objective 1 >

Multiply.

$$\frac{2x^3}{5y^2} \cdot \frac{10y}{3x^2} = \frac{20x^3y}{15x^2y^2}$$

$$= \frac{\overset{1}{\cancel{5x^2y}} \cdot 4x}{\underset{1}{\cancel{5x^2y}} \cdot 3y}$$

Divide by the common factor $5x^2y$ to simplify.

$$= \frac{4x}{3y}$$

NOTE

The factoring methods in Chapter 5 are used to simplify rational expressions.

Check Yourself 1

Multiply.

$$\frac{9a^2b^3}{5ab^4} \cdot \frac{20ab^2}{27ab^3}$$

Generally, you will find it best to divide by any common factors before you multiply, as Example 2 illustrates.

Example 2 Multiplying Rational Expressions

Multiply as indicated.

(a) $\frac{x}{x^2 - 3x} \cdot \frac{6x - 18}{9x}$ Factor.

$= \frac{x}{x(x - 3)} \cdot \frac{6(x - 3)}{9x}$ Divide by the common factors of 3, x, and $x - 3$.

$= \frac{2}{3x}$

(b) $\frac{x^2 - y^2}{5x^2 - 5xy} \cdot \frac{10xy}{x^2 + 2xy + y^2}$ Factor and divide by the common factors of 5, x, $x - y$, and $x + y$.

$= \frac{(x + y)(x - y)}{5x(x - y)} \cdot \frac{10xy}{(x + y)(x + y)}$

$= \frac{2y}{x + y}$

RECALL

$\frac{2 - x}{x - 2} = -1$

(c) $\frac{4}{x^2 - 2x} \cdot \frac{10x - 5x^2}{8x + 24}$ Factor and divide by the common factors of 4, x, and $x - 2$.

$= \frac{4}{x(x - 2)} \cdot \frac{5x(2 - x)}{8(x + 3)}$

$= \frac{-5}{2(x + 3)}$

Check Yourself 2

Multiply as indicated.

(a) $\frac{x^2 - 5x - 14}{4x^2} \cdot \frac{8x + 56}{x^2 - 49}$ (b) $\frac{x}{2x - 6} \cdot \frac{3x - x^2}{2}$

The following algorithm summarizes our work in multiplying rational expressions.

Step by Step

Multiplying Rational Expressions

Step 1 Write each numerator and denominator in completely factored form.
Step 2 Divide by any common factors appearing in both the numerator and denominator.
Step 3 Multiply as needed to form the product.

NOTE

We invert the *divisor* (the second fraction) and multiply.

In dividing rational expressions, you can again use your experience from arithmetic. Recall that

$$\frac{3}{5} \div \frac{2}{3} = \frac{3}{5} \cdot \frac{3}{2} = \frac{9}{10}$$

Once more, the pattern in algebra is identical.

Property

Dividing Rational Expressions

For polynomials P, Q, R, and S,

$$\frac{P}{Q} \div \frac{R}{S} = \frac{P}{Q} \cdot \frac{S}{R} = \frac{PS}{QR}$$

when $Q \neq 0$, $R \neq 0$, and $S \neq 0$.

To divide rational expressions, invert the divisor and multiply as before, as Example 3 illustrates.

Example 3 **Dividing Rational Expressions**

< Objective 2 >

Divide as indicated.

NOTE

Invert the divisor and multiply.

(a) $\dfrac{3x^2}{8x^3y} \div \dfrac{9x^2y^2}{4y^4} = \dfrac{\cancel{3}\cancel{x^2}}{\cancel{8}x^3y} \cdot \dfrac{\cancel{4}y^4}{\cancel{9}\cancel{x^2}y^2} = \dfrac{\cancel{y^4}}{6x^3\cancel{y^3}} = \dfrac{y}{6x^3}$

(b) $\dfrac{2x^2 + 4xy}{9x - 18y} \div \dfrac{4x + 8y}{3x - 6y} = \dfrac{2x^2 + 4xy}{9x - 18y} \cdot \dfrac{3x - 6y}{4x + 8y}$

$= \dfrac{\cancel{2}x\cancel{(x + 2y)}}{\cancel{9}\cancel{(x - 2y)}} \cdot \dfrac{\cancel{3}\cancel{(x - 2y)}}{\cancel{4}\cancel{(x + 2y)}} = \dfrac{x}{6}$

> CAUTION

Be Careful! Invert the divisor, and then factor.

(c) $\dfrac{2x^2 - x - 6}{4x^2 + 6x} \div \dfrac{x^2 - 4}{4x} = \dfrac{2x^2 - x - 6}{4x^2 + 6x} \cdot \dfrac{4x}{x^2 - 4}$

$= \dfrac{\cancel{(2x + 3)}\cancel{(x - 2)}}{\cancel{2}\cancel{x}\cancel{(2x + 3)}} \cdot \dfrac{\cancel{4x}}{(x + 2)\cancel{(x - 2)}} = \dfrac{2}{x + 2}$

Check Yourself 3

Divide and simplify.

(a) $\dfrac{5xy}{7x^3} \div \dfrac{10y^2}{14x^3}$

(b) $\dfrac{3x - 9y}{2x + 10y} \div \dfrac{x^2 - 3xy}{4x^2 + 20xy}$

(c) $\dfrac{x^2 - 9}{x^3 - 27} \div \dfrac{x^2 - 2x - 15}{2x^2 - 10x}$

We summarize our work in dividing fractions with the following algorithm.

Step by Step

Dividing Rational Expressions

Step 1 Invert the divisor (the *second* rational expression) to write the problem as one of multiplication.

Step 2 Proceed as in the algorithm for the multiplication of rational expressions.

The product of two rational functions is always a rational function. Given two rational functions, $f(x)$ and $g(x)$, we can rename the product, so

$$h(x) = f(x) \cdot g(x)$$

This will always be true for values of x for which both f and g are defined. So, for example, $h(1) = f(1) \cdot g(1)$ as long as both $f(1)$ and $g(1)$ exist.

Example 4 illustrates this concept.

Example 4 Multiplying Rational Functions

< Objective 3 >

Given the rational functions

$$f(x) = \frac{x^2 - 3x - 10}{x + 1} \quad \text{and} \quad g(x) = \frac{x^2 - 4x - 5}{x - 5}$$

find the following.

(a) $f(0) \cdot g(0)$

Because $f(0) = -10$ and $g(0) = 1$, then $f(0) \cdot g(0) = (-10)(1) = -10$.

(b) $f(5) \cdot g(5)$

Although we can find $f(5)$, $g(5)$ is undefined. 5 is an excluded value for the domain of the function g. Therefore, $f(5) \cdot g(5)$ is undefined.

(c) $h(x) = f(x) \cdot g(x)$

$$h(x) = \frac{x^2 - 3x - 10}{x + 1} \cdot \frac{x^2 - 4x - 5}{x - 5}$$

$$= \frac{(x - 5)(x + 2)}{\cancel{(x + 1)}} \cdot \frac{\cancel{(x + 1)}\cancel{(x - 5)}}{\cancel{(x - 5)}}$$

$$= (x - 5)(x + 2) \qquad x \neq -1, x \neq 5$$

NOTE

In part **(c)**, $x \neq -1$ and $x \neq 5$ for $h(x)$ because of the definition of $h(x)$ *before* simplifying.

(d) $h(0)$

$$h(0) = (0 - 5)(0 + 2) = -10$$

(e) $h(5)$

Although the temptation is to substitute 5 for x in part **(c)**, notice that the function is undefined when x is -1 or 5. As was true in part **(b)**, the function is undefined at that point.

Check Yourself 4

Given the rational functions

$$f(x) = \frac{x^2 - 2x - 8}{x + 2} \quad \text{and} \quad g(x) = \frac{x^2 - 3x - 10}{x - 4}$$

find the following.

(a) $f(0) \cdot g(0)$ **(b)** $f(4) \cdot g(4)$ **(c)** $h(x) = f(x) \cdot g(x)$
(d) $h(0)$ **(e)** $h(4)$

When we divide two rational functions to create a third rational function, we must be certain to exclude values for which the denominator is equal to zero, as Example 5 illustrates.

Example 5 Dividing Rational Functions

< Objective 4 >

Given the rational functions

$$f(x) = \frac{x^3 - 2x^2}{x + 2} \quad \text{and} \quad g(x) = \frac{x^2 - 3x + 2}{x - 4}$$

complete the following.

(a) Find $\frac{f(0)}{g(0)}$.

Because $f(0) = 0$ and $g(0) = -\frac{1}{2}$, then

$$\frac{f(0)}{g(0)} = \frac{0}{-\frac{1}{2}} = 0$$

(b) Find $\frac{f(1)}{g(1)}$.

Although we can find both $f(1)$ and $g(1)$, $g(1) = 0$, so division is undefined when $x = 1$. 1 is an excluded value for the domain of the quotient.

(c) Find $h(x) = \frac{f(x)}{g(x)}$.

$$h(x) = \frac{\dfrac{x^3 - 2x^2}{x + 2}}{\dfrac{x^2 - 3x + 2}{x - 4}}$$

Invert and multiply.

$$= \frac{x^3 - 2x^2}{x + 2} \cdot \frac{x - 4}{x^2 - 3x + 2}$$

$$= \frac{x^2\overset{1}{\cancel{(x - 2)}}}{x + 2} \cdot \frac{x - 4}{(x - 1)\underset{1}{\cancel{(x - 2)}}}$$

$$= \frac{x^2(x - 4)}{(x + 2)(x - 1)} \qquad x \neq -2, 1, 2, 4$$

NOTE

$f(x)$ is undefined at $x = -2$, $g(x)$ is undefined at $x = 4$, and $g(x) = 0$ is undefined at $x = 1$ and $x = 2$.

(d) For which values of x is $h(x)$ undefined?

$h(x)$ will be undefined for any value of x for which $f(x)$ is undefined, $g(x)$ is undefined, or $g(x) = 0$.

$h(x)$ is undefined for the values -2, 1, 2, and 4.

Check Yourself 5

Given the rational functions

$$f(x) = \frac{x^2 - 2x + 1}{x + 3} \quad \text{and} \quad g(x) = \frac{x^2 - 5x + 4}{x - 2}$$

complete the following.

(a) Find $\frac{f(0)}{g(0)}$. **(b)** Find $\frac{f(1)}{g(1)}$. **(c)** Find $h(x) = \frac{f(x)}{g(x)}$.

(d) For which values of x is $h(x)$ undefined?

Check Yourself ANSWERS

1. $\frac{4a}{3b^2}$ **2. (a)** $\frac{2(x + 2)}{x^2}$; **(b)** $\frac{-x^2}{4}$ **3. (a)** $\frac{x}{y}$; **(b)** 6; **(c)** $\frac{2x}{x^2 + 3x + 9}$

4. (a) -10; **(b)** undefined; **(c)** $h(x) = (x - 5)(x + 2)$ $x \neq 4, x \neq -2$; **(d)** -10; **(e)** undefined **5. (a)** $-\frac{1}{6}$; **(b)** undefined; **(c)** $h(x) = \frac{(x - 1)(x - 2)}{(x + 3)(x - 4)}$; **(d)** $x \neq -3, 1, 2, 4$

Reading Your Text

The following fill-in-the-blank exercises are designed to ensure that you understand some of the key vocabulary used in this section.

SECTION 6.2

(a) In arithmetic, we find the product of two fractions by ____________ the numerators and denominators.

(b) The first step when multiplying rational expressions is to ____________ the numerators and denominators.

(c) When dividing two rational expressions, ____________ the divisor and multiply.

(d) When dividing rational expressions, the divisor cannot equal ____________.

6.2 exercises

Basic Skills | Advanced Skills | Vocational-Technical Applications | Calculator/Computer | Above and Beyond

Name ____________

Section ______ Date ______

< Objectives 1 and 2 >

In exercises 1 to 30, multiply or divide as indicated. Express your result in simplest form.

1. $\frac{x^2}{3} \cdot \frac{6x}{x^4}$

2. $\frac{-y^3}{10} \cdot \frac{15y}{y^6}$

3. $\frac{a}{7a^3} \div \frac{a^2}{21}$

4. $\frac{p^5}{8} \div \frac{-p^2}{12p}$

5. $\frac{4xy^2}{15x^3} \cdot \frac{25xy}{16y^3}$

6. $\frac{3x^3y}{10xy^3} \cdot \frac{5xy^2}{-9xy^3}$

7. $\frac{8b^3}{15ab} \div \frac{2ab^2}{20ab^3}$

8. $\frac{4x^2y^2}{9x^3} \div \frac{-8y^2}{27xy}$

9. $\frac{m^3n}{2mn} \cdot \frac{6mn^2}{m^3n} \div \frac{3mn}{5m^2n}$

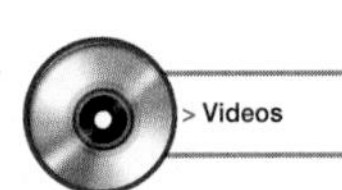

10. $\frac{4cd^2}{5cd} \cdot \frac{3c^3d}{2c^2d} \div \frac{9cd}{20cd^3}$

11. $\frac{5x+15}{3x} \cdot \frac{9x^2}{2x+6}$

12. $\frac{a^2-3a}{5a} \cdot \frac{20a^2}{3a-9}$

13. $\frac{3b-15}{6b} \div \frac{4b-20}{9b^2}$

14. $\frac{7m^2+28m}{4m} \div \frac{5m+20}{12m^2}$

15. $\frac{x^2-3x-10}{5x} \cdot \frac{15x^2}{3x-15}$

16. $\frac{y^2-8y}{4y} \cdot \frac{12y^2}{y^2-64}$

17. $\frac{c^2+2c-8}{6c} \div \frac{5c+20}{18c}$

18. $\frac{m^2-49}{5m} \div \frac{3m+21}{20m^2}$

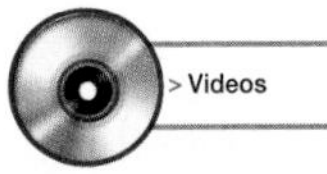

19. $\frac{x^2-2x-8}{4x-16} \cdot \frac{10x}{x^2-4}$

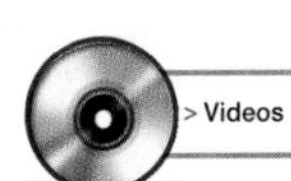

20. $\frac{y^2+7y+10}{y^2+5y} \cdot \frac{2y}{y^2-4}$

Answers

1. $\frac{2}{x}$
2. $\frac{-3}{2y^2}$
3. $\frac{3}{a^4}$
4. $\frac{-3p^4}{2}$
5. $\frac{5}{12x}$
6. $\frac{-x^2}{6y^3}$
7. $\frac{16b^3}{3a}$
8. $\frac{-3y}{2}$
9. $5mn$
10. $\frac{8cd^3}{3}$
11. $\frac{15x}{2}$
12. $\frac{4a^2}{3}$
13. $\frac{9b}{8}$
14. $\frac{21m^2}{5}$
15. $x(x+2)$
16. $\frac{3y^2}{y+8}$
17. $\frac{3(c-2)}{5}$
18. $\frac{4m(m-7)}{3}$
19. $\frac{5x}{2(x-2)}$
20. $\frac{2}{y-2}$

21. $\frac{d^2 - 3d - 18}{16d - 96} \div \frac{d^2 - 9}{20d}$

22. $\frac{b^2 + 6b + 8}{b^2 + 4b} \div \frac{b^2 - 4}{2b}$

23. $\frac{2x^2 - x - 3}{3x^2 + 7x + 4} \cdot \frac{3x^2 - 11x - 20}{4x^2 - 9}$

24. $\frac{4p^2 - 1}{2p^2 - 9p - 5} \cdot \frac{3p^2 - 13p - 10}{9p^2 - 4}$

25. $\frac{a^2 - 9}{2a^2 - 6a} \div \frac{2a^2 + 5a - 3}{4a^2 - 1}$

26. $\frac{2x^2 - 5x - 7}{4x^2 - 9} \div \frac{5x^2 + 5x}{2x^2 + 3x}$

27. $\frac{2w - 6}{w^2 + 2w} \cdot \frac{3w}{3 - w}$

28. $\frac{3y - 15}{y^2 + 3y} \cdot \frac{4y}{5 - y}$

29. $\frac{a - 7}{2a + 6} \div \frac{21 - 3a}{a^2 + 3a}$

30. $\frac{x - 4}{x^2 + 2x} \div \frac{16 - 4x}{3x + 6}$

< Objective 3 >

31. Let $f(x) = \frac{x^2 - 3x - 4}{x + 2}$ and $g(x) = \frac{x^2 - 2x - 8}{x - 4}$. Find **(a)** $f(0) \cdot g(0)$, **(b)** $f(4) \cdot g(4)$, **(c)** $h(x) = f(x) \cdot g(x)$, **(d)** $h(0)$, and **(e)** $h(4)$.

32. Let $f(x) = \frac{x^2 - 4x + 3}{x + 5}$ and $g(x) = \frac{x^2 + 7x + 10}{x - 3}$. Find **(a)** $f(1) \cdot g(1)$, **(b)** $f(3) \cdot g(3)$, **(c)** $h(x) = f(x) \cdot g(x)$, **(d)** $h(1)$, and **(e)** $h(3)$.

33. Let $f(x) = \frac{2x^2 - 3x - 5}{x + 2}$ and $g(x) = \frac{3x^2 + 5x - 2}{x + 1}$. Find **(a)** $f(1) \cdot g(1)$, **(b)** $f(-2) \cdot g(-2)$, **(c)** $h(x) = f(x) \cdot g(x)$, **(d)** $h(1)$, and **(e)** $h(-2)$.

34. Let $f(x) = \frac{x^2 - 1}{x - 3}$ and $g(x) = \frac{x^2 - 9}{x - 1}$. Find **(a)** $f(2) \cdot g(2)$, **(b)** $f(3) \cdot g(3)$, **(c)** $h(x) = f(x) \cdot g(x)$, **(d)** $h(2)$, and **(e)** $h(3)$.

Answers

21. $\frac{5d}{4(d - 3)}$

22. $\frac{2}{b - 2}$

23. $\frac{x - 5}{2x + 3}$

24. $\frac{2p - 1}{3p - 2}$

25. $\frac{2a + 1}{2a}$

26. $\frac{2x - 7}{5(2x - 3)}$

27. $\frac{-6}{w + 2}$

28. $\frac{-12}{y + 3}$

29. $\frac{-a}{6}$

30. $\frac{-3}{4x}$

31. (a) -4; (b) undefined; (c) $(x + 1)(x - 4)$, $x \neq -2, 4$; (d) -4; (e) undefined

32. (a) 0; (b) undefined; (c) $(x - 1)(x + 2)$, $x \neq -5, 3$; (d) 0; (e) undefined

33. (a) -6; (b) undefined; (c) $(2x - 5)(3x - 1)$, $x \neq -2, -1$; (d) -6; (e) undefined

34. (a) 15; (b) undefined; (c) $(x + 1)(x + 3)$, $x \neq 1, 3$; (d) 15; (e) undefined

Answers

35. (a) $-\frac{4}{5}$; (b) $\frac{5}{4}$; (c) $\frac{(3x-2)(x+4)}{(x-2)(x-5)}$, $x \neq -4, -1, 2, 5$; (d) 2, −4, −1, 5

36. (a) 0; (b) $\frac{-3}{2}$; (c) $\frac{x(x+1)}{(x-3)(x+2)}$ $x \neq -2, 3, 5$; (d) −2, 3, 5

37. $\frac{2}{x}$

38. $\frac{a}{2b}$

39. $\frac{3}{m}$

40. $\frac{y}{4}$

41. $\frac{5}{x}$

42. $3a$

43. $\frac{x^2+2}{4}$

44. $\frac{3}{5a}$

< Objective 4 >

35. Let $f(x) = \dfrac{3x^2 + x - 2}{x - 2}$ and $g(x) = \dfrac{x^2 - 4x - 5}{x + 4}$. Find **(a)** $\dfrac{f(0)}{g(0)}$, **(b)** $\dfrac{f(1)}{g(1)}$, **(c)** $h(x) = \dfrac{f(x)}{g(x)}$, and **(d)** the values of x for which $h(x)$ is undefined.

36. Let $f(x) = \dfrac{x^2 + x}{x - 5}$ and $g(x) = \dfrac{x^2 - x - 6}{x - 5}$. Find **(a)** $\dfrac{f(0)}{g(0)}$, **(b)** $\dfrac{f(2)}{g(2)}$, **(c)** $h(x) = \dfrac{f(x)}{g(x)}$, and **(d)** the values of x for which $h(x)$ is undefined.

Basic Skills | **Advanced Skills** | Vocational-Technical Applications | Calculator/Computer | Above and Beyond

Multiply or divide as indicated. Express your result in simplest form.

37. $\dfrac{x^2 - 9y^2}{2x^2 - xy - 15y^2} \cdot \dfrac{4x + 10y}{x^2 + 3xy}$

38. $\dfrac{2a^2 - 7ab - 15b^2}{2ab - 10b^2} \cdot \dfrac{2a^2 - 3ab}{4a^2 - 9b^2}$

39. $\dfrac{3m^2 - 5mn + 2n^2}{9m^2 - 4n^2} \div \dfrac{m^3 - m^2n}{9m^2 + 6mn}$

40. $\dfrac{2x^2y - 5xy^2}{4x^2 - 25y^2} \div \dfrac{4x^2 + 20xy}{2x^2 + 15xy + 25y^2}$

41. $\dfrac{x^3 + 8}{x^2 - 4} \cdot \dfrac{5x - 10}{x^3 - 2x^2 + 4x}$

42. $\dfrac{a^3 - 27}{a^2 - 9} \div \dfrac{a^3 + 3a^2 + 9a}{3a^3 + 9a^2}$

Basic Skills | Advanced Skills | Vocational-Technical Applications | **Calculator/Computer** | Above and Beyond

The results from multiplying and dividing rational expressions can be checked by using a graphing calculator. To do this, define one expression in Y_1 and the other in Y_2. Then define the operation in Y_3 as $Y_1 \cdot Y_2$ or $Y_1 \div Y_2$. Put your simplified result in Y_4 (sorry, you still must simplify algebraically). Deselect the graphs for Y_1 and Y_2. If you have correctly simplified the expression, the graphs of Y_3 and Y_4 will be identical. On the TI-84, to access the Y_1 and Y_2 variables for your equations, use the following path:

Y-VARS
1: Function.

Use this technique in exercises 43 to 46.

43. $\dfrac{x^3 - 3x^2 + 2x - 6}{x^2 - 9} \cdot \dfrac{5x^2 + 15x}{20x}$

44. $\dfrac{3a^3 + a^2 - 9a - 3}{15a^2 + 5a} \cdot \dfrac{3a^2 + 9}{a^4 - 9}$

45. $\dfrac{x^4 - 16}{x^2 + x - 6} \div (x^3 + 4x)$

46. $\dfrac{w^3 + 27}{w^2 + 2w - 3} \div (w^3 - 3w^2 + 9w)$

Basic Skills | Advanced Skills | Vocational-Technical Applications | Calculator/Computer | **Above and Beyond**

Perform the indicated operations, and express the results in simplest form.

47. $\dfrac{x^2 - 2x - 8}{2x - 8} \cdot \dfrac{x^2 + 5x}{x^2 + 5x + 6} \div \dfrac{x^2 + 2x - 15}{x^2 - 9}$

48. $\dfrac{14x - 7}{x^2 + 3x - 4} \cdot \dfrac{x^2 + 6x + 8}{2x^2 + 5x - 3} \div \dfrac{x^2 + 2x}{x^2 + 2x - 3}$

49. $\dfrac{x^2 + 5x}{3x - 6} \cdot \dfrac{x^2 - 4}{3x^2 + 15x} \cdot \dfrac{6x}{x^2 + 6x + 8}$

50. $\dfrac{m^2 - n^2}{m^2 - mn} \cdot \dfrac{6m}{2m^2 + mn - n^2} \cdot \dfrac{8m - 4n}{12m^2 + 12mn}$

51. **STATISTICS** Herbicides constitute $\frac{2}{3}$ of all pesticides used in the United States. Insecticides are $\frac{1}{4}$ of all pesticides used in the United States. The ratio of herbicides to insecticides used in the United States can be written as $\frac{2}{3} \div \frac{1}{4}$. Write this ratio in simplest form.

52. **STATISTICS** Fungicides account for $\frac{1}{10}$ of the pesticides used in the United States. Insecticides account for $\frac{1}{4}$ of all the pesticides used in the United States. The ratio of fungicides to insecticides used in the United States can be written as $\frac{1}{10} \div \frac{1}{4}$. Write this ratio in simplest form.

53. **STATISTICS** The ratio of insecticides to herbicides applied to wheat, soybeans, corn, and cotton can be expressed as $\frac{7}{10} \div \frac{4}{5}$. Simplify this ratio.

Answers

45. $\dfrac{x + 2}{x(x + 3)}$

46. $\dfrac{1}{w(w - 1)}$

47. $\dfrac{x}{2}$

48. $\dfrac{7}{x}$

49. $\dfrac{2x}{3(x + 4)}$

50. $\dfrac{2}{m(m + n)}$

51. $\dfrac{8}{3}$

52. $\dfrac{2}{5}$

53. $\dfrac{7}{8}$

Answers

54. $\dfrac{2(3x - 2)}{x - 1}$

55. $\dfrac{2}{3}$

54. GEOMETRY Find the area of the rectangle shown.

$\dfrac{2x - 4}{x - 1}$

$\dfrac{3x - 2}{x - 2}$

55. GEOMETRY Find the area of the rectangle shown.

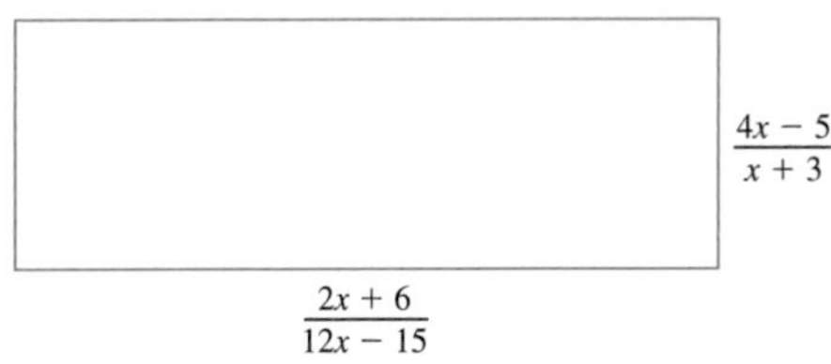

Answers

1. $\frac{2}{x}$ **3.** $\frac{3}{a^4}$ **5.** $\frac{5}{12x}$ **7.** $\frac{16b^3}{3a}$ **9.** $5mn$ **11.** $\frac{15x}{2}$ **13.** $\frac{9b}{8}$

15. $x(x + 2)$ **17.** $\frac{3(c - 2)}{5}$ **19.** $\frac{5x}{2(x - 2)}$ **21.** $\frac{5d}{4(d - 3)}$

23. $\frac{x - 5}{2x + 3}$ **25.** $\frac{2a + 1}{2a}$ **27.** $\frac{-6}{w + 2}$ **29.** $\frac{-a}{6}$

31. **(a)** -4; **(b)** undefined; **(c)** $(x + 1)(x - 4), x \neq -2, 4$; **(d)** -4; **(e)** undefined

33. **(a)** -6; **(b)** undefined; **(c)** $(2x - 5)(3x - 1), x \neq -2, -1$; **(d)** -6; **(e)** undefined

35. **(a)** $-\frac{4}{5}$; **(b)** $\frac{5}{4}$; **(c)** $\frac{(3x - 2)(x + 4)}{(x - 2)(x - 5)}, x \neq -4, -1, 2, 5$; **(d)** $2, -4, -1, 5$

37. $\frac{2}{x}$ **39.** $\frac{3}{m}$ **41.** $\frac{5}{x}$ **43.** $\frac{x^2 + 2}{4}$ **45.** $\frac{x + 2}{x(x + 3)}$

47. $\frac{x}{2}$ **49.** $\frac{2x}{3(x + 4)}$ **51.** $\frac{8}{3}$ **53.** $\frac{7}{8}$ **55.** $\frac{2}{3}$

6.3 Addition and Subtraction of Rational Expressions and Functions

< 6.3 Objectives >

1 > Add two rational expressions

2 > Subtract two rational expressions

3 > Add two rational functions

4 > Subtract two rational functions

Recall that adding or subtracting two arithmetic fractions with the same denominator is straightforward. The same is true in algebra. To add or subtract two rational expressions with the same denominator, we add or subtract their numerators and then write that sum or difference over the common denominator.

Property

Adding or Subtracting Rational Expressions

$$\frac{P}{R} + \frac{Q}{R} = \frac{P + Q}{R}$$

and

$$\frac{P}{R} - \frac{Q}{R} = \frac{P - Q}{R}$$

when $R \neq 0$.

Example 1 Adding and Subtracting Rational Expressions

< Objectives 1 and 2 >

Perform the indicated operations.

$$\frac{3}{2a^2} - \frac{1}{2a^2} + \frac{5}{2a^2} = \frac{3 - 1 + 5}{2a^2}$$

$$= \frac{7}{2a^2}$$

NOTE

Because we have common denominators, we simply perform the indicated operations on the numerators.

Check Yourself 1

Perform the indicated operations.

$$\frac{5}{3y^2} + \frac{4}{3y^2} - \frac{7}{3y^2}$$

The sum or difference of rational expressions should always be expressed in simplest form. Consider Example 2.

Example 2 Adding and Subtracting Rational Expressions

Add or subtract as indicated.

(a) $\frac{5x}{x^2 - 9} + \frac{15}{x^2 - 9}$ Add the numerators.

$= \frac{5x + 15}{x^2 - 9}$

$= \frac{5\overset{1}{\cancel{(x + 3)}}}{(x - 3)\underset{1}{\cancel{(x + 3)}}} = \frac{5}{x - 3}$ Factor and divide by the common factor.

(b) $\frac{3x + y}{2x} - \frac{x - 3y}{2x} = \frac{(3x + y) - (x - 3y)}{2x}$ Be sure to *enclose the second numerator* in parentheses.

$= \frac{3x + y - x + 3y}{2x}$ Remove the parentheses by *changing each sign.*

$= \frac{2x + 4y}{2x}$ Combine like terms.

$= \frac{\overset{1}{\cancel{2}}(x + 2y)}{\underset{1}{\cancel{2}}x}$ Factor and divide by the common factor of 2.

$= \frac{x + 2y}{x}$

Check Yourself 2

Perform the indicated operations.

(a) $\frac{6a}{a^2 - 2a - 8} + \frac{12}{a^2 - 2a - 8}$ **(b)** $\frac{5x - y}{3y} - \frac{2x - 4y}{3y}$

NOTE

By **inspection,** we mean you look at the denominators and find that the LCD is obvious (as in Example 2).

Now, what if our rational expressions *do not* have common denominators? In that case, we must use the least common denominator (LCD). The **least common denominator** is the simplest polynomial that is divisible by each of the individual denominators. Each expression in the desired sum or difference is then "built up" to an equivalent expression having that LCD as a denominator. We can then add or subtract as before.

Although in many cases we can find the LCD by inspection, we can state an algorithm for finding the LCD that is similar to the one used in arithmetic.

Step by Step

Finding the Least Common Denominator

Step 1 Write each of the denominators in completely factored form.

Step 2 Write the LCD as the product of each prime factor to the highest power to which it appears in the factored form of any individual denominator.

Example 3 illustrates the procedure.

Example 3 Finding the LCD for Two Rational Expressions

Find the LCD for each of the following pairs of rational expressions.

(a) $\dfrac{3}{4x^2}$ and $\dfrac{5}{6xy}$

Factor the denominators.

$4x^2 = 2^2 \cdot x^2$

$6xy = 2 \cdot 3 \cdot x \cdot y$

The LCD must have the factors

$2^2 \cdot 3 \cdot x^2 \cdot y$

and so $12x^2y$ is the desired LCD.

NOTE

You may very well be able to find this LCD by inspecting the numerical coefficients and the variable factors.

(b) $\dfrac{7}{x - 3}$ and $\dfrac{2}{x + 5}$

Here, neither denominator can be factored. The LCD must have the factors $x - 3$ and $x + 5$. So the LCD is

$(x - 3)(x + 5)$

NOTE

It is generally best to leave the LCD in this factored form to help with simplifying (see Example 6).

Check Yourself 3

Find the LCD for the following pairs of rational expressions.

(a) $\dfrac{3}{8a^3}$ and $\dfrac{5}{6a^2}$ **(b)** $\dfrac{4}{x + 7}$ and $\dfrac{3}{x - 5}$

Let us see how factoring techniques are applied in Example 4.

Example 4 Finding the LCD for Two Rational Expressions

Find the LCD for the following pairs of rational expressions.

(a) $\dfrac{2}{x^2 - x - 6}$ and $\dfrac{1}{x^2 - 9}$

Factoring, we have

$x^2 - x - 6 = (x + 2)(x - 3)$

and

$x^2 - 9 = (x + 3)(x - 3)$

The LCD of the given expressions is then

$(x + 2)(x - 3)(x + 3)$

NOTES

The LCD must contain *each* of the factors appearing in the original denominators.

Because $(x - 3)$ appears only once in each denominator, it appears only once in the LCD.

(b) $\dfrac{5}{x^2 - 4x + 4}$ and $\dfrac{3}{x^2 + 2x - 8}$

NOTE

The LCD must contain $(x - 2)^2$ as a factor because $x - 2$ appears *twice* as a factor in the first denominator.

Again, we factor:

$x^2 - 4x + 4 = (x - 2)^2$

$x^2 + 2x - 8 = (x - 2)(x + 4)$

The LCD is then

$(x - 2)^2 (x + 4)$

Check Yourself 4

Find the LCD for the following pairs of rational expressions.

(a) $\dfrac{3}{x^2 - 2x - 15}$ and $\dfrac{5}{x^2 - 25}$

(b) $\dfrac{5}{y^2 + 6y + 9}$ and $\dfrac{3}{y^2 - y - 12}$

Let us look at Example 5, in which the concept of the LCD is applied in adding and subtracting rational expressions.

Example 5 Adding and Subtracting Rational Expressions

Add or subtract as indicated.

(a) $\dfrac{5}{4xy} + \dfrac{3}{2x^2}$

The LCD for $2x^2$ and $4xy$ is $4x^2y$. We rewrite each of the rational expressions with the LCD as a denominator.

NOTE

Notice that in each case we are multiplying by 1: $\frac{x}{x}$ in the first fraction and $\frac{2y}{2y}$ in the second fraction, which is why the resulting fractions are equivalent to the original ones.

$$\frac{5}{4xy} + \frac{3}{2x^2} = \frac{5 \cdot x}{4xy \cdot x} + \frac{3 \cdot 2y}{2x^2 \cdot 2y}$$

$$= \frac{5x}{4x^2y} + \frac{6y}{4x^2y} = \frac{5x + 6y}{4x^2y}$$

Multiply the first rational expression by $\frac{x}{x}$ and the second by $\frac{2y}{2y}$ to form the LCD of $4x^2y$.

(b) $\dfrac{3}{a - 3} - \dfrac{2}{a}$

The LCD for a and $a - 3$ is $a(a - 3)$. We rewrite each of the rational expressions with that LCD as a denominator.

$$\frac{3}{a - 3} - \frac{2}{a}$$

$$= \frac{3a}{a(a - 3)} - \frac{2(a - 3)}{a(a - 3)}$$

Subtract the numerators.

$$= \frac{3a - 2(a - 3)}{a(a - 3)}$$

Remove the parentheses in the numerator, and combine like terms.

$$= \frac{3a - 2a + 6}{a(a - 3)} = \frac{a + 6}{a(a - 3)}$$

Check Yourself 5

Perform the indicated operations.

(a) $\dfrac{3}{2ab} + \dfrac{4}{5b^2}$ (b) $\dfrac{5}{y+2} - \dfrac{3}{y}$

Let us proceed to Example 6, in which factoring will be required in forming the LCD.

Example 6 Adding and Subtracting Rational Expressions

Add or subtract as indicated.

(a) $\dfrac{-5}{x^2 - 3x - 4} + \dfrac{8}{x^2 - 16}$

We first factor the two denominators.

$$x^2 - 3x - 4 = (x+1)(x-4)$$
$$x^2 - 16 = (x+4)(x-4)$$

We see that the LCD must be

$$(x+1)(x+4)(x-4)$$

Again, rewriting the original expressions with factored denominators gives

$$\frac{-5}{(x+1)(x-4)} + \frac{8}{(x-4)(x+4)}$$

$$= \frac{-5(x+4)}{(x+1)(x-4)(x+4)} + \frac{8(x+1)}{(x-4)(x+4)(x+1)}$$

$$= \frac{-5(x+4) + 8(x+1)}{(x+1)(x-4)(x+4)}$$ Now add the numerators.

$$= \frac{-5x - 20 + 8x + 8}{(x+1)(x-4)(x+4)}$$ Combine like terms in the numerator.

$$= \frac{3x - 12}{(x+1)(x-4)(x+4)}$$ Factor.

$$= \frac{3\overset{1}{\cancel{(x-4)}}}{(x+1)\underset{1}{\cancel{(x-4)}}(x+4)}$$ Divide by the common factor $x - 4$.

$$= \frac{3}{(x+1)(x+4)}$$

NOTE

We use the facts that

$\dfrac{x+4}{x+4} = 1$ and $\dfrac{x+1}{x+1} = 1$

(b) $\dfrac{5}{x^2 - 5x + 6} - \dfrac{3}{4x - 12}$

Again, factor the denominators.

$$x^2 - 5x + 6 = (x-2)(x-3)$$
$$4x - 12 = 4(x-3)$$

The LCD is $4(x - 2)(x - 3)$, and proceeding as before, we have

$$\frac{5}{(x-2)(x-3)} - \frac{3}{4(x-3)}$$

$$= \frac{5 \cdot 4}{4(x-2)(x-3)} - \frac{3(x-2)}{4(x-2)(x-3)}$$

$$= \frac{20 - 3(x-2)}{4(x-2)(x-3)}$$

$$= \frac{20 - 3x + 6}{4(x-2)(x-3)} = \frac{-3x + 26}{4(x-2)(x-3)}$$

Simplify the numerator and combine like terms.

Check Yourself 6

Add or subtract as indicated.

(a) $\frac{-4}{x^2 - 4} + \frac{7}{x^2 - 3x - 10}$ **(b)** $\frac{5}{3x - 9} - \frac{2}{x^2 - 9}$

Example 7 looks slightly different from those you have seen thus far, but the reasoning involved in performing the subtraction is exactly the same.

Example 7 Subtracting Rational Expressions

Subtract.

$$3 - \frac{5}{2x - 1}$$

To perform the subtraction, remember that 3 is equivalent to the fraction $\frac{3}{1}$, so

$$3 - \frac{5}{2x-1} = \frac{3}{1} - \frac{5}{2x-1}$$

The LCD for 1 and $2x - 1$ is just $2x - 1$. We now rewrite the first expression with that denominator.

$$3 - \frac{5}{2x-1} = \frac{3(2x-1)}{(2x-1)} - \frac{5}{2x-1}$$

$$= \frac{3(2x-1) - 5}{2x-1} = \frac{6x - 3 - 5}{2x-1} = \frac{6x - 8}{2x - 1}$$

Check Yourself 7

Subtract.

$$\frac{4}{3x + 1} - 3$$

Example 8 uses an observation from Section 6.1. Recall that

$$a - b = -(b - a)$$
$$= -1(b - a)$$

Let us see how this is used in adding rational expressions.

Example 8 Adding and Subtracting Rational Expressions

Add.

$$\frac{x^2}{x - 5} + \frac{3x + 10}{5 - x}$$

Your first thought might be to use a denominator of $(x - 5)(5 - x)$. However, we can simplify our work considerably if we multiply the numerator and denominator of the second fraction by -1 to find a common denominator.

NOTES

Use $\frac{-1}{-1} = 1$.

Notice that $(-1)(5 - x) = x - 5$. The fractions now have a common denominator, and we can add as before.

$$\frac{x^2}{x - 5} + \frac{3x + 10}{5 - x}$$
$$= \frac{x^2}{x - 5} + \frac{(-1)(3x + 10)}{(-1)(5 - x)}$$
$$= \frac{x^2}{x - 5} + \frac{-3x - 10}{x - 5}$$
$$= \frac{x^2 - 3x - 10}{x - 5}$$
$$= \frac{(x + 2)\overset{1}{\cancel{(x - 5)}}}{\underset{1}{\cancel{x - 5}}}$$
$$= x + 2$$

Check Yourself 8

Add.

$$\frac{x^2}{x - 7} + \frac{10x - 21}{7 - x}$$

The sum of two rational functions is always a rational function. Given two rational functions, $f(x)$ and $g(x)$, we can rename the sum, so $h(x) = f(x) + g(x)$. This will always be true for values of x for which both f and g are defined. So, for example, $h(-2) = f(-2) + g(-2)$, so long as both $f(-2)$ and $g(-2)$ exist.

Example 9 illustrates this approach.

Example 9 Adding Two Rational Functions

< Objective 3 >

Given

$$f(x) = \frac{3x}{x + 5} \quad \text{and} \quad g(x) = \frac{x}{x - 4}$$

complete the following.

(a) Find $f(1) + g(1)$.

Because $f(1) = \frac{1}{2}$ and $g(1) = -\frac{1}{3}$, then

$$f(1) + g(1) = \frac{1}{2} + \left(-\frac{1}{3}\right)$$
$$= \frac{3}{6} + \left(-\frac{2}{6}\right)$$
$$= \frac{1}{6}$$

(b) Find $h(x) = f(x) + g(x)$.

$$h(x) = \frac{3x}{x + 5} + \frac{x}{x - 4}$$
$$= \frac{3x(x - 4) + x(x + 5)}{(x + 5)(x - 4)}$$
$$= \frac{3x^2 - 12x + x^2 + 5x}{(x + 5)(x - 4)}$$
$$= \frac{4x^2 - 7x}{(x + 5)(x - 4)} \qquad x \neq -5, 4$$

(c) Find the ordered pair $(1, h(1))$.

$$h(1) = \frac{-3}{-18} = \frac{1}{6}$$

The ordered pair is $\left(1, \frac{1}{6}\right)$.

Check Yourself 9

Given

$$f(x) = \frac{x}{2x - 5} \quad \text{and} \quad g(x) = \frac{2x}{3x - 1}$$

complete the following.

(a) Find $f(1) + g(1)$.
(b) Find $h(x) = f(x) + g(x)$.
(c) Find the ordered pair $(1, h(1))$.

When subtracting rational functions, you must take particular care with the signs in the numerator of the expression being subtracted.

Example 10 Subtracting Rational Functions

< Objective 4 >

Given

$$f(x) = \frac{3x}{x + 5} \quad \text{and} \quad g(x) = \frac{x - 2}{x - 4}$$

complete the following.

(a) Find $f(1) - g(1)$.

Because $f(1) = \frac{1}{2}$ and $g(1) = \frac{1}{3}$, then

$$\begin{aligned} f(1) - g(1) &= \frac{1}{2} - \frac{1}{3} \\ &= \frac{3}{6} - \frac{2}{6} \\ &= \frac{1}{6} \end{aligned}$$

(b) Find $h(x) = f(x) - g(x)$.

$$\begin{aligned} h(x) &= \frac{3x}{x + 5} - \frac{x - 2}{x - 4} \\ &= \frac{3x(x - 4) - (x - 2)(x + 5)}{(x + 5)(x - 4)} \\ &= \frac{(3x^2 - 12x) - (x^2 + 3x - 10)}{(x + 5)(x - 4)} \\ &= \frac{2x^2 - 15x + 10}{(x + 5)(x - 4)} \qquad x \neq -5, 4 \end{aligned}$$

(c) Find the ordered pair $(1, h(1))$.

$$h(1) = \frac{-3}{-18} = \frac{1}{6}$$

The ordered pair is $\left(1, \frac{1}{6}\right)$.

Check Yourself 10

Given

$$f(x) = \frac{x}{2x - 5} \quad \text{and} \quad g(x) = \frac{2x - 1}{3x - 1}$$

complete the following.

(a) Find $f(1) - g(1)$.
(b) Find $h(x) = f(x) - g(x)$.
(c) Find the ordered pair $(1, h(1))$.

Check Yourself ANSWERS

1. $\frac{2}{3y^2}$ **2. (a)** $\frac{6}{a-4}$; **(b)** $\frac{x+y}{y}$ **3. (a)** $24a^3$; **(b)** $(x+7)(x-5)$
4. (a) $(x-5)(x+5)(x+3)$; **(b)** $(y+3)^2(y-4)$
5. (a) $\frac{8a+15b}{10ab^2}$; **(b)** $\frac{2y-6}{y(y+2)}$ **6. (a)** $\frac{3}{(x-2)(x-5)}$;
(b) $\frac{5x+9}{3(x+3)(x-3)}$ **7.** $\frac{-9x+1}{3x+1}$ **8.** $x-3$
9. (a) $\frac{2}{3}$; **(b)** $h(x) = \frac{7x^2-11x}{(2x-5)(3x-1)}$, $x \neq \frac{1}{3}, \frac{5}{2}$; **(c)** $\left(1, \frac{2}{3}\right)$
10. (a) $-\frac{5}{6}$; **(b)** $h(x) = \frac{-x^2+11x-5}{(2x-5)(3x-1)}$, $x \neq \frac{1}{3}, \frac{5}{2}$; **(c)** $\left(1, -\frac{5}{6}\right)$

Reading Your Text

The following fill-in-the-blank exercises are designed to ensure that you understand some of the key vocabulary used in this section.

SECTION 6.3

(a) To add or subtract two rational expressions with the same denominator, we add or subtract their ______________ and then write that result over the ______________.

(b) When adding rational expressions, the final step is to write the result in ______________ form.

(c) Rational expressions can be simplified if the numerator and denominator have a common ______________.

(d) The sum of two rational functions is always a ______________ function.

Basic Skills | Advanced Skills | Vocational-Technical Applications | Calculator/Computer | Above and Beyond

6.3 exercises

< Objectives 1 and 2 >

Perform the indicated operations. Express your results in simplest form.

1. $\frac{7}{2x^2} + \frac{5}{2x^2}$

2. $\frac{11}{3b^3} - \frac{2}{3b^3}$

3. $\frac{5}{3a + 7} + \frac{2}{3a + 7}$

4. $\frac{6}{5x + 3} - \frac{3}{5x + 3}$

5. $\frac{2x}{x - 3} - \frac{6}{x - 3}$

6. $\frac{7w}{w + 3} + \frac{21}{w + 3}$

7. $\frac{y^2}{2y + 8} + \frac{3y - 4}{2y + 8}$

8. $\frac{x^2}{4x - 12} - \frac{9}{4x - 12}$

9. $\frac{4m - 7}{m - 5} - \frac{2m + 3}{m - 5}$

10. $\frac{3b - 8}{b - 6} + \frac{b - 16}{b - 6}$

11. $\frac{x - 7}{x^2 - x - 6} + \frac{2x - 2}{x^2 - x - 6}$

12. $\frac{5x - 12}{x^2 - 8x + 15} - \frac{3x - 2}{x^2 - 8x + 15}$

13. $\frac{5}{3x} + \frac{3}{2x}$

14. $\frac{4}{5w} - \frac{3}{4w}$

15. $\frac{6}{a} + \frac{3}{a^2}$

16. $\frac{3}{p} - \frac{7}{p^2}$

17. $\frac{2}{m} - \frac{2}{n}$

18. $\frac{3}{x} + \frac{3}{y}$

19. $\frac{3}{4b^2} - \frac{5}{3b^3}$

20. $\frac{4}{5x^3} - \frac{3}{2x^2}$

21. $\frac{2}{a} - \frac{1}{a - 2}$

22. $\frac{4}{c} + \frac{3}{c + 1}$

23. $\frac{2}{x + 1} + \frac{3}{x + 2}$

24. $\frac{4}{y - 1} + \frac{2}{y + 3}$

Name ______________

Section ________ Date ________

Answers

1. $\frac{6}{x^2}$
2. $\frac{3}{b^3}$
3. $\frac{7}{3a + 7}$
4. $\frac{3}{5x + 3}$
5. 2
6. 7
7. $\frac{y - 1}{2}$
8. $\frac{x + 3}{4}$
9. 2
10. 4
11. $\frac{3}{x + 2}$
12. $\frac{2}{x - 3}$
13. $\frac{19}{6x}$
14. $\frac{1}{20w}$
15. $\frac{6a + 3}{a^2}$
16. $\frac{3p - 7}{p^2}$
17. $\frac{2n - 2m}{mn}$
18. $\frac{3x + 3y}{xy}$
19. $\frac{9b - 20}{12b^3}$
20. $\frac{8 - 15x}{10x^3}$
21. $\frac{a - 4}{a(a - 2)}$
22. $\frac{7c + 4}{c(c + 1)}$
23. $\frac{5x + 7}{(x + 1)(x + 2)}$
24. $\frac{6y + 10}{(y + 3)(y - 1)}$

Answers

25. $\frac{12x + 5}{3x + 2}$

26. $\frac{-12x - 19}{2x + 3}$

27. $\frac{3w^2 - 11w}{(w - 7)(w - 2)}$

28. $\frac{4n^2 - 7n}{(n + 5)(n - 4)}$

29. $\frac{7x}{(3x - 2)(2x + 1)}$

30. $\frac{7}{x - 1}$

31. $\frac{4}{m - 7}$

32. $\frac{8}{a - 5}$

33. 1

34. $\frac{2y + 11}{(y + 2)(y + 3)}$

35. $\frac{3m + 1}{(m - 1)(m - 2)}$

36. $\frac{-x - 2}{(x + 1)(x - 1)}$

37. (a) $\frac{1}{2}$; (b) $\frac{5x^2 - 7x}{(x + 1)(x - 3)}$; (c) $\left(1, \frac{1}{2}\right)$

38. (a) $\frac{7}{6}$; (b) $\frac{5x^2 + 4x - 16}{(x - 4)(x + 1)}$; (c) $\left(1, \frac{7}{6}\right)$

39. (a) $\frac{3}{4}$; (b) $\frac{x^2 + x + 1}{(x + 1)^2}$; (c) $\left(1, \frac{3}{4}\right)$

40. (a) $-\frac{1}{5}$; (b) $\frac{2x^2 + 5x - 4}{x^2 - 16}$; (c) $\left(1, -\frac{1}{5}\right)$

25. $4 - \frac{3}{3x + 2}$

26. $-6 - \frac{1}{2x + 3}$

27. $\frac{2w}{w - 7} + \frac{w}{w - 2}$

28. $\frac{3n}{n + 5} + \frac{n}{n - 4}$

29. $\frac{3x}{3x - 2} - \frac{2x}{2x + 1}$

30. $\frac{4}{x - 1} - \frac{3}{1 - x}$

31. $\frac{6}{m - 7} + \frac{2}{7 - m}$

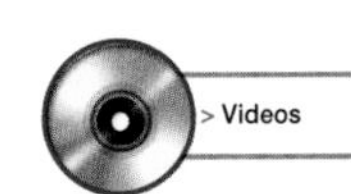

32. $\frac{5}{a - 5} - \frac{3}{5 - a}$

33. $\frac{2x}{2x - 3} + \frac{3}{3 - 2x}$

34. $\frac{5}{y^2 + 5y + 6} + \frac{2}{y + 2}$

35. $\frac{4m}{m^2 - 3m + 2} - \frac{1}{m - 2}$

36. $\frac{x}{x^2 - 1} - \frac{2}{x - 1}$

< Objective 3 >

In exercises 37 to 40, find **(a)** $f(1) + g(1)$, **(b)** $h(x) = f(x) + g(x)$, *and* **(c)** *the ordered pair* $(1, h(1))$.

37. $f(x) = \frac{3x}{x + 1}$ and $g(x) = \frac{2x}{x - 3}$

38. $f(x) = \frac{4x}{x - 4}$ and $g(x) = \frac{x + 4}{x + 1}$

39. $f(x) = \frac{x}{x + 1}$ and $g(x) = \frac{1}{x^2 + 2x + 1}$

40. $f(x) = \frac{x + 2}{x - 4}$ and $g(x) = \frac{x + 3}{x + 4}$

< Objective 4 >

In exercises 41 to 44, find **(a)** $f(1) - g(1)$, **(b)** $h(x) = f(x) - g(x)$, *and* **(c)** *the ordered pair* $(1, h(1))$.

41. $f(x) = \dfrac{x+5}{x-5}$ and $g(x) = \dfrac{x-5}{x+5}$

42. $f(x) = \dfrac{2x}{x-4}$ and $g(x) = \dfrac{3x}{x+7}$

43. $f(x) = \dfrac{x+9}{4x-36}$ and $g(x) = \dfrac{x-9}{x^2-18x+81}$

44. $f(x) = \dfrac{4x+1}{x+5}$ and $g(x) = -\dfrac{2}{x}$

In exercises 45 to 54, evaluate each expression at the given variable value(s).

45. $\dfrac{5x+5}{x^2+3x+2} - \dfrac{x-3}{x^2+5x+6}$, $x = -4$

46. $\dfrac{y-3}{y^2-6y+8} + \dfrac{2y-6}{y^2-4}$, $y = 3$

47. $\dfrac{2m+2n}{m^2-n^2} + \dfrac{m-2n}{m^2+2mn+n^2}$, $m = 3, n = 2$

48. $\dfrac{w-3z}{w^2-2wz+z^2} - \dfrac{w+2z}{w^2-z^2}$, $w = 2, z = 1$

49. $\dfrac{1}{a-3} - \dfrac{1}{a+3} + \dfrac{2a}{a^2-9}$, $a = 4$

50. $\dfrac{1}{m+1} + \dfrac{1}{m-3} - \dfrac{4}{m^2-2m-3}$, $m = -2$

51. $\dfrac{3w^2+16w-8}{w^2+2w-8} + \dfrac{w}{w+4} - \dfrac{w-1}{w-2}$, $w = 3$

52. $\dfrac{4x^2-7x-45}{x^2-6x+5} - \dfrac{x+2}{x-1} - \dfrac{x}{x-5}$, $x = -3$

53. $\dfrac{a^2-9}{2a^2-5a-3} \cdot \left(\dfrac{1}{a-2} + \dfrac{1}{a+3}\right)$, $a = -3$

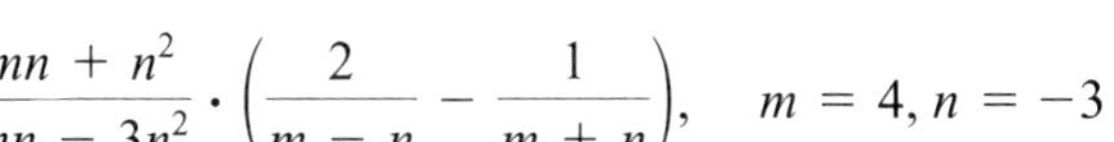

54. $\dfrac{m^2-2mn+n^2}{m^2+2mn-3n^2} \cdot \left(\dfrac{2}{m-n} - \dfrac{1}{m+n}\right)$, $m = 4, n = -3$

Answers

41. (a) $-\dfrac{5}{6}$; (b) $\dfrac{20x}{(x-5)(x+5)}$; (c) $\left(1, -\dfrac{5}{6}\right)$

42. (a) $-\dfrac{25}{24}$; (b) $\dfrac{-x^2+26x}{(x-4)(x+7)}$; (c) $\left(1, -\dfrac{25}{24}\right)$

43. (a) $-\dfrac{3}{16}$; (b) $\dfrac{(x+5)}{4(x-9)}$; (c) $\left(1, -\dfrac{3}{16}\right)$

44. (a) $\dfrac{17}{6}$; (b) $\dfrac{4x^2+3x+10}{x(x+5)}$; (c) $\left(1, \dfrac{17}{6}\right)$

45. 1

46. 0

47. $\dfrac{49}{25}$

48. $-\dfrac{7}{3}$

49. 2

50. −2

51. 8

52. $-\dfrac{1}{4}$

53. Undefined

54. 1

Basic Skills | Advanced Skills | Vocational-Technical Applications | **Calculator/Computer** | Above and Beyond

As we saw in Section 6.2 exercises, the graphing calculator can be used to check our work. To do this, enter the first rational expression in Y_1 and the second in Y_2. In Y_3, you will enter either $Y_1 + Y_2$ or $Y_1 - Y_2$. Enter your algebraically simplified rational expression in Y_4. The graphs of Y_3 and Y_4 will be identical if you have correctly simplified the expression. On the TI-84, to access the Y_1 and Y_2 variables for your equations, use the following path:

Y-VARS
1: Function

Use this technique in exercises 55 to 60.

55. $\dfrac{6y}{y^2 - 8y + 15} + \dfrac{9}{y - 3}$

56. $\dfrac{8a}{a^2 - 8a + 12} + \dfrac{4}{a - 2}$

57. $\dfrac{6x}{x^2 - 10x + 24} - \dfrac{18}{x - 6}$

58. $\dfrac{21p}{p^2 - 3p - 10} - \dfrac{15}{p - 5}$

59. $\dfrac{2}{z^2 - 4} + \dfrac{3}{z^2 + 2z - 8}$

60. $\dfrac{5}{x^2 - 3x - 10} + \dfrac{2}{x^2 - 25}$

Basic Skills | Advanced Skills | Vocational-Technical Applications | Calculator/Computer | **Above and Beyond**

Add or subtract, as indicated. Express your results in simplest form.

61. $\dfrac{1}{a - 3} - \dfrac{1}{a + 3} + \dfrac{2a}{a^2 - 9}$

62. $\dfrac{1}{p + 1} + \dfrac{1}{p - 3} - \dfrac{4}{p^2 - 2p - 3}$

63. **Geometry** Find the perimeter of the given figure.

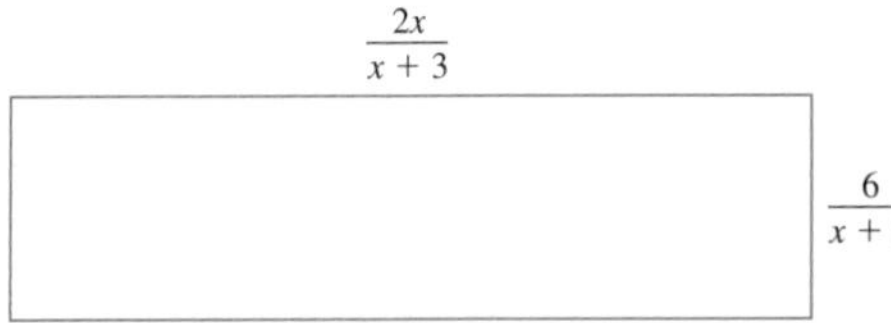

64. **Geometry** Find the perimeter of the given figure.

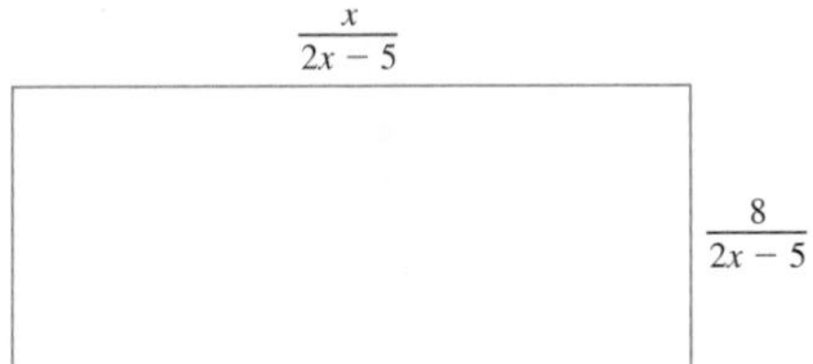

Answers

55. $\dfrac{15}{y - 5}$

56. $\dfrac{12}{a - 6}$

57. $\dfrac{-12}{x - 4}$

58. $\dfrac{6}{p + 2}$

59. $\dfrac{5z + 14}{(z + 2)(z - 2)(z + 4)}$

60. $\dfrac{7x + 29}{(x + 5)(x - 5)(x + 2)}$

61. $\dfrac{2}{a - 3}$

62. $\dfrac{2}{p + 1}$

63. 4

64. $\dfrac{2x + 16}{2x - 5}$

65. **Number Problem** Use a rational expression to represent the sum of the reciprocals of two consecutive even integers. Let x represent the first even integer.

66. **Number Problem** One number is two less than another. Use a rational expression to represent the sum of the reciprocals of the two numbers. Let x represent the first number.

67. **Geometry** Refer to the rectangle in the figure. Find an expression that represents its perimeter.

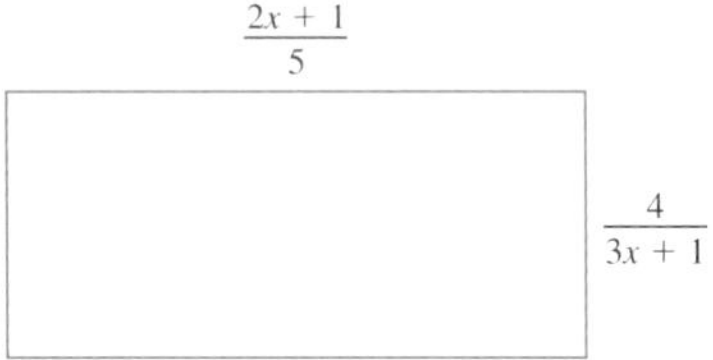

68. **Geometry** Refer to the triangle in the figure. Find an expression that represents its perimeter.

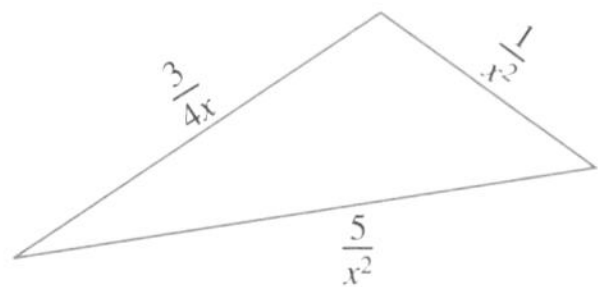

Answers

65. $\dfrac{2x+2}{x(x+2)}$

66. $\dfrac{2x-2}{x(x-2)}$

67. $\dfrac{12x^2+10x+42}{5(3x+1)}$

68. $\dfrac{3x+24}{4x^2}$

Probability and Pari-Mutual Betting

In most gambling games, payoffs are determined by the **odds.** At horse and dog tracks, the odds (D) are a ratio that is calculated by taking into account the total amount wagered (A), the amount wagered on a particular animal (a), and the government share, called the take-out (f). The ratio is then rounded down to a comparison of integers like 99 to 1, 3 to 1, or 5 to 2. Following is the formula that tracks use to find odds.

$$D = \frac{A(1-f)}{a} - 1$$

Work with a partner to complete the following.

1. Assume that the government takes 10%, and simplify the expression for D. Use this formula to compute the odds on each horse if a total of \$10,000 was bet on all the horses and the amounts were distributed as shown in the table.

Horse	Total Amount Wagered on This Horse to Win	Odds: Amount Paid on Each Dollar Bet If Horse Wins
1	\$5,000	
2	\$1,000	
3	\$2,000	
4	\$1,500	
5	\$ 500	

2. Odds can be used as a guide in determining the chance that a given horse will win. The probability of a horse winning is related to many variables, such as track condition, how the horse is feeling, and weather. However, the odds do reflect the consensus opinion of racing fans and can be used to give some idea of the probability.

The relationship between odds and probability is given by the equations

$$P(\text{win}) = \frac{1}{D + 1}$$

and $P(\text{loss}) = 1 - P(\text{win})$

or $P(\text{loss}) = 1 - \dfrac{1}{D + 1}$

Solve this equation for D, the odds against the horse winning. Do the probabilities for each horse winning all add up to 1? Should they add to 1?

Answers

1. $\frac{6}{x^2}$ **3.** $\frac{7}{3a + 7}$ **5.** 2 **7.** $\frac{y - 1}{2}$ **9.** 2 **11.** $\frac{3}{x + 2}$

13. $\frac{19}{6x}$ **15.** $\frac{6a + 3}{a^2}$ **17.** $\frac{2n - 2m}{mn}$ **9.** $\frac{9b - 20}{12b^3}$

21. $\frac{a - 4}{a(a - 2)}$ **23.** $\frac{5x + 7}{(x + 1)(x + 2)}$ **25.** $\frac{12x + 5}{3x + 2}$

27. $\frac{3w^2 - 11w}{(w - 7)(w - 2)}$ **29.** $\frac{7x}{(3x - 2)(2x + 1)}$ **31.** $\frac{4}{m - 7}$ **33.** 1

35. $\frac{3m + 1}{(m - 1)(m - 2)}$ **37. (a)** $\frac{1}{2}$; **(b)** $\frac{5x^2 - 7x}{(x + 1)(x - 3)}$; **(c)** $\left(1, \frac{1}{2}\right)$

39. (a) $\frac{3}{4}$; **(b)** $\frac{x^2 + x + 1}{(x + 1)^2}$; **(c)** $\left(1, \frac{3}{4}\right)$

41. (a) $-\frac{5}{6}$; **(b)** $\frac{20x}{(x - 5)(x + 5)}$; **(c)** $\left(1, -\frac{5}{6}\right)$

43. (a) $-\frac{3}{16}$; **(b)** $\frac{x + 5}{4(x - 9)}$; **(c)** $\left(1, -\frac{3}{16}\right)$ **45.** 1 **47.** $\frac{49}{25}$ **49.** 2

51. 8 **53.** Undefined **55.** $\frac{15}{y - 5}$ **57.** $\frac{-12}{x - 4}$

59. $\frac{5z + 14}{(z + 2)(z - 2)(z + 4)}$ **61.** $\frac{2}{a - 3}$ **63.** 4 **65.** $\frac{2x + 2}{x(x + 2)}$

67. $\frac{12x^2 - 10x + 42}{5(3x + 1)}$

6.4 Complex Fractions

< 6.4 Objectives >

1 > Use the fundamental principle to simplify a complex fraction

2 > Use division to simplify a complex fraction

Our work in this section deals with two methods for simplifying complex fractions. We begin with a definition. A **complex fraction** is a fraction that has a fraction in its numerator or denominator (or both). Some examples are

$$\frac{\frac{5}{6}}{\frac{3}{4}}, \qquad \frac{\frac{4}{x}}{\frac{3}{x+1}}, \qquad \text{and} \qquad \frac{1+\frac{1}{x}}{1-\frac{1}{x}}.$$

> **NOTE**
>
> Fundamental principle:
>
> $\frac{P}{Q} = \frac{PR}{QR}$
>
> when $Q \neq 0$ and $R \neq 0$.

Two methods can be used to simplify complex fractions. Method 1 involves the fundamental principle, and Method 2 involves inverting and multiplying.

Recall that by the *fundamental principle* we can always multiply the numerator and denominator of a fraction by the same nonzero quantity. In simplifying a complex fraction, we multiply the numerator and denominator by the LCD of all fractions that appear within the complex fraction.

Here the denominators are 5 and 10, so we can write

> **NOTE**
>
> Again, we are multiplying by $\frac{10}{10}$ or 1.

$$\frac{\frac{3}{5}}{\frac{7}{10}} = \frac{\frac{3}{5}\cdot 10}{\frac{7}{10}\cdot 10} = \frac{6}{7}$$

Our second approach interprets the complex fraction as indicating division and applies our earlier work in dividing fractions in which we *invert and multiply.*

$$\frac{\frac{3}{5}}{\frac{7}{10}} = \frac{3}{5} \div \frac{7}{10} = \frac{3}{5} \cdot \frac{10}{7} = \frac{6}{7}$$ Invert and multiply.

Which method is better? The answer depends on the expression you are trying to simplify. Both approaches are effective, and you should be familiar with both. With practice you will be able to tell which method may be easier to use in a particular situation.

Let us look at the same two methods applied to the simplification of an algebraic complex fraction.

Example 1 Simplifying Complex Fractions

< Objective 1 >

Simplify.

$$\frac{1 + \frac{2x}{y}}{2 - \frac{x}{y}}$$

Method 1 The LCD of 1, $\frac{2x}{y}$, 2, and $\frac{x}{y}$ is y. So we multiply the numerator and denominator by y.

$$\frac{1 + \frac{2x}{y}}{2 - \frac{x}{y}} = \frac{\left(1 + \frac{2x}{y}\right) \cdot y}{\left(2 - \frac{x}{y}\right) \cdot y}$$ Distribute y over the numerator and denominator.

$$= \frac{1 \cdot y + \frac{2x}{y} \cdot y}{2 \cdot y - \frac{x}{y} \cdot y}$$ Simplify.

$$= \frac{y + 2x}{2y - x}$$

Method 2 In this approach, we must *first work separately* in the numerator and denominator to form single fractions.

NOTE

Make sure you understand the steps in forming a single fraction in the numerator and denominator. If necessary, review Section 6.3.

$$\frac{1 + \frac{2x}{y}}{2 - \frac{x}{y}} = \frac{\frac{y}{y} + \frac{2x}{y}}{\frac{2y}{y} - \frac{x}{y}} = \frac{\frac{y + 2x}{y}}{\frac{2y - x}{y}}$$

$$= \frac{y + 2x}{y} \cdot \frac{y}{2y - x}$$ Invert the divisor and multiply.

$$= \frac{y + 2x}{2y - x}$$

Check Yourself 1

Simplify.

$$\frac{\frac{x}{y} - 1}{\frac{2x}{y} + 2}$$

Again, simplifying a complex fraction means writing an equivalent simple fraction in lowest terms, as Example 2 illustrates.

Example 2 Simplifying Complex Fractions

Simplify.

$$\frac{1 - \frac{2y}{x} + \frac{y^2}{x^2}}{1 - \frac{y^2}{x^2}}$$

We choose the first method of simplification in this case. The LCD of all the fractions that appear is x^2. So we multiply the numerator and denominator by x^2.

$$\frac{1 - \frac{2y}{x} + \frac{y^2}{x^2}}{1 - \frac{y^2}{x^2}} = \frac{\left(1 - \frac{2y}{x} + \frac{y^2}{x^2}\right) \cdot x^2}{\left(1 - \frac{y^2}{x^2}\right) \cdot x^2}$$

Distribute x^2 over the numerator and denominator and simplify.

$$= \frac{x^2 - 2xy + y^2}{x^2 - y^2}$$

Factor the numerator and denominator.

$$= \frac{(x - y)\overset{1}{\cancel{(x - y)}}}{(x + y)\underset{1}{\cancel{(x - y)}}}$$

Divide by the common factor $x - y$.

$$= \frac{x - y}{x + y}$$

Check Yourself 2

Simplify.

$$\frac{1 + \frac{5}{x} + \frac{6}{x^2}}{1 - \frac{9}{x^2}}$$

In Example 3, we will illustrate the second method of simplification for purposes of comparison.

Example 3 Simplifying Complex Fractions

< Objective 2 >

Simplify.

$$\frac{1 - \frac{1}{x + 2}}{x - \frac{2}{x - 1}}$$

NOTE

Again, take time to make sure you understand how the numerator and denominator are rewritten as single fractions.

$$\frac{1 - \dfrac{1}{x + 2}}{x - \dfrac{2}{x - 1}} = \frac{\dfrac{x + 2}{x + 2} - \dfrac{1}{x + 2}}{\dfrac{x(x - 1)}{x - 1} - \dfrac{2}{x - 1}} = \frac{\dfrac{x + 1}{x + 2}}{\dfrac{x^2 - x - 2}{x - 1}}$$

Invert the divisor and multiply.

$$= \frac{x + 1}{x + 2} \cdot \frac{x - 1}{x^2 - x - 2}$$

Factor.

$$= \frac{\overset{1}{\cancel{x + 1}}}{x + 2} \cdot \frac{x - 1}{(x - 2)\underset{1}{\cancel{(x + 1)}}}$$

Divide by the common factor $x + 1$.

$$= \frac{x - 1}{(x + 2)(x - 2)}$$

NOTE

Method 2 is probably the more efficient in this case. The LCD of the denominators would be $(x + 2)(x - 1)$, leading to a somewhat more complicated process if Method 1 were used.

Check Yourself 3

Simplify.

$$\frac{2 + \dfrac{5}{x - 3}}{x - \dfrac{1}{2x + 1}}$$

The following algorithm summarizes our work with complex fractions.

Step by Step

Simplifying Complex Fractions

Method 1

Step 1 Multiply the numerator and denominator of the complex fraction by the LCD of all the fractions that appear within the numerator and denominator.

Step 2 Simplify the resulting rational expression, writing the expression in lowest terms.

Method 2

Step 1 Write the numerator and denominator of the complex fraction as single fractions, if necessary.

Step 2 Invert the denominator and multiply as before, writing the result in lowest terms.

Check Yourself ANSWERS

1. $\dfrac{x - y}{2x + 2y}$ **2.** $\dfrac{x + 2}{x - 3}$ **3.** $\dfrac{2x + 1}{(x - 3)(x + 1)}$

Reading Your Text

The following fill-in-the-blank exercises are designed to ensure that you understand some of the key vocabulary used in this section.

SECTION 6.4

(a) A complex fraction is a fraction that has a ______________ in its numerator or denominator (or both).

(b) We can always multiply the numerator and denominator of a fraction by the same ______________ quantity.

(c) To simplify a complex fraction, multiply the numerator and denominator by the ______________ of all fractions that appear within the complex fraction.

(d) A second approach to simplifying a complex fraction interprets the complex fraction as indicating division and applies to the rule for dividing fractions, which is ______________ and multiply.

6.4 exercises

Basic Skills | Advanced Skills | Vocational-Technical Applications | Calculator/Computer | Above and Beyond

MathZone

Boost your grade at mathzone.com!
- > Practice Problems
- > NetTutor
- > Self-Tests
- > e-Professors
- > Videos

Name ______________

Section ________ Date ________

< Objectives 1 and 2 >

Simplify each complex fraction.

1. $\dfrac{\frac{2}{3}}{\frac{6}{8}}$

2. $\dfrac{\frac{5}{6}}{\frac{10}{15}}$

3. $\dfrac{\frac{2}{3}+\frac{1}{2}}{\frac{3}{4}-\frac{1}{3}}$

4. $\dfrac{\frac{3}{4}+\frac{1}{2}}{\frac{7}{8}-\frac{1}{4}}$

5. $\dfrac{2+\frac{1}{3}}{3-\frac{1}{5}}$

6. $\dfrac{1+\frac{3}{4}}{2-\frac{1}{8}}$

7. $\dfrac{\frac{x}{8}}{\frac{x^2}{4}}$

8. $\dfrac{\frac{a^2}{10}}{\frac{a^3}{15}}$

9. $\dfrac{\frac{3}{m}}{\frac{6}{m^2}}$ > Videos

10. $\dfrac{\frac{15}{x^2}}{\frac{20}{x^3}}$

11. $\dfrac{\frac{y+1}{y}}{\frac{y-1}{2y}}$

12. $\dfrac{\frac{x+3}{4x}}{\frac{x-3}{2x}}$

13. $\dfrac{\frac{a+2b}{3a}}{\frac{a^2+2ab}{9b}}$ > Videos

14. $\dfrac{\frac{m-3n}{4m}}{\frac{m^2-3mn}{8n}}$

15. $\dfrac{\frac{x-2}{x^2-9}}{\frac{x^2-4}{x^2+3x}}$ > Videos

16. $\dfrac{\frac{x+5}{x^2-6x}}{\frac{x^2-25}{x^2-36}}$

Answers

1. $\frac{8}{9}$
2. $\frac{5}{4}$
3. $\frac{14}{5}$
4. 2
5. $\frac{5}{6}$
6. $\frac{14}{15}$
7. $\frac{1}{2x}$
8. $\frac{3}{2a}$
9. $\frac{m}{2}$
10. $\frac{3x}{4}$
11. $\frac{2(y+1)}{y-1}$
12. $\frac{x+3}{2(x-3)}$
13. $\frac{3b}{a^2}$
14. $\frac{2n}{m^2}$
15. $\frac{x}{(x+2)(x-3)}$
16. $\frac{x+6}{x(x-5)}$

17. $\dfrac{2 - \dfrac{1}{x}}{2 + \dfrac{1}{x}}$

18. $\dfrac{3 + \dfrac{1}{b}}{3 - \dfrac{1}{b}}$

19. $\dfrac{\dfrac{1}{x} - \dfrac{1}{y}}{\dfrac{1}{xy}}$ > Videos

20. $\dfrac{\dfrac{1}{ab}}{\dfrac{1}{a} + \dfrac{1}{b}}$

21. $\dfrac{\dfrac{x^2}{y^2} - 1}{\dfrac{x}{y} + 1}$

22. $\dfrac{\dfrac{m}{n} + 2}{\dfrac{m^2}{n^2} - 4}$

23. $\dfrac{1 + \dfrac{3}{a} - \dfrac{4}{a^2}}{1 + \dfrac{2}{a} - \dfrac{3}{a^2}}$

24. $\dfrac{1 - \dfrac{2}{x} - \dfrac{8}{x^2}}{1 - \dfrac{1}{x} - \dfrac{6}{x^2}}$

25. $\dfrac{\dfrac{x^2}{y} + 2x + y}{\dfrac{1}{y^2} - \dfrac{1}{x^2}}$

26. $\dfrac{\dfrac{a}{b} + 1 - \dfrac{2b}{a}}{\dfrac{1}{b^2} - \dfrac{4}{a^2}}$

27. $\dfrac{1 + \dfrac{1}{x - 1}}{1 - \dfrac{1}{x - 1}}$ > Videos

28. $\dfrac{2 - \dfrac{1}{m - 2}}{2 + \dfrac{1}{m - 2}}$

29. $\dfrac{1 - \dfrac{1}{y - 1}}{y - \dfrac{8}{y + 2}}$

30. $\dfrac{1 + \dfrac{1}{x + 2}}{x - \dfrac{18}{x - 3}}$

Basic Skills | **Advanced Skills** | Vocational-Technical Applications | Calculator/Computer | Above and Beyond

Simplify each complex fraction.

31. $\dfrac{\dfrac{1}{x - 3} + \dfrac{1}{x + 3}}{\dfrac{1}{x - 3} - \dfrac{1}{x + 3}}$

32. $\dfrac{\dfrac{2}{m - 2} + \dfrac{1}{m - 3}}{\dfrac{2}{m - 2} - \dfrac{1}{m - 3}}$

33. $\dfrac{\dfrac{x}{x + 1} + \dfrac{1}{x - 1}}{\dfrac{x}{x - 1} - \dfrac{1}{x + 1}}$

34. $\dfrac{\dfrac{y}{y - 4} + \dfrac{1}{y + 2}}{\dfrac{4}{y - 4} - \dfrac{1}{y + 2}}$

Answers

17. $\dfrac{2x - 1}{2x + 1}$

18. $\dfrac{3b + 1}{3b - 1}$

19. $y - x$

20. $\dfrac{1}{b + a}$

21. $\dfrac{x - y}{y}$

22. $\dfrac{n}{m - 2n}$

23. $\dfrac{a + 4}{a + 3}$

24. $\dfrac{x - 4}{x - 3}$

25. $\dfrac{x^2y(x + y)}{x - y}$

26. $\dfrac{ab(a - b)}{a - 2b}$

27. $\dfrac{x}{x - 2}$

28. $\dfrac{2m - 5}{2m - 3}$

29. $\dfrac{y + 2}{(y - 1)(y + 4)}$

30. $\dfrac{x - 3}{(x + 2)(x - 6)}$

31. $\dfrac{x}{3}$

32. $\dfrac{3m - 8}{m - 4}$

33. 1

34. $\dfrac{y - 1}{3}$

Answers

35. $\frac{2a}{a^2+1}$

36. $\frac{4x}{x^2+4}$

37. $\frac{2x+1}{x+1}$

38. $\frac{2y-1}{y-1}$

39. $\frac{3x+2}{2x+1}$

40. See exercise

41. See exercise

42. (a) $1+\cfrac{1}{1+\cfrac{1}{1+\cfrac{1}{1+\cfrac{1}{x}}}}$

(b) $\frac{5x+3}{3x+2}$

35. $\dfrac{\dfrac{a+1}{a-1}-\dfrac{a-1}{a+1}}{\dfrac{a+1}{a-1}+\dfrac{a-1}{a+1}}$

36. $\dfrac{\dfrac{x+2}{x-2}-\dfrac{x-2}{x+2}}{\dfrac{x+2}{x-2}+\dfrac{x-2}{x+2}}$

37. $1+\cfrac{1}{1+\cfrac{1}{x}}$ > Videos

38. $1+\cfrac{1}{1-\cfrac{1}{y}}$

39. $1+\cfrac{1}{1+\cfrac{1}{1+\cfrac{1}{x}}}$

Basic Skills | Advanced Skills | Vocational-Technical Applications | **Calculator/Computer** | Above and Beyond

In exercises 40 and 41, use the table utility on your graphing calculator to complete the table. Comment on the equivalence of the two expressions.

40.

x	−3	−2	−1	0	1	2	3
$\dfrac{-8+\dfrac{20}{x}}{4-\dfrac{25}{x^2}}$	−12	8	$\frac{4}{3}$	error	$\frac{-4}{7}$	$\frac{-8}{9}$	$\frac{-12}{11}$
$\dfrac{-4x}{2x+5}$	−12	8	$\frac{4}{3}$	0	$\frac{-4}{7}$	$\frac{-8}{9}$	$\frac{-12}{11}$

41.

x	−3	−2	−1	0	1	2	3
$\dfrac{1-\dfrac{2}{x}}{1-\dfrac{4}{x^2}}$	3	error	−1	error	$\frac{1}{3}$	error	$\frac{3}{5}$
$\dfrac{x}{x+2}$	3	error	−1	0	$\frac{1}{3}$	$\frac{1}{2}$	$\frac{3}{5}$

Basic Skills | Advanced Skills | Vocational-Technical Applications | Calculator/Computer | **Above and Beyond**

42. **(a)** Extend the "continued fraction" patterns in exercises 37 and 39 to write the next complex fraction. **(b)** Simplify the complex fraction obtained in part **(a)**.

43. Compare your results in exercises 37, 39, and 42. Could you have predicted the result?

44. Outline the two different methods used to simplify a complex fraction. What are the advantages of each method?

45. Can the expression $\dfrac{x^{-1} + y^{-1}}{x^{-2} + y^{-2}}$ be written as $\dfrac{x^2 + y^2}{x + y}$? If not, what is the correct simplified form?

46. Write and simplify a complex fraction that is the reciprocal of $x + \dfrac{6}{x - 1}$.

47. Let $f(x) = \dfrac{3}{x}$. Write and simplify a complex fraction whose numerator is $f(3 + h) - f(3)$ and whose denominator is h.

48. Write and simplify a complex fraction that is the arithmetic mean of $\dfrac{1}{x}$ and $\dfrac{1}{x - 1}$.

49. Write and simplify a complex fraction that is the reciprocal of $\dfrac{1}{x} + \dfrac{1}{y}$.

Consider the following:

Suppose you drive at 40 mi/h from city A to city B. You then return along the same route from city B to city A at 50 mi/h. What is your average rate for the round trip? Your obvious guess would be 45 mi/h, but you are in for a surprise.

Suppose that the cities are 200 mi apart. Your time from city A to city B is the distance divided by the rate, or

$$\frac{200 \text{ mi}}{40 \text{ mi/h}} = 5 \text{ h}$$

Similarly, your time from city B to city A is

$$\frac{200 \text{ mi}}{50 \text{ mi/h}} = 4 \text{ h}$$

The total time is then 9 h, and now using *rate equals distance divided by time,* we have

$$\frac{400 \text{ mi}}{9 \text{ h}} = \frac{400}{9} \text{ mi/h} = 44\frac{4}{9} \text{ mi/h}$$

Note that the rate for the round trip is independent of the distance involved. For instance, try the same computations if cities A and B are 400 mi apart.

The answer to the preceding problem is the complex fraction

$$R = \frac{2}{\dfrac{1}{R_1} + \dfrac{1}{R_2}}$$

in which R_1 = rate going
R_2 = rate returning
R = rate for round trip

Answers

43. Above and Beyond

44. Above and Beyond

45. No; $\dfrac{xy(x + y)}{y^2 + x^2}$

46. $\dfrac{1}{x + \dfrac{6}{x - 1}} = \dfrac{x - 1}{x^2 - x + 6}$

47. $\dfrac{\dfrac{3}{3 + h} - 1}{h} = \dfrac{-1}{3 + h}$

48. $\dfrac{\dfrac{1}{x} + \dfrac{1}{x - 1}}{2} = \dfrac{2x - 1}{2x(x - 1)}$

49. $\dfrac{xy}{x + y}$

Answers

50. Above and Beyond

51. $44\frac{4}{9}$ mi/h

52. $54\frac{6}{11}$ mi/h

53. $54\frac{6}{11}$ mi/h

54. Above and Beyond

55. Above and Beyond

Use this information to solve exercises 50 to 53.

50. Verify that if $R_1 = 40$ mi/h and $R_2 = 50$ mi/h, then $R = 44\frac{4}{9}$ mi/h, by simplifying the complex fraction *after* substituting those values.

51. Simplify the given complex fraction first. *Then* substitute 40 for R_1 and 50 for R_2 to calculate R.

52. Repeat exercise 50, with $R_1 = 50$ mi/h and $R_2 = 60$ mi/h.

53. Use the procedure in exercise 51 with the values in exercise 52 for R_1 and R_2.

54. The following inequality is used when the U.S. House of Representatives seats are apportioned (see the chapter's introduction for more information).

$$\frac{\frac{E}{e} - \frac{A}{a+1}}{\frac{A}{a+1}} < \frac{\frac{A}{a} - \frac{E}{e+1}}{\frac{E}{e+1}}$$

Show that this inequality can be simplified to

$$\frac{A}{\sqrt{a(a+1)}} > \frac{E}{\sqrt{e(e+1)}}.$$

Here, A and E represent the populations of two states of the United States, and a and e are the number of representatives each of these two states have in the U.S. House of Representatives.

55. Mathematicians have shown that there are situations in which the method for apportionment described in the chapter's introduction does not work, and a state may not even get its basic quota of representatives. They give the following table of a hypothetical seven states and their populations as an example.

State	Population	Exact Quota	Number of Reps.
A	325	1.625	2
B	788	3.940	4
C	548	2.740	3
D	562	2.810	3
E	4,263	21.315	21
F	3,219	16.095	15
G	295	1.475	2
Total	10,000	50	50

In this case, the total population of all states is 10,000, and there are 50 representatives in all, so there should be no more than 10,000/50 or 200 people per representative. The quotas are found by dividing the population by 200. Whether a state, A, should get an additional representative before another state, E, should get one is decided in this method by using the following simplified inequality. If the ratio

$$\frac{A}{\sqrt{a(a+1)}} > \frac{E}{\sqrt{e(e+1)}}$$

is true, then A gets an extra representative before E does.

(a) If you go through the process of comparing the inequality for each pair of states, state F loses a representative to state G. Do you see how this happens? Will state F complain?

(b) Alexander Hamilton, one of the signers of the Constitution, proposed that the extra representative positions be given one at a time to states with the largest remainder until all the "extra" positions were filled. How would this affect the table? Do you agree or disagree?

56. In Italy in the 1500s, Pietro Antonio Cataldi expressed square roots as infinite, continued fractions. It is not a difficult process to follow. For instance, if you want the square root of 5, then let

$$x + 1 = \sqrt{5}$$

Squaring both sides gives

$$(x + 1)^2 = 5 \quad \text{or} \quad x^2 + 2x + 1 = 5$$

which can be written

$$x(x + 2) = 4$$

$$x = \frac{4}{x + 2}$$

One can continue replacing x with $\frac{4}{x+2}$:

$$x = \cfrac{4}{2 + \cfrac{4}{2 + \cfrac{4}{2 + \cfrac{4}{2 + \dots}}}}$$

to obtain

$$\sqrt{5} - 1$$

(a) Evaluate this complex fraction and then add 1 and see how close it is to the square root of 5. What should you put where the ellipses (. . .) are? Try a number you feel is close to $\sqrt{5}$. How far would you have to go to get the square root correct to the nearest hundredth?

(b) Develop an infinite complex fraction for $\sqrt{10}$.

Answers

56. Above and Beyond

Answers

57. Above and Beyond

58. $\dfrac{\frac{1}{2}}{3} = \dfrac{1}{6}$ or $\dfrac{1}{\frac{2}{3}} = \dfrac{3}{2}$

57. Here is yet another method for simplifying a complex fraction. Suppose we want to simplify

$$\dfrac{\frac{3}{5}}{\frac{7}{10}}$$

Multiply the numerator and denominator of the complex fraction by $\frac{10}{7}$.

(a) What principle allows you to do this?

(b) Why was $\frac{10}{7}$ chosen?

(c) When learning to divide fractions, you may have heard the saying "Yours is not to reason why . . . just invert and multiply." How does this method serve to explain the "reason why" we invert and multiply?

58. Suppose someone wrote a fraction as follows $\begin{matrix}1\\ \hline 2\\ \hline 3\end{matrix}$. Give two ways that this fraction can be interpreted, and simplify each. Do you see why it is important to clearly indicate the "main fraction line"? On your graphing calculator, type 1/2/3 and press ENTER. Which way is your calculator interpreting the fraction?

Answers

1. $\frac{8}{9}$ **3.** $\frac{14}{5}$ **5.** $\frac{5}{6}$ **7.** $\frac{1}{2x}$ **9.** $\frac{m}{2}$ **11.** $\frac{2(y+1)}{y-1}$ **13.** $\frac{3b}{a^2}$

15. $\frac{x}{(x+2)(x-3)}$ **17.** $\frac{2x-1}{2x+1}$ **19.** $y - x$ **21.** $\frac{x-y}{y}$

23. $\frac{a+4}{a+3}$ **25.** $\frac{x^2y(x+y)}{x-y}$ **27.** $\frac{x}{x-2}$ **29.** $\frac{y+2}{(y-1)(y+4)}$

31. $\frac{x}{3}$ **33.** 1 **35.** $\frac{2a}{a^2+1}$ **37.** $\frac{2x+1}{x+1}$ **39.** $\frac{3x+2}{2x+1}$

41.

x	−3	−2	−1	0	1	2	3
$\dfrac{1-\frac{2}{x}}{1-\frac{4}{x^2}}$	3	error	−1	error	$\frac{1}{3}$	error	$\frac{3}{5}$
$\dfrac{x}{x+2}$	3	error	−1	0	$\frac{1}{3}$	$\frac{1}{2}$	$\frac{3}{5}$

43. Above and Beyond **45.** No; $\frac{xy(x+y)}{y^2+x^2}$ **47.** $\frac{-1}{3+h}$ **49.** $\frac{xy}{x+y}$

51. $44\frac{4}{9}$ mi/h **53.** $54\frac{6}{11}$ mi/h **55.** Above and Beyond

57. Above and Beyond

6.5 Solving Rational Equations

< 6.5 Objectives >

1 > Rewrite a rational equation by clearing the fractions

2 > Solve an equation that contains a rational expression

3 > Find the zeros of a rational equation

4 > Solve a literal equation that involves a rational expression

5 > Solve an application that involves a rational equation

Applications of your work in algebra will often result in equations involving rational expressions. Our objective in this section is to develop methods to find the solutions of such equations.

The usual technique is to multiply both sides of the equation by the lowest common denominator (LCD) of all the rational expressions appearing in the equation. The resulting equation will be cleared of fractions, and we can then proceed to solve the equation as before. Example 1 illustrates the process.

Example 1 Clearing Equations of Fractions

< Objective 1 >

Solve.

$$\frac{2x}{3} + \frac{x}{5} = 13$$

The LCM for 3 and 5 is 15. Multiplying both sides of the equation by 15, we have

$$15\left(\frac{2x}{3} + \frac{x}{5}\right) = 15 \cdot 13 \qquad \text{Distribute 15 on the left.}$$

$$15 \cdot \frac{2x}{3} + 15 \cdot \frac{x}{5} = 15 \cdot 13$$

$$10x + 3x = 195 \qquad \text{Simplify. The equation is now cleared of fractions.}$$

$$13x = 195$$

$$x = 15$$

NOTE

The LCM for 3 and 5 is 15.

The LCD for $\frac{2x}{3}$ and $\frac{x}{5}$ is 15.

To check, substitute 15 in the original equation.

$$\frac{2 \cdot 15}{3} + \frac{15}{5} \stackrel{?}{=} 13$$

$$10 + 3 \stackrel{?}{=} 13$$

$$13 = 13 \qquad \text{A true statement.}$$

So 15 is the solution for the equation.

> CAUTION

Be Careful! A common mistake is to confuse an *equation* such as

$$\frac{2x}{3} + \frac{x}{5} = 13$$

and an *expression* such as

$$\frac{2x}{3} + \frac{x}{5}$$

Let us compare.

Equation: $\frac{2x}{3} + \frac{x}{5} = 13$

Here we want to *solve the equation for x,* as in Example 1. We multiply both sides by the LCD to clear fractions and proceed as before.

Expression: $\frac{2x}{3} + \frac{x}{5}$

Here we want to find *a third fraction* that is equivalent to the given expression. We write each fraction as an equivalent fraction with the LCD as a common denominator.

$$\frac{2x}{3} + \frac{x}{5} = \frac{2x \cdot 5}{3 \cdot 5} + \frac{x \cdot 3}{5 \cdot 3}$$

$$= \frac{10x}{15} + \frac{3x}{15} = \frac{10x + 3x}{15}$$

$$= \frac{13x}{15}$$

Check Yourself 1

Solve.

$$\frac{3x}{2} - \frac{x}{3} = 7$$

The process is similar when variables are in the denominators. Consider Example 2.

Example 2 Solving an Equation Involving Rational Expressions

< Objective 2 >

NOTE

We assume that x cannot have the value 0. Do you see why?

Solve.

$$\frac{7}{4x} - \frac{3}{x^2} = \frac{1}{2x^2}$$

The LCM of $4x$, x^2, and $2x^2$ is $4x^2$. So, the LCD for the equation is $4x^2$. Multiplying both sides by $4x^2$, we have

$$4x^2\left(\frac{7}{4x} - \frac{3}{x^2}\right) = 4x^2 \cdot \frac{1}{2x^2}$$ Distribute $4x^2$ on the left side.

$$4x^2 \cdot \frac{7}{4x} - 4x^2 \cdot \frac{3}{x^2} = 4x^2 \cdot \frac{1}{2x^2}$$ Simplify.

$$7x - 12 = 2$$

$$7x = 14$$

$$x = 2$$

We leave the check of the solution, $x = 2$, to you. Be sure to return to the original equation and substitute 2 for x.

Check Yourself 2

Solve.

$$\frac{5}{2x} - \frac{4}{x^2} = \frac{7}{2x^2}$$

Example 3 illustrates the same solution process when there are binomials in the denominators.

Example 3 Solving an Equation Involving Rational Expressions

NOTES

Here we assume that x *cannot* have the value −2 or 3.

Notice that multiplying *each term* by the LCD is the same as multiplying both sides of the equation by the LCD.

Solve.

$$\frac{4}{x+2} + 3 = \frac{3x}{x-3}$$

The LCD is $(x + 2)(x - 3)$. Multiplying by that LCD, we have

$$(x+2)(x-3)\left(\frac{4}{x+2}\right) + (x+2)(x-3)(3) = (x+2)(x-3)\left(\frac{3x}{x-3}\right)$$

Or, simplifying each term, we have

$$\begin{aligned} 4(x-3) + 3(x+2)(x-3) &= 3x(x+2) \\ 4x - 12 + 3(x^2 - x - 6) &= 3x^2 + 6x \\ 4x - 12 + 3x^2 - 3x - 18 &= 3x^2 + 6x \\ 3x^2 + x - 30 &= 3x^2 + 6x \\ x - 30 &= 6x \\ -5x &= 30 \\ x &= -6 \end{aligned}$$

Again, we leave the check of this solution to you.

Check Yourself 3

Solve.

$$\frac{5}{x-4} + 2 = \frac{2x}{x-3}$$

Factoring plays an important role in solving equations containing rational expressions.

Example 4 Solving an Equation Involving Rational Expressions

Solve.

$$\frac{3}{x-3} - \frac{7}{x+3} = \frac{2}{x^2-9}$$

In factored form, the denominator on the right side is $(x - 3)(x + 3)$, which forms the LCD, and we multiply each term by that LCD.

$$(x - 3)(x + 3)\left(\frac{3}{x - 3}\right) - (x - 3)(x + 3)\left(\frac{7}{x + 3}\right) = (x - 3)(x + 3)\left[\frac{2}{(x - 3)(x + 3)}\right]$$

Again, simplifying each term on the right and left sides, we have

$$3(x + 3) - 7(x - 3) = 2$$
$$3x + 9 - 7x + 21 = 2$$
$$-4x + 30 = 2$$
$$-4x = -28$$
$$x = 7$$

Be sure to check this result by substitution in the original equation.

Check Yourself 4

Solve $\dfrac{4}{x - 4} - \dfrac{3}{x + 1} = \dfrac{5}{x^2 - 3x - 4}$.

NOTE

An extraneous solution is an extra value that appears with certain algebraic manipulations, but does not work in the original problem. We will study these again in Section 7.4.

Whenever we multiply both sides of an equation by an expression containing a variable, there is the possibility that a proposed solution may make that multiplier 0. As we pointed out earlier, multiplying by 0 does not give an equivalent equation, and therefore verifying solutions by substitution serves not only as a check of our work but also as a check for *extraneous* solutions. Consider Example 5.

Example 5 Solving an Equation Involving Rational Expressions

NOTES

Notice that we must assume that $x \neq 2$.

Notice that each of the three terms gets multiplied by $(x - 2)$.

Solve.

$$\frac{x}{x - 2} - 7 = \frac{2}{x - 2}$$

The LCD is $x - 2$, and multiplying, we have

$$\left(\frac{x}{x - 2}\right)(x - 2) - 7(x - 2) = \left(\frac{2}{x - 2}\right)(x - 2)$$

Simplifying yields

$$x - 7(x - 2) = 2$$
$$x - 7x + 14 = 2$$
$$-6x + 14 = 2$$
$$-6x = -12$$
$$x = 2$$

> CAUTION

Because division by 0 is undefined, we conclude that 2 is *not a solution* for the original equation. It is an extraneous solution. Since there were no other values, the original equation has no solution.

To check this result, by substituting 2 for x, we have

$$\frac{2}{2-2} - 7 \stackrel{?}{=} \frac{2}{2-2}$$

$$\frac{2}{0} - 7 \stackrel{?}{=} \frac{2}{0}$$

Check Yourself 5

Solve $\dfrac{x-3}{x-4} = 4 + \dfrac{1}{x-4}$.

Equations involving rational expressions may also lead to quadratic equations, as illustrated in Example 6.

Example 6 Solving an Equation Involving Rational Expressions

NOTE

Assume $x \neq 3$ and $x \neq 4$.

Solve.

$$\frac{x}{x-4} = \frac{15}{x-3} - \frac{2x}{x^2 - 7x + 12}$$

After factoring the trinomial denominator on the right, the LCD of $x - 4$, $x - 3$, and $x^2 - 7x + 12$ is $(x - 3)(x - 4)$. Multiplying by that LCD, we have

$$(x-3)(x-4)\left(\frac{x}{x-4}\right) = (x-3)(x-4)\left(\frac{15}{x-3}\right) - (x-3)(x-4)\left[\frac{2x}{(x-3)(x-4)}\right]$$

Simplifying yields

$$x(x-3) = 15(x-4) - 2x$$

$$x^2 - 3x = 15x - 60 - 2x \qquad \text{Write in standard form and factor.}$$

$$x^2 - 16x + 60 = 0$$

$$(x-6)(x-10) = 0$$

So

$x = 6$ or $x = 10$

Verify that 6 and 10 are both solutions for the original equation.

Check Yourself 6

Solve $\dfrac{3x}{x+2} - \dfrac{2}{x+3} = \dfrac{36}{x^2 + 5x + 6}$.

The following algorithm summarizes our work in solving equations containing rational expressions.

Step by Step

Solving Equations Containing Rational Expressions

Step 1 Clear the equation of fractions by multiplying both sides of the equation by the LCD of all the fractions that appear.

Step 2 Solve the equation resulting from step 1.

Step 3 Check all solutions by substitution in the original equation.

The techniques we have just discussed can also be used to find the zeros of rational functions. Remember that a zero of a function is a value of x for which $f(x) = 0$.

Example 7 Finding the Zeros of a Function

< Objective 3 >

> CAUTION

This is different from finding values for which the rational function does not exist. In that case, we found x-values that caused division by zero. Here, we set the entire function equal to zero and find the x-values that make the statement true.

Find the zeros of

$$f(x) = \frac{1}{x} - \frac{3}{7x} - \frac{4}{21}$$

Set the function equal to 0, and solve the resulting equation for x.

$$f(x) = \frac{1}{x} - \frac{3}{7x} - \frac{4}{21} = 0$$

The LCM for x, $7x$, and 21 is $21x$. Multiplying both sides by $21x$, we have

$$21x\left(\frac{1}{x} - \frac{3}{7x} - \frac{4}{21}\right) = 21x \cdot 0$$

$$21x \cdot \frac{1}{x} - 21x \cdot \frac{3}{7x} - 21x \cdot \frac{4}{21} = 0$$

$$21 - 9 - 4x = 0$$

$$12 - 4x = 0$$

$$12 = 4x$$

$$3 = x$$

So 3 is the value of x for which $f(x) = 0$; that is, 3 is a zero of $f(x)$.

Check Yourself 7

Find the zeros of the function.

$$f(x) = \frac{5x + 2}{x - 6} - \frac{11}{4}$$

Now that we have solved rational equations, we will see several applications of those techniques. Given a literal equation such as

$$\frac{1}{R} = \frac{1}{R_1} + \frac{1}{R_2}$$

we can use the techniques from earlier in this section to solve for one of the variables.

Example 8 Solving a Literal Equation

< Objective 4 >

NOTE

This is a parallel electric circuit. The symbol for a resistor is .

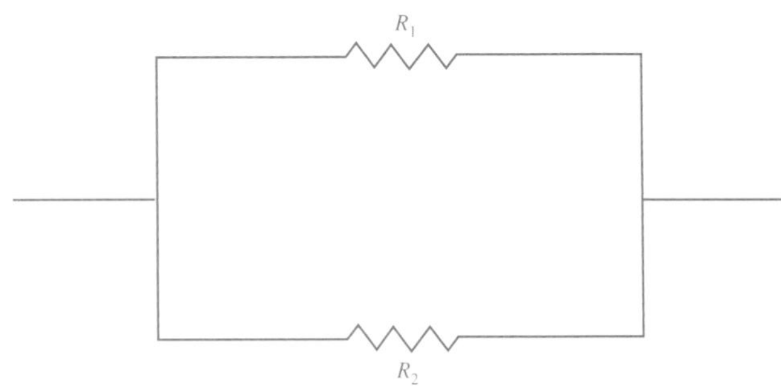

RECALL

The numbers 1 and 2 are *subscripts*. We read R_1 as "R sub 1" and R_2 as "R sub 2."

If two resistors with resistances R_1 and R_2 are connected in parallel, the combined resistance R can be found from

$$\frac{1}{R} = \frac{1}{R_1} + \frac{1}{R_2}$$

Solve the formula for R.

First, the LCD is RR_1R_2, and we multiply:

$$RR_1R_2 \cdot \frac{1}{R} = RR_1R_2 \cdot \frac{1}{R_1} + RR_1R_2 \cdot \frac{1}{R_2}$$

NOTE

Reversing the left and right sides of an equation uses the symmetric property of equality.

Simplifying yields

$$R_1R_2 = RR_2 + RR_1 \quad \text{Factor out } R \text{ on the right.}$$

$$R_1R_2 = R(R_2 + R_1) \quad \text{Divide by } R_2 + R_1 \text{ to isolate } R.$$

$$\frac{R_1R_2}{R_2 + R_1} = R \quad \text{or} \quad R = \frac{R_1R_2}{R_1 + R_2}$$

NOTE

This formula involves the focal length of a convex lens.

Check Yourself 8

Solve for D_1.

$$\frac{1}{F} = \frac{1}{D_1} + \frac{1}{D_2}$$

Many distance problems also lead to rational equations. You will recall that distance (d), rate (r), and time (t) are related by the following formula.

Property

The Distance Relationship I	$d = r \cdot t$

Treating this as a literal equation, we can produce two variations that frequently lead to rational equations.

Property

The Distance Relationship II $r = \dfrac{d}{t}$

and

Property

The Distance Relationship III $t = \dfrac{d}{r}$

Example 9 Finding a Rate

< Objective 5 >

A boat, which moves at 36 mi/h in still water, travels 28 mi downstream in the same amount of time that it takes to travel 20 mi upstream. Find the speed of the current.

When solving an application that involves the distance relationship, it is usually best to begin by completing the following table.

	Distance	Rate	Time
Upstream			
Downstream			

Letting r represent the rate of the current, we have the following information:

	Distance	Rate	Time
Upstream	20	$36 - r$	
Downstream	28	$36 + r$	

Using relationship III, we can complete the last column of the table.

	Distance	Rate	Time
Upstream	20	$36 - r$	$\dfrac{20}{36 - r}$
Downstream	28	$36 + r$	$\dfrac{28}{36 + r}$

Having completed the table, we go back to the original problem. The key phrase is "in the same amount of time." That means that the time going upstream is the same as the time going downstream. This leads to the equation

$$\frac{28}{36 + r} = \frac{20}{36 - r}$$

The LCD is $(36 + r)(36 - r)$. Clearing the fractions, we get

$$\begin{aligned} 28(36 - r) &= 20(36 + r) \\ 1{,}008 - 28r &= 720 + 20r \\ 288 &= 48r \\ r &= 6 \end{aligned}$$

The rate of the current is 6 mi/h.

Check Yourself 9

A boat, which moves at 30 mi/h in still water, travels 3 mi downstream in the same amount of time that it takes to travel 2 mi upstream. Find the speed of the current.

Another type of application that frequently leads to a rational equation is something called a **work problem.** Solving a work problem is simplified by using the following work principles.

Property

Work Principle I

If a job takes t hours to complete, then, for each hour,

$$\frac{1}{t}$$

represents the portion of the job that has been completed.

This principle confirms that, if a job takes 2 h to do, then $\frac{1}{2}$ of the job is done each hour. If a job takes 10 h to do, then $\frac{1}{10}$ of the job is done each hour.

Extending the idea behind the first principle, we find the second work principle.

Property

Work Principle II

If two entities are working on the same job, and the first would take a hours to complete the job alone and the second b hours to complete the job alone, then the expression

$$\frac{1}{a} + \frac{1}{b}$$

represents the portion of the job completed each hour if both entities are at work.

Combining these two principles, we get an equation that will allow us to find the total time it takes to complete a job.

Property

Work Principle III

If two entities are working on the same job, and the first would take a hours to complete the job alone and the second b hours to complete the job alone, then the equation

$$\frac{1}{a} + \frac{1}{b} = \frac{1}{t}$$

can be used to find t, the time it will take to complete the job.

We will use this equation in Example 10.

Example 10 Solving a Work Problem

Jason and Hilger are required to paint over the graffiti on a wall. If Jason worked alone, it would take him 20 h to repaint. Working alone, Hilger could do the job in 15 h. How long will it take them to do the painting if they work together?

Using the work principle, we get the equation

$$\frac{1}{20} + \frac{1}{15} = \frac{1}{t}$$

Clearing the fractions (LCD = $60t$) yields

$$3t + 4t = 60$$
$$7t = 60$$
$$t = \frac{60}{7}$$

Working together, they will finish the job in $8\frac{4}{7}$ h. Note that, when working together, it will always take less time to complete a job than it will take either individual!

Check Yourself 10

Filling a hot tub with a hose will take 4 h. Draining the same tub takes 7 h. If the drain is open, how long will it take to fill the tub? (*Hint:* Treat the draining time as a negative number.)

The techniques used with rational equations are also used when performing **unit conversions.** The following table contains some of the common conversion factors.

Common Conversion Factors
1 mile = 5,280 feet
1 hour = 60 minutes
1 minute = 60 seconds
1 kilogram = 1,000 grams
1 second = 1,000,000 microseconds
1 gigabyte = 1,000,000,000 bytes

Each of the conversion factors can be rewritten as one of two fractions that are equal to one. For example, we can rewrite the statement 1 kilogram = 1,000 grams as either

$$\frac{1 \text{ kilogram}}{1{,}000 \text{ grams}} = 1 \quad \text{or} \quad \frac{1{,}000 \text{ grams}}{1 \text{ kilogram}} = 1$$

Example 11 Converting Units

An SST can fly over 2,000 mi/h. To the nearest tenth, how many miles does it cover each second?

First, note that 2,000 mi/h can be written in several different forms. When doing unit conversion, it is best to write a rate (like 2,000 mi/h) as a ratio, so we write it as

$$\frac{2{,}000 \text{ mi}}{1 \text{ h}}$$

This is now multiplied by the appropriate conversion ratios. To figure out what those ratios should be, it is best to first write the units of the desired result.

$$\frac{2{,}000 \text{ mi}}{1 \text{ h}} = \quad \cdots \quad = \frac{\text{mi}}{1 \text{ sec}}$$

To convert hours to seconds, use the conversion ratio $\frac{1 \text{ h}}{60 \text{ min}} \cdot \frac{1 \text{ min}}{60 \text{ sec}} = \frac{1 \text{ h}}{3{,}600 \text{ sec}}$

$$\frac{2{,}000 \text{ mi}}{1 \text{ h}} \cdot \frac{1 \text{ h}}{3{,}600 \text{ sec}} = \frac{2{,}000 \text{ mi}}{3{,}600 \text{ sec}} = \frac{5 \text{ mi}}{9 \text{ sec}} \approx \frac{0.55 \text{ mi}}{1 \text{ sec}}$$

When traveling at 2,000 mi/h, the SST covers 0.55 mi every second.

Check Yourself 11

A roller coaster reaches a maximum speed of 75 ft/sec. To the nearest tenth, convert the speed to miles per hour.

Check Yourself ANSWERS

1. 6 **2.** 3 **3.** 9 **4.** -11 **5.** No solution **6.** $-5, \frac{8}{3}$
7. $-\frac{74}{9}$ **8.** $\frac{FD_2}{D_2 - F}$ **9.** 6 mi/h **10.** $\frac{28}{3}$ h or $9\frac{1}{3}$ h **11.** 51.1 mi/h

Reading Your Text

The following fill-in-the-blank exercises are designed to ensure that you understand some of the key vocabulary used in this section.

SECTION 6.5

(a) To solve a rational equation, we multiply each term by the ______________ of any fractions in the equation.

(b) Verifying solutions to rational equations by substitution is necessary to check for ___________________ solutions.

(c) The key equation for solving motion problems relates the distance traveled, the speed, and the _____________.

(d) Time is distance divided by ____________________.

6.5 exercises

Basic Skills | Advanced Skills | Vocational-Technical Applications | Calculator/Computer | Above and Beyond

MathZone

Boost your grade at mathzone.com!
> Practice Problems
> NetTutor
> Self-Tests
> e-Professors
> Videos

Name ______________

Section ________ Date ________

Decide whether each of the following is an expression or an equation. If it is an equation, solve it. If it is an expression, write it as a single fraction.

1. $\frac{x}{2} - \frac{x}{3} = 6$

2. $\frac{x}{4} - \frac{x}{7} = 3$

3. $\frac{x}{2} - \frac{x}{5}$

4. $\frac{x}{6} - \frac{x}{8}$

5. $\frac{3x + 1}{4} = x - 1$

6. $\frac{3x - 1}{2} - \frac{x}{5} - \frac{x + 3}{4}$

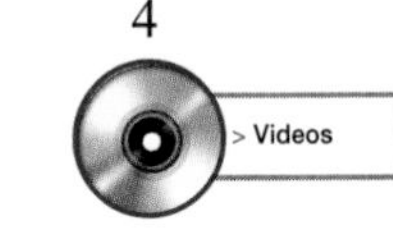

7. $\frac{x}{4} = \frac{x}{12} + \frac{1}{2}$

8. $\frac{2x - 1}{3} + \frac{x}{2}$

< Objectives 1 and 2 >

Solve each equation.

9. $\frac{x}{3} + \frac{3}{2} = \frac{x}{6} + \frac{7}{3}$

10. $\frac{x}{10} - \frac{1}{5} = \frac{x}{5} + \frac{1}{2}$

11. $\frac{4}{x} + \frac{3}{4} = \frac{10}{x}$

12. $\frac{3}{x} = \frac{5}{3} - \frac{7}{x}$

13. $\frac{5}{4x} - \frac{1}{2} = \frac{1}{2x}$

14. $\frac{7}{6x} - \frac{1}{3} = \frac{1}{2x}$

15. $\frac{3}{x + 4} = \frac{2}{x + 3}$

16. $\frac{5}{x - 2} = \frac{4}{x - 1}$

17. $\frac{9}{x} + 2 = \frac{2x}{x + 3}$

18. $\frac{6}{x} + 3 = \frac{3x}{x + 1}$

19. $\frac{3}{x + 2} - \frac{5}{x} = \frac{13}{x + 2}$

20. $\frac{7}{x} - \frac{2}{x - 3} = \frac{6}{x}$

Answers

1. Equation, 36
2. Equation, 28
3. Expression, $\frac{3x}{10}$
4. Expression, $\frac{x}{24}$
5. Equation, 5
6. Expression, $\frac{21x - 25}{20}$
7. Equation, 3
8. Expression, $\frac{7x - 2}{6}$
9. 5
10. -7
11. 8
12. 6
13. $\frac{3}{2}$
14. 2
15. -1
16. -3
17. $-\frac{9}{5}$
18. $-\frac{2}{3}$
19. $-\frac{2}{3}$
20. -3

21. $\frac{3}{2} + \frac{2}{2x - 4} = \frac{1}{x - 2}$

22. $\frac{2}{x - 1} + \frac{5}{2x - 2} = \frac{3}{4}$

23. $\frac{x}{3x + 12} + \frac{x - 1}{x + 4} = \frac{5}{3}$

24. $\frac{x}{4x - 12} - \frac{x - 4}{x - 3} = \frac{1}{8}$

25. $\frac{x - 1}{x + 3} - \frac{x - 3}{x} = \frac{3}{x^2 + 3x}$

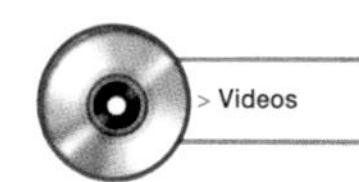

26. $\frac{x + 1}{x - 2} - \frac{3}{x} = \frac{6}{x^2 - 2x}$

27. $\frac{1}{x - 2} - \frac{2}{x + 2} = \frac{2}{x^2 - 4}$

28. $\frac{1}{x + 4} + \frac{1}{x - 4} = \frac{12}{x^2 - 16}$

29. $\frac{7}{x + 5} - \frac{1}{x - 5} = \frac{x}{x^2 - 25}$

30. $\frac{2}{x - 2} = \frac{3}{x + 2} + \frac{x}{x^2 - 4}$

31. $\frac{11}{x + 2} - \frac{5}{x^2 - x - 6} = \frac{1}{x - 3}$

32. $\frac{5}{x - 4} = \frac{1}{x + 2} - \frac{2}{x^2 - 2x - 8}$

33. $\frac{5}{x - 2} - \frac{3}{x + 3} = \frac{24}{x^2 + x - 6}$

34. $\frac{3}{x + 1} - \frac{5}{x + 6} = \frac{2}{x^2 + 7x + 6}$

35. $\frac{x}{x - 3} - 2 = \frac{3}{x - 3}$

36. $\frac{x}{x - 5} + 2 = \frac{5}{x - 5}$

37. $\frac{2}{x^2 - 3x} - \frac{1}{x^2 + 2x} = \frac{2}{x^2 - x - 6}$

38. $\frac{2}{x^2 - x} - \frac{4}{x^2 + 5x - 6} = \frac{3}{x^2 + 6x}$

39. $\frac{2}{x^2 - 4x + 3} - \frac{3}{x^2 - 9} = \frac{2}{x^2 + 2x - 3}$

40. $\frac{2}{x^2 - 4} - \frac{1}{x^2 + x - 2} = \frac{3}{x^2 - 3x + 2}$

Answers

21. No solution
22. 7
23. −23
24. 5
25. 6
26. No solution
27. 4
28. 6
29. 8
30. 5
31. 4
32. −4
33. $\frac{3}{2}$
34. $\frac{11}{2}$
35. No solution
36. No solution
37. 7
38. 3
39. 5
40. −3

Answers

41. $2, -\frac{3}{2}$
42. $-\frac{2}{3}, 3$
43. 5, 6
44. −6, 1
45. 4, 6
46. $-\frac{7}{3}, 5$
47. $-\frac{1}{2}, 6$
48. −4, 3
49. $-\frac{1}{2}$
50. $\frac{2}{3}$
51. 24
52. 0
53. $\frac{25}{7}$
54. 3
55. $\frac{3}{4}$
56. 1
57. 3, 13
58. −9, 8
59. $\frac{ab}{b-a}$
60. $\frac{bx}{b-x}$

41. $2 - \frac{6}{x^2} = \frac{1}{x}$

42. $3 - \frac{7}{x} - \frac{6}{x^2} = 0$

43. $1 - \frac{7}{x-2} + \frac{12}{(x-2)^2} = 0$

44. $1 + \frac{3}{x+1} = \frac{10}{(x+1)^2}$

45. $1 + \frac{3}{x^2-9} = \frac{10}{x+3}$

46. $3 - \frac{7}{x^2-x-6} = \frac{5}{x-3}$

47. $\frac{2x}{x-3} + \frac{2}{x-5} = \frac{3x}{x^2-8x+15}$

48. $\frac{x}{x-4} = \frac{5x}{x^2-x-12} - \frac{3}{x+3}$

49. $\frac{2x}{x+2} = \frac{5}{x^2-x-6} - \frac{1}{x-3}$

50. $\frac{3x}{x-1} = \frac{2}{x-2} - \frac{2}{x^2-3x+2}$

< Objective 3 >

Find the zeros of each function.

51. $f(x) = \frac{x}{10} - \frac{12}{5}$

52. $f(x) = \frac{4x}{3} - \frac{x}{6}$

53. $f(x) = \frac{12}{x+5} - \frac{5}{x}$

54. $f(x) = \frac{1}{x-2} - \frac{3}{x}$

55. $f(x) = \frac{1}{x-3} + \frac{2}{x} - \frac{5}{3x}$

56. $f(x) = \frac{2}{x} - \frac{1}{x+1} - \frac{3}{x^2+x}$

57. $f(x) = 1 + \frac{39}{x^2} - \frac{16}{x}$

58. $f(x) = x - \frac{72}{x} + 1$

< Objective 4 >

Solve each equation for the indicated variable.

59. $\frac{1}{x} = \frac{1}{a} - \frac{1}{b}$ for x

60. $\frac{1}{x} = \frac{1}{a} + \frac{1}{b}$ for a

61. $\frac{1}{R} = \frac{1}{R_1} + \frac{1}{R_2}$ for R_1 > Videos

62. $\frac{1}{F} = \frac{1}{D_1} + \frac{1}{D_2}$ for D_2

63. $y = \frac{x + 1}{x - 1}$ for x

64. $y = \frac{x - 3}{x - 2}$ for x

65. $t = \frac{A - P}{Pr}$ for P

66. $I = \frac{nE}{R + nr}$ for n

< Objective 5 >

Solve the following problems.

67. **Science and Medicine** A motorboat can travel 20 mi/h in still water. If the boat can travel 3 mi downstream on a river in the same time it takes to travel 2 mi upstream, what is the rate of the river's current?

68. **Science and Medicine** A small jet has an airspeed (the rate in still air) of 300 mi/h. During one day's flights, the pilot noted that the plane could fly 85 mi with a tailwind in the same time it took to fly 65 mi against that same wind. What was the rate of the wind?

69. **Science and Medicine** A plane flew 720 mi with a steady 30-mi/h tailwind. The pilot then returned to the starting point, flying against that same wind. If the round-trip flight took 10 h, what was the plane's airspeed?

70. **Science and Medicine** Janet and Michael took a canoeing trip, traveling 6 mi upstream along a river, against a 2-mi/h current. They then returned downstream to the starting point of their trip. If their entire trip took 4 h, what was their rate in still water?

Answers

61. $\frac{RR_2}{R_2 - R}$

62. $\frac{D_1F}{D_1 - F}$

63. $\frac{y + 1}{y - 1}$

64. $\frac{2y - 3}{y - 1}$

65. $\frac{A}{1 + rt}$

66. $\frac{IR}{E - Ir}$

67. 4 mi/h

68. 40 mi/h

69. 150 mi/h

70. 4 mi/h

Answers

71. Bicycling: 25 mi/h, driving: 55 mi/h

72. Freight train: 45 mi/h, passenger train: 55 mi/h

73. First leg: 3 h, second leg: 2 h

74. First day: 5 h, second day: 3 h

75. Bus: 50 mi/h, train: 70 mi/h

76. Private plane: 180 mi/h, commercial plane: 360 mi/h

77. 6 h

78. 36 min

79. 15 h

71. **Science and Medicine** Po Ling can bicycle 75 mi in the same time it takes her to drive 165 mi. If her driving rate is 30 mi/h faster than her rate on the bicycle, find each rate.

72. **Science and Medicine** A passenger train can travel 275 mi in the same time a freight train takes to travel 225 mi. If the speed of the passenger train is 10 mi/h more than that of the freight train, find the speed of each train.

73. **Science and Medicine** A light plane took 1 h longer to fly 540 mi on the first portion of a trip than to fly 360 mi on the second. If the rate was the same for each portion, what was the flying time for each leg of the trip?

74. **Science and Medicine** Gilbert took 2 h longer to drive 240 mi on the first day of a business trip than to drive 144 mi on the second day. If his rate was the same both days, what was his driving time for each day?

75. **Science and Medicine** An express train and a passenger bus leave the same city, at the same time, for a destination 350 mi away. The rate of the train is 20 mi/h faster than the rate of the bus. If the train arrives at its destination 2 h ahead of the bus, find each rate.

76. **Science and Medicine** A private plane and a commercial plane take off from an airport at the same time for a city 720 mi away. The rate of the private plane is 180 mi/h less than that of the commercial plane. If the commercial plane arrives 2 h ahead of the private plane, find each plane's rate.

77. **Science and Medicine** One road crew can pave a section of highway in 15 h. A second crew, working with newer equipment, can do the same job in 10 h. How long would it take to pave that same section of highway if both crews worked together?

78. **Science and Medicine** One computer printer can print a company's weekly payroll checks in 60 min. A second printer would take 90 min to complete the job. How long would it take the two printers, operating together, to print the checks?

79. **Science and Medicine** An inlet pipe can fill a tank in 10 h. An outlet pipe can drain that same tank in 30 h. The inlet valve is opened, but the outlet valve is accidentally left open. How long will it take to fill the tank with both valves open?

80. **Science and Medicine** A bathtub can be filled in 8 min. It takes 12 min for the bathtub to drain. If the faucet is turned on but the drain is also left open, how long will it take to fill the tub?

81. **Science and Medicine** An electrician can wire a house in 20 h. If she works with an apprentice, the same job can be completed in 12 h. How long would it take the apprentice, working alone, to wire the house?

82. **Science and Medicine** A landscaper can prepare and seed a new lawn in 12 h. If he works with an assistant, the job takes 8 h. How long would it take the assistant, working alone, to complete the job?

83. **Science and Medicine** An experienced roofer can work twice as fast as her helper. Working together, they can shingle a new section of roof in 4 h. How long would it take the experienced roofer, working alone, to complete the same job?

84. **Science and Medicine** One model copier operates at 3 times the speed of another. Working together, the copiers can copy a report in 8 min. The faster model breaks down, and the other model must be used. How long will the job take with the machine that is available?

85. **Science and Medicine** A college uses two optical scanners to grade multiple-choice tests. One model takes 12 min longer to complete the scoring of a test than the other model. If by both models working together the test can be scored in 8 min, how long would each model take to score the same test, used by itself?

86. **Science and Medicine** Virginia can complete her company's monthly report in 5 h less time than Carl. If they work together, the report will take them 6 h to finish. How long would it take Virginia, working alone?

87. **Number Problem** The sum of the reciprocals of two consecutive integers is equal to 11 times the reciprocal of the product of those integers. What are the two integers?

Answers

80. 24 min
81. 30 h
82. 24 h
83. 6 h
84. 32 min
85. 12 min, 24 min
86. 10 h
87. 5, 6

Answers

88. 4, 6

89. 10

90. 9

91. 6, 8

92. 2, 5

93. 40.9 mi/h

94. 2,592,000 sec

95. 2,000,000,000 bytes

96. 3.7 ft/sec

97. \$2,430

98. It is impossible!

88. **Number Problem** The sum of the reciprocals of two consecutive even integers is equal to 10 times the reciprocal of the product of those integers. Find the two integers.

89. **Number Problem** If the same number is added to the numerator and denominator of $\frac{2}{5}$, the result is $\frac{4}{5}$. What is that number?

90. **Number Problem** If the same number is subtracted from the numerator and denominator of $\frac{11}{15}$, the result is $\frac{1}{3}$. Find that number.

91. **Number Problem** One positive number is 2 more than another. If the sum of the reciprocals of the two numbers is $\frac{7}{24}$, what are those numbers?

92. **Number Problem** One integer is 3 less than another. If the sum of the reciprocals of the two numbers is $\frac{7}{10}$, find the two integers.

93. A car is traveling at the rate of 60 ft/sec. To the nearest tenth, convert the speed to miles per hour.

94. How many seconds are there in the month of June?

95. Arlene's hard drive has 2 gigabytes of memory. How many bytes is this?

96. Mr. Fernandez can walk 5 mi in 2 h. What is his speed in feet per second, to the nearest tenth?

97. Trucks in Sam's home state are taxed at the rate of 0.15¢ per gram. His truck weighs 1,620 kg. What is his annual tax?

Basic Skills | Advanced Skills | Vocational-Technical Applications | Calculator/Computer | **Above and Beyond**

98. Suppose you travel to a certain destination at an average speed of 30 mi/h. What should your speed be on the return trip to bring your overall average speed to 60 mi/h?

Answers

1. Equation, 36 **3.** Expression, $\frac{3x}{10}$ **5.** Equation, 5 **7.** Equation, 3
9. 5 **11.** 8 **13.** $\frac{3}{2}$ **15.** -1 **17.** $-\frac{9}{5}$ **19.** $-\frac{2}{3}$
21. No solution **23.** -23 **25.** 6 **27.** 4 **29.** 8 **31.** 4
33. $\frac{3}{2}$ **35.** No solution **37.** 7 **39.** 5 **41.** $2, -\frac{3}{2}$ **43.** 5, 6
45. 4, 6 **47.** $-\frac{1}{2}, 6$ **49.** $-\frac{1}{2}$ **51.** 24 **53.** $\frac{25}{7}$ **55.** $\frac{3}{4}$
57. 3, 13 **59.** $\frac{ab}{b - a}$ **61.** $\frac{RR_2}{R_2 - R}$ **63.** $\frac{y + 1}{y - 1}$ **65.** $\frac{A}{1 + rt}$
67. 4 mi/h **69.** 150 mi/h **71.** Bicycling: 25 mi/h, driving: 55 mi/h
73. First leg: 3 h, second leg: 2 h **75.** Bus: 50 mi/h, train: 70 mi/h
77. 6 h **79.** 15 h **81.** 30 h **83.** 6 h **85.** 12 min, 24 min
87. 5, 6 **89.** 10 **91.** 6, 8 **93.** 40.9 mi/h **95.** 2,000,000,000 bytes
97. $2,430

6.6 Variation

< 6.6 Objectives >

1 > Solve problems involving direct variation

2 > Solve problems involving inverse variation

3 > Solve problems involving direct, inverse, and joint variation

NOTE

Considering these special functions is called the study of *variation* because the quantity varies.

NOTE

The idea that the circumference is a constant times the diameter was known to the Babylonians as early as 2000 B.C.

We have seen that equations can describe a relationship between two quantities. One particular type of equation is so common that there exists a precise terminology to describe the relationship. That type of equation is our focus in this section. In each case we will see that a quantity is *varying* with respect to one or more other quantities in a particular fashion.

Suppose that our quantities are related in a manner such that one is a constant multiple of the other. There are many real-world applications.

The circumference of a circle is a constant multiple of the length of its diameter:

$$C = \pi d$$

Circumference — The constant pi — Diameter

If a rate or speed is constant, the distance traveled is a constant multiple of time.

$$d = rt$$

Distance — Rate—a constant — Time

If you earn a fixed hourly pay, your total pay is a constant multiple of the number of hours that you worked.

$$T = ph$$

Total pay — Hourly pay—a constant — Hours worked

In all the preceding cases, the changes in one variable are proportional to the changes in the other. For instance, if the diameter of a circle is *doubled,* its circumference is *doubled.* This leads to our first definition.

Definition

Direct Variation

If y is a constant multiple of x, we write

$y = kx$ $\quad$ k is a constant

and say that *y varies directly* as x, or that y is *directly proportional* to x. The constant k is called the *constant of variation*.

Typically, in a variation problem, you will be given the type of variation involved and related values for the variables. From this information you can determine the constant of variation and, therefore, the equation relating the quantities. The following examples illustrate.

Example 1 Solving a Direct Variation Problem

< Objective 1 >

If y varies directly as x and $y = 40$ when $x = 8$, find the equation relating x and y. Also find the value of y when $x = 10$.

Because y varies directly with x, from our definition we have

$$y = kx$$

We need to determine k, and this is done by using the information given and letting $x = 8$ and $y = 40$:

$$40 = k(8)$$
$$k = 5$$

The desired equation relating x and y is then

$$y = 5x$$

To complete the example, if $x = 10$,

$$y = 5(10) = 50$$

> **NOTE**
>
> As you will see, in direct variation, as the absolute value of one variable *increases,* the absolute value of the other also *increases.*

Check Yourself 1

If y varies directly as x and $y = 72$ when $x = 9$, find the value of y when $x = 12$.

As we said, problems of variation occur frequently in applications of mathematics to many fields. The following is a typical example.

Example 2 Solving a Direct Variation Application

In physics, it is known that the force F needed to stretch a spring x units varies directly with x. If a force of 18 lb stretches a spring 3 in., how far will the same spring be stretched by a force of 30 lb?

From the problem we know that $F = kx$, and letting $F = 18$ and $x = 3$, we have

$$18 = k(3)$$
$$k = 6$$

Therefore, $F = 6x$ relates the two variables. Now, to find x when $F = 30$, we write

$$30 = 6x$$
$$x = 5$$

So the force of 30 lb would stretch the spring 5 in.

> **NOTE**
>
> Example 2 is an application of Hooke's law.

Check Yourself 2

The pressure at a point under water is directly proportional to the depth. If the pressure at a depth of 2 ft is 125 lb/ft², find the pressure at a depth of 10 ft.

NOTE

We also say that "*y* varies directly with the square of *x*."

Many applications require that one variable be directly proportional to some power of a second variable. For instance, we might say that *y* is directly proportional to the square of *x* and write

$$y = kx^2$$

Consider Example 3.

Example 3 Solving a Direct Variation Problem

The distance *s* that an object will fall from rest (neglecting air resistance) varies directly with the square of the time *t*. If an object falls 64 feet in 2 seconds, how far will it fall in 5 seconds?

The relating equation in this example is

$$s = kt^2$$

By letting $s = 64$ and $t = 2$, we can determine k:

$$64 = k(2)^2$$

$$64 = 4k$$

so

$$k = 16$$

We now know that the desired equation is $s = 16t^2$, and substituting 5 for t, we have

$$s = 16(5)^2 = 400 \text{ feet}$$

NOTE

Perhaps the most common example of inverse variation is the relationship between rate and time. The faster something travels (rate *increases*), the sooner it arrives (time *decreases*).

Check Yourself 3

The distance that an object falls from rest varies directly with the square of time *t*. If an object falls 144 feet in 3 seconds, how far does it fall in 6 seconds?

If two quantities are related so that an *increase* in the absolute value of the first gives a proportional *decrease* in the absolute value of the second, we say that the variables *vary inversely* with each other. This leads to our second definition.

Definition

Inverse Variation

If *y varies inversely* as *x*, we write

$$y = \frac{k}{x} \qquad k \text{ is a constant}$$

We can also say that *y* is *inversely proportional* to *x*.

Example 4 Solving an Inverse Variation Problem

< Objective 2 >

If y varies inversely as x and $y = 18$ when $x = \frac{1}{2}$, find the equation relating x and y. Also find the value of y when $x = 3$.

Because y varies inversely as x, we can write

$$y = \frac{k}{x}$$

Now with $y = 18$ and $x = \frac{1}{2}$, we have

$$18 = \frac{k}{\frac{1}{2}}$$

$$9 = k$$

We now have the desired equation relating x and y:

$$y = \frac{9}{x}$$

and when $x = 3$,

$$y = \frac{9}{3} = 3$$

Check Yourself 4

If w is inversely proportional to z and $w = 15$ when $z = 5$, find the equation relating z and w. Also find the value of w when $z = 3$.

Let us consider an application that involves the idea of inverse variation.

Example 5 Solving an Inverse Variation Application

The intensity of illumination I of a light source varies inversely as the square of the distance d from that source. If the illumination 4 ft from the source is 9 foot-candles (fc), find the illumination 6 ft from the source.

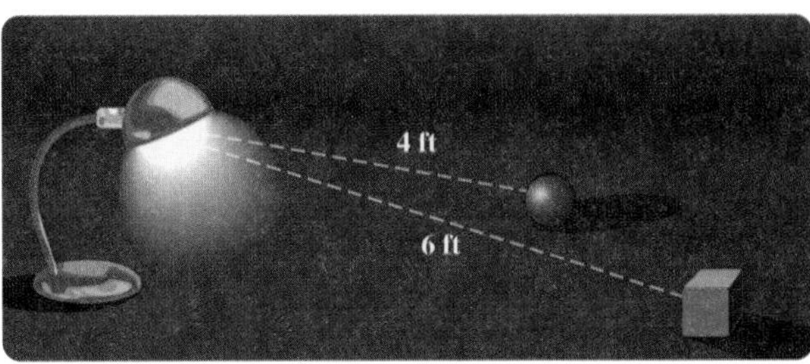

From the given information we know that

$$I = \frac{k}{d^2}$$

Letting $d = 4$ and $I = 9$, we first find the constant of variation k:

$$9 = \frac{k}{4^2} \quad \text{or} \quad 9 = \frac{k}{16}$$

and

$$k = 144$$

The equation relating I and d is then

$$I = \frac{144}{d^2}$$

and when $d = 6$,

$$I = \frac{144}{6^2} = \frac{144}{36} = 4 \text{ fc}$$

Check Yourself 5

At a constant temperature, the volume of a gas varies inversely as the pressure. If a gas has volume 200 ft^3 under a pressure of 40 pounds per square inch (lb/in.^{2}), what will be its volume under a pressure of 50 lb/in.^{2}?

NOTE

You probably recognize that k, the constant of variation, is π in the formula.

It is also common for one quantity to depend on *several* others. We can find a familiar example from geometry.

The volume of a cylinder depends on its height and the square of its radius.

This is an example of *joint variation.* We say that the volume V varies jointly with the height h and the square of the radius r. We can write

$$V = khr^2$$

In general:

Definition

Joint Variation

If z *varies jointly* as x and y, we write

$z = kxy$ $\quad$ k is a constant

The solution techniques for problems involving joint variation are similar to those used earlier, as Example 6 illustrates.

Example 6 Solving a Joint Variation Problem

Assume that z varies jointly as x and y. If $z = 100$ when $x = 2$ and $y = 20$, find the value of z if $x = 4$ and $y = 30$.

From the given information we have

$$z = kxy$$

Letting $z = 100$, $x = 2$, and $y = 20$ gives

$$100 = k(2)(20) \quad \text{or} \quad k = \frac{5}{2}$$

The equation relating z with x and y is then

$$z = \frac{5}{2}xy$$

and when $x = 4$ and $y = 30$, by substitution

$$z = \frac{5}{2}(4)(30) = 300$$

Check Yourself 6

Assume that r varies jointly as s and t. If $r = 64$ when $s = 3$ and $t = 8$, find the value of r when $s = 16$ and $t = 12$.

Once again there are many physical applications of the concept of joint variation. The following is a typical example.

Example 7 Solving a Joint Variation Application

The "safe load" for a wooden rectangular beam varies jointly as its width and the square of its depth.

If the safe load of a beam 2 in. wide and 8 in. deep is 640 lb, what is the safe load of a beam 4 in. wide and 6 in. deep?

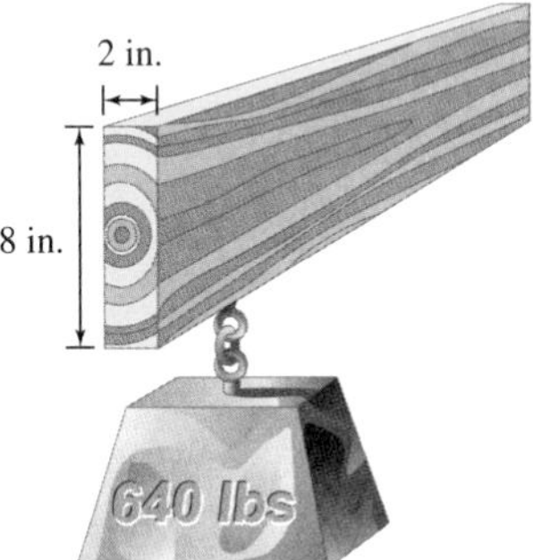

> **NOTE**
>
> S is the safe load, w the width, and d the depth.

From the given information,

$$S = kwd^2$$

Substituting the given values yields

$$640 = k(2)(8)^2$$
$$k = 5$$

We then have the equation

$$S = 5wd^2$$

and, for the 4 by 6 in. beam,

$$S = 5(4)(6)^2 = 720 \text{ lb}$$

Check Yourself 7

The force of a wind F blowing on a vertical wall varies jointly as the surface area of the wall A and the square of the wind velocity v.

If a wind of 20 mi/h has a force of 100 lb on a wall with area 50 ft^2, what force will a wind of 40 mi/h produce on the same wall?

There is one final category of variation problems. This category involves applications in which inverse variation is combined with direct or joint variation in stating the equation relating the variables.

These are called *combined variation* problems. In general, a typical statement form is as follows:

Definition

Combined Variation

If z varies directly as x and inversely as y, we write

$$z = \frac{kx}{y} \qquad k \text{ is a constant}$$

Example 8 **Solving a Combined Variation Problem**

< Objective 3 >

Assume that w varies directly as x and inversely as the square of y. When $x = 8$ and $y = 4$, $w = 18$. Find w if $x = 4$ and $y = 6$.

From the given information we can write

$$w = \frac{kx}{y^2}$$

Substituting the known values, we have

$$18 = \frac{k \cdot 8}{4^2} \quad \text{or} \quad k = 36$$

We now have the equation

$$w = \frac{36x}{y^2}$$

and letting $x = 4$ and $y = 6$, we get

$$w = \frac{36 \cdot 4}{6^2} = 4$$

Check Yourself 8

Ohm's law for an electric circuit states that the current I varies directly as the electromotive force E and inversely as the resistance R.

If the current is 10 amperes (A), the electromotive force is 110 volts (V) and the resistance is 11 ohms (Ω). Find the current for an electromotive force of 220 V and a resistance of 5 Ω.

Translating verbal problems to algebraic equations is the basis for all variation applications. The following table gives some typical examples from our work in this section.

Variation Statement	Algebraic Equation
y varies directly as x.	$y = kx$
y varies inversely as x.	$y = \frac{k}{x}$
z varies jointly as x and as y.	$z = kxy$
z varies directly as x and inversely as y.	$z = \frac{kx}{y}$

All four basic types of variation problems involve essentially the same solution technique. The following algorithm summarizes the steps involved in all the variation problems that we have considered.

Step by Step

Solving Problems Involving Variation

Step 1 Translate the given problem to an algebraic equation involving the constant of variation k.

Step 2 Use the given values to find that constant.

Step 3 Replace k with the value found in step 2 to form the general equation relating the variables.

Step 4 Substitute the appropriate values of the variables to solve for the corresponding value of the desired unknown quantity.

Check Yourself ANSWERS

1. $y = 96$ **2.** 625 lb/ft^2 **3.** 576 ft **4.** $w = \frac{75}{z}$, $w = 25$ **5.** 160 ft^3 **6.** $r = 512$ **7.** 400 lb **8.** $I = \frac{kE}{R}$ and $k = 1$, so $I = 44$ A

Reading Your Text

The following fill-in-the-blank exercises are designed to ensure that you understand some of the key vocabulary used in this section.

SECTION 6.6

(a) For $y = kx$, that is, y varies directly as x, the constant k is called the constant of ____________.

(b) If two quantities are related so that an increase in the absolute value of the first gives a proportional decrease in the absolute value of the second, we say that the variables vary ____________ with each other.

(c) One quantity depending on several others is an example of ____________ variation.

(d) Applications in which inverse variation is combined with direct or joint variation in stating the equation relating the variables are called ____________ variation problems.

6.6 exercises

Basic Skills | Advanced Skills | Vocational-Technical Applications | Calculator/Computer | Above and Beyond

MathZone

Boost your grade at mathzone.com!
- Practice Problems
- NetTutor
- Self-Tests
- e-Professors
- Videos

Name ____________

Section ________ Date ________

In exercises 1 to 10, translate each of the statements of variation to an algebraic equation, using k as the constant of variation.

1. s varies directly as the square of x.

2. z is directly proportional to the square root of w.

3. r is inversely proportional to s.

4. m varies inversely as the cube of n.

5. V varies directly as T and inversely as P.

6. A varies jointly as x and y.

7. V varies jointly as h and the square of r.

8. t is directly proportional to d and inversely proportional to r.

9. w varies jointly as x and y and inversely as the square of z.

10. p varies jointly as r and the square of s and inversely as the cube of t.

In exercises 11 to 20, find k, the constant of variation, given each set of conditions.

11. y varies directly with x; $y = 54$ when $x = 6$.

12. m varies inversely with p; $m = 5$ when $p = 3$.

13. r is inversely proportional to the square of s; $r = 5$ when $s = 4$.

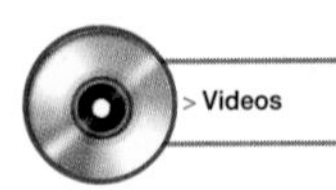

14. u varies directly with the square of w; $u = 75$ when $w = 5$.

Answers

1. $s = kx^2$
2. $z = k\sqrt{w}$
3. $r = \frac{k}{s}$
4. $m = \frac{k}{n^3}$
5. $V = \frac{kT}{P}$
6. $A = kxy$
7. $V = khr^2$
8. $t = \frac{kd}{r}$
9. $w = \frac{kxy}{z^2}$
10. $p = \frac{krs^2}{t^3}$
11. $k = 9$
12. $k = 15$
13. $k = 80$
14. $k = 3$

15. V varies jointly as x and y; $V = 100$ when $x = 5$ and $y = 4$.

16. w is directly proportional to u and inversely proportional to v; $w = 20$ when $u = 10$ and $v = 3$.

17. z varies directly as the square of x and inversely as y; $z = 20$ when $x = 2$ and $y = 4$.

> Videos

18. p varies jointly as r and the square of q; $p = 144$ when $q = 6$ and $r = 2$.

19. m varies jointly as n and the square of p and inversely as r; $m = 40$ when $n = 5$, $p = 2$, and $r = 4$.

> Videos

20. x varies directly as the square of y and inversely as w and z; $x = 8$ when $y = 4$, $w = 3$, and $z = 2$.

< Objectives 1–3 >

In exercises 21 to 26, solve each variation problem.

21. Let y vary directly with x. If $y = 60$ when $x = 5$, find the value of y when $x = 8$.

22. Suppose that z varies inversely as the square of w and that $z = 3$ when $w = 4$. Find the value of z when $w = 6$.

23. Variable A varies jointly with x and y, and $A = 120$ when $x = 6$ and $y = 5$. Find the value of A when $x = 8$ and $y = 3$.

> Videos

24. Let p be directly proportional to q and inversely proportional to the square of r. If $p = 3$ when $q = 8$ and $r = 4$, find p when $q = 9$ and $r = 6$.

25. Suppose that s varies directly with r and inversely with the square of t. If $s = 4$ when $r = 12$ and $t = 6$, find the value of s when $r = 8$ and $t = 4$.

> Videos

26. Variable p varies jointly with the square root of r and the square of q. If $p = 72$ when $r = 16$ and $q = 3$, find the value of p when $r = 25$ and $q = 2$.

In exercises 27 to 40, solve each variation application.

27. **Science and Medicine** The length that a spring will stretch varies directly as the force applied to the spring. If a force of 10 lb will stretch a spring 2 in., what force will stretch the same spring 3 in.?

Answers

15. $k = 5$
16. $k = 6$
17. $k = 20$
18. $k = 2$
19. $k = 8$
20. $k = 3$
21. $y = 96$
22. $z = \frac{4}{3}$
23. $A = 96$
24. $p = \frac{3}{2}$
25. $s = 6$
26. $p = 40$
27. 15 lb

Answers

28. 6 ft^3
29. 22 A
30. 100 ft
31. 32π cm^3
32. 1,280 lb
33. 180 ft
34. 4.4 sec
35. 75 mi
36. 12 fc

28. **Science and Medicine** If the temperature of a gas is held constant, the volume occupied by that gas varies inversely as the pressure to which the gas is subjected. If the volume of a gas is 8 ft^3 when the pressure is 12 lb/in.^{2}, find the volume of the gas if the pressure is 16 lb/in.^{2}

29. **Science and Medicine** If the current, in amperes, in an electric circuit is inversely proportional to the resistance, the current is 55 A when the resistance is 2 Ω. Find the current when the resistance is 5 Ω.

30. **Science and Medicine** The distance that a ball rolls down an inclined plane varies directly as the square of the time. If the ball rolls 36 ft in 3 sec, how far will it roll in 5 sec?

31. **Geometry** The volume of a right circular cone varies jointly as the height and the square of the radius. If the volume of the cone is 15π cm^3 when the height is 5 cm and the radius is 3 cm, find the volume when the height is 6 cm and the radius is 4 cm.

32. **Science and Medicine** The safe load of a rectangular beam varies jointly as its width and the square of its depth. If the safe load of a beam is 1,000 lb when the width is 2 in. and the depth is 10 in., find its safe load when the width is 4 in. and the depth is 8 in.

33. **Science and Medicine** The stopping distance (in feet) of an automobile varies directly as the square of its speed (in miles per hour). If a car can stop in a distance of 80 ft from 40 mi/h, how much distance will it take to stop from a speed of 60 mi/h?

34. **Science and Medicine** The period (the time required for one complete swing) of a simple pendulum is directly proportional to the square root of its length. If a pendulum with length 9 cm has a period of 3.3 sec, find the period of a pendulum with length 16 cm.

35. **Science and Medicine** The distance (in miles) that a person can see to the horizon from a point above Earth's surface is directly proportional to the square root of the height (in feet) of that point. If a person 100 ft above Earth's surface can see 12.5 mi, how far can an observer in a light airplane at 3,600 ft see to the horizon?

36. **Science and Medicine** The illumination produced by a light source on a surface varies inversely as the square of the distance of that surface from the source. If a light source produces an illumination of 48 fc on a wall 4 ft from the source, what will be the illumination (in foot-candles) of a wall 8 ft from the source?

37. **Science and Medicine** The electrical resistance of a wire varies directly as its length and inversely as the square of its diameter. If a wire with length 200 ft and diameter 0.1 in. has a resistance of 2 Ω, what will be the resistance in a wire of length 400 ft with diameter 0.2 in.?

38. **Science and Medicine** The frequency of a guitar string varies directly as the square root of the tension on the string and inversely as the length of the string. If a frequency of 440 cycles per second, or *hertz* (Hz), is produced by a tension of 36 lb on a string of length 60 cm, what frequency (in hertz) will be produced by a tension of 64 lb on a string of length 40 cm?

39. **Science and Medicine** The temperature of the steam from a geothermal source is inversely proportional to the distance it is transported. Write an algebraic equation relating temperature (t) to distance (d).

40. **Science and Medicine** Power available from a wind generator varies jointly as the square of the diameter of the rotor and the cube of the wind velocity. Write an algebraic equation relating power (p), rotor diameter (d), and wind speed (v).

Basic Skills | Advanced Skills | **Vocational-Technical Applications** | Calculator/Computer | Above and Beyond

Solve each variation application.

41. **Allied Health** If the temperature remains constant, then the pressure, P [measured in millimeters of mercury (mmHg)], being exerted on a gas is inversely proportional to the volume, V [measured in liters (L)], of the gas. Suppose that the initial volume of a gas is 6.3 L with an initial pressure of 725 mmHg. What is the new pressure if the volume changes to 4.75 L?

42. **Allied Health** The number of mAs, the product of the milliamperage and the time in seconds, varies directly with the square of the distance between the source of the radiation and the object receiving the radiation. If 10 mAs were used to produce a satisfactory radiograph at a distance of 30 inches, what mAs would be required at a distance of 45 inches?

43. **Manufacturing Technology** The tensile strength of a steel reinforcement rod varies directly with the square of the radius. If a $\frac{3}{8}$-in.-diameter rod has a tensile strength of 320 pounds, what is the tensile strength of a $\frac{1}{2}$-in.-diameter rod?

44. **Manufacturing Technology** The revolutions per minute (rpm) of a gear varies inversely with the number of teeth it has. If a gear with 8 teeth is spinning at 400 rpm, how many revolutions per minute is a gear with 5 teeth spinning?

Answers

37. 1 Ω
38. 880 Hz
39. $t = \frac{k}{d}$
40. $P = kd^2v^3$
41. 962 mmHg
42. 22.5 mAs
43. 569 lb
44. 640 rpm

Answers

45. 4×10^8 m

46. 1.95 sec

45. Information Technology The distance a packet travels is directly proportional to the time it takes to transmit the bit. If the rate of the transmission in a wire is 2×10^8 m/sec, and it took 2 sec to transmit a packet, what distance did the packet travel?

46. Information Technology The time it takes to transmit a packet over a certain distance is inversely proportional to the rate of transmission. If the rate of transmission is 1.2×10^9 m/sec and the distance traveled is 2.34×10^9 m, how long did it take transmit the packet?

Answers

1. $s = kx^2$ **3.** $r = \frac{k}{s}$ **5.** $V = \frac{kT}{P}$ **7.** $V = khr^2$ **9.** $w = \frac{kxy}{z^2}$
11. $k = 9$ **13.** $k = 80$ **15.** $k = 5$ **17.** $k = 20$ **19.** $k = 8$
21. $y = 96$ **23.** $A = 96$ **25.** $s = 6$ **27.** 15 lb **29.** 22 A
31. 32π cm^3 **33.** 180 ft **35.** 75 mi **37.** 1 Ω **39.** $t = \frac{k}{d}$
41. 962 mmHg **43.** 569 lb **45.** 4×10^8 m

Definition/Procedure	Example	Reference
Simplification of Rational Expressions and Functions		**Section 6.1**
Rational expressions have the form $\frac{P}{Q}$ in which P and Q are polynomials and $Q(x) \neq 0$ for all x.	$\frac{x^2 - 5x}{x - 3}$ is a rational expression. The variable x cannot have the value 3.	p. 544
Fundamental Principle of Rational Expressions		
For polynomials P, Q, and R, $\frac{P}{Q} = \frac{PR}{QR}$ when $Q \neq 0$ and $R \neq 0$. This principle can be used in two ways. We can multiply or divide the numerator and denominator of a rational expression by the same nonzero polynomial.	This uses the fact that $\frac{R}{R} = 1$ when $R \neq 0$.	p. 546
Simplifying Rational Expressions		
To simplify a rational expression, use the following algorithm. **Step 1** Completely factor both the numerator and denominator of the expression. **Step 2** Divide the numerator and denominator by *all* common factors. **Step 3** The resulting expression will be in simplest form (or in lowest terms).	$\frac{x^2 - 4}{x^2 - 2x - 8}$ $= \frac{(x - 2)(x + 2)}{(x - 4)(x + 2)}$ $= \frac{x - 2}{x - 4}$	p. 548
Identifying Rational Functions		
A rational function is a function that is defined by a rational expression. It can be written as $f(x) = \frac{P}{Q}$ in which P and Q are polynomials, $Q \neq 0$		p. 548
Simplifying Rational Functions		
When we simplify a rational function, it is important that we note the x-values that need to be excluded, particularly when we are trying to draw the graph of a function. The set of ordered pairs of the simplified function will be exactly the same as the set of ordered pairs of the original function. If we plug the excluded value(s) for x into the simplified expression, we get a set of ordered pairs that represent "holes" in the graph. These holes are breaks in the curve. We use an open circle to designate them on a graph.		p. 549

Continued

Definition/Procedure	Example	Reference
Multiplication and Division of Rational Expressions and Functions		Section 6.2
Multiplying Rational Expressions		
For polynomials P, Q, R, and S, $\frac{P}{Q} \cdot \frac{R}{S} = \frac{PR}{QS}$ when $Q \neq 0, S \neq 0$ In practice, we apply the following algorithm to multiply two rational expressions. **Step 1** Write each numerator and denominator in completely factored form. **Step 2** Divide by any common factors appearing in both the numerator and denominator. **Step 3** Multiply as needed to form the desired product.	$\frac{2x - 6}{x^2 - 9} \cdot \frac{x^2 + 3x}{6x + 24}$ $= \frac{2(x - 3)}{(x - 3)(x + 3)} \cdot \frac{x(x + 3)}{6(x + 4)}$ $= \frac{x}{3(x + 4)}$	*pp.* 560, 561
Dividing Rational Expressions		
For polynomials P, Q, R, and S, $\frac{P}{Q} \div \frac{R}{S} = \frac{P}{Q} \cdot \frac{S}{R} = \frac{PS}{QR}$ when $Q \neq 0, R \neq 0, S \neq 0$ To divide two rational expressions, you can apply the following algorithm. **Step 1** Invert the divisor (the *second* rational expression) to write the problem as one of multiplication. **Step 2** Proceed as in the algorithm for the multiplication of rational expressions.	$\frac{5y}{2y - 8} \div \frac{10y^2}{y^2 - y - 12}$ $= \frac{5y}{2y - 8} \cdot \frac{y^2 - y - 12}{10y^2}$ $= \frac{5y}{2(y - 4)} \cdot \frac{(y - 4)(y + 3)}{10y^2}$ $= \frac{y + 3}{4y}$	*pp.* 562, 563
Addition and Subtraction of Rational Expressions and Functions		Section 6.3
Adding and Subtracting Rational Expressions		
To add or subtract rational expressions with the same denominator, add or subtract their numerators and then write that sum over the common denominator. The result should be written in lowest terms. In symbols, $\frac{P}{R} + \frac{Q}{R} = \frac{P + Q}{R}$ and $\frac{P}{R} - \frac{Q}{R} = \frac{P - Q}{R}$ when $R \neq 0$.	$\frac{5w}{w^2 - 16} - \frac{20}{w^2 - 16}$ $= \frac{5w - 20}{w^2 - 16}$ $= \frac{5(w - 4)}{(w + 4)(w - 4)}$ $= \frac{5}{w + 4}$	*p.* 571

Definition/Procedure	Example	Reference
Least Common Denominator		
The **least common denominator (LCD)** of a group of rational expressions is the simplest polynomial that is divisible by each of the individual denominators of the rational expressions. To find the LCD, use the following algorithm. **Step 1** Write each of the denominators in completely factored form. **Step 2** Write the LCD as the product of each prime factor, to the highest power to which it appears in the factored form of any individual denominators.	To find the LCD for $\frac{2}{x^2 + 2x + 1}$ and $\frac{3}{x^2 + x}$ write $x^2 + 2x + 1 = (x + 1)(x + 1)$ $x^2 + x = x(x + 1)$ The LCD is $x(x + 1)(x + 1)$	p. 572
Now to add or subtract rational expressions with different denominators, we first find the LCD by the procedure just outlined. We then rewrite each of the rational expressions with that LCD as a common denominator. Then we can add or subtract as before.	$\frac{2}{(x + 1)^2} - \frac{3}{x(x + 1)}$ $= \frac{2 \cdot x}{(x + 1)^2 x} - \frac{3(x + 1)}{x(x + 1)(x + 1)}$ $= \frac{2x - 3(x + 1)}{x(x + 1)(x + 1)}$ $= \frac{-x - 3}{x(x + 1)(x + 1)}$	p. 574
Complex Fractions		**Section 6.4**
Complex fractions are fractions that have a fraction in their numerator or denominator (or both). There are two commonly used methods for simplifying complex fractions: Methods 1 and 2. ***Method 1*** **Step 1** Multiply the numerator and denominator of the complex fraction by the LCD of all the fractions that appear within the numerator and denominator. **Step 2** Simplify the resulting rational expression, writing the result in lowest terms.	Simplify $\frac{1 - \frac{2}{x}}{1 - \frac{4}{x^2}}$ Method 1: $\frac{\left(1 - \frac{2}{x}\right)x^2}{\left(1 - \frac{4}{x^2}\right)x^2}$ $= \frac{x^2 - 2x}{x^2 - 4} = \frac{x(x - 2)}{(x + 2)(x - 2)}$ $= \frac{x}{x + 2}$	pp. 587, 590
Method 2 **Step 1** Write the numerator and denominator of the complex fraction as single fractions, if necessary. **Step 2** Invert the denominator and multiply as before, writing the result in lowest terms.	Method 2: $\frac{\frac{x - 2}{x}}{\frac{x^2 - 4}{x^2}}$ $= \frac{x - 2}{x} \cdot \frac{x^2}{x^2 - 4}$ $= \frac{x - 2}{x} \cdot \frac{x^2}{(x + 2)(x - 2)}$ $= \frac{x}{x + 2}$	

Continued

Definition/Procedure	Example	Reference
Solving Rational Equations		**Section 6.5**
To solve an equation involving rational expressions, you should apply the following algorithm. **Step 1** Clear the equation of fractions by multiplying both sides of the equation by the LCD of all the fractions that appear. **Step 2** Solve the equation resulting from step 1. **Step 3** Check all solutions by substitution in the original equation.	Solve $\frac{3}{x-3} - \frac{2}{x+2} = \frac{19}{x^2 - x - 6}$ Multiply by the LCD $(x-3)(x+2)$: $3(x+2) - 2(x-3) = 19$ $3x + 6 - 2x + 6 = 19$ $x = 7$ Check: $\frac{3}{4} - \frac{2}{9} \stackrel{?}{=} \frac{19}{36}$ $\frac{19}{36} = \frac{19}{36}$ True	p. 604
Solve a Literal Equation That Involves a Rational Expression		
Formulas and **literal equations** express a relationship between more than one variable or letter. Solving a formula or literal equation for a variable means isolating that specified variable on one side of the equation. The steps used in the process are very similar to those used in solving linear equations.	Solve $t = \frac{A - P}{Pr}$ for A $Pr \cdot t = A - P$ $Prt + P = A$	p. 605
Variation		**Section 6.6**
Direct Variation		
If y *varies directly* as x (or y is *directly proportional* to x), we write $y = kx$ in which k is the *constant of variation.*	If y varies directly as x and $y = 64$ when $x = 4$, find the equation relating x and y. $y = kx$ $64 = k \cdot 4$ so $k = 16$ so $y = 16x$	p. 620
Inverse Variation		
If y *varies inversely* as x (or y is *inversely proportional* to x), we write $y = \frac{k}{x}$	If r varies inversely as the square of s, the relating equation is $r = \frac{k}{s^2}$	p. 622
Joint Variation		
If z *varies jointly* as x and y, we write $z = kxy$	If m varies jointly as n and the square root of p, the relating equation is $m = kn\sqrt{p}$	p. 624
Combined Variation		
If z varies directly as x and inversely as y, we write $z = \frac{kx}{y}$	If V varies directly as T and inversely as P, the relating equation is $V = \frac{kT}{P}$	p. 626

This summary exercise set is provided to give you practice with each of the objectives of this chapter. Each exercise is keyed to the appropriate chapter section. When you are finished, you can check your answers to the odd-numbered exercises against those presented in the back of the text. If you have difficulty with any of these questions, go back and reread the examples from that section. The answers to the even-numbered exercises appear in the *Instructor's Solutions Manual.* Your instructor will give you guidelines on how to best use these exercises in your instructional setting.

6.1 *For what value of the variable will each of the following rational expressions be undefined?*

1. $\frac{x}{2}$ Never undefined

2. $\frac{3}{y}$ $y \neq 0$

3. $\frac{2}{x - 5}$ $x \neq 5$

4. $\frac{3x}{2x - 5}$ $x \neq \frac{5}{2}$

Simplify each of the following rational expressions.

5. $\frac{18x^5}{24x^3}$ $\frac{3x^2}{4}$

6. $\frac{15m^3n}{-5mn^2}$ $\frac{-3m^2}{n}$

7. $\frac{8y - 64}{y - 8}$ 8

8. $\frac{5x - 20}{x^2 - 16}$ $\frac{5}{x + 4}$

9. $\frac{9 - x^2}{x^2 + 2x - 15}$ $-\frac{x + 3}{x + 5}$

10. $\frac{3w^2 + 8w - 35}{2w^2 + 13w + 15}$ $\frac{3w - 7}{2w + 3}$

11. $\frac{6a^2 - ab - b^2}{9a^2 - b^2}$ $\frac{2a - b}{3a - b}$

12. $\frac{6w - 3z}{8w^3 - z^3}$ $\frac{3}{4w^2 + 2wz + z^2}$

Graph the following rational functions. Indicate the coordinates of the hole in the graph.

13. $f(x) = \frac{x^2 - 3x - 4}{x + 1}$

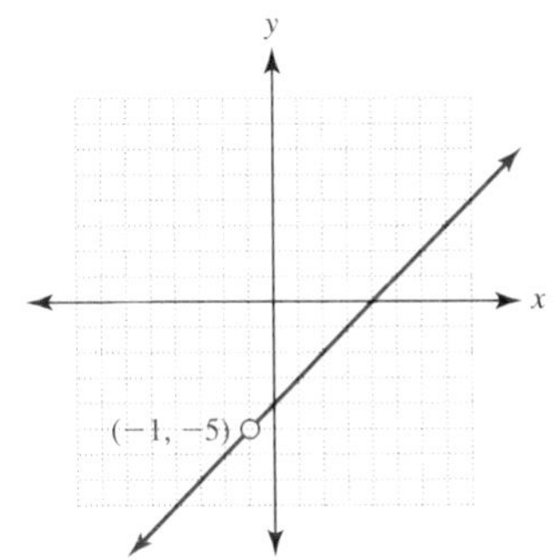

14. 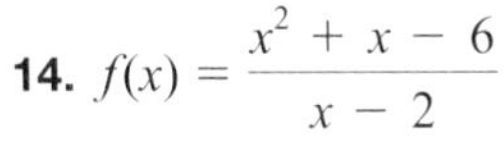 $f(x) = \frac{x^2 + x - 6}{x - 2}$

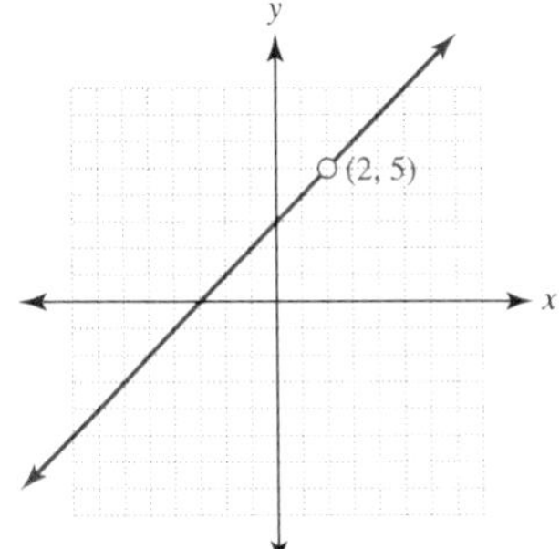

6.2 *Multiply or divide as indicated. Express your results in simplest form.*

15. $\frac{x^5}{24} \cdot \frac{20}{x^3}$ $\frac{5x^2}{6}$

16. $\frac{a^3b}{4ab^2} \div \frac{ab}{12ab^2}$ $3a^2$

17. $\frac{6y - 18}{9y} \cdot \frac{10}{5y - 15}$ $\frac{4}{3y}$

18. $\frac{m^2 - 3m}{m^2 - 5m + 6} \cdot \frac{m^2 - 4}{m^2 + 7m + 10}$ $\frac{m}{m + 5}$

19. $\frac{a^2 - 2a}{a^2 - 4} \div \frac{2a^2}{3a + 6}$ $\frac{3}{2a}$

20. $\frac{r^2 + 2rs}{r^3 - r^2s} \div \frac{5r + 10s}{r^2 - 2rs + s^2}$ $\frac{r - s}{5r}$

21. $\frac{x^2 - 2xy - 3y^2}{x^2 - xy - 2y^2} \cdot \frac{x^2 - 4y^2}{x^2 - 8xy + 15y^2}$ $\frac{x + 2y}{x - 5y}$

22. $\frac{w^3 + 3w^2 + 2w + 6}{w^4 - 4} \div (w^3 + 27)$ $\frac{1}{(w^2 - 2)(w^2 - 3w + 9)}$

23. Let $f(x) = \frac{x^2 - 16}{x - 5}$ and $g(x) = \frac{x^2 - 25}{x + 4}$. Find **(a)** $f(3) \cdot g(3)$, **(b)** $h(x) = f(x) \cdot g(x)$, **(c)** $h(3)$.

(a) -8; (b) $x^2 + x - 20$; (c) -8

24. Let $f(x) = \frac{2x^2 - 5x - 3}{x - 4}$ and $g(x) = \frac{x^2 - 3x - 4}{2x^2 + 5x + 2}$. Find **(a)** $f(3) \cdot g(3)$, **(b)** $h(x) = f(x) \cdot g(x)$, **(c)** $h(3)$.

(a) 0; (b) $\frac{x^2 - 2x - 3}{x + 2}$; (c) 0

6.3 *Perform the indicated operations. Express your results in simplified form.*

25. $\frac{5x + 7}{x + 4} - \frac{2x - 5}{x + 4}$ 3

26. $\frac{3}{4x^2} + \frac{5}{6x}$ $\frac{10x + 9}{12x^2}$

27. $\frac{2}{x - 5} - \frac{1}{x}$ $\frac{x + 5}{x(x - 5)}$

28. $\frac{2}{y + 5} + \frac{3}{y + 4}$ $\frac{5y + 23}{(y + 5)(y + 4)}$

29. $\frac{2}{3m - 3} - \frac{5}{2m - 2}$ $\frac{-11}{6(m - 1)}$

30. $\frac{7}{x - 3} - \frac{5}{3 - x}$ $\frac{12}{x - 3}$

31. $\frac{5}{4x + 4} + \frac{5}{2x - 2}$ $\frac{15x + 5}{4(x + 1)(x - 1)}$

32. $\frac{2a}{a^2 - 9a + 20} + \frac{8}{a - 4}$ $\frac{10}{a - 5}$

33. $\frac{2}{s-1} - \frac{6s}{s^2+s-2}$ $\frac{-4}{s+2}$

34. $\frac{4}{x^2-9} - \frac{3}{x^2-4x+3}$ $\frac{x-13}{(x+3)(x-3)(x-1)}$

35. $\frac{x^2-14x-8}{x^2-2x-8} + \frac{2x}{x-4} - \frac{3}{x+2}$ $\frac{3x-1}{x+2}$

36. $\frac{w^2+2wz+z^2}{w^2-wz-2z^2} \cdot \left(\frac{3}{w+z} - \frac{1}{w-z}\right)$ $\frac{2}{w-z}$

37. Let $f(x) = \frac{2x}{x-2}$ and $g(x) = \frac{x}{x-3}$. Find **(a)** $f(4) + g(4)$, **(b)** $h(x) = f(x) + g(x)$, **(c)** the ordered pair $(4, h(4))$.

(a) 8; (b) $\frac{3x^2-8x}{(x-2)(x-3)}$; (c) (4, 8)

38. Let $f(x) = \frac{x+2}{x-2}$ and $g(x) = \frac{x+1}{x-7}$. Find **(a)** $f(3) - g(3)$, **(b)** $h(x) = f(x) - g(x)$, **(c)** the ordered pair $(3, h(3))$.

(a) 6; (b) $\frac{-4x-12}{(x-2)(x-7)}$; (c) (3, 6)

6.4 *Simplify each of the following complex fractions.*

39. $\frac{\frac{x^2}{12}}{\frac{x^3}{8}}$ $\frac{2}{3x}$

40. $\frac{\frac{y-1}{y^2-4}}{\frac{y^2-1}{y^2-y-2}}$ $\frac{1}{y+2}$

41. $\frac{1+\frac{a}{b}}{1-\frac{a}{b}}$ $\frac{b+a}{b-a}$

42. $\frac{2-\frac{x}{y}}{4-\frac{x^2}{y^2}}$ $\frac{y}{2y+x}$

43. $\frac{\frac{1}{r}-\frac{1}{s}}{\frac{1}{r^2}-\frac{1}{s^2}}$ $\frac{rs}{s+r}$

44. $\frac{1-\frac{1}{x+2}}{1+\frac{1}{x+2}}$ $\frac{x+1}{x+3}$

45. $\frac{1-\frac{2}{x-1}}{x+\frac{3}{x-4}}$ $\frac{x-4}{(x-1)(x-1)}$

46. $\frac{\frac{w}{w+1}-\frac{1}{w-1}}{\frac{w}{w-1}+\frac{1}{w+1}}$ $\frac{w^2-2w-1}{w^2+2w-1}$

47. $\dfrac{1}{1 - \dfrac{1}{1 - \dfrac{1}{y - 1}}}$ $-y + 2$

48. $1 - \dfrac{1}{1 + \dfrac{1}{1 - \dfrac{1}{x}}}$ $\dfrac{x}{2x - 1}$

49. $\dfrac{1 - \dfrac{1}{x - 1}}{x - \dfrac{8}{x + 2}}$ $\dfrac{x + 2}{(x - 1)(x + 4)}$

50. $\dfrac{1}{1 - \dfrac{1}{1 + \dfrac{1}{y + 1}}}$ $y + 2$

6.5 *Solve each of the following equations.*

51. $\dfrac{1}{2x} + \dfrac{1}{3x} = \dfrac{1}{6}$ 5

52. $\dfrac{5}{2x^2} - \dfrac{1}{4x} = \dfrac{1}{x}$ 2

53. $\dfrac{x}{x - 2} + 1 = \dfrac{x + 4}{x - 2}$ 6

54. $\dfrac{2x - 1}{x - 3} - \dfrac{5}{x - 3} = 1$ No solution

55. $\dfrac{2}{3x + 1} = \dfrac{1}{x + 2}$ 3

56. $\dfrac{5}{x + 1} + \dfrac{1}{x - 2} = \dfrac{7}{x + 1}$ 5

57. $\dfrac{4}{x - 1} - \dfrac{5}{3x - 7} = \dfrac{3}{x - 1}$ −1

58. $\dfrac{7}{x} - \dfrac{1}{x - 3} = \dfrac{9}{x^2 - 3x}$ 5

59. $\dfrac{2}{x - 3} - \dfrac{11}{x^2 - 9} = \dfrac{3}{x + 3}$ 4

60. $\dfrac{5}{x + 3} + \dfrac{1}{x - 5} = 1$ 1, 7

61. $\dfrac{2}{x - 4} = \dfrac{x}{x - 2} - \dfrac{x + 4}{x^2 - 6x + 8}$ 0, 7

62. $\dfrac{x}{x - 5} = \dfrac{3x}{x^2 - 7x + 10} + \dfrac{8}{x - 2}$ 8

Solve each equation for the indicated variable.

63. $\dfrac{1}{T} + \dfrac{1}{T_1} = \dfrac{1}{T_2}$ for T_1 $\dfrac{TT_2}{T - T_2}$

64. $R = \dfrac{R_1R_2}{R_1 + R_2}$ for R_1 $\dfrac{RR_2}{R_2 - R}$

65. $\dfrac{1}{F} = \dfrac{1}{D_1} + \dfrac{1}{D_2}$ for D_2 $\dfrac{FD_1}{D_1 - F}$

66. $\dfrac{1}{x} = \dfrac{1}{a} + \dfrac{1}{b}$ for x $\dfrac{ab}{a + b}$

6.5

67. Science and Medicine On the first day of a business trip, Min Yeh drove 225 mi. On her second day, it took her 2 h longer to drive 315 mi. If her rate was the same each day, what was her driving time each day? 5 h, 7 h

68. Science and Medicine Brett made a trip of 240 mi using the freeway. Returning by a different route, he found that the distance was only 200 mi but that traffic slowed his speed by 8 mi/h. If the trip took the same time in both directions, what was Brett's rate each way? 48 mi/h, 40 mi/h

69. Science and Medicine A painter could paint an office complex in 10 h although it would take his helper 15 h. How long would it take to complete the job if the two worked together? 6 h

70. Science and Medicine A water tank can be filled through an inlet pipe in 10 h. The tank will take 15 h to drain through an outlet pipe. The inlet pipe is opened to begin filling the tank, but the outlet valve is also inadvertently left open. How long will it take to fill the tank? 30 h

71. Science and Medicine Salvatore and Susan can construct a fence in 6 h. If Susan could complete the same job by herself in 9 h, how long would it take Salvatore, working alone? 18 h

72. Science and Medicine One model printer can print a company's monthly billings three times as fast as another model. If the two printers, working together, can complete the job in 9 h, how long will it take the faster model, working alone? 12 h

73. Number Problem The sum of the reciprocal of an integer and the square of the reciprocal of that integer is $\frac{4}{9}$. Find the integer. 3

74. Number Problem The difference between the reciprocal of an integer and the square of its reciprocal is $\frac{3}{16}$. What is the integer? 4

75. Number Problem The same number is added to the numerator and denominator of $\frac{7}{10}$. If the resulting fraction is equal to $\frac{5}{6}$, what number was added to the numerator and denominator? 8

76. Number Problem One integer is 2 more than another. If the sum of the reciprocals of the integers is $\frac{5}{12}$, find the two integers. 4, 6

6.6 *Translate each of the following statements of variation to an algebraic equation, using k as the constant of variation.*

77. d varies directly as the square of t. $d = kt^2$

78. r varies inversely as the square root of s. $r = \frac{k}{\sqrt{s}}$

79. y is directly proportional to x and inversely proportional to w. $y = \frac{kx}{w}$

80. z varies jointly as the cube of x and the square root of y. $z = kx^3\sqrt{y}$

Find k, the constant of variation, given each of the following sets of conditions.

81. y varies directly as the cube root of x; $y = 12$ when $x = 8$. $k = 6$

82. p is inversely proportional to the square of q; $p = 3$ when $q = 4$. $k = 48$

83. r varies jointly as s and the square of t; $r = 150$ when $s = 2$ and $t = 5$. $k = 3$

84. t varies directly as the square of u and inversely as v; $t = 36$ when $u = 3$ and $v = 2$. $k = 8$

Solve each of the following variation problems.

85. Let z vary inversely as the square of w. If $z = 3$ when $w = 4$, find the value of z when $w = 2$. $z = 12$

86. Suppose that s varies directly as the square of t and that $s = 90$ when $t = 3$. Find the value of s when $t = 5$. $s = 250$

87. The variable m varies jointly as p and the square of n. If $m = 144$ when $n = 2$ and $p = 3$, find the value of m when $n = 3$ and $p = 4$. $m = 432$

88. Let p be directly proportional to the square of q and inversely proportional to r. If $p = 2$ when $q = 2$ and $r = 12$, find the value of p when $q = 4$ and $r = 24$. $p = 4$

89. The distance that a ball will fall (neglecting air resistance) is directly proportional to the square of time. If the ball falls 64 feet in 2 sec, how far will it fall in 5 sec? 400 ft

90. If the temperature of a gas is held constant, the volume occupied by that gas varies inversely as the pressure. A gas has volume 200 ft^3 when it is subjected to a pressure of 20 lb/in.^2 What will its volume be under a pressure of 25 lb/in.^2?
160 ft^3

self-test 6

Name ______________________

Section __________ Date __________

The purpose of this chapter test is to help you check your progress so that you can find sections and concepts that you need to review before the next exam. Allow yourself about an hour to take this test. At the end of that hour, check your answers against those given in the back of this text. If you missed any, note the section reference that accompanies the answer. Go back to that section and reread the examples until you have mastered that particular concept.

6.1

Simplify each of the following rational expressions.

1. $\dfrac{-21x^5y^3}{28xy^5}$ **2.** $\dfrac{3w^2 + w - 2}{3w^2 - 8w + 4}$ **3.** $\dfrac{x^3 + 2x^2 - 3x}{x^3 - 3x^2 + 2x}$

4. Graph the following. Indicate the coordinates of the hole in the graph.

$$f(x) = \frac{x^2 - 5x + 4}{x - 4}$$

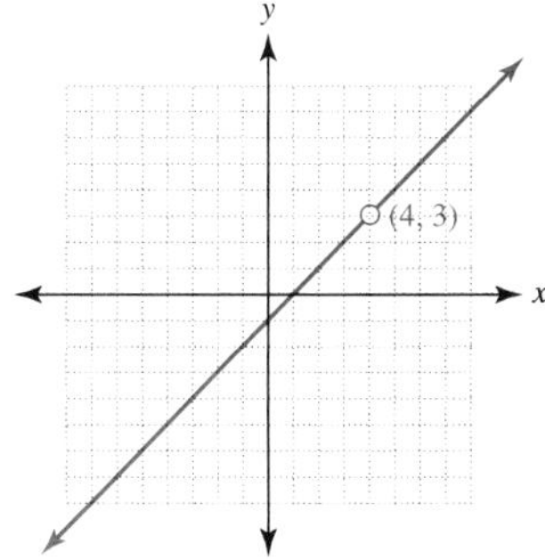

6.2

Multiply or divide as indicated.

5. $\dfrac{3ab^2}{5ab^3} \cdot \dfrac{20a^2b}{21b}$ **6.** $\dfrac{m^2 - 3m}{m^2 - 9} \div \dfrac{4m}{m^2 - m - 12}$

7. $\dfrac{x^2 - 3x}{5x^2} \cdot \dfrac{10x}{x^2 - 4x + 3}$ **8.** $\dfrac{x^2 + 3xy}{2x^3 - x^2y} \div \dfrac{x^2 + 6xy + 9y^2}{4x^2 - y^2}$

9. $\dfrac{9x^2 - 9x - 4}{6x^2 - 11x + 3} \cdot \dfrac{15 - 10x}{3x - 4}$

6.3

Add or subtract as indicated.

10. $\dfrac{5}{x - 2} - \dfrac{1}{x}$ **11.** $\dfrac{2}{x + 3} + \dfrac{12}{x^2 - 9}$

12. $\dfrac{6x}{x^2 - x - 2} - \dfrac{2}{x + 1}$ **13.** $\dfrac{3}{x^2 - 3x - 4} + \dfrac{5}{x^2 - 16}$

Answers

1. $\dfrac{-3x^4}{4y^2}$
2. $\dfrac{w + 1}{w - 2}$
3. $\dfrac{x + 3}{x - 2}$
4. See exercise
5. $\dfrac{4a^2}{7b}$
6. $\dfrac{m - 4}{4}$
7. $\dfrac{2}{x - 1}$
8. $\dfrac{2x + y}{x(x + 3y)}$
9. $\dfrac{-15x - 5}{3x - 1}$
10. $\dfrac{4x + 2}{x(x - 2)}$
11. $\dfrac{2}{x - 3}$
12. $\dfrac{4}{x - 2}$
13. $\dfrac{8x + 17}{(x - 4)(x + 1)(x + 4)}$

Answers

14. $\frac{y}{3y + x}$

15. $\frac{z - 1}{2(z + 3)}$

16. $\frac{1}{xy(x - y)}$

17. 9

18. $-\frac{1}{2}, 4$

19. 3, 6

20. Going: 50 mi/h, returning: 45 mi/h

21. Juan: 10 days, Ariel: 40 days

22. 3

23. $s = 2$

24. $p = 75$

25. $z = 12$

26. 500 lb/ft²

6.4

Simplify each of the following complex fractions.

14. $\dfrac{3 - \dfrac{x}{y}}{9 - \dfrac{x^2}{y^2}}$ **15.** $\dfrac{1 - \dfrac{10}{z + 3}}{2 - \dfrac{12}{z - 1}}$ **16.** $\dfrac{\dfrac{1}{x} + \dfrac{1}{y}}{x^2 - y^2}$

6.5

Solve the following equations.

17. $\dfrac{x}{x + 3} + 1 = \dfrac{3x - 6}{x + 3}$ **18.** $\dfrac{2x}{x + 1} = \dfrac{3}{x - 2} + \dfrac{1}{x^2 - x - 2}$

Solve each of the following applications.

19. One positive number is 3 more than another. If the sum of the reciprocals of the two numbers is $\frac{1}{2}$, find the two numbers.

20. Stephen drove 250 mi to visit Sandra. Returning by a shorter route, he found that the trip was only 225 mi, but traffic slowed his speed by 5 mi/h. If the two trips took exactly the same time, what was his rate each way?

21. Juan can paint the neighbor's house four times as fast as Ariel can. The year they worked together it took them 8 days. How long would it take each to paint the house alone?

22. Given the fraction $\frac{4}{7}$, the numerator is multiplied by a certain number, and the same number is added to the denominator. The result is $\frac{6}{5}$. What is the number?

6.6

Solve each of the following.

23. Let s vary inversely as the cube of t. If $s = 16$ when $t = 2$, find the value of s when $t = 4$.

24. Variable p is jointly proportional to r and the square root of s. If $p = 80$ when $r = 4$ and $s = 16$, find the value of p when $r = 3$ and $s = 25$.

25. Suppose that z is directly proportional to x and inversely proportional to the square of y. If $z = 32$ when $x = 4$ and $y = 2$, find the value of z when $x = 6$ and $y = 4$.

26. The pressure at a point under water varies directly as the depth. If the pressure at a point 4 ft below the surface of the water is 250 pounds per square foot (lb/ft²), find the pressure at a depth of 8 ft.

Activity 6 :: Determining State Apportionment

Each chapter in this text concludes with a chapter activity such as this one. These activities provide you with the opportunity to apply the math you studied in that chapter to a relevant topic. Your instructor will determine how best to use these activities in your instructional setting. You may find yourself working in class or outside of class; you may find yourself working alone or in small groups; you may even be asked to perform research in a library or on the Internet.

The introduction to this chapter referred to the ratio of the people in a particular state to their total number of representatives in the U.S. House based on the 1990 census. It was noted that the ratio of the total population of the country to the 435 representatives in Congress should equal the state apportionment if it is fair. That is, $\frac{A}{a} = \frac{P}{r}$, where A is the population of the state, a is the number of representatives for that state, P is the total population of the United States, and r is the total number of representatives in Congress (435).

Pick 5 states (your own included) and search the Internet to find the following.

1. Determine the 2000 population of each state.
2. Note the number of representatives for each state and any increase or decrease.
3. Find the number of people per representative for each state.
4. Compare that with the national average of the number of people per representative.
5. Solve the rational equation $\frac{A}{a} = \frac{P}{r}$ for a. For each state substitute the number values for the variables, A, P, and r. Find a. Based on your findings,
   (a) Which states have a greater number of representatives than they should (that is, the number has been rounded up)?
   (b) Which states have a smaller number of representatives than they should (that is, the number has been rounded down)?

You can find out more about apportionment counts and how they are determined from the U.S. Census website.

cumulative review chapters 1–6

Name ____________

Section ________ Date ________

The following exercises are presented to help you review concepts from earlier chapters. This is meant as review material and not as a comprehensive exam. The answers are presented in the back of the text. Beside each answer is a section reference for the concept. If you have difficulty with any of these exercises, be certain to at least read through the summary related to that section.

Answers

1. 12
2. −14
3. $6x + 7y = -21$
4. x-int: $(-6, 0)$, y-int: $(0, 7)$
5. $6x^2 - 5x - 2$
6. $2x^3 + 5x^2 - 3x$
7. Domain: $\{2\}$, range: all real numbers
8. 16
9. $x(2x + 3)(3x - 1)$
10. $(4x^8 + 3y^4)(4x^8 - 3y^4)$
11. $\frac{3}{x - 1}$
12. $\frac{1}{(x + 1)(x - 1)}$

2.1

1. Solve the equation $5x - 3(2x + 6) = 4 - (3x - 2)$.

3.2

2. If $f(x) = 5x^4 - 3x^2 + 7x - 9$, find $f(-1)$.

3.4

3. Find the equation of the line that is parallel to the line $6x + 7y = 42$ and has a y-intercept of $(0, -3)$.

3.1

4. Find the x- and y-intercepts of the equation $7x - 6y = -42$.

Simplify.

1.4

5. $3x - 2(x - (3x - 1)) + 6x(x - 2)$

5.2

6. $x(2x - 1)(x + 3)$

3.1

7. Find the domain and range of the relation $7x - 14 = 0$.

1.2

8. Evaluate the expression $6^2 - (16 \div 8 \cdot 2) - 4^2$.

Factor each of the following completely.

5.8

9. $6x^3 + 7x^2 - 3x$

10. $16x^{16} - 9y^8$

Simplify each of the following rational expressions.

6.3

11. $\frac{5}{x - 1} - \frac{2x + 6}{x^2 + 2x - 3}$

6.2

12. $\frac{x + 1}{x^2 - 5x - 6} \div \frac{x^2 - 1}{x - 6}$

6.4

13. $\dfrac{1 - \dfrac{3}{x+3}}{\dfrac{1}{x^2 - 9}}$

Solve the following equations.

2.1

14. $7x + (x - 10) = -12(x - 5)$

2.5

15. $|-9x - 6| = 2$

2.1

16. $-4(7x + 6) = 8(5x + 12)$

5.9

17. $2x^2 - 5x - 12 = 0$

Solve the following inequalities.

2.5

18. $-4(-2x - 7) > -6x$

19. $|5x - 4| < 3$

20. $-6|2x + 6| \le -12$

6.5

21. Solve the equation $\dfrac{5}{x} = \dfrac{2}{x+3}$ for x.

4.1

22. Solve the system of equations

$$\begin{aligned} 4x - 3y &= 15 \\ x + y &= 2 \end{aligned}$$

1.5

23. Simplify the expression

$$\left(\frac{a^{-2}b}{a^3b^{-2}}\right)^2$$

Answers

13. $x^2 - 3x$

14. $\frac{7}{2}$

15. $-\frac{8}{9}, -\frac{4}{9}$

16. $-\frac{30}{17}$

17. $-\frac{3}{2}, 4$

18. $x > -2$

19. $\frac{1}{5} < x < \frac{7}{5}$

20. $x \le -4$ or $x \ge -2$

21. $x = -5$

22. $(3, -1)$

23. $\frac{b^6}{a^{10}}$

Answers

24. Barry: 3 h, Don: 6 h

25. Width: 10 cm, length: 18 cm

26. $y = 96$

Solve the following applications.

6.5

24. When each works alone, Barry can mow a lawn in 3 h less time than Don. When they work together, it takes 2 h. How long does it take each to do the job by himself?

5.9

25. The length of a rectangle is 2 cm less than twice the width. The area of the rectangle is 180 cm^2. Find the length and width of the rectangle.

6.6

26. Let y vary directly with x. If $y = 60$ when $x = 5$, find the value of y when $x = 8$.

CHAPTER

7

Radicals and Rational Exponents

INTRODUCTION

A weight suspended on the end of a string is a pendulum. One type of pendulum you may have seen in a museum is called a Foucault pendulum (pronounced "foo-koh"). This is named for the French physicist Jean Foucault who first used it in 1851 to demonstrate the rotation of Earth. The fascinating thing about a Foucault pendulum is that if you start a Foucault pendulum swinging in one direction, after a few hours you will notice that it is swinging in a quite different direction!

The regular back-and-forth motion of a pendulum is periodic, and one such cycle of motion is called a period. The time, in seconds, that it takes for one period is given by the radical equation

$$T = k\sqrt{L}$$

in which k is a constant and L is the length of the pendulum in meters.

More specifically, we can write this as

$$T = 2\pi\sqrt{\frac{L}{g}}$$

in which g is the force of gravity (a constant). In this chapter we will work with the radicals used to express this relationship. Then at the end of the chapter, you will find a more in-depth activity exploring the swing of a pendulum.

CHAPTER 7 OUTLINE

7 pretest

Name ____________

Section ________ Date ________

This pretest provides a preview of the types of exercises you will encounter in each section of this chapter. The answers for these exercises can be found in the back of the text. If you are working on your own, or ahead of the class, this pretest can help you identify the sections in which you should focus more of your time.

7.1–7.2 Simplify each expression. Assume that all variables represent positive real numbers in all subsequent problems.

1. $\sqrt{25t^6}$

2. $\sqrt{\dfrac{3a}{8b}}$

7.2 Simplify each expression if necessary. Then add or subtract as indicated.

3. $3\sqrt{7} - 2\sqrt{7} + 6\sqrt{7}$

7.3 Multiply or divide as indicated. Then simplify your result.

4. $(\sqrt{3} + 2)(\sqrt{3} + 3)$

5. $\dfrac{44 - \sqrt{605}}{11}$

7.4 Solve the equation for x. Be sure to check any solutions.

6. $\sqrt{x - 3} = 9$

7.5 Find the missing length in each problem. Write your answer to the nearest hundredth.

7.

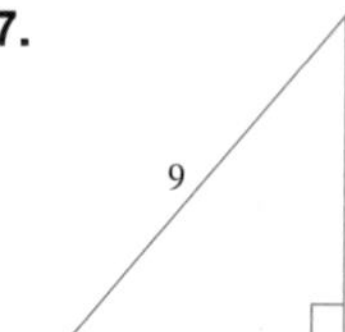

8. If the diagonal of a rectangle is 25 cm and the width of the rectangle is 16 cm, what is the length of the rectangle?

7.6 Write the expression in radical form and simplify.

9. $(a^3b^7)^{2/5}$

Write the expression using rational exponents. Then simplify.

10. $\sqrt[4]{16x^{12}y^8}$

7.7 Perform the indicated operations.

11. $(-7 - 5i) - (2 + 3i)$

12. $\dfrac{10 + 20i}{3 + i}$

Answers

1. $5t^3$
2. $\dfrac{\sqrt{6ab}}{4b}$
3. $7\sqrt{7}$
4. $9 + 5\sqrt{3}$
5. $4 - \sqrt{5}$
6. $x = 84$
7. $x = 4.12$
8. 19.21 cm
9. $ab^2\sqrt[5]{ab^4}$
10. $2x^3y^2$
11. $-9 - 8i$
12. $5 + 5i$

7.1 Roots and Radicals

< 7.1 Objectives >

1 > Use radical notation to represent roots

2 > Approximate a square root

3 > Distinguish between rational and irrational numbers

4 > Simplify expressions that contain radicals

In Chapter 1, we discussed the properties of exponents. In this section and Sections 7.2 and 7.3, we will work with a new notation that "reverses" the process of raising to a power.

From our work in Chapter 1, we know that when we have a statement such as

$$x^2 = 9$$

it is read as "x squared equals 9."

Here we are concerned with the relationship between the variable x and the number 9. We call that relationship the **square root** and say, equivalently, that "x is the square root of 9."

We know from experience that x must be 3 (because $3^2 = 9$) or -3 [because $(-3)^2 = 9$]. We see that 9 has two square roots, 3 and -3. In fact, every positive number will have *two* square roots. In general, if $x^2 = a$, we call x a *square root* of a.

We are now ready for our new notation. The symbol $\sqrt{}$ is called a **radical sign.** We just saw that 3 was the positive square root of 9. We also call 3 the **principal square root** of 9 and write

$$\sqrt{9} = 3$$

to indicate that 3 is the principal square root of 9.

NOTE

The symbol $\sqrt{}$ first appeared in print in 1525. In Latin, *radix* means "root," and this was contracted to a small *r*. The present symbol may have evolved from the manuscript form of that small *r*.

Definition

Square Root $\sqrt{a}$ is the *positive* (or *principal*) square root of a. It is the positive number whose square is a.

Example 1 Finding Principal Square Roots

< Objective 1 >

Find the following square roots.

(a) $\sqrt{49} = 7$ Because 7 is the positive number we must square to get 49.

(b) $\sqrt{\frac{4}{9}} = \frac{2}{3}$ Because $\frac{2}{3}$ is the positive number we must square to get $\frac{4}{9}$.

Check Yourself 1

Find the following square roots.

(a)  $\sqrt{64}$ **(b)** $\sqrt{144}$ **(c)** $\sqrt{\frac{16}{25}}$

NOTES

When you use the radical sign, you are referring to the *positive square root:*

$\sqrt{25} = 5$

$-\sqrt{x}$ is the negative square root of x.

Each nonnegative number has two square roots. For instance, 25 has square roots of 5 and -5 because

$5^2 = 25$ and $(-5)^2 = 25$

If you want to indicate the negative square root, you must use a minus sign in front of the radical.

$-\sqrt{25} = -5$

Example 2 Finding Square Roots

Find the following square roots.

(a) $\sqrt{100} = 10$ The principal root

(b) $-\sqrt{100} = -10$ The negative square root

(c) $-\sqrt{\frac{9}{16}} = -\frac{3}{4}$

Check Yourself 2

Find the following square roots.

(a) $\sqrt{16}$ **(b)** $-\sqrt{16}$ **(c)** $-\sqrt{\frac{16}{25}}$

> CAUTION

Be Careful! Do not confuse

$-\sqrt{9}$ with $\sqrt{-9}$

The expression $-\sqrt{9}$ is -3, whereas $\sqrt{-9}$ is not a real number.

Every number that we have encountered in this text is a **real number.** The square roots of negative numbers are *not* real numbers. For instance, $\sqrt{-9}$ is *not* a real number because there is *no* real number x such that

$x^2 = -9$

Example 3 summarizes our discussion thus far.

Example 3 Finding Square Roots

Evaluate each of the following square roots.

(a) $\sqrt{36} = 6$

(b) $\sqrt{121} = 11$

(c) $-\sqrt{64} = -8$

(d) $\sqrt{-64}$ is not a real number.

(e) $\sqrt{0} = 0$ (Because $0 \cdot 0 = 0$)

Check Yourself 3

Evaluate, if possible.

(a) $\sqrt{81}$ **(b)** $\sqrt{49}$ **(c)** $-\sqrt{49}$ **(d)** $\sqrt{-49}$

Not every square root is an integer. In fact, there are only 10 whole-number square roots for the numbers from 1 to 100. They are the square roots of 1, 4, 9, 16, 25, 36, 49, 64, 81, and 100. However, we can approximate square roots that are not integers. For example, we know that the square root of 12 is not an integer. We also know that its value must lie somewhere between the square root of 9 ($\sqrt{9} = 3$) and the square root of 16 ($\sqrt{16} = 4$). That is, $\sqrt{12}$ is between 3 and 4.

Example 4 Approximating Square Roots

< Objective 2 >

Approximate $\sqrt{29}$.

$\sqrt{25} = 5$ and $\sqrt{36} = 6$, so $\sqrt{29}$ must be between 5 and 6.

Check Yourself 4

$\sqrt{29}$ is between which two numbers?

(a) 4 and 5 **(b)** 5 and 6 **(c)** 6 and 7

Now that we can get an estimate of the value of a square root, let us consider how we can use our calculators to help us find an even better approximation. All calculators have square root keys, but only the integers for which the calculator gives the exact value of the square root are perfect square integers. For all other positive integers, a calculator gives only an approximation of the correct answer. In Example 5 you will use your calculator to approximate square roots.

Example 5 Approximating Square Roots

NOTE

On most graphing calculators the $\sqrt{}$ symbol is the "2nd function" or "inverse" of the x^2 key. This follows from the idea of the square root "undoing" the squaring operation.

Use your calculator to approximate each square root to the nearest thousandth.

(a) $\sqrt{17}$

On most graphing calculators, press the 2nd key, and then press the x^2 key. Now enter 1, 7,), and ENTER.

The screen shown is the TI-84 Plus display. Rounded to the nearest thousandth, the result is 4.123.

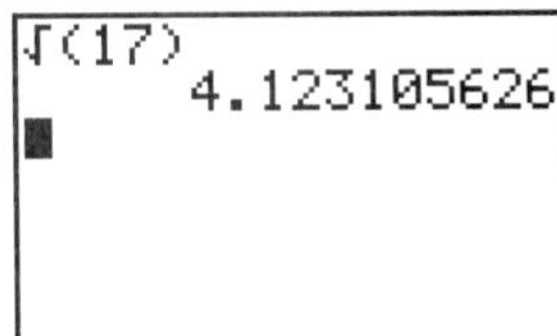

NOTE

The error message as displayed by the TI-84 Plus calculator.

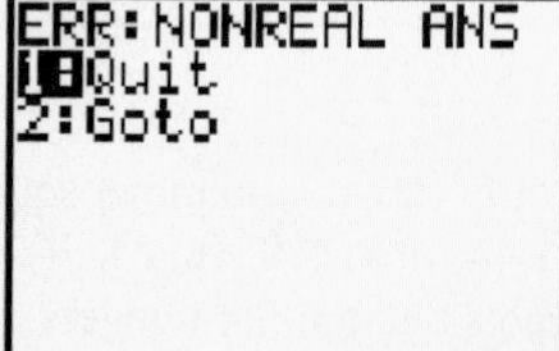

(b) $\sqrt{28}$

Press [2nd], [x^2], [2], [8], [)], and [ENTER]. The display should read 5.291502622. Rounded to the nearest thousandths, the result is 5.292.

(c) $\sqrt{-11}$

Press [2nd], [x^2], [(-)], [1], [1], [)], and [ENTER].

This time the display shows an error message. This indicates that -11 does not have a real square root.

Check Yourself 5

Use a calculator to find the decimal approximation for each square root. Round each answer to the nearest thousandth.

(a) $\sqrt{13}$ **(b)** $\sqrt{38}$ **(c)** $\sqrt{-21}$

From Example 5, we see that

$$\sqrt{17} \approx 4.123 \quad \text{and} \quad \sqrt{28} \approx 5.292$$

NOTES

$\sqrt[3]{8}$ is read "the cube root of 8."

The index for $\sqrt[3]{a}$ is 3.

The index of 2 for square roots is generally not written. We understand that $\sqrt{a}$ is the principal square root of *a*.

So, we have the result $\sqrt{17} < \sqrt{28}$. This follows directly from the fact that $17 < 28$. In fact, for positive numbers a and b, if $a < b$, then $\sqrt{a} < \sqrt{b}$.

As we mentioned earlier, finding the square root of a number is the reverse of squaring a number. We can extend that idea to work with other roots of numbers. For instance, the **cube root** of a number is the number we must cube (or raise to the third power) to get that number. For example, the cube root of 8 is 2 because $2^3 = 8$, and we write

$$\sqrt[3]{8} = 2$$

The parts of a radical expression are summarized as follows.

Definition

Parts of a Radical Expression

Every radical expression contains three parts as shown here. The principal *n*th root of *a* is written as

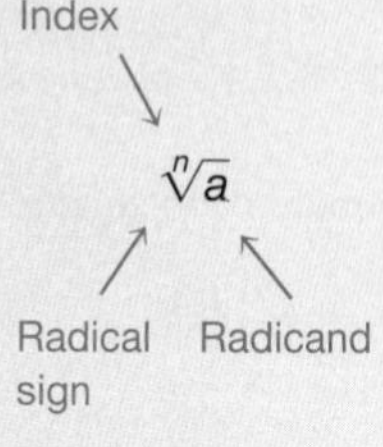

To illustrate, the *cube root* of 64 is written

Index of 3 ⟶ $\sqrt[3]{64} = 4$

because $4^3 = 64$. And

Index of 4 ⟶ $\sqrt[4]{81} = 3$

is the *fourth root* of 81 because $3^4 = 81$.

We can find roots of negative numbers as long as the index is *odd* (3, 5, etc.). For example,

$\sqrt[3]{-64} = -4$

because $(-4)^3 = -64$.

If the index is *even* (2, 4, etc.), roots of negative numbers are *not* real numbers. For example,

$\sqrt[4]{-16}$

is not a real number because there is no real number x such that $x^4 = -16$.

The following table shows the most common roots.

NOTES

The *even power* of a real number is always *positive* or *zero*.

It would be helpful for your work here and in future mathematics classes to memorize these roots.

Square Roots		Cube Roots	Fourth Roots
$\sqrt{1} = 1$	$\sqrt{49} = 7$	$\sqrt[3]{1} = 1$	$\sqrt[4]{1} = 1$
$\sqrt{4} = 2$	$\sqrt{64} = 8$	$\sqrt[3]{8} = 2$	$\sqrt[4]{16} = 2$
$\sqrt{9} = 3$	$\sqrt{81} = 9$	$\sqrt[3]{27} = 3$	$\sqrt[4]{81} = 3$
$\sqrt{16} = 4$	$\sqrt{100} = 10$	$\sqrt[3]{64} = 4$	$\sqrt[4]{256} = 4$
$\sqrt{25} = 5$	$\sqrt{121} = 11$	$\sqrt[3]{125} = 5$	$\sqrt[4]{625} = 5$
$\sqrt{36} = 6$	$\sqrt{144} = 12$		

You can use the above table to do Example 6, which summarizes the discussion so far.

Example 6 Evaluating Roots

NOTES

The cube root of a negative number will be negative.

The fourth root of a negative number is not a real number.

Evaluate each of the following.

(a) $\sqrt[5]{32} = 2$ because $2^5 = 32$.

(b) $\sqrt[3]{-125} = -5$ because $(-5)^3 = -125$.

(c) $\sqrt[4]{-81}$ is not a real number.

Check Yourself 6

Evaluate, if possible.

(a) $\sqrt[3]{64}$ **(b)** $\sqrt[4]{16}$ **(c)** $\sqrt[4]{-256}$ **(d)** $\sqrt[5]{-243}$

We can also use a graphing calculator to evaluate roots other than square roots. Calculators differ in their commands and syntax for this, so you may need to consult your instructor, the owner's manual, or even the manufacturer's website.

In Example 7, we use the TI-84 Plus calculator. On the TI-84 Plus, the *n*th root functions are found in the Math menu. Using your own calculators you should obtain similar results.

Example 7 Approximating Radical Expressions

NOTE

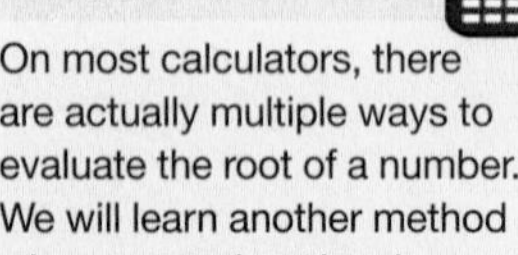

On most calculators, there are actually multiple ways to evaluate the root of a number. We will learn another method when we study rational exponents in Section 7.6.

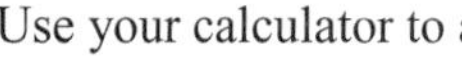

Use your calculator to approximate each root to the nearest thousandth.

(a) $\sqrt[3]{78}$

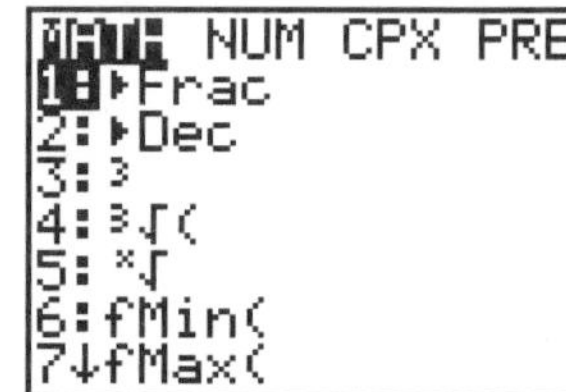

On the TI-84 Plus calculator, press MATH to access the Math menu and display the screen shown. Press 4 for the option 4: $\sqrt[3]{\ }$(, and enter the value 78. Close the parentheses and press ENTER.

The display should read 4.272658682. Rounded to the nearest thousandth, the result is 4.273.

(b) $\sqrt[4]{12}$

```
³√(78)
      4.272658682
4ˣ√(12)
      1.861209718
```

On the TI-84 Plus calculator, enter the index (root) 4, and then press MATH, 5 to call the *n*th root function 5: $\sqrt[x]{\ }$. Press (, 1, 2,), ENTER.

The screen display is shown. To three decimal places, the result is 1.861.

(c) $\sqrt[5]{27}$

To three decimal places, the result is 1.933.

Check Yourself 7

Use a calculator to give a three-decimal-place approximation for each root.

(a) $\sqrt[3]{-102}$ **(b)** $\sqrt[4]{35}$ **(c)** $\sqrt[5]{29}$

NOTE

Notice that each radicand is a **perfect-square integer** (that is, an integer that is the square of another integer).

The radical notation helps us to distinguish between two important types of numbers: rational numbers and irrational numbers.

A **rational number** can be represented by a fraction whose numerator and denominator are integers and whose denominator is not zero. The form of a rational number is

$$\frac{a}{b} \qquad a \text{ and } b \text{ are integers, } b \neq 0$$

Certain square roots are rational numbers also. For example,

$$\sqrt{4} \qquad \sqrt{25} \qquad \text{and} \qquad \sqrt{64}$$

represent the rational numbers 2, 5, and 8, respectively.

An **irrational number** is a number that *cannot* be written as the ratio of two integers. For example, the square root of any positive number that is not itself a perfect square is an irrational number. Because the radicands are *not* perfect squares, the expressions $\sqrt{2}$, $\sqrt{3}$, and $\sqrt{5}$ represent irrational numbers. The fact that the square root of 2 is irrational will be proved in later mathematics courses and was known to Greek mathematicians over 2,000 years ago.

Example 8 Identifying Rational Numbers

< Objective 3 >

Which of the following numbers are rational and which are irrational?

$$\sqrt{\frac{2}{3}} \qquad \sqrt{\frac{4}{9}} \qquad \sqrt{7} \qquad \sqrt{16} \qquad \sqrt{25}$$

Here $\sqrt{7}$ and $\sqrt{\frac{2}{3}}$ are irrational numbers. The numbers $\sqrt{16}$ and $\sqrt{25}$ are rational because 16 and 25 are perfect squares. Also $\sqrt{\frac{4}{9}}$ is rational because $\sqrt{\frac{4}{9}} = \frac{2}{3}$.

Check Yourself 8

Determine whether each root is rational or irrational.

(a) $\sqrt{26}$ **(b)** $\sqrt{49}$ **(c)** $\sqrt{\frac{6}{7}}$ **(d)** $\sqrt{105}$ **(e)** $\sqrt{\frac{16}{9}}$

NOTE

The decimal representation of a rational number always terminates or repeats. For instance,

$\frac{3}{8} = 0.375$

$\frac{5}{11} = 0.454545\ldots$

An important fact about the irrational numbers is that their decimal representations are always *nonterminating* and *nonrepeating*. We can therefore only approximate irrational numbers with a decimal that has been rounded. A calculator can be used to find roots. However, note that the values found for the irrational roots are only approximations. For instance, $\sqrt{2}$ is approximately 1.414 (to three decimal places), and we can write

$\sqrt{2} \approx 1.414$

With a calculator we find that

$(1.414)^2 = 1.999396$

The set of all rational numbers and the set of all irrational numbers together form the set of *real numbers*. The real numbers will represent every point that can be pictured on the number line. Some examples are shown.

NOTE

For this reason we refer to the number line as the **real number line.**

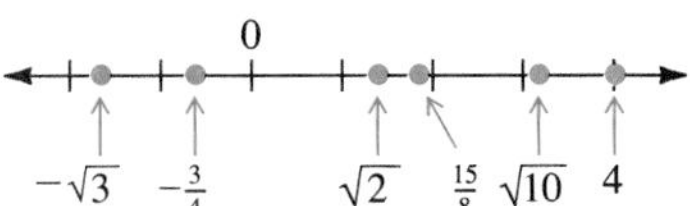

The following diagram summarizes the relationships among the various numeric sets.

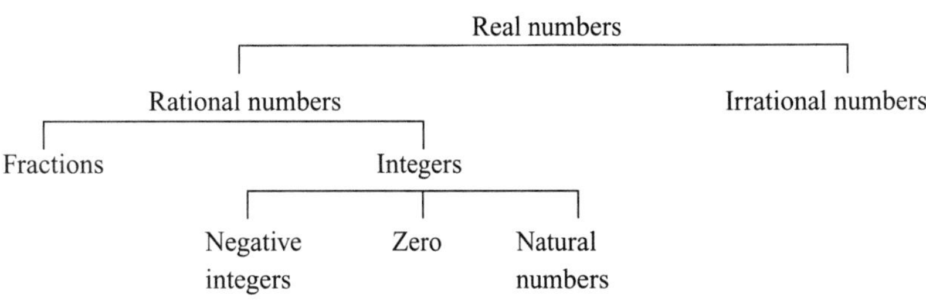

A certain amount of caution should be exercised in dealing with principal even roots. Start by looking at two numerical examples.

$\sqrt{2^2} = \sqrt{4} = 2$

$\sqrt{(-2)^2} = \sqrt{4} = 2$ because $(-2)^2 = 4$

NOTE

This is because the principal square root of a number is always positive or zero.

Consider the value of $\sqrt{x^2}$ when x is positive or negative.

In the first equation when $x = 2$:

$\sqrt{2^2} = 2$

In the second equation when $x = -2$:

$\sqrt{(-2)^2} \neq -2$

$\sqrt{(-2)^2} = -(-2) = 2$

Comparing the results of these two equations, we see that $\sqrt{x^2}$ is x if x is positive (or 0) and $\sqrt{x^2}$ is $-x$ if x is negative. We can write

$$\sqrt{x^2} = \begin{cases} x & \text{when } x \geq 0 \\ -x & \text{when } x < 0 \end{cases}$$

From your earlier work with absolute values you will remember that

$$|x| = \begin{cases} x & \text{when } x \geq 0 \\ -x & \text{when } x < 0 \end{cases}$$

and we can summarize the discussion by writing

$\sqrt{x^2} = |x|$ for any real number x

This last statement can be extended to $\sqrt[n]{x^n} = |x|$ when n is even.

Example 9 Evaluating Radical Expressions

< Objective 4 >

Evaluate.

(a) $\sqrt{5^2} = |5| = 5$

(b) $\sqrt{(-4)^2} = |-4| = 4$

(c) $\sqrt[4]{2^4} = |2| = 2$

(d) $\sqrt[4]{(-7)^4} = |-7| = 7$

NOTE

Alternately we could write $\sqrt{(-4)^2} = \sqrt{16} = 4$

Check Yourself 9

Evaluate.

(a) $\sqrt{6^2}$ **(b)** $\sqrt{(-6)^2}$ **(c)** $\sqrt[4]{3^4}$ **(d)** $\sqrt[4]{(-3)^4}$

The case for roots with indices that are odd does *not* require the use of absolute value. For instance,

$\sqrt[3]{3^3} = \sqrt[3]{27} = 3$

$\sqrt[3]{(-3)^3} = \sqrt[3]{-27} = -3$

and we see that

$$\sqrt[n]{x^n} = x \quad \text{when } n \text{ is odd.}$$

To summarize, we can write

$$\sqrt[n]{x^n} = \begin{cases} |x| & \text{when } n \text{ is even} \\ x & \text{when } n \text{ is odd} \end{cases}$$

We turn now to a final example in which variables are involved in the radicand.

Example 10 Simplifying Radical Expressions

Simplify each radical expression.

NOTE

We can determine the power of the variable in our root by dividing the power in the radicand by the index. In Example 10(d), $8 \div 4 = 2$.

(a) $\sqrt[3]{a^3} = a$

(b) $\sqrt{16m^2} = 4|m|$

(c) $\sqrt[5]{32x^5} = 2x$

(d) $\sqrt[4]{x^8} = x^2$ Note that $(x^2)^4 = x^8$.

(e) $\sqrt[3]{27y^6} = 3y^2$

Check Yourself 10

Simplify.

(a) $\sqrt[4]{x^4}$ **(b)** $\sqrt{49w^2}$ **(c)** $\sqrt[5]{a^{10}}$ **(d)** $\sqrt[3]{8y^9}$

Check Yourself ANSWERS

1. (a) 8; **(b)** 12; **(c)** $\frac{4}{5}$ **2. (a)** 4; **(b)** -4; **(c)** $-\frac{4}{5}$ **3. (a)** 9; **(b)** 7; **(c)** -7; **(d)** not a real number **4.** (b) **5. (a)** 3.606; **(b)** 6.164; **(c)** not a real number **6. (a)** 4; **(b)** 2; **(c)** not a real number; **(d)** -3 **7. (a)** -4.672; **(b)** 2.432; **(c)** 1.961 **8. (a)** Irrational; **(b)** rational (because $\sqrt{49} = 7$); **(c)** irrational; **(d)** irrational; **(e)** rational $\left(\text{because } \sqrt{\frac{16}{9}} = \frac{4}{3}\right)$ **9. (a)** 6; **(b)** 6; **(c)** 3; **(d)** 3 **10. (a)** $|x|$; **(b)** $7|w|$; **(c)** a^2; **(d)** $2y^3$

Reading Your Text

The following fill-in-the-blank exercises are designed to ensure that you understand some of the key vocabulary used in this section.

SECTION 7.1

(a) $\sqrt{a}$ is the positive (or ____________) square root of a.

(b) A calculator gives only an ____________ to the correct value for finding the square root of an integer that is not a perfect square.

(c) Every radical expression contains three parts: the radical sign, the index, and the ____________.

(d) A(n) ____________ number is a number that cannot be written as the ratio of two integers.

7.1 exercises

MathZone

Boost your grade at mathzone.com!
> Practice Problems
> NetTutor
> Self-Tests
> e-Professors
> Videos

Name ______________

Section ________ Date ________

< Objective 1 >

Evaluate, if possible.

1. $\sqrt{49}$
2. $-\sqrt{36}$
3. $\pm\sqrt{81}$
4. $\sqrt{-49}$ > Videos
5. $\sqrt[3]{27}$
6. $\sqrt[3]{-64}$ > Videos
7. $-\sqrt[3]{216}$
8. $\sqrt[4]{81}$
9. $\sqrt[5]{-32}$
10. $-\sqrt[4]{16}$
11. $\sqrt[4]{-16}$
12. $-\sqrt[5]{243}$
13. $\sqrt{\frac{4}{9}}$
14. $\sqrt[3]{-\frac{27}{64}}$
15. $\sqrt{6^2}$
16. $\sqrt{(-3)^2}$
17. $\sqrt[3]{4^3}$
18. $\sqrt[4]{(-2)^4}$

< Objective 2 >

Without using a calculator, select the correct approximation.

19. Is $\sqrt{23}$ between **(a)** 3 and 4, **(b)** 4 and 5, or **(c)** 5 and 6?
20. Is $\sqrt{15}$ between **(a)** 1 and 2, **(b)** 2 and 3, or **(c)** 3 and 4?
21. Is $\sqrt{44}$ between **(a)** 6 and 7, **(b)** 7 and 8, or **(c)** 8 and 9?

22. Is $\sqrt{31}$ between **(a)** 3 and 4, **(b)** 4 and 5, or **(c)** 5 and 6?

Using a calculator, evaluate the following. Round each answer to the nearest thousandth.

23. $\sqrt{15}$
24. $\sqrt{156}$
25. $\sqrt{-79}$
26. $\sqrt{\frac{2}{5}}$

Answers

1. 7
2. −6
3. ±9
4. Not a real number
5. 3
6. −4
7. −6
8. 3
9. −2
10. −2
11. Not a real number
12. −3
13. $\frac{2}{3}$
14. $-\frac{3}{4}$
15. 6
16. 3
17. 4
18. 2
19. (b)
20. (c)
21. (a)
22. (c)
23. 3.873
24. 12.490
25. Not a real number
26. 0.633

27. $-\sqrt{18}$

28. $\sqrt[3]{83}$

29. $\sqrt[5]{123}$

30. $\sqrt[3]{-15}$

< Objective 3 >

State whether each of the following roots is rational or irrational.

31. $\sqrt{21}$

32. $\sqrt{100}$

33. $\sqrt[4]{16}$

34. $\sqrt[3]{9}$

35. $\sqrt{\dfrac{9}{15}}$

36. $\sqrt[3]{-27}$

< Objective 4 >

Simplify each of the following roots.

37. $\sqrt{x^2}$

38. $\sqrt[5]{y^5}$

39. $\sqrt{9x^2}$

40. $\sqrt{a^4b^6}$

41. $\sqrt{16x^4}$

42. $\sqrt[4]{y^{20}}$

43. $\sqrt[4]{m^8n^{12}}$

44. $\sqrt[3]{125a^3}$

45. $\sqrt[5]{32x^5y^{15}}$

Label each of the following statements as **true** *or* **false.**

46. $\sqrt{16x^{16}} = 4x^4$

47. $\sqrt{36c^2} = 6c$

48. $\sqrt[3]{(4x^6y^9)^3} = 4x^6y^9$

49. $\sqrt[4]{(x-4)^4} = x - 4$

50. $\sqrt{16x^{-4}y^{-4}}$ is not a real number.

51. $\sqrt[3]{-8x^6y^6}$ is not a real number.

For exercises 52 to 56, find the two expressions that are equivalent.

52. $-\sqrt{25}, -5, \sqrt{-25}$

53. $\sqrt[3]{-125}, -\sqrt[3]{125}, |-5|$

54. $\sqrt[5]{-32}, -\sqrt[5]{32}, |-2|$

55. $\sqrt[4]{10{,}000}$, 100, $\sqrt[3]{1{,}000}$

56. $10^2, \sqrt{10{,}000}, \sqrt[3]{100{,}000}$

Answers

27. −4.243
28. 4.362
29. 2.618
30. −2.466
31. Irrational
32. Rational
33. Rational
34. Irrational
35. Irrational
36. Rational
37. $|x|$
38. y
39. $3|x|$
40. $|a^2b^3|$
41. $4x^2$
42. $|y^5|$
43. $|m^2n^3|$
44. $5a$
45. $2xy^3$
46. False
47. False
48. True
49. False
50. False
51. False
52. $-\sqrt{25}, -5$
53. $\sqrt[3]{-125}, -\sqrt[3]{125}$
54. $\sqrt[5]{-32}, -\sqrt[5]{32}$
55. $\sqrt[4]{10{,}000}, \sqrt[3]{1{,}000}$
56. $10^2, \sqrt{10{,}000}$

Basic Skills | **Advanced Skills** | Vocational-Technical Applications | Calculator/Computer | Above and Beyond

Solve the following application problems.

57. **GEOMETRY** The area of a square is 32 ft^2. Find the length of a side to the nearest hundredth.

58. **GEOMETRY** The area of a square is 83 ft^2. Find the length of the side to the nearest hundredth.

59. **GEOMETRY** The area of a circle is 147 ft^2. Find the radius to the nearest hundredth.

60. **GEOMETRY** If the area of a circle is 72 cm^2, find the radius to the nearest hundredth.

61. **SCIENCE AND MEDICINE** The time in seconds that it takes for an object to fall from rest is given by $t = \frac{1}{4}\sqrt{d}$, in which d is the distance fallen. Find the time required for an object to fall to the ground from a building that is 800 ft high.

62. **SCIENCE AND MEDICINE** Find the time required for an object to fall to the ground from a building that is 1,400 ft high. (Use the formula found in exercise 61.)

In exercises 63 to 65, the area is given in square feet. Find the length of a side of the square. Round your answer to the nearest hundredth of a foot.

63.

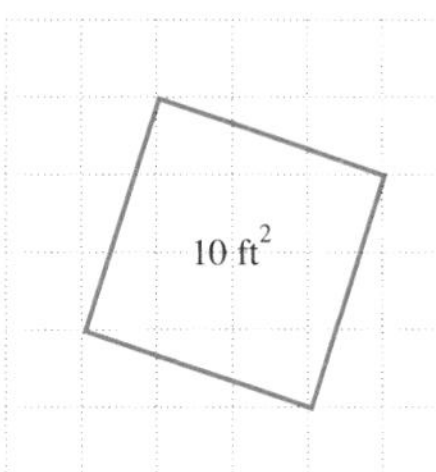

64.

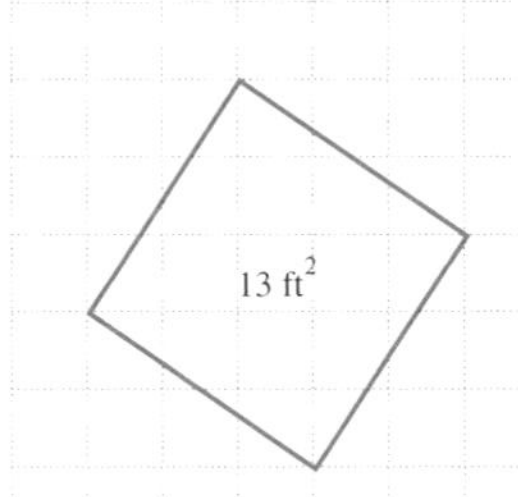

65.

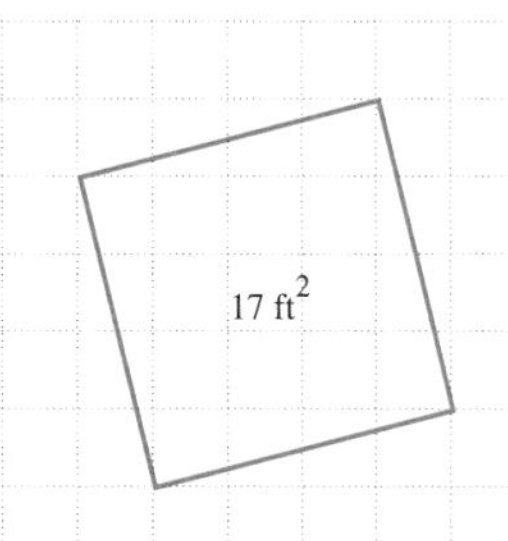

Basic Skills | Advanced Skills | Vocational-Technical Applications | **Calculator/Computer** | Above and Beyond

66. Try the following using your calculator.
    (a) Choose a number greater than 1 and find its square root. Then find the square root of the result and continue in this manner, observing the successive square roots. Do these numbers seem to be approaching a certain value? If so, what?
    (b) Choose a number greater than 0 but less than 1 and find its square root. Then find the square root of the result, and continue in this manner, observing successive square roots. Do these numbers seem to be approaching a certain value? If so, what?

Answers

57. 5.66 ft
58. 9.11 ft
59. 6.84 ft
60. 4.79 cm
61. 7.07 sec
62. 9.35 sec
63. 3.16 ft
64. 3.61 ft
65. 4.12 ft
66. Answers will vary

Answers

67. (a) 1.1 sec; (b) 1.4 sec; (c) 1.7 sec; (d) 1.9 sec; (e) 2.1 sec

68. No

69. 0, 1

70. Above and Beyond

71. Above and Beyond

67. Suppose that a weight is attached to a string of length L, and the other end of the string is held fixed. If we pull the weight and then release it, allowing the weight to swing back and forth, we can observe the behavior of a simple pendulum. The period, T, is the time required for the weight to complete a full cycle, swinging forward and then back. The following formula may be used to describe the relationship between T and L.

chapter 7 > Make the Connection

$$T = 2\pi\sqrt{\frac{L}{g}}$$

If L is expressed in centimeters, then $g = 980\ \text{cm/sec}^2$. For each of the following string lengths, calculate the corresponding period. Round to the nearest tenth of a second.

(a) 30 cm **(b)** 50 cm **(c)** 70 cm **(d)** 90 cm **(e)** 110 cm

Basic Skills | Advanced Skills | Vocational-Technical Applications | Calculator/Computer | **Above and Beyond**

68. Is there any prime number whose square root is an integer? Explain your answer.

69. Determine two consecutive integers whose square roots are also consecutive integers.

70. **(a)** Can a number be equal to its own square root? If so, list all such numbers.
(b) Other than the number(s) found in part **(a)**, is a number always greater than its square root? Investigate.

71. Let a and b be positive numbers. If a is greater than b, is it always true that the square root of a is greater than the square root of b? Investigate.

Answers

1. 7 **3.** ± 9 **5.** 3 **7.** -6 **9.** -2 **11.** Not a real number **13.** $\frac{2}{3}$ **15.** 6 **17.** 4 **19.** (b) **21.** (a) **23.** 3.873 **25.** Not a real number **27.** -4.243 **29.** 2.618 **31.** Irrational **33.** Rational **35.** Irrational **37.** $|x|$ **39.** $3|x|$ **41.** $4x^2$ **43.** $|m^2n^3|$ **45.** $2xy^3$ **47.** False **49.** False **51.** False **53.** $\sqrt[3]{-125}, -\sqrt[3]{125}$ **55.** $\sqrt[4]{10{,}000}, \sqrt[3]{1{,}000}$ **57.** 5.66 ft **59.** 6.84 ft **61.** 7.07 sec **63.** 3.16 ft **65.** 4.12 ft **67. (a)** 1.1 sec; **(b)** 1.4 sec; **(c)** 1.7 sec; **(d)** 1.9 sec; **(e)** 2.1 sec **69.** 0, 1 **71.** Above and Beyond

7.2 Simplification of Radical Expressions

< 7.2 Objectives >

1 > Use the product property to simplify a radical expression

2 > Use the quotient property to simplify a radical expression

3 > Rationalize a denominator

NOTE

A precise set of conditions for a radical to be in simplified form will follow in this section.

In Section 7.1, we introduced radical notation. For some applications, we will want to make sure that all radical expressions are written in *simplified form.* To accomplish this objective, we will need two basic properties. In stating these properties, and in our subsequent examples, we will assume that all variables represent positive real numbers whenever the index of a radical is even. To develop our first property, consider an expression such as

$$\sqrt{25 \cdot 4}$$

One approach to simplify the expression would be

$$\sqrt{25 \cdot 4} = \sqrt{100} = 10$$

NOTE

As we stated in the first paragraph, a and b are assumed to be positive real numbers when n is an even integer in the following properties.

Now what happens if we separate the original radical as follows?

$$\sqrt{25 \cdot 4} = \sqrt{25} \cdot \sqrt{4}$$
$$= 5 \cdot 2 = 10$$

The result in either case is the same, and this suggests our first property for radicals.

Property

Product Property for Radicals

$$\sqrt[n]{ab} = \sqrt[n]{a} \cdot \sqrt[n]{b}$$

In words, the radical of a product is equal to the product of the radicals.

The second property we will need is similar.

Property

Quotient Property for Radicals

$$\sqrt[n]{\frac{a}{b}} = \frac{\sqrt[n]{a}}{\sqrt[n]{b}}$$

In words, the radical of a quotient is the quotient of the radicals.

To convince yourself that the quotient property is true, at least for square roots, let $a = 100$ and $b = 4$ and then evaluate both sides of the equation. The left side of the equation would give us

$$\sqrt{\frac{100}{4}} = \sqrt{25} = 5$$

The right side of the equation would give us

$$\frac{\sqrt{100}}{\sqrt{4}} = \frac{10}{2} = 5$$

Therefore, we can see both sides are the same.

Be Careful! Students sometimes assume that because

$$\sqrt{a \cdot b} = \sqrt{a} \cdot \sqrt{b}$$

then it should also be true that

$$\sqrt{a + b} = \sqrt{a} + \sqrt{b}$$ This is *not* true.

Again, we can see this is not true by picking values for a and b. Consider $a = 9$ and $b = 16$. The left side would give us

$$\sqrt{9 + 16} = \sqrt{25} = 5$$

The right side would give us

$$\sqrt{9} + \sqrt{16} = 3 + 4 = 7$$

Since 5 does not equal 7, the two sides are not equal and this is not a true statement.

With these two properties, we are now ready to define the simplified form for a radical expression. A radical is in simplified form if the following three conditions are satisfied.

Definition

Simplified Form for a Radical Expression

1. The radicand has no factor raised to a power greater than or equal to the index.
2. No fraction appears in the radical.
3. No radical appears in a denominator.

Our initial example deals with satisfying the first of the given conditions. Essentially, we want to find the largest perfect-square factor (in the case of a square root) in the radicand and then apply the product property to simplify the expression.

Example 1 **Simplifying Radical Expressions**

< Objective 1 >

Write each expression in simplified form.

(a) $\sqrt{18} = \sqrt{9 \cdot 2}$

$= \sqrt{9} \cdot \sqrt{2}$ Apply the product property.

$= 3\sqrt{2}$

NOTES

In part **(a)**, the largest perfect-square factor of 18 is 9.

In part **(b)**, the largest perfect-square factor of 75 is 25.

In part **(c)**, the largest perfect-square factor of $27x^3$ is $9x^2$. Note that the exponent must be *even* in a perfect square.

(b) $\sqrt{75} = \sqrt{25 \cdot 3}$
$= \sqrt{25} \cdot \sqrt{3}$
$= 5\sqrt{3}$

(c) $\sqrt{27x^3} = \sqrt{9x^2 \cdot 3x}$
$= \sqrt{9x^2} \cdot \sqrt{3x}$
$= 3x\sqrt{3x}$

(d) $\sqrt{72a^3b^4} = \sqrt{36a^2b^4 \cdot 2a}$
$= \sqrt{36a^2b^4} \cdot \sqrt{2a}$
$= 6ab^2\sqrt{2a}$

Check Yourself 1

Write each expression in simplified form.

(a) $\sqrt{45}$ **(b)** $\sqrt{200}$ **(c)** $\sqrt{75p^5}$ **(d)** $\sqrt{98m^3n^4}$

Writing a cube root in simplest form involves finding factors of the radicand that are perfect cubes, as we see in Example 2. The process illustrated in this example is extended in an identical fashion to simplify radical expressions with any index.

Example 2 Simplifying Radical Expressions

Write each expression in simplified form.

NOTE

In a perfect cube, the exponent must be a *multiple of* 3.

(a) $\sqrt[3]{48} = \sqrt[3]{8 \cdot 6}$
$= \sqrt[3]{8} \cdot \sqrt[3]{6} = 2\sqrt[3]{6}$

(b) $\sqrt[3]{24x^4} = \sqrt[3]{8x^3 \cdot 3x}$
$= \sqrt[3]{8x^3} \cdot \sqrt[3]{3x} = 2x\sqrt[3]{3x}$

(c) $\sqrt[3]{54a^7b^4} = \sqrt[3]{27a^6b^3 \cdot 2ab}$
$= \sqrt[3]{27a^6b^3} \cdot \sqrt[3]{2ab} = 3a^2b\sqrt[3]{2ab}$

Check Yourself 2

Write each expression in simplified form.

(a) $\sqrt[3]{128w^4}$ **(b)** $\sqrt[3]{40x^5y^7}$ **(c)** $\sqrt[4]{48a^8b^5}$

Satisfying our second condition for a radical to be in simplified form (no fractions should appear inside the radical) requires the quotient property for radicals. Consider Example 3.

Example 3 Simplifying Radical Expressions

< Objective 2 >

Write each expression in simplified form.

(a) $\sqrt{\frac{5}{9}} = \frac{\sqrt{5}}{\sqrt{9}}$ Apply the quotient property.

$= \frac{\sqrt{5}}{3}$

(b) $\sqrt{\frac{a^4}{25}} = \frac{\sqrt{a^4}}{\sqrt{25}} = \frac{a^2}{5}$

(c) $\sqrt[3]{\frac{5x^2}{8}} = \frac{\sqrt[3]{5x^2}}{\sqrt[3]{8}} = \frac{\sqrt[3]{5x^2}}{2}$

Check Yourself 3

Write each expression in simplified form.

(a) $\sqrt{\frac{7}{16}}$ (b) $\sqrt{\frac{3}{25a^2}}$ (c) $\sqrt[3]{\frac{5x}{27}}$

Example 4 also begins with the application of the quotient property for radicals. However, an additional step is required because, as we will see, the third condition (no radicals can appear in a denominator) must also be satisfied during the process.

Example 4 Rationalizing the Denominator

< Objective 3 >

Write $\sqrt{\frac{3}{5}}$ in simplified form.

$$\sqrt{\frac{3}{5}} = \frac{\sqrt{3}}{\sqrt{5}}$$

The application of the quotient property satisfies the second condition—there are now no fractions *inside* a radical. However, we now have a radical in the denominator, violating the third condition. The expression is not simplified until that radical is removed.

To remove the radical in the denominator, we multiply the numerator and denominator by the *same* expression, here $\sqrt{5}$. This is called *rationalizing the denominator.*

$$\frac{\sqrt{3}}{\sqrt{5}} = \frac{\sqrt{3} \cdot \sqrt{5}}{\sqrt{5} \cdot \sqrt{5}}$$

$$= \frac{\sqrt{15}}{\sqrt{25}} = \frac{\sqrt{15}}{5}$$

NOTES

The value of the expression is *not* changed as we multiply by $\frac{\sqrt{5}}{\sqrt{5}}$, or 1.

The point here is to arrive at a perfect square inside the radical in the denominator. This is done by multiplying the numerator and denominator by $\sqrt{5}$ because

$\sqrt{5} \cdot \sqrt{5} = \sqrt{5^2}$

$= \sqrt{25}$

$= 5$

Check Yourself 4

Simplify $\sqrt{\dfrac{3}{7}}$.

We will look at some further examples that involve rationalizing the denominator of an expression.

Example 5 Rationalizing the Denominator

> **NOTE**
>
> We could also have multiplied the numerator and denominator in part **(a)** by $\sqrt{8}$, but then we would have more simplifying to do.

Write each expression in simplified form.

(a) $\dfrac{3}{\sqrt{8}} = \dfrac{3 \cdot \sqrt{2}}{\sqrt{8} \cdot \sqrt{2}}$ Multiply the numerator and denominator by $\sqrt{2}$ to get a perfect square inside the radical in the denominator.

$$= \frac{3\sqrt{2}}{\sqrt{16}} = \frac{3\sqrt{2}}{4}$$

(b) $\sqrt[3]{\dfrac{5}{4}} = \dfrac{\sqrt[3]{5}}{\sqrt[3]{4}}$

Now note that

$$\sqrt[3]{4} \cdot \sqrt[3]{2} = \sqrt[3]{8} = 2$$

so multiplying the numerator and denominator by $\sqrt[3]{2}$ will produce a perfect cube inside the radical in the denominator. Continuing, we have

> **NOTE**
>
> 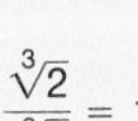
>
> $\dfrac{\sqrt[3]{2}}{\sqrt[3]{2}} = 1$

$$\frac{\sqrt[3]{5}}{\sqrt[3]{4}} = \frac{\sqrt[3]{5} \cdot \sqrt[3]{2}}{\sqrt[3]{4} \cdot \sqrt[3]{2}}$$

$$= \frac{\sqrt[3]{10}}{\sqrt[3]{8}} = \frac{\sqrt[3]{10}}{2}$$

Check Yourself 5

Simplify each expression.

(a) $\dfrac{5}{\sqrt{12}}$ (b) $\sqrt[3]{\dfrac{2}{9}}$

As our final example, we illustrate the process of rationalizing a denominator when variables are involved in a rational expression.

Example 6 Rationalizing Variable Denominators

Simplify each expression.

(a) $\sqrt{\dfrac{8x^3}{3y}}$

By the quotient property we have

$$\sqrt{\frac{8x^3}{3y}} = \frac{\sqrt{8x^3}}{\sqrt{3y}}$$

Because the numerator can be simplified in this case, we will start with that procedure.

$$\frac{\sqrt{8x^3}}{\sqrt{3y}} = \frac{\sqrt{4x^2} \cdot \sqrt{2x}}{\sqrt{3y}} = \frac{2x\sqrt{2x}}{\sqrt{3y}}$$

Multiplying the numerator and denominator by $\sqrt{3y}$ will rationalize the denominator.

$$\frac{2x\sqrt{2x} \cdot \sqrt{3y}}{\sqrt{3y} \cdot \sqrt{3y}} = \frac{2x\sqrt{6xy}}{\sqrt{9y^2}} = \frac{2x\sqrt{6xy}}{3y}$$

(b) $\dfrac{2}{\sqrt[3]{3x}}$

To satisfy the third condition, we must remove the radical from the denominator. For this we need a perfect cube inside the radical in the denominator. Multiplying the numerator and denominator by $\sqrt[3]{9x^2}$ will provide the perfect cube. So

$$\frac{2\sqrt[3]{9x^2}}{\sqrt[3]{3x} \cdot \sqrt[3]{9x^2}} = \frac{2\sqrt[3]{9x^2}}{\sqrt[3]{27x^3}}$$
$$= \frac{2\sqrt[3]{9x^2}}{3x}$$

Check Yourself 6

Simplify each expression.

(a) $\sqrt{\dfrac{12a^3}{5b}}$ **(b)** $\dfrac{3}{\sqrt[3]{2w^2}}$

The following algorithm summarizes our work in simplifying radical expressions.

Step by Step

Simplifying Radical Expressions

Step 1 To satisfy the first condition: Determine the largest perfect-square factor of the radicand. Apply the product property to "remove" that factor from inside the radical.

Step 2 To satisfy the second condition: Use the quotient property to write the expression in the form

If *b* is a perfect square, remove the radical and replace it with the root of *b* in the denominator. If that is not the case, proceed to step 3.

Step 3 Multiply the numerator and denominator of the radical expression by an appropriate radical to remove the radical in the denominator. Simplify the resulting expression when necessary.

NOTE

In the case of a cube root, steps 1 and 2 would refer to perfect cubes, and so forth.

Check Yourself ANSWERS

1. **(a)** $3\sqrt{5}$; **(b)** $10\sqrt{2}$; **(c)** $5p^2\sqrt{3p}$; **(d)** $7mn^2\sqrt{2m}$

2. **(a)** $4w\sqrt[3]{2w}$; **(b)** $2xy^2\sqrt[3]{5x^2y}$; **(c)** $2a^2b\sqrt[4]{3b}$ **3.** **(a)** $\frac{\sqrt{7}}{4}$; **(b)** $\frac{\sqrt{3}}{5a}$; **(c)** $\frac{\sqrt[3]{5x}}{3}$

4. $\frac{\sqrt{21}}{7}$ **5.** **(a)** $\frac{5\sqrt{3}}{6}$; **(b)** $\frac{\sqrt[3]{6}}{3}$ **6.** **(a)** $\frac{2a\sqrt{15ab}}{5b}$; **(b)** $\frac{3\sqrt[3]{4w}}{2w}$

Reading Your Text

The following fill-in-the-blank exercises are designed to ensure that you understand some of the key vocabulary used in this section.

SECTION 7.2

(a) Although the radical of a product is equal to the ______________ of the radicals, the radical of a sum is not equal to the ______________ of the redicals.

(b) For an expression involving square roots to be in simplest form, there will be no perfect square ______________ in a radicand.

(c) For an expression involving a radical to be in simplest form, there will be no ______________ under the radical sign.

(d) Rationalizing the denominator is a process that ______________ a radical in the denominator.

7.2 exercises

Basic Skills | Advanced Skills | Vocational-Technical Applications | Calculator/Computer | Above and Beyond

Name ______________

Section ________ Date ________

< Objective 1 >

Use the product property to write each expression in simplified form.

1. $\sqrt{50}$
2. $\sqrt{28}$
3. $-\sqrt{108}$
4. $-\sqrt{96}$
5. $\sqrt{288}$
6. $-\sqrt{300}$
7. $-\sqrt{72}$ > Videos
8. $\sqrt{48}$
9. $\sqrt{200}$
10. $\sqrt{96}$
11. $\sqrt[3]{16}$
12. $\sqrt[3]{-54}$
13. $\sqrt[3]{-48}$
14. $\sqrt[3]{-160}$
15. $\sqrt[4]{243}$
16. $\sqrt[4]{96}$

Use the product property to write each expression in simplified form. Assume that all variables represent positive real numbers.

17. $\sqrt{x^3y^2}$
18. $\sqrt{a^6b^4c}$

19. $\sqrt{3w^4}$
20. $\sqrt{54m^5}$
21. $\sqrt{18z^2}$
22. $\sqrt{45a^2}$
23. $\sqrt{63x^4}$
24. $\sqrt{75a^5}$
25. $\sqrt{80x^2y^3}$
26. $\sqrt{108p^5q^2}$

Answers

1. $5\sqrt{2}$
2. $2\sqrt{7}$
3. $-6\sqrt{3}$
4. $-4\sqrt{6}$
5. $12\sqrt{2}$
6. $-10\sqrt{3}$
7. $-6\sqrt{2}$
8. $4\sqrt{3}$
9. $10\sqrt{2}$
10. $4\sqrt{6}$
11. $2\sqrt[3]{2}$
12. $-3\sqrt[3]{2}$
13. $-2\sqrt[3]{6}$
14. $-2\sqrt[3]{20}$
15. $3\sqrt[4]{3}$
16. $2\sqrt[4]{6}$
17. $xy\sqrt{x}$
18. $a^3b^2\sqrt{c}$
19. $w^2\sqrt{3}$
20. $3m^2\sqrt{6m}$
21. $3z\sqrt{2}$
22. $3a\sqrt{5}$
23. $3x^2\sqrt{7}$
24. $5a^2\sqrt{3a}$
25. $4xy\sqrt{5y}$
26. $6p^2q\sqrt{3p}$

27. $\sqrt[3]{48p^9}$

28. $\sqrt[3]{-80a^6}$

29. $\sqrt[3]{54m^7}$

30. $\sqrt[3]{250x^{13}}$

31. $\sqrt[3]{-24a^5b^4}$

32. $\sqrt[3]{128r^6s^2}$

33. $\sqrt[4]{96w^5z^{13}}$

34. $\sqrt[4]{128a^{12}b^{17}}$

< Objective 2 >

Use the quotient property to write each expression in simplified form. Assume that all variables represent positive real numbers.

35. $\sqrt{\frac{5}{16}}$

36. $\sqrt{\frac{11}{36}}$

37. $\sqrt{\frac{5}{9y^4}}$

38. $\sqrt{\frac{7}{25x^2}}$

39. $\sqrt[3]{\frac{5}{8}}$

40. $\sqrt[3]{\frac{3}{64}}$

41. $\sqrt[3]{\frac{4x^2}{27}}$

42. $\sqrt[4]{\frac{5x^3}{16}}$

< Objective 3 >

Write each expression in simplified form. Assume that all variables represent positive real numbers.

43. $\sqrt{\frac{4}{5}}$

44. $\frac{3}{\sqrt{10}}$

45. $\sqrt{\frac{5}{8}}$

46. $\frac{\sqrt{6}}{\sqrt{7}}$

47. $\frac{2\sqrt{3}}{\sqrt{10}}$

48. $\sqrt[3]{\frac{7}{4}}$

49. $\sqrt{\frac{3}{x}}$

50. $\sqrt{\frac{12}{w}}$

Answers

27. $2p^3\sqrt[3]{6}$
28. $-2a^2\sqrt[3]{10}$
29. $3m^2\sqrt[3]{2m}$
30. $5x^4\sqrt[3]{2x}$
31. $-2ab\sqrt[3]{3a^2b}$
32. $4r^2\sqrt[3]{2s^2}$
33. $2wz^3\sqrt[4]{6wz}$
34. $2a^3b^4\sqrt[4]{8b}$
35. $\frac{\sqrt{5}}{4}$
36. $\frac{\sqrt{11}}{6}$
37. $\frac{\sqrt{5}}{3y^2}$
38. $\frac{\sqrt{7}}{5x}$
39. $\frac{\sqrt[3]{5}}{2}$
40. $\frac{\sqrt[3]{3}}{4}$
41. $\frac{\sqrt[3]{4x^2}}{3}$
42. $\frac{\sqrt[4]{5x^3}}{2}$
43. $\frac{2\sqrt{5}}{5}$
44. $\frac{3\sqrt{10}}{10}$
45. $\frac{\sqrt{10}}{4}$
46. $\frac{\sqrt{42}}{7}$
47. $\frac{\sqrt{30}}{5}$
48. $\frac{\sqrt[3]{14}}{2}$
49. $\frac{\sqrt{3x}}{x}$
50. $\frac{2\sqrt{3w}}{w}$

Answers

51. $\frac{\sqrt[3]{5y^2}}{y}$ 52. $\frac{3\sqrt[3]{4x^2}}{2x}$

53. False 54. False

55. False 56. True

57. False 58. True

59. See exercise

60. See exercise

61. See exercise

62. See exercise

63. See exercise

64. See exercise

65. See exercise

66. See exercise

67. See exercise

68. See exercise

69. See exercise

70. See exercise

71. See exercise

72. See exercise

73. x^5y^5

74. c^4d^4

75. (a) 6; (b) 6; (c) 12; (d) 12; (e) 10; (f) Not possible; (g) Answers will vary

51. $\sqrt[3]{\frac{5}{y}}$

52. $\frac{3}{\sqrt[3]{2x}}$

Label each of the following statements as **true** *or* **false.**

53. $\sqrt{x^4 + 16} = x^2 + 4$

54. $\sqrt[3]{x^8 + 27} = x^2 + 3$

55. $\sqrt{x^2 + y^2} = x + y$

56. $\frac{\sqrt{x^2 - 25}}{\sqrt{x - 5}} = \sqrt{x + 5}$

57. $\sqrt[3]{x^6} \cdot \sqrt[3]{x^3 - 1} = x^2\sqrt[3]{x - 1}$

58. $\frac{\sqrt[3]{8x^3}}{\sqrt[3]{2x}} = \sqrt[3]{4x^2}$

Complete the following chart.

	x	$\sqrt{x}$	Classify $\sqrt{x}$ as Rational, Irrational, or Not a Real Number
59.	36	6	Rational
60.	8	$2\sqrt{2}$	Irrational
61.	16	4	Rational
62.	-9	Not a real number	Not a real number
63.	1	1	Rational
64.	17	$\sqrt{17}$	Irrational
65.	-3	Not a real number	Not a real number
66.	72	$6\sqrt{2}$	Irrational
67.	25	5	Rational
68.	18	$3\sqrt{2}$	Irrational
69.	7	$\sqrt{7}$	Irrational
70.	45	$3\sqrt{5}$	Irrational
71.	42	$\sqrt{42}$	Irrational
72.	0	0	Rational

Basic Skills | **Advanced Skills** | Vocational-Technical Applications | Calculator/Computer | Above and Beyond

Simplify.

73. $\frac{7\sqrt{x^2y^4} \cdot \sqrt{36xy}}{6\sqrt{x^{-6}y^{-2}} \cdot \sqrt{49x^{-1}y^{-3}}}$

74. $\frac{3\sqrt[3]{32c^{12}d^2} \cdot \sqrt[3]{2c^5d^4}}{4\sqrt[3]{9c^8d^{-2}} \cdot \sqrt[3]{3c^{-3}d^{-4}}}$

75. In parts **(a)** through **(f),** evaluate when possible.

(a) $\sqrt{4 \cdot 9}$ **(b)** $\sqrt{4} \cdot \sqrt{9}$ **(c)** $\sqrt{9 \cdot 16}$

(d) $\sqrt{9} \cdot \sqrt{16}$ **(e)** $\sqrt{(-4)(-25)}$ **(f)** $\sqrt{-4} \cdot \sqrt{-25}$

(g) Based on parts **(a)** through **(f),** make a general conjecture concerning $\sqrt{ab}$. Be careful to specify any restrictions on possible values for a and b.

76. In parts **(a)** through **(d)**, evaluate when possible.

(a) $\sqrt{9 + 16}$ **(b)** $\sqrt{9} + \sqrt{16}$ **(c)** $\sqrt{36 + 64}$ **(d)** $\sqrt{36} + \sqrt{64}$

(e) Based on parts **(a)** through **(d)**, what can you say about $\sqrt{a + b}$ and $\sqrt{a} + \sqrt{b}$?

Basic Skills | Advanced Skills | Vocational-Technical Applications | **Calculator/Computer** | Above and Beyond

77. Use a calculator to evaluate the expressions in parts **(a)** through **(d).** Round your answer to the nearest hundredth.

(a) $3\sqrt{5} + 4\sqrt{5}$ **(b)** $7\sqrt{5}$ **(c)** $2\sqrt{6} + 3\sqrt{6}$ **(d)** $5\sqrt{6}$

(e) Based on parts **(a)** through **(d)**, make a conjecture concerning $a\sqrt{m} + b\sqrt{m}$. Check your conjecture on an example of your own similar to parts **(a)** through **(d)**.

78. Suppose you are given the basic square root function, $y = \sqrt{x}$.

(a) Use a calculator to complete the table (round answers to the nearest tenth).

x	0	1	2	3	4	5	6	7	8	9	10
y	0	1	1.4	1.7	2	2.2	2.4	2.6	2.8	3	3.2

(b) Plot the points on graph paper.

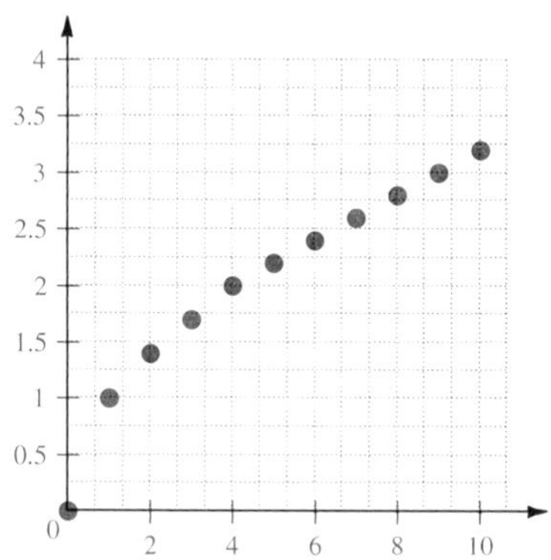

(c) Connect the points with a smooth curve.

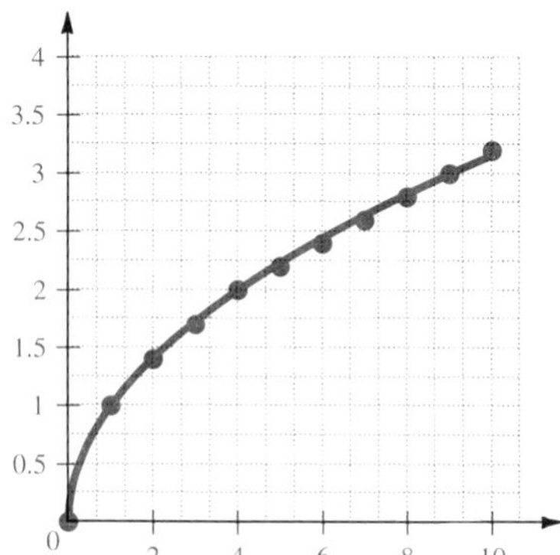

Answers

76. (a) 5; (b) 7; (c) 10; (d) 14; (e) Answers will vary

77. (a) 15.65; (b) 15.65; (c) 12.25; (d) 12.25; (e) Answers will vary

78. See exercise

Answers

79. (a), (c) See exercise; (b) The constant k describes a vertical stretch or shrink of the graph.

80. Above and Beyond

81. $\sqrt{3} + 2$

82. $k = \frac{T\sqrt{L}}{L}$

83. (a) See exercise; (b) 0.199

79. Use a graphing calculator to view the graphs of

$f(x) = \sqrt{x}$

$g(x) = 2\sqrt{x}$

$h(x) = 3\sqrt{x}$

Try the following window: Xmin = 0, Xmax = 10, Ymin = 0, Ymax = 10.

(a) Sketch the graphs shown by your calculator.

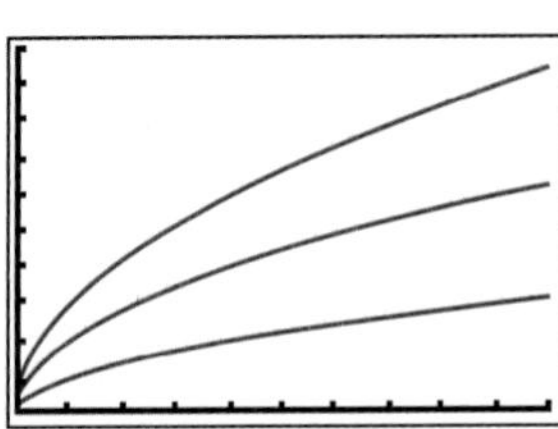

(b) Describe the effect of k on the graph of $y = k\sqrt{x}$.

(c) View and sketch the graph of $y = 4\sqrt{x}$ to test your description in part **(b)**.

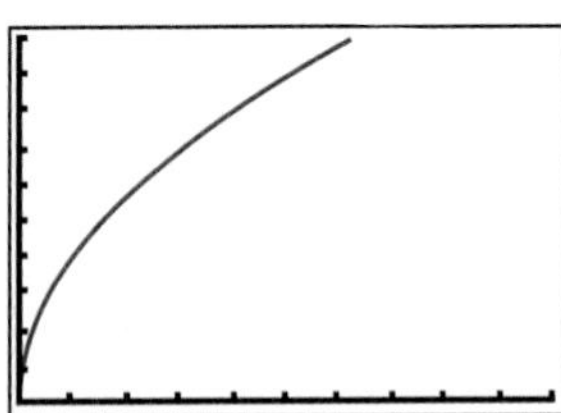

Basic Skills | Advanced Skills | Vocational-Technical Applications | Calculator/Computer | **Above and Beyond**

80. Explain the difference between a pair of binomials in which the middle sign is changed, and the opposite of a binomial. To illustrate, use $4 - \sqrt{7}$.

81. Determine the missing binomial in the following:

$(\sqrt{3} - 2)(\qquad) = -1$

82. Solve the equation $T = k\sqrt{L}$ for k (simplify your result).

83. Complete the following chart of pendulum data using the function $T = k\sqrt{L}$.

(a) Beginning with $L = 10$ cm, compute the value of k for each given value of T. Round each value of k to the nearest thousandth.

L	10	20	30	40	50	60	70
T	0.633	0.9	1.1	1.267	1.4	1.533	1.633
k	0.200	0.201	0.201	0.200	0.198	0.198	0.195

(b) Find the average (mean) of these seven values for k found in part **(a)**. Round to the nearest thousandth.

84. A standard physics text gives us the theoretical function relating the period of a pendulum to the length of the pendulum as

$$T = 2\pi\sqrt{\frac{L}{g}}$$

in which g is the constant for gravity. If the units involved are centimeters and seconds, then the constant g is given by $g = 980 \text{ cm/sec}^2$.

(a) Use the properties of radicals to rewrite the given function in the form $T = k\sqrt{L}$. Round k to the nearest thousandth.

(b) How does the theoretical k found in part **(a)** compare with the experimental k found in exercise 83(b)?

Answers

84. (a) $T = 0.201\sqrt{L}$; (b) Within 0.002

Answers

1. $5\sqrt{2}$ **3.** $-6\sqrt{3}$ **5.** $12\sqrt{2}$ **7.** $-6\sqrt{2}$ **9.** $10\sqrt{2}$
11. $2\sqrt[3]{2}$ **13.** $-2\sqrt[3]{6}$ **15.** $3\sqrt[4]{3}$ **17.** $xy\sqrt{x}$ **19.** $w^2\sqrt{3}$
21. $3z\sqrt{2}$ **23.** $3x^2\sqrt{7}$ **25.** $4xy\sqrt{5y}$ **27.** $2p^3\sqrt[3]{6}$
29. $3m^2\sqrt[3]{2m}$ **31.** $-2ab\sqrt[3]{3a^2b}$ **33.** $2wz^3\sqrt[4]{6wz}$ **35.** $\frac{\sqrt{5}}{4}$
37. $\frac{\sqrt{5}}{3y^2}$ **39.** $\frac{\sqrt[3]{5}}{2}$ **41.** $\frac{\sqrt[3]{4x^2}}{3}$ **43.** $\frac{2\sqrt{5}}{5}$ **45.** $\frac{\sqrt{10}}{4}$
47. $\frac{\sqrt{30}}{5}$ **49.** $\frac{\sqrt{3x}}{x}$ **51.** $\frac{\sqrt[3]{5y^2}}{y}$ **53.** False **55.** False
57. False **59.** 6, rational **61.** 16, rational **63.** 1, rational
65. Not a real number, not a real number **67.** 25, rational
69. 7, irrational **71.** $\sqrt{42}$, irrational **73.** x^5y^5
75. **(a)** 6; **(b)** 6; **(c)** 12; **(d)** 12; **(e)** 10; **(f)** not possible; **(g)** Answers will vary
77. **(a)** 15.65; **(b)** 15.65; **(c)** 12.25; **(d)** 12.25; **(e)** Answers will vary
79. **(a)**

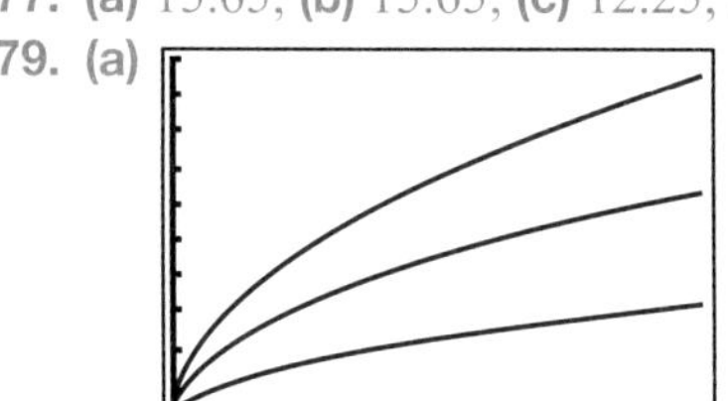

(b) The constant k describes a vertical stretch or shrink of the graph;
(c)

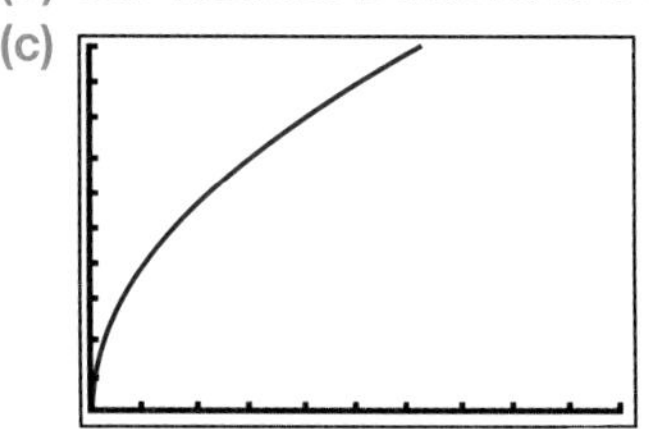

81. $\sqrt{3} + 2$
83. **(a)**

L	10	20	30	40	50	60	70
T	0.633	0.9	1.1	1.267	1.4	1.533	1.633
k	0.200	0.201	0.201	0.200	0.198	0.198	0.195

(b) 0.199

7.3 Operations on Radical Expressions

< 7.3 Objectives >

1 > Add or subtract radical expressions

2 > Multiply radical expressions

3 > Divide radical expressions

NOTE

This uses the distributive property.

The addition and subtraction of radical expressions exactly parallel our earlier work with polynomials containing like terms. We will review for a moment.

To add $3x^2 + 4x^2$, we have

$$3x^2 + 4x^2 = (3 + 4)x^2$$
$$= 7x^2$$

Keep in mind that we were able to simplify or combine the preceding expressions because of like terms in x^2. (Recall that like terms have the same variable factor raised to the same power.)

RECALL

In general,
$\sqrt{a} + \sqrt{b} \neq \sqrt{a + b}$

We *cannot* combine terms such as

$$4a^3 + 3a^2 \quad \text{or} \quad 3x - 5y$$

By extending these ideas, radical expressions can be combined *only* if they are *similar,* that is, if the expressions contain the same radicand with the same index. This idea is illustrated in Example 1.

Example 1 Adding or Subtracting Radical Expressions

< Objective 1 >

Add or subtract as indicated.

NOTES

Apply the distributive property.

In part **(d)**, the expressions have different radicands, $\sqrt{5}$ and $\sqrt{3}$.

In part **(e)**, the expressions have different indices, 2 and 3.

In part **(h)**, the radicands are *not* the same.

(a) $3\sqrt{7} + \sqrt{7} = (3 + 1)\sqrt{7}$ $\qquad \sqrt{7} = 1 \cdot \sqrt{7}$
$= 4\sqrt{7}$

(b) $7\sqrt{3} - 4\sqrt{3} = (7 - 4)\sqrt{3} = 3\sqrt{3}$

(c) $5\sqrt{10} - 3\sqrt{10} + 2\sqrt{10} = (5 - 3 + 2)\sqrt{10}$
$= 4\sqrt{10}$

(d) $2\sqrt{5} + 3\sqrt{3}$ cannot be further simplified.

(e) $\sqrt{7} + \sqrt[3]{7}$ cannot be further simplified.

(f) $5\sqrt{x} + 2\sqrt{x} = (5 + 2)\sqrt{x}$
$= 7\sqrt{x}$

(g) $5\sqrt{3ab} - 2\sqrt{3ab} + 3\sqrt{3ab} = (5 - 2 + 3)\sqrt{3ab} = 6\sqrt{3ab}$

(h) $\sqrt[3]{3x^2} + \sqrt[3]{3x}$ cannot be further simplified.

Check Yourself 1

Add or subtract as indicated.

(a) $5\sqrt{3} + 2\sqrt{3}$
(b) $7\sqrt{5} - 2\sqrt{5} + 3\sqrt{5}$
(c) $2\sqrt{3} + 3\sqrt{2}$
(d) $\sqrt{2y} + 5\sqrt{2y} - 3\sqrt{2y}$
(e) $2\sqrt[3]{3m} - 5\sqrt[3]{3m}$
(f) $\sqrt{5x} - \sqrt[3]{5x}$

Often it is necessary to simplify radical expressions by the methods of Section 7.2 before they can be combined. Example 2 illustrates how the product property is applied.

Example 2 Adding or Subtracting Radical Expressions

Add or subtract as indicated.

(a) $\sqrt{48} + 2\sqrt{3}$

In this form, the radicals cannot be combined. However, note that the first radical can be simplified by our earlier methods because 48 has the perfect-square factor 16.

$$\sqrt{48} = \sqrt{16 \cdot 3} = 4\sqrt{3}$$

With this result we can proceed as before.

$$\begin{aligned}\sqrt{48} + 2\sqrt{3} &= 4\sqrt{3} + 2\sqrt{3}\\ &= (4 + 2)\sqrt{3} = 6\sqrt{3}\end{aligned}$$

(b) $$\begin{aligned}\sqrt{50} - \sqrt{32} + \sqrt{98} &= \sqrt{25 \cdot 2} - \sqrt{16 \cdot 2} + \sqrt{49 \cdot 2}\\ &= 5\sqrt{2} - 4\sqrt{2} + 7\sqrt{2}\\ &= (5 - 4 + 7)\sqrt{2} = 8\sqrt{2}\end{aligned}$$

(c) $x\sqrt{2x} + 3\sqrt{8x^3}$

Note that

$$\begin{aligned}3\sqrt{8x^3} &= 3\sqrt{4x^2 \cdot 2x}\\ &= 3\sqrt{4x^2} \cdot \sqrt{2x}\\ &= 3 \cdot 2x\sqrt{2x} = 6x\sqrt{2x}\end{aligned}$$

So

$$\begin{aligned}x\sqrt{2x} + 3\sqrt{8x^3} &= x\sqrt{2x} + 6x\sqrt{2x}\\ &= (x + 6x)\sqrt{2x} = 7x\sqrt{2x}\end{aligned}$$

NOTE

We can now combine the similar radicals.

(d) $$\begin{aligned}\sqrt[3]{2a} - \sqrt[3]{16a} + \sqrt[3]{54a} &= \sqrt[3]{2a} - 2\sqrt[3]{2a} + 3\sqrt[3]{2a}\\ &= (1 - 2 + 3)\sqrt[3]{2a}\\ &= 2\sqrt[3]{2a}\end{aligned}$$

Check Yourself 2

Add or subtract as indicated.

(a) $\sqrt{125} + 3\sqrt{5}$
(b) $\sqrt{75} - \sqrt{27} + \sqrt{48}$
(c) $5\sqrt{24y^3} - y\sqrt{6y}$
(d) $\sqrt[3]{81x} - \sqrt[3]{3x} + \sqrt[3]{24x}$

It may also be necessary to apply the quotient property before combining rational expressions. Consider Example 3.

Example 3 Adding or Subtracting Radical Expressions

Add or subtract as indicated.

(a) $2\sqrt{6} + \sqrt{\frac{2}{3}}$

We apply the quotient property to the *second term* and rationalize the denominator.

NOTE

Multiply by $\frac{\sqrt{3}}{\sqrt{3}}$, or 1.

$$\sqrt{\frac{2}{3}} = \frac{\sqrt{2}}{\sqrt{3}} = \frac{\sqrt{2} \cdot \sqrt{3}}{\sqrt{3} \cdot \sqrt{3}} = \frac{\sqrt{6}}{3}$$

So

$$2\sqrt{6} + \sqrt{\frac{2}{3}} = 2\sqrt{6} + \frac{\sqrt{6}}{3}$$

$$= \left(2 + \frac{1}{3}\right)\sqrt{6} = \frac{7}{3}\sqrt{6} \quad \text{or} \quad \frac{7\sqrt{6}}{3}$$

NOTE

$\frac{\sqrt{6}}{3}$ and $\frac{1}{3}\sqrt{6}$ are equivalent since

$\frac{1}{3}\sqrt{6} = \frac{1}{3} \cdot \frac{\sqrt{6}}{1} = \frac{\sqrt{6}}{3}$

(b) $\sqrt{20x} - \sqrt{\frac{x}{5}}$

Again we first simplify the two expressions. So

$$\sqrt{20x} - \sqrt{\frac{x}{5}} = 2\sqrt{5x} - \frac{\sqrt{x} \cdot \sqrt{5}}{\sqrt{5} \cdot \sqrt{5}}$$

$$= 2\sqrt{5x} - \frac{\sqrt{5x}}{5}$$

$$= \left(2 - \frac{1}{5}\right)\sqrt{5x} = \frac{9}{5}\sqrt{5x} \quad \text{or} \quad \frac{9\sqrt{5x}}{5}$$

Check Yourself 3

Add or subtract as indicated.

(a) $3\sqrt{7} + \sqrt{\frac{1}{7}}$ **(b)** $\sqrt{40x} - \sqrt{\frac{2x}{5}}$

Example 4 illustrates the need to apply our earlier methods for adding fractions when working with radical expressions.

Example 4 Adding Radical Expressions

Add $\frac{\sqrt{5}}{3} + \frac{2}{\sqrt{5}}$

Our first step will be to rationalize the denominator of the second fraction, to write the sum as

$$\frac{\sqrt{5}}{3} + \frac{2 \cdot \sqrt{5}}{\sqrt{5} \cdot \sqrt{5}}$$

or

$$\frac{\sqrt{5}}{3} + \frac{2\sqrt{5}}{5}$$

The LCD of the fractions is 15, and rewriting each fraction with that denominator, we have

$$\frac{\sqrt{5} \cdot 5}{3 \cdot 5} + \frac{2\sqrt{5} \cdot 3}{5 \cdot 3} = \frac{5\sqrt{5} + 6\sqrt{5}}{15}$$
$$= \frac{11\sqrt{5}}{15}$$

Check Yourself 4

Subtract $\frac{3}{\sqrt{10}} - \frac{\sqrt{10}}{5}$.

NOTE

We actually used the multiplication property to rationalize denominators.

In Section 7.2 we introduced the product and quotient properties for radical expressions. At that time they were used for simplifying radicals.

If we turn those properties around, we have our rules for the multiplication and division of radical expressions. For multiplication:

Property

Multiplying Radical Expressions

$$\sqrt[n]{a} \cdot \sqrt[n]{b} = \sqrt[n]{a \cdot b}$$

In words, the product of radicals is the radical of the product.

A use of this multiplication rule is illustrated in Example 5. As we did in Section 7.2, we assume that all variables represent positive real numbers.

Example 5 Multiplying Radical Expressions

< Objective 2 >

Multiply.

NOTE

Multiply the radicands.

(a) $\sqrt{7} \cdot \sqrt{5} = \sqrt{7 \cdot 5} = \sqrt{35}$

(b) $\sqrt{3x} \cdot \sqrt{10y} = \sqrt{3x \cdot 10y}$
$= \sqrt{30xy}$

(c) $\sqrt[3]{4x} \cdot \sqrt[3]{7x} = \sqrt[3]{4x \cdot 7x}$
$= \sqrt[3]{28x^2}$

Check Yourself 5

Multiply.

(a) $\sqrt{6} \cdot \sqrt{7}$

(b) $\sqrt{5a} \cdot \sqrt{11b}$

(c) $\sqrt[3]{3y} \cdot \sqrt[3]{5y}$

Keep in mind that all radical expressions should be written in simplified form. Often we have to apply the methods of Section 7.2 to simplify a product once it has been formed.

Example 6 Multiplying Radical Expressions

> **NOTE**
> In part **(a)**, $\sqrt{18}$ is *not* in simplified form. 9 is a perfect-square factor of 18.

Multiply and simplify.

(a) $\sqrt{3} \cdot \sqrt{6} = \sqrt{18}$
$= \sqrt{9 \cdot 2} = \sqrt{9}\sqrt{2}$
$= 3\sqrt{2}$

(b) $\sqrt{5x} \cdot \sqrt{15x} = \sqrt{75x^2}$
$= \sqrt{25x^2 \cdot 3} = \sqrt{25x^2} \cdot \sqrt{3}$
$= 5x\sqrt{3}$

> **NOTE**
> Now, for part **(c)**, we want a factor that is a *perfect cube.*

(c) $\sqrt[3]{4a^2b} \cdot \sqrt[3]{10a^2b^2} = \sqrt[3]{40a^4b^3} = \sqrt[3]{8a^3b^3 \cdot 5a}$
$= \sqrt[3]{8a^3b^3} \cdot \sqrt[3]{5a} = 2ab\sqrt[3]{5a}$

Check Yourself 6

Multiply and simplify.

(a) $\sqrt{10} \cdot \sqrt{20}$ **(b)** $\sqrt{6x} \cdot \sqrt{15x}$
(c) $\sqrt[3]{9p^2q^2} \cdot \sqrt[3]{6pq^2}$

We are now ready to combine multiplication with the techniques for addition and subtraction of radicals. This will allow us to multiply radical expressions with more than one term. Consider Examples 7 and 8, which combine these techniques.

Example 7 Using the Distributive Property

Multiply and simplify.

(a) $\sqrt{2}(\sqrt{5} + \sqrt{7})$

Distributing $\sqrt{2}$, we have

$\sqrt{2} \cdot \sqrt{5} + \sqrt{2} \cdot \sqrt{7} = \sqrt{10} + \sqrt{14}$

The expression cannot be simplified further.

> **NOTE**
> Alternately, in part **(c)**, we could choose to simplify $\sqrt{8x}$ in the original expression as our first step. We leave it to the reader to verify that the result would be the same.

(b) $\sqrt{3}(\sqrt{6} + 2\sqrt{15}) = \sqrt{3} \cdot \sqrt{6} + \sqrt{3} \cdot 2\sqrt{15}$ Distribute $\sqrt{3}$.
$= \sqrt{18} + 2\sqrt{45}$
$= 3\sqrt{2} + 6\sqrt{5}$

(c) $\sqrt{x}(\sqrt{2x} + \sqrt{8x}) = \sqrt{x} \cdot \sqrt{2x} + \sqrt{x} \cdot \sqrt{8x}$
$= \sqrt{2x^2} + \sqrt{8x^2}$
$= x\sqrt{2} + 2x\sqrt{2} = 3x\sqrt{2}$

Check Yourself 7

Multiply and simplify.

(a) $\sqrt{3}(\sqrt{10} + \sqrt{2})$ **(b)** $\sqrt{2}(3 + 2\sqrt{6})$ **(c)** $\sqrt{a}(\sqrt{3a} + \sqrt{12a})$

If both of the radical expressions involved in a multiplication statement have two terms, we must apply the patterns for multiplying polynomials developed in Chapter 5. Example 8 illustrates the use of FOIL.

Example 8 Multiplying Radical Binomials

Multiply and simplify.

(a) $(\sqrt{3} + 1)(\sqrt{3} + 5)$

To write the desired product, we use the FOIL pattern for multiplying binomials.

$(\sqrt{3} + 1)(\sqrt{3} + 5)$

$= \underbrace{\sqrt{3} \cdot \sqrt{3}}_{\text{First}} + \underbrace{5 \cdot \sqrt{3}}_{\text{Outer}} + \underbrace{1 \cdot \sqrt{3}}_{\text{Inner}} + \underbrace{1 \cdot 5}_{\text{Last}}$ Outer and inner products are similar radicals, so combine.

$= 3 + 6\sqrt{3} + 5$ First and last products are like terms, so combine.

$= 8 + 6\sqrt{3}$

NOTE

The sum of the outer and inner products $-\sqrt{12} + \sqrt{12}$ is 0.

(b) $(\sqrt{6} + \sqrt{2})(\sqrt{6} - \sqrt{2})$

Multiplying as before, we have

$\sqrt{6} \cdot \sqrt{6} - \sqrt{6} \cdot \sqrt{2} + \sqrt{6} \cdot \sqrt{2} - \sqrt{2} \cdot \sqrt{2} = 6 - 2 = 4$

Two binomial radical expressions that differ *only* in the sign of the second term are called **conjugates** of each other. So

$\sqrt{6} + \sqrt{2}$ and $\sqrt{6} - \sqrt{2}$

are conjugates, and their product does *not* contain a radical—the product is a rational number. That will always be the case with two conjugates. This will have particular significance later in this section.

NOTE

The form of the product

$(a + b)(a - b)$

gives

$a^2 - b^2$

When a and b are square roots, the product will be rational.

(c) $(\sqrt{2} + \sqrt{5})^2$

$(\sqrt{2} + \sqrt{5})^2 = (\sqrt{2} + \sqrt{5})(\sqrt{2} + \sqrt{5})$

Multiplying as before, we have

$$\begin{aligned}(\sqrt{2} + \sqrt{5})^2 &= \sqrt{2} \cdot \sqrt{2} + \sqrt{2} \cdot \sqrt{5} + \sqrt{2} \cdot \sqrt{5} + \sqrt{5} \cdot \sqrt{5} \\ &= 2 + \sqrt{10} + \sqrt{10} + 5 \\ &= 7 + 2\sqrt{10}\end{aligned}$$

This square can also be evaluated by using our earlier formula for the square of a binomial

$(a + b)^2 = a^2 + 2ab + b^2$

in which $a = \sqrt{2}$ and $b = \sqrt{5}$. Then

$$\begin{aligned}(\sqrt{2} + \sqrt{5})^2 &= (\sqrt{2})^2 + 2(\sqrt{2})(\sqrt{5}) + (\sqrt{5})^2 \\ &= 2 + 2\sqrt{10} + 5 \\ &= 7 + 2\sqrt{10}\end{aligned}$$

Check Yourself 8

Multiply and simplify.

(a) $(\sqrt{2} + 3)(\sqrt{2} + 5)$ (b) $(\sqrt{5} - \sqrt{3})(\sqrt{5} + \sqrt{3})$
(c) $(\sqrt{7} - \sqrt{3})^2$

We are now ready to state our basic rule for the division of radical expressions. Again, it is simply a restatement of our earlier quotient property.

Property

Dividing Radical Expressions

$$\frac{\sqrt[n]{a}}{\sqrt[n]{b}} = \sqrt[n]{\frac{a}{b}}$$

In words, the quotient of radicals is the radical of the quotient.

Although we illustrate the use of this property in the examples that follow, the division of radical expressions is most often carried out by rationalizing the denominator. This process can be divided into two types of problems, those with a monomial divisor and those with binomial divisors.

Example 9 Dividing Radical Expressions

< Objective 3 >

NOTE

$\frac{\sqrt{5}}{\sqrt{5}} = 1$

Simplify each expression. Again assume that all variables represent positive real numbers.

(a) $\frac{3}{\sqrt{5}} = \frac{3 \cdot \sqrt{5}}{\sqrt{5} \cdot \sqrt{5}} = \frac{3\sqrt{5}}{5}$

We multiply numerator and denominator by $\sqrt{5}$ to rationalize the denominator.

(b) $\frac{\sqrt{7x}}{\sqrt{10y}} = \frac{\sqrt{7x} \cdot \sqrt{10y}}{\sqrt{10y} \cdot \sqrt{10y}}$

$= \frac{\sqrt{70xy}}{10y}$

(c) $\frac{3}{\sqrt[3]{2}} = \frac{3\sqrt[3]{4}}{\sqrt[3]{2} \cdot \sqrt[3]{4}}$

$= \frac{3\sqrt[3]{4}}{2}$

In this case we want a perfect cube in the denominator, so we multiply numerator and denominator by $\sqrt[3]{4}$, which gives $\sqrt[3]{8} = 2$.

These division problems are identical to those we saw earlier in Section 7.2 when we were simplifying radical expressions. They are shown here to illustrate this case of division with radicals.

Check Yourself 9

Simplify each expression.

(a) $\frac{5}{\sqrt{7}}$ (b) $\frac{\sqrt{3a}}{\sqrt{5b}}$ (c) $\frac{5}{\sqrt[3]{9}}$

Example 10 shows that our division rule can be particularly useful if the radicands in the numerator and denominator have common factors.

Example 10 Dividing Radical Expressions

Simplify

$$\frac{\sqrt{10}}{\sqrt{15a}}$$

NOTE

There is a common factor of 5 in the radicand of the numerator and denominator.

We apply the division rule so that the radicand can be reduced as a fraction:

$$\frac{\sqrt{10}}{\sqrt{15a}} = \sqrt{\frac{10}{15a}} = \sqrt{\frac{2}{3a}}$$

Now we use the quotient property and rationalize the denominator:

$$\sqrt{\frac{2}{3a}} = \frac{\sqrt{2}}{\sqrt{3a}} = \frac{\sqrt{2} \cdot \sqrt{3a}}{\sqrt{3a} \cdot \sqrt{3a}}$$

$$= \frac{\sqrt{6a}}{3a}$$

Check Yourself 10

Simplify $\frac{\sqrt{15}}{\sqrt{18x}}$.

We now turn our attention to another type of division problem involving radical expressions. Here the divisors (the denominators) are binomials. This next example will use the idea of conjugates that we saw earlier in Example 8.

Example 11 Rationalizing Radical Denominators

Rationalize each denominator.

NOTE

If a radical expression has a sum or difference in the denominator, multiply the numerator and denominator by the *conjugate* of the denominator to rationalize.

(a) $\frac{6}{\sqrt{6} + \sqrt{2}}$

Recall that $\sqrt{6} - \sqrt{2}$ is the conjugate of $\sqrt{6} + \sqrt{2}$, and the product of such conjugates is *always a rational number*. Therefore, to rationalize the denominator, we multiply by $\sqrt{6} - \sqrt{2}$.

$$\frac{6}{\sqrt{6} + \sqrt{2}} = \frac{6(\sqrt{6} - \sqrt{2})}{(\sqrt{6} + \sqrt{2})(\sqrt{6} - \sqrt{2})}$$

$$= \frac{6(\sqrt{6} - \sqrt{2})}{4}$$ Divide 2 out of 6 and 4 to simplify.

$$= \frac{3(\sqrt{6} - \sqrt{2})}{2}$$

NOTE

See Example 8(b) for details of the multiplication in the denominator.

(b) $\dfrac{\sqrt{5} + \sqrt{3}}{\sqrt{5} - \sqrt{3}}$

Multiply the numerator and denominator by $\sqrt{5} + \sqrt{3}$.

$$\frac{(\sqrt{5} + \sqrt{3})(\sqrt{5} + \sqrt{3})}{(\sqrt{5} - \sqrt{3})(\sqrt{5} + \sqrt{3})} = \frac{5 + \sqrt{15} + \sqrt{15} + 3}{5 - 3}$$ Combine like terms.

$$= \frac{8 + 2\sqrt{15}}{2} = \frac{2(4 + \sqrt{15})}{2}$$ Factor.

$$= 4 + \sqrt{15}$$ Divide numerator and denominator by 2 to simplify.

Check Yourself 11

Rationalize the denominator.

(a) $\dfrac{4}{\sqrt{3} - \sqrt{2}}$ (b) $\dfrac{\sqrt{6} + \sqrt{3}}{\sqrt{6} - \sqrt{3}}$

Check Yourself ANSWERS

1. **(a)** $7\sqrt{3}$; **(b)** $8\sqrt{5}$; **(c)** cannot be simplified; **(d)** $3\sqrt{2y}$; **(e)** $-3\sqrt[3]{3m}$; **(f)** cannot be simplified **2.** **(a)** $8\sqrt{5}$; **(b)** $6\sqrt{3}$; **(c)** $9y\sqrt{6y}$; **(d)** $4\sqrt[3]{3x}$ **3.** **(a)** $\frac{22}{7}\sqrt{7}$ or $\frac{22\sqrt{7}}{7}$; **(b)** $\frac{9}{5}\sqrt{10x}$ or $\frac{9\sqrt{10x}}{5}$ **4.** $\frac{\sqrt{10}}{10}$ **5.** **(a)** $\sqrt{42}$; **(b)** $\sqrt{55ab}$; **(c)** $\sqrt[3]{15y^2}$ **6.** **(a)** $10\sqrt{2}$; **(b)** $3x\sqrt{10}$; **(c)** $3pq\sqrt[3]{2q}$ **7.** **(a)** $\sqrt{30} + \sqrt{6}$; **(b)** $3\sqrt{2} + 4\sqrt{3}$; **(c)** $3a\sqrt{3}$ **8.** **(a)** $17 + 8\sqrt{2}$; **(b)** 2; **(c)** $10 - 2\sqrt{21}$ **9.** **(a)** $\frac{5\sqrt{7}}{7}$; **(b)** $\frac{\sqrt{15ab}}{5b}$; **(c)** $\frac{5\sqrt[3]{3}}{3}$ **10.** $\frac{\sqrt{30x}}{6x}$ **11.** **(a)** $4(\sqrt{3} + \sqrt{2})$; **(b)** $3 + 2\sqrt{2}$

Reading Your Text

The following fill-in-the-blank exercises are designed to ensure that you understand some of the key vocabulary used in this section.

SECTION 7.3

(a) Radicals that have the same index and the same ____________ are called like radicals.

(b) Like radicals can be added by using the ____________ property.

(c) The product of two radicals is equal to the ____________ of the products.

(d) The product of conjugates is always a ____________.

Basic Skills | Advanced Skills | Vocational-Technical Applications | Calculator/Computer | Above and Beyond

7.3 exercises

MathZone

Boost your grade at mathzone.com!
> Practice Problems
> NetTutor
> Self-Tests
> e-Professors
> Videos

Name ______________

Section ________ Date ________

< Objective 1 >

Add or subtract as indicated. Assume that all variables represent positive real numbers.

1. $3\sqrt{5} + 4\sqrt{5}$
2. $5\sqrt{x} + 3\sqrt{x}$
3. $8\sqrt{3a} - 11\sqrt{3a}$
4. $7\sqrt{m} + 6\sqrt{n}$
5. $2\sqrt[3]{2} + 7\sqrt[3]{2}$
6. $8\sqrt{6} - 2\sqrt{6} + 3\sqrt{6}$

Simplify the radical expressions when necessary. Then add or subtract as indicated. Again assume that all variables represent positive real numbers.

7. $\sqrt{20} + \sqrt{5}$
8. $\sqrt{27} + \sqrt{3}$
9. $\sqrt{18} + \sqrt{50}$
10. $\sqrt{28} + \sqrt{63}$
11. $\sqrt{72} + \sqrt{50}$
12. $\sqrt{27} - \sqrt{12}$
13. $3\sqrt{12} - \sqrt{48}$
14. $5\sqrt{8} + 2\sqrt{18}$
15. $2\sqrt{5} + \sqrt{12}$
16. $\sqrt{98} - 3\sqrt{5}$
17. $4\sqrt{28} - \sqrt{63}$
18. $2\sqrt{40} + \sqrt{90}$
19. $\sqrt{12} + \sqrt{27} - \sqrt{3}$
20. $\sqrt{50} + \sqrt{32} - \sqrt{8}$
21. $\sqrt{98} - \sqrt{18} + \sqrt{8}$
22. $\sqrt{108} - \sqrt{27} + \sqrt{75}$

23. $3\sqrt{24} - \sqrt{54} + \sqrt{6}$
24. $\sqrt{63} - 2\sqrt{28} + 5\sqrt{7}$
25. $\sqrt[3]{81} + \sqrt[3]{3}$
26. $\sqrt[3]{16} - \sqrt[3]{2}$
27. $2\sqrt[3]{128} - 3\sqrt[3]{2}$

28. $3\sqrt[3]{81} - 2\sqrt[3]{3}$

Answers

1. $7\sqrt{5}$
2. $8\sqrt{x}$
3. $-3\sqrt{3a}$
4. Cannot be simplified
5. $9\sqrt[3]{2}$
6. $9\sqrt{6}$
7. $3\sqrt{5}$
8. $4\sqrt{3}$
9. $8\sqrt{2}$
10. $5\sqrt{7}$
11. $11\sqrt{2}$
12. $\sqrt{3}$
13. $2\sqrt{3}$
14. $16\sqrt{2}$
15. $2\sqrt{5} + 2\sqrt{3}$
16. $7\sqrt{2} - 3\sqrt{5}$
17. $5\sqrt{7}$
18. $7\sqrt{10}$
19. $4\sqrt{3}$
20. $7\sqrt{2}$
21. $6\sqrt{2}$
22. $8\sqrt{3}$
23. $4\sqrt{6}$
24. $4\sqrt{7}$
25. $4\sqrt[3]{3}$
26. $\sqrt[3]{2}$
27. $5\sqrt[3]{2}$
28. $7\sqrt[3]{3}$

Answers

29. $\sqrt{6w}$ 30. $8\sqrt{3p}$

31. $5x\sqrt{2x}$ 32. $3y\sqrt{5y}$

33. $a\sqrt{3}$ 34. $-y\sqrt{2}$

35. $(5x + 6)\sqrt{3x}$ 36. $(7a - 2)\sqrt{2a}$

37. $5x\sqrt[3]{2x}$ 38. $a\sqrt[3]{3a^2}$

39. $3w\sqrt[3]{2w^2}$ 40. $2z\sqrt[4]{2z^3}$

41. $\frac{4}{3}\sqrt{3}$ or $\frac{4\sqrt{3}}{3}$

42. $\frac{5}{6}\sqrt{6}$ or $\frac{5\sqrt{6}}{6}$

43. $\frac{2}{3}\sqrt{6}$ or $\frac{2\sqrt{6}}{3}$

44. $\frac{6}{5}\sqrt{10}$ or $\frac{6\sqrt{10}}{5}$

45. $\frac{3}{2}\sqrt[3]{6}$ or $\frac{3\sqrt[3]{6}}{2}$

46. $\frac{7}{3}\sqrt[3]{12}$ or $\frac{7\sqrt[3]{12}}{3}$

47. $\frac{2}{3}\sqrt{6}$ or $\frac{2\sqrt{6}}{3}$

48. $\frac{2}{5}\sqrt{10}$ or $\frac{2\sqrt{10}}{5}$

49. $\frac{1}{3}\sqrt{3}$ or $\frac{\sqrt{3}}{3}$

50. $\frac{4}{5}\sqrt{5}$ or $\frac{4\sqrt{5}}{5}$

51. $\sqrt{42}$ 52. $\sqrt{11a}$

53. $\sqrt{42}$ 54. $\sqrt[3]{36}$

55. 6 56. 7

57. $3p\sqrt[3]{2}$ 58. $2xy\sqrt[3]{5y}$

59. $\sqrt{6} + 5\sqrt{2}$ 60. $\sqrt{15} - \sqrt{10}$

29. $\sqrt{54w} - \sqrt{24w}$

30. $\sqrt{27p} + \sqrt{75p}$

31. $\sqrt{18x^3} + \sqrt{8x^3}$

32. $\sqrt{125y^3} - \sqrt{20y^3}$

33. $a\sqrt{27} - 2\sqrt{3a^2}$

34. $5\sqrt{2y^2} - 3y\sqrt{8}$

35. $5\sqrt{3x^3} + 2\sqrt{27x}$

36. $7\sqrt{2a^3} - \sqrt{8a}$

37. $\sqrt[3]{54x^4} - \sqrt[3]{16x^4} + \sqrt[3]{128x^4}$

38. $\sqrt[3]{81a^5} + \sqrt[3]{24a^5} - \sqrt[3]{192a^5}$

39. $\sqrt[3]{16w^5} + 2w\sqrt[3]{2w^2} - \sqrt[3]{2w^5}$

40. $\sqrt[4]{2z^7} - z\sqrt[4]{32z^3} + \sqrt[4]{162z^7}$

41. $\sqrt{3} + \sqrt{\frac{1}{3}}$

42. $\sqrt{6} - \sqrt{\frac{1}{6}}$

43. $\sqrt{6} - \sqrt{\frac{2}{3}}$

44. $\sqrt{10} + \sqrt{\frac{2}{5}}$

45. $\sqrt[3]{48} - \sqrt[3]{\frac{3}{4}}$

46. $\sqrt[3]{96} + \sqrt[3]{\frac{4}{9}}$

47. $\frac{\sqrt{6}}{2} + \frac{1}{\sqrt{6}}$

48. $\frac{\sqrt{10}}{2} - \frac{1}{\sqrt{10}}$ > Videos

49. $\frac{\sqrt{12}}{3} - \frac{1}{\sqrt{3}}$

50. $\frac{\sqrt{20}}{5} + \frac{2}{\sqrt{5}}$

< Objective 2 >

Multiply each of the following expressions.

51. $\sqrt{7} \cdot \sqrt{6}$

52. $\sqrt{a} \cdot \sqrt{11}$

53. $\sqrt{3} \cdot \sqrt{7} \cdot \sqrt{2}$

54. $\sqrt[3]{4} \cdot \sqrt[3]{9}$

Multiply and simplify each of the following expressions.

55. $\sqrt{3} \cdot \sqrt{12}$

56. $\sqrt{7} \cdot \sqrt{7}$

57. $\sqrt[3]{9p^2} \cdot \sqrt[3]{6p}$

58. $\sqrt[3]{4x^2y} \cdot \sqrt[3]{10xy^3}$

59. $\sqrt{2}(\sqrt{3} + 5)$

60. $\sqrt{5}(\sqrt{3} - \sqrt{2})$

61. $\sqrt{3}(5\sqrt{2} - \sqrt{18})$

62. $\sqrt{x}(\sqrt{3x} + \sqrt{27x})$

63. $\sqrt[3]{4}(\sqrt[3]{4} + \sqrt[3]{32})$

64. $(\sqrt{2} + 3)(\sqrt{2} - 4)$

65. $(\sqrt{3} - 2)(\sqrt{3} - 5)$

66. $(\sqrt{2} + 3\sqrt{5})(\sqrt{2} - 2\sqrt{5})$

67. $(\sqrt{5} + 3)(\sqrt{5} - 3)$

68. $(\sqrt{a} + \sqrt{3})(\sqrt{a} - \sqrt{3})$

69. $(\sqrt{3} - 5)^2$

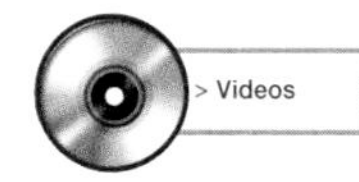

70. $(\sqrt{a} + 3)^2$

71. $(\sqrt{r} - \sqrt{s})^2$

< Objective 3 >

Rationalize the denominator in each of the following expressions. Simplify when necessary.

72. $\dfrac{\sqrt{3}}{\sqrt{7}}$

73. $\dfrac{\sqrt{5}}{\sqrt{3}}$

74. $\dfrac{\sqrt{2a}}{\sqrt{3b}}$

75. $\dfrac{\sqrt{5x}}{\sqrt{6y}}$

76. $\dfrac{3}{\sqrt[3]{4}}$ > Videos

77. $\dfrac{2}{\sqrt[3]{9}}$

78. $\dfrac{1}{2 + \sqrt{3}}$

79. $\dfrac{2}{3 - \sqrt{2}}$ > Videos

80 $\dfrac{8}{3 - \sqrt{5}}$

81. $\dfrac{\sqrt{7} - 2}{\sqrt{7} + 2}$

82. $\dfrac{\sqrt{6} + \sqrt{3}}{\sqrt{6} - \sqrt{3}}$

83. $\dfrac{\sqrt{w} + 3}{\sqrt{w} - 3}$

84. $\dfrac{\sqrt{x} - \sqrt{y}}{\sqrt{x} + \sqrt{y}}$

Answers

61. $2\sqrt{6}$

62. $4x\sqrt{3}$

63. $6\sqrt[3]{2}$

64. $-10 - \sqrt{2}$

65. $13 - 7\sqrt{3}$

66. $-28 + \sqrt{10}$

67. -4

68. $a - 3$

69. $28 - 10\sqrt{3}$

70. $a + 6\sqrt{a} + 9$

71. $r - 2\sqrt{rs} + s$

72. $\dfrac{\sqrt{21}}{7}$

73. $\dfrac{\sqrt{15}}{3}$

74. $\dfrac{\sqrt{6ab}}{3b}$

75. $\dfrac{\sqrt{30xy}}{6y}$

76. $\dfrac{3\sqrt[3]{2}}{2}$

77. $\dfrac{2\sqrt[3]{3}}{3}$

78. $2 - \sqrt{3}$

79. $\dfrac{6 + 2\sqrt{2}}{7}$

80. $6 + 2\sqrt{5}$

81. $\dfrac{11 - 4\sqrt{7}}{3}$

82. $3 + 2\sqrt{2}$

83. $\dfrac{w + 6\sqrt{w} + 9}{w - 9}$

84. $\dfrac{x - 2\sqrt{xy} + y}{x - y}$

Basic Skills | **Advanced Skills** | Vocational-Technical Applications | Calculator/Computer | Above and Beyond

Simplify each of the following radical expressions.

85. $x\sqrt[3]{8x^4} + 4\sqrt[3]{27x^7}$

86. $\sqrt[3]{8x^2} - \sqrt[3]{27x^2}$

87. $\sqrt[4]{16a^5} + \sqrt[4]{81a^5}$

88. $\sqrt[4]{256x^7} - 2\sqrt[4]{81x^7}$

89. $\dfrac{\sqrt{2x^2 + 3x}}{\sqrt{x}}$

90. $\dfrac{\sqrt{x^2 - 9}}{\sqrt{x + 3}}$

For exercises 91 and 92, the period T, in seconds, of a pendulum is given by the function

$$T = 2\pi\sqrt{\frac{L}{g}}$$

in which L is the length of the pendulum and g is the gravitational constant.

91. If we measure the length of the pendulum in feet, then the gravitational constant is given by $g = 32$ ft/sec^2. Use this value for g, and simplify the pendulum period function (rationalize the denominator). chapter 7 > Make the Connection

92. Rewrite the pendulum equation so that L and g are given in inches. Simplify your answer. chapter 7 > Make the Connection

Basic Skills | Advanced Skills | Vocational-Technical Applications | Calculator/Computer | **Above and Beyond**

Simplify each of the following radical expressions.

93. $3(2\sqrt{6} - 5\sqrt{3}) - 2(3\sqrt{15} - 8\sqrt{6}) + (\sqrt{15} + 3\sqrt{6} + \sqrt{15})$

94. $\sqrt{13 + 7\sqrt{13 + 3\sqrt{16}}} - \sqrt{72}$

95. **Geometry** Find the perimeter of the triangle shown in the figure.

4

$\sqrt{5} - \sqrt{3}$

$\sqrt{5} + \sqrt{3}$

96. **Geometry** Find the perimeter and the area of the rectangle shown in the figure.

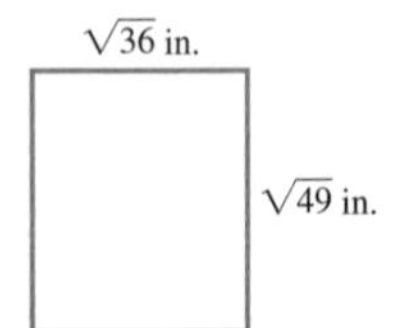

Answers

85. $14x^2\sqrt[3]{x}$

86. $-\sqrt[3]{x^2}$

87. $5a\sqrt[4]{a}$

88. $-2x\sqrt[4]{x^3}$

89. $\sqrt{2x + 3}$

90. $\sqrt{x - 3}$

91. $T = \dfrac{\pi\sqrt{2L}}{4}$

92. $T = \dfrac{\pi\sqrt{6L}}{24}$

93. $-15\sqrt{3} + 25\sqrt{6} - 4\sqrt{15}$

94. $4\sqrt{3} - 6\sqrt{2}$

95. Perimeter: $2\sqrt{5} + 4$

96. Perimeter: 26 in., area: 42 in.^{2}

97. **Geometry** Find the perimeter and the area of the rectangle shown in the figure. Write your answer in radical form.

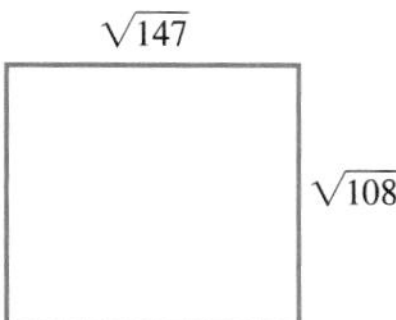

98. Find the area and perimeter of this square:

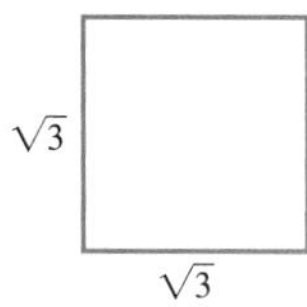

One of these measures, the area, is a rational number, and the other, the perimeter, is an irrational number. Explain how this happened. Will the area always be a rational number? Explain.

99. **(a)** Evaluate the three expressions $\frac{n^2 - 1}{2}$, n, $\frac{n^2 + 1}{2}$ using odd values of n: 1, 3, 5, 7, and so forth. Make a chart like the one that follows and complete it.

n	$a = \frac{n^2 - 1}{2}$	$b = n$	$c = \frac{n^2 + 1}{2}$	a^2	b^2	c^2
1						
3						
5						
7						
9						
11						
13						
15						

(b) Check for each of these sets of three numbers to see if this statement is true: $\sqrt{a^2 + b^2} = \sqrt{c^2}$. For how many of your sets of three did this work? Sets of three numbers for which this statement is true are called *Pythagorean triples* because $a^2 + b^2 = c^2$. Can the radical equation be written in this way: $\sqrt{a^2 + b^2} = a + b$? Explain your answer.

Answers

97. Perimeter: $26\sqrt{3}$, area: 126

98. Above and Beyond

99. Above and Beyond

Answers

1. $7\sqrt{5}$ **3.** $-3\sqrt{3a}$ **5.** $9\sqrt[3]{2}$ **7.** $3\sqrt{5}$ **9.** $8\sqrt{2}$ **11.** $11\sqrt{2}$
13. $2\sqrt{3}$ **15.** $2\sqrt{5} + 2\sqrt{3}$ **17.** $5\sqrt{7}$ **19.** $4\sqrt{3}$ **21.** $6\sqrt{2}$
23. $4\sqrt{6}$ **25.** $4\sqrt[3]{3}$ **27.** $5\sqrt[3]{2}$ **29.** $\sqrt{6w}$ **31.** $5x\sqrt{2x}$

33. $a\sqrt{3}$ **35.** $(5x + 6)\sqrt{3x}$ **37.** $5x\sqrt[3]{2x}$ **39.** $3w\sqrt[3]{2w^2}$

41. $\frac{4}{3}\sqrt{3}$ or $\frac{4\sqrt{3}}{3}$ **43.** $\frac{2}{3}\sqrt{6}$ or $\frac{2\sqrt{6}}{3}$ **45.** $\frac{3}{2}\sqrt[3]{6}$ or $\frac{3\sqrt[3]{6}}{2}$

47. $\frac{2}{3}\sqrt{6}$ or $\frac{2\sqrt{6}}{3}$ **49.** $\frac{1}{3}\sqrt{3}$ or $\frac{\sqrt{3}}{3}$ **51.** $\sqrt{42}$ **53.** $\sqrt{42}$ **55.** 6

57. $3p\sqrt[3]{2}$ **59.** $\sqrt{6} + 5\sqrt{2}$ **61.** $2\sqrt{6}$ **63.** $6\sqrt[3]{2}$ **65.** $13 - 7\sqrt{3}$

67. -4 **69.** $28 - 10\sqrt{3}$ **71.** $r - 2\sqrt{rs} + s$ **73.** $\frac{\sqrt{15}}{3}$

75. $\frac{\sqrt{30xy}}{6}$ **77.** $\frac{2\sqrt[3]{3}}{3}$ **79.** $\frac{6 + 2\sqrt{2}}{7}$ **81.** $\frac{11 - 4\sqrt{7}}{3}$

83. $\frac{w + 6\sqrt{w} + 9}{w - 9}$ **85.** $14x^2\sqrt[3]{x}$ **87.** $5a\sqrt[4]{a}$ **89.** $\sqrt{2x + 3}$

91. $T = \frac{\pi\sqrt{2L}}{4}$ **93.** $-15\sqrt{3} + 25\sqrt{6} - 4\sqrt{15}$

95. Perimeter: $2\sqrt{5} + 4$ **97.** Perimeter: $26\sqrt{3}$, area: 126

99. Above and Beyond

7.4 Solving Radical Equations

< 7.4 Objectives >

1 > Solve an equation containing a radical expression

2 > Solve an equation containing two radical expressions

In this section we wish to establish procedures for solving equations involving radicals. The basic technique we will use involves raising both sides of an equation to some power. However, doing so requires some caution.

Let us illustrate this with a simple equation. Consider the following.

$$x = 3$$

Squaring both sides gives us

$$x^2 = 9$$

Solving for x then shows us that

$$x^2 - 9 = 0$$
$$(x + 3)(x - 3) = 0$$

So the answers are 3 and -3.

However, -3 is not a solution to the original equation! Since -3 is an "extra" solution that was produced when we squared each side of the equation, we call -3 an *extraneous solution.* In fact, since -3 does not work in the original equation, it cannot be listed as a solution to the original equation.

We must be aware of the possibility of extraneous solutions any time we raise both sides of an equation to any even power. Having said this, we are now prepared to introduce the power property of equality.

Property

The Power Property of Equality

Given any two expressions a and b and any positive integer n,

If $a = b$, then $a^n = b^n$.

Although you will never lose a solution when applying the power property, as we discussed before, you will often find an extraneous one as a result of raising both sides of the equation to some power. Because of this, it is very important that you *check all solutions.*

Example 1 Solving a Radical Equation

< Objective 1 >

> **NOTE**
>
> Notice that
> $(\sqrt{x + 2})^2 = x + 2$
> That is why squaring both sides of the equation removes the radical.

Solve $\sqrt{x + 2} = 3$.

Squaring each side, we have

$$(\sqrt{x + 2})^2 = 3^2$$
$$x + 2 = 9$$
$$x = 7$$

Substituting 7 into the original equation, we find

$$\sqrt{7 + 2} \stackrel{?}{=} 3$$
$$\sqrt{9} \stackrel{?}{=} 3$$
$$3 = 3$$

Because 7 is the only value that makes this a true statement, the solution is 7.

Check Yourself 1

Solve the equation $\sqrt{x - 5} = 4$.

Example 2 Solving a Radical Equation

> **NOTE**
>
> Applying the power property will only remove the radical if that radical is isolated on one side of the equation.

Solve $\sqrt{4x + 5} + 1 = 0$.

We must *first isolate the radical* on the left side:

$$\sqrt{4x + 5} = -1$$

Then, squaring both sides, we have

$$(\sqrt{4x + 5})^2 = (-1)^2 \qquad (-1)^2 = 1$$
$$4x + 5 = 1$$

and solving for x, we find that

$$x = -1$$

> **NOTE**
>
> $\sqrt{1} = 1$, the principal root.

Now we will check the solution by substituting -1 for x in the original equation:

$$\sqrt{4(-1) + 5} + 1 \stackrel{?}{=} 0$$
$$\sqrt{1} + 1 \stackrel{?}{=} 0$$

and $2 \neq 0$

> **NOTE**
>
> $2 \neq 0$ and is clearly a false statement, so -1 is *not* a solution for the original equation.

Because -1 is an extraneous solution, there are *no solutions* to the original equation.

Since $\sqrt{4x + 5}$ represents the nonnegative principal square root, we might have seen immediately after isolating the radical that there is no solution: $\sqrt{4x + 5} \neq -1$.

Check Yourself 2

Solve $\sqrt{3x - 2} + 2 = 0$.

We will consider an example in which the procedure we have described involves squaring a binomial.

Example 3 Solving a Radical Equation

NOTES

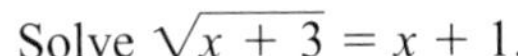

These problems can also be solved graphically. With a graphing utility, plot the two graphs $Y_1 = \sqrt{x + 3}$ and $Y_2 = x + 1$. Note that the graphs intersect at $x = 1$.

We solved similar equations in Section 5.9.

Solve $\sqrt{x + 3} = x + 1$.

We can square each side, as before.

$$(\sqrt{x + 3})^2 = (x + 1)^2$$
$$x + 3 = x^2 + 2x + 1$$

Simplifying this gives us the quadratic equation

$$x^2 + x - 2 = 0$$

Factoring, we have

$$(x - 1)(x + 2) = 0$$

which gives us the possible solutions

$$x = 1 \quad \text{or} \quad x = -2$$

Now we check for extraneous solutions and find that $x = 1$ is a valid solution, but that $x = -2$ does not yield a true statement.

> CAUTION

Be Careful! Sometimes (as in this example), one side of the equation contains a binomial. In that case, we must remember the middle term when we square the binomial. The square of a binomial *is always a trinomial.*

NOTE

Verify this for yourself by substituting 1 and then −2 for x in the original equation.

Check Yourself 3

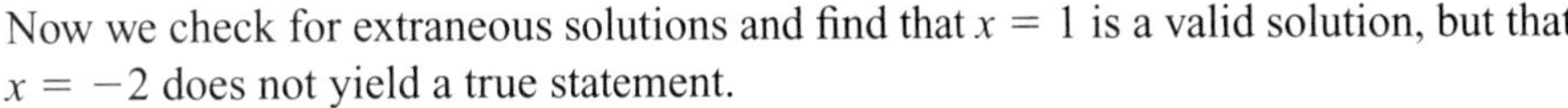

Solve $\sqrt{x - 5} = x - 7$.

It is not always the case that one of the solutions is extraneous. We may have zero, one, or two valid solutions when we generate a quadratic from a radical equation.

In Example 4 we see a case in which both of the solutions derived will satisfy the equation.

Example 4 Solving a Radical Equation

NOTE

Again, with a graphing utility plot $Y_1 = \sqrt{7x + 1}$ and $Y_2 = 2x + 1$. Where do they intersect?

Solve $\sqrt{7x + 1} - 1 = 2x$.

First, *we must isolate the term involving the radical.*

$$\sqrt{7x + 1} = 2x + 1$$

We can now square both sides of the equation.

$$7x + 1 = 4x^2 + 4x + 1$$

Now we write the quadratic equation in standard form.

$$4x^2 - 3x = 0$$

Factoring, we have

$$x(4x - 3) = 0$$

which yields two possible solutions

$$x = 0 \quad \text{and} \quad x = \frac{3}{4}$$

Checking the solutions by substitution, we find that both values for x give true statements, as follows.

Letting x be 0, we have

$$\sqrt{7(0) + 1} - 1 \stackrel{?}{=} 2(0)$$
$$\sqrt{1} - 1 \stackrel{?}{=} 0$$
$$0 = 0 \quad \text{A true statement.}$$

Letting x be $\frac{3}{4}$, we have

$$\sqrt{7\left(\frac{3}{4}\right) + 1} - 1 \stackrel{?}{=} 2\left(\frac{3}{4}\right)$$
$$\sqrt{\frac{25}{4}} - 1 \stackrel{?}{=} \frac{3}{2}$$
$$\frac{5}{2} - 1 \stackrel{?}{=} \frac{3}{2}$$
$$\frac{3}{2} = \frac{3}{2} \quad \text{Again a true statement.}$$

The solutions are 0 and $\frac{3}{4}$.

Check Yourself 4

Solve $\sqrt{5x + 1} - 1 = 3x$.

Example 5 Solving an Equation Containing Two Radicals

< Objective 2 >

Solve $\sqrt{2x - 5} = \sqrt{x + 2}$.

Since the radicals are each isolated on a side, we can square both sides to get

$$(\sqrt{2x - 5})^2 = (\sqrt{x + 2})^2$$
$$2x - 5 = x + 2$$

And solving for x, we find that

$$x = 7$$

Checking this answer:

$$\sqrt{2(7) - 5} \stackrel{?}{=} \sqrt{(7) + 2}$$
$$\sqrt{9} \stackrel{?}{=} \sqrt{9}$$
$$3 = 3 \quad \text{True}$$

Therefore, we have found the solution to be $x = 7$.

Check Yourself 5

Solve $\sqrt{4x + 25} = \sqrt{6x + 13}$.

Example 6 Solving an Equation Containing Two Radicals

Solve $3\sqrt{x} = \sqrt{8x + 16}$.

As we saw in Example 5, since the radicals are each isolated on a side, we can square both sides to get

$$(3\sqrt{x})^2 = (\sqrt{8x + 16})^2$$

$$9x = 8x + 16 \qquad (3\sqrt{x})^2 = (3\sqrt{x})(3\sqrt{x}) = 9\sqrt{x^2} = 9x$$

And solving for x, we find that

$$x = 16$$

Checking this answer:

$$3\sqrt{16} \stackrel{?}{=} \sqrt{8(16) + 16}$$

$$3 \cdot 4 \stackrel{?}{=} \sqrt{144}$$

$$12 = 12 \qquad \text{True}$$

Therefore, we have found the solution to be $x = 16$.

Check Yourself 6

Solve $4\sqrt{x} = \sqrt{15x + 10}$.

Sometimes when an equation involves more than one radical, we must apply the power property more than once. In such a case, it is generally best to avoid having to work with two radicals on the same side of the equation. Example 7 illustrates one approach to the solution of such equations.

Example 7 Solving an Equation Containing Two Radicals

NOTE

$1 + \sqrt{2x - 6}$ is a binomial of the form $a + b$, in which a is 1 and b is $\sqrt{2x - 6}$. The square on the right then has the form $a^2 + 2ab + b^2$.
so $(1)^2 + 2(1)(\sqrt{2x - 6}) + (\sqrt{2x - 6})^2 = 1 + 2\sqrt{2x - 6} + 2x - 6$

Solve $\sqrt{x - 2} - \sqrt{2x - 6} = 1$.

First we isolate $\sqrt{x - 2}$ by adding $\sqrt{2x - 6}$ to both sides of the equation. This gives

$$\sqrt{x - 2} = 1 + \sqrt{2x - 6}$$

Then squaring each side, we have

$$x - 2 = 1 + 2\sqrt{2x - 6} + 2x - 6$$

We now isolate the radical that remains on the right side.

$$-x + 3 = 2\sqrt{2x - 6}$$

We must square again to remove that radical.

Remember to square the *coefficient* of the radical term.

$$x^2 - 6x + 9 = 4(2x - 6)$$

Now solve the quadratic equation that results.

$$x^2 - 14x + 33 = 0$$
$$(x - 3)(x - 11) = 0$$

So the possible solutions are

$$x = 3 \quad \text{and} \quad x = 11$$

Checking the possible solutions, you will find that $x = 3$ yields the only valid solution. You should verify that for yourself.

Check Yourself 7

Solve $\sqrt{x + 3} - \sqrt{2x + 4} + 1 = 0$.

As with other types of equations, those involving radical expressions may be identities or contradictions.

Example 8 Solving Equations Containing Radical Expressions

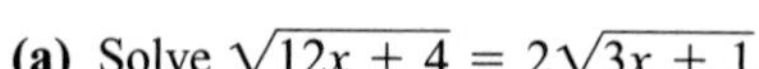

(a) Solve $\sqrt{12x + 4} = 2\sqrt{3x + 1}$.

$\sqrt{12x + 4} = 2\sqrt{3x + 1}$	Square both sides.
$12x + 4 = 4(3x + 1)$	Distribute through the grouping symbol.
$12x + 4 = 12x + 4$	
$12x = 12x$	
$0 = 0$	A true statement.

NOTE

(a) is an identity.

Because this last statement is true for all real numbers, the solution of the original equation is the set of all numbers that produce a nonnegative under the radical. Here,

$$12x + 4 \ge 0$$
$$12x \ge -4$$
$$x \ge -\frac{1}{3}$$

Likewise,

$$3x + 1 \ge 0$$
$$3x \ge -1$$
$$x \ge -\frac{1}{3}$$

so the solution is $x \ge -\frac{1}{3}$.

(b) Solve $\sqrt{3x + 1} = \sqrt{3x + 2}$.

$$\sqrt{3x + 1} = \sqrt{3x + 2}$$

NOTE

(b) is a contradiction.

$$3x + 1 = 3x + 2$$
$$3x = 3x + 1$$
$$0 = 1 \quad \text{False!}$$

Because this last statement is always false, there are no solutions to the original equation.

Check Yourself 8

Solve each equation.

(a) $\sqrt{x+1} = -3$ **(b)** $3\sqrt{1-2x} = \sqrt{9-18x}$

Earlier in this section, we noted that extraneous roots were possible whenever we raised both sides of the equation to an *even power*. In Example 9, we will raise both sides of the equation to an odd power. We still check the solutions, but in this case it will simply be a check of our work and not a search for extraneous solutions.

Example 9 Solving a Radical Equation

NOTE

Because a *cube root* is involved, we *cube* both sides to remove the radical.

Solve $\sqrt[3]{x^2 + 23} = 3$.

Cubing each side, we have

$$x^2 + 23 = 27$$

which results in the quadratic equation

$$x^2 - 4 = 0$$

This has two solutions:

$$x = 2 \quad \text{and} \quad x = -2$$

Checking the solutions, we find that both result in true statements. Again you should verify this result.

Check Yourself 9

Solve $\sqrt[3]{x^2 - 8} - 2 = 0$.

We summarize our work in this section in the following algorithm for solving equations involving radicals.

Step by Step

Solving Equations Involving Radicals

Step 1 Isolate a radical on one side of the equation.

Step 2 Raise each side of the equation to the smallest power that will eliminate the isolated radical.

Step 3 If any radicals remain in the equation derived in step 2, return to step 1 and continue until no radical remains.

Step 4 Solve the resulting equation to determine any possible solutions.

Step 5 Check all solutions to determine whether extraneous solutions may have resulted from step 2.

Check Yourself ANSWERS

1. 21 **2.** No solution **3.** 9 **4.** 0, $-\frac{1}{9}$ **5.** 6 **6.** 10 **7.** 6
8. **(a)** No solution; **(b)** $x \le \frac{1}{2}$ **9.** 4, −4

Reading Your Text

The following fill-in-the-blank exercises are designed to ensure that you understand some of the key vocabulary used in this section.

SECTION 7.4

(a) The basic technique for solving a radical equation is to raise both ________ of an equation to some power.

(b) We must be aware of the possibility of __________ solutions any time we raise both sides of an equation to any even power.

(c) You will never __________ a solution using the power property of equality.

(d) Squaring a binomial will always result in __________ terms.

Basic Skills | Advanced Skills | Vocational-Technical Applications | Calculator/Computer | Above and Beyond

7.4 exercises

< Objective 1 >

Solve each of the equations. Be sure to check your solutions.

1. $\sqrt{x} = 2$

2. $\sqrt{x} - 3 = 0$

3. $\sqrt{a} + 3 = 1$

4. $10 - \sqrt{p} = 12$

5. $2\sqrt{y} - 1 = 0$

> Videos

6. $3\sqrt{2z} = 9$

7. $\sqrt{m + 5} = 3$

8. $\sqrt{y + 7} = 5$

9. $\sqrt{2x + 4} - 4 = 0$

10. $\sqrt{3x + 3} - 6 = 0$

11. $\sqrt{3x - 2} + 2 = 0$

12. $\sqrt{4x + 1} + 3 = 0$

13. $\sqrt{x - 1} = \sqrt{1 - x}$

14. $\sqrt{x + 1} = \sqrt{1 + x}$

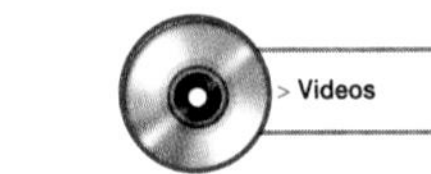

15. $\sqrt{w + 3} = \sqrt{3 + w}$

16. $\sqrt{w - 3} = \sqrt{3 - w}$

17. $\sqrt{2x - 3} + 1 = 3$

18. $\sqrt{3x + 1} - 2 = -1$

19. $2\sqrt{3z + 2} - 1 = 5$

20. $3\sqrt{4q - 1} - 2 = 7$

21. $\sqrt{15 - 2x} = x$

22. $\sqrt{48 - 2y} = y$

23. $\sqrt{p^2 - 2p - 10} = p$

24. $r = \sqrt{r^2 + 5r + 15}$

25. $\sqrt{x + 5} = x - 1$

26. $\sqrt{2x - 1} = x - 8$

27. $\sqrt{3m - 2} + m = 10$

28. $\sqrt{2x + 1} + x = 7$

MathZone

Boost your grade at mathzone.com!

- > Practice Problems
- > NetTutor
- > Self-Tests
- > e-Professors
- > Videos

Name ____________________

Section ________ Date ________

Answers

1. 4
2. 9
3. No solution
4. No solution
5. $\frac{1}{4}$
6. $\frac{9}{2}$
7. 4
8. 18
9. 6
10. 11
11. No solution
12. No solution
13. 1
14. $x \geq -1$
15. $w \geq -3$
16. 3
17. $\frac{7}{2}$
18. 0
19. $\frac{7}{3}$
20. $\frac{5}{2}$
21. 3
22. 6
23. No solution
24. No solution
25. 4
26. 13
27. 6
28. 4

Answers

29. 7
30. 9
31. $0, \frac{1}{2}$
32. $0, \frac{1}{9}$
33. 32
34. 2
35. 3, −3
36. 4, −4
37. 1
38. $\frac{1}{2}$
39. 1
40. 5
41. $-\frac{7}{4}$
42. $-\frac{11}{4}$
43. 3, 7
44. 1, 5
45. 0
46. 5
47. 6
48. 15
49. never
50. sometimes
51. always
52. sometimes

29. $\sqrt{t + 9} + 3 = t$

30. $\sqrt{2y + 7} + 4 = y$

31. $\sqrt{6x + 1} - 1 = 2x$

32. $\sqrt{7x + 1} - 1 = 3x$

> Videos

33. $\sqrt[3]{x - 5} = 3$

34. $\sqrt[3]{x + 6} = 2$

35. $\sqrt[3]{x^2 - 1} = 2$

36. $\sqrt[3]{x^2 + 11} = 3$

< Objective 2 >

Solve each of the equations. Be sure to check your solutions.

37. $\sqrt{2x} = \sqrt{x + 1}$

38. $\sqrt{3x} = \sqrt{5x - 1}$

39. $2\sqrt{3r} = \sqrt{r + 11}$

40. $5\sqrt{2q - 7} = \sqrt{15q}$

41. $\sqrt{x + 2} + 1 = \sqrt{x + 4}$

42. $\sqrt{x + 5} - 1 = \sqrt{x + 3}$

43. $\sqrt{4m - 3} - 2 = \sqrt{2m - 5}$

44. $\sqrt{2c - 1} = \sqrt{3c + 1} - 1$

45. $\sqrt{x + 1} + \sqrt{x} = 1$

46. $\sqrt{z - 1} - \sqrt{6 - z} = 1$

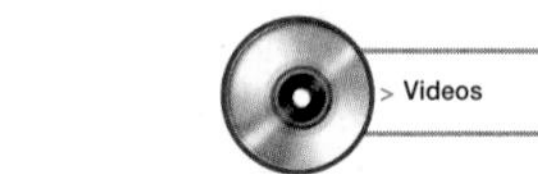

47. $\sqrt{5x + 6} - \sqrt{x + 3} = 3$

48. $\sqrt{5y + 6} - \sqrt{3y + 4} = 2$

In each of the following statements, fill in the blank with **always, sometimes,** *or* **never.**

49. When applying the power property of equality, you will _________ lose a solution.

50. If you square both sides of an equation, you will _________ find an extraneous solution.

51. The square of a binomial is _________ a trinomial.

52. If we generate a quadratic equation from a radical, we will _________ find more than one solution.

Basic Skills | **Advanced Skills** | Vocational-Technical Applications | Calculator/Computer | Above and Beyond

Solve each of the equations. Be sure to check your solutions.

53. $\sqrt{y^2 + 12y} - 3\sqrt{5} = 0$

54. $\sqrt{x^2 + 2x} - 2\sqrt{6} = 0$

55. $\sqrt{x + x^2} = 2\sqrt{3}$

56. $\sqrt{-5x + x^2} = 2\sqrt{6}$

57. $\sqrt{\dfrac{x - 3}{x + 2}} = \dfrac{2}{3}$

58. $\dfrac{\sqrt{x - 2}}{x - 2} = \dfrac{x - 5}{\sqrt{x - 2}}$

59. $\sqrt{\sqrt{t} + 5} = 3$

60. $\sqrt{\sqrt{s} - 1} = \sqrt{s - 7}$

Solve for the indicated variable.

61. $h = \sqrt{pq}$ for q

62. $c = \sqrt{a^2 + b^2}$ for a

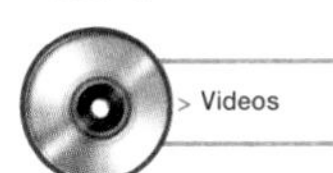

63. $v = \sqrt{2gR}$ for R

64. $v = \sqrt{2gR}$ for g

65. $r = \sqrt{\dfrac{S}{2\pi}}$ for S

66. $r = \sqrt{\dfrac{3V}{4\pi}}$ for V

67. $r = \sqrt{\dfrac{2V}{\pi h}}$ for V

68. $r = \sqrt{\dfrac{2V}{\pi h}}$ for h

69. $d = \sqrt{(x - 1)^2 + (y - 2)^2}$ for x

70. $d = \sqrt{(x - 1)^2 + (y - 2)^2}$ for y

Basic Skills | Advanced Skills | Vocational-Technical Applications | **Calculator/Computer** | Above and Beyond

For each given equation, use a graphing calculator to solve. Express solutions to the nearest hundredth. (Hint: Define Y_1 by the expression on the left side of the equation and define Y_2 by the expression on the right side. Graph these functions and locate any intersection points. For each such point, the x-value represents a solution.)

71. $\sqrt{2 - x} = x + 4$

72. $\sqrt{x + 4} = x - 3$

73. $5 - 3\sqrt{2 - x} = 3 - 4x$

74. $3 - 2\sqrt{x + 4} = 2x - 5$

Answers

53. −15, 3

54. −6, 4

55. −4, 3

56. −3, 8

57. 7

58. 6

59. 16

60. 9

61. $q = \dfrac{h^2}{p}$

62. $a = \sqrt{c^2 - b^2}$

63. $R = \dfrac{v^2}{2g}$

64. $g = \dfrac{v^2}{2R}$

65. $S = 2\pi r^2$

66. $V = \dfrac{4}{3}\pi r^2$

67. $V = \dfrac{\pi h r^2}{2}$

68. $h = \dfrac{2V}{\pi r^2}$

69. $x = 1 \pm \sqrt{d^2 - (y - 2)^2}$

70. $y = 2 \pm \sqrt{d^2 - (x - 1)^2}$

71. −2

72. 6.19

73. 0.44

74. 1.63

Answers

75. $x \geq 1$

76. All real numbers

77. $L = \frac{g}{4\pi^2}T^2 = \frac{245}{\pi^2}T^2$

78. $L \approx 25$ cm

79. $L \approx 99$ cm

80. $L \approx 621$ cm

81. $L \approx 894$ cm $= 8.94$ m

82. $L \approx 1{,}589$ cm $= 15.89$ m

Basic Skills | Advanced Skills | Vocational-Technical Applications | Calculator/Computer | **Above and Beyond**

75. For what values of x is $\sqrt{(x-1)^2} = x - 1$ a true statement?

76. For what values of x is $\sqrt[3]{(x-1)^3} = x - 1$ a true statement?

In exercises 77 to 82, use the theoretical function relating to the pendulum activity $T = 2\pi\sqrt{\frac{L}{g}}$, *with the gravitational constant* $g = 980$ *cm/sec*^{2}.

77. Express the length L of the pendulum as a function of the period T.

chapter 7 > Make the Connection

78. If $T = 1$ sec, find L to the nearest centimeter.

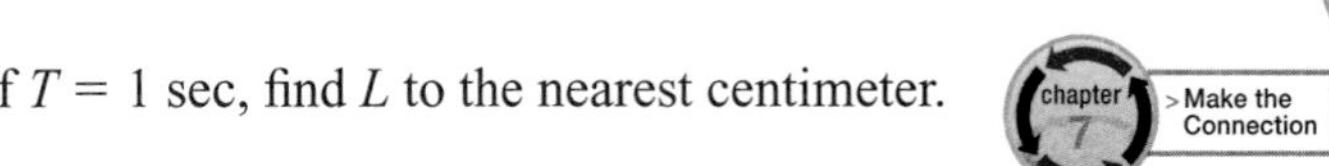

79. If $T = 2$ sec, find L to the nearest centimeter.

80. If $T = 5$ sec, find L to the nearest centimeter.

chapter 7 > Make the Connection

81. The Foucault (pronounced "foo-koh") pendulum in the California Academy of Sciences, located in San Francisco, has a period of 6 sec. How long is the pendulum (to the nearest centimeter)? Convert this result to meters.

82. The Foucault pendulum in the Smithsonian Institution, located in Washington, D.C., has a period of 8 sec. How long is the pendulum (to the nearest centimeter)? Convert this result to meters.

chapter 7 > Make the Connection

Answers

1. 4 **3.** No solution **5.** $\frac{1}{4}$ **7.** 4 **9.** 6 **11.** No solution **13.** 1 **15.** $w \geq -3$ **17.** $\frac{7}{2}$ **19.** $\frac{7}{3}$ **21.** 3 **23.** No solution **25.** 4 **27.** 6 **29.** 7 **31.** $0, \frac{1}{2}$ **33.** 32 **35.** ± 3 **37.** 1 **39.** 1 **41.** $-\frac{7}{4}$ **43.** 3, 7 **45.** 0 **47.** 6 **49.** never **51.** always **53.** $-15, 3$ **55.** $-4, 3$ **57.** 7 **59.** 16 **61.** $q = \frac{h^2}{p}$ **63.** $R = \frac{v^2}{2g}$ **65.** $S = 2\pi r^2$ **67.** $V = \frac{\pi h r^2}{2}$ **69.** $x = 1 \pm \sqrt{d^2 - (y-2)^2}$ **71.** -2 **73.** 0.44 **75.** $x \geq 1$ **77.** $L = \frac{245}{\pi^2}T^2$ **79.** $L \approx 99$ cm **81.** $L \approx 894$ cm $= 8.94$ m

7.5 Geometric and Other Applications

< 7.5 Objectives >

1 > Solve applications that involve radical equations

2 > Solve applications of the Pythagorean theorem

3 > Solve applications of the golden ratio

Now that we have learned how to solve radical equations, we will look at some of the many applications that can be solved using the methods we have seen.

Did you ever stand on a beach and wonder how far out into the ocean you could see? Or have you wondered how close a ship has to be to spot land? In either case, the function

$$d(h) = \sqrt{2h}$$

can be used to estimate the distance to the horizon (in miles) from a given height (in feet).

Example 1 Estimating a Distance

< Objective 1 >

Cordelia stood on a cliff gazing out at the ocean. Her eyes were 100 ft above the ocean. She saw a ship on the horizon. Approximately how far was she from that ship?

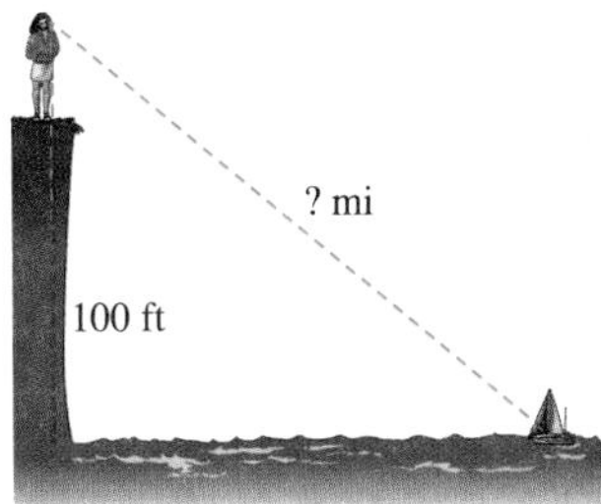

Substituting 100 for h in the equation, we get

$$d(h) = \sqrt{2(100)}$$

$$d(h) = \sqrt{200}$$

$$d(h) \approx 14 \text{ mi}$$

Check Yourself 1

From a plane flying at 35,000 ft, how far away is the horizon?

Perhaps the most famous of all mathematical theorems is the **Pythagorean theorem** (sometimes called Pythagoras's theorem). Although the Greek mathematician, Pythagoras, and his followers gave name to the theorem, it was known to the Babylonians around 2000 B.C.E., about 1,500 years before the time of the Pythagoreans.

Property

Pythagorean Theorem

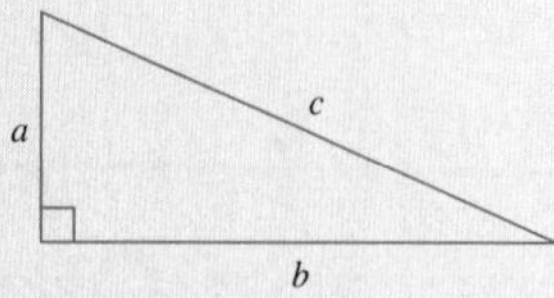

$$a^2 + b^2 = c^2$$

In a right triangle, the sum of the squares of the two legs is equal to the square of the hypotenuse.

Example 2 Applying the Pythagorean Theorem

< Objective 2 >

Fredrica and Thanh are building a set for the school play. They need to put together several wooden 8 ft × 3 ft rectangles, each with a diagonal support piece. How long is each diagonal piece?

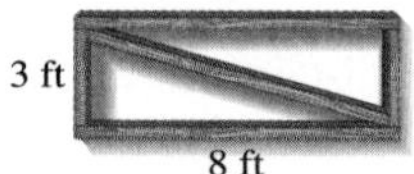

NOTE

In the movie *The Wizard of Oz*, the scarecrow misstates this theorem.

From the Pythagorean theorem, we have

$$a^2 + b^2 = c^2$$
$$8^2 + 3^2 = c^2$$
$$64 + 9 = c^2$$
$$73 = c^2$$
$$c = \sqrt{73}$$
$$c \approx 8.54 \text{ ft}$$

Each diagonal should be about $8\frac{1}{2}$ ft long.

Check Yourself 2

Fernando needs to build a handicap-access ramp into the gym. The Americans with Disabilities Act requires such a ramp to have a rise of no more than 1 in. for each 12 in. of run. With this in mind, Fernando has established a run of 19 ft for a rise of 18 in. Find the length of the ramp to the nearest tenth of an inch.

We can also use the Pythagorean theorem to find the length of a missing side, as in Example 3.

Example 3 Applying the Pythagorean Theorem

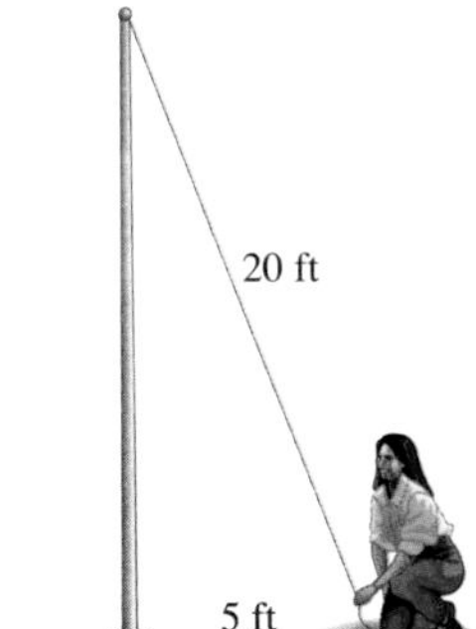

A flagpole has a 20-ft rope hanging from the top. When extended to the ground, the rope touches a spot 5 ft from the pole. How high is the flagpole?

Let the pole have height h. We have

$$h^2 = 20^2 - 5^2 \quad \text{If } a^2 + b^2 = c^2, \text{ then } b^2 = c^2 - a^2.$$
$$h^2 = 400 - 25$$
$$h^2 = 375$$
$$h = \sqrt{375}$$
$$h \approx 19.4 \text{ ft}$$

Check Yourself 3

A 10-ft tent pole is to be stabilized by a 12-ft guy wire. How far will the wire be staked from the pole?

The Pythagoreans were interested in mathematics, music, and art. They were particularly interested in areas in which mathematics could be connected to music or art. One of their discoveries was the **golden rectangle.** This became an important element in painting and sculpture. It is still used today in many fields.

What follows is the method that Euclid used around 300 B.C.E. to develop the golden rectangle.

Start with a square with sides of length 2 and connect corner B to the midpoint of side CD, which we label as O.

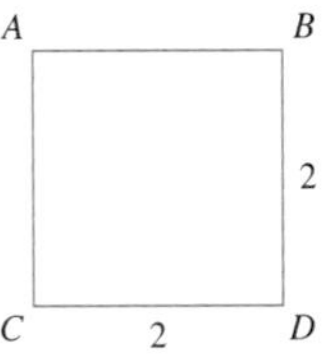

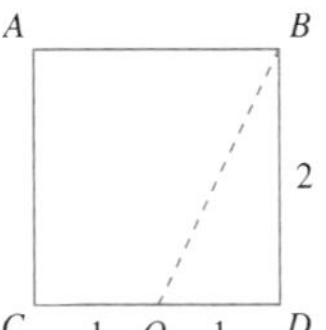

Pivot the length OB on point O so that it passes through D. Label the end of that segment as E.

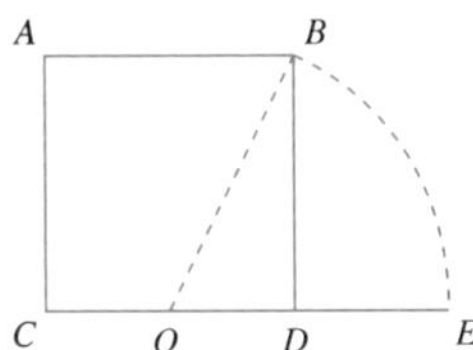

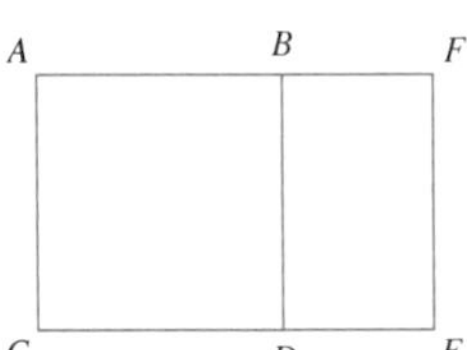

Create rectangle $AFEC$. This is a golden rectangle.

Example 4 Finding the Golden Ratio

< Objective 3 >

The ratio of the length of a golden rectangle to its width is called the **golden ratio.** Use the rectangle given to find the golden ratio.

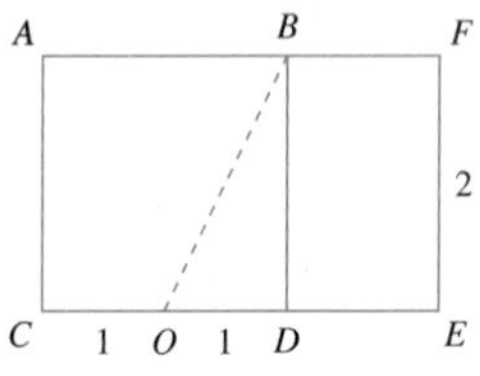

We want $\frac{CE}{FE}$.

$$CE = CO + OE$$
$$= 1 + OE$$

NOTE

$OE = OB$ from how the golden rectangle was constructed.

OE is the same as *OB*, which is the hypotenuse of triangle *BOD.*

$$OB^2 = 2^2 + 1^2 = 5$$
$$OB = \sqrt{5} = OE$$
$$CE = 1 + \sqrt{5}$$
$$\frac{CE}{FE} = \frac{1 + \sqrt{5}}{2}$$

This is the golden ratio.

Check Yourself 4

The reciprocal of the golden ratio is $\frac{2}{1 + \sqrt{5}}$. Rewrite this ratio, rationalizing the denominator.

The golden ratio is also called the **divine section,** a term first used by Franciscan monk and mathematician Luca Pacioli in the sixteenth century. It was believed to be the most important ratio in all of art and architecture. Example 5 illustrates one such case.

Example 5 Applying the Golden Ratio

The public façade for almost all Greek buildings used the golden ratio. Such a façade is pictured here; it has a base of approximately 20 m. What is the height of the façade?

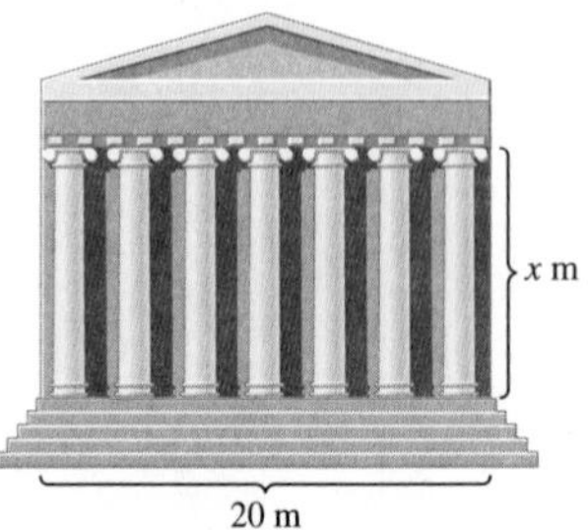

The ratio of the shorter side to the longer must be $\dfrac{2}{1 + \sqrt{5}}$. In this case,

$$\frac{2}{1 + \sqrt{5}} = \frac{x}{20}$$

Clearing the fractions, we have

$$(1 + \sqrt{5})x = 40$$

$$x = \frac{40}{1 + \sqrt{5}}$$

$$x \approx 12.4 \text{ m}$$

The height of the façade is just over 12 m.

Check Yourself 5

In Greek sculpture, the human torso was always sculpted using the golden ratio. If the height of a torso was to be 3 ft, what would the width have been?

Check Yourself ANSWERS

1. $d(h) \approx 265$ mi **2.** 228.7 in. **3.** Approximately 6.6 ft
4. $\dfrac{\sqrt{5} - 1}{2}$ **5.** $h \approx 1.85$ ft

Reading Your Text

The following fill-in-the-blank exercises are designed to ensure that you understand some of the key vocabulary used in this section.

SECTION 7.5

(a) In a right triangle, the sum of the square of the two legs is equal to the ______________.

(b) We can use the Pythagorean theorem to find the length of a ______________.

(c) The ratio of the length of a golden rectangle to its width is called the ______________.

(d) The golden ratio is also called the ______________ and was believed to be the most important ratio in all of art and architecture.

7.5 exercises

Basic Skills | Advanced Skills | Vocational-Technical Applications | Calculator/Computer | Above and Beyond

MathZone

Boost your grade at mathzone.com!
> Practice Problems
> NetTutor
> Self-Tests
> e-Professors
> Videos

Name ______________________

Section ________ Date ________

Answers

1. 9
2. 16
3. 16
4. 25
5. ≈245 mi
6. ≈22.4 mi
7. $\frac{d^2}{2}$
8. 5,000 ft
9. $x = 10$
10. $x = 25$
11. $x = 8$
12. $x = 8$

< Objective 1 >

Solve each of the applications.

1. **Number Problem** The sum of an integer and its square root is 12. Find the integer.

2. **Number Problem** The difference between an integer and its square root is 12. What is the integer? > Videos

3. **Number Problem** The sum of an integer and twice its square root is 24. What is the integer?

4. **Number Problem** The sum of an integer and 3 times its square root is 40. Find the integer. > Videos

Use the function $d(h) = \sqrt{2h}$ *from Example* 1 *to solve the applications in exercises 5 to 8.*

5. **Science and Medicine** If a plane flies at 30,000 ft, how far away is the horizon?

6. **Science and Medicine** Neil was looking out across the ocean from his hotel room on the beach. His eyes were 250 ft above the ground. He saw a ship on the horizon. Approximately how far was the ship from him?

7. **Science and Medicine** Given a distance, d, to the horizon, what altitude would allow you to see that far?

8. **Science and Medicine** From what altitude would the horizon be 100 mi away?

< Objective 2 >

Using the Pythagorean theorem for exercises 9 to 14, find the length x in each triangle. Write answers to the nearest tenth.

9.

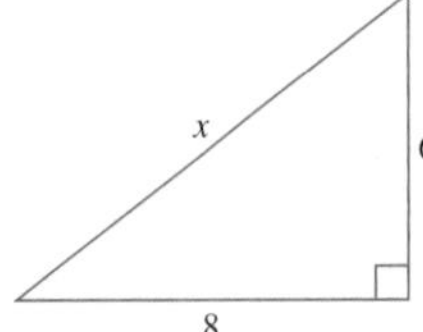

10.

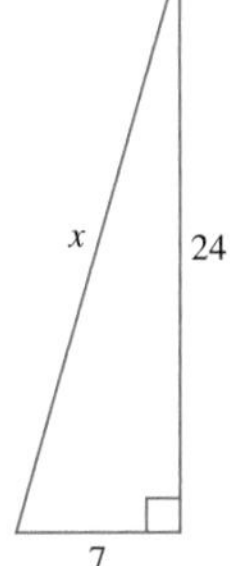

11.

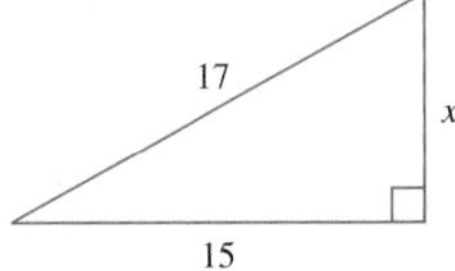

12.

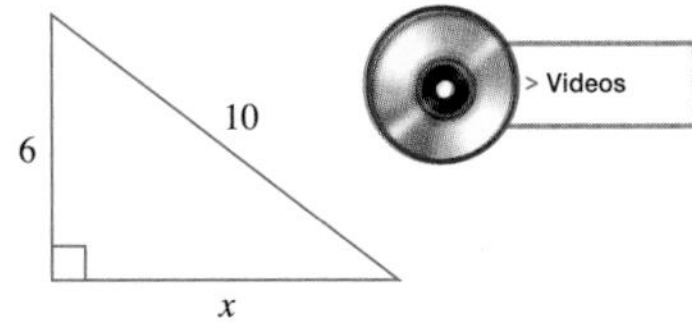

13.

8

x

6

14.

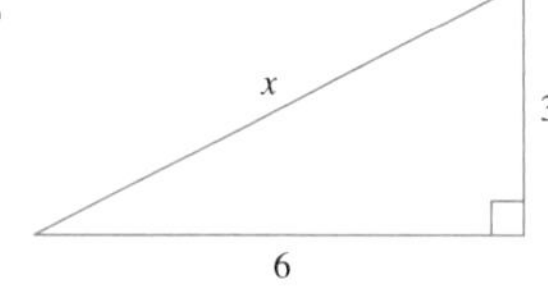

Solve each of the applications.

15. GEOMETRY Find the length of the diagonal of a rectangle whose length is 11 cm and whose width is 7 cm.

16. GEOMETRY Find the length of the diagonal of a rectangle whose width is 4 in. and whose length is 7 in.

17. GEOMETRY Find the width of a rectangle whose diagonal is 13 ft and whose length is 10 ft.

18. GEOMETRY Find the length of a rectangle whose diagonal is 9 in. and whose width is 5 in.

19. SCIENCE AND MEDICINE How long must a wire be to run from the top of a 20-ft pole to a point on the ground 7 ft from the base of the pole?

20. SCIENCE AND MEDICINE The base of a 14-ft ladder is 5 ft away from a wall. How high from the floor is the top of the ladder?

21. SCIENCE AND MEDICINE An air traffic controller is tracking two planes at the same altitude converging on a point in space as they fly at right angles to each other. One plane is 75 mi from the point when the other plane is 100 mi from the point. How far apart are the two planes?

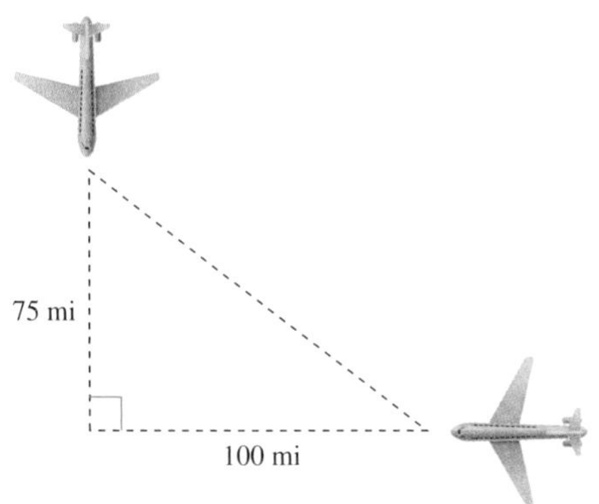

Answers

13. $x = 5.3$

14. $x = 6.7$

15. 13.0 cm

16. 8.1 in.

17. 8.3 ft

18. 7.5 in.

19. 21.2 ft

20. 13.1 ft

21. 125 mi

Answers

22. 127.3 ft

23. 62 ft

24. ≈3.24 units

25. 3.1 ft or 8.1 ft

26. 15 cm

22. Science and Medicine A baseball diamond is in the shape of a square. The vertices of the square are the three bases and home plate. If the distance from first base to second base is 90 ft, what is the distance between home plate and second base?

> Videos

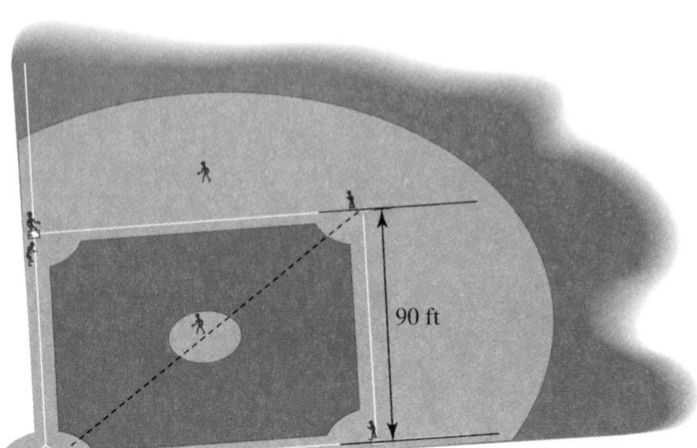

< Objective 3 >

Solve each of the applications.

23. Science and Medicine The Parthenon in Athens is an example of a building with a width to height ratio that is almost equal to the golden ratio. If the Parthenon is 101 ft wide, what is its height (to the nearest foot) if we assume the dimensions are in the golden ratio?

24. Geometry If a rectangle is to have sides related by the golden ratio, what is the length if the width (the shorter side) is 2 units?

25. Science and Medicine If a window is 5 ft wide, how high should it be, to the nearest tenth of a foot, to be a golden rectangle?

> Videos

26. Crafts A photograph is to be printed on a rectangle in the golden ratio. If it is 9 cm on its shorter side, how wide is it, to the nearest centimeter?

Label the following statements as **true** *or* **false.**

27. It is possible to have a right triangle that has two equal sides.

28. The hypotenuse is always the longest side of a right triangle.

29. The ratio of the width of a golden rectangle to its length is called the golden ratio.

30. Any rectangle can be called a golden rectangle.

Basic Skills | **Advanced Skills** | Vocational-Technical Applications | Calculator/Computer | Above and Beyond

A weight suspended on the end of a string is a *pendulum*. The most common example of a pendulum (this side of Edgar Allen Poe) is found in many clocks.

The regular back-and-forth motion of the pendulum is *periodic,* and one such cycle of motion is called a *period*. The time, in seconds, that it takes for one period is given by the radical equation

$$T = 2\pi\sqrt{\frac{L}{g}}$$

in which g is the force of gravity (approximately 10 m/sec^2) and L is the length of the pendulum in meters.

Use this equation to solve exercises 31 to 34.

31. Find the period (to the nearest hundredth of a second) if the pendulum is 0.9 m long. chapter 7 > Make the Connection

32. Find the period if the pendulum is 0.049 m long. chapter 7 > Make the Connection

33. Solve the equation for length L.

34. How long would the pendulum be if the period were exactly 1 second?

Answers

27. True

28. True

29. False

30. False

31. 1.88 sec

32. 0.44 sec

33. $L = \frac{t^2 g}{4\pi^2}$

34. $\approx$0.25 m

Answers

35. ≈36 ft

36. ≈33 ft

37. ≈28 ft

38. $\frac{s^2}{20}$

39. 6 in., 8 in.

40. 9 cm, 12 cm

41. Yes

42. ≈1.04 mi or ≈5,489 ft

43. (a) 5 in. by 3 in.
(b) 1.67 (about the same as the golden ratio)

When a car comes to a sudden stop on dry road, you can determine the skidding distance (in feet) for a given speed (in miles per hour) using the formula $s(x) = 2\sqrt{5x}$, in which s is skidding distance and x is speed.

Calculate the skidding distance for the given speeds in exercises 35 to 37.

35. 65 mi/h

36. 55 mi/h

37. 40 mi/h

38. Given the skidding distance, s, what formula would allow you to calculate the speed in miles per hour?

Solve each of the applications.

39. The length of one leg of a right triangle is 2 in. more than the other. If the length of the hypotenuse is 10 in., what are the lengths of the two legs?

40. The length of one side of a rectangle is 3 cm more than the other side. If the diagonal is 15 cm, find the lengths of the two sides.

41. To "square" the wall of a house being built by a carpenter, measurements are taken, as shown in the figure. Is the corner a right angle?

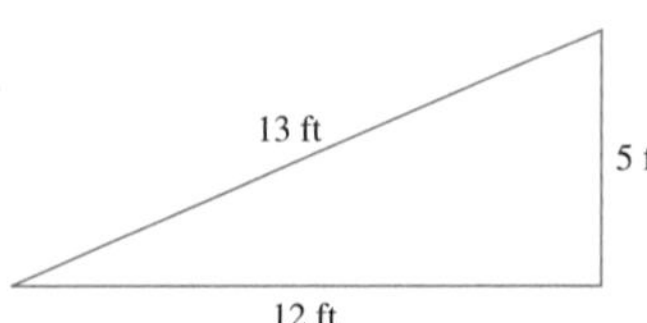

42. A television camera at ground level is filming the liftoff of a space shuttle that is rising vertically. The camera is 1,500 ft from the launch pad. How far apart are the camera and the shuttle when the shuttle is 1 mi directly above the launch pad?
(*Hint:* 1 mi = 5,280 ft.)

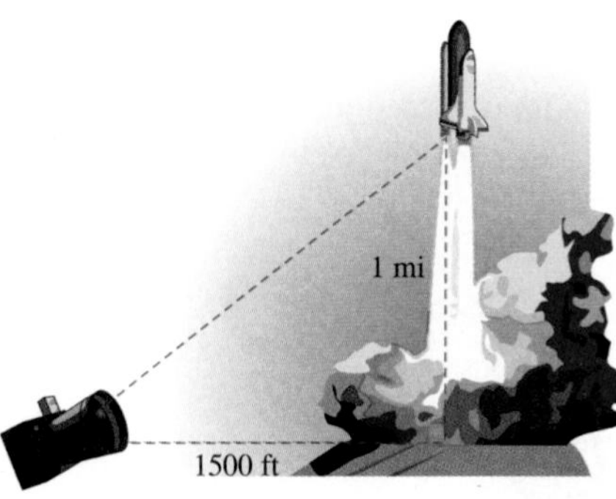

43. **(a)** What are the dimensions of a standard index card?
(b) Find the ratio of length to width and compare it with the golden ratio.

44. The Great Pyramid of Giza has these dimensions: height, $h = 481$ ft; base, $b = 756$ ft; and slant height, $s = 612$ ft. Find the ratio of s to $\frac{1}{2}b$ and b to h. Are either of these ratios equal to the golden ratio?

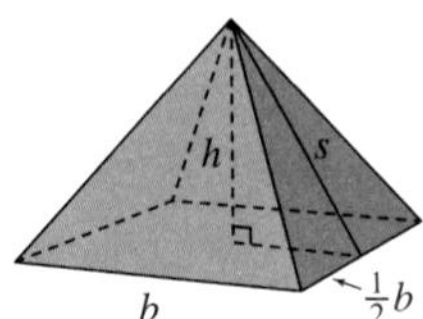

In exercises 45 and 46, use the theoretical function relating to the pendulum activity $T = 2\pi\sqrt{\frac{L}{g}}$, *with L measured in feet and the gravitational constant* $g = 32$ ft/sec^2.

45. Determine the period of a pendulum if its length is 9 in. Check your answer by using $\frac{3}{4}$ ft in the pendulum equation. chapter 7 > Make the Connection

46. Determine the period of a pendulum if its length is 8 in. Check your answer by using $\frac{2}{3}$ ft in the pendulum equation. chapter 7 > Make the Connection

Basic Skills | Advanced Skills | Vocational-Technical Applications | Calculator/Computer | **Above and Beyond**

For problems 47 and 48 consider the following four copies of the same triangle:

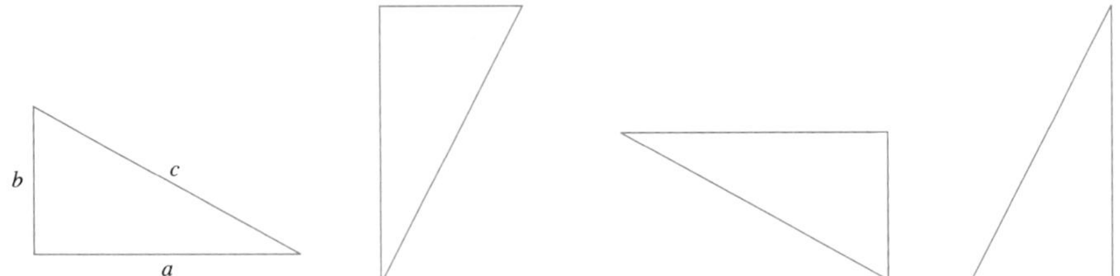

47. Let us put the four triangles together to make the following square:

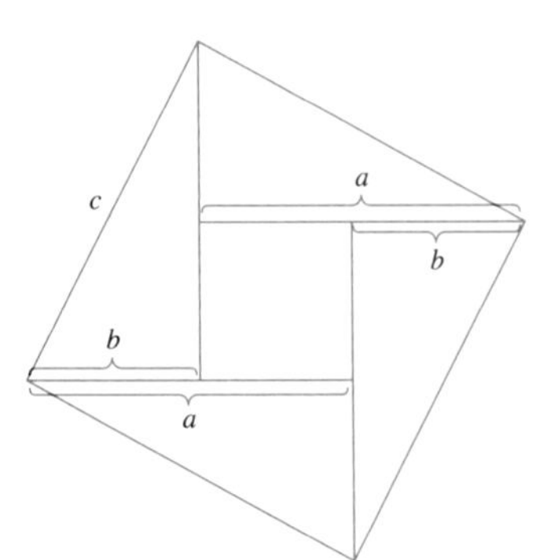

Answers

44. Ratio of s to $\frac{1}{2}b$ is 1.62; b to h is 1.57; these are both about the same as the golden ratio.

45. ≈0.96 sec

46. ≈0.91 sec

Answers

47. (a) $\frac{1}{2}ab$; (b) c; (c) c^2; (d) $a - b$; (e) $(a - b)^2$; (f) $4\left(\frac{1}{2}ab\right) + (a - b)^2 = 2ab + a^2 - 2ab + b^2 = a^2 + b^2$; (g) Both (c) and (f) measure the same area, so they must be equal. This means $c^2 = a^2 + b^2$. A proof of the Pythagorean theorem!

48. (a) $\frac{1}{2}ab$; (b) $a + b$; (c) $(a + b)^2$; (d) c; (e) c^2; (f) $4\left(\frac{1}{2}ab\right) + c^2 = 2ab + c^2$; (g) Both parts (c) and (f) measure the same area, so they must be equal. This means

$$(a + b)^2 = 2ab + c^2$$
$$a^2 + 2ab + b^2 = 2ab + c^2$$
$$a^2 + b^2 = c^2$$

Another proof of the Pythagorean theorem!

49. Above and Beyond

(a) What is the area of one triangle?

(b) What is the length of the side of the new big square?

(c) What, therefore, is the area of the new big square?

(d) What is the length of the side of the small inside square?

(e) What, therefore, is the area of the small inside square?

(f) We can also compute the area of the large big square by adding the areas of the four triangles and the area of the small inside square. Compute this area now.

(g) How does your answer in part **(c)**, compare with your answer in part **(f)**?

48. Suppose we put the four triangles together in a different way to make the following square:

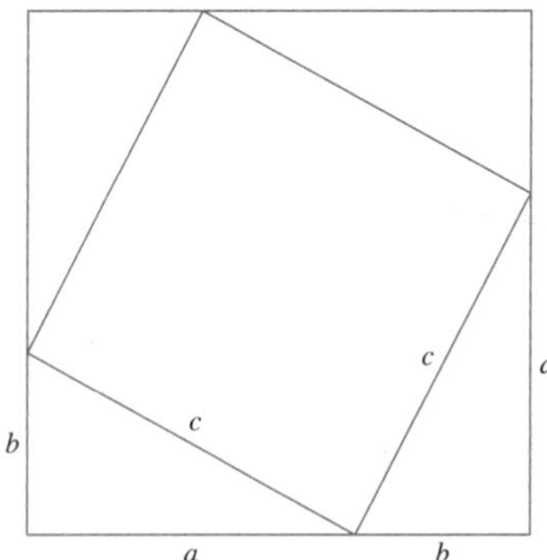

(a) What is the area of one triangle?

(b) What is the length of the side of the new big square?

(c) What, therefore, is the area of the new big square?

(d) What is the length of the side of the smaller inside square?

(e) What, therefore, is the area of the smaller inside square?

(f) We can also compute the area of the large big square by adding the areas of the four triangles and the area of the inside square. Compute this area now.

(g) How does your answer in part **(c)**, compare with your answer in part **(f)**?

49. **Business and Finance** Your architectural firm just received this memo.

To:	Algebra Expert Architecture, Inc.
From:	Microbeans Coffee Company, Inc.
Re:	Design for On-Site Day Care Facility
Date:	Aug. 10, 2003

We are requesting that you submit a design for a nursery for preschool children. We are planning to provide free on-site day care for the workers at our corporate headquarters.

The nursery should be large enough to serve the needs of 20 preschoolers. There will be three child care workers in this facility. We want the nursery to be 3,000 ft^2 in area. It needs a playroom, a small kitchen and eating space, and bathroom facilities. There should be some space to store toys and books, many of which should be accessible to children. The company plans to put this facility on the first floor on an outside wall so the children can go outside to play without disturbing workers. You are free to add to this design as you see fit.

Please send us your design drawn to a scale of 1 ft to 0.25 in., with precise measurements and descriptions. We would like to receive this design 1 week from today. Please give us some estimate of the cost of this renovation to our building.

Submit a design, keeping in mind that the design has to conform to strict design specifications for buildings designated as nurseries, including:

1. Number of exits: Two exits for the first 7 people and one exit for every additional 7 people.
2. Width of exits: The total width of exits in inches shall not be less than the total occupant load served by an exit multiplied by 0.3 for stairs and 0.2 for other exits. No exit shall be less than 3 ft wide and 6 ft 8 in. high.
3. Arrangements of exits: If two exits are required, they shall be placed a distance apart equal to but not less than one-half the length of the maximum overall diagonal dimension of the building or area to be served measured in a straight line between exits. Where three or more exits are required, two shall be placed as stated and the additional exits arranged a reasonable distance apart.
4. Distance to exits: Maximum distance to travel from any point to an exterior door shall not exceed 100 ft.

Answers

1. 9 **3.** 16 **5.** ≈245 mi **7.** $\frac{d^2}{2}$ **9.** $x = 10$ **11.** $x = 8$ **13.** $x = 5.3$
15. 13.0 cm **17.** 8.3 ft **19.** 21.2 ft **21.** 125 mi **23.** 62 ft
25. 3.1 ft or 8.1 ft **27.** True **29.** False **31.** 1.88 sec
33. $L = \frac{t^2 g}{4\pi^2}$ **35.** ≈36 ft **37.** ≈28 ft **39.** 6 in., 8 in. **41.** Yes
43. **(a)** 5 in. by 3 in.; **(b)** 1.67 (about the same as the golden ratio)
45. ≈ 0.96 sec **47.** **(a)** $\frac{1}{2}ab$; **(b)** c; **(c)** c^2; **(d)** $a - b$; **(e)** $(a - b)^2$;
(f) $4\left(\frac{1}{2}ab\right) + (a - b)^2 = 2ab + a^2 - 2ab + b^2 = a^2 + b^2$;
(g) Both (c) and (f) measure the same area, so they must be equal. This means $c^2 = a^2 + b^2$. A proof of the Pythagorean theorem!
49. Above and Beyond

7.6 Rational Exponents

< 7.6 Objectives >

1 > Define rational exponents

2 > Simplify expressions containing rational exponents

3 > Use a calculator to estimate the value of an expression containing rational exponents

4 > Write an expression in radical or exponential form

In Section 7.1, we discussed radical notation and the concept of roots. In this section, we use that concept to develop a new notation. We use exponents to provide an alternate way of writing these roots.

This new notation involves **rational numbers as exponents.** To start the development, we extend all the previous properties of exponents to include rational exponents.

Given that extension, suppose that

$a = 4^{1/2}$

Squaring both sides of the equation yields

$a^2 = (4^{1/2})^2$

or

$a^2 = 4^{(1/2)(2)}$

$a^2 = 4^1$

$a^2 = 4$

NOTES

We will see later in this section that the property $(x^m)^n = x^{mn}$ holds for rational numbers m and n.

$4^{1/2}$ indicates the *principal square root* of 4, so it is nonnegative.

From the final equation we see that a is the number whose square is 4; that is, a is the principal square root of 4. Using our earlier notation, we can write

$a = \sqrt{4}$

But from the first equation,

$a = 4^{1/2}$

so we must have

$4^{1/2} = \sqrt{4}$

This argument can be repeated for any exponent of the form $\frac{1}{n}$, which leads to the following definition.

Definition

Rational Exponents

If a is any real number and n is a positive integer ($n > 1$), then

$a^{1/n} = \sqrt[n]{a}$

We restrict a so that a is nonnegative when n is even. In words, $a^{1/n}$ indicates the principal nth root of a.

Example 1 illustrates the use of rational exponents to represent roots.

Example 1 Writing Expressions in Radical Form

< Objective 1 >

Write each expression in radical form and then simplify.

(a) $25^{1/2} = \sqrt{25} = 5$

(b) $27^{1/3} = \sqrt[3]{27} = 3$ — $27^{1/3}$ is the *cube root* of 27.

(c) $-36^{1/2} = -\sqrt{36} = -6$

(d) $(-36)^{1/2} = \sqrt{-36}$ is not a real number.

(e) $32^{1/5} = \sqrt[5]{32} = 2$ — $32^{1/5}$ is the *fifth root* of 32.

Check Yourself 1

Write each expression in radical form and simplify.

(a) $8^{1/3}$ (b) $-64^{1/2}$ (c) $81^{1/4}$

NOTES

This is because

$$\frac{m}{n} = (m)\left(\frac{1}{n}\right) = \left(\frac{1}{n}\right)(m)$$

The two radical forms for $a^{m/n}$ are equivalent, and the choice of which form to use generally depends on whether we are evaluating numerical expressions or rewriting expressions containing variables in radical form.

We are now ready to extend our exponent notation to allow *any* rational exponent, again assuming that our previous exponent properties must still be valid. Note that

$$a^{m/n} = (a^{1/n})^m = (a^m)^{1/n}$$

From our earlier work, we know that $a^{1/n} = \sqrt[n]{a}$, and combining this with the previous equation, we offer the following definition for $a^{m/n}$.

Definition

Rational Exponents

For any real number a and positive integers m and n with $n > 1$,

$$a^{m/n} = (\sqrt[n]{a})^m = \sqrt[n]{a^m}$$

This new extension of our rational exponent notation is applied in Example 2.

Example 2 Simplifying Expressions with Rational Exponents

< Objective 2 >

Simplify each expression.

(a) $9^{3/2} = (9^{1/2})^3 = (\sqrt{9})^3$
$= 3^3 = 27$

(b) $\left(\frac{16}{81}\right)^{3/4} = \left[\left(\frac{16}{81}\right)^{1/4}\right]^3 = \left(\sqrt[4]{\frac{16}{81}}\right)^3$
$= \left(\frac{2}{3}\right)^3 = \frac{8}{27}$

(c) $(-8)^{2/3} = [(-8)^{1/3}]^2 = (\sqrt[3]{-8})^2$
$= (-2)^2 = 4$

RECALL

If $n = 2$, we have a square root. In this case, we omit the index.

NOTE

This illustrates why we use $(\sqrt[n]{a})^m$ for $a^{m/n}$ when evaluating numerical expressions. The numbers involved will be smaller and easier to work with.

In part **(a)** we could also have evaluated the expression as

$$9^{3/2} = \sqrt{9^3} = \sqrt{729}$$
$$= 27$$

Check Yourself 2

Simplify each expression.

(a) $16^{3/4}$ **(b)** $\left(\frac{8}{27}\right)^{2/3}$ **(c)** $(-32)^{3/5}$

RECALL

$a^{-p} = \frac{1}{a^p}$

Now we want to extend our rational exponent notation. Using the definition of negative exponents, we can write

$$a^{-m/n} = \frac{1}{a^{m/n}}$$

Example 3 illustrates the use of negative rational exponents.

Example 3 Simplifying Expressions with Rational Exponents

NOTE

The sign of the exponent has no effect on the sign of the base. A negative exponent indicates reciprocal.

Simplify each expression.

(a) $16^{-1/2} = \frac{1}{16^{1/2}} = \frac{1}{4}$

(b) $27^{-2/3} = \frac{1}{27^{2/3}} = \frac{1}{(\sqrt[3]{27})^2} = \frac{1}{3^2} = \frac{1}{9}$

Check Yourself 3

Simplify each expression.

(a) $16^{-1/4}$ **(b)** $81^{-3/4}$

Graphing calculators can be used to evaluate expressions that contain rational exponents by using the [∧] key and the parentheses keys.

Example 4 Estimating Exponential Expressions Using a Calculator

< Objective 3 >

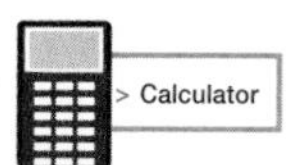

NOTE

The rational exponent must be enclosed in parentheses.

Using a graphing calculator, evaluate each exponential expression. Round all answers to three decimal places.

(a) $45^{2/5}$

Enter 45 and press the [∧] key. Then use the following keystrokes:

[(] 2 [÷] 5 [)]

Press [ENTER], and the display will read 4.584426407. Rounded to three decimal places, the result is 4.584.

NOTE

The $\boxed{(-)}$ key changes the sign of the exponent to negative.

(b) $38^{-2/3}$

Enter 38 and press the $\boxed{\wedge}$ key. Then use the following keystrokes:

$\boxed{(}\ \boxed{(-)}\ 2\ \boxed{\div}\ 3\ \boxed{)}$

Press $\boxed{\text{ENTER}}$, and the display will read 0.088473037. Rounded to three decimal places, the result is 0.088.

Check Yourself 4

Evaluate each exponential expression by using a calculator. Round each answer to three decimal places.

(a) $23^{3/5}$ **(b)** $18^{-4/7}$

As we mentioned earlier in this section, we assume that all our previous exponent properties will continue to hold for rational exponents. Those properties are restated here.

Property

Properties of Exponents

For any nonzero real numbers a and b and rational numbers m and n,

1. Product rule $a^m \cdot a^n = a^{m+n}$
2. Quotient rule $\dfrac{a^m}{a^n} = a^{m-n}$
3. Power rule $(a^m)^n = a^{mn}$
4. Product to a power rule $(ab)^m = a^m b^m$
5. Quotient to a power rule $\left(\dfrac{a}{b}\right)^m = \dfrac{a^m}{b^m}$

We restrict a and b to being nonnegative real numbers when m or n indicates an even root.

Example 5 illustrates the use of our extended properties to simplify expressions involving rational exponents. Here, we assume that all variables represent positive real numbers.

Example 5 Simplifying Expressions

NOTES

Product rule—add the exponents.

Quotient rule—subtract the exponents.

Simplify each expression.

(a) $x^{2/3} \cdot x^{1/2} = x^{2/3+1/2}$

$= x^{4/6+3/6} = x^{7/6}$

(b) $\dfrac{w^{3/4}}{w^{1/2}} = w^{3/4-1/2}$

$= w^{3/4-2/4} = w^{1/4}$

NOTE

Power rule—multiply the exponents.

(c) $(a^{2/3})^{3/4} = a^{(2/3)(3/4)}$
$= a^{1/2}$

Check Yourself 5

Simplify each expression.

(a) $z^{3/4} \cdot z^{1/2}$ **(b)** $\dfrac{x^{5/6}}{x^{1/3}}$ **(c)** $(b^{5/6})^{2/5}$

As you would expect from your previous experience with exponents, simplifying expressions often involves using several exponent properties.

Example 6 Simplifying Expressions

Simplify each expression.

(a) $(x^{2/3} \cdot y^{5/6})^{3/2}$

$= (x^{2/3})^{3/2} \cdot (y^{5/6})^{3/2}$ Product to a power rule

$= x^{(2/3)(3/2)} \cdot y^{(5/6)(3/2)} = xy^{5/4}$ Power rule

(b) $\left(\dfrac{r^{-1/2}}{s^{1/3}}\right)^6 = \dfrac{(r^{-1/2})^6}{(s^{1/3})^6}$ Quotient to a power rule

$= \dfrac{r^{-3}}{s^2} = \dfrac{1}{r^3s^2}$ Power rule

(c) $\left(\dfrac{4a^{-2/3} \cdot b^2}{a^{1/3} \cdot b^{-4}}\right)^{1/2} = \left(\dfrac{4b^2 \cdot b^4}{a^{1/3} \cdot a^{2/3}}\right)^{1/2} = \left(\dfrac{4b^6}{a}\right)^{1/2}$ We simplify inside the parentheses as the first step.

$= \dfrac{(4b^6)^{1/2}}{a^{1/2}} = \dfrac{4^{1/2}(b^6)^{1/2}}{a^{1/2}}$

$= \dfrac{2b^3}{a^{1/2}}$

Check Yourself 6

Simplify each expression.

(a) $(a^{3/4} \cdot b^{1/2})^{2/3}$ **(b)** $\left(\dfrac{w^{1/2}}{z^{-1/4}}\right)^4$

(c) $\left(\dfrac{8x^{-3/4}y}{x^{1/4} \cdot y^{-5}}\right)^{1/3}$

We can also use the relationships between rational exponents and radicals to write expressions involving rational exponents as radicals and vice versa.

Example 7 Writing Expressions in Radical Form

< Objective 4 >

NOTES

Here we use $a^{m/n} = \sqrt[n]{a^m}$, which is generally the preferred form in this situation.

In part **(c)** the exponent applies *only* to the variable *y*.

In part **(d)** the exponent now applies to 2*y* because of the parentheses.

Write each expression in radical form.

(a) $a^{3/5} = \sqrt[5]{a^3}$

(b) $(mn)^{3/4} = \sqrt[4]{(mn)^3}$
$= \sqrt[4]{m^3n^3}$

(c) $2y^{5/6} = 2\sqrt[6]{y^5}$

(d) $(2y)^{5/6} = \sqrt[6]{(2y)^5}$
$= \sqrt[6]{32y^5}$

Check Yourself 7

Write each expression in radical form.

(a) $(ab)^{2/3}$ **(b)** $3x^{3/4}$ **(c)** $(3x)^{3/4}$

Example 8 Writing Expressions in Exponential Form

Rewrite each expression using rational exponents and simplify.

(a) $\sqrt[3]{5x} = (5x)^{1/3}$

(b) $\sqrt{9a^2b^4} = (9a^2b^4)^{1/2}$
$= 9^{1/2}(a^2)^{1/2}(b^4)^{1/2} = 3ab^2$

(c) $\sqrt[4]{16w^{12}z^8} = (16w^{12}z^8)^{1/4}$
$= 16^{1/4}(w^{12})^{1/4}(z^8)^{1/4} = 2w^3z^2$

Check Yourself 8

Rewrite each expression using rational exponents and simplify.

(a) $\sqrt{7a}$ **(b)** $\sqrt[3]{27p^6q^9}$ **(c)** $\sqrt[4]{81x^8y^{16}}$

Check Yourself ANSWERS

1. (a) 2; **(b)** −8; **(c)** 3 **2. (a)** 8; **(b)** $\frac{4}{9}$; **(c)** −8 **3. (a)** $\frac{1}{2}$; **(b)** $\frac{1}{27}$

4. (a) 6.562; **(b)** 0.192 **5. (a)** $z^{5/4}$; **(b)** $x^{1/2}$; **(c)** $b^{1/3}$

6. (a) $a^{1/2}b^{1/3}$; **(b)** w^2z; **(c)** $\frac{2y^2}{x^{1/3}}$ **7. (a)** $\sqrt[3]{a^2b^2}$; **(b)** $3\sqrt[4]{x^3}$; **(c)** $\sqrt[4]{27x^3}$

8. (a) $(7a)^{1/2}$; **(b)** $3p^2q^3$; **(c)** $3x^2y^4$

Reading Your Text

The following fill-in-the-blank exercises are designed to ensure that you understand some of the key vocabulary used in this section.

SECTION 7.6

(a) Exponents can be integers or ______________ numbers.

(b) $a^{1/n}$ indicates the ______________ of a.

(c) $\sqrt[n]{a^m}$ = ______________.

(d) The product rule of exponents states we should ______________ the exponents; the quotient rule of exponents states we should ______________ the exponents; and the power rule of exponents states we should ______________ the exponents.

7.6 exercises

< Objective 1 >

Use the definition of $a^{1/n}$ to evaluate each expression.

1. $36^{1/2}$

2. $100^{1/2}$

3. $-25^{1/2}$

4. $(-64)^{1/2}$

5. $(-49)^{1/2}$

6. $-49^{1/2}$

7. $27^{1/3}$

8. $(-64)^{1/3}$

9. $\left(\frac{4}{9}\right)^{1/2}$

10. $\left(\frac{27}{8}\right)^{1/3}$

Use the definition of $a^{m/n}$ to evaluate each expression.

11. $27^{2/3}$

12. $16^{3/2}$

13. $(-8)^{4/3}$

14. $125^{2/3}$

15. $32^{2/5}$

16. $-81^{3/4}$

17. $\left(\frac{8}{27}\right)^{2/3}$

18. $\left(\frac{9}{4}\right)^{3/2}$

Use the definition of $a^{-m/n}$ to evaluate the following expressions. Use your calculator to check each answer.

19. $25^{-1/2}$

20. $27^{-1/3}$

21. $9^{-3/2}$

22. $16^{-3/4}$

23. $\left(\frac{4}{25}\right)^{-1/2}$

24. $\left(\frac{27}{8}\right)^{-2/3}$

< Objective 2 >

Use the properties of exponents to simplify each expression. Assume all variables represent positive real numbers. Write your answers with positive exponents only.

25. $x^{1/2} \cdot x^{1/2}$

26. $a^{2/3} \cdot a^{1/3}$

27. $y^{3/5} \cdot y^{1/5}$

28. $m^{1/4} \cdot m^{5/4}$

Name ____________

Section ________ Date ________

Answers

1. 6 **2.** 10

3. -5

4. Not a real number

5. Not a real number

6. -7

7. 3 **8.** -4

9. $\frac{2}{3}$ **10.** $\frac{3}{2}$

11. 9 **12.** 64

13. 16 **14.** 25

15. 4 **16.** -27

17. $\frac{4}{9}$ **18.** $\frac{27}{8}$

19. $\frac{1}{5}$ **20.** $\frac{1}{3}$

21. $\frac{1}{27}$ **22.** $\frac{1}{8}$

23. $\frac{5}{2}$ **24.** $\frac{4}{9}$

25. x **26.** a

27. $y^{4/5}$ **28.** $m^{3/2}$

Answers

29. $b^{13/6}$
30. $p^{3/2}$
31. $x^{1/3}$
32. $a^{2/3}$
33. s
34. z^3
35. $w^{3/4}$
36. $b^{1/2}$
37. x
38. y
39. $a^{3/5}$
40. $p^{1/2}$
41. $\frac{1}{y^6}$
42. $\frac{1}{w^4}$
43. a^4b^9
44. p^3q^{10}
45. $32xy^3$
46. $81m^3n^5$
47. $4pq^{5/3}$
48. $8a^{1/4}b^{1/2}$
49. $a^{1/2}b^{1/4}$
50. $x^{1/6}y^{1/4}$
51. $\frac{s^2}{r^4}$
52. $\frac{1}{w^4z^2}$
53. $\frac{x^3}{y^2}$
54. $\frac{p^3}{q^2}$
55. $\frac{1}{mn^2}$
56. r^2s^5
57. 9.946
58. 2.449
59. 0.370
60. 0.068

29. $b^{2/3} \cdot b^{3/2}$

30. $p^{5/6} \cdot p^{2/3}$

31. $\frac{x^{2/3}}{x^{1/3}}$

32. $\frac{a^{5/6}}{a^{1/6}}$

33. $\frac{s^{7/5}}{s^{2/5}}$

34. $\frac{z^{9/2}}{z^{3/2}}$

35. $\frac{w^{5/4}}{w^{1/2}}$

36. $\frac{b^{7/6}}{b^{2/3}}$

37. $(x^{3/4})^{4/3}$

38. $(y^{4/3})^{3/4}$

39. $(a^{2/5})^{3/2}$

40. $(p^{3/4})^{2/3}$

41. $(y^{-3/4})^8$

42. $(w^{-2/3})^6$

43. $(a^{2/3} \cdot b^{3/2})^6$

44. $(p^{3/4} \cdot q^{5/2})^4$

45. $(2x^{1/5} \cdot y^{3/5})^5$

46. $(3m^{3/4} \cdot n^{5/4})^4$

47. $(8p^{3/2} \cdot q^{5/2})^{2/3}$

48. $(16a^{1/3} \cdot b^{2/3})^{3/4}$

49. $\frac{a^{5/6} \cdot b^{3/4}}{a^{1/3} \cdot b^{1/2}}$

50. $\frac{x^{2/3} \cdot y^{3/4}}{x^{1/2} \cdot y^{1/2}}$

51. $\frac{(r^{-1} \cdot s^{1/2})^3}{r \cdot s^{-1/2}}$

52. $\frac{(w^{-2} \cdot z^{-1/4})^6}{w^{-8}z^{1/2}}$

> Videos

53. $\left(\frac{x^{12}}{y^8}\right)^{1/4}$

54. $\left(\frac{p^9}{q^6}\right)^{1/3}$

55. $\left(\frac{m^{-1/4}}{n^{1/2}}\right)^4$

56. $\left(\frac{r^{1/5}}{s^{-1/2}}\right)^{10}$

< Objective 3 >

Evaluate each expression, using a calculator. Round each answer to three decimal places.

57. $46^{3/5}$

58. $23^{2/7}$

59. $12^{-2/5}$

60. $36^{-3/4}$

< Objective 4 >

Write each expression in radical form. Do not simplify.

61. $a^{3/4}$

62. $m^{5/6}$

63. $2x^{2/3}$

64. $3m^{-2/5}$

65. $(3x)^{2/5}$

66. $(2y)^{-3/4}$

Write each expression using rational exponents, and simplify when necessary.

67. $\sqrt{7a}$

68. $\sqrt{25w^4}$

69. $\sqrt[3]{8m^6n^9}$

70. $\sqrt[5]{32r^{10}s^{15}}$

Basic Skills | **Advanced Skills** | Vocational-Technical Applications | Calculator/Computer | Above and Beyond

Apply the appropriate multiplication patterns. Then simplify your result.

71. $a^{1/2}(a^{3/2} + a^{3/4})$

72. $2x^{1/4}(3x^{3/4} - 5x^{-1/4})$

73. $(a^{1/2} + 2)(a^{1/2} - 2)$

74. $(w^{1/3} - 3)(w^{1/3} + 3)$

75. $(x^{1/2} + 2)^2$

76. $(a^{1/3} - 3)^2$

As is suggested by several of the preceding exercises, certain expressions containing rational exponents are factorable. For instance, to factor $x^{2/3} - x^{1/3} - 6$, let $u = x^{1/3}$. Note that $x^{2/3} = (x^{1/3})^2 = u^2$.

Substituting, we have $u^2 - u - 6$, and factoring yields $(u - 3)(u + 2)$ or $(x^{1/3} - 3)(x^{1/3} + 2)$.

Use this technique to factor each expression.

77. $x^{2/3} + 4x^{1/3} + 3$

78. $y^{2/5} - 2y^{1/5} - 8$

79. $x^{4/3} - 4$

80. $x^{2/5} - 16$

Perform the indicated operations. Assume that n represents a positive integer and that the denominators are not zero.

81. $x^{3n} \cdot x^{2n}$

82. $p^{1-n} \cdot p^{n+3}$

83. $(y^2)^{2n}$

84. $(a^{3n})^3$

Answers

61. $\sqrt[4]{a^3}$
62. $\sqrt[6]{m^5}$
63. $2\sqrt[3]{x^2}$
64. $\frac{3}{\sqrt[5]{m^2}}$
65. $\sqrt[5]{9x^2}$
66. $\frac{1}{\sqrt[4]{8y^3}}$
67. $(7a)^{1/2}$
68. $5w^2$
69. $2m^2n^3$
70. $2r^2s^3$
71. $a^2 + a^{5/4}$
72. $6x - 10$
73. $a - 4$
74. $w^{2/3} - 9$
75. $x + 4x^{1/2} + 4$
76. $a^{2/3} - 6a^{1/3} + 9$
77. $(x^{1/3} + 1)(x^{1/3} + 3)$
78. $(y^{1/5} - 4)(y^{1/5} + 2)$
79. $(x^{2/3} - 2)(x^{2/3} + 2)$
80. $(x^{1/5} + 4)(x^{1/5} - 4)$
81. x^{5n}
82. p^4
83. y^{4n}
84. a^{9n}

85. $\frac{r^{n+2}}{r^n}$

86. $\frac{w^n}{w^{n-3}}$

87. $(a^3 \cdot b^2)^{2n}$

88. $(c^4 \cdot d^2)^{3m}$

89. $\left(\frac{x^{n+2}}{x^n}\right)^{1/2}$

90. $\left(\frac{b^n}{b^{n-3}}\right)^{1/3}$

Write each expression in exponential form, simplify, and give the result as a single radical.

91. $\sqrt{\sqrt{x}}$

92. $\sqrt[3]{\sqrt{a}}$

93. $\sqrt[4]{\sqrt{y}}$

94. $\sqrt{\sqrt[3]{w}}$

Simplify each expression. Write your answer in scientific notation.

95. $(4 \times 10^8)^{1/2}$

96. $(8 \times 10^6)^{1/3}$

97. $(16 \times 10^{-12})^{1/4}$

98. $(9 \times 10^{-4})^{1/2}$

Basic Skills | Advanced Skills | **Vocational-Technical Applications** | Calculator/Computer | Above and Beyond

Solve the following applications.

99. **Agricultural Technology** While investigating rainfall runoff in a region of semiarid farmland, a researcher encounters the following formula:

$$t = C\left(\frac{L}{xy^2}\right)^{1/3}$$

Evaluate t when $C = 20$, $L = 600$, $x = 3$, and $y = 5$.

100. **Agricultural Technology** The average velocity of water in an open irrigation ditch is given by the formula

$$V = \frac{1.5x^{2/3}y^{1/2}}{z}$$

Evaluate V when $x = 27$, $y = 16$, and $z = 12$.

Basic Skills | Advanced Skills | Vocational-Technical Applications | **Calculator/Computer** | Above and Beyond

101. On your calculator, try evaluating $(-9)^{4/2}$ in the following two ways:

(a) $[(-9)^4]^{1/2}$ **(b)** $[(-9)^{1/2}]^4$

Discuss the results.

Answers

85. r^2

86. w^3

87. $a^{6n}b^{4n}$

88. $c^{12m}d^{6m}$

89. x

90. b

91. $\sqrt[4]{x}$

92. $\sqrt[6]{a}$

93. $\sqrt[8]{y}$

94. $\sqrt[6]{w}$

95. 2×10^4

96. 2×10^2

97. 2×10^{-3}

98. 3×10^{-2}

99. 40

100. 4.5

101. (a) 81; (b) not defined

102. In this exercise, you will use a regression utility in your graphing calculator to find a function that "fits" pendulum data. We will fit a power function to the data, that is, a function of the form $y = ax^b$.

(a) Enter the data as ordered pairs into your calculator as seen, in the following screen. To enter statistical data into the TI-84 calculator, press STAT and ENTER and use the arrows and numbers to store your data.

L1	L2	L3 2
10	.633	------
20	.9	
30	1.1	
40	1.267	
50	1.4	
60	1.533	
70	1.633	

L2(7) =1.633

(b) Find and execute the **power regression** utility in your calculator. This will likely be found by locating a Statistics menu, and then a Calculate option. You should obtain a function of the form $y = ax^b$. Write this equation, rounding the values of a and b to the nearest thousandth.

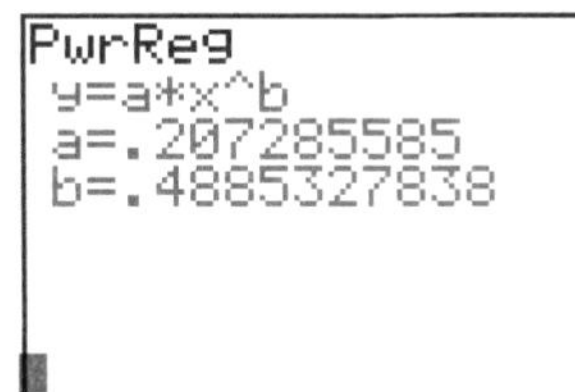

(c) Determine a simple fraction that is near in value to b.

(d) Using the rational exponent from part **(c)**, rewrite the function found in part **(b)** in radical notation.

(e) Compare the constant a (determined by the regression) with the experimental k found in exercise 83 of Section 7.2.

(f) Compare the constant a (determined by the regression) with the theoretical k found in exercise 84(a) of Section 7.2.

Basic Skills | Advanced Skills | Vocational-Technical Applications | Calculator/Computer | **Above and Beyond**

103. Describe the difference between x^{-2} and $x^{1/2}$.

104. Some rational exponents, like $\frac{1}{2}$, can easily be rewritten as terminating decimals (0.5). Others, like $\frac{1}{3}$, cannot. What is it that determines which rational numbers can be rewritten as terminating decimals?

105. Use the properties of exponents to decide what x should be to make each statement true. Explain your choices regarding which properties of exponents you decide to use.

(a) $(a^{2/3})^x = a$ **(b)** $(a^{5/6})^x = \frac{1}{a}$

(c) $a^{2x} \cdot a^{3/2} = 1$ **(d)** $(\sqrt{a^{2/3}})^x = a$

Answers

102. (a) See exercise; (b) $y = 0.207x^{0.489}$; (c) $b \approx 0.5 = \frac{1}{2}$; (d) $y = 0.207\sqrt{x}$; (e) within 0.008; (f) within 0.006

103. Above and Beyond

104. Above and Beyond

105. Above and Beyond

Answers

(a) $\sqrt[6]{5{,}400}$;
(b) $b\sqrt[10]{b^9}$;
106. (c) $\sqrt[12]{d^5}$

106. Consider the following problem: $\sqrt[4]{5x} \cdot \sqrt{3y}$. So far we have only multiplied radicals with the same index. However, we can do this problem by rewriting the radicals so they *do* have the same index.

$\sqrt[4]{5x} \cdot \sqrt{3y}$	Rewrite the radical using rational exponents.
$= (5x)^{1/4}(3y)^{1/2}$	Find common denominators for the exponents.
$= (5x)^{1/4}(3y)^{2/4}$	Rewrite the rational exponents as radicals.
$= \sqrt[4]{5x} \cdot \sqrt[4]{(3y)^2}$	Now we have the same index, so we can multiply.
$= \sqrt[4]{5x \cdot (3y)^2}$	Simplify.
$= \sqrt[4]{5x \cdot 9y^2}$	
$= \sqrt[4]{45xy^2}$	

Using this same method, simplify the following radical expressions.

(a) $\sqrt[3]{5} \cdot \sqrt{6}$

(b) $\sqrt[5]{b^2} \cdot \sqrt{b^3}$

(c) $\dfrac{\sqrt[3]{d^2}}{\sqrt[4]{d}}$

Answers

1. 6 **3.** -5 **5.** Not a real number **7.** 3 **9.** $\frac{2}{3}$ **11.** 9
13. 16 **15.** 4 **17.** $\frac{4}{9}$ **19.** $\frac{1}{5}$ **21.** $\frac{1}{27}$ **23.** $\frac{5}{2}$ **25.** x
27. $y^{4/5}$ **29.** $b^{13/6}$ **31.** $x^{1/3}$ **33.** s **35.** $w^{3/4}$ **37.** x **39.** $a^{3/5}$
41. $\frac{1}{y^6}$ **43.** a^4b^9 **45.** $32xy^3$ **47.** $4pq^{5/3}$ **49.** $a^{1/2}b^{1/4}$ **51.** $\frac{s^2}{r^4}$
53. $\frac{x^3}{y^2}$ **55.** $\frac{1}{mn^2}$ **57.** 9.946 **59.** 0.370 **61.** $\sqrt[4]{a^3}$ **63.** $2\sqrt[3]{x^2}$
65. $\sqrt[5]{9x^2}$ **67.** $(7a)^{1/2}$ **69.** $2m^2n^3$ **71.** $a^2 + a^{5/4}$ **73.** $a - 4$
75. $x + 4x^{1/2} + 4$ **77.** $(x^{1/3} + 1)(x^{1/3} + 3)$ **79.** $(x^{2/3} - 2)(x^{2/3} + 2)$
81. x^{5n} **83.** y^{4n} **85.** r^2 **87.** $a^{6n}b^{4n}$ **89.** x **91.** $\sqrt[4]{x}$ **93.** $\sqrt[8]{y}$
95. 2×10^4 **97.** 2×10^{-3} **99.** 40 **101.** **(a)** 81; **(b)** not defined
103. Above and Beyond **105.** Above and Beyond

7.7 Complex Numbers

< 7.7 Objectives >

1 > Use the number i

2 > Add and subtract complex numbers

3 > Multiply complex numbers

4 > Divide complex numbers

Radicals such as

$\sqrt{-4}$ and $\sqrt{-49}$

are *not* real numbers because no real number squared produces a negative number. Our work in this section will extend our number system to include these **imaginary numbers,** which will allow us to consider radicals such as $\sqrt{-4}$.

Definition

The Imaginary Number i

The number i is defined as

$$i = \sqrt{-1}$$

Since $i = \sqrt{-1}$, we also know

$$i^2 = (\sqrt{-1})^2 = -1$$

The number i gives us a means of indicating the square root of a negative number.

Property

Writing an Imaginary Number

When a is a positive real number,

$$\sqrt{-a} = i\sqrt{a}$$

Example 1 **Using the Number i**

< Objective 1 >

Write each expression as a multiple of i.

(a) $\sqrt{-4} = i\sqrt{4} = 2i$

(b) $\sqrt{-8} = i\sqrt{8} = 2i\sqrt{2}$

NOTE

In Example 1 **(b)**, we simplify $\sqrt{8}$ as $2\sqrt{2}$. Note that we write the *i in front of* the radical to make it clear that *i* is *not part of* the radicand.

Check Yourself 1

Write each radical as a multiple of *i*.

(a) $\sqrt{-25}$ **(b)** $\sqrt{-24}$

We have just defined $\sqrt{-4} = i\sqrt{4} = 2i$ in the process of expressing the square root of a negative number as a multiple of i. Particular care must be taken with products in which two negative radicands are involved. The product property for radicals does not apply if both radicands are negative.

Example 2 Multiplying Two Negative Radicands

$\sqrt{-3} \cdot \sqrt{-12}$

$= i\sqrt{3} \cdot i\sqrt{12}$ Write each radical in standard form as an expression as a multiple of i.

$= i^2\sqrt{36}$ Multiply using the product rule for radicals.

$= (-1)\sqrt{36}$ Since $i^2 = (\sqrt{-1})^2 = -1$

$= -6$ Simplify.

If we tried to apply the product property for radicals to the original problem, we would have

$\sqrt{-3} \cdot \sqrt{-12} \stackrel{?}{=} \sqrt{(-3)(-12)} = \sqrt{36} = 6$ which is *not* correct.

The property $\sqrt{a} \cdot \sqrt{b} = \sqrt{ab}$ is not applicable in the case in which a and b are both negative. Radicals such as $\sqrt{-a}$ must be written in the standard form $i\sqrt{a}$ *before* multiplying, to use the rules for real-valued radicals.

NOTE

The term *imaginary number* was introduced by René Descartes in 1637. Euler used *i* to indicate $\sqrt{-1}$ in 1748, but it was not until 1831 that Gauss used the term *complex number*.

Check Yourself 2

$\sqrt{-8} \cdot \sqrt{-3}$

We are now ready to define complex numbers in terms of the number i.

Definition

Complex Number

A **complex number** is any number that can be written in the form

$a + bi$

in which a and b are real numbers and

$i = \sqrt{-1}$

NOTE

$5i$ is sometimes called a **pure imaginary** number.

The form $a + bi$ is called the **standard form** of a complex number. We call a the **real part** of the complex number and bi the **imaginary part.** Some examples follow.

$3 + 7i$ is an example of a complex number with real part 3 and imaginary part $7i$.

$5i$ is also a complex number because it can be written as $0 + 5i$.

-3 is a complex number because it can be written as $-3 + 0i$.

The basic operations of addition and subtraction on complex numbers are defined here.

Property

Adding and Subtracting Complex Numbers

For the complex numbers $a + bi$ and $c + di$,

$$(a + bi) + (c + di) = (a + c) + (b + d)i$$

$$(a + bi) - (c + di) = (a - c) + (b - d)i$$

In words, we add or subtract the real parts and the imaginary parts of the complex numbers.

NOTE

The real numbers, $\mathbb{R}$, can be considered a subset of the set of complex numbers, $\mathbb{C}$.

$3i$ and $7i$ can be thought of as like terms. We have seen that $2x$ and $3x$ can be added or subtracted since they are like terms, and we have seen that $4\sqrt{2}$ and $5\sqrt{2}$ can be added or subtracted since they are similar radicals. Similarly, $3i$ and $7i$ can be added or subtracted since they are both imaginary parts of a complex number.

Example 3 illustrates the use of the definitions.

Example 3 Adding and Subtracting Complex Numbers

< Objective 2 >

Perform the indicated operations.

(a) $(5 + 3i) + (6 - 7i) = (5 + 6) + (3 - 7)i = 11 - 4i$

(b) $5 + (7 - 5i) = (5 + 7) + (-5i) = 12 - 5i$

(c) $(8 - 2i) - (3 - 4i) = (8 - 3) + [-2 - (-4)]i = 5 + 2i$

NOTE

The regrouping is essentially a matter of combining like terms.

Check Yourself 3

Perform the indicated operations.

(a) $(4 - 7i) + (3 - 2i)$ **(b)** $-7 + (-2 + 3i)$ **(c)** $(-4 + 3i) - (-2 - i)$

Because complex numbers are binomial in form, the product of two complex numbers is found by applying our earlier multiplication pattern for binomials (FOIL), as Example 4 illustrates.

Example 4 Multiplying Complex Numbers

Multiply.

$$\begin{aligned}(2 + 3i)(3 - 4i) &= 2 \cdot 3 + 2(-4i) + (3i)3 + (3i)(-4i)\\ &= 6 + (-8i) + 9i + (-12i^2)\\ &= 6 - 8i + 9i + (-12)(-1)\\ &= 6 + i + 12\\ &= 18 + i\end{aligned}$$

NOTE

We can replace i^2 with -1 because of the definition of i, and we usually do so because of the resulting simplification.

Check Yourself 4

Multiply $(2 - 5i)(3 - 2i)$.

Property

Multiplying Complex Numbers

For the complex numbers $a + bi$ and $c + di$,

$$\begin{aligned}(a + bi)(c + di) &= ac + adi + bci + bdi^2 \\ &= ac + adi + bci - bd \\ &= (ac - bd) + (ad + bc)i\end{aligned}$$

RECALL

Two binomials that differ only in the signs of their second terms are called *conjugates*.

This formula for the general product of two complex numbers can be memorized. However, you will find it much easier to use FOIL as it is applied to complex numbers than to memorize this formula.

There is one particular product form that will seem very familiar. We call $a + bi$ and $a - bi$ **complex conjugates.** For instance,

$3 + 2i$ and $3 - 2i$

are complex conjugates.

Consider the product

$$\begin{aligned}(3 + 2i)(3 - 2i) &= 3^2 - (2i)^2 \\ &= 9 - 4i^2 = 9 - 4(-1) \\ &= 9 + 4 = 13\end{aligned}$$

> CAUTION

$(a + bi)(a - bi) = a^2 \pm b^2$
$(a + bi)(a - bi) = a^2 - b^2i^2$ by multiplication. However, $i^2 = -1$ so $a^2 - b^2i^2 = a^2 - b^2(-1)$ which is $a^2 \pm b^2$.

The product of $3 + 2i$ and $3 - 2i$ is a real number. We can write the product of two complex conjugates as

$$(a + bi)(a - bi) = a^2 + b^2$$

The fact that this product is always a real number will be very useful when we consider the division of complex numbers later in this section.

Example 5 Multiplying Complex Numbers

< Objective 3 >

Multiply.

$$\begin{aligned}(7 - 4i)(7 + 4i) &= 7^2 - (4i)^2 = 7^2 - 4^2(-1) \\ &= 7^2 + 4^2 = 49 + 16 = 65\end{aligned}$$

NOTE

We could get the same result by applying the preceding formula with $a = 7$ and $b = 4$. We could also use FOIL:

$$\begin{aligned}&(7)(7) + (7)(4i) + (-4i)(7) \\ &\quad + (-4i)(4i) \\ &= 49 + 28i - 28i - 16i^2 \\ &= 49 - 16(-1) \\ &= 49 + 16 \\ &= 65\end{aligned}$$

Check Yourself 5

Multiply $(5 + 3i)(5 - 3i)$.

We are now ready to discuss the division of complex numbers. We find the quotient by multiplying the numerator and denominator by the conjugate of the denominator, as Example 6 illustrates.

Example 6 Dividing Complex Numbers

< Objective 4 >

Divide.

(a) $\dfrac{6 + 9i}{3i}$

$$\frac{6 + 9i}{3i} = \frac{(6 + 9i)(-3i)}{(3i)(-3i)}$$

The conjugate of $3i$ is $-3i$, and so we multiply the numerator and denominator by $-3i$.

$$= \frac{-18i - 27i^2}{-9i^2}$$

$$= \frac{-18i - 27(-1)}{(-9)(-1)}$$

$$= \frac{27 - 18i}{9} = 3 - 2i$$

NOTE

Think of $3i$ as $0 + 3i$ and of its conjugate as $0 - 3i$, or $-3i$.

(b) $$\frac{3 - i}{3 + 2i} = \frac{(3 - i)(3 - 2i)}{(3 + 2i)(3 - 2i)}$$

$$= \frac{9 - 6i - 3i + 2i^2}{9 - 4i^2}$$

$$= \frac{9 - 9i - 2}{9 + 4}$$

$$= \frac{7 - 9i}{13} = \frac{7}{13} - \frac{9}{13}i$$

NOTES

Multiplying by $\frac{i}{i} = 1$ in the original expression would yield the same result. Try it yourself.

We multiply by $\frac{3 - 2i}{3 - 2i}$, which equals 1.

Check Yourself 6

Divide.

(a) $\dfrac{5 + i}{5 - 3i}$ (b) $\dfrac{4 + 10i}{2i}$

We conclude this section with a diagram that summarizes the structure of the system of complex numbers.

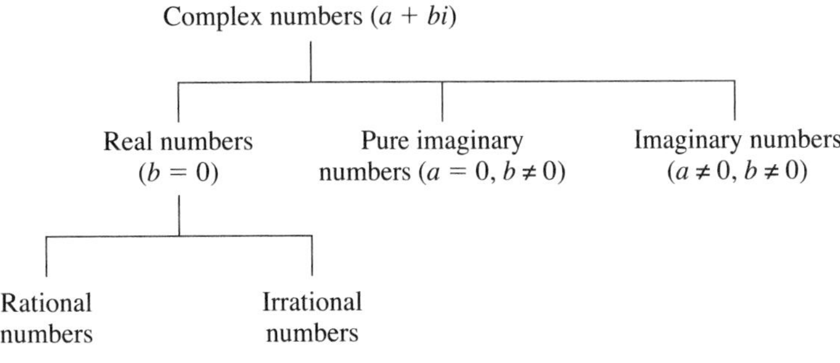

Check Yourself ANSWERS

1. (a) $5i$; **(b)** $2i\sqrt{6}$ **2.** $-2\sqrt{6}$ **3. (a)** $7 - 9i$; **(b)** $-9 + 3i$; **(c)** $-2 + 4i$
4. $-4 - 19i$ **5.** 34 **6. (a)** $\frac{11}{17} + \frac{10}{17}i$; **(b)** $5 - 2i$

Reading Your Text

The following fill-in-the-blank exercises are designed to ensure that you understand some of the key vocabulary used in this section.

SECTION 7.7

(a) The number i is defined as ________ and $i^2 =$ ________.

(b) A ________ is any number that can be written in the form $a + bi$, in which a and b are real numbers and $i = \sqrt{-1}$.

(c) In $a + bi$, a is called the ________ of the complex number and bi is called the ________.

(d) $a + bi$ and $a - bi$ are called ________.

Basic Skills | Advanced Skills | Vocational-Technical Applications | Calculator/Computer | Above and Beyond

7.7 exercises

MathZone

Boost your grade at mathzone.com!
> Practice Problems
> NetTutor
> Self-Tests
> e-Professors
> Videos

Name ____________

Section ________ Date ________

< Objective 1 >

Write each root as a multiple of i. Simplify your results when necessary.

1. $\sqrt{-16}$
2. $\sqrt{-36}$
3. $-\sqrt{-64}$
4. $-\sqrt{-25}$
5. $\sqrt{-21}$
6. $\sqrt{-19}$
7. $\sqrt{-12}$
8. $\sqrt{-24}$
9. $-\sqrt{-108}$

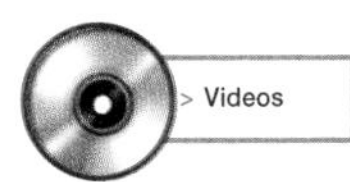

10. $-\sqrt{-192}$

Find each product.

11. $\sqrt{-5} \cdot \sqrt{-7}$
12. $\sqrt{-3} \cdot \sqrt{-10}$
13. $\sqrt{-2} \cdot \sqrt{-18}$
14. $\sqrt{-4} \cdot \sqrt{-25}$
15. $\sqrt{-6} \cdot \sqrt{-15}$
16. $\sqrt{-5} \cdot \sqrt{-30}$
17. $\sqrt{-10} \cdot \sqrt{-10}$
18. $\sqrt{-11} \cdot \sqrt{-11}$

< Objective 2 >

Perform the indicated operations.

19. $(3 + i) + (5 + 2i)$
20. $(2 + 3i) + (4 + 5i)$
21. $(3 - 2i) + (-2 + 7i)$
22. $(-5 + 3i) + (-2 + 7i)$
23. $(5 + 4i) - (3 + 2i)$
24. $(7 + 6i) - (3 + 5i)$
25. $(8 - 5i) - (3 + 2i)$
26. $(7 - 3i) - (-2 - 5i)$
27. $(5 + i) + (2 + 3i) + 7i$
28. $(3 - 2i) + (2 + 3i) + 7i$
29. $(2 + 3i) - (3 - 5i) + (4 + 3i)$
30. $(5 - 7i) + (7 + 3i) - (2 - 7i)$
31. $(7 + 3i) - [(3 + i) - (2 - 5i)]$
32. $(8 - 2i) - [(4 + 3i) - (-2 + i)]$

33. $(5 + 3i) + (-5 - 3i)$
34. $(8 - 7i) + (-8 + 7i)$

Answers

1. $4i$
2. $6i$
3. $-8i$
4. $-5i$
5. $i\sqrt{21}$
6. $i\sqrt{19}$
7. $2i\sqrt{3}$
8. $2i\sqrt{6}$
9. $-6i\sqrt{3}$
10. $-8i\sqrt{3}$
11. $-\sqrt{35}$
12. $-\sqrt{30}$
13. -6
14. -10
15. $-3\sqrt{10}$
16. $-5\sqrt{6}$
17. -10
18. -11
19. $8 + 3i$
20. $6 + 8i$
21. $1 + 5i$
22. $-7 + 10i$
23. $2 + 2i$
24. $4 + i$
25. $5 - 7i$
26. $9 + 2i$
27. $7 + 11i$
28. $5 + 8i$
29. $3 + 11i$
30. $10 + 3i$
31. $6 - 3i$
32. $2 - 4i$
33. 0
34. 0

Answers

35. $-15 + 9i$
36. $-6 + 14i$
37. $28 + 12i$
38. $-6 + 12i$
39. $-6 - 8i$
40. $-35 - 10i$
41. $-5 + 4i$
42. $-3 + 2i$
43. $13i$
44. $13 - 11i$
45. $23 + 14i$
46. $25 - 8i$
47. $18 + i$
48. $11 + 23i$
49. $21 - 20i$
50. $-40 + 42i$
51. $3 + 2i$, 13
52. $5 - 2i$, 29
53. $2 - 3i$, 13
54. $7 + i$, 50
55. $-3 + 2i$, 13
56. $-5 + 7i$, 74
57. $-5i$, 25
58. $3i$, 9
59. $2 - 3i$
60. $3 + 5i$
61. $-2 - 3i$
62. $-3 + 2i$
63. $\frac{6}{29} - \frac{15}{29}i$
64. $\frac{10}{13} + \frac{15}{13}i$

< Objective 3 >

Find each product. Write your answer in standard form.

35. $3i(3 + 5i)$

36. $2i(7 + 3i)$

37. $4i(3 - 7i)$

38. $2i(6 + 3i)$

39. $-2i(4 - 3i)$

40. $-5i(2 - 7i)$

41. $6i\left(\frac{2}{3} + \frac{5}{6}i\right)$

42. $4i\left(\frac{1}{2} + \frac{3}{4}i\right)$

43. $(3 + 2i)(2 + 3i)$

44. $(5 - 2i)(3 - i)$

45. $(4 - 3i)(2 + 5i)$

46. $(7 + 2i)(3 - 2i)$

47. $(-2 - 3i)(-3 + 4i)$

48. $(-5 - i)(-3 - 4i)$

49. $(5 - 2i)^2$

50. $(3 + 7i)^2$

Write the conjugate of each complex number. Then find the product of the given number and the conjugate.

51. $3 - 2i$

52. $5 + 2i$

53. $2 + 3i$

54. $7 - i$

55. $-3 - 2i$

56. $-5 - 7i$

57. $5i$

58. $-3i$

< Objective 4 >

Find each quotient, and write your answer in standard form.

59. $\frac{3 + 2i}{i}$

60. $\frac{5 - 3i}{-i}$

61. $\frac{6 - 4i}{2i}$

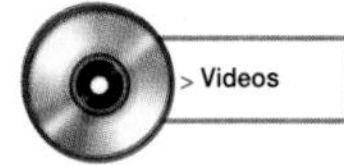

62. $\frac{8 + 12i}{-4i}$

63. $\frac{3}{2 + 5i}$

64. $\frac{5}{2 - 3i}$

65. $\dfrac{13}{2 + 3i}$

66. $\dfrac{-17}{3 + 5i}$

67. $\dfrac{2 + 3i}{4 + 3i}$

68. $\dfrac{4 - 2i}{5 - 3i}$

> Videos

69. $\dfrac{3 - 4i}{3 + 4i}$

70. $\dfrac{7 + 2i}{7 - 2i}$

Label each of the following statements as **true** *or* **false.**

71. If a is a negative number, then $\sqrt{-a}$ will be an imaginary number.

72. When subtracting two complex numbers, we subtract the real parts and then the imaginary parts.

73. When multiplying two complex numbers, we multiply the real parts and then the imaginary parts.

74. The product of two complex conjugates will be a real number.

Basic Skills | **Advanced Skills** | Vocational-Technical Applications | Calculator/Computer | Above and Beyond

Because $i^2 = -1$, the positive integral powers of i form an interesting pattern. Consider these.

$i = i$ $\qquad i^5 = i^4 \cdot i = 1 \cdot i = i$

$i^2 = -1$ $\qquad i^6 = i^4 \cdot i^2 = 1(-1) = -1$

$i^3 = i^2 \cdot i = (-1)i = -i$ $\qquad i^7 = i^4 \cdot i^3 = 1(-i) = -i$

$i^4 = i^2 \cdot i^2 = (-1)(-1) = 1$ $\qquad i^8 = i^4 \cdot i^4 = 1 \cdot 1 = 1$

Given this pattern, do you see that any power of i will simplify to i, -1, $-i$, or 1? This is often referred to as the *cyclic nature* of i. The answers of i, -1, $-i$, and 1 will repeat in the same order. For instance, i^9 will be i again and $i^{10} = -1$, and so forth. The easiest approach to simplifying higher powers of i is to write that power in terms of i^4 (because $1^4 = 1$). As an example,

$$i^{18} = i^{16} \cdot i^2 = (i^4)^4 \cdot i^2 = 1^4(-1) = -1$$

In exercises 75 to 82, use these comments to simplify each power of i.

75. i^{10}

76. i^9

77. i^{20}

78. i^{15}

79. i^{38}

80. i^{40}

81. i^{51}

82. i^{61}

Answers

65. $2 - 3i$

66. $-\frac{3}{2} + \frac{5}{2}i$

67. $\frac{17}{25} + \frac{6}{25}i$

68. $\frac{13}{17} + \frac{1}{17}i$

69. $-\frac{7}{25} - \frac{24}{25}i$

70. $\frac{45}{53} + \frac{28}{53}i$

71. False

72. True

73. False

74. True

75. -1

76. i

77. 1

78. $-i$

79. -1

80. 1

81. $-i$

82. i

7.7 exercises

Answers

83. Above and Beyond

84. $\mathbb{N}, \mathbb{Z}, \mathbb{Q}, \mathbb{R}, \mathbb{C}$

Basic Skills | Advanced Skills | Vocational-Technical Applications | Calculator/Computer | **Above and Beyond**

83. Show that a square root of i is $\frac{\sqrt{2}}{2} + \frac{\sqrt{2}}{2}i$. That is, $\left(\frac{\sqrt{2}}{2} + \frac{\sqrt{2}}{2}i\right)^2 = i$.

84. To what standard sets of numbers does 1 belong?

Answers

1. $4i$ **3.** $-8i$ **5.** $i\sqrt{21}$ **7.** $2i\sqrt{3}$ **9.** $-6i\sqrt{3}$ **11.** $-\sqrt{35}$
13. -6 **15.** $-3\sqrt{10}$ **17.** -10 **19.** $8 + 3i$ **21.** $1 + 5i$
23. $2 + 2i$ **25.** $5 - 7i$ **27.** $7 + 11i$ **29.** $3 + 11i$ **31.** $6 - 3i$
33. 0 **35.** $-15 + 9i$ **37.** $28 + 12i$ **39.** $-6 - 8i$ **41.** $-5 + 4i$
43. $13i$ **45.** $23 + 14i$ **47.** $18 + i$ **49.** $21 - 20i$ **51.** $3 + 2i, 13$
53. $2 - 3i, 13$ **55.** $-3 + 2i, 13$ **57.** $-5i, 25$ **59.** $2 - 3i$
61. $-2 - 3i$ **63.** $\frac{6}{29} - \frac{15}{29}i$ **65.** $2 - 3i$ **67.** $\frac{17}{25} + \frac{6}{25}i$
69. $-\frac{7}{25} - \frac{24}{25}i$ **71.** False **73.** False **75.** -1 **77.** 1 **79.** -1
81. $-i$ **83.** Above and Beyond

Definition/Procedure	Example	Reference
Roots and Radicals		Section 7.1
Square Roots Every positive number has two square roots. The positive or principal square root of a number a is denoted $\sqrt{a}$ The negative square root is written as $-\sqrt{a}$	$\sqrt{25} = 5$ 5 is the principal square root of 25 because $5^2 = 25$.	*pp.* 651, 654, 659
Higher Roots Cube roots, fourth roots, and so on are denoted by using an index and a radical. The principal nth root of a is written as 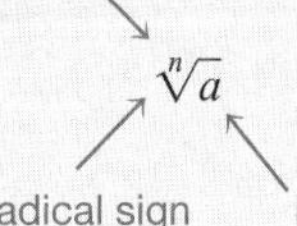	$\sqrt[3]{27} = 3$ $\sqrt[3]{-64} = -4$ $\sqrt[4]{81} = 3$ $\sqrt{4^2} = 4$ $\sqrt{(-5)^2} = 5$ $\sqrt[3]{(-3)^3} = -3$ $\sqrt{m^2} = \|m\|$ $\sqrt[3]{27x^3} = 3x$	
Radicals Containing Variables In general, $\sqrt[n]{x^n} = \begin{cases} \|x\| & \text{if } n \text{ is even} \\ x & \text{if } n \text{ is odd} \end{cases}$		
Simplification of Radical Expressions		Section 7.2
Simplifying radical expressions entails applying two properties for radicals.		*pp.* 665, 666
Product Property $\sqrt[n]{ab} = \sqrt[n]{a} \cdot \sqrt[n]{b}$	$\sqrt{35} = \sqrt{5 \cdot 7} = \sqrt{5} \cdot \sqrt{7}$	
Quotient Property $\sqrt[n]{\frac{a}{b}} = \frac{\sqrt[n]{a}}{\sqrt[n]{b}}, \quad b \neq 0$	$\sqrt{\frac{2}{5}} = \frac{\sqrt{2}}{\sqrt{5}}$	
Simplified Form for Radicals A radical is in *simplified form* if the following three conditions are satisfied. **1.** The radicand has no factor raised to a power greater than or equal to the index. **2.** No fraction appears in the radical. **3.** No radical appears in a denominator. **Note:** Satisfying the third condition may require *rationalizing the denominator.*	$\sqrt{18x^3} = \sqrt{9x^2 \cdot 2x} = \sqrt{9x^2} \cdot \sqrt{2x} = 3x\sqrt{2x}$ $\sqrt{\frac{5}{9}} = \frac{\sqrt{5}}{\sqrt{9}} = \frac{\sqrt{5}}{3}$ $\sqrt{\frac{3}{7x}} = \frac{\sqrt{3}}{\sqrt{7x}} = \frac{\sqrt{3} \cdot \sqrt{7x}}{\sqrt{7x} \cdot \sqrt{7x}} = \frac{\sqrt{21x}}{\sqrt{49x^2}} = \frac{\sqrt{21x}}{7x}$	

Continued

Definition/Procedure	Example	Reference
Operations on Radical Expressions		Section 7.3
Addition and Subtraction Radical expressions may be combined only if they are *similar*, that is, if they have the same radicand with the same index. Similar radicals are combined by applying the distributive property.	$8\sqrt{5} + 3\sqrt{5} = (8 + 3)\sqrt{5}$ $= 11\sqrt{5}$ $2\sqrt{18} - 4\sqrt{2}$ $= 2\sqrt{9 \cdot 2} - 4\sqrt{2}$ $= 2\sqrt{9} \cdot \sqrt{2} - 4\sqrt{2}$ $= 2 \cdot 3\sqrt{2} - 4\sqrt{2}$ $= 6\sqrt{2} - 4\sqrt{2} = (6 - 4)\sqrt{2}$ $= 2\sqrt{2}$	*pp.* 678–679
Multiplication To multiply two radical expressions, we use $\sqrt[n]{a} \cdot \sqrt[n]{b} = \sqrt[n]{ab}$ and simplify the product. If binomial expressions are involved, we use the distributive property or the FOIL method.	$\sqrt{3x} \cdot \sqrt{6x^2} = \sqrt{18x^3}$ $= \sqrt{9x^2 \cdot 2x}$ $= \sqrt{9x^2} \cdot \sqrt{2x}$ $= 3x\sqrt{2x}$ $\sqrt{2}(5 + \sqrt{8}) = \sqrt{2} \cdot 5 + \sqrt{2} \cdot \sqrt{8}$ $= 5\sqrt{2} + 4$ $(3 + \sqrt{2})(5 - \sqrt{2})$ $= 15 - 3\sqrt{2} + 5\sqrt{2} - 2$ $= 13 + 2\sqrt{2}$	*p.* 681
Division To divide two radical expressions, rationalize the denominator by multiplying the numerator and denominator by the appropriate radical. If the divisor (the denominator) is a binomial, multiply the numerator and denominator by the conjugate of the denominator.	$\frac{5}{\sqrt{8}} = \frac{5 \cdot \sqrt{2}}{\sqrt{8} \cdot \sqrt{2}} = \frac{5\sqrt{2}}{\sqrt{16}}$ $= \frac{5\sqrt{2}}{4}$ **Note:** $3 + \sqrt{5}$ is the conjugate of $3 - \sqrt{5}$. $\frac{2}{3 - \sqrt{5}} = \frac{2(3 + \sqrt{5})}{(3 - \sqrt{5})(3 + \sqrt{5})}$ $= \frac{2(3 + \sqrt{5})}{4}$ $= \frac{3 + \sqrt{5}}{2}$	*p.* 684
Solving Radical Equations		Section 7.4
Power Property of Equality If $a = b$, then $a^n = b^n$.	If $\sqrt{x + 1} = 5$, then $(\sqrt{x + 1})^2 = 5^2$ $x + 1 = 25$ $x = 24$	*p.* 693

Definition/Procedure	Example	Reference
If an equation involves two radicals, rewrite the equation so that there is one radical on each side and then use the power property to solve the equation.	Given $\sqrt{x} + \sqrt{x+7} = 7$, $\sqrt{x} = 7 - \sqrt{x+7}$ $x = 49 - 14\sqrt{x+7} + (x+7)$ $x = 56 + x - 14\sqrt{x+7}$ $-56 = -14\sqrt{x+7}$ $4 = \sqrt{x+7}$ $16 = x + 7$ $x = 9$	pp. 696–698
Geometric and Other Applications		Section 7.5
Pythagorean Theorem 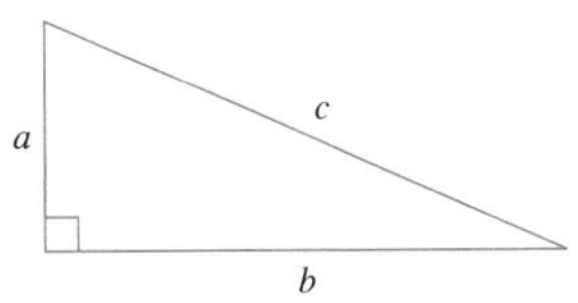 $a^2 + b^2 = c^2$ In a right triangle, the sum of the squares of the two sides is equal to the square of the hypotenuse.	Given triangle 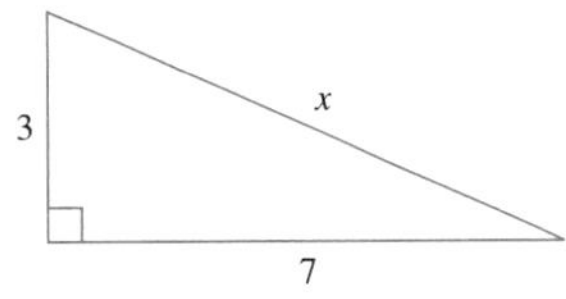 $x^2 = 7^2 + 3^2$ $x^2 = 49 + 9$ $x = \sqrt{58}$ ≈ 7.6	p. 706
Rational Exponents		Section 7.6
Rational exponents are an alternate way of indicating roots. We use the following definition. If a is any real number and n is a positive integer ($n > 1$), $a^{1/n} = \sqrt[n]{a}$ We restrict a so that a is nonnegative when n is even. We also define the following. For any real number a and positive integers m and n, with $n > 1$, $a^{m/n} = (\sqrt[n]{a})^m = \sqrt[n]{a^m}$	$36^{1/2} = \sqrt{36} = 6$ $-27^{1/3} = -\sqrt[3]{27} = -3$ $243^{1/5} = \sqrt[5]{243} = 3$ $25^{-1/2} = \frac{1}{\sqrt{25}} = \frac{1}{5}$ $27^{2/3} = (\sqrt[3]{27})^2$ $= 3^2 = 9$ $(a^4b^8)^{3/4} = \sqrt[4]{(a^4b^8)^3}$ $= \sqrt[4]{a^{12}b^{24}} = a^3b^6$	pp. 718–719
Properties of Exponents The following five properties for exponents continue to hold for rational exponents.		p. 721
Product Rule $a^m \cdot a^n = a^{m+n}$	$x^{1/2} \cdot x^{1/3} = x^{1/2+1/3} = x^{5/6}$	
Quotient Rule $\frac{a^m}{a^n} = a^{m-n}$	$\frac{x^{3/2}}{x^{1/2}} = x^{3/2-1/2} = x^{2/2} = x$	

Continued

 The Streeter/Hutchison Series in Mathematics Intermediate Algebra

Definition/Procedure	Example	Reference
Power Rule $(a^m)^n = a^{m \cdot n}$	$(x^{1/3})^5 = x^{1/3 \cdot 5} = x^{5/3}$	p. 721
Product to a Power Rule $(ab)^m = a^m b^m$	$(2xy)^{1/2} = 2^{1/2}x^{1/2}y^{1/2}$	
Quotient to a Power Rule $\left(\frac{a}{b}\right)^m = \frac{a^m}{b^m}$	$\left(\frac{x^{1/3}}{3}\right)^2 = \frac{(x^{1/3})^2}{3^2} = \frac{x^{2/3}}{9}$	
Complex Numbers		Section 7.7
The number i is defined as $i = \sqrt{-1}$ such that $i^2 = -1$	$\sqrt{-16} = 4i$ $\sqrt{-8} = 2i\sqrt{2}$	p. 731
A **complex number** is any number that can be written in the form $a + bi$ in which a and b are real numbers and $i = \sqrt{-1}$		p. 732
Addition and Subtraction		
For the complex numbers $a + bi$ and $c + di$, $(a + bi) + (c + di) = (a + c) + (b + d)i$ and $(a + bi) - (c + di) = (a - c) + (b - d)i$	$(2 + 3i) + (-3 - 5i)$ $= (2 - 3) + (3 - 5)i$ $= -1 - 2i$ $(5 - 2i) - (3 - 4i)$ $= (5 - 3) + [-2 - (-4)]i$ $= 2 + 2i$	p. 733
Multiplication For the complex numbers $a + bi$ and $c + di$, $(a + bi)(c + di) = (ac - bd) + (ad + bc)i$ **Note:** It is generally easier to use the FOIL multiplication pattern and the definition of i, rather than to apply this formula.	$(2 + 5i)(3 - 4i)$ $= 6 - 8i + 15i - 20i^2$ $= 6 + 7i - 20(-1)$ $= 26 + 7i$	p. 734
Division		
To divide two complex numbers, we multiply the numerator and denominator by the complex conjugate of the denominator and write the result in standard form.	$\frac{3 + 2i}{3 - 2i} = \frac{(3 + 2i)(3 + 2i)}{(3 - 2i)(3 + 2i)}$ $= \frac{9 + 6i + 6i + 4i^2}{9 - 4i^2}$ $= \frac{9 + 12i + 4(-1)}{9 - 4(-1)}$ $= \frac{5 + 12i}{13} = \frac{5}{13} + \frac{12}{13}i$	p. 735

This summary exercise set is provided to give you practice with each of the objectives of this chapter. Each exercise is keyed to the appropriate chapter section. When you are finished, you can check your answers to the odd-numbered exercises against those presented in the back of the text. If you have difficulty with any of these questions, go back and reread the examples from that section. The answers to the even-numbered exercises appear in the *Instructor's Solutions Manual.* Your instructor will give you guidelines on how best to use these exercises in your instructional setting.

7.1 *Evaluate each of the roots over the set of real numbers.*

1. $\sqrt{121}$ 11

2. $-\sqrt{64}$ −8

3. $\sqrt{-81}$ Not a real number

4. $\sqrt[3]{64}$ 4

5. $\sqrt[3]{-64}$ −4

6. $\sqrt[4]{81}$ 3

7. $\sqrt{\frac{9}{16}}$ $\frac{3}{4}$

8. $\sqrt[3]{-\frac{8}{27}}$ $-\frac{2}{3}$

9. $\sqrt{8^2}$ 8

Simplify each of the expressions. Assume that all variables represent positive real numbers for all subsequent exercises in this exercise set.

10. $\sqrt{4x^2}$ $2x$

11. $\sqrt{a^4}$ a^2

12. $\sqrt{36y^2}$ $6y$

13. $\sqrt{49w^4z^6}$ $7w^2z^3$

14. $\sqrt[3]{x^9}$ x^3

15. $\sqrt[3]{-27b^6}$ $-3b^2$

16. $\sqrt[3]{8r^3s^9}$ $2rs^3$

17. $\sqrt[4]{16x^4y^8}$ $2xy^2$

18. $\sqrt[5]{32p^5q^{15}}$ $2pq^3$

7.2 *Use the product property to write each of the expressions in simplified form.*

19. $\sqrt{45}$ $3\sqrt{5}$

20. $-\sqrt{75}$ $-5\sqrt{3}$

21. $\sqrt{60x^2}$ $2x\sqrt{15}$

22. $\sqrt{108a^3}$ $6a\sqrt{3a}$

23. $\sqrt[3]{32}$ $2\sqrt[3]{4}$

24. $\sqrt[3]{-80w^4z^3}$ $-2wz\sqrt[3]{10w}$

Use the quotient property to write each of the expressions in simplified form.

25. $\sqrt{\frac{9}{16}}$ $\frac{3}{4}$

26. $\sqrt{\frac{7}{36}}$ $\frac{\sqrt{7}}{6}$

27. $\sqrt{\frac{y^4}{49}}$ $\frac{y^2}{7}$

28. $\sqrt{\frac{2x}{9}}$ $\frac{\sqrt{2x}}{3}$

29. $\sqrt{\frac{5}{16x^2}}$ $\frac{\sqrt{5}}{4x}$

30. $\sqrt[3]{\frac{5a^2}{27}}$ $\frac{\sqrt[3]{5a^2}}{3}$

7.3 *Simplify each of the expressions if necessary. Then add or subtract as indicated.*

31. $7\sqrt{10} + 4\sqrt{10}$ $11\sqrt{10}$

32. $5\sqrt{3x} - 2\sqrt{3x}$ $3\sqrt{3x}$

33. $7\sqrt[3]{2x} + 3\sqrt[3]{2x}$ $10\sqrt[3]{2x}$

34. $8\sqrt{10} - 3\sqrt{10} + 2\sqrt{10}$ $7\sqrt{10}$

35. $\sqrt{72} + \sqrt{50}$ $11\sqrt{2}$

36. $\sqrt{54} - \sqrt{24}$ $\sqrt{6}$

37. $9\sqrt{7} - 2\sqrt{63}$ $3\sqrt{7}$

38. $\sqrt{20} - \sqrt{45} + 2\sqrt{125}$ $9\sqrt{5}$

39. $2\sqrt[3]{16} + 3\sqrt[3]{54}$ $13\sqrt[3]{2}$

40. $\sqrt{27w^3} - w\sqrt{12w}$ $w\sqrt{3w}$

41. $\sqrt[3]{128a^5} + 6a\sqrt[3]{2a^2}$ $10a\sqrt[3]{2a^2}$

42. $\sqrt{20} + \dfrac{3}{\sqrt{5}}$ $\dfrac{13}{5}\sqrt{5}$ or $\dfrac{13\sqrt{5}}{5}$

43. $\sqrt{72x} - \sqrt{\dfrac{x}{2}}$ $\dfrac{11}{2}\sqrt{2x}$ or $\dfrac{11\sqrt{2x}}{2}$

44. $\sqrt[3]{81a^4} - a\sqrt[3]{\dfrac{a}{9}}$ $\dfrac{8a\sqrt[3]{3a}}{3}$

45. $\dfrac{\sqrt{15}}{3} - \dfrac{1}{\sqrt{15}}$ $\dfrac{4}{15}\sqrt{15}$ or $\dfrac{4\sqrt{15}}{15}$

Multiply and simplify each of the expressions.

46. $\sqrt{3x} \cdot \sqrt{7y}$ $\sqrt{21xy}$

47. $\sqrt{6x^2} \cdot \sqrt{18}$ $6x\sqrt{3}$

48. $\sqrt[3]{4a^2b} \cdot \sqrt[3]{ab^2}$ $ab\sqrt[3]{4}$

49. $\sqrt{5}(\sqrt{3} + 2)$ $\sqrt{15} + 2\sqrt{5}$

50. $\sqrt{6}(\sqrt{8} - \sqrt{2})$ $2\sqrt{3}$

51. $\sqrt{a}(\sqrt{5a} + \sqrt{125a})$ $6a\sqrt{5}$

52. $(\sqrt{3} + 5)(\sqrt{3} - 7)$ $-32 - 2\sqrt{3}$

53. $(\sqrt{7} - \sqrt{2})(\sqrt{7} + \sqrt{3})$ $7 + \sqrt{21} - \sqrt{14} - \sqrt{6}$

54. $(\sqrt{5} - 2)(\sqrt{5} + 2)$ 1

55. $(\sqrt{7} - \sqrt{3})(\sqrt{7} + \sqrt{3})$ 4

56. $(2 + \sqrt{3})^2$ $7 + 4\sqrt{3}$

57. $(\sqrt{5} - \sqrt{2})^2$ $7 - 2\sqrt{10}$

Rationalize the denominator, and write each of the expressions in simplified form.

58. $\sqrt{\dfrac{3}{7}}$ $\dfrac{\sqrt{21}}{7}$

59. $\dfrac{\sqrt{12}}{\sqrt{x}}$ $\dfrac{2\sqrt{3x}}{x}$

60. $\dfrac{\sqrt{10a}}{\sqrt{5b}}$ $\dfrac{\sqrt{2ab}}{b}$

61. $\sqrt[3]{\dfrac{3}{a^2}}$ $\dfrac{\sqrt[3]{3a}}{a}$

62. $\dfrac{2}{\sqrt[3]{3x}}$ $\dfrac{2\sqrt[3]{9x^2}}{3x}$

63. $\dfrac{\sqrt[3]{x^2}}{\sqrt[3]{y^5}}$ $\dfrac{\sqrt[3]{x^2y}}{y^2}$

Divide and simplify each of the expressions.

64. $\dfrac{1}{3 + \sqrt{2}}$ $\dfrac{3 - \sqrt{2}}{7}$

65. $\dfrac{11}{5 - \sqrt{3}}$ $\dfrac{5 + \sqrt{3}}{2}$

66. $\dfrac{\sqrt{5} - 2}{\sqrt{5} + 2}$ $9 - 4\sqrt{5}$

67. $\dfrac{\sqrt{x} - 3}{\sqrt{x} + 3}$ $\dfrac{x - 6\sqrt{x} + 9}{x - 9}$

7.4 *Solve each of the equations. Be sure to check your solutions.*

68. $\sqrt{3x - 2} + 2 = 5$ $\frac{11}{3}$

69. $\sqrt{x - 5} = 4$ 21

70. $\sqrt{2x - 1} + x = 8$ 5

71. $\sqrt{y + 7} = y - 5$ 9

72. $\sqrt[3]{x^2 + 2} - 3 = 0$ ± 5

73. $\sqrt[3]{5x + 2} = 3$ 5

74. $\sqrt{4x + 5} - \sqrt{x - 1} = 3$ 1, 5

75. $\sqrt{z + 7} = 1 + \sqrt{z}$ 9

Solve each of the equations for the indicated variable.

76. $t = 2\pi\sqrt{\frac{l}{10}}$ for l $l = \frac{5t^2}{2\pi^2}$

77. $r = \sqrt{x^2 + y^2}$ for x $x = \pm\sqrt{r^2 - y^2}$

7.5 *Use the Pythagorean theorem to find each missing length. Write answers to the nearest tenth.*

78. 13.5 cm

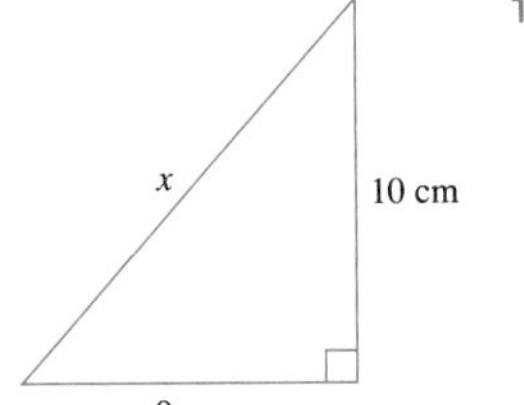

79. 11.5 in.

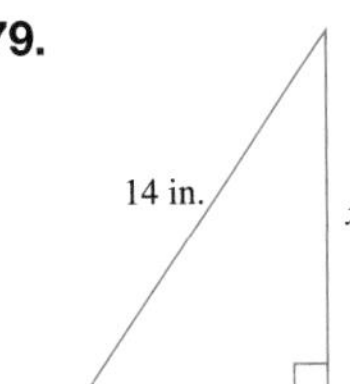

80. Find the width of a rectangle whose diagonal is 12 ft and whose length is 6 ft. 10.4 ft

81. If a window is 3 ft on its shorter side, how high should it be, to the nearest tenth of a foot, to be a golden rectangle? 4.9 ft

82. The base of a ladder that is 16 ft long is placed 4 ft from a wall of a building. How high up the wall is the top of the ladder? 15.5 ft

83. How long must a ladder be to reach 8 m up the side of a building when the base of the ladder is 2 m from the building? 8.2 m

7.6 *Evaluate each of the expressions.*

84. $49^{1/2}$ 7

85. $-100^{1/2}$ -10

86. $(-27)^{1/3}$ -3

87. $16^{1/4}$ 2

88. $64^{2/3}$ 16

89. $25^{3/2}$ 125

90. $\left(\frac{4}{9}\right)^{3/2}$ $\frac{8}{27}$

91. $49^{-1/2}$ $\frac{1}{7}$

92. $81^{-3/4}$ $\frac{1}{27}$

Use the properties of exponents to simplify each of the expressions.

93. $x^{3/2} \cdot x^{5/2}$ x^4

94. $b^{2/3} \cdot b^{3/2}$ $b^{13/6}$

95. $\frac{r^{8/5}}{r^{3/5}}$ r

96. $\frac{a^{5/4}}{a^{1/2}}$ $a^{3/4}$

97. $(x^{3/5})^{2/3}$ $x^{2/5}$

98. $(y^{-4/3})^6$ $\frac{1}{y^8}$

99. $(x^{4/5}y^{3/2})^{10}$ x^8y^{15}

100. $(16x^{1/3} \cdot y^{2/3})^{3/4}$ $8x^{1/4}y^{1/2}$

101. $\left(\frac{x^{-2}y^{-1/6}}{x^{-4}y}\right)^3$ $\frac{x^6}{y^{7/2}}$

102. $\left(\frac{27y^3z^{-6}}{x^{-3}}\right)^{1/3}$ $\frac{3xy}{z^2}$

Write each of the expressions in radical form.

103. $x^{3/4}$ $\sqrt[4]{x^3}$

104. $(w^2z)^{2/5}$ $\sqrt[5]{w^4z^2}$

105. $3a^{2/3}$ $3\sqrt[3]{a^2}$

106. $(3a)^{2/3}$ $\sqrt[3]{9a^2}$

Write each of the expressions using rational exponents, and simplify when necessary.

107. $\sqrt[5]{7x}$ $(7x)^{1/5}$

108. $\sqrt{16w^4}$ $4w^2$

109. $\sqrt[3]{27p^3q^9}$ $3pq^3$

110. $\sqrt[4]{16a^8b^{16}}$ $2a^2b^4$

7.7 *Write each of the roots as a multiple of i. Simplify your result.*

111. $\sqrt{-49}$ $7i$

112. $\sqrt{-13}$ $i\sqrt{13}$

113. $-\sqrt{-60}$ $-2i\sqrt{15}$

Perform the indicated operations.

114. $(2 + 3i) + (3 - 5i)$ $5 - 2i$

115. $(7 - 3i) + (-3 - 2i)$ $4 - 5i$

116. $(5 - 3i) - (2 + 5i)$ $3 - 8i$

117. $(-4 + 2i) - (-1 - 3i)$ $-3 + 5i$

Find each of the products.

118. $4i(7 - 2i)$ $8 + 28i$

119. $(5 - 2i)(3 + 4i)$ $23 + 14i$

120. $(3 - 4i)^2$ $-7 - 24i$

121. $(2 - 3i)(2 + 3i)$ 13

Find each of the quotients, and write your answer in standard form.

122. $\frac{5 - 15i}{5i}$ $-3 - i$

123. $\frac{10}{3 - 4i}$ $\frac{6}{5} + \frac{8}{5}i$

124. $\frac{3 - 2i}{3 + 2i}$ $\frac{5}{13} - \frac{12}{13}i$

125. $\frac{5 + 10i}{2 + i}$ $4 + 3i$

self-test 7

Name ______________________

Section __________ Date __________

The purpose of this chapter test is to help you check your progress so that you can find sections and concepts that you need to review before the next exam. Allow yourself about an hour to take this test. At the end of that hour, check your answers against those given in the back of this text. If you missed any, note the section reference that accompanies the answer. Go back to that section and reread the examples until you have mastered that particular concept.

7.1

Simplify each expression. Assume that all variables represent positive real numbers in all subsequent problems.

1. $\sqrt{49a^4}$

2. $\sqrt[3]{-27w^6z^9}$

7.2

Use the product or quotient properties to write each expression in simplified form.

3. $\sqrt[3]{9p^7q^5}$

4. $\dfrac{7x}{\sqrt{64y^2}}$

Rationalize the denominator, and write each expression in simplified form.

5. $\sqrt{\dfrac{5x}{8y}}$

6. $\dfrac{3}{\sqrt[3]{9x}}$

7.3

Simplify each expression if necessary. Then add or subtract as indicated.

7. $\sqrt{3x^3} + x\sqrt{75x} - \sqrt{27x^3}$

8. $\sqrt[3]{54m^4} + m\sqrt[3]{16m}$

Multiply or divide as indicated. Then simplify your result.

9. $\sqrt{6x}(\sqrt{18x} - \sqrt{2x})$

10. $\dfrac{\sqrt{6} - \sqrt{3}}{\sqrt{6} + \sqrt{3}}$

7.4

Solve the following equations. Be sure to check your solutions.

11. $\sqrt{x-7} - 2 = 0$

12. $\sqrt{3w+4} + w = 8$

7.5

13. Use the Pythagorean theorem to find the length x in the given triangle. Write your answer to the nearest tenth.

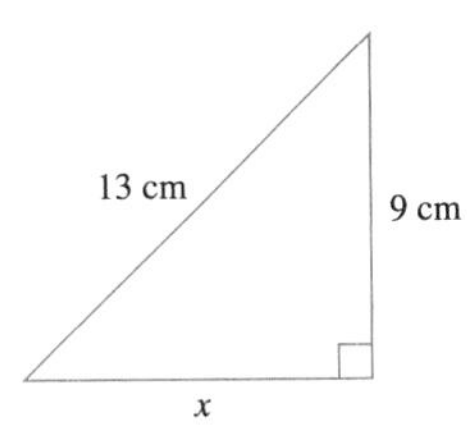

Answers

1. $7a^2$
2. $-3w^2z^3$
3. $p^2q\sqrt[3]{9pq^2}$
4. $\dfrac{7x}{8y}$
5. $\dfrac{\sqrt{10xy}}{4y}$
6. $\dfrac{\sqrt[3]{3x^2}}{x}$
7. $3x\sqrt{3x}$
8. $5m\sqrt[3]{2m}$
9. $4x\sqrt{3}$
10. $3 - 2\sqrt{2}$
11. 11
12. 4
13. 9.4 cm

Answers

14. ≈ 21.9 ft

15. 3.7 cm

16. 9.0 cm

17. 69.3 cm

18. $64x^6$

19. $\frac{9m}{n^4}$

20. $\frac{8s^3}{r}$

21. $a^2b\sqrt[5]{a^4b}$

22. $5p^3q^2$

23. $3 + 10i$

24. $-14 + 22i$

25. $5 - 5i$

14. Find the width of a rectangle whose diagonal is 25 ft and whose length is 12 ft.

15. If the longer side of a rectangle is 6 cm, find the width (to the nearest tenth of a centimeter) to make the rectangle a golden rectangle.

16. What is the length of a diagonal in a rectangle with sides 4.5 cm and 7.8 cm? Give your answer to the nearest tenth of a centimeter.

17. In a right triangle, one leg has a length of 40 cm and the hypotenuse is 80 cm. Find the length of the other leg to the nearest tenth of a centimeter.

7.6

Use the properties of exponents to simplify each expression.

18. $(16x^4)^{3/2}$

19. $(27m^{3/2}n^{-6})^{2/3}$

20. $\left(\dfrac{16r^{-1/3}s^{5/3}}{rs^{-7/3}}\right)^{3/4}$

Write the expression in radical form and simplify.

21. $(a^7b^3)^{2/5}$

Write the expression, using rational exponents. Then simplify.

22. $\sqrt[3]{125p^9q^6}$

7.7

Perform the indicated operations.

23. $(-2 + 3i) - (-5 - 7i)$

24. $(5 - 3i)(-4 + 2i)$

25. $\dfrac{10 - 20i}{3 - i}$

Activity 7 :: The Swing of a Pendulum

Each chapter in this text concludes with a chapter activity such as this one. These activities provide you with the opportunity to apply the math you studied in that chapter to a relevant topic. Your instructor will determine how best to use these activities in your instructional setting. You may find yourself working in class or outside of class; you may find yourself working alone or in small groups; you may even be asked to perform research in a library or on the Internet.

The action of a pendulum seems simple. Scientists have studied the characteristics of a swinging pendulum and found them to be quite useful. In 1851 in Paris, Jean Foucault (pronounced "foo-koh") used a pendulum to clearly demonstrate the rotation of Earth about its own axis.

A pendulum can be as simple as a string or cord with a weight fastened to one end. The other end is fixed, and the weight is allowed to swing. We define the **period** of a pendulum to be the amount of time required for the pendulum to make one complete swing (back and forth). The question we will pose is: How does the *period* of a pendulum relate to the *length* of the pendulum?

For this activity, you will need a piece of string that is approximately 1m long. Fasten a weight (such as a small hexagonal nut) to one end, and then place clear marks on the string every 10 cm up to 70 cm, measured from the center of the weight.

1. Working with one or two partners, hold the string at the mark that is 10 cm from the weight. Pull the weight to the side with your other hand and let it swing freely. To estimate the period, let the weight swing through 30 periods, record the time in the given table, and then divide by 30. Round your result to the nearest hundredth of a second and record it. (*Note:* If you are unable to perform the experiment and collect your own data, you can use the sample data collected in this manner and presented at the end of this activity.)

   Repeat the described procedure for each length indicated in the given table.

Length of string, cm	10	20	30	40	50	60	70
Time for 30 periods, sec							
Time for 1 period, sec							

2. Let L represent the length of the pendulum and T represent the time period that results from swinging that pendulum. Fill out the table:

L	10	20	30	40	50	60	70
T							

3. Which variable, L or T, is viewed here as the independent variable?

4. On graph paper, draw horizontal and vertical axes, but plan to graph the data points in the first quadrant only. Explain why this is so.

5. With the independent variable marked on the horizontal axis, scale the axes appropriately, keeping an eye on your data.

6. Plot your data points. Should you connect them with a smooth curve?
7. What period T would correspond to a string length of 0? Include this point on your graph.
8. Use your graph to predict the period for a string length of 80 cm.
9. Verify your prediction by measuring the period when the string is held at 80 cm (as described in step 1). How close did your experimental estimate come to the prediction made in step 8?

You have created a graph showing T as a function of L. The shape of the graph should be familiar to you now. In Chapter 7, we studied square root functions, and we have seen that the shape of your pendulum graph fits that of a square root function.

Sample Data

Length of string, cm	10	20	30	40	50	60	70
Time for 30 periods, sec	19	27	33	38	42	46	49

cumulative review chapters 1-7

Name ____________

Section ______ Date ______

The following exercises are presented to help you review concepts from earlier chapters. This is meant as review material and not as a comprehensive exam. The answers are presented in the back of the text. Beside each answer is a section reference for the concept. If you have difficulty with any of these exercises, be certain to at least read through the summary related to that section.

2.1

1. Solve the equation $7x - 6(x - 1) = 2(5 + x) + 11$.

3.2

2. If $f(x) = 3x^6 - 4x^3 + 9x^2 - 11$, find $f(-1)$.

3.5

3. Find the equation of the line that has a y-intercept of $(0, -6)$ and is parallel to the line $6x - 4y = 18$.

2.5

4. Solve the equation $|3x - 5| = 4$.

Simplify each of the following polynomial functions.

5.1

5. $f(x) = 5x^2 - 8x + 11 - (-3x^2 - 2x + 8) - (-2x^2 - 4x + 3)$

5.2

6. $f(x) = (5x + 3)(2x - 9)$

Factor each of the following completely.

5.7

7. $2x^3 + x^2 - 3x$

5.5

8. $9x^4 - 36y^4$

5.4

9. $4x^2 + 8xy - 5x - 10y$

Simplify each of the following rational expressions.

6.1

10. $\dfrac{2x^2 + 13x + 15}{6x^2 + 7x - 3}$

6.3

11. $\dfrac{3}{x - 5} - \dfrac{2}{x - 1}$

6.2

12. $\dfrac{a^2 - 4a}{a^2 - 6a + 8} \cdot \dfrac{a^2 - 4}{2a^2}$

6.3

13. $\dfrac{a^2 - 9}{a^2 - a - 12} - \dfrac{a^2 - a - 6}{a^2 - 2a - 8}$

7.3

Simplify each of the following radical expressions. Assume that all variables represent positive real numbers.

14. $\sqrt{3x^3y}\,\sqrt{4x^5y^6}$

15. $(\sqrt{3} - 5)(\sqrt{2} + 3)$

16. $\sqrt{50x^3} - x\sqrt{32x}$

Answers

1. $x = -15$
2. 5
3. $3x - 2y = 12$
4. $x = 3$ or $x = \frac{1}{3}$
5. $f(x) = 10x^2 - 2x$
6. $f(x) = 10x^2 - 39x - 27$
7. $x(x - 1)(2x + 3)$
8. $9(x^2 + 2y^2)(x^2 - 2y^2)$
9. $(x + 2y)(4x - 5)$
10. $\dfrac{x + 5}{3x - 1}$
11. $\dfrac{x + 7}{(x - 5)(x - 1)}$
12. $\dfrac{a + 2}{2a}$
13. 0
14. $2x^4y^3\sqrt{3y}$
15. $\sqrt{6} - 5\sqrt{2} + 3\sqrt{3} - 15$
16. $x\sqrt{2x}$

Answers

17. $\frac{c^{12}}{a^6b^4}$

18. See exercise

19. $15 + 18i$

20. $23 - 14i$

21. $x = 11$

22. $(9, 1)$

23. $x \le 17$

24. $-1 \le x \le 9$

25. 16

7.6

17. Use the properties of exponents to simplify the expression $\left(\frac{a^{-2}b^{-1/4}c^{3}}{a^{-1/2}b^{3/4}c^{0}}\right)^4$.

3.3

18. Graph the equation $2x - 3y = 12$.

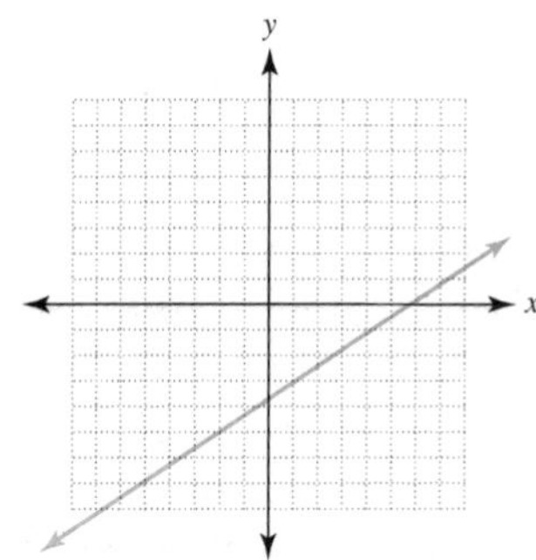

7.7

Find each of the following products.

19. $3i(6 - 5i)$

20. $(5 + 2i)(3 - 4i)$

7.4

21. Solve the equation $\sqrt{x + 14} - x + 6 = 0$.

4.1

22. Solve the system

$$2x - 5y = 13$$
$$x + 3y = 12$$

Solve the following inequalities.

2.4

23. $3x - 5 \le 4x - 2(x - 6)$

2.5

24. $|x - 4| \le 5$

7.5

25. The difference between an integer and its square root is 12. Find the integer.

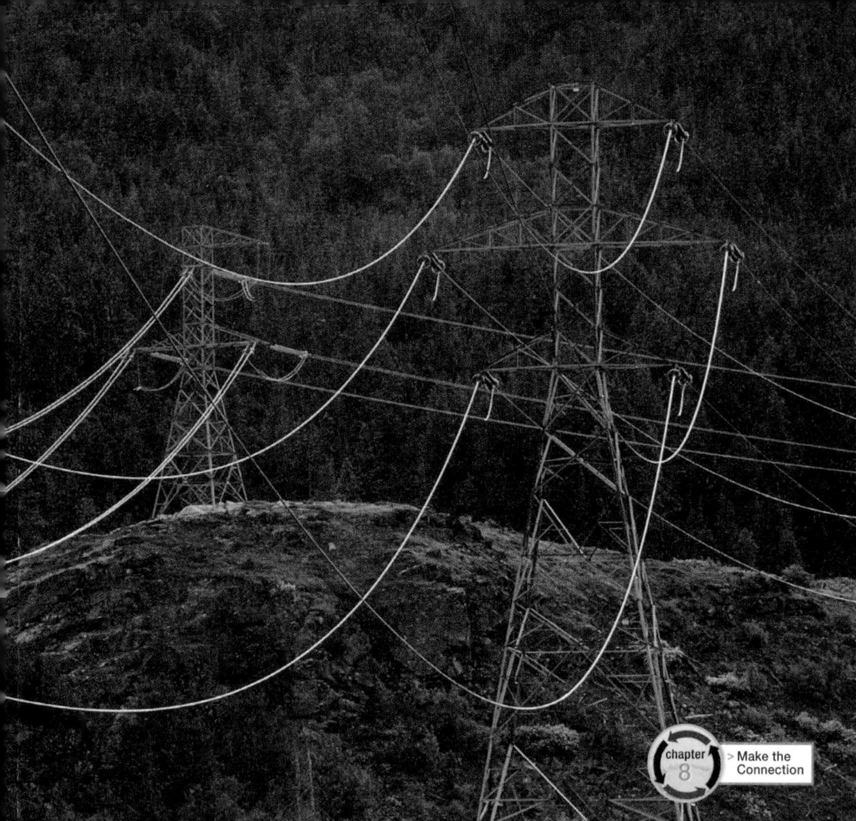

CHAPTER

8

Quadratic Equations and Inequalities

INTRODUCTION

Running power lines from a power plant, wind farm, or hydroelectric plant to a city is a very costly enterprise. Land must be cleared, towers built, and conducting wires strung from tower to tower across miles of countryside. Typical construction designs run from about 300- to 1,200-ft spans, with towers about 75 to 200 ft high. Of course, if a lot of towers are needed, and many of them must be tall, the construction costs skyrocket.

Power line construction carries a unique set of problems. Towers must be built tall enough and close together enough to keep the conducting lines well above the ground. The sag of these wires (how much they droop from the towers) is a function of the weight of the conductor, the span length, and the tension in the wires. The amount of this sag, measured in feet, is approximated by the following formula:

$$\text{Sag} = \frac{wS^2}{8T}$$

in which w = weight of wires in pounds per foot

S = span length in feet

T = tension in wires measured in pounds

CHAPTER 8 OUTLINE

If the weight of the conducting wires is 2,074 lb per 1,000 ft, and the tension on the wires is 5,000 lb, the relationship between the sag and the span is given by the following equation:

$$\text{Sag} = \frac{2.074S^2}{8(5,000)}$$

The following graph shows how the sag increases as the distance between the towers increases.

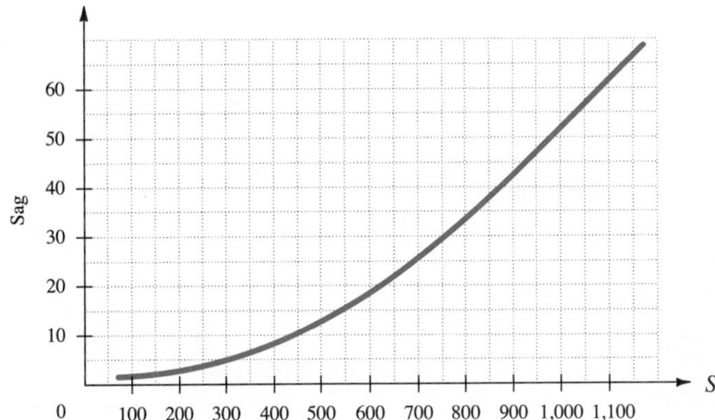

There would be a different graph for every combination of wire weight and tension. This graph represents a wire weight of 2.074 lb/ft and a 5,000-lb tension on the conductor.

In this graph, when the towers are 600 ft apart, the conducting wires will sag 18.7 ft; if the towers are 1,000 ft apart, the wires will sag 51.8 ft. Which will be the best for a particular area? The building planners must know what kind of clearance is needed over the terrain to decide which costs less: very tall towers spaced far apart or shorter towers placed closer together.

The actual curve of the power lines is called a **catenary curve.** The curve that we use to approximate the sag is a **parabola,** one of the conic sections we study in this chapter. At the end of the chapter, you will find an in-depth activity involving another relationship defined by a quadratic-trajectory and height.

pretest 8

Name ____________________

Section __________ Date __________

This pretest will provide a preview of the types of exercises you will encounter in each section of this chapter. The answers for these exercises can be found in the back of the text. If you are working on your own, or ahead of the class, this pretest can help you identify the sections in which you should focus more of your time.

8.1 **1.** Find the zeros of the function $f(x) = 3x^2 + 7x - 6$.

2. Find the coordinates of the vertex of $f(x) = x^2 + 4x - 12$.

3. Graph $f(x) = x^2 - x - 6$.

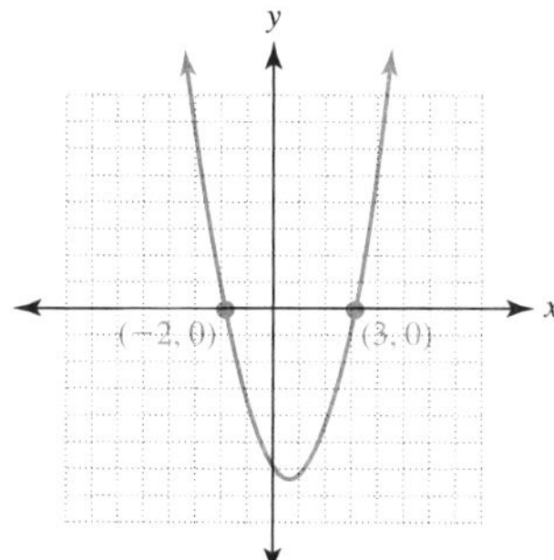

8.2 **4.** Solve $3x^2 - 21 = 0$ using the square root method.

5. Solve $x^2 + 3x - 10 = 0$ by completing the square.

6. The length of a rectangle is 2 cm less than 3 times its width. If the area of the rectangle is 96 cm^2, what are the dimensions of the rectangle.

7. If a ball is thrown upward from the ground, the equation to find the height, h, of such a ball thrown with an initial velocity of 64 ft/sec is $h(t) = 64t - 16t^2$. Find the time it takes the ball to reach a height of 48 ft.

8.3 **8.** Solve $x^2 - 4x + 2 = 0$ using the quadratic formula.

9. One leg of a right triangle is twice the length of the other. The hypotenuse is 6 m long. Find the length of each leg.

8.4 Solve by factoring directly or by substitution.

10. $x^4 - 6x^2 + 8 = 0$

11. $y - 9\sqrt{y} + 18 = 0$

8.5 Solve the inequalities and graph the solution.

12. $2x^2 + 6x - 20 \le 0$

−5 0 2

$-5 \le x \le 2$

13. $\dfrac{x+1}{x-1} > 0$

−1 0 1

$x < -1$ or $x > 1$

Answers

1. $\frac{2}{3}, -3$
2. (−2, −16)
3. See exercise
4. $\pm\sqrt{7}$
5. −5, 2
6. Width: 6 cm, length: 16 cm
7. 1 sec, 3 sec
8. $2 \pm \sqrt{2}$
9. $\sqrt{7.2} \approx 2.7$ m, $2\sqrt{7.2} \approx 5.4$ m
10. $\pm\sqrt{2}, \pm 2$
11. 9, 36
12. See exercise
13. See exercise

8.1 Graphs of Quadratic Functions

< 8.1 Objectives >

1 > Find the zeros of a factorable quadratic function

2 > Find the vertex for the graph of a factorable quadratic function

3 > Sketch the graph of a factorable quadratic function

If you know how fast a ball is thrown (its **initial velocity**) straight up into the air, you can find its maximum height and predict the number of seconds it will be in the air. If you know how long it was in the air, you can find both its maximum height and its initial velocity.

To analyze such a problem, we use a quadratic function.

Definition

Quadratic Function

A function that can be written in the form

$f(x) = ax^2 + bx + c,$ for real numbers a, b, and c, $a \neq 0$

is called a **quadratic function.**

> **NOTE**
>
> The coefficient -16 accounts for the gravitational pull of Earth.

The height of a ball (in feet) thrown up from the ground is determined by the quadratic function

$$h(x) = -16x^2 + v_o x$$

in which v_o represents the initial velocity and x represents the number of seconds that have passed since the ball was thrown.

The function

$$h(x) = -16x^2 + 64x$$

gives us the height, after x seconds, of a ball thrown with an initial velocity of 64 ft/sec.

Example 1 Finding the Zeros of a Quadratic Function

< Objective 1 >

RECALL

The zeros of a function are those points where the y-coordinate is zero. That is, the x-intercepts of the graph.

Find the zeros for the function

$$h(x) = -16x^2 + 64x$$

The zeros of the function are the values of x for which $h(x) = 0$. We wish to solve the equation

$$0 = -16x^2 + 64x$$

or

$$16x^2 - 64x = 0$$

In Section 5.9, we solved quadratic equations by the method of factoring. Using that technique, we find

$$16x(x - 4) = 0$$

The zero-product principle tells us that there are two solutions, $x = 0$ or $x = 4$. Applying this answer to our ball-throwing example tells us that the ball is at ground level twice, at 0 seconds (just before the ball is thrown) and after 4 seconds (when the ball lands back on the ground).

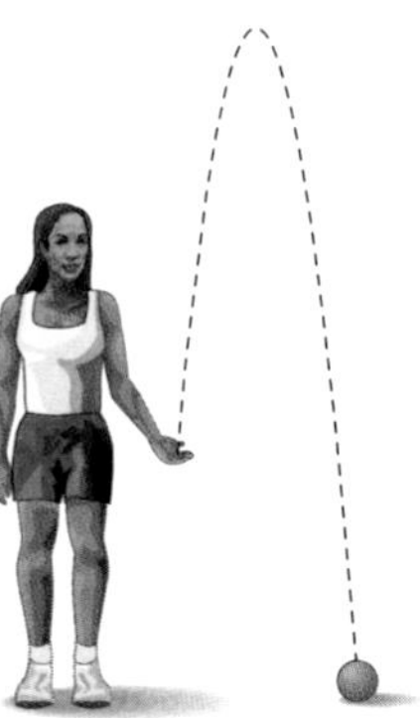

NOTE

This should not be confused with a "sketch" of the flight of the ball!

Check Yourself 1

Find the zeros for the function

$$h(x) = -16x^2 + 48x$$

In Example 2, we sketch the graph of the function $h(x)$.

Example 2 Graphing a Quadratic Function

Sketch the graph of the function

$$h(x) = -16x^2 + 64x$$

From the given table, we can plot five points.

x	$h(x)$
0	0
1	48
2	64
3	48
4	0

We will sketch our graph using only the first quadrant. We plot the five points, and then connect them with a smooth curve.

NOTE

In $h(x)$, the coefficient of x^2 is negative, so the parabola opens down.

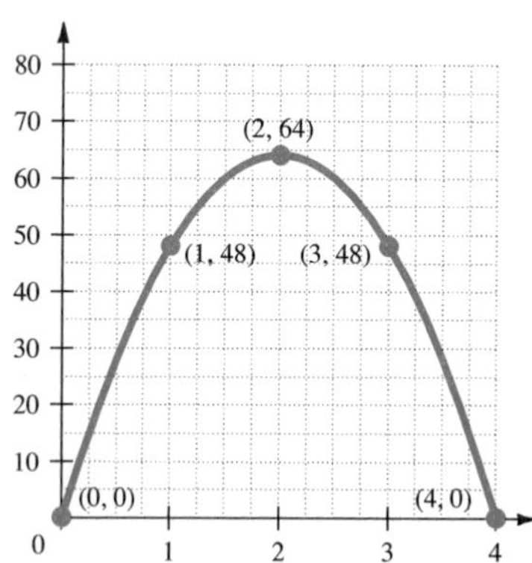

The shape of the graph of a quadratic function is called a **parabola.** Note that the curve at its peak is not angled or pointed.

Check Yourself 2

Sketch the graph of the function

$h(x) = -16x^2 + 48x$

An important point for many mathematical applications is called the **vertex.**

Definition

Vertex The highest or lowest point on the graph of a quadratic function is called its **vertex.**

In the case of a ball thrown into the air, the vertex is the highest point the ball reaches.

Example 3 **Finding the Vertex**

< Objective 2 >

Find the vertex for the function

$h(x) = -16x^2 + 64x$

The vertex of the function is the ordered pair $(x, h(x))$ for which $h(x)$ has the greatest value. We look at a table of values that will help us identify the vertex.

x	$h(x)$
0	0
1	48
2	64
3	48
4	0

Note that there seems to be a symmetric pattern. It takes the ball exactly as much time to reach its vertex as it takes the ball to fall from its vertex to the ground (because the acceleration due to gravity is constant).

The ball reaches its vertex exactly halfway between its time of release and the time it returns to the ground. In this case, it reaches its vertex after $\frac{0+4}{2} = 2$ seconds.

NOTE

Alternatively, the formula $x_v = \frac{-b}{2a}$ gives the x-coordinate of the vertex. In this case, $x_v = \frac{-(64)}{2(-16)} = 2$ seconds.

To find its height at the vertex, substitute 2 for the x.

$$\begin{aligned} h(2) &= -16(2)^2 + 64(2) \\ &= -64 + 128 \\ &= 64 \end{aligned}$$

The vertex is represented by the ordered pair (2, 64). The maximum height of the ball is 64 ft.

NOTE

In this section, we are graphing only factorable quadratic functions.

Check Yourself 3

Find the vertex for the function

$h(x) = -16x^2 + 48x$

Example 3 demonstrated a method for sketching the graph of any factorable quadratic function. This method is summarized in the following algorithm.

Step by Step

Sketching the Graph of a Quadratic Function

Step 1 Factor the quadratic.

Step 2 Using the zero-product principle, plot the points associated with the zeros of the function on the x-axis.

Step 3 Find the vertex (the mean of the two x-values in step 2 and the function value for that x) and plot the associated point.

Step 4 Draw a smooth curve connecting the three plotted points.

Example 4 Sketching the Graph of a Quadratic Function

< Objective 3 >

Sketch the graph of the function

$f(x) = x^2 + 4x - 5$

Factoring, we have

$$f(x) = (x - 1)(x + 5)$$

Using the zero-product principle, we find the two points (1, 0) and (−5, 0). We plot those points.

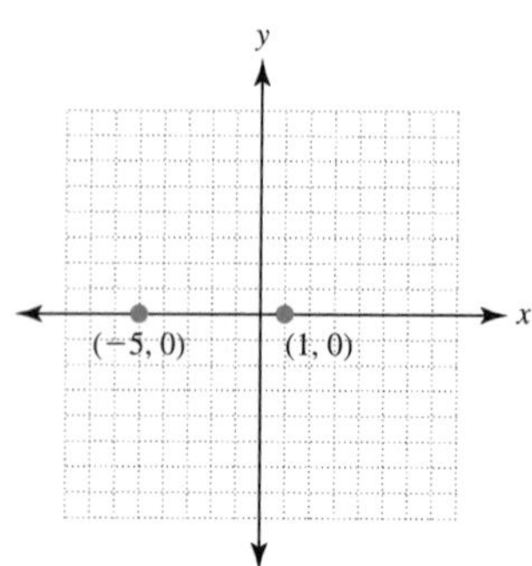

To find the vertex, we find the mean of 1 and −5, which is −2, and then we find $f(-2)$.

$$\begin{aligned} f(-2) &= (-2)^2 + 4(-2) - 5 \\ &= 4 - 8 - 5 \\ &= -9 \end{aligned}$$

Plotting the vertex, (−2, −9), and connecting the points with a smooth curve, we get

NOTE

In $f(x)$, the coefficient of x^2 is positive, so the parabola opens up.

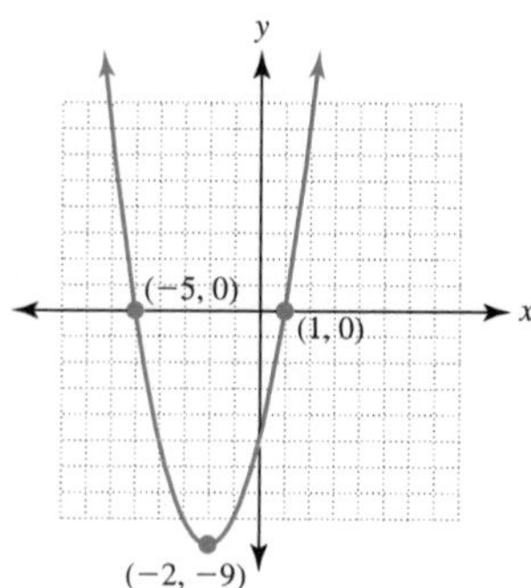

Check Yourself 4

Sketch the graph of the function

$$f(x) = x^2 - 2x - 8$$

We *can* sketch the graphs of quadratic functions even when they are not factorable. Such graphs will be covered in Chapter 9.

Check Yourself ANSWERS

1. $x = 0$ or $x = 3$

2.

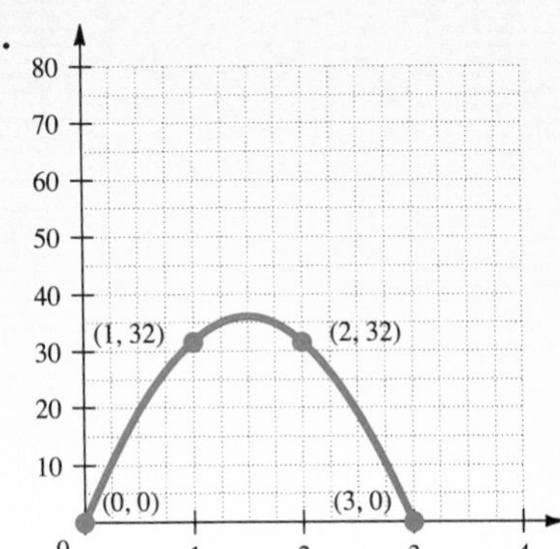

3. $\left(\frac{3}{2}, 36\right)$

4.

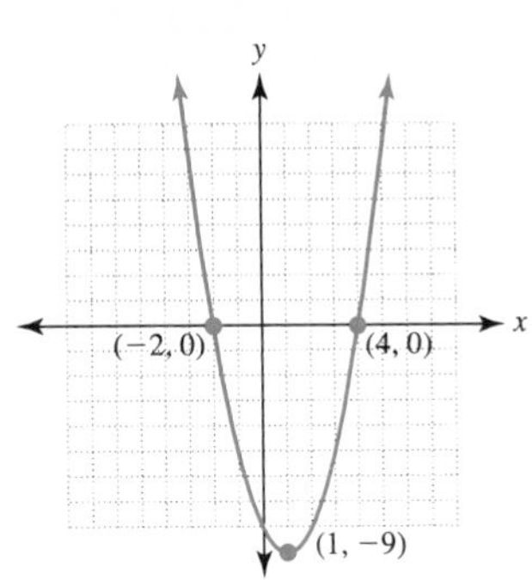

Reading Your Text

The following fill-in-the-blank exercises are designed to ensure that you understand some of the key vocabulary used in this section.

SECTION 8.1

(a) The graph of $y = ax^2 + bx + c$, where $a \neq 0$, is always a curve called a ________________.

(b) If the coefficient of x^2 is negative, the parabola opens ________________.

(c) The highest or lowest point on the graph of a parabola is called its ________________.

(d) The zeros of a function are those points where the y-coordinate is ________________.

8.1 exercises

Basic Skills | Advanced Skills | Vocational-Technical Applications | Calculator/Computer | Above and Beyond

MathZone

Boost your grade at mathzone.com!
> Practice Problems
> NetTutor
> Self-Tests
> e-Professors
> Videos

Name ______________

Section ________ Date ________

Answers

1. −3, −1; (−2, −1)
2. −4, 6; (1, −25)
3. −2, 6; (2, −16)
4. 2, 6; (4, −12)
5. −5, 1; (−2, −36)
6. 3, 2; $\left(\frac{5}{2}, -\frac{1}{2}\right)$
7. 0, 2; (1, −8)
8. 0, −4; (−2, −36)
9. 0, −4; (−2, 20)
10. 0, 4; (2, 24)
11. 3, −1; (1, 4)
12. 2, 6; (4, 4)
13. See exercise
14. See exercise
15. See exercise
16. See exercise

< Objectives 1 and 2 >

Find the zeros and the vertex of the given quadratic function.

1. $f(x) = x^2 + 4x + 3$

2. $f(x) = x^2 - 2x - 24$

3. $f(x) = x^2 - 4x - 12$

4. $f(x) = 3x^2 - 24x + 36$

5. $f(x) = 4x^2 + 16x - 20$

6. $f(x) = 2x^2 - 10x + 12$

7. $f(x) = 8x^2 - 16x$

8. $f(x) = 9x^2 + 36x$

9. $f(x) = -5x^2 - 20x$

10. $f(x) = -6x^2 + 24x$

11. $f(x) = -x^2 + 2x + 3$

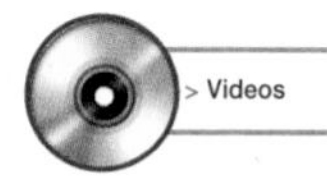

12. $f(x) = -x^2 + 8x - 12$

< Objective 3 >

Sketch the graph of the given quadratic function.

13. $f(x) = x^2 + 4x + 3$

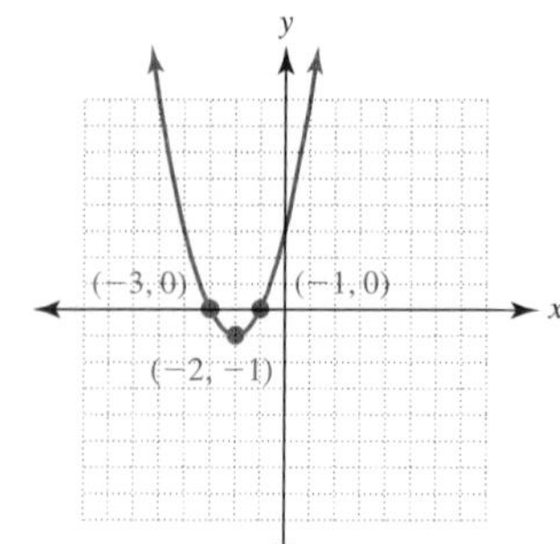

14. $f(x) = x^2 + x - 2$

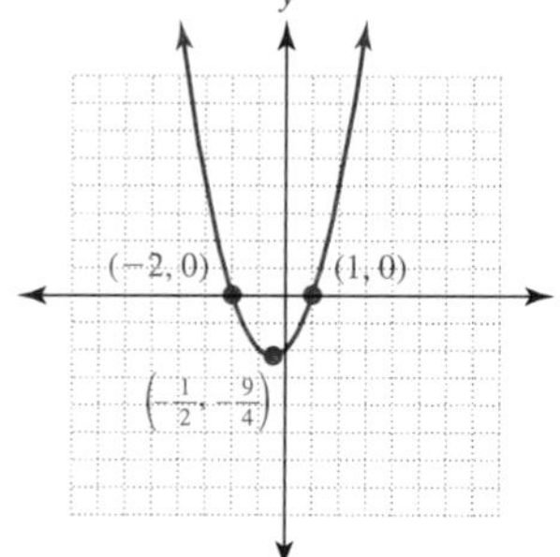

15. $f(x) = x^2 - 2x - 8$

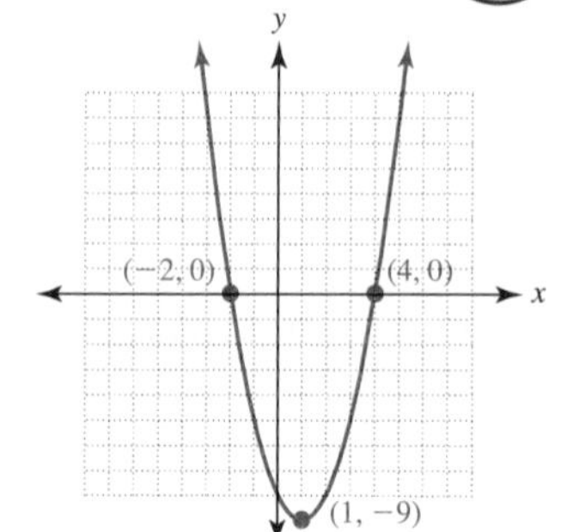

16. $f(x) = -3x^2 + 9x$

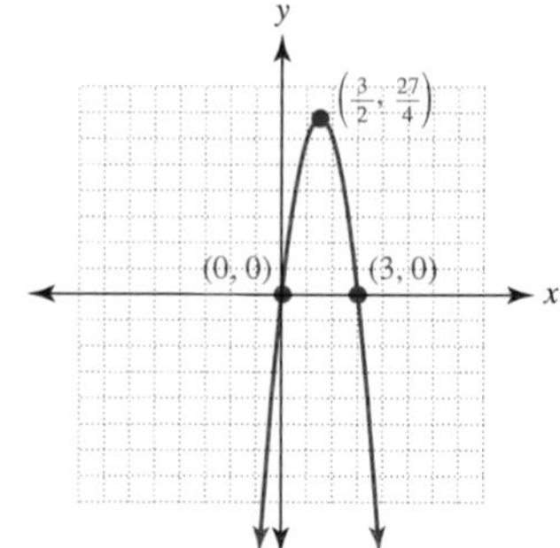

17. $f(x) = x^2 - x - 6$

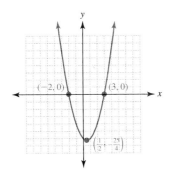

18. $f(x) = -x^2 + 2x + 3$

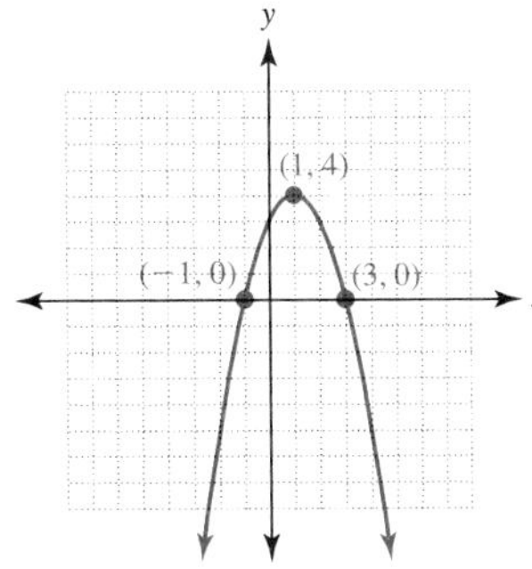

19. $f(x) = x(x - 6)$

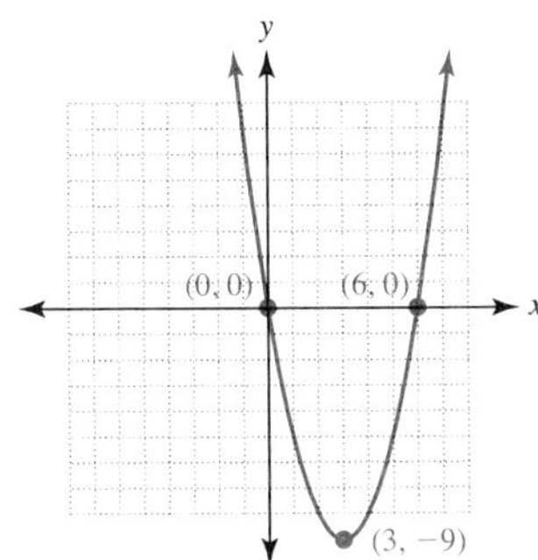

20. $f(x) = -2x^2 + 6x$

> Videos

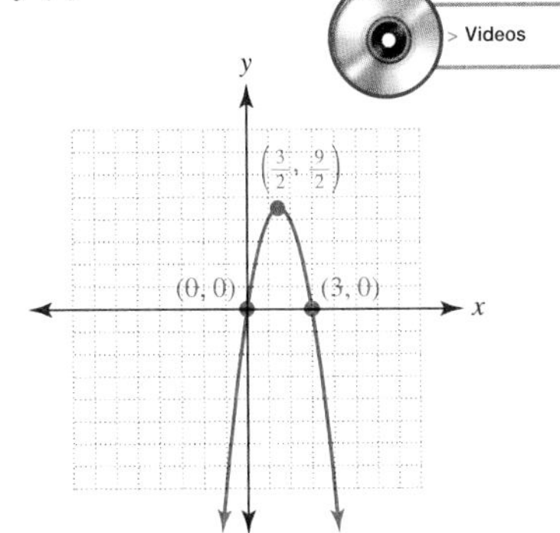

Basic Skills | **Advanced Skills** | Vocational-Technical Applications | Calculator/Computer | Above and Beyond

21. **(a)** Define a quadratic function that has zeros of 2 and 3. Express your function first in factored form, and then in standard form [$f(x) = ax^2 + bx + c$].

(b) Define another quadratic function with the same zeros.

22. Let $f(x) = ax^2 + bx$

(a) Write $f(x)$ in factored form.

(b) Find the zeros of $f(x)$.

(c) Find the x-value of the vertex.

Basic Skills | Advanced Skills | **Vocational-Technical Applications** | Calculator/Computer | Above and Beyond

23. **Allied Health** An experimental drug is being tested on a bacteria colony. It is found that t days after treating the colony, the number N of bacteria per cubic centimeter is given by the function $N(t) = 15t^2 - 100t + 700$.

(a) When will the bacteria colony be at a minimum?

(b) What is the minimum number?

24. **Allied Health** The number of people who are sick t days after the outbreak of a flu epidemic is given by the function $P(t) = -t^2 + 120t + 20$.

(a) On what day will the maximum number of people be sick?

(b) How many people will be sick on that day?

Answers

17. See exercise

18. See exercise

19. See exercise

20. See exercise

21. (a) $f(x) = (x - 2)(x - 3)$, $f(x) = x^2 - 5x + 6$; (b) one example is $f(x) = 2x^2 - 10x + 12$

22. (a) $f(x) = x(ax + b)$; (b) $x = 0, x = \frac{-b}{a}$; (c) $x = \frac{-b}{2a}$

23. (a) 3.3 days; (b) 533 bacteria

24. (a) 60th day; (b) 3,620 people

Answers

1. $-3, -1; (-2, -1)$ **3.** $-2, 6; (2, -16)$ **5.** $-5, 1; (-2, -36)$ **7.** $0, 2; (1, -8)$ **9.** $0, -4; (-2, 20)$ **11.** $3, -1; (1, 4)$

13.

y
(−3, 0)
(−1, 0)
x
(−2, −1)

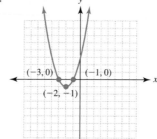

15.

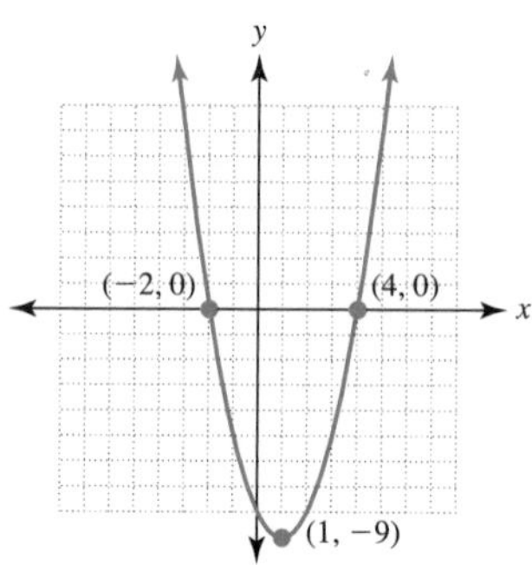

17.

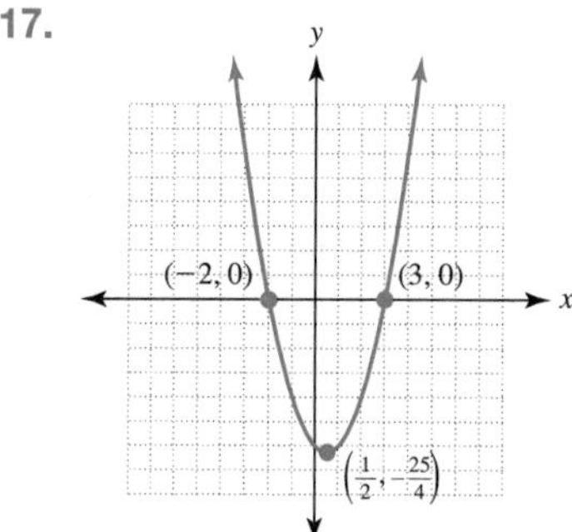

19.

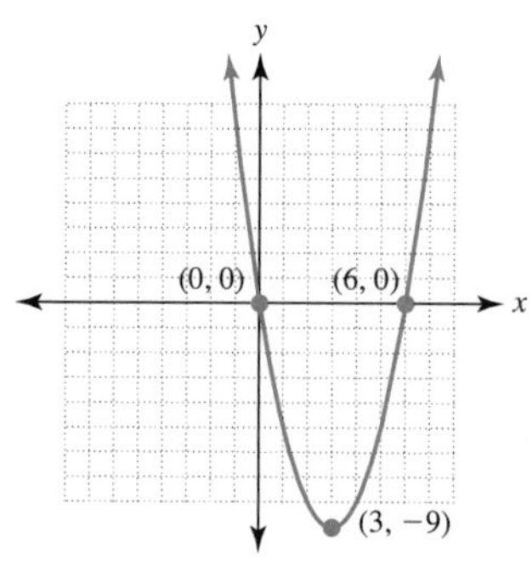

21. **(a)** $f(x) = (x - 2)(x - 3)$, $f(x) = x^2 - 5x + 6$; **(b)** one example is $f(x) = 2x^2 - 10x + 12$ **23.** **(a)** 3.3 days; **(b)** 533 bacteria

8.2 Solving Quadratic Equations by Completing the Square

< 8.2 Objectives >

1 > Solve a quadratic equation by the square root method

2 > Solve a quadratic equation by completing the square

3 > Solve a geometric application involving a quadratic equation

In Section 5.9, we solved quadratic equations by factoring and using the zero-product principle. However, not all equations are factorable over the integers. In this section, we will look at another method that can be used to solve a quadratic equation, called the **square root method.** First, we will solve a special type of equation using a factoring method from Chapter 5.

 Example 1 — Solving Equations by Factoring

Solve the quadratic equation $x^2 = 16$ by factoring.

We write the equation in standard form:

$$x^2 - 16 = 0$$

Factoring, we have

$$(x + 4)(x - 4) = 0$$

Finally, the solutions are

$$x = -4 \quad \text{or} \quad x = 4$$

NOTE

Here, we factor the quadratic member of the equation as a difference of squares.

Check Yourself 1

Solve each of the following quadratic equations.

(a) $5x^2 = 180$ **(b)** $x^2 = 25$

The equation in Example 1 could have been solved in an alternative fashion. We could have used what is called the **square root method.** Again, given the equation

$$x^2 = 16$$

NOTE

Be sure to include *both* the positive and the negative square roots when you use the square root method.

we can write the equivalent statement

$x = \sqrt{16}$ or $x = -\sqrt{16}$

This yields the solutions

$x = 4$ or $x = -4$

This discussion leads us to the following general result.

Property

Square Root Property

If $x^2 = k$, when k is a complex number, then

$x = \sqrt{k}$ or $x = -\sqrt{k}$

Example 2 further illustrates the use of this property.

Example 2 Using the Square Root Method

< Objective 1 >

Solve each equation by using the square root method.

(a) $x^2 = 9$

By the square root property,

$x = \sqrt{9}$ or $x = -\sqrt{9}$

$x = 3$ or $x = -3$

we can also write this as $x = \pm 3$.

NOTE

If a calculator were used, $\sqrt{17} = 4.123$ (rounded to three decimal places).

(b) $x^2 - 17 = 0$

Add 17 to both sides of the equation.

$x^2 = 17$

so $x = \pm\sqrt{17}$

(c) $2x^2 - 3 = 0$

$$2x^2 = 3$$

$$x^2 = \frac{3}{2}$$

$$x = \pm\sqrt{\frac{3}{2}}$$

$$x = \pm\frac{\sqrt{6}}{2}$$

NOTE

In Example 2(d) we see that complex-number solutions may result.

(d) $x^2 + 1 = 0$

$$x^2 = -1$$

$$x = \pm\sqrt{-1}$$

$$x = \pm i$$

Check Yourself 2

Solve each equation.

(a) $x^2 = 5$ **(b)** $x^2 - 2 = 0$ **(c)** $3x^2 - 8 = 0$ **(d)** $x^2 + 9 = 0$

We can also use the approach in Example 2 to solve an equation of the form

$(x + 3)^2 = 16$

As before, by the square root property we have

$x + 3 = \pm 4$ Subtract 3 from both sides of the equation.

Solving for x yields

$x = -3 \pm 4$

which means that there are two solutions:

$x = -3 + 4$ or $x = -3 - 4$

$x = 1$ or $x = -7$

Example 3 Using the Square Root Method

NOTES

The two solutions $5 + \sqrt{5}$ and $5 - \sqrt{5}$ are abbreviated as $5 \pm \sqrt{5}$. Using a calculator, we find the approximate solutions are 2.76 and 7.24.

We have solved for y and rationalized the denominator.

$$\sqrt{\frac{2}{3}} = \frac{\sqrt{2}}{\sqrt{3}} = \frac{\sqrt{2}\cdot\sqrt{3}}{\sqrt{3}\cdot\sqrt{3}} = \frac{\sqrt{6}}{3}$$

Then we combine the terms on the right, using the common denominator of 3.

Use the square root method to solve each equation.

(a) $(x - 5)^2 - 5 = 0$

$$(x - 5)^2 = 5$$
$$x - 5 = \pm\sqrt{5}$$
$$x = 5 \pm \sqrt{5}$$

(b) $3(y + 1)^2 - 2 = 0$

$$3(y + 1)^2 = 2$$
$$(y + 1)^2 = \frac{2}{3}$$
$$y + 1 = \pm\sqrt{\frac{2}{3}}$$
$$y = -1 \pm \frac{\sqrt{6}}{3}$$

so
$$y = \frac{-3 \pm \sqrt{6}}{3}$$

The approximate solutions are -1.82 and -0.18.

Check Yourself 3

Using the square root method, solve each equation.

(a) $(x - 2)^2 - 3 = 0$ **(b)** $2(x - 1)^2 = 1$

Not all quadratic equations can be solved directly by factoring or using the square root method. We must extend our techniques.

The square root method is useful in this process because any quadratic equation can be written in the form

$$(x + h)^2 = k$$

which yields the solution

$$x = -h \pm \sqrt{k}$$

NOTE

If $(x + h)^2 = k$, then $x + h = \pm\sqrt{k}$ and $x = -h \pm \sqrt{k}$

The process of changing an equation in standard form

$$ax^2 + bx + c = 0$$

to the form

$$(x + h)^2 = k$$

is called the method of **completing the square,** and it is based on the relationship between the middle term and the last term of any perfect-square trinomial.

Let us look at three perfect-square trinomials to see whether we can detect a pattern:

$$x^2 + 4x + 4 = (x + 2)^2$$

$$x^2 - 6x + 9 = (x - 3)^2$$

$$x^2 + 8x + 16 = (x + 4)^2$$

Note that in each case the last (or constant) term is the square of one-half of the coefficient of x in the middle (or linear) term. For example, in the second equation,

NOTE

This relationship is true *only* if the leading, or x^2, coefficient is 1. That will be important later.

$$x^2 - 6x + 9 = (x - 3)^2$$

$\frac{1}{2}$ of this coefficient is -3, and $(-3)^2 = 9$, the constant.

Verify this relationship for yourself in the third equation. To summarize, in perfect-square trinomials, the constant is always the square of one-half the coefficient of x.

We are now ready to use the preceding observation in the solution of quadratic equations by completing the square. Consider Example 4.

Example 4 Completing the Square to Solve an Equation

< Objective 2 >

Solve $x^2 + 8x - 7 = 0$ by completing the square.

First, we rewrite the equation with the constant on the *right-hand side:*

$$x^2 + 8x = 7$$

Our objective is to have a perfect-square trinomial on the left-hand side. We know that we must add the square of one-half of the x-coefficient to complete the square. In this case, that value is 16, so now we add 16 to each side of the equation.

NOTES

Remember that if $(x + h)^2 = k$, then $x = -h \pm \sqrt{k}$.

$\frac{1}{2} \cdot 8 = 4$ and $4^2 = 16$

$$x^2 + 8x + 16 = 7 + 16$$

Factor the perfect-square trinomial on the left, and combine like terms on the right to yield

$$(x + 4)^2 = 23$$

NOTE

When you graph the related function, $y = x^2 + 8x - 7$, you will note that the x-values for the x-intercepts are just below 1 and just above -9. Be certain that you see how these points relate to the exact solutions, $-4 + \sqrt{23}$ and $-4 - \sqrt{23}$.

Now the square root property yields

$$x + 4 = \pm\sqrt{23}$$

Subtracting 4 from both sides of the equation gives

$$x = -4 \pm \sqrt{23}$$

As decimals, these solutions are approximated by -8.8 and 0.8.

Check Yourself 4

Solve $x^2 - 6x - 2 = 0$ by completing the square.

Example 5 Completing the Square to Solve an Equation

Solve $x^2 + 5x - 3 = 0$ by completing the square.

NOTE

Add the square of one-half of the x-coefficient to both sides of the equation. Note that

$$\frac{1}{2} \cdot 5 = \frac{5}{2}$$

$$x^2 + 5x - 3 = 0 \qquad \text{Add 3 to both sides.}$$

$$x^2 + 5x = 3 \qquad \text{Make the left-hand side a perfect square.}$$

$$x^2 + 5x + \left(\frac{5}{2}\right)^2 = 3 + \left(\frac{5}{2}\right)^2$$

$$\left(x + \frac{5}{2}\right)^2 = \frac{37}{4} \qquad \text{Take the square root of both sides.}$$

$$x + \frac{5}{2} = \pm\frac{\sqrt{37}}{2} \qquad \text{Solve for } x.$$

$$x = \frac{-5 \pm \sqrt{37}}{2}$$

The approximate solutions are -5.54 and 0.54.

Check Yourself 5

Solve $x^2 + 3x - 7 = 0$ by completing the square.

Some equations have nonreal complex solutions, as Example 6 illustrates.

Example 6 Completing the Square to Solve an Equation

Solve $x^2 + 4x + 13 = 0$ by completing the square.

$$x^2 + 4x + 13 = 0 \qquad \text{Subtract 13 from both sides.}$$

$$x^2 + 4x = -13 \qquad \text{Add } \left[\frac{1}{2}(4)\right]^2 \text{ to both sides.}$$

$$x^2 + 4x + 4 = -13 + 4$$ Factor the left-hand side.

$$(x + 2)^2 = -9$$ Take the square root of both sides.

$$x + 2 = \pm\sqrt{-9}$$ Simplify the radical.

$$x + 2 = \pm i\sqrt{9}$$

$$x + 2 = \pm 3i$$

$$x = -2 \pm 3i$$

NOTE

Using your calculator you will see that the graph of $y = x^2 + 4x + 13$ does not intercept the x-axis.

Check Yourself 6

Solve $x^2 + 10x + 41 = 0$.

Example 7 illustrates a situation in which the leading coefficient of the quadratic member is not equal to 1. As you will see, an extra step is required.

Example 7 Completing the Square to Solve an Equation

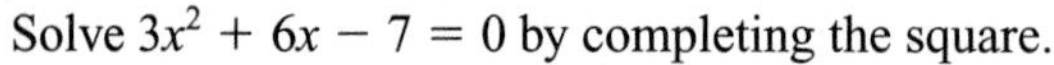

> CAUTION

Before you can complete the square on the left, the coefficient of x^2 must be equal to 1. Otherwise, we must *divide* both sides of the equation by that coefficient.

Solve $3x^2 + 6x - 7 = 0$ by completing the square.

$$3x^2 + 6x - 7 = 0$$ Add 7 to both sides.

$$3x^2 + 6x = 7$$ Divide both sides by 3.

$$x^2 + 2x = \frac{7}{3}$$ Now, complete the square on the left.

$$x^2 + 2x + 1 = \frac{7}{3} + 1$$ The left side is now a perfect square.

$$(x + 1)^2 = \frac{10}{3}$$

$$x + 1 = \pm\sqrt{\frac{10}{3}}$$

$$x = -1 \pm \sqrt{\frac{10}{3}}$$

so $$x = \frac{-3 \pm \sqrt{30}}{3}$$

NOTE

We have rationalized the denominator and combined the terms on the right side.

Check Yourself 7

Solve $2x^2 - 8x + 3 = 0$ by completing the square.

The following algorithm summarizes our work in this section with solving quadratic equations by completing the square.

Step by Step

Completing the Square

Step 1 Isolate the constant on the right side of the equation.

Step 2 Divide both sides of the equation by the coefficient of the x^2 term if that coefficient is not equal to 1.

Step 3 Add the square of one-half of the coefficient of the linear term to both sides of the equation. This will give a perfect-square trinomial on the left side of the equation.

Step 4 Write the left side of the equation as the square of a binomial, and simplify on the right side.

Step 5 Use the square root property, and then solve the resulting linear equations.

Let us proceed now to applications involving geometry.

Example 8 Applying the Completing of a Square

< Objective 3 >

The length of a rectangle is 4 cm greater than its width. If the area of the rectangle is 108 cm^2, what are the approximate dimensions of the rectangle?

Step 1 You are asked to find the dimensions (the length and the width) of the rectangle.

Step 2 Whenever geometric figures are involved in an application, start by drawing, and *then labeling,* a sketch of the problem. Letting x represent the width and $x + 4$ the length, we have

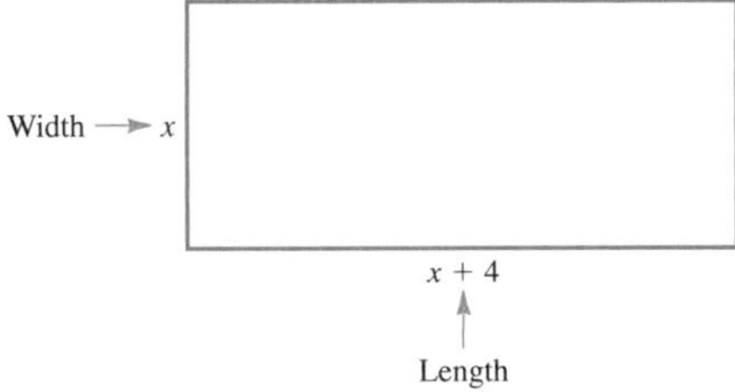

Step 3 The area of a rectangle is the product of its length and width, so

$x(x + 4) = 108$

NOTE

Multiply and complete the square.

Step 4

$$x(x + 4) = 108$$
$$x^2 + 4x = 108$$
$$x^2 + 4x + 4 = 108 + 4$$
$$(x + 2)^2 = 112$$
$$x + 2 = \pm\sqrt{112}$$
$$x = -2 \pm \sqrt{112}$$

Step 5 We reject $-2 - \sqrt{112}$ (cm) as a solution. A length cannot be negative, and so we must consider only $-2 + \sqrt{112}$ (cm) in finding the required dimensions.

The width x is approximately 8.6 cm, and the length $x + 4$ is 12.6 cm. Because (8.6 cm)(12.6 cm) gives a rectangle of area 108.36 cm^2, the solution is verified.

Check Yourself 8

In a triangle, the base is 4 in. less than its height. If its area is 35 in.^{2}, find the length of the base and the height of the triangle.

Example 9 Applying the Completing of a Square

An open box is formed from a rectangular piece of cardboard, whose length is 2 in. more than its width, by cutting 2-in. squares from each corner and folding up the sides. If the volume of the box is to be 100 in.^{3}, what must be the size of the original piece of cardboard?

Step 1 We are asked for the dimensions of the sheet of cardboard.

Step 2 Again sketch the problem.

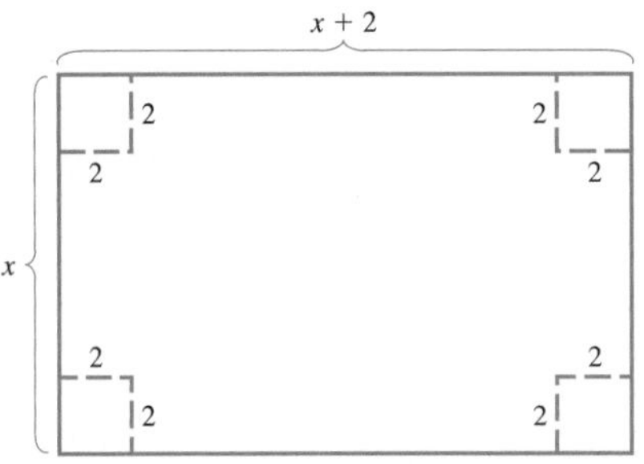

Step 3 To form an equation for volume, we sketch the completed box.

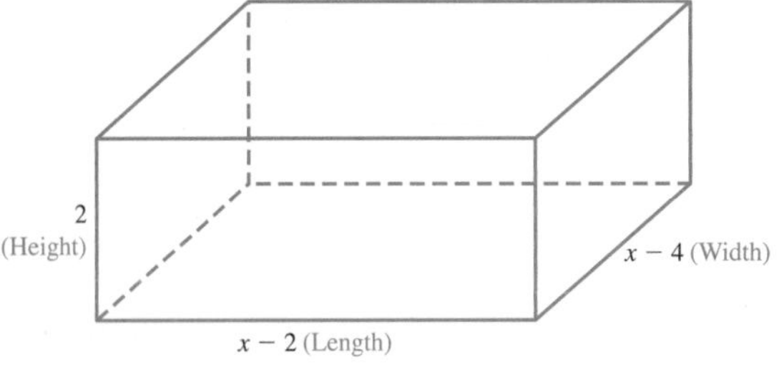

NOTE

The original width of the cardboard was x. Removing two 2-in. squares leaves $x - 4$ for the width of the box. Similarly, the length of the box is $x - 2$. Do you see why?

Because volume is the product of height, length, and width,

$$2(x - 2)(x - 4) = 100$$

Step 4

$$\begin{aligned} 2(x - 2)(x - 4) &= 100 \\ (x - 2)(x - 4) &= 50 \\ x^2 - 6x + 8 &= 50 \\ x^2 - 6x &= 42 \\ x^2 - 6x + 9 &= 42 + 9 \\ (x - 3)^2 &= 51 \\ x - 3 &= \pm\sqrt{51} \\ x &= 3 \pm \sqrt{51} \end{aligned}$$

Divide both sides by 2, and multiply on the left. Then solve as before.

Step 5 Again, we need consider only the positive solution. The width x of the original piece of cardboard is approximately 10.14 in., and its length $x + 2$ is 12.14 in. The dimensions of the completed box will be 6.14 by 8.14 by 2 in., which gives volume of an approximate 100 in.^{3}

Check Yourself 9

A similar box is to be made by cutting 3-cm squares from a piece of cardboard that is 4 cm longer than it is wide. If the required volume is 300 cm^3, find the dimensions of the original sheet of cardboard.

Check Yourself ANSWERS

1. **(a)** $-6, 6$; **(b)** $-5, 5$

2. **(a)** $\pm\sqrt{5}$; **(b)** $\pm\sqrt{2}$; **(c)** $\pm\frac{2\sqrt{6}}{3}$; **(d)** $\pm 3i$

3. **(a)** $2 \pm \sqrt{3}$; **(b)** $\frac{2 \pm \sqrt{2}}{2}$ **4.** $3 \pm \sqrt{11}$ **5.** $\frac{-3 \pm \sqrt{37}}{2}$

6. $-5 \pm 4i$ **7.** $\frac{4 \pm \sqrt{10}}{2}$ **8.** Base $\approx$ 6.6 in., height $\approx$ 10.6 in.

9. 14.2 cm by 18.2 cm

Reading Your Text

The following fill-in-the-blank exercises are designed to ensure that you understand some of the key vocabulary used in this section.

SECTION 8.2

(a) An alternative method to solving an equation of the form $x^2 = k$ is called the ______________ method.

(b) The process of changing an equation in standard form, $ax^2 + bx + c = 0$, to the form $(x - h)^2 = k$ is called ______________.

(c) Equations of the form $(x - h)^2 = k$ can be solved by taking the ______________ of both sides.

(d) To obtain a perfect-square trinomial of an equation with a leading coefficient of 1, add the square of one-half of the ______________ of the linear term to both sides of the equation.

8.2 exercises

Basic Skills | Advanced Skills | Vocational-Technical Applications | Calculator/Computer | Above and Beyond

Name ____________

Section ________ Date ________

Solve by factoring.

1. $x^2 + 6x + 5 = 0$

2. $x^2 + 5x + 6 = 0$

3. $z^2 - 2z - 35 = 0$

4. $q^2 - 5q - 24 = 0$

5. $2x^2 - 5x - 3 = 0$

6. $3x^2 + 10x - 8 = 0$

7. $6y^2 - y - 2 = 0$

8. $10z^2 + 3z - 1 = 0$

< Objective 1 >

Use the square root method to find solutions for the equations.

9. $x^2 = 36$

10. $x^2 = 144$

11. $y^2 = 7$

12. $p^2 = 18$

13. $2x^2 - 12 = 0$

14. $3x^2 - 66 = 0$

15. $2t^2 + 12 = 4$

16. $3u^2 - 5 = -32$

17. $(x + 1)^2 = 12$

18. $(2x - 3)^2 = 5$

19. $(2z + 1)^2 - 3 = 0$

20. $(3p - 4)^2 + 9 = 0$

Answers

1. $-5, -1$
2. $-2, -3$
3. $-5, 7$
4. $8, -3$
5. $-\frac{1}{2}, 3$
6. $\frac{2}{3}, -4$
7. $-\frac{1}{2}, \frac{2}{3}$
8. $\frac{1}{5}, -\frac{1}{2}$
9. ± 6
10. ± 12
11. $\pm\sqrt{7}$
12. $\pm 3\sqrt{2}$
13. $\pm\sqrt{6}$
14. $\pm\sqrt{22}$
15. $\pm 2i$
16. $\pm 3i$
17. $-1 \pm 2\sqrt{3}$
18. $\frac{3 \pm \sqrt{5}}{2}$
19. $\frac{-1 \pm \sqrt{3}}{2}$
20. $\frac{4 \pm 3i}{3}$

< Objective 2 >

In exercises 21 to 32, find the constant that must be added to each binomial expression to form a perfect-square trinomial.

21. $x^2 + 12x$

22. $r^2 - 14r$

23. $y^2 - 8y$

24. $w^2 + 16w$

25. $x^2 - 3x$

26. $z^2 + 5z$

27. $n^2 + n$

28. $x^2 - x$

29. $x^2 + \frac{1}{2}x$

30. $x^2 - \frac{1}{3}x$

31. $y^2 + 2ay$

32. $y^2 - 4ay$

Solve each equation by completing the square.

33. $x^2 + 12x - 2 = 0$

34. $x^2 - 14x - 7 = 0$

35. $y^2 - 2y = 8$

36. $z^2 + 4z - 72 = 0$

37. $x^2 - 2x - 5 = 0$

38. $x^2 - 2x = 3$

39. $x^2 + 10x + 13 = 0$

40. $x^2 + 3x - 17 = 0$

41. $z^2 - 5z - 7 = 0$

42. $q^2 - 8q + 20 = 0$

43. $m^2 - m - 3 = 0$

44. $y^2 + y - 5 = 0$

45. $x^2 + \frac{1}{2}x = 1$

46. $x^2 - \frac{1}{3}x = 2$

Answers

21. 36
22. 49
23. 16
24. 64
25. $\frac{9}{4}$
26. $\frac{25}{4}$
27. $\frac{1}{4}$
28. $\frac{1}{4}$
29. $\frac{1}{16}$
30. $\frac{1}{36}$
31. a^2
32. $4a^2$
33. $-6 \pm \sqrt{38}$
34. $7 \pm 2\sqrt{14}$
35. $-2, 4$
36. $-2 \pm 2\sqrt{19}$
37. $1 \pm \sqrt{6}$
38. $-1, 3$
39. $-5 \pm 2\sqrt{3}$
40. $\frac{-3 \pm \sqrt{77}}{2}$
41. $\frac{5 \pm \sqrt{53}}{2}$
42. $4 \pm 2i$
43. $\frac{1 \pm \sqrt{13}}{2}$
44. $\frac{-1 \pm \sqrt{21}}{2}$
45. $\frac{-1 \pm \sqrt{17}}{4}$
46. $\frac{1 \pm \sqrt{73}}{6}$

Answers

47. $\frac{-1 \pm \sqrt{3}}{2}$

48. $\frac{3 \pm \sqrt{21}}{6}$

49. $\frac{3 \pm \sqrt{15}}{3}$

50. $\frac{-2 \pm \sqrt{5}}{2}$

51. $\frac{1 \pm i\sqrt{35}}{3}$

52. $\frac{1 \pm 2i\sqrt{5}}{7}$

53. $-4 \pm 2i$

54. $1 \pm 3i$

55. Width: 7 ft, length: 10 ft

56. Width: 7 cm, length: 12 cm

57. Width: 5 cm, length: 17 cm

58. Width: 6 ft, length: 9 ft

59. a^2

60. a^2b^2

61. $\frac{9}{4}a^2$

62. $\frac{a^2b^2}{4}$

63. 1

64. $4b^2$

65. $-a \pm \sqrt{a^2 + 4}$

66. $-a \pm \sqrt{a^2 + 8}$

67. Width: 5 cm, length: 6 cm

---

47. $2x^2 + 2x - 1 = 0$ 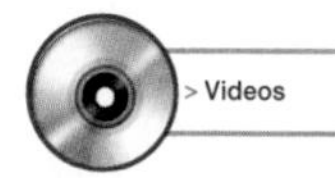

48. $3x^2 - 3x = 1$

49. $3x^2 - 6x = 2$

50. $4x^2 + 8x - 1 = 0$

51. $3x^2 - 2x + 12 = 0$

52. $7y^2 - 2y + 3 = 0$

53. $x^2 + 8x + 20 = 0$

54. $x^2 - 2x + 10 = 0$

< Objective 3 >

Solve the following applications.

55. **Geometry** The width of a rectangle is 3 ft less than its length. If the area of the rectangle is 70 ft^2, what are the dimensions of the rectangle?

56. **Geometry** The length of a rectangle is 5 cm more than its width. If the area of the rectangle is 84 cm^2, find the dimensions of the rectangle.

57. **Geometry** The length of a rectangle is 2 cm more than 3 times its width. If the area of the rectangle is 85 cm^2, find the dimensions of the rectangle.

58. **Geometry** If the length of a rectangle is 3 ft less than twice its width and the area of the rectangle is 54 ft^2, what are the dimensions of the rectangle?

Basic Skills | **Advanced Skills** | Vocational-Technical Applications | Calculator/Computer | Above and Beyond

In exercises 59 to 64, find the constant that must be added to each binomial to form a perfect-square trinomial. Let x be the variable; other letters represent constants.

59. $x^2 + 2ax$

60. $x^2 + 2abx$

61. $x^2 + 3ax$

62. $x^2 + abx$

63. $a^2x^2 + 2ax$

64. $a^2x^2 + 4abx$

In exercises 65 and 66, solve each equation by completing the square.

65. $x^2 + 2ax = 4$

66. $x^2 + 2ax - 8 = 0$

Solve the following applications.

67. **Geometry** The length of a rectangle is 1 cm more than its width. If the length of the rectangle is doubled, the area of the rectangle is increased by 30 cm^2. What were the dimensions of the original rectangle?

68. **GEOMETRY** A box is to be made from a rectangular piece of tin that is twice as long as it is wide. To accomplish this, a 10-cm square is cut from each corner, and the sides are folded up. The volume of the finished box is to be 5,000 cm^3. Find the dimensions of the original piece of tin.

Hint: To solve this equation, you will want to use the following sketch of the piece of tin. Note that the original dimensions are represented by x and $2x$. Do you see why? Also recall that the volume of the resulting box will be the product of the length, width, and height. See Example 9 if you need more help.

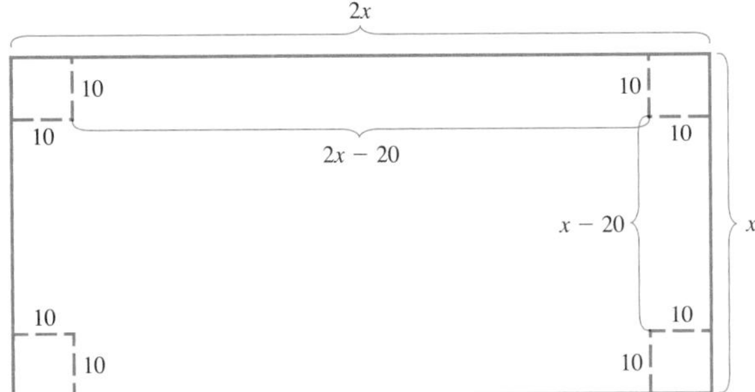

69. **GEOMETRY** An open box is formed from a square piece of material by cutting 2-in. squares from each corner of the material and folding up the sides. If the volume of the box that is formed is 72 $in.^3$, what was the size of the original piece of material?

70. **GEOMETRY** An open carton is formed from a rectangular piece of cardboard that is 4 ft longer than it is wide, by removing 1-ft squares from each corner and folding up the sides. If the volume of the carton is then 12 ft^3, what were the dimensions of the original piece of cardboard?

71. **GEOMETRY** A box that has a volume of 2,000 $in.^3$ was made from a square piece of tin. The square piece cut from each corner had sides of length 4 in. What were the original dimensions of the square?

72. **GEOMETRY** A square piece of cardboard is to be formed into a box. After 5-cm squares are cut from each corner and the sides are folded up, the resulting box will have a volume of 400 cm^3. Find the length of a side of the original piece of cardboard.

Basic Skills | Advanced Skills | **Vocational-Technical Applications** | Calculator/Computer | Above and Beyond

73. **CONSTRUCTION TECHNOLOGY** The shape of a beam loaded with a single concentrated load is described by the equation $d = \dfrac{x^2 - 64}{200}$, where x is the distance from the center of the beam and d is the deflection of the beam under the load. Find the points where the deflection equals 0.

Answers

68. $15 + 5\sqrt{11}$ by $30 + 10\sqrt{11}$ or 31.6 cm by 63.2 cm

69. 10 in. by 10 in.

70. 4 ft by 8 ft

71. $8 + 10\sqrt{5}$ in. or 30.4 in.

72. $10 + 4\sqrt{5}$ cm or 18.9 cm

73. 8 units on either side of center

Answers

74. 11 h

75. 5.5 days

76. 6.5 days

77. See exercise

78. See exercise

79. See exercise

80. See exercise

81. (a) None; (b) $\pm i$; (c) No x-intercepts, no real zeros

74. ALLIED HEALTH A toxic chemical is introduced into a protozoan culture. The number of deaths per hour, N, is given by the function $N(t) = 363 - 3t^2$, where t is the number of hours after the chemical's introduction. How long will it take before the protozoa stop dying?

75. ALLIED HEALTH One technique of controlling a certain type of cancer is to use radiation therapy. After such a treatment, the total number of cancerous cells, N, in thousands, can be estimated by the function $N(t) = 121 - 4t^2$, where t is the number of days of treatment. How many days of treatment are required to kill all the cancer cells?

76. ALLIED HEALTH After radiation therapy for another type of cancer, the total number of cancerous cells, N, in thousands, can be estimated by the function $N(t) = 169 - 4t^2$, where t is the number of days of treatment. How many days of treatment are required to kill all the cancer cells?

Basic Skills | Advanced Skills | Vocational-Technical Applications | **Calculator/Computer** | Above and Beyond

In exercises 77 to 80, use your graphing utility to find the graph. For each graph, approximate the x-intercepts to the nearest tenth. (You may have to adjust the viewing window to see both intercepts.)

77. $y = x^2 + 12x - 2$

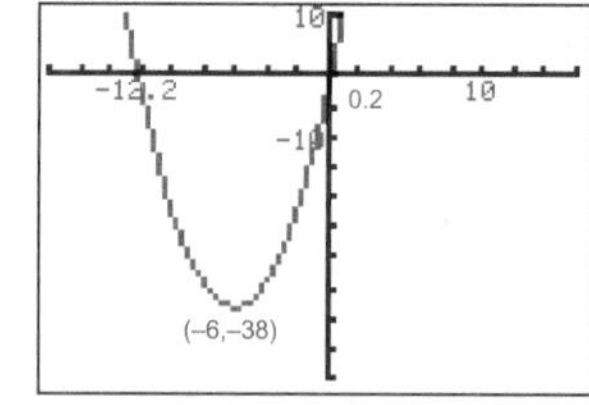

78. $y = x^2 - 14x - 7$

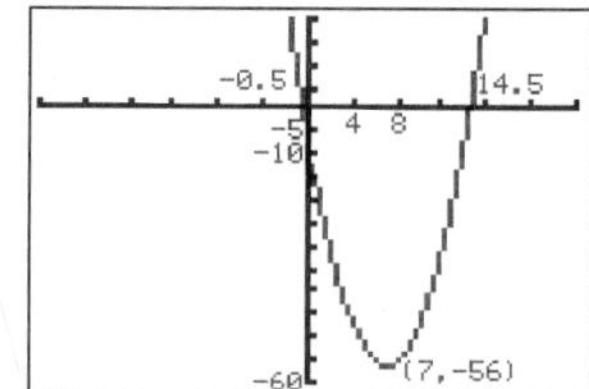

79. $y = x^2 - 2x - 8$

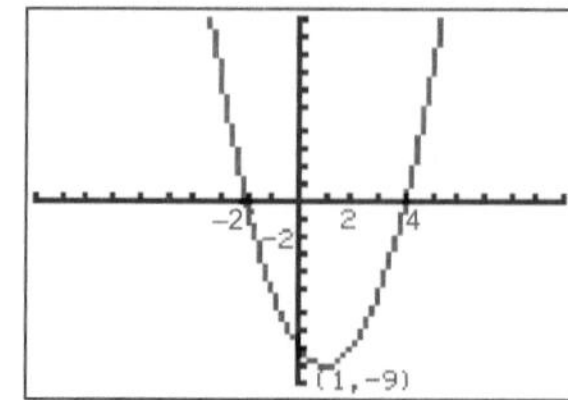

80. $y = x^2 + 4x - 72$

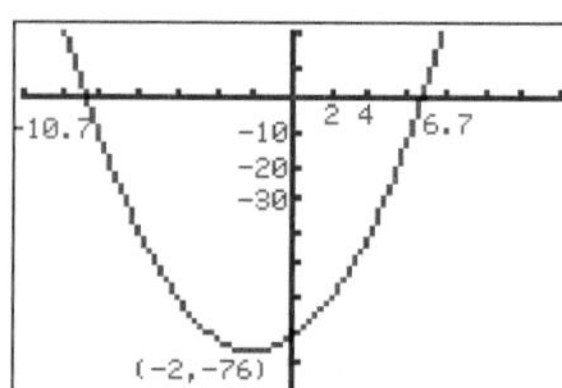

81. On your graphing calculator, view the graph of $f(x) = x^2 + 1$.

(a) What can you say about the x-intercepts of the graph?

(b) Determine the zeros of the function, using the square root method.

(c) How does your answer to part **(a)** relate to your answer to part **(b)**?

Basic Skills | Advanced Skills | Vocational-Technical Applications | Calculator/Computer | **Above and Beyond**

82. Why must the leading coefficient of the quadratic member be set equal to 1 before using the technique of completing the square?

83. What relationship exists between the solutions of a quadratic equation and the graph of a quadratic function?

84. Consider the following representation of "completing the square": Suppose we wish to complete the square for $x^2 + 10x$. A square with dimensions x by x has area equal to x^2.

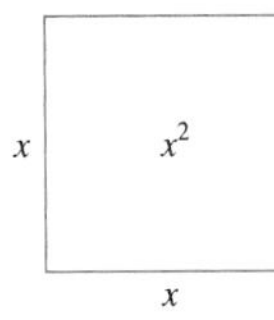

We divide the quantity $10x$ by 2 and get $5x$. If we extend the base x by 5 units, and draw the rectangle attached to the square, the rectangle's dimensions are 5 by x with an area of $5x$.

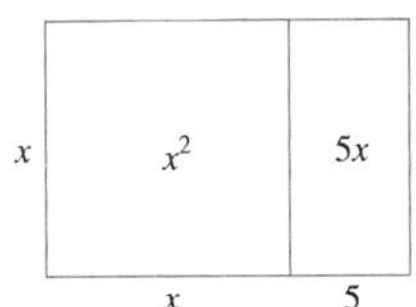

Now we extend the height by 5 units, and draw another rectangle whose area is $5x$.

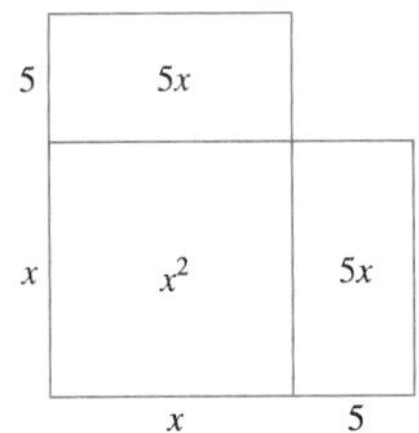

(a) What is the total area represented in the figure so far?

(b) How much area must be added to the figure to "complete the square"?

(c) Write the area of the completed square as a binomial squared.

85. Repeat the process described in exercise 84 with $x^2 + 16x$.

Answers

1. $-5, -1$ **3.** $-5, 7$ **5.** $-\frac{1}{2}, 3$ **7.** $-\frac{1}{2}, \frac{2}{3}$ **9.** ± 6
11. $\pm\sqrt{7}$ **13.** $\pm\sqrt{6}$ **15.** $\pm 2i$ **17.** $-1 \pm 2\sqrt{3}$
19. $\frac{-1 \pm \sqrt{3}}{2}$ **21.** 36 **23.** 16 **25.** $\frac{9}{4}$ **27.** $\frac{1}{4}$ **29.** $\frac{1}{16}$
31. a^2 **33.** $-6 \pm \sqrt{38}$ **35.** $-2, 4$ **37.** $1 \pm \sqrt{6}$

Answers

82. Above and Beyond

83. Above and Beyond

84. (a) $x^2 + 10x$; (b) 25; (c) $(x + 5)^2$

85. (a) $x^2 + 16x$; (b) 64; (c) $(x + 8)^2$

39. $-5 \pm 2\sqrt{3}$ **41.** $\frac{5 \pm \sqrt{53}}{2}$ **43.** $\frac{1 \pm \sqrt{13}}{2}$ **45.** $\frac{-1 \pm \sqrt{17}}{4}$
47. $\frac{-1 \pm \sqrt{3}}{2}$ **49.** $\frac{3 \pm \sqrt{15}}{3}$ **51.** $\frac{1 \pm i\sqrt{35}}{3}$ **53.** $-4 \pm 2i$
55. Width: 7 ft, length: 10 ft **57.** Width: 5 cm, length: 17 cm
59. a^2 **61.** $\frac{9}{4}a^2$ **63.** 1 **65.** $-a \pm \sqrt{a^2 + 4}$
67. Width: 5 cm, length: 6 cm **69.** 10 in. by 10 in.
71. $8 + 10\sqrt{5}$ in. or 30.4 in. **73.** 8 units on either side of center **75.** 5.5 days

77.
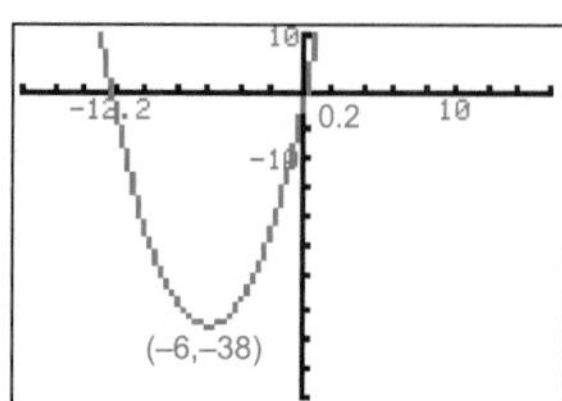

79.
-2
-2
2
4
(1,-9)

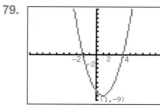

81. **(a)** None; **(b)** $\pm i$; **(c)** No x-intercepts, no real zeroes
83. Above and Beyond **85.** **(a)** $x^2 + 16x$; **(b)** 64; **(c)** $(x + 8)^2$

8.3 Solving Quadratic Equations by Using the Quadratic Formula

< 8.3 Objectives >

1 > Solve a quadratic equation by using the quadratic formula

2 > Determine the nature of the solutions of a quadratic equation by using the discriminant

3 > Solve applications involving quadratic equations

4 > Use the Pythagorean theorem to solve a geometric application

Every quadratic equation can be solved by using the quadratic formula. In this section, we will first describe how the quadratic formula is derived, and then we will examine its use. Recall that a quadratic equation is any equation that can be written in the form

$$ax^2 + bx + c = 0 \quad \text{when } a \neq 0$$

Step by Step

Deriving the Quadratic Formula

Step 1 Isolate the constant on the right side of the equation.

$$ax^2 + bx = -c$$

Step 2 Divide both sides by the coefficient of the x^2 term.

$$x^2 + \frac{b}{a}x = -\frac{c}{a}$$

Step 3 Add the square of one-half the x-coefficient to both sides.

$$x^2 + \frac{b}{a}x + \frac{b^2}{4a^2} = -\frac{c}{a} + \frac{b^2}{4a^2}$$

Step 4 Factor the left side as a perfect-square binomial. Then apply the square root property.

$$\left(x + \frac{b}{2a}\right)^2 = \frac{-4ac + b^2}{4a^2}$$

$$x + \frac{b}{2a} = \pm\sqrt{\frac{b^2 - 4ac}{4a^2}}$$

Step 5 Solve the resulting linear equations.

$$x = -\frac{b}{2a} \pm \frac{\sqrt{b^2 - 4ac}}{2a}$$

Step 6 Simplify.

$$x = \frac{-b \pm \sqrt{b^2 - 4ac}}{2a}$$

We now use the result just derived to state the **quadratic formula,** a formula that allows us to find the solutions for any quadratic equation.

Property

The Quadratic Formula Given any quadratic equation in the form

$ax^2 + bx + c = 0 \quad \text{when } a \neq 0$

the two solutions to the equation are found using the formula

$$x = \frac{-b \pm \sqrt{b^2 - 4ac}}{2a}$$

Example 1 uses an equation in standard form.

Example 1 Using the Quadratic Formula

< Objective 1 >

Solve, using the quadratic formula.

$6x^2 - 7x - 3 = 0$

First, we determine the values for a, b, and c. Here,

$a = 6 \qquad b = -7 \qquad c = -3$

Substituting those values into the quadratic formula, we have

$$x = \frac{-(-7) \pm \sqrt{(-7)^2 - 4(6)(-3)}}{2(6)}$$

Simplifying inside the radical gives us

$$x = \frac{7 \pm \sqrt{121}}{12}$$

$$= \frac{7 \pm 11}{12}$$

This gives us the solutions

$$x = \frac{3}{2} \quad \text{or} \quad x = -\frac{1}{3}$$

Note that because the solutions for the equation of this example are rational, the original equation could have been solved by our earlier method of factoring.

NOTE

The equation is in standard form, so we can right away find a, b, and c.

Because $b^2 - 4ac = 121$ is a perfect square, the two solutions in this case are rational numbers.

NOTE

Compare these solutions to the graph of $y = 6x^2 - 7x - 3$.

Check Yourself 1

Solve, using the quadratic formula.

$3x^2 + 2x - 8 = 0$

To use the quadratic formula, we often must write the equation in standard form. Example 2 illustrates this approach.

Example 2 Using the Quadratic Formula

> **NOTE**
>
> The equation *must be in standard form* to determine *a*, *b*, and *c*.

Solve by using the quadratic formula.

$9x^2 = 12x - 4$

First, we must write the equation in standard form.

$9x^2 - 12x + 4 = 0$

Second, we find the values of *a*, *b*, and *c*. Here,

$a = 9 \qquad b = -12 \qquad c = 4$

Substituting these values into the quadratic formula, we find

$$x = \frac{-(-12) \pm \sqrt{(-12)^2 - 4(9)(4)}}{2(9)}$$

$$= \frac{12 \pm \sqrt{0}}{18}$$

and simplifying yields

$$x = \frac{2}{3}$$

> **NOTE**
>
> The graph of
>
> $y = 9x^2 - 12x + 4$
>
> intercepts the *x*-axis only at the point $\left(\frac{2}{3}, 0\right)$.

Check Yourself 2

Use the quadratic formula to solve the equation.

$4x^2 - 4x = -1$

Thus far our examples and exercises have led to rational solutions. That is not always the case, as Example 3 illustrates.

Example 3 Using the Quadratic Formula

Using the quadratic formula, solve

$x^2 - 3x = 5$

Once again, to use the quadratic formula, we write the equation in standard form.

$x^2 - 3x - 5 = 0$

We now determine values for *a*, *b*, and *c* and substitute.

> **NOTE**
>
> $a = 1$,
> $b = -3$, and
> $c = -5$.

$$x = \frac{-(-3) \pm \sqrt{(-3)^2 - 4(1)(-5)}}{2(1)}$$

Simplifying as before, we have

$$x = \frac{3 \pm \sqrt{29}}{2}$$

Check Yourself 3

Using the quadratic equation, solve $2x^2 = x + 7$.

Example 4 requires some special care in simplifying the solution.

Example 4 Using the Quadratic Formula

Using the quadratic formula, solve

$3x^2 - 6x + 2 = 0$

Here, we have $a = 3$, $b = -6$, and $c = 2$. Substituting gives

$$x = \frac{-(-6) \pm \sqrt{(-6)^2 - 4(3)(2)}}{2(3)}$$

$$= \frac{6 \pm \sqrt{12}}{6}$$ We now look for the largest perfect-square factor of 12, the radicand.

> CAUTION

Students are sometimes tempted to reduce this result to

$\frac{6 \pm 2\sqrt{3}}{6} \stackrel{?}{=} 1 \pm 2\sqrt{3}$

This is *not a valid step.* We must divide *each of the terms* in the numerator by 2 when simplifying the expression.

Simplifying, we note that $\sqrt{12}$ is equal to $\sqrt{4 \cdot 3}$, or $2\sqrt{3}$. We can then write the solutions as

$$x = \frac{6 \pm 2\sqrt{3}}{6} = \frac{2(3 \pm \sqrt{3})}{6} = \frac{3 \pm \sqrt{3}}{3}$$

Check Yourself 4

Solve by using the quadratic formula.

$x^2 - 4x = 6$

Let us examine a case in which the solutions are nonreal complex numbers.

Example 5 Using the Quadratic Formula

Solve by using the quadratic formula.

$x^2 - 2x = -2$

NOTE

The solutions will have an imaginary part any time $\sqrt{b^2 - 4ac}$ is negative.

Rewriting in standard form, we have

$x^2 - 2x + 2 = 0$

Labeling the coefficients, we find that

$a = 1 \qquad b = -2 \qquad c = 2$

NOTES

The graph of

$y = x^2 - 2x + 2$

does not intercept the x-axis, so there are no real solutions.

Although not necessarily distinct or real, every second-degree equation has two solutions.

Graphically, we can see the number of real solutions as the number of times the related quadratic function intercepts the x-axis.

Applying the quadratic formula, we have

$$x = \frac{2 \pm \sqrt{-4}}{2}$$

and noting that $\sqrt{-4}$ is $2i$, we can simplify to

$$x = 1 \pm i$$

Check Yourself 5

Solve by using the quadratic formula.

$x^2 - 4x + 6 = 0$

In attempting to solve a quadratic equation, you should first try the factoring method. If this method does not work, you can apply the quadratic formula or the square root method to find the solution. The following algorithm outlines the steps for solving equations using the quadratic formula.

Step by Step

Solving a Quadratic Equation by Using the Quadratic Formula

Step 1 Write the equation in standard form (one side is equal to 0).

$ax^2 + bx + c = 0$

Step 2 Determine the values for a, b, and c.

Step 3 Substitute those values into the quadratic formula.

$$x = \frac{-b \pm \sqrt{b^2 - 4ac}}{2a}$$

Step 4 Simplify.

Given a quadratic equation, the radicand $b^2 - 4ac$ determines the number of real solutions. Because of this, we call it the **discriminant**. Since the value of the discriminant is a real number, there are three possibilities.

Property

The Discriminant

If $b^2 - 4ac$ $\begin{cases} < 0 & \text{there are } \textit{no real solutions}\text{, but two imaginary solutions} \\ = 0 & \text{there is } \textit{one real solution} \text{ (a double solution)} \\ > 0 & \text{there are } \textit{two distinct real solutions} \end{cases}$

Example 6 Analyzing the Discriminant

< Objective 2 >

How many real solutions are there for each of the following quadratic equations?

(a) $x^2 + 7x - 15 = 0$

The discriminant can be found by computing $49 - 4(1)(-15)$. So the value is 109. Since it is positive, it indicates that there are two real solutions.

(b) $3x^2 - 5x + 7 = 0$

The value of the discriminant is -59. Since it is negative there are no real solutions.

(c) $9x^2 - 12x + 4 = 0$

The value of the discriminant is 0. There is exactly one real solution (a double solution).

Check Yourself 6

How many real solutions are there for each of the following quadratic equations?

(a) $2x^2 - 3x + 2 = 0$ **(b)** $3x^2 + x - 11 = 0$
(c) $4x^2 - 4x + 1 = 0$ **(d)** $x^2 = -5x - 7$

NOTE

We could find two imaginary solutions by using the quadratic formula.

Consider the following two applications involving thrown balls that can be solved by using the quadratic formula.

Example 7 Solving a Thrown-Ball Application

< Objective 3 >

If a ball is thrown upward from the ground, the equation to find the height h of such a ball thrown with an initial velocity of 80 ft/sec is

$h(t) = 80t - 16t^2$

NOTE

Here h measures the height above the ground, in feet, t seconds after the ball is thrown upward.

Find the time it takes the ball to reach a height of 48 ft.

First we substitute 48 for h, and then we rewrite the equation in standard form.

$$16t^2 - 80t + 48 = 0$$

To simplify the computation, we divide both sides of the equation by the common factor, 16. This yields

$$t^2 - 5t + 3 = 0$$

NOTE

The result of dividing by 16

$$\frac{0}{16} = 0$$

is 0 on the right.

We solve for t as before, using the quadratic equation, with the result

$$t = \frac{5 \pm \sqrt{13}}{2}$$

NOTE

There are two solutions because the ball reaches the height *twice,* once on the way up and once on the way down.

This gives us two solutions, $\frac{5 + \sqrt{13}}{2}$ and $\frac{5 - \sqrt{13}}{2}$. But, because we have specified units of time, we generally estimate the answer to the nearest tenth or hundredth of a second.

In this case, estimating to the nearest tenth of a second gives solutions of 0.7 seconds and 4.3 seconds.

Check Yourself 7

The equation to find the height h of a ball thrown upward with an initial velocity of 64 ft/sec is

$h(t) = 64t - 16t^2$

Find the time it takes the ball to reach a height of 32 ft.

Example 8 Solving a Thrown-Ball Application

The height, h, of a ball thrown downward from the top of a 240-ft building with an initial velocity of 64 ft/sec is given by

$h(t) = 240 - 64t - 16t^2$

At what time will the ball reach a height of 176 ft?

Let $h(t) = 176$, and write the equation in standard form.

$$176 = 240 - 64t - 16t^2$$
$$0 = 64 - 64t - 16t^2$$
$$16t^2 + 64t - 64 = 0 \quad \text{Divide both sides of the equation by 16}$$

or

$$t^2 + 4t - 4 = 0$$

Applying the quadratic formula with $a = 1$, $b = 4$, and $c = -4$ yields

$$t = -2 \pm 2\sqrt{2}$$

Estimating these solutions, we have $t = -4.8$ and $t = 0.8$, but of these two values only the *positive value* makes any sense. (To accept the negative solution would be to say that the ball reached the specified height before it was thrown.) Therefore, the ball has a height of 176 ft at approximately 0.8 seconds.

NOTE

The graph of

$h(t) = 240 - 64t - 16t^2$

shows the height, h, at any time t.

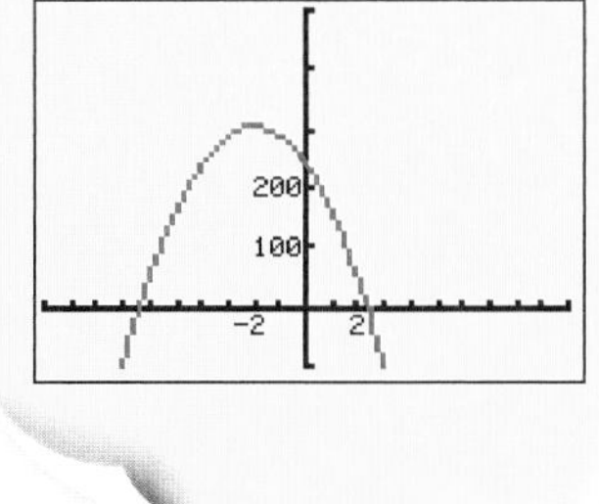

Check Yourself 8

The height h of a ball thrown upward from the top of a 96-ft building with an initial velocity of 16 ft/s is given by

$h(t) = 96 + 16t - 16t^2$

When will the ball have a height of 32 ft above the ground? (Estimate your answer to the nearest tenth of a second.)

Another geometric result that generates quadratic equations in applications is the **Pythagorean theorem,** which we discussed in Section 7.5.

In Example 9, the solution of the quadratic equation contains radicals. Substituting a pair of solutions such as $\dfrac{3 \pm \sqrt{5}}{2}$ is a very difficult process. As in our thrown-ball applications, always check the "reasonableness" of the answer.

Example 9 A Triangular Application

< Objective 4 >

One leg of a right triangle is 4 cm longer than the other leg. The length of the hypotenuse of the triangle is 12 cm. Find the length of the two legs.

As in any geometric problem, a sketch of the information will help us visualize.

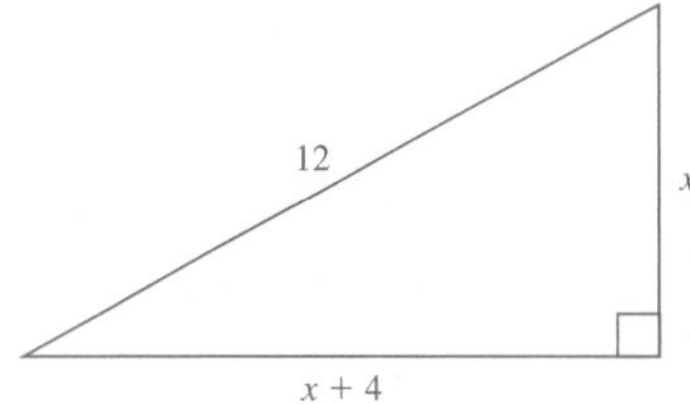

We assign variable x to the shorter leg and $x + 4$ to the other leg.

NOTE

The sum of the squares of the legs of the triangle is equal to the square of the hypotenuse.

Now we apply the Pythagorean theorem to write an equation.

$$x^2 + (x + 4)^2 = (12)^2$$

$$x^2 + x^2 + 8x + 16 = 144$$

or

$$2x^2 + 8x - 128 = 0$$

NOTE

Dividing both sides of a quadratic equation by a common factor is always an important step. It is often necessary in order to make the coefficient of x^2 equal to one. In general, it simplifies your work with the quadratic formula.

Dividing both sides by 2, we have the equivalent equation

$$x^2 + 4x - 64 = 0$$

Using the quadratic formula, we get

$$x = -2 + 2\sqrt{17} \quad \text{or} \quad x = -2 - 2\sqrt{17}$$

Now, we check our answers for reasonableness. We can reject $-2 - 2\sqrt{17}$ (Do you see why?), but we should still check the reasonableness of the value $-2 + 2\sqrt{17}$. We could substitute $-2 + 2\sqrt{17}$ into the original equation, but it seems better to simply check that it "makes sense" as a solution. Remembering that $\sqrt{16} = 4$, we estimate $-2 + 2\sqrt{17}$ as

NOTE

$\sqrt{17}$ is just slightly *more* than $\sqrt{16}$ or 4.

$$-2 + 2(4) = 6$$

Our equation,

$$x^2 + (x + 4)^2 \overset{?}{\approx} (12)^2$$

when x equals 6, becomes

$$36 + 100 \approx 144$$

NOTE

$-2 + 2\sqrt{17}$ is approximately 6.2.

This indicates that our answer is at least reasonable. Therefore, the lengths of the two legs are approximately 6.2 cm and 10.2 cm.

Check Yourself 9

One leg of a right triangle is 2 cm longer than the other. The hypotenuse is 1 cm less than twice the length of the shorter leg. Find the length of each side of the triangle.

An important economic application involves supply and demand. Our last example illustrates that application.

Example 10 An Economic Application

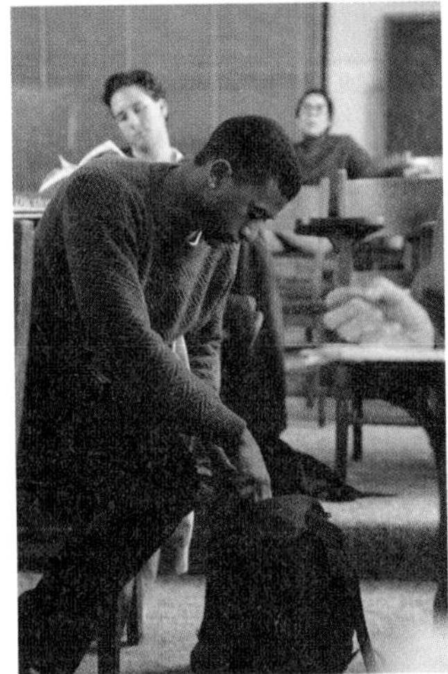

The number of intermediate algebra workbooks that a publisher is willing to produce is determined by the supply curve

$S(p) = -p^2 + 30p - 180$ in which p is the unit price in dollars

The demand for these workbooks is determined by the equation

$$D(p) = -10p + 130$$

Find the equilibrium price (the price at which supply and demand are equal).

Because supply equals demand ($S = D$ at equilibrium), we can write

$$-p^2 + 30p - 180 = -10p + 130$$

Rewriting this statement as a quadratic equation in standard form yields

$$p^2 - 40p + 310 = 0$$

When we apply the quadratic formula, we find the solutions

$$p = 20 \pm 3\sqrt{10}$$

$$p \approx 10.51 \quad \text{or} \quad p \approx 29.49$$

Although you might assume that the publisher will choose the higher price, it will, in fact, choose \$10.51. If you want to discover why, try substituting the two solutions into the original demand equation.

Check Yourself 10

The demand equation for CDs that accompany a text is predicted to be

$D = -6p + 30$ in which p is the unit price in dollars

The supply equation is predicted to be

$S = -p^2 + 12p - 20$

Find the equilibrium price.

Check Yourself ANSWERS

1. $-2, \frac{4}{3}$ **2.** $\frac{1}{2}$ **3.** $\frac{1 \pm \sqrt{57}}{4}$ **4.** $2 \pm \sqrt{10}$ **5.** $2 \pm i\sqrt{2}$
6. **(a)** None; **(b)** two; **(c)** one; **(d)** none **7.** 0.6 sec and 3.4 sec **8.** 2.6 sec
9. Approximately 4.3 cm, 6.3 cm, and 7.7 cm **10.** $\approx$\$3.43

Reading Your Text

The following fill-in-the-blank exercises are designed to ensure that you understand some of the key vocabulary used in this section.

SECTION 8.3

(a) Every quadratic equation can be solved using the ______________.

(b) To use the quadratic formula, we must write the equation in ______________ form.

(c) The part of the quadratic formula that is under the radical is called the ______________.

(d) If the discriminant is positive and a perfect square, there are two ______________ solutions to the equation.

8.3 exercises

< Objective 1 >

Solve each quadratic equation by first factoring and then using the quadratic formula.

1. $x^2 - 5x - 14 = 0$

2. $x^2 + 7x - 18 = 0$

3. $t^2 + 8t - 65 = 0$

4. $q^2 + 3q - 130 = 0$

5. $5x^2 + 4x - 1 = 0$

6. $3x^2 + 2x - 1 = 0$

7. $16t^2 - 24t + 9 = 0$

8. $6m^2 - 23m + 10 = 0$

In exercises 9 to 20, solve each quadratic equation by **(a)** *completing the square, and* **(b)** *using the quadratic formula.*

9. $x^2 - 2x - 5 = 0$

10. $x^2 + 6x - 1 = 0$

11. $x^2 + 3x - 27 = 0$

12. $t^2 + 4t - 7 = 0$

13. $2x^2 - 6x - 3 = 0$

14. $2x^2 - 6x + 1 = 0$

15. $2q^2 - 4q + 1 = 0$

16. $4r^2 - 2r + 1 = 0$

17. $3x^2 - x - 2 = 0$

18. $2x^2 - 8x + 3 = 0$

19. $2y^2 - y - 5 = 0$

20. $3m^2 + 2m - 1 = 0$

MathZone

Boost your grade at mathzone.com!

- > Practice Problems
- > NetTutor
- > Self-Tests
- > e-Professors
- > Videos

Name ______________

Section ________ Date ________

Answers

1. $-2, 7$
2. $-9, 2$
3. $-13, 5$
4. $-13, 10$
5. $-1, \frac{1}{5}$
6. $-1, \frac{1}{3}$
7. $\frac{3}{4}$
8. $\frac{1}{2}, \frac{10}{3}$
9. $1 \pm \sqrt{6}$
10. $-3 \pm \sqrt{10}$
11. $\frac{-3 \pm 3\sqrt{13}}{2}$
12. $-2 \pm \sqrt{11}$
13. $\frac{3 \pm \sqrt{15}}{2}$
14. $\frac{3 \pm \sqrt{7}}{2}$
15. $\frac{2 \pm \sqrt{2}}{2}$
16. $\frac{1 \pm i\sqrt{3}}{4}$
17. $-\frac{2}{3}, 1$
18. $\frac{4 \pm \sqrt{10}}{2}$
19. $\frac{1 \pm \sqrt{41}}{4}$
20. $-1, \frac{1}{3}$

 The Streeter/Hutchison Series in Mathematics Intermediate Algebra

Solve each equation by using the quadratic formula.

21. $x^2 - 4x + 3 = 0$

22. $x^2 - 7x + 3 = 0$

23. $p^2 - 8p + 16 = 0$

24. $u^2 + 7u - 30 = 0$

25. $2x^2 - 2x - 3 = 0$

26. $2x^2 - 3x - 7 = 0$

27. $-3s^2 + 2s - 1 = 0$

28. $5t^2 - 2t - 2 = 0$

< Objective 2 >

For each quadratic equation, find the value of the discriminant and give the number of real solutions.

29. $2x^2 - 5x = 0$

30. $3x^2 + 8x = 0$

31. $m^2 - 8m + 16 = 0$

32. $4p^2 + 12p + 9 = 0$

33. $3x^2 - 7x + 1 = 0$

34. $2x^2 - x + 5 = 0$

35. $2w^2 - 5w + 11 = 0$

36. $7q^2 - 3q + 1 = 0$

In exercises 37 to 42, find all the solutions of each quadratic equation. Use any applicable method.

37. $x^2 - 8x + 16 = 0$

38. $4x^2 + 12x + 9 = 0$

39. $3t^2 - 7t + 1 = 0$

40. $2z^2 - z + 5 = 0$

41. $5y^2 - 2y = 0$

42. $7z^2 - 6z - 2 = 0$

< Objective 3 >

The equation

$h(t) = 112t - 16t^2$

is the equation for the height of an arrow, shot upward from the ground with an initial velocity of 112 ft/sec, in which t is the time, in seconds, after the arrow leaves the ground.

Use this information to solve exercises 43 and 44. Your answers should be expressed to the nearest tenth of a second.

43. Find the time it takes for the arrow to reach a height of 112 ft.

44. Find the time it takes for the arrow to reach a height of 144 ft.

Answers

21. 1, 3
22. $\frac{7 \pm \sqrt{37}}{2}$
23. 4
24. −10, 3
25. $\frac{1 \pm \sqrt{7}}{2}$
26. $\frac{3 \pm \sqrt{65}}{4}$
27. $\frac{1 \pm i\sqrt{2}}{3}$
28. $\frac{1 \pm \sqrt{11}}{5}$
29. 25, two
30. 64, two
31. 0, one
32. 0, one
33. 37, two
34. −39, none
35. −63, none
36. −19, none
37. 4
38. $-\frac{3}{2}$
39. $\frac{7 \pm \sqrt{37}}{6}$
40. $\frac{1 \pm i\sqrt{39}}{4}$
41. $0, \frac{2}{5}$
42. $\frac{3 \pm \sqrt{23}}{7}$
43. 1.2 sec or 5.8 sec
44. 1.7 sec or 5.3 sec

The equation

$$h(t) = 320 - 32t - 16t^2$$

is the equation for the height of a ball, thrown downward from the top of a 320-ft building with an initial velocity of 32 ft/sec, in which t is the time after the ball is thrown down from the top of the building.

Use this information to solve exercises 45 and 46. Express your results to the nearest tenth of a second.

45. Find the time it takes for the ball to reach a height of 240 ft.

46. Find the time it takes for the ball to reach a height of 96 ft.

47. NUMBER PROBLEM The product of two consecutive integers is 72. What are the two integers?

48. NUMBER PROBLEM The sum of the squares of two consecutive whole numbers is 61. Find the two whole numbers.

49. GEOMETRY The width of a rectangle is 3 ft less than its length. If the area of the rectangle is 70 ft^2, what are the dimensions of the rectangle?

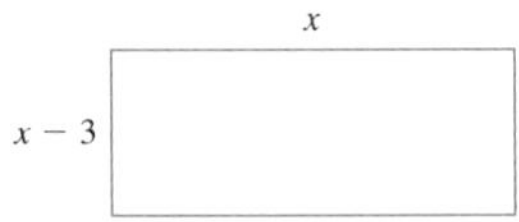

50. GEOMETRY The length of a rectangle is 5 cm more than its width. If the area of the rectangle is 84 cm^2, find the dimensions.

51. GEOMETRY The length of a rectangle is 2 cm more than 3 times its width. If the area of the rectangle is 85 cm^2, find the dimensions of the rectangle.

52. GEOMETRY If the length of a rectangle is 3 ft less than twice its width, and the area of the rectangle is 54 ft^2, what are the dimensions of the rectangle?

< Objective 4 >

53. GEOMETRY One leg of a right triangle is twice the length of the other. The hypotenuse is 6 m long. Find the length of each leg.

Answers

45. 1.4 sec
46. 2.9 sec
47. −9, −8 or 8, 9
48. 5, 6
49. 7 ft by 10 ft
50. 7 cm by 12 cm
51. 5 cm by 17 cm
52. 6 ft by 9 ft
53. 2.7 m, 5.4 m

Answers

54. 8.8 ft, 10.8 ft

55. 5.5 in., 6.5 in., 8.5 in.

56. 8.5 cm, 10.5 cm, 13.5 cm

57. 3.2 m, 21.8 m

58. 2.8 cm, 7.2 cm, 7.8 cm

59. 50 chairs

60. 40 appliances

54. GEOMETRY One leg of a right triangle is 2 ft longer than the shorter side. If the length of the hypotenuse is 14 ft, how long is each leg?

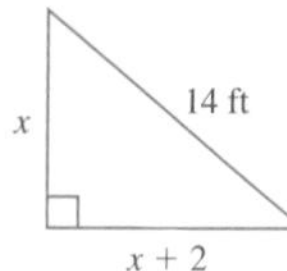

55. GEOMETRY One leg of a right triangle is 1 in. shorter than the other leg. The hypotenuse is 3 in. longer than the shorter side. Find the length of each side.

56. GEOMETRY The hypotenuse of a given right triangle is 5 cm longer than the shorter leg. The length of the shorter leg is 2 cm less than that of the longer leg. Find the length of the three sides.

57. GEOMETRY The sum of the lengths of the two legs of a right triangle is 25 m. The hypotenuse is 22 m long. Find the length of the two legs.

58. GEOMETRY The sum of the lengths of one side of a right triangle and the hypotenuse is 15 cm. The other leg is 5 cm shorter than the hypotenuse. Find the length of each side.

Solve the following applications.

59. BUSINESS AND FINANCE Suppose that the cost, $C(x)$, in dollars, of producing x chairs is given by

$$C(x) = 2{,}400 - 40x + 2x^2$$

How many chairs can be produced for $5,400?

60. BUSINESS AND FINANCE Suppose that the profit, $T(x)$, in dollars, of producing and selling x appliances is given by

$$T(x) = -3x^2 + 240x - 1{,}800$$

How many appliances must be produced and sold to achieve a profit of $3,000?

If a ball is thrown upward from the roof of a building 70 m tall with an initial velocity of 15 m/sec, its approximate height, h, after t seconds is given by

$$h(t) = 70 + 15t - 5t^2$$

Note: The difference between this equation and the one we used in Example 8 has to do with the units used. When we used feet, the t^2 coefficient was −16 (from the fact that the acceleration due to gravity is approximately 32 ft/sec^2). When we use meters as the height, the t^2 coefficient is −5 (that same acceleration becomes approximately 10 m/sec^2).

Use this information to solve exercises 61 and 62.

61. **Science and Medicine** How long does it take the ball to fall back to the ground?

62. **Science and Medicine** When will the ball reach a height of 80 m?

Changing the initial velocity to 25 m/sec will only change the t-coefficient. Our new equation becomes

$$h(t) = 70 + 25t - 5t^2$$

Use this information to solve exercises 63 and 64.

63. **Science and Medicine** How long will it take the ball to return to the thrower?

64. **Science and Medicine** When will the ball reach a height of 85 m?

65. **Business and Finance** A small manufacturer's weekly profit in dollars is given by

$$P(x) = -3x^2 + 270x$$

Find the number of items x that must be produced to realize a profit of \$5,100.

66. **Business and Finance** Suppose the profit in dollars is given by

$$P(x) = -2x^2 + 240x$$

Now how many items must be sold to realize a profit of \$5,100?

67. **Business and Finance** The demand equation for a certain computer chip is given by

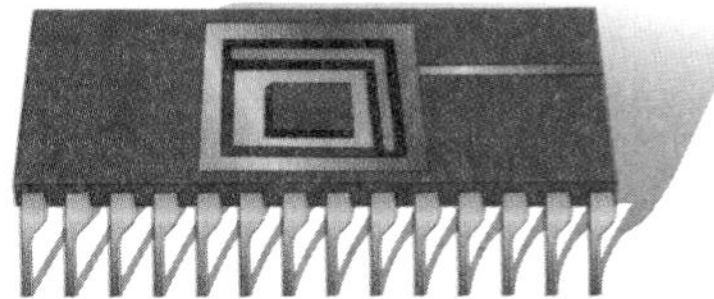

$$D = -2p + 14$$

in which p is the unit price in dollars. The supply equation is predicted to be

$$S = -p^2 + 16p - 2$$

Find the equilibrium price.

68. **Business and Finance** The demand equation for a certain type of print is predicted to be

$$D = -200p + 36,000$$

in which p is the unit price in dollars. The supply equation is predicted to be

$$S = -p^2 + 400p - 24,000$$

Find the equilibrium price.

Answers

61. 5.5 sec
62. 1 sec, 2 sec
63. 5 sec
64. 0.7 sec, 4.3 sec
65. 63 items or 27 items
66. 28 items or 92 items
67. \$0.94
68. \$126.79

Basic Skills | **Advanced Skills** | Vocational-Technical Applications | Calculator/Computer | Above and Beyond

Solve each equation by using the quadratic formula. (Hint: *Clear each of the following equations of fractions or parentheses first.*)

69. $2x^2 - \frac{1}{2}x - 5 = 0$

70. $3x^2 + \frac{1}{3}x - 3 = 0$

71. $5t^2 - 2t - \frac{2}{3} = 0$

72. $3y^2 + 2y + \frac{3}{4} = 0$

73. $(x - 2)(x + 3) = 4$

74. $(x + 1)(x - 8) = 3$

75. $(t + 1)(2t - 4) - 7 = 0$

76. $(2w + 1)(3w - 2) = 1$

77. $3x - 5 = \frac{1}{x}$

78. $x + 3 = \frac{1}{x}$

79. $2t - \frac{3}{t} = 3$

80. $4p - \frac{1}{p} = 6$

81. $\frac{5}{y^2} + \frac{2}{y} - 1 = 0$

82. $\frac{6}{x^2} - \frac{2}{x} = 1$

Find all solutions. Use any applicable method.

83. $(x - 1)(2x + 7) = -6$

84. $4x^2 - 3 = 0$

85. $x^2 + 9 = 0$

86. $(4x - 5)(x + 2) = 1$

87. $x - 3 - \frac{10}{x} = 0$

88. $1 + \frac{2}{x} + \frac{2}{x^2} = 0$

89. Science and Medicine If a ball is thrown vertically upward from the ground, its height, h, after t seconds is given by

$h(t) = 64t - 16t^2$

(a) How long does it take the ball to return to the ground? [*Hint:* Let $h(t) = 0$.]

(b) How long does it take the ball to reach a height of 48 ft on the way up?

Answers

69. $\frac{1 \pm \sqrt{161}}{8}$

70. $\frac{-1 \pm 5\sqrt{13}}{18}$

71. $\frac{3 \pm \sqrt{39}}{15}$

72. $\frac{-2 \pm i\sqrt{5}}{6}$

73. $\frac{-1 \pm \sqrt{41}}{2}$

74. $\frac{7 \pm \sqrt{93}}{2}$

75. $\frac{1 \pm \sqrt{23}}{2}$

76. $\frac{1 \pm \sqrt{73}}{12}$

77. $\frac{5 \pm \sqrt{37}}{6}$

78. $\frac{-3 \pm \sqrt{13}}{2}$

79. $\frac{3 \pm \sqrt{33}}{4}$

80. $\frac{3 \pm \sqrt{13}}{4}$

81. $1 \pm \sqrt{6}$

82. $-1 \pm \sqrt{7}$

83. $\frac{-5 \pm \sqrt{33}}{4}$

84. $\pm\frac{\sqrt{3}}{2}$

85. $-3i, 3i$

86. $\frac{-3 \pm \sqrt{185}}{8}$

87. $-2, 5$

88. $-1 \pm i$

89. (a) 4 sec; (b) 1 sec

90. **Science and Medicine** If a ball is thrown vertically upward from the ground, its height, h, after t seconds is given by

$$h(t) = 96t - 16t^2$$

(a) How long does it take the ball to return to the ground?

(b) How long does it take the ball to pass through a height of 128 ft on the way back down to the ground?

The only part of the height equation that we have not discussed is the constant. You have probably noticed that the constant is always equal to the initial height of the ball (70 m in exercises 61 to 64). Now, let's have *you* develop an equation.

A ball is thrown upward from the roof of a 100-*m building with an initial velocity of* 20 *m/sec. Use this information to solve exercises 91 to 94.*

91. **Science and Medicine** Find the equation for the height, h, of the ball after t seconds.

92. **Science and Medicine** How long will it take the ball to fall back to the ground?

93. **Science and Medicine** When will the ball reach a height of 75 m?

94. **Science and Medicine** Will the ball ever reach a height of 125 m? (*Hint:* Check the discriminant.)

A ball is thrown upward from the roof of a 100-*ft building with an initial velocity of* 20 *ft/sec. Use this information to solve exercises 95 to 98.*

95. **Science and Medicine** Find the equation for the height, h, of the ball after t seconds.

96. **Science and Medicine** How long will it take the ball to fall back to the ground?

97. **Science and Medicine** When will the ball reach a height of 80 ft?

98. **Science and Medicine** Will the ball ever reach a height of 120 ft? Explain.

Answers

90. (a) 6 sec; (b) 4 sec

91. $h(t) = 100 + 20t - 5t^2$

92. 6.9 sec

93. 5 sec

94. No

95. $h(t) = 100 + 20t - 16t^2$

96. 3.2 sec

97. 1.9 sec

98. No, at 120 ft "t" is not a real number.

Answers

99. (a) −1.2, 4.2; (b) −1.2, 4.2; (c) Solutions to the quadratic equation are the x-intercepts of the graph.

100. (a) 3, −1; (b) 3, −1; (c) Solutions to the equation are the x-coordinates of the points of intersection of the graphs of f and g.

101. Above and Beyond

102. Above and Beyond

103. $\pm\sqrt{z^2 - y^2}$

104. $\pm\dfrac{\sqrt{2}}{2yz}$

105. $\pm 6a$

106. $\pm\dfrac{3b\sqrt{a}}{a}$

107. $-3a, \dfrac{a}{2}$

108. $\dfrac{b}{3}, 5b$

109. $\dfrac{-a \pm a\sqrt{17}}{4}$

110. $\dfrac{b \pm b\sqrt{7}}{3}$

111. $-1 \pm \sqrt{6}$

112. $\dfrac{1 \pm \sqrt{3}}{2}$

113. $-1, \dfrac{1 \pm i\sqrt{3}}{2}$

Basic Skills | Advanced Skills | Vocational-Technical Applications | **Calculator/Computer** | Above and Beyond

99. **(a)** Use the quadratic formula to solve $x^2 - 3x - 5 = 0$. For each solution give a decimal approximation to the nearest tenth.

(b) Graph the function $f(x) = x^2 - 3x - 5$ on your graphing calculator. Use a zoom utility and estimate the x-intercepts to the nearest tenth.

(c) Describe the connection between parts **(a)** and **(b)**.

100. **(a)** Solve the following equation using any appropriate method:

$$x^2 - 2x = 3$$

(b) Graph the following functions on your graphing calculator:

$$f(x) = x^2 - 2x \quad \text{and} \quad g(x) = 3$$

Estimate the points of intersection of the graphs of f and g. In particular, note the x-coordinates of these points.

(c) Describe the connection between parts **(a)** and **(b)**.

Basic Skills | Advanced Skills | Vocational-Technical Applications | Calculator/Computer | **Above and Beyond**

101. Can the solution of a quadratic equation with integer coefficients include one real and one imaginary number? Justify your answer.

102. Explain how the discriminant is used to predict the nature of the solutions of a quadratic equation.

In exercises 103 to 110, solve each equation for x.

103. $x^2 + y^2 = z^2$

104. $2x^2y^2z^2 = 1$

105. $x^2 - 36a^2 = 0$

106. $ax^2 - 9b^2 = 0$

107. $2x^2 + 5ax - 3a^2 = 0$

108. $3x^2 - 16bx + 5b^2 = 0$

109. $2x^2 + ax - 2a^2 = 0$

110. $3x^2 - 2bx - 2b^2 = 0$

111. Given that the polynomial $x^3 - 3x^2 - 15x + 25 = 0$ has as one of its solutions $x = 5$, find the other two solutions. (*Hint:* If you divide the given polynomial by $x - 5$, the quotient will be a quadratic equation. The remaining solutions will be the solutions for *that* equation.)

112. Given that $2x^3 + 2x^2 - 5x - 2 = 0$ has as one of its solutions $x = -2$, find the other two solutions. (*Hint:* In this case, divide the original polynomial by $x + 2$.)

113. Find all the zeros of the function $f(x) = x^3 + 1$.

114. Find the zeros of the function $f(x) = x^2 + x + 1$.

115. Find all six solutions to the equation $x^6 - 1 = 0$. (*Hint:* Factor the left-hand side of the equation first as the difference of squares, and then as the sum and difference of cubes.)

116. Find all six solutions to $x^6 = 64$.

Answers

114. $\frac{-1 \pm i\sqrt{3}}{2}$

115. $-1, 1, \frac{1 \pm i\sqrt{3}}{2}, \frac{-1 \pm i\sqrt{3}}{2}$

116. $-2, 2, 1 \pm i\sqrt{3}, -1 \pm i\sqrt{3}$

Answers

1. $-2, 7$ **3.** $-13, 5$ **5.** $-1, \frac{1}{5}$ **7.** $\frac{3}{4}$ **9.** $1 \pm \sqrt{6}$

11. $\frac{-3 \pm 3\sqrt{13}}{2}$ **13.** $\frac{3 \pm \sqrt{15}}{2}$ **15.** $\frac{2 \pm \sqrt{2}}{2}$ **17.** $-\frac{2}{3}, 1$

19. $\frac{1 \pm \sqrt{41}}{4}$ **21.** $1, 3$ **23.** 4 **25.** $\frac{1 \pm \sqrt{7}}{2}$

27. $\frac{1 \pm i\sqrt{2}}{3}$ **29.** 25, two **31.** 0, one **33.** 37, two

35. -63, none **37.** 4 **39.** $\frac{7 \pm \sqrt{37}}{6}$ **41.** $0, \frac{2}{5}$

43. 1.2 sec or 5.8 sec **45.** 1.4 sec **47.** $-9, -8$, or $8, 9$ **49.** 7 ft by 10 ft
51. 5 cm by 17 cm **53.** 2.7 m, 5.4 m **55.** 5.5 in., 6.5 in., 8.5 in.
57. 3.2 m, 21.8 m **59.** 50 chairs **61.** 5.5 sec **63.** 5 sec

65. 63 items or 27 items **67.** \$0.94 **69.** $\frac{1 \pm \sqrt{161}}{8}$ **71.** $\frac{3 \pm \sqrt{39}}{15}$

73. $\frac{-1 \pm \sqrt{41}}{2}$ **75.** $\frac{1 \pm \sqrt{23}}{2}$ **77.** $\frac{5 \pm \sqrt{37}}{6}$ **79.** $\frac{3 \pm \sqrt{33}}{4}$

81. $1 \pm \sqrt{6}$ **83.** $\frac{-5 \pm \sqrt{33}}{4}$ **85.** $-3i, 3i$ **87.** $-2, 5$

89. **(a)** 4 sec; **(b)** 1 sec **91.** $h(t) = 100 + 20t - 5t^2$ **93.** 5 sec
95. $h(t) = 100 + 20t - 16t^2$ **97.** 1.9 sec **99.** **(a)** $-1.2, 4.2$; **(b)** $-1.2, 4.2$;
(c) Solutions to the quadratic equation are the x-intercepts of the graph.
101. Above and Beyond **103.** $\pm\sqrt{z^2 - y^2}$ **105.** $\pm 6a$

107. $-3a, \frac{a}{2}$ **109.** $\frac{-a \pm a\sqrt{17}}{4}$ **111.** $-1 \pm \sqrt{6}$

113. $-1, \frac{1 \pm i\sqrt{3}}{2}$ **115.** $-1, 1, \frac{1 \pm i\sqrt{3}}{2}, \frac{-1 \pm i\sqrt{3}}{2}$

8.4 Equations That Are Quadratic in Form

< 8.4 Objectives >

1 > Solve a radical equation that is quadratic in form

2 > Solve other equations that are quadratic in form

NOTES

Let $u = \sqrt{x}$ in the first equation.

Let $u = x^2$ in the second equation.

Let $u = x^2 - x$ in the third equation.

Consider the following equations:

$$2x - 5\sqrt{x} + 3 = 0$$
$$x^4 - 4x^2 + 3 = 0$$
$$(x^2 - x)^2 - 8(x^2 - x) + 12 = 0$$

None of these equations are quadratic, yet each can be readily solved by using quadratic methods.

Compare the following quadratic equations to the original three equations.

$$2u^2 - 5u + 3 = 0$$
$$u^2 - 4u + 3 = 0$$
$$u^2 - 8u + 12 = 0$$

In each case, a simple substitution has been made that resulted in a quadratic equation. Equations that can be rewritten in this manner are said to be *equations in quadratic form.*

Example 1 Solving a Radical Equation

< Objective 1 >

NOTES

Notice that $u^2 = x$ because $u = \sqrt{x}$.

By intermediate solutions we mean values for u rather than for the original variable x.

Solve.

$$2x - 5\sqrt{x} + 3 = 0$$

By substituting u for $\sqrt{x}$, we have

$$2u^2 - 5u + 3 = 0$$

Factoring yields

$$(2u - 3)(u - 1) = 0$$

which gives the intermediate solutions

$$u = \frac{3}{2} \quad \text{or} \quad u = 1$$

NOTE

We square both sides in each equation.

We must now solve for x and then check our solutions. Because $\sqrt{x} = u$, we can write

$$\sqrt{x} = \frac{3}{2} \quad \text{or} \quad \sqrt{x} = 1$$

$$x = \frac{9}{4} \qquad\qquad x = 1$$

To check these solutions, we again simply substitute these values into the original equation. You should verify that each is a valid solution.

Check Yourself 1

Solve $3x - 8\sqrt{x} + 4 = 0$.

For certain equations in quadratic form, we can either solve by substitution (as we did in Example 1) or solve directly by treating the equation as quadratic in some other power of the variable (this will be x^2 in the case of the equation of Example 2). In Example 2, we show both methods of solution.

Example 2 Solving a Fourth-Degree Equation

< Objective 2 >

(a) Solve $x^4 - 4x^2 + 3 = 0$ by substitution.

Let $u = x^2$. Then

$$u^2 - 4u + 3 = 0$$

NOTE

$u^2 = (x^2)^2 = x^4$

Factoring, we have

$$(u - 1)(u - 3) = 0$$

so

$$u = 1 \quad \text{or} \quad u = 3$$

Given these intermediate solutions, because $u = x^2$, we can write

$$x^2 = 1 \quad \text{or} \quad x^2 = 3$$

which, by using the square root method, yields the four solutions

$$x = \pm 1 \quad \text{or} \quad x = \pm\sqrt{3}$$

NOTE

There are *four* solutions to the original *fourth-degree* equation.

We can check each of these solutions by substituting into the original equation. When we do so, we find that all four are valid solutions to the original equation.

(b) Solve $x^4 - 4x^2 + 3 = 0$ directly.

By treating the equation as quadratic in x^2, we can factor the left member, to write

$$(x^2 - 1)(x^2 - 3) = 0$$

This gives us the two equations

$$x^2 - 1 = 0 \quad \text{or} \quad x^2 - 3 = 0$$

Now

$$x^2 = 1 \quad \text{or} \quad x^2 = 3$$

NOTE

We apply the square root property.

Again, we have the four possible solutions

$x = \pm 1 \quad \text{or} \quad x = \pm\sqrt{3}$

All check when they are substituted into the original equation.

Check Yourself 2

Solve $x^4 - 9x^2 + 20 = 0$ by substitution and by factoring directly.

In Example 3, a binomial is replaced with u to make it easier to proceed with the solution.

Example 3 Solving a Fourth-Degree Equation

Solve.

$(x^2 - x)^2 - 8(x^2 - x) + 12 = 0$

Because of the repeated factor $x^2 - x$, we substitute u for $x^2 - x$. Factoring the resulting equation

$u^2 - 8u + 12 = 0$

gives

$(u - 6)(u - 2) = 0$

So

$u = 6 \quad \text{or} \quad u = 2$

We now have two intermediate solutions to work with. Because $u = x^2 - x$, we have two cases:

NOTE

Write in standard form. Then factor the quadratic member.

If $u = 6$, then

$$x^2 - x = 6$$
$$x^2 - x - 6 = 0$$
$$(x - 3)(x + 2) = 0$$
$$x = 3 \quad \text{or} \quad x = -2$$

If $u = 2$, then

$$x^2 - x = 2$$
$$x^2 - x - 2 = 0$$
$$(x - 2)(x + 1) = 0$$
$$x = 2 \quad \text{or} \quad x = -1$$

The quadratic equations now yield four solutions that we must check. Substituting them into the original equation, we will find that all four are valid solutions.

Check Yourself 3

Solve for x:

$$(x^2 - 2x)^2 - 11(x^2 - 2x) + 24 = 0$$

An equation involving rational exponents can sometimes be solved as quadratic in form as Example 4 illustrates.

Example 4 Solving an Equation with Rational Exponents

NOTE

$u^2 = (x^{1/4})^2 = x^{1/2}$

(a) Solve $x^{1/2} - 5x^{1/4} + 6 = 0$ by substitution.

Let $u = x^{1/4}$. Then by substitution

$u^2 - 5u + 6 = 0$

Factoring, we have

$(u - 3)(u - 2) = 0$

So

$u - 3 = 0$ or $u - 2 = 0$
$u = 3$ $u = 2$

NOTE

$(x^{1/4})^4 = x$

Given these intermediate solutions, because $u = x^{1/4}$, we can write

$x^{1/4} = 3$ or $x^{1/4} = 2$

Raising both sides of each equation to the fourth power yields the solutions

$(x^{1/4})^4 = 3^4$ or $(x^{1/4})^4 = 2^4$
$x = 81$ $x = 16$

We can check these solutions by substituting them in the original equation. When we do so, we find that the solutions are valid.

RECALL

$x^{1/2} = \sqrt{x}$

$x^{1/4} = \sqrt[4]{x}$

(b) Solve $x^{1/2} - 5x^{1/4} + 6 = 0$ directly.

By treating the equation as a quadratic in x^2, we can factor the left member to write

$(x^{1/4} - 3)(x^{1/4} - 2) = 0$

This gives us the two equations

$x^{1/4} - 3 = 0$ or $x^{1/4} - 2 = 0$

Now

$x^{1/4} = 3$ or $x^{1/4} = 2$

Again we have the two solutions

$(x^{1/4})^4 = 3^4$ or $(x^{1/4})^4 = 2^4$
$x = 81$ $x = 16$

Check Yourself 4

Solve $x^{1/2} - 4x^{1/4} + 3 = 0$ by substitution and by factoring directly.

Certain equations involving rational expressions can also be solved as quadratic in form as illustrated in Example 5.

Example 5 Solving Equations with Rational Expressions

(a) Solve $\frac{1}{y^2} - 2\frac{1}{y} - 3 = 0$ by substitution.

NOTE

$\frac{1}{y^2} - 2\frac{1}{y} - 3 = 0$ can also be written as $y^{-2} - 2y^{-1} - 3 = 0$

Let $u = \frac{1}{y}$. Then by substitution

$$u^2 - 2u - 3 = 0$$

Factoring, we have

$$(u - 3)(u + 1) = 0$$

So

$$u - 3 = 0 \quad \text{or} \quad u + 1 = 0$$
$$u = 3 \qquad\qquad u = -1$$

Given these intermediate solutions, because $u = \frac{1}{y}$, we can write

$$\frac{1}{y} = 3 \quad \text{or} \quad \frac{1}{y} = -1$$

Multiplying both sides of each equation by y and then solving for y yields

$$1 = 3y \quad \text{or} \quad 1 = -1y$$
$$\frac{1}{3} = y \qquad\qquad -1 = y$$
$$y = \frac{1}{3} \qquad\qquad y = -1$$

We can check these solutions by substituting in the original equation. When we do so, we find that the solutions are valid.

(b) Solve $\frac{1}{y^2} - 2\frac{1}{y} - 3 = 0$ directly.

By treating the equation as a quadratic in y^2, we can factor the left member to write

$$\left(\frac{1}{y} - 3\right)\left(\frac{1}{y} + 1\right) = 0$$

This gives us two equations:

$$\frac{1}{y} - 3 = 0 \quad \text{or} \quad \frac{1}{y} + 1 = 0$$

Now

$$\frac{1}{y} = 3 \quad \text{or} \quad \frac{1}{y} = -1$$

Again we have the two solutions (multiplying both sides of each equation by y and solving for y).

$$y = \frac{1}{3} \quad \text{or} \quad y = -1$$

Check Yourself 5

Solve $\frac{1}{y^2} - \frac{2}{y} - 8 = 0$ by substitution and by factoring directly.

To summarize our work with equations in quadratic form, two approaches are commonly used. The first involves substitution of a new intermediate variable to make the original equation quadratic. The second solves the original equation directly by treating the equation as quadratic in some other power of the original variable. The following algorithms outline the two approaches.

Step by Step

Solving by Substitution

Step 1 Make an appropriate substitution so that the equation becomes quadratic.
Step 2 Solve the resulting equation for the intermediate variable.
Step 3 Use the intermediate values found in step 2 to find possible solutions for the original variable.
Step 4 Check the solutions of step 3 by substitution into the original equation.

Step by Step

Solving by Factoring

Step 1 Treat the original equation as quadratic in some power of the variable, and factor.
Step 2 Solve the resulting equations.
Step 3 Check the solutions of step 2 by substitution into the original equation.

Check Yourself ANSWERS

1. $\frac{4}{9}, 4$ **2.** $\pm 2, \pm\sqrt{5}$ **3.** $-1, -2, 3, 4$ **4.** $1, 81$ **5.** $-\frac{1}{2}, \frac{1}{4}$

Reading Your Text

The following fill-in-the-blank exercises are designed to ensure that you understand some of the key vocabulary used in this section.

SECTION 8.4

(a) Equations that are quadratic in form can be solved by using ______________ methods.

(b) For certain equations in quadratic form, we can either solve by ______________ or directly.

(c) A fourth-degree equation will yield ______________ solutions.

(d) We can check solutions to equations quadratic in form by substituting into the ______________ equations.

8.4 exercises

Basic Skills | Advanced Skills | Vocational-Technical Applications | Calculator/Computer | Above and Beyond

MathZone

Boost your grade at mathzone.com!
> Practice Problems
> NetTutor
> Self-Tests
> e-Professors
> Videos

Name ______________

Section ________ Date ________

< Objectives 1 and 2 >

Solve each of the following equations by factoring directly and then applying the zero-product principle.

1. $x^4 - 9x^2 + 20 = 0$ 

2. $t^4 - 7t^2 + 12 = 0$

3. $x^4 + x^2 - 12 = 0$

4. $x^4 - 7x^2 - 18 = 0$

5. $2w^4 - 9w^2 + 4 = 0$

6. $3x^4 - 5x^2 + 2 = 0$

7. $x^4 - 4x^2 + 4 = 0$

8. $y^4 - 6y^2 + 9 = 0$

9. $3x^4 + 16x^2 - 12 = 0$

10. $2x^4 + 9x^2 - 5 = 0$

11. $2z^4 + 4z^2 - 70 = 0$

12. $3y^4 + 10y^2 - 8 = 0$

13. $4t^4 - 20t^2 = 0$

14. $r^4 - 81 = 0$

Solve each of the following equations.

15. $x^4 - x^2 - 12 = 0$

16. $w^4 + w^2 - 6 = 0$

17. $2y^4 + y^2 - 15 = 0$

18. $4x^4 - 5x^2 - 9 = 0$

19. $b - 20\sqrt{b} + 64 = 0$ 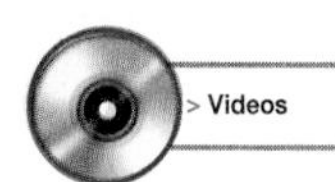

20. $z - 6\sqrt{z} + 8 = 0$

21. $t - 8\sqrt{t} - 9 = 0$

22. $y - 24\sqrt{y} - 25 = 0$

Answers

1. $\pm\sqrt{5}, \pm 2$
2. $\pm\sqrt{3}, \pm 2$
3. $\pm\sqrt{3}, \pm 2i$
4. $\pm 3, \pm i\sqrt{2}$
5. $\pm\frac{\sqrt{2}}{2}, \pm 2$
6. $\pm\frac{\sqrt{6}}{3}, \pm 1$
7. $\pm\sqrt{2}$
8. $\pm\sqrt{3}$
9. $\pm\frac{\sqrt{6}}{3}, \pm i\sqrt{6}$
10. $\pm\frac{\sqrt{2}}{2}, \pm i\sqrt{5}$
11. $\pm\sqrt{5}, \pm i\sqrt{7}$
12. $\pm\frac{\sqrt{6}}{3}, \pm 2i$
13. $0, \pm\sqrt{5}$
14. $\pm 3, \pm 3i$
15. $\pm 2, \pm i\sqrt{3}$
16. $\pm\sqrt{2}, \pm i\sqrt{3}$
17. $\pm\frac{\sqrt{10}}{2}, \pm i\sqrt{3}$
18. $\pm\frac{3}{2}, \pm i$
19. 16, 256
20. 4, 16
21. 81
22. 625

23. $(x - 2)^2 - 3(x - 2) - 10 = 0$

24. $(w + 1)^2 - 5(w + 1) + 6 = 0$

25. $(x^2 + 2x)^2 + 3(x^2 + 2x) + 2 = 0$

26. $(x^2 - 4x)^2 - (x^2 - 4x) - 12 = 0$

Solve each of the following equations by any method.

27. $7m - 41\sqrt{m} - 6 = 0$

28. $(x + 1) - 6\sqrt{x + 1} + 8 = 0$

29. $(w - 3)^2 - 2(w - 3) = 15$

30. $(x^2 - 4x)^2 + 7(x^2 - 4x) + 12 = 0$

31. $2y^4 - 5y^2 = 12$

32. $4t^4 - 29t^2 + 25 = 0$

33. $w^{1/2} - 4w^{1/4} + 3 = 0$

34. $x^{1/2} - 5x^{1/4} + 6 = 0$

35. $x^{1/2} - x^{1/4} = 2$

36. $2x^{1/2} + x^{1/4} - 1 = 0$

37. $x^{2/3} + 2x^{1/3} - 3 = 0$

38. $x^{2/5} - x^{1/5} = 6$

39. $\frac{1}{x^2} - \frac{6}{x} + 8 = 0$

40. $\frac{2}{x^2} - \frac{1}{x} = 3$

Basic Skills | **Advanced Skills** | Vocational-Technical Applications | Calculator/Computer | Above and Beyond

Solve each of the following equations.

41. $\frac{3}{x^2} - \frac{5}{x} = 2$

42. $\frac{1}{(x + 1)^2} - \frac{5}{x + 1} + 4 = 0$

43. $\frac{1}{(x - 2)^2} + \frac{1}{x - 2} = 6$

44. $\frac{8}{(x - 3)^2} - \frac{2}{x - 3} = 1$

Answers

23. 7, 0
24. 1, 2
25. $-1, -1 \pm i$
26. $1, 3, 2 \pm 2\sqrt{2}$
27. 36
28. 3, 15
29. 0, 8
30. 1, 2, 3
31. $\pm 2, \pm \frac{i\sqrt{6}}{2}$
32. $\pm 1, \pm \frac{5}{2}$
33. 1, 81
34. 16, 81
35. 16
36. $\frac{1}{16}$
37. $-27, 1$
38. $-32, 243$
39. $\frac{1}{4}, \frac{1}{2}$
40. $-1, \frac{2}{3}$
41. $-3, \frac{1}{2}$
42. $-\frac{3}{4}, 0$
43. $\frac{5}{3}, \frac{5}{2}$
44. $-1, 5$

Answers

45. 16

46. 25

47. 2

48. 3

Solve each of the following applications.

45. **Number Problem** The sum of an integer and twice its square root is 24. What is the integer?

46. **Number Problem** The sum of an integer and 3 times its square root is 40. Find the integer.

47. **Number Problem** The sum of the reciprocal of an integer and the square of its reciprocal is $\frac{3}{4}$. What is the integer?

48. **Number Problem** The difference between the reciprocal of an integer and the square of its reciprocal is $\frac{2}{9}$. Find the integer.

Answers

1. $\pm\sqrt{5}, \pm 2$ **3.** $\pm\sqrt{3}, \pm 2i$ **5.** $\pm\frac{\sqrt{2}}{2}, \pm 2$ **7.** $\pm\sqrt{2}$
9. $\pm\frac{\sqrt{6}}{3}, \pm i\sqrt{6}$ **11.** $\pm\sqrt{5}, \pm i\sqrt{7}$ **13.** $0, \pm\sqrt{5}$
15. $\pm 2, \pm i\sqrt{3}$ **17.** $\pm\frac{\sqrt{10}}{2}, \pm i\sqrt{3}$ **19.** 16, 256 **21.** 81
23. 7, 0 **25.** $-1, -1 \pm i$ **27.** 36 **29.** 0, 8 **31.** $\pm 2, \pm\frac{i\sqrt{6}}{2}$
33. 1, 81 **35.** 16 **37.** $-27, 1$ **39.** $\frac{1}{4}, \frac{1}{2}$ **41.** $-3, \frac{1}{2}$ **43.** $\frac{5}{3}, \frac{5}{2}$
45. 16 **47.** 2

8.5 Quadratic Inequalities and Rational Inequalities

< 8.5 Objectives >

1 > Solve a quadratic inequality graphically

2 > Solve a quadratic inequality algebraically

3 > Solve a quadratic inequality in two variables

4 > Solve a rational inequality

A **quadratic inequality** is an inequality that can be written in the form

$$ax^2 + bx + c < 0 \quad \text{when } a \neq 0$$

Note that the inequality symbol, $<$, can be replaced by the symbol $>$, $\leq$, or $\geq$ in this definition.

In this section, we will solve quadratic inequalities.

Example 1 Solving a Quadratic Inequality Graphically

< Objective 1 >

Solve the inequality

$$x^2 - x - 12 \leq 0$$

First, use the techniques in Section 8.1 to graph the function $f(x) = x^2 - x - 12$.

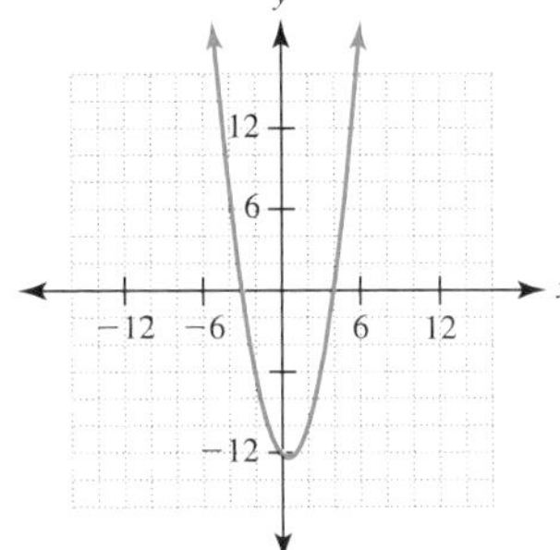

Note that $x^2 - x - 12$ factors as $(x - 4)(x + 3)$. The parabola therefore has x-intercepts of $(4, 0)$ and $(-3, 0)$.

Next, looking at the graph, determine the values of x that make $x^2 - x - 12 \leq 0$ a true statement.

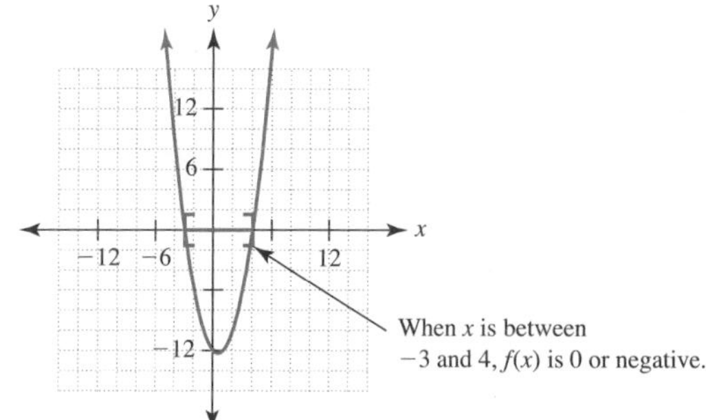

We ask, "For what values of x is the graph *on or below* the x-axis?"

NOTE

If we expand the binomial product in Example 2, we get

$x^2 - 2x - 3 < 0$

Looking at the graph of

$y = x^2 - 2x - 3,$

where is y less than 0 on the graph?

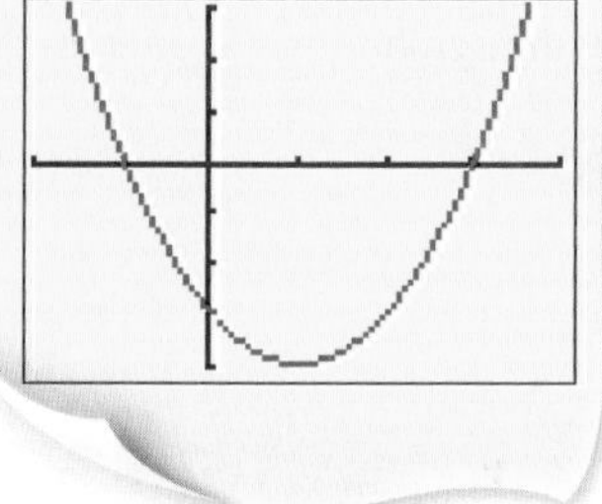

Notice that the graph is on or below the x-axis for values of x between -3 and 4. The graph intercepts the x-axis when x is -3 or 4. The solution for the inequality is $-3 \leq x \leq 4$.

Check Yourself 1

Use a graph to solve the inequality.

$x^2 - 3x - 10 \geq 0$

Algebraic methods can also be used to find the solutions to a quadratic inequality. Subsequent examples in this section will discuss algebraic methods. When solving an equation or inequality algebraically, it is always a good idea to compare the graph to the algebraic solutions.

Example 2 Solving a Quadratic Inequality Algebraically

< Objective 2 >

Solve $(x - 3)(x + 1) < 0$.

We start by finding the solutions of the corresponding quadratic equation. So

$(x - 3)(x + 1) = 0$

has solutions 3 and -1.

Our process depends on determining where each factor is positive or negative. To help visualize that process, we start with a number line and label it as shown. We begin with our first zero of -1.

NOTES

$x + 1$ is negative if x is less than -1 and $x + 1$ is positive if x is greater than -1.

$x - 3$ is negative if x is less than 3 and $x - 3$ is positive if x is greater than 3.

Sign of $x + 1$ − − − − |+ + + + + + + + + + +

−1

We now continue in the same manner with the second zero, 3.

Sign of $x - 3$ − − − − − − − − − − − − |+ + + +

3

In practice, we combine the two steps for the following result.

Sign of $x + 1$ − − − −|+ + + + + + +|+ + + +
Sign of $x - 3$ − − − −|− − − − − − −|+ + + +
−1 3
Sign of product + + + + − − − − − − − − + + + +

Examining the signs of the factors, we see that in this case:

For any x less than -1, the product is positive.

For any x between -1 and 3, the product is negative.

For any x greater than 3, the product is again positive.

NOTES

Both factors are negative.

The factors have opposite signs.

Both factors are positive.

The product of the two binomials must be negative.

We return to the original inequality:

$(x - 3)(x + 1) < 0$

We can see that this is true only between -1 and 3. The solution can be written as

$-1 < x < 3$

On a number line, the graph of the solution is

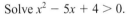

Check Yourself 2

Solve and graph the solution.

$(x - 2)(x + 4) < 0$

We now consider an example in which we factor the quadratic member of the inequality.

Example 3 Solving a Quadratic Inequality Algebraically

Solve $x^2 - 5x + 4 > 0$.

Factoring the quadratic member, we have

$(x - 1)(x - 4) > 0$

NOTE

Examine the graph of $y = x^2 - 5x + 4$. For what values of x is y (the graph) greater than zero?

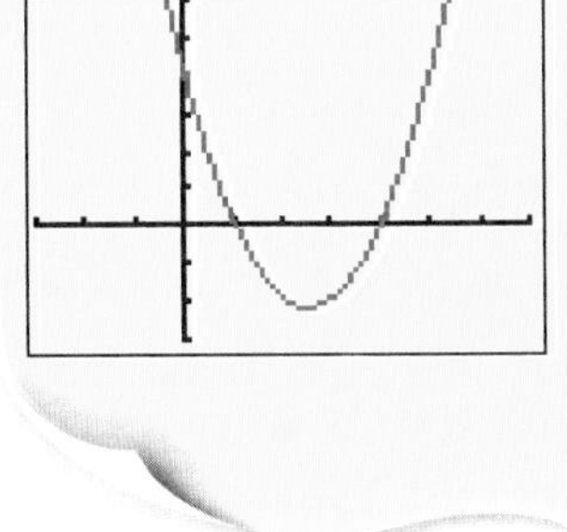

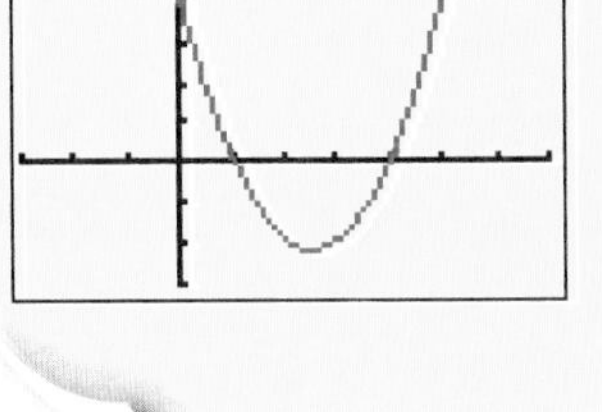

The critical values (the zeros of the binomials) are 1 and 4, and we form the sign graph as before.

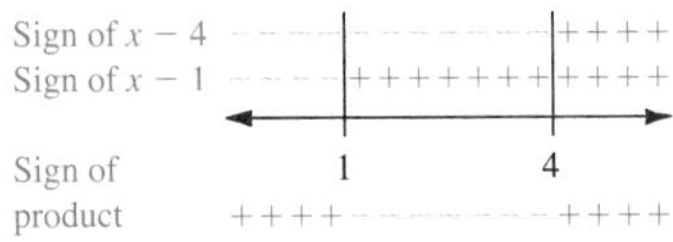

In this case, we want those values of x for which the product is *positive,* and we can see from the sign graph that the solution is

$x < 1$ or $x > 4$

The graph of the solution is shown here.

1 4

Check Yourself 3

Solve and graph the solution.

$2x^2 - x - 3 > 0$

The method used in Examples 1 to 3 works *only* when one side of the inequality is factorable and the other is 0. It is sometimes necessary to rewrite the inequality in an equivalent form, as Example 4 illustrates.

Example 4 Solving a Quadratic Inequality Algebraically

Solve $(x + 1)(x - 4) \geq 6$.

First, we multiply to clear the parentheses.

$x^2 - 3x - 4 \geq 6$

NOTE

Use a calculator to graph both $f(x) = x^2 - 3x - 4$ and $g(x) = 6$. Where is $f(x)$ above $g(x)$? Compare this to the algebraic solution.

Now we subtract 6 from both sides so that the right side of the inequality is 0:

$x^2 - 3x - 10 \geq 0$

Factoring the quadratic member, we have

$(x - 5)(x + 2) \geq 0$

We can now proceed with the sign graph method as before.

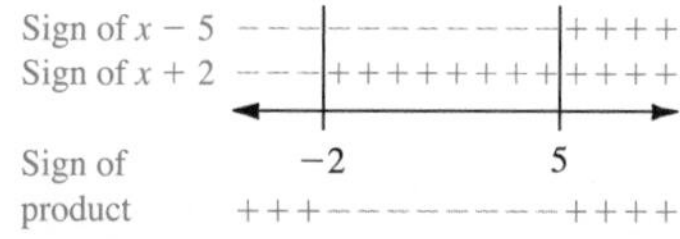

NOTE

Both factors are negative if x is less than -2. Both factors are positive if x is greater than 5.

From the sign graph we see that the solution is

$x \leq -2$ or $x \geq 5$

The graph of the solution is shown here.

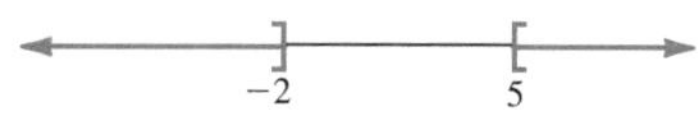

Check Yourself 4

Solve and graph the solution set.

$(x - 5)(x + 7) \leq -11$

The following algorithm summarizes our work to this point in solving a quadratic inequality in one variable.

Step by Step

Solving a Quadratic Inequality Algebraically

Step 1 Clear the inequality of parentheses and fractions.

Step 2 Rewrite the inequality so that one side is zero.

Step 3 Factor the quadratic expression.

Step 4 Use a sign graph to find the values for x that make the inequality a true statement.

Step 5 Use a number line to graph the solution.

Each of the quadratic inequalities we have investigated in this section has included only one variable. What does the solution for a quadratic inequality in two variables look like? Example 5 illustrates.

Example 5 Solving a Quadratic Inequality in Two Variables

< Objective 3 >

Use a graphing calculator to find the solution for the inequality

$$y \le x^2 - 3x - 10$$

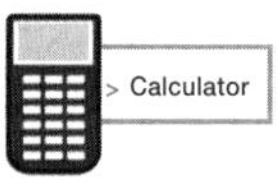

Recall from Section 4.4 that the solution for a linear inequality in two variables was a set of points in the plane. Further recall that, to find that set of points, we first graphed the line of the related equation. We will use a graphing calculator to graph

$$f(x) = x^2 - 3x - 10$$

Because the graph of $f(x)$ is a parabola, the solution has a parabolic boundary.

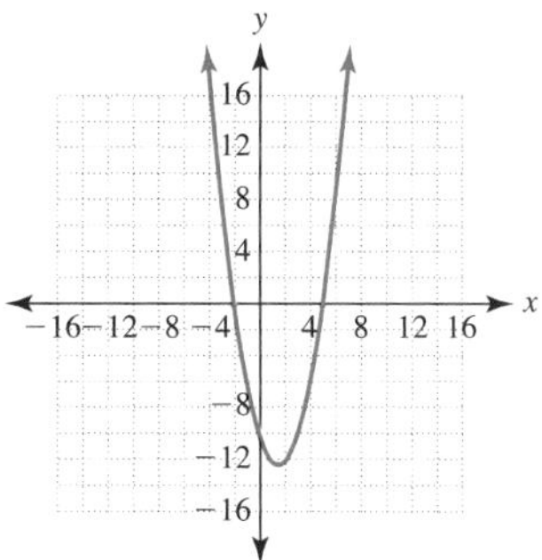

Now we decide which half-plane to shade. As we did with linear inequalities, we select a test point and find whether the test point is part of the solution. The origin is usually the easiest test point to use.

$$0 \overset{?}{\le} (0)^2 - 3(0) - 10$$

$0 \le -10$ is not a true statement. We will shade the half-plane that does not include the origin.

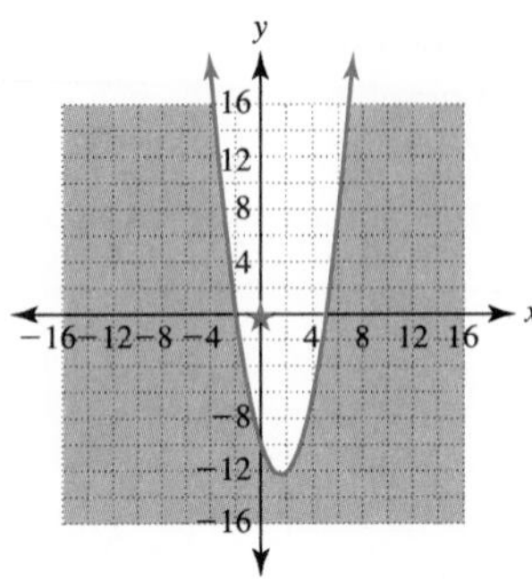

Check Yourself 5

Graph the solution for the inequality.

$y \ge x^2 - 7x + 12$

Now we will turn our attention to solving rational inequalities. **A rational inequality** is an inequality that can be written in the form

$$\frac{x + a}{x + b} < 0 \quad \text{when } x + b \ne 0$$

Note that the inequality symbol, $<$, can be replaced by the symbol, $<$, $\le$, or $\ge$ in the definition.

The algebraic method of solution is similar to that of solving quadratic inequalities. Example 6 illustrates this.

Example 6 Solving a Rational Inequality

< Objective 4 >

Solve the inequality

$$\frac{x - 3}{x + 2} < 0$$

The inequality states that the quotient of $(x - 3)$ and $(x + 2)$ must be negative (less than 0). This means the numerator and denominator have opposite signs. The critical values (those values of x for which the numerator and denominator are zero) are 3 and -2, and we form the following sign graph.

Sign of $x - 3$	− − −	− − − − − − − − −	+ + + +
Sign of $x + 2$	− − −	+ + + + + + + +	+ + + +
		-2	3
Sign of the quotient	+ + +	− − − − − − − − −	+ + + +

In this case, we want those values of x for which the quotient is negative, and we can see from the sign graph that the solution is

$-2 < x < 3$ or $(-2, 3)$

The graph of the solution is shown here.

Check Yourself 6

Solve and graph the solution.

$$\frac{x - 4}{x + 2} > 0$$

The solution process illustrated in Example 6 is valid only when the rational expression is isolated on one side of the inequality as the first step, as Example 7 illustrates.

Example 7 Solving a Rational Inequality

Solve the inequality

$$\frac{2x - 3}{x + 1} \geq 1$$

$$\frac{2x - 3}{x + 1} - 1 \geq 0$$ Subtract 1 from both sides.

$$\frac{2x - 3}{x + 1} - \frac{x + 1}{x + 1} \geq 0$$ Expand 1 to an equivalent fraction with a denominator of $x + 1$.

$$\frac{2x - 3 - (x + 1)}{x + 1} \geq 0$$ Combine the expressions.

$$\frac{2x - 3 - x - 1}{x + 1} \geq 0$$ Simplify.

$$\frac{x - 4}{x + 1} \geq 0$$

We can now proceed as before since the rational expression is related to 0. The critical points are 4 and -1, and the sign graph is formed as follows.

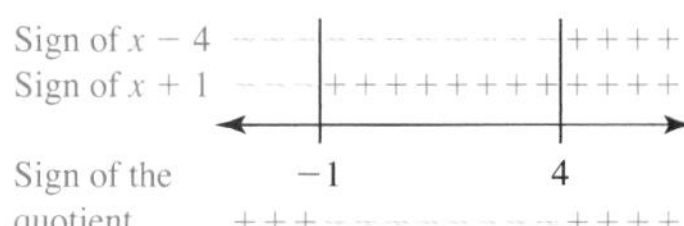

Since the inequality is greater than *or equal to,* the critical points themselves must also be tested. From the sign graph the solution is

$x < -1$ or $x \geq 4$ or $(-\infty, -1) \cup [4, \infty)$

Note that 4 is included in the solution but -1 is not. Do you see why?

The graph is shown here.

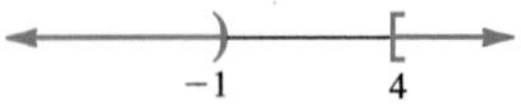

Check Yourself 7

Solve and graph the solution.

$$\frac{2x - 3}{x - 2} \le 1$$

The following algorithm summarizes our work to this point in solving a rational inequality in one variable.

Step by Step

Solving a Rational Inequality Algebraically

Step 1 Isolate the inequality on the left side and relate it to 0.

Step 2 Form a common denominator on the left side of the inequality.

Step 3 Combine the expressions on the left side.

Step 4 Use a sign graph to find the values for x that make the inequality a true statement.

Step 5 Use a number line to graph the solution.

Check Yourself ANSWERS

1. $x \le -2$ or $x \ge 5$

2.  $-4 < x < 2$ or $(-4, 2)$

3. 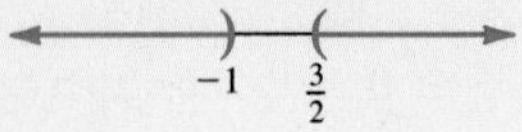 $x < -1$ or $x > \frac{3}{2}$ or $(-\infty, -1) \cup \left(\frac{3}{2}, \infty\right)$

4.  $-6 \le x \le 4$ or $[-6, 4]$

5.

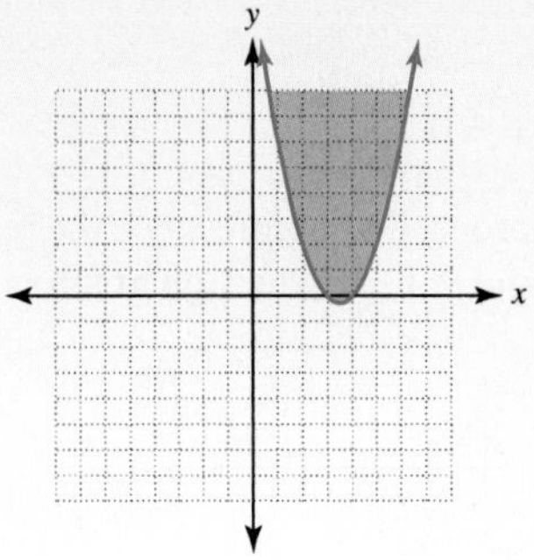

6. $x < -2$ or $x > 4$

$(-\infty, -2) \cup (4, \infty)$

7. $1 \le x < 2$ or $[1, 2)$ 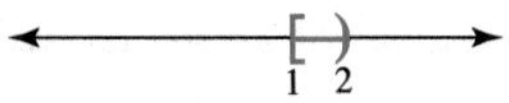

Reading Your Text

The following fill-in-the-blank exercises are designed to ensure that you understand some of the key vocabulary used in this section.

SECTION 8.5

(a) A quadratic inequality can be solved graphically or ______________.

(b) When solving a quadratic inequality algebraically, the zeros of the related equation are called its ______________ values.

(c) If the quadratic inequality is less than zero, we want those values of the variable for which the product is ______________.

(d) The algebraic method of solving rational inequalities is similar to that of solving ______________ inequalities.

8.5 exercises

Basic Skills | Advanced Skills | Vocational-Technical Applications | Calculator/Computer | Above and Beyond

MathZone

Boost your grade at mathzone.com!
- > Practice Problems
- > NetTutor
- > Self-Tests
- > e-Professors
- > Videos

Name ____________

Section ______ Date ______

Answers

1. See exercise
2. See exercise
3. See exercise
4. See exercise
5. See exercise
6. See exercise
7. See exercise
8. See exercise
9. See exercise
10. See exercise
11. See exercise
12. See exercise
13. See exercise
14. See exercise
15. See exercise
16. See exercise
17. See exercise
18. See exercise

In exercises 1 to 8, solve each inequality, and graph the solution.

1. $(x - 3)(x + 4) < 0$

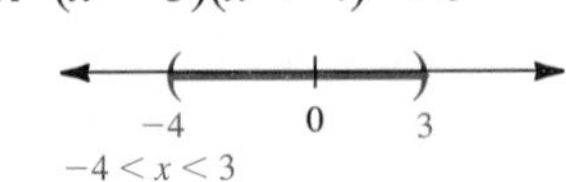

$-4 < x < 3$

2. $(x - 2)(x + 5) > 0$

−5 0 2

$x < -5$ or $x > 2$

3. $(x - 3)(x + 4) > 0$

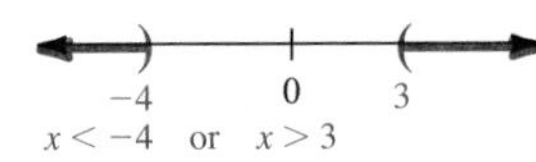

$x < -4$ or $x > 3$

4. $(x - 2)(x + 5) < 0$

−5 0 2

$-5 < x < 2$

5. $(x - 3)(x + 4) \le 0$

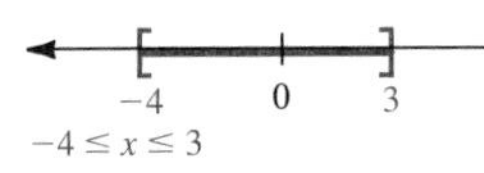

$-4 \le x \le 3$

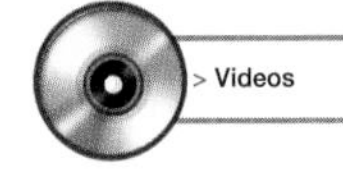

6. $(x - 2)(x + 5) \ge 0$

−5 0 2

$x \le -5$ or $x \ge 2$

7. $(x - 3)(x + 4) \ge 0$

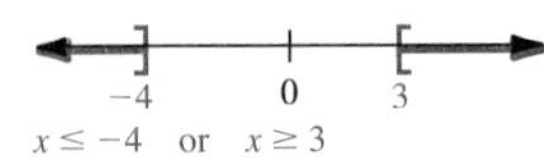

$x \le -4$ or $x \ge 3$

8. $(x - 2)(x + 5) \le 0$

−5 0 2

$-5 \le x \le 2$

In exercises 9 to 38, solve each inequality, and graph the solution.

9. $x^2 - 3x - 4 > 0$

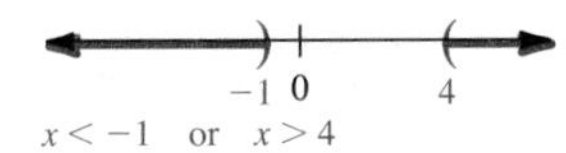

$x < -1$ or $x > 4$

10. $x^2 - 2x - 8 < 0$

−2 0 4

$-2 < x < 4$

11. $x^2 + x - 12 \le 0$

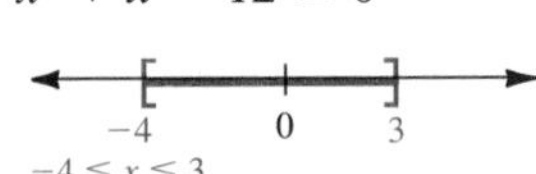

$-4 \le x \le 3$

12. $x^2 - 2x - 15 \ge 0$

−3 0 5

$x \le -3$ or $x \ge 5$

13. $x^2 - 5x + 6 \ge 0$

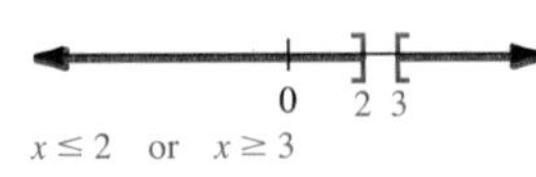

$x \le 2$ or $x \ge 3$

14. $x^2 + 7x + 10 \le 0$

−5 −2 0

$-5 \le x \le -2$

15. $x^2 + 2x \le 24$

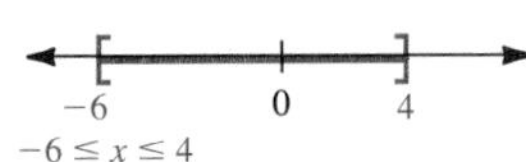

$-6 \le x \le 4$

16. $x^2 - 3x > 18$

−3 0 6

$x < -3$ or $x > 6$

17. $x^2 > 27 - 6x$

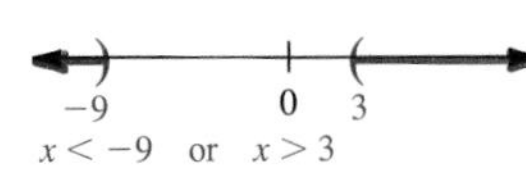

$x < -9$ or $x > 3$

18. $x^2 \le 7x - 12$

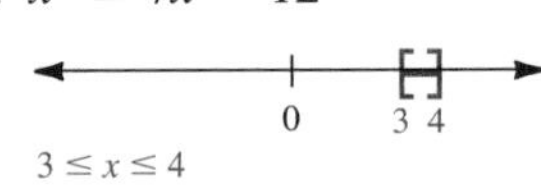

$3 \le x \le 4$

19. $2x^2 + x - 6 \le 0$

$-2 \le x \le \frac{3}{2}$

20. $3x^2 - 10x - 8 < 0$

$-\frac{2}{3} < x < 4$

21. $4x^2 + x < 3$

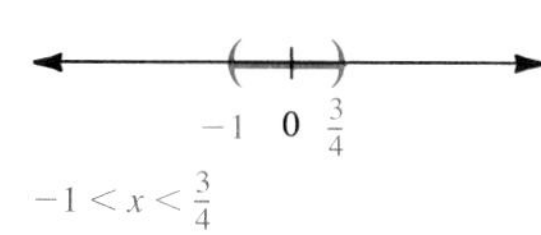

$-1 < x < \frac{3}{4}$

22. $5x^2 - 13x \ge 6$

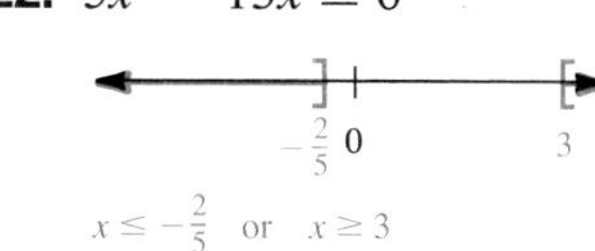

$x \le -\frac{2}{5}$ or $x \ge 3$

23. $x^2 - 16 \le 0$

$-4 \le x \le 4$

24. $x^2 - 9 > 0$

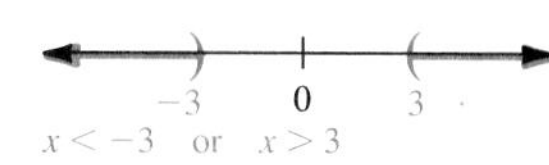

$x < -3$ or $x > 3$

25. $x^2 \ge 25$

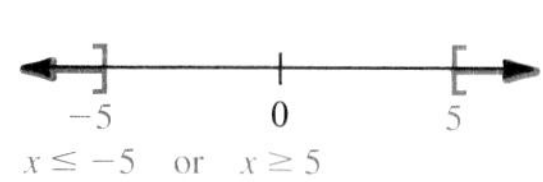

$x \le -5$ or $x \ge 5$

26. $x^2 < 49$

$-7 < x < 7$

27. $4 - x^2 < 0$

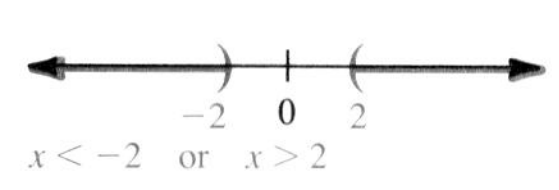

$x < -2$ or $x > 2$

> Videos

28. $36 - x^2 \ge 0$

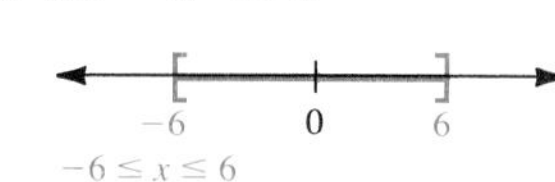

$-6 \le x \le 6$

29. $x^2 - 4x \le 0$

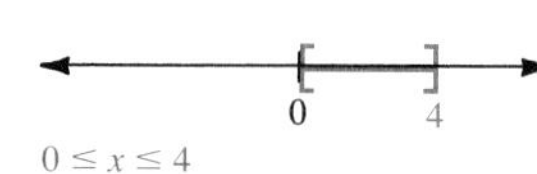

$0 \le x \le 4$

30. $x^2 + 5x > 0$

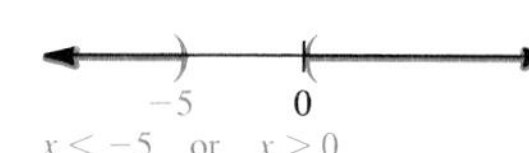

$x < -5$ or $x > 0$

31. $x^2 \ge 6x$

$x \le 0$ or $x \ge 6$

32. $x^2 < 3x$

$0 < x < 3$

33. $4x > x^2$

$0 < x < 4$

34. $6x \le x^2$

$x \le 0$ or $x \ge 6$

35. $x^2 - 4x + 4 \le 0$

$x = 2$

> Videos

36. $x^2 + 6x + 9 \ge 0$

All real numbers

37. $(x + 3)(x - 6) \le 10$

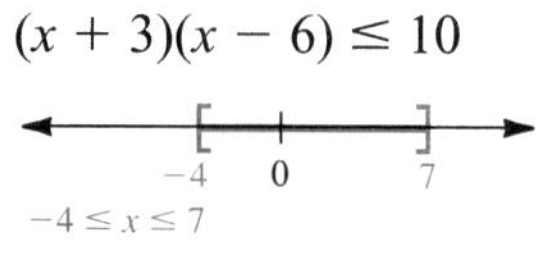

$-4 \le x \le 7$

38. $(x + 4)(x - 5) > 22$

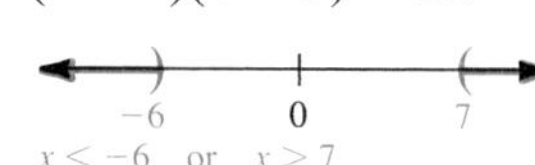

$x < -6$ or $x > 7$

Answers

19. See exercise
20. See exercise
21. See exercise
22. See exercise
23. See exercise
24. See exercise
25. See exercise
26. See exercise
27. See exercise
28. See exercise
29. See exercise
30. See exercise
31. See exercise
32. See exercise
33. See exercise
34. See exercise
35. See exercise
36. See exercise
37. See exercise
38. See exercise

Answers

39. See exercise
40. See exercise
41. See exercise
42. See exercise
43. See exercise
44. See exercise
45. See exercise
46. See exercise
47. See exercise
48. See exercise

Solve each inequality and graph the solution on a number line.

39. $\dfrac{x-2}{x+1} < 0$ > Videos

$-1 \quad 2$

$-1 < x < 2$

40. $\dfrac{x+3}{x-2} > 0$

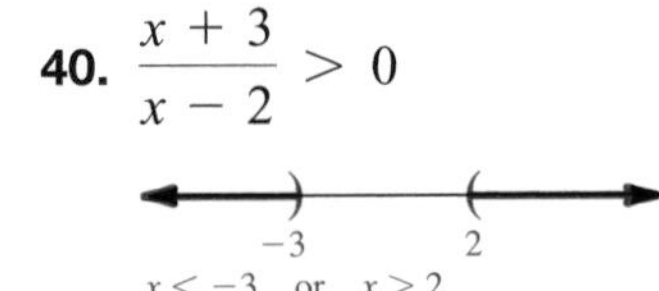

$-3 \quad 2$

$x < -3$ or $x > 2$

41. $\dfrac{2x-1}{x+3} \ge 0$

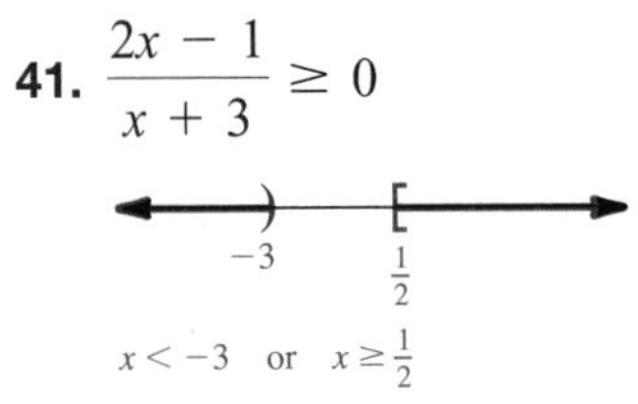

$-3 \quad \frac{1}{2}$

$x < -3$ or $x \ge \frac{1}{2}$

42. $\dfrac{3x-2}{x-4} \le 0$

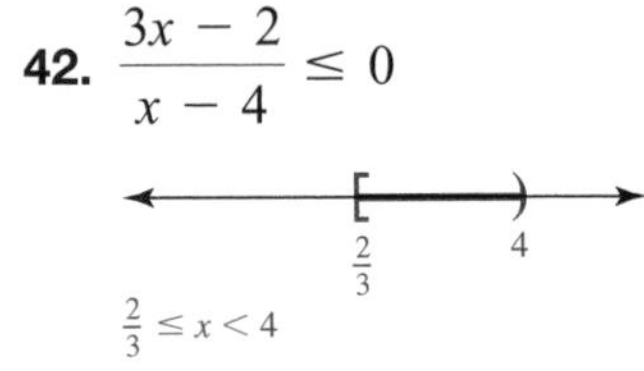

$\frac{2}{3} \quad 4$

$\frac{2}{3} \le x < 4$

43. $\dfrac{2x-5}{x-2} > 1$

$2 \quad 3$

$x < 2$ or $x > 3$

44. $\dfrac{2x+3}{x+4} \ge 1$

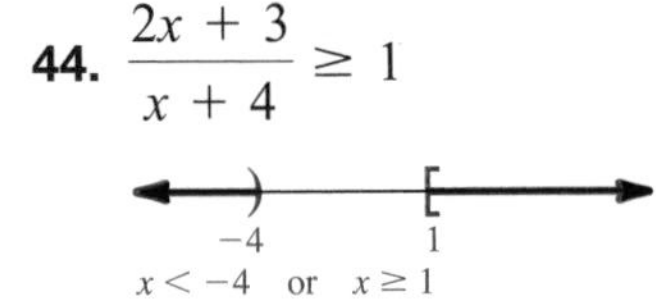

$-4 \quad 1$

$x < -4$ or $x \ge 1$

Basic Skills | Advanced Skills | Vocational-Technical Applications | **Calculator/Computer** | Above and Beyond

In exercises 45 to 48, use a graphing calculator to find the solution for each inequality.

45. $y < x^2 + 6x$

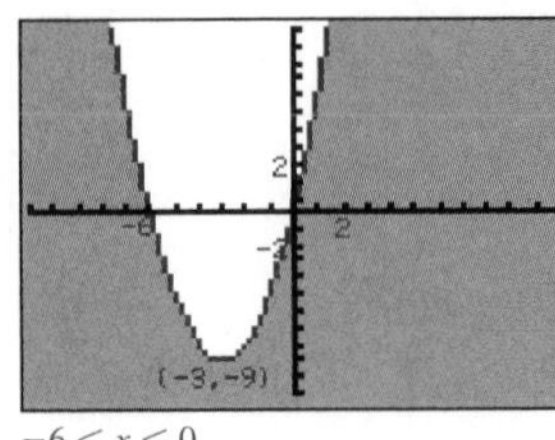

$-6 < x < 0$

46. $y \ge x^2 - 49$

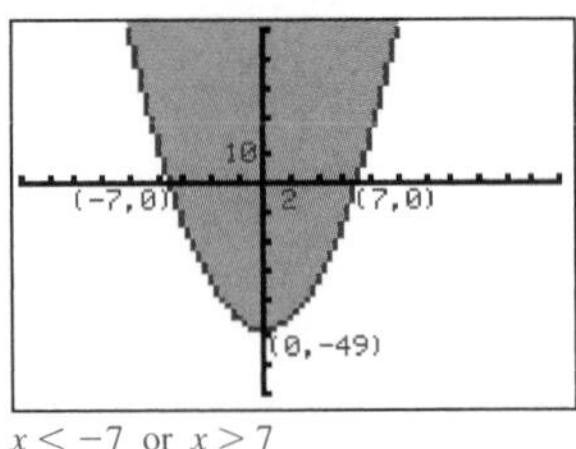

$x < -7$ or $x > 7$

47. $y > x^2 - 5x - 6$

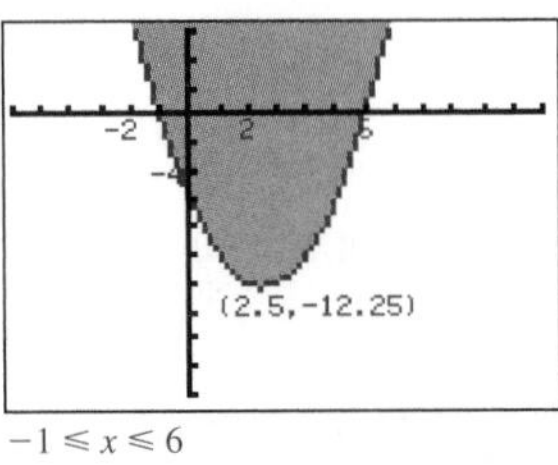

$-1 \le x \le 6$

48. $y < 2x^2 + 7x - 15$

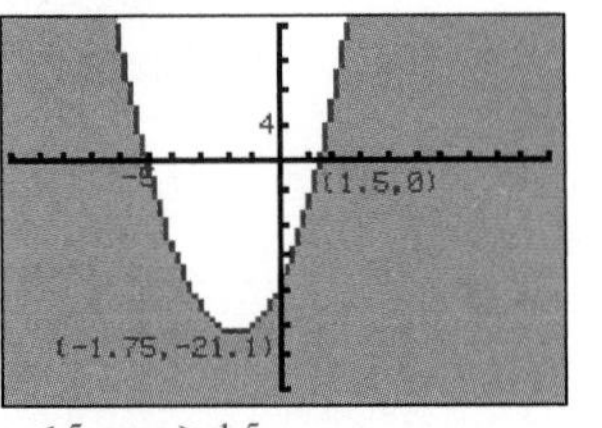

$x < 5$ or $x > 1.5$

Basic Skills | Advanced Skills | Vocational-Technical Applications | Calculator/Computer | **Above and Beyond**

49. Can a quadratic inequality be solved if the quadratic member of the inequality is not factorable? If so, explain how the solution can be found. If not, explain why not.

50. Is it necessary to relate a quadratic inequality to 0 to solve it? Why or why not?

An inequality of the form

$(x - a)(x - b)(x - c) < 0$

can be solved by using a sign graph to consider the signs of *all three factors*.

In exercises 51 to 56, use this suggestion to solve each inequality. Then graph the solution.

51. $x(x - 2)(x + 1) < 0$

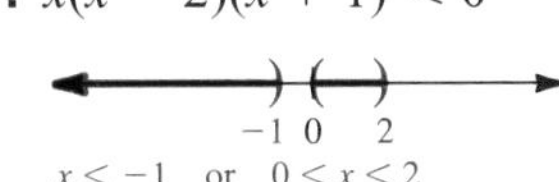

$x < -1$ or $0 < x < 2$

52. $x(x + 3)(x - 2) \geq 0$

−3 0 2

$-3 \leq x \leq 0$ or $x \geq 2$

53. $(x - 3)(x + 2)(x - 1) \geq 0$

−2 0 1 3

$-2 \leq x \leq 1$ or $x \geq 3$

54. $(x - 5)(x + 1)(x - 4) < 0$

−1 0 4 5

$x < -1$ or $4 < x < 5$

55. $x^3 - 2x^2 - 15x \leq 0$

−3 0 5

$x \leq -3$ or $0 \leq x \leq 5$

56. $x^3 + 2x^2 - 24x > 0$

−6 0 4

$-6 < x < 0$ or $x > 4$

Answers

1. −4 0 3

$-4 < x < 3$

3. −4 0 3

$x < -4$ or $x > 3$

5. −4 0 3

$-4 \leq x \leq 3$

7. −4 0 3

$x \leq -4$ or $x \geq 3$

9. −1 0 4

$x < -1$ or $x > 4$

11. −4 0 3

$-4 \leq x \leq 3$

13. 0 2 3

$x \leq 2$ or $x \geq 3$

15. −6 0 4

$-6 \leq x \leq 4$

17. −9 0 3

$x < -9$ or $x > 3$

19. −2 $\frac{3}{2}$

$-2 \leq x \leq \frac{3}{2}$

Answers

49. Above and Beyond

50. Above and Beyond

51. See exercise

52. See exercise

53. See exercise

54. See exercise

55. See exercise

56. See exercise

21. $-1 < x < \frac{3}{4}$

23. $-4 \le x \le 4$

25. $x \le -5$ or $x \ge 5$

27. 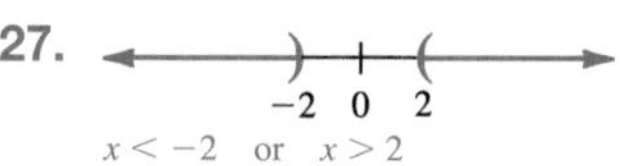

$x < -2$ or $x > 2$

29. $0 \le x \le 4$

31. 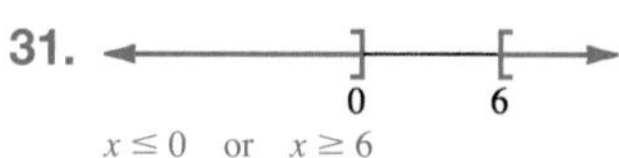

$x \le 0$ or $x \ge 6$

33. $0 < x < 4$

35. $x = 2$

37. $-4 \le x \le 7$

39. $-1 < x < 2$

41. $x < -3$ or $x \ge \frac{1}{2}$

43. 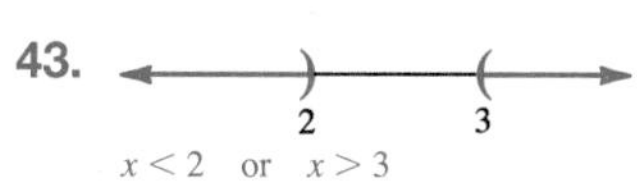

$x < 2$ or $x > 3$

45. 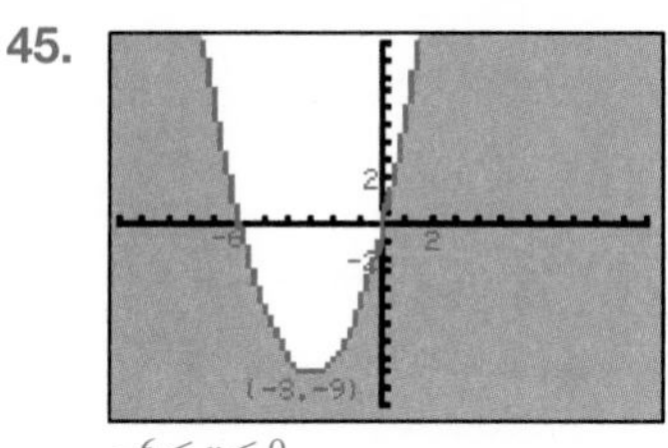

$-6 < x < 0$

47. 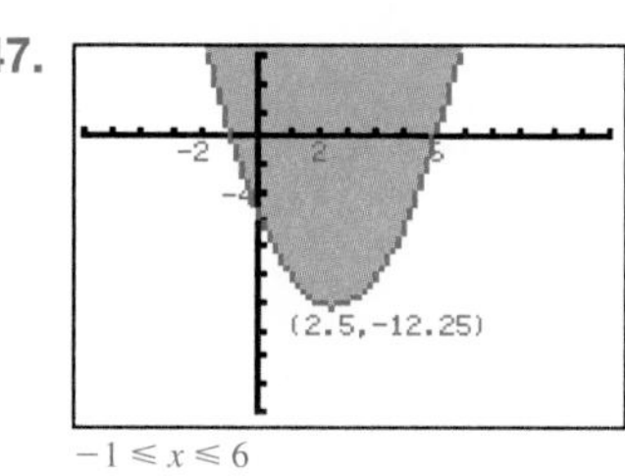

$-1 \le x \le 6$

49. Above and Beyond

51. 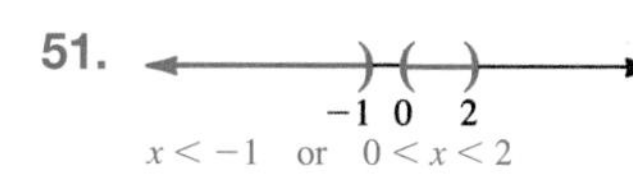

$x < -1$ or $0 < x < 2$

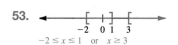

53. $-2 \le x \le 1$ or $x \ge 3$

55. $x \le -3$ or $0 \le x \le 5$

Definition/Procedure	Example	Reference
Graphs of Quadratic Functions		Section 8.1
A function that can be written in the form $f(x) = ax^2 + bx + c$ is called a **quadratic function.**	$f(x) = 2x^2 - 3x + 2$ is a quadratic function.	*p.* 758
The height of a ball (in feet) thrown up from the ground is determined by the quadratic function $h(x) = -16x^2 + v_0x$ in which v_0 represents the initial velocity and x represents the number of seconds that have passed since the ball was thrown.	If a ball has an initial velocity of 64 ft/sec, its height is determined by $h(x) = -16x^2 + 64x$.	*p.* 758
The zeros of the function are the values of x for which $h(x) = 0$.	If $0 = -16x^2 + 64x$, $0 = -16x(x - 4)$ $x = 0$ or $x = 4$	*p.* 759
Solving Quadratic Equations by Completing the Square		Section 8.2
Square Root Property		
If $x^2 = k$, when k is a complex number, then $x = \sqrt{k}$ or $x = -\sqrt{k}$.	To solve: $(x - 3)^2 = 5$ $x - 3 = \pm\sqrt{5}$ $x = 3 \pm \sqrt{5}$	*p.* 768
Completing the Square		
Step 1 Isolate the constant on the right side of the equation. **Step 2** Divide both sides of the equation by the coefficient of the x^2 term if that coefficient is not equal to 1. **Step 3** Add the square of one-half of the coefficient of the linear term to both sides of the equation. This will give a perfect-square trinomial on the left side of the equation. **Step 4** Write the left side of the equation as the square of a binomial, and simplify on the right side. **Step 5** Use the square root property, and then solve the resulting linear equations.	To solve: $x^2 + x = \frac{1}{2}$ $x^2 + x + \left(\frac{1}{2}\right)^2 = \frac{1}{2} + \left(\frac{1}{2}\right)^2$ $\left(x + \frac{1}{2}\right)^2 = \frac{3}{4}$ $x + \frac{1}{2} = \pm\sqrt{\frac{3}{4}}$ $x = \frac{-1 \pm \sqrt{3}}{2}$	*p.* 773

Continued

Definition/Procedure	Example	Reference
Solving Quadratic Equations by Using the Quadratic Formula		Section 8.3
Any quadratic equation can be solved by using the following algorithm. **Step 1** Write the equation in standard form (set it equal to 0). $ax^2 + bx + c = 0$ **Step 2** Determine the values for a, b, and c. **Step 3** Substitute those values into the quadratic formula $x = \frac{-b \pm \sqrt{b^2 - 4ac}}{2a}$ **Step 4** Write the solutions in simplest form.	To solve $x^2 - 2x = 4$ Write the equation as $x^2 - 2x - 4 = 0$ $a = 1 \quad b = -2 \quad c = -4$ $x = \frac{-(-2) \pm \sqrt{(-2)^2 - 4(1)(-4)}}{2 \cdot 1}$ $= \frac{2 \pm \sqrt{20}}{2}$ $= \frac{2 \pm 2\sqrt{5}}{2}$ $= 1 \pm \sqrt{5}$	*p.* 787
The Discriminant		
The expression $b^2 - 4ac$ is called the **discriminant** for a quadratic equation. There are three possibilities: **1.** If $b^2 - 4ac < 0$, there are no real solutions (but two imaginary solutions). **2.** If $b^2 - 4ac = 0$, there is one real solution (a double solution). **3.** If $b^2 - 4ac > 0$, there are two distinct real solutions.	Given $2x^2 - 5x + 3 = 0$ $a = 2, \quad b = -5, \quad c = 3$ $b^2 - 4ac = 25 - 4(2)(3)$ $= 25 - 24$ $= 1$ There are two distinct real solutions.	*p.* 787
Equations That Are Quadratic in Form		Section 8.4
There are a variety of equations that are quadratic in form. $2x - 11\sqrt{x} + 12 = 0$ is quadratic in $\sqrt{x}$. $x^4 - 3x^2 - 10 = 0$ is quadratic in x^2. $(x^2 - 1)^2 + 2(x^2 - 1) - 8 = 0$ is quadratic in $x^2 - 1$. These equations can be solved by one of two techniques. ***Solving by Substitution*** **Step 1** Make an appropriate substitution so that the equation becomes quadratic. **Step 2** Solve the resulting equation for the intermediate variable. **Step 3** Use the intermediate values found in step 2 to find possible solutions for the original variable. **Step 4** Check the solutions of step 3 by substitution into the original equation.	To solve $2x - 11\sqrt{x} + 12 = 0$ let $u = \sqrt{x}$. Then $2u^2 - 11u + 12 = 0$ $(u - 4)(2u - 3) = 0$ $u = 4 \quad \text{or} \quad u = \frac{3}{2}$ Because $u = \sqrt{x}$, $\sqrt{x} = 4 \quad \text{or} \quad \sqrt{x} = \frac{3}{2}$ $x = 16 \qquad x = \frac{9}{4}$ Both solutions are valid.	*pp.* 802, 807

Definition/Procedure	Example	Reference

Solving by Factoring

Step 1 Treat the original equation as quadratic in some power of the variable, and factor.
Step 2 Solve the resulting equations.
Step 3 Check the solutions of step 2 by substitution into the original equation.

To solve

$x^4 - 3x^2 - 10 = 0$

$(x^2 - 5)(x^2 + 2) = 0$

$x^2 = 5$ or $x^2 = -2$

$x = \pm\sqrt{5}$ $x = \pm i\sqrt{2}$

All four solutions are valid.

p. 807

Quadratic Inequalities and Rational Inequalities

Section 8.5

Solving a Quadratic Inequality Graphically

1. Graph $f(x) = ax^2 + bx + c$.
2. The x-values of the points on the graph that are *above* the x-axis form the solution of

   $ax^2 + bx + c > 0$

   and x-values of the graph that are *below* the x-axis form the solution set of

   $ax^2 + bx + c < 0$

Solve

$x^2 - 4x + 3 < 0$

Graph

$f(x) = x^2 - 4x + 3$

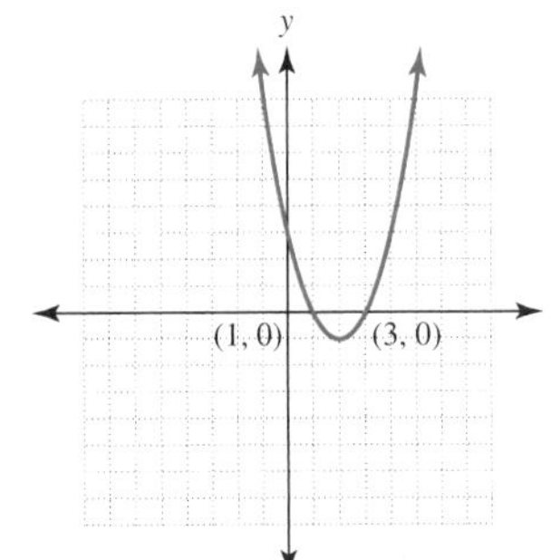

The graph is below the x-axis for values of x between 1 and 3. Since the inequality is *less than 0,* the solution is

$1 < x < 3$ or $(1, 3)$

p. 811

Solving a Quadratic Inequality Algebraically

Step 1 Clear the inequality of parentheses and fractions.
Step 2 Rewrite the inequality such that the expression is related to zero.
Step 3 Factor the quadratic member and find the critical values of x.
Step 4 Use a sign graph to find the values for x that make the inequality a true statement.
Step 5 Use a number line to graph the solution.

To solve

$x^2 - 3x < 18$

$x^2 - 3x - 18 < 0$

$(x - 6)(x + 3) < 0$

The critical values of x are

-3 and 6

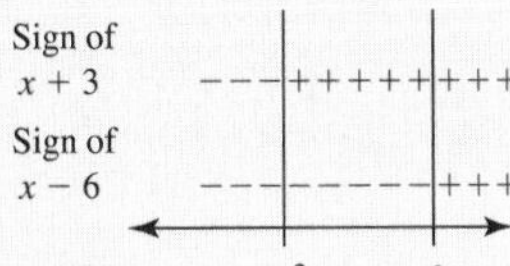

The solution is

$-3 < x < 6$

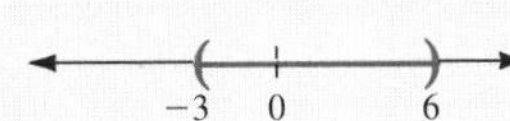

p. 815

Continued

Definition/Procedure	Example	Reference

Solving a Rational Inequality

Step 1 Isolate the inequality on the left side and relate it to 0.

Step 2 Form a common denominator on the left side of the inequality.

Step 3 Simplify and combine the expressions on the left side.

Step 4 Use a sign graph to find the values for x that make the inequality a true statement.

Step 5 Use a number line to graph the solution.

Solve

$$\frac{2x + 2}{x - 1} \geq 1$$

$$\frac{2x + 2}{x - 1} - 1 \geq 0$$

$$\frac{2x + 2}{x - 1} - \frac{x - 1}{x - 1} \geq 0$$

$$\frac{2x + 2 - (x - 1)}{x - 1} \geq 0$$

$$\frac{2x + 2 - x + 1}{x + 1} \geq 0$$

$$\frac{x + 3}{x - 1} \geq 0$$

The critical values are -3 and 1.

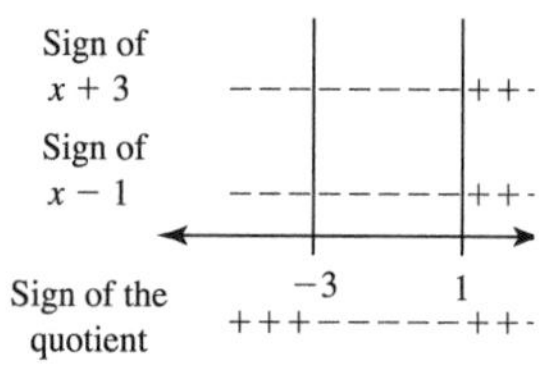

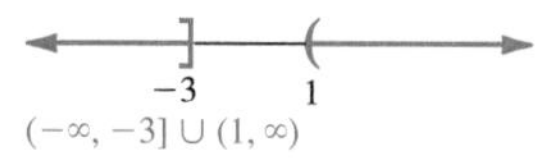

p. 818

summary exercises :: chapter 8

This summary exercise set is provided to give you practice with each of the objectives of this chapter. Each exercise is keyed to the appropriate chapter section. When you are finished, you can check your answers to the odd-numbered exercises against those presented in the back of the text. If you have difficulty with any of these questions, go back and reread the examples from that section. The answers to the even-numbered exercises appear in the *Instructor's Solutions Manual.* Your instructor will give you guidelines on how best to use these exercises in your instructional setting.

8.1 *Graph each function.*

1. $f(x) = x^2 + 5x$

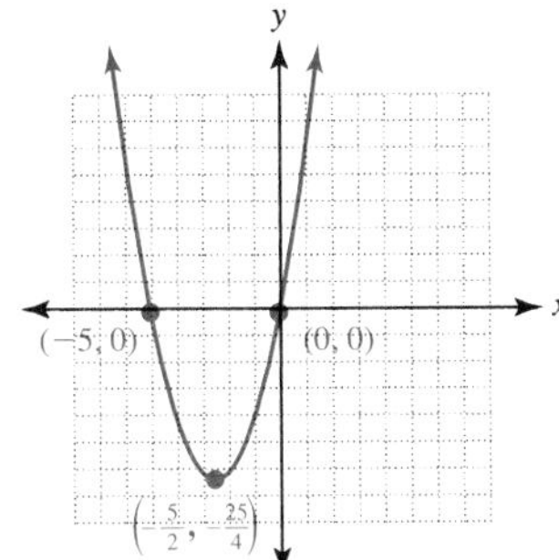

2. $f(x) = x^2 + 3x$

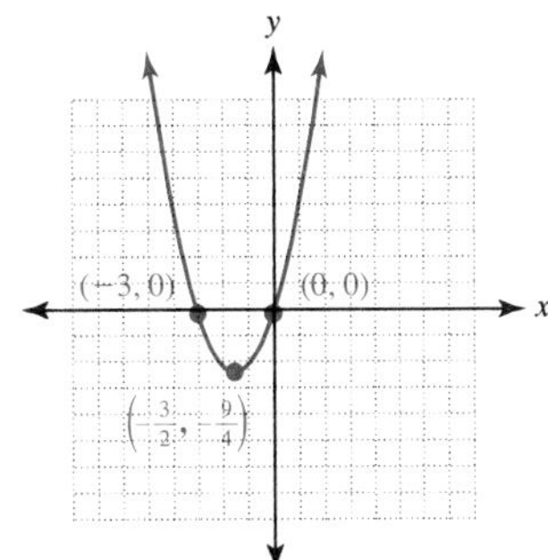

3. $f(x) = x^2 - 4x$

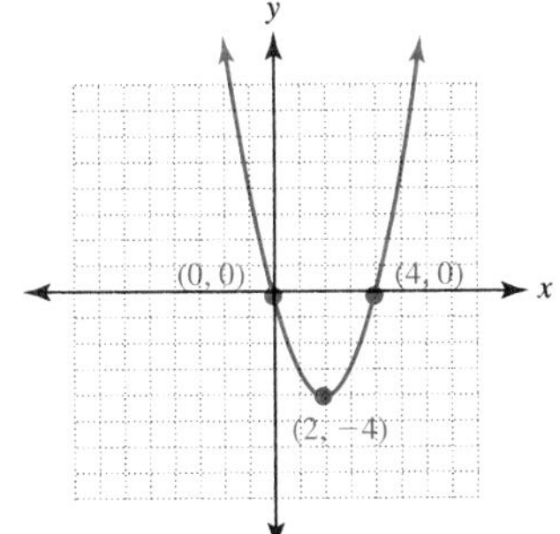

4. $f(x) = -x^2 + 2x$

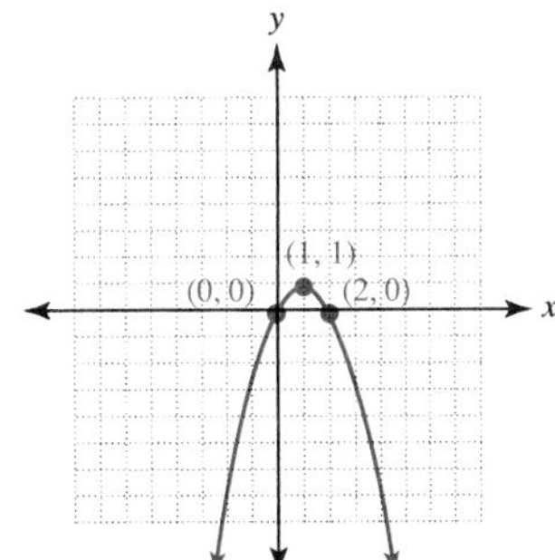

5. $f(x) = x^2 + 2x - 3$

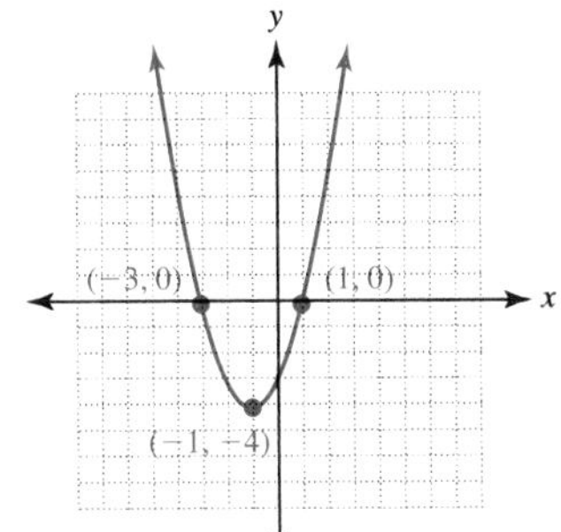

6. $f(x) = x^2 - 4x + 3$

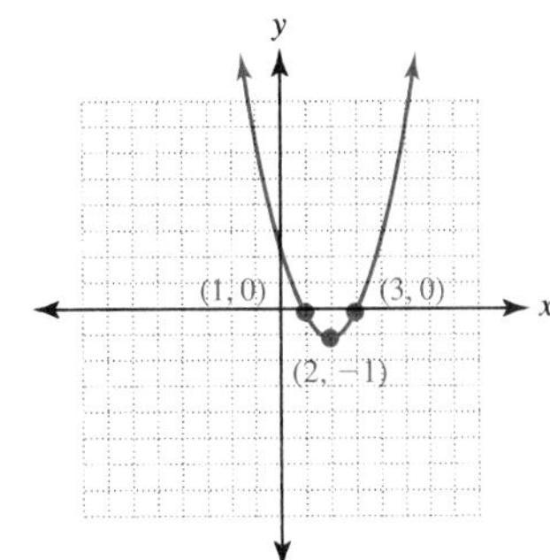

7. $f(x) = -x^2 - x + 6$

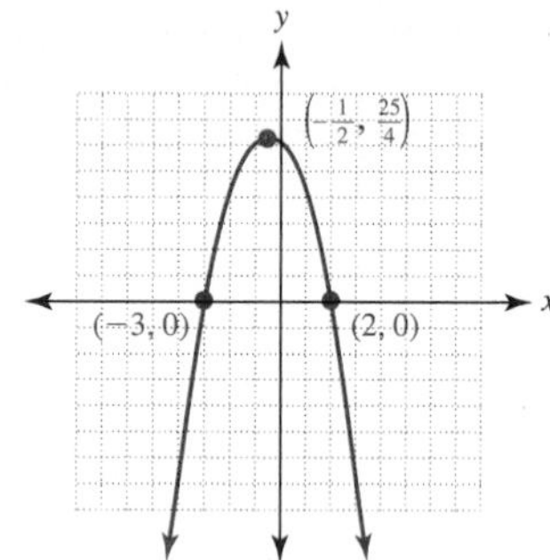

8. $f(x) = -x^2 + 3x + 4$

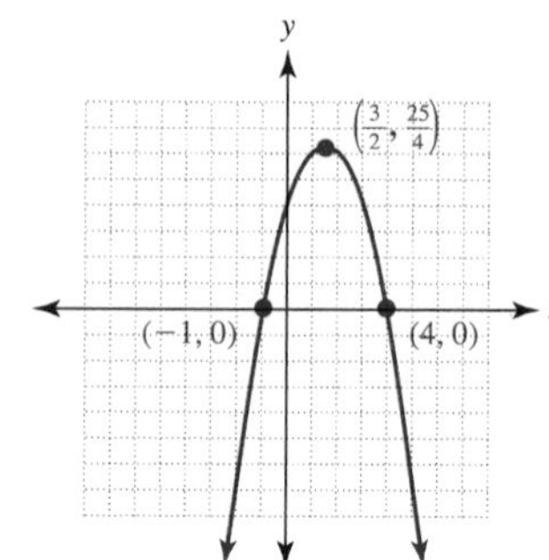

Find the coordinates for the vertex of each function's graph.

9. $f(x) = x^2 + 2x - 8$ (−1, −9)

10. $f(x) = x^2 - 2x$ (1, −1)

11. $f(x) = 8x^2 + 16x$ (−1, −8)

12. $f(x) = x^2 - 6x + 9$ (3, 0)

13. $f(x) = x^2 + 4x + 4$ (−2, 0)

14. $f(x) = x^2 - 2x - 8$ (1, −9)

15. $f(x) = x^2 - 4x - 5$ (2, −9)

16. $f(x) = -x^2 - 2x - 15$ (−1, −14)

17. $f(x) = x^2 - 4x + 3$ (2, −1)

18. $f(x) = x^2 + 6x + 8$ (−3, −1)

19. $f(x) = x^2 + 2x - 3$ (−1, −4)

20. $f(x) = -x^2 - 8x$ (−4, 16)

21. $f(x) = -x^2 - 2x + 8$ (−1, 9)

22. $f(x) = x^2 + 4x - 5$ (−2, −9)

8.2 *Solve each of the equations for x by the square root method.*

23. $x^2 = 10$ $\pm\sqrt{10}$

24. $x^2 = 48$ $\pm 4\sqrt{3}$

25. $x^2 - 20 = 0$ $\pm 2\sqrt{5}$

26. $x^2 + 2 = 8$ $\pm\sqrt{6}$

27. $(x - 1)^2 = 5$ $1 \pm \sqrt{5}$

28. $(x + 2)^2 = 8$ $-2 \pm 2\sqrt{2}$

29. $(x + 3)^2 = 5$ $-3 \pm \sqrt{5}$

30. $64x^2 - 25 = 0$ $\pm\frac{5}{8}$

31. $4x^2 + 27 = 0$ $\frac{\pm 3i\sqrt{3}}{2}$

32. $9x^2 - 20 = 0$ $\frac{\pm 2\sqrt{5}}{3}$

33. $25x^2 - 7 = 0$ $\frac{\pm\sqrt{7}}{5}$

34. $7x^2 + 3 = 0$ $\frac{\pm i\sqrt{21}}{7}$

Find the constant that must be added to each of the binomials to form a perfect-square trinomial.

35. $x^2 - 12x$ 36

36. $y^2 + 3y$ $\frac{9}{4}$

Solve the equations by completing the square.

37. $x^2 - 4x - 5 = 0$ −1, 5

38. $x^2 + 8x + 12 = 0$ −6, −2

39. $w^2 - 10w - 3 = 0$ $5 \pm 2\sqrt{7}$

40. $y^2 + 3y - 1 = 0$ $\frac{-3 \pm \sqrt{13}}{2}$

41. $2x^2 - 8x - 5 = 0$ $\frac{4 \pm \sqrt{26}}{2}$

42. $3x^2 + 3x - 1 = 0$ $\frac{-3 \pm \sqrt{21}}{6}$

8.3 *Solve each of the equations using the quadratic formula.*

43. $x^2 - 5x - 24 = 0$ $\quad -3, 8$

44. $w^2 + 10w + 25 = 0$ $\quad -5$

45. $x^2 = 3x + 3$ $\quad \frac{3 \pm \sqrt{21}}{2}$

46. $2y^2 - 5y + 2 = 0$ $\quad \frac{1}{2}, 2$

47. $3y^2 + 4y = 1$ $\quad \frac{-2 \pm \sqrt{7}}{3}$

48. $2y^2 + 5y + 4 = 0$ $\quad \frac{-5 \pm i\sqrt{7}}{4}$

49. $(x - 5)(x + 3) = 13$ $\quad 1 \pm \sqrt{29}$

50. $\frac{1}{x^2} - \frac{4}{x} + 1 = 0$ $\quad 2 \pm \sqrt{3}$

51. $3x^2 + 2x + 5 = 0$ $\quad \frac{-1 \pm i\sqrt{14}}{3}$

52. $(x - 1)(2x + 3) = -5$ $\quad \frac{-1 \pm i\sqrt{15}}{4}$

Find the value of the discriminant and give the number of real solutions.

53. $x^2 - 2x + 5$ $\quad -16$, none

54. $2x^2 - x + 1$ $\quad -7$, none

55. $3x^2 - 2x - 6$ $\quad 76$, two

56. $5x^2 - 5x - 7$ $\quad 165$, two

Find the zeros of the functions.

57. $f(x) = x^2 - x - 2$ $\quad x = 2, -1$

58. $f(x) = 6x^2 + 7x + 2$ $\quad x = -\frac{2}{3}, -\frac{1}{2}$

59. $f(x) = -2x^2 - 7x - 6$ $\quad x = -\frac{3}{2}, -2$

60. $f(x) = -x^2 - 1$ $\quad x = -i, i$

8.4 *Solve each of the equations.*

61. $x^4 - 11x^2 + 18 = 0$ $\quad \pm\sqrt{2}, \pm 3$

62. $x^4 + x^2 = 20$ $\quad \pm 2, \pm i\sqrt{5}$

63. $w^4 = 9w^2$ $\quad 0, \pm 3$

64. $p^4 - 16 = 0$ $\quad \pm 2, \pm 2i$

65. $m - \sqrt{m} - 12 = 0$ $\quad 16$

66. $(x - 3)^2 + 5(x - 3) = 14$ $\quad -4, 5$

67. $(t^2 - 2t)^2 - 9(t^2 - 2t) + 8 = 0$ $\quad 1 \pm \sqrt{2}, -2, 4$

68. $x^{1/2} - 2x^{1/4} - 3 = 0$ $\quad 81$

69. $x^{2/3} + x^{1/3} = 2$ $\quad -8, 1$

70. $\frac{10}{p^2} + \frac{3}{p} - 1 = 0$ $\quad -2, 5$

8.5 *Solve the inequalities and graph the solution set.*

71. $(x - 2)(x + 5) > 0$ $\quad x < -5$ or $x > 2$

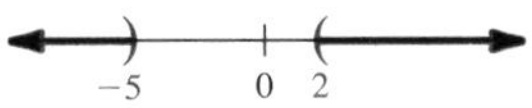

72. $(x - 1)(x - 6) < 0$ $\quad 1 < x < 6$

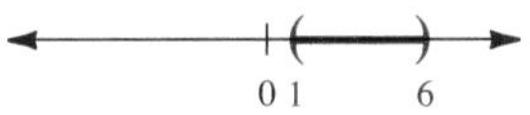

73. $(x + 1)(x + 3) \le 0$ $\quad -3 \le x \le -1$

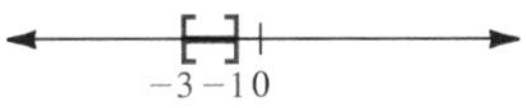

74. $(x + 4)(x - 5) \ge 0$ $\quad x \le -4$ or $x \ge 5$

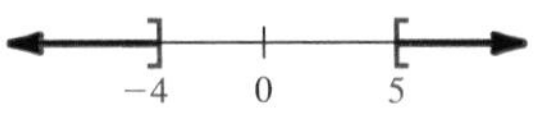

75. $x^2 - 5x - 24 \le 0$ $\quad -3 \le x \le 8$

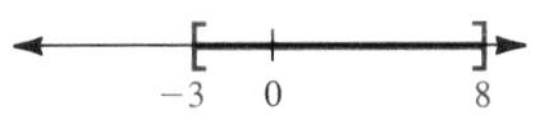

76. $x^2 + 4x \geq 21$ $x \leq -7$ or $x \geq 3$

77. $x^2 \geq 64$ $x \leq -8$ or $x \geq 8$

78. $x^2 + 5x \geq 0$ $x \leq -5$ or $x \geq 0$

79. $(x + 2)(x - 6) < 9$ $-3 < x < 7$

80. $(x - 1)(x + 2) \geq 4$ $x \leq -3$ or $x \geq 2$

81. $\frac{x - 4}{x - 2} > 0$ $x < 2$ or $x > 4$

82. $\frac{x + 6}{x + 3} < 0$ $-6 < x < -3$

83. $\frac{x - 5}{x + 3} \leq 0$ $-3 < x \leq 5$

84. $\frac{x + 3}{x - 2} \leq 0$ $-3 \leq x < 2$

85. $\frac{2x + 1}{x - 3} \geq 1$ $x \leq -4$ or $x > 3$

86. $\frac{3x - 1}{x + 1} \leq 1$ $-1 < x \leq 1$

8.2–8.5

87. **Science and Medicine** If a ball is thrown vertically upward from the ground with an initial velocity of 64 ft/sec, its approximate height is given by $h(t) = -16t^2 + 64t$. When will the ball reach a height of at least 48 ft? 1 sec $\leq t \leq$ 3 sec

88. **Business and Finance** Suppose that the cost, in dollars, of producing x stereo systems is given by the equation $C(x) = 3{,}000 - 60x + 3x^2$. How many systems can be produced if the cost cannot exceed $7,500? 50 systems or less

89. **Geometry** The length of a rectangle is 2 ft more than its width. If the area of the rectangle is 80 ft², what are the dimensions of the rectangle? Width: 8 ft, length: 10 ft

90. **Geometry** The length of a rectangle is 3 cm less than twice its width. The area of the rectangle is 35 cm². Find the length and width of the rectangle. Width: 5 cm, length: 7 cm

91. **Geometry** An open box is formed by cutting 3-in. squares from each corner of a rectangular piece of cardboard that is 3 in. longer than it is wide. If the box is to have a volume of 120 in.³, what must be the size of the original piece of cardboard? Width: 11 in., length: 14 in.

92. **Business and Finance** Suppose that a manufacturer's weekly profit P is given by

$P(x) = -3x^2 + 240x$

in which x is the number of items manufactured and sold. Find the number of items that must be manufactured and sold if the profit is to be at least $4,500. 30 items $\leq x \leq$ 50 items

93. **Science and Medicine** If a ball is thrown vertically upward from the ground with an initial velocity of 96 ft/sec, its approximate height is given by

$h(t) = -16t^2 + 96t$

When will the ball reach a height of at least 80 ft? 1 sec $\leq t \leq$ 5 sec

94. **Geometry** The length of a rectangle is 1 cm more than twice its width. If the length is doubled, the area of the new rectangle is 36 cm² more than that of the old. Find the dimensions of the original rectangle. Width: 4 cm, length: 9 cm

self-test 8

The purpose of this chapter test is to help you check your progress so that you can find sections and concepts that you need to review before the next exam. Allow yourself about an hour to take this test. At the end of that hour, check your answers against those given in the back of this text. If you missed any, note the section reference that accompanies the answer. Go back to that section and reread the examples until you have mastered that particular concept.

Name ____________

Section ________ Date ________

8.1

1. Find the zeros of the function $f(x) = 3x^2 - 10x - 8$.

Find the coordinates of the vertex of each of the following.

2. $f(x) = x^2 + x - 2$

3. $f(x) = x^2 - 4x - 5$

Graph the following functions.

4. $f(x) = x^2 + x - 6$

5. $f(x) = 2x^2 + 4x - 3$

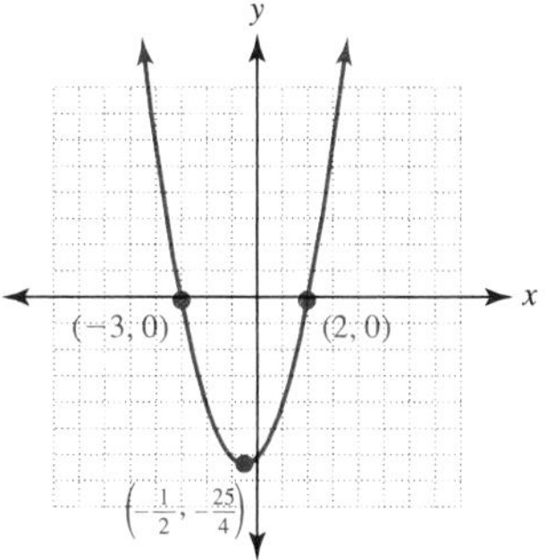

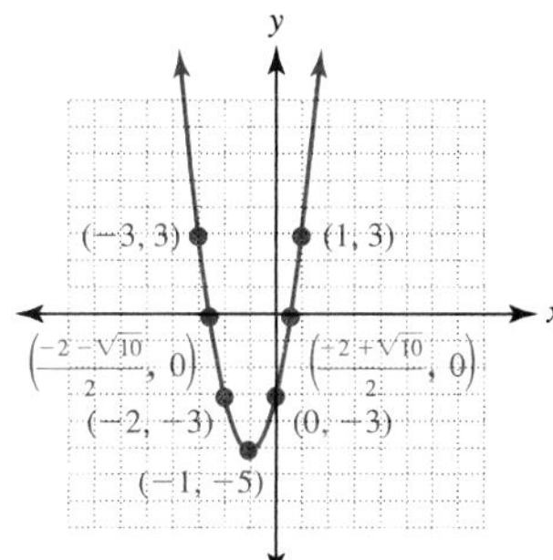

6. The length of a rectangle is 2 cm more than 3 times its width. If the area of the rectangle is 85 cm^2, what are the dimensions of the rectangle?

7. Suppose that the height (in feet) of a ball thrown upward from a raised platform is approximated by

$h(t) = -16t^2 + 32t + 32$

t seconds after the ball has been released. How long will it take the ball to hit the ground? Write your answer to the nearest tenth of a second.

8.2

Solve each of the following equations, using the square root method.

8. $4w^2 - 20 = 0$

9. $(x - 1)^2 = 10$

10. $4(x - 1)^2 = 23$

Answers

1. $-\frac{2}{3}, 4$
2. $\left(-\frac{1}{2}, -\frac{9}{4}\right)$
3. (2, −9)
4. See exercise
5. See exercise
6. Width: 5 cm, length: 17 cm
7. 2.7 sec
8. $\pm\sqrt{5}$
9. $1 \pm \sqrt{10}$
10. $\frac{2 \pm \sqrt{23}}{2}$

Answers

11. $\frac{-3 \pm \sqrt{13}}{2}$
12. $\frac{5 \pm \sqrt{19}}{2}$
13. $\frac{5 \pm \sqrt{37}}{2}$
14. $-2 \pm \sqrt{11}$
15. $\pm\sqrt{3}, \pm 3$
16. 4, 81
17. −3, 5
18. 3, −2
19. See exercise
20. See exercise
21. See exercise
22. See exercise

Solve each of the following equations by completing the square.

11. $m^2 + 3m - 1 = 0$

12. $2x^2 - 10x + 3 = 0$

8.3

Solve each of the following equations, using the quadratic formula.

13. $x^2 - 5x - 3 = 0$

14. $x^2 + 4x = 7$

8.4

Solve the following equations either by factoring directly or by substitution.

15. $x^4 - 12x^2 + 27 = 0$

16. $y - 11\sqrt{y} + 18 = 0$

17. $(m - 2)^2 + 2(m - 2) = 15$

18. $\frac{6}{x^2} + \frac{1}{x} - 1 = 0$

8.5

Solve each of the following inequalities, and graph the solution.

19. $x^2 + 5x - 14 < 0$

−7 2

$-7 < x < 2$

20. $x^2 - 3x \geq 18$

−3 6

$x \leq -3$ or $x \geq 6$

21. $\frac{x + 5}{x - 3} \leq 0$

−5 3

$-5 \leq x < 3$

22. $\frac{3x + 1}{x - 1} > 1$

−1 1

$x < -1$ or $x > 1$

Activity 8 :: Trajectory and Height

Each chapter in this text concludes with a chapter activity such as this one. These activities provide you with the opportunity to apply the math you studied in that chapter to a relevant topic. Your instructor will determine how best to use these activities in your instructional setting. You may find yourself working in class or outside of class; you may find yourself working alone or in small groups; you may even be asked to perform research in a library or on the Internet.

The introduction to this chapter referred to the curve used to approximate the sag between power lines. This sag was dependent upon the distance between the towers, wire weight, and tension, which would dictate the appearance of the curve. The equation used to define the relationship between the sag and the span is a quadratic, which when graphed gives us the parabola. Another relationship defined by a quadratic is that of trajectory and height.

Trajectory and Height

So far in this chapter you have done many exercises involving balls that have been thrown upward with varying velocities. How does trajectory—the angle at which the ball is thrown—affect its height and time in the air?

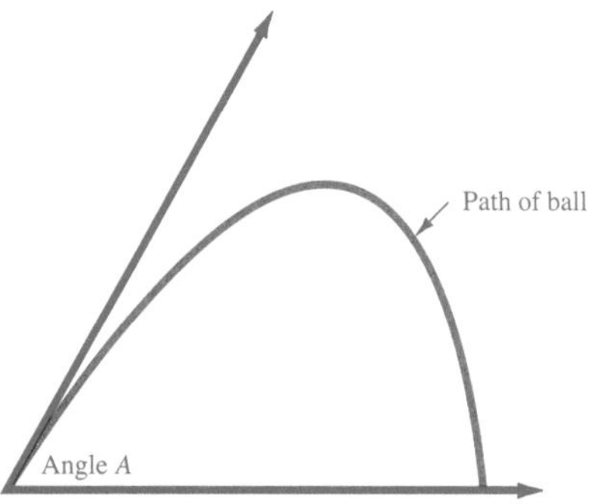

If you throw a ball from ground level with an initial upward velocity of 70 ft/sec, the equation

$$h = -16t^2 + \partial(70)t$$

gives you the height, h, in feet, t seconds after the ball has been thrown at a certain angle, A. The value of ∂ in the equation depends on the angle A and is given in the accompanying table.

Measure of Angle A in Degrees	Value of ∂
0	0.000
5	0.087
10	0.174
15	0.259
20	0.342

(Continued)

 The Streeter/Hutchison Series in Mathematics Intermediate Algebra

Measure of Angle A in Degrees	Value of ∂
25	0.423
30	0.500
35	0.574
40	0.643
45	0.707
50	0.766
55	0.819
60	0.866
65	0.906
70	0.940
75	0.966
80	0.985
85	0.996
90 (straight up)	1.000

Investigate the following questions and write your conclusions to each one in complete sentences, showing all charts and graphs. Indicate what initial velocity you are using in each case.

1. Suppose an object is thrown from ground level with an initial upward velocity of 70 ft/sec and at an angle of 45 degrees. What will be the height of the ball in 1 sec (nearest tenth of a foot)? How long is the ball in the air?
2. Does the ball stay in the air longer if the angle of the throw is greater?
3. If you double the angle of the throw, will the ball stay in the air double the length of time?
4. If you double the angle of the throw, will the ball go twice as high?
5. Is the height of the ball directly related to the angle at which you throw it? That is, does the ball go higher if the angle of the throw is larger?
6. Repeat this exercise using another initial upward velocity.

The following exercises are presented to help you review concepts from earlier chapters. This is meant as review material and not as a comprehensive exam. The answers are presented in the back of the text. Beside each answer is a section reference for the concept. If you have difficulty with any of these exercises, be certain to at least read through the summary related to that section.

Name ____________________

Section ________ Date ________

3.1

1. Graph the following equation.

$2x - 3y = 6$

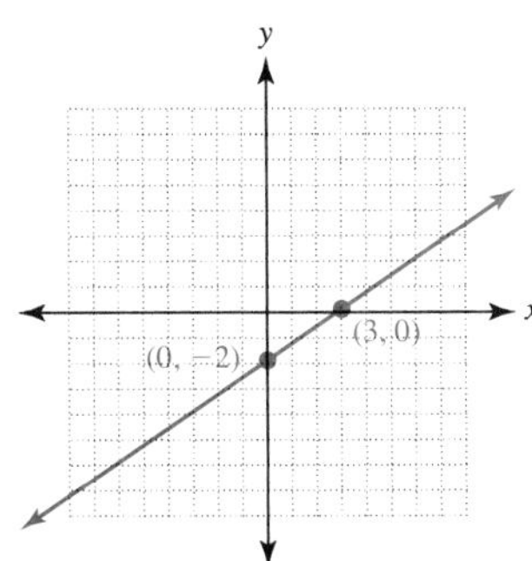

3.3

2. Find the slope of the line determined by the set of points.

$(-4, 7)$ and $(-3, 4)$

4.1

3. Solve the system

$2x + 5y = 4$
$x + 3y = 1$

5.3

4. Divide: $(3x^2 - 5x + 4) \div (x - 2)$.

5.8

5. Completely factor the expression $x^3 + x^2 - 6x$.

6.3

6. Simplify the expression $\dfrac{2}{x + 2} - \dfrac{3x - 2}{x^2 - x - 6}$.

7.3

7. Simplify the expression $(\sqrt{7} - \sqrt{2})(\sqrt{3} + \sqrt{6})$.

Solve each equation.

2.1

8. $2x - 7 = 0$

9. $3x - 5 = 5x + 3$

5.9

10. $0 = (x - 3)(x + 5)$

11. $x^2 - 3x + 2 = 0$

Answers

1. See exercise

2. -3

3. $(7, -2)$

4. $3x + 1 + \dfrac{6}{x - 2}$

5. $x(x + 3)(x - 2)$

6. $\dfrac{-x - 4}{(x - 3)(x + 2)}$

7. $\sqrt{21} - \sqrt{6} + \sqrt{42} - 2\sqrt{3}$

8. $\dfrac{7}{2}$

9. -4

10. $-5, 3$

11. $1, 2$

Answers

12. −10, 3
13. $\frac{3 \pm \sqrt{21}}{2}$
14. $3 \pm \sqrt{5}$
15. −2, 5
16. 4
17. 7
18. $x + 2y = 6$
19. $x \le -5$ or $x \ge 13$
20. $-3 \le x \le 5$
21. xy^2
22. $3 - 4i$
23. −13
24. $-2 + 2\sqrt{97}, 2 + 2\sqrt{97}$ or 17.7 ft, 21.7 ft
25. Between 21 and 59 units

8.3

12. $x^2 + 7x - 30 = 0$

13. $x^2 - 3x - 3 = 0$

8.2

14. $(x - 3)^2 = 5$

2.5

15. $|2x - 3| = 7$

6.5

16. $\frac{6}{x + 3} + \frac{2}{x - 3} = \frac{20}{x^2 - 9}$

7.4

17. $\sqrt{4x - 3} - 3 = 2$

3.5

18. Find the equation of the line, L, that has y-intercept of (0, 3) and is perpendicular to the line $2y - 4x = 5$.

Solve the following inequalities.

2.5

19. $|x - 4| \ge 9$

8.5

20. $x^2 - 2x - 15 \le 0$

7.6

21. Simplify the expression $\left(\frac{x^{-3}y^{11/8}}{x^{-5}y^{-21/8}}\right)^{1/2}$.

7.7

22. Simplify the expression $(3 - i)^2 - (5 - 2i)$.

Solve the following word problems.

2.3

23. NUMBER PROBLEM Five times a number decreased by 7 is −72. Find the number.

8.3

24. GEOMETRY One leg of a right triangle is 4 ft longer than the shorter leg. If the hypotenuse is 28 ft, how long is each leg?

25. BUSINESS AND FINANCE Suppose that a manufacturer's weekly profit, P, is given by

$P(x) = -4x^2 + 320x$

in which x is the number of units manufactured and sold. Find the number of items that must be manufactured and sold to guarantee a profit of at least $4,956.

9

Conic Sections

INTRODUCTION

You can find examples of conic sections as far away as the planets and as near as your own home!

Astronomy has many examples of conic sections. The orbit of a planet is an ellipse with the sun as one of its focal points. If the planet were to speed up, the curve would open up into a parabola, and then a hyperbola. An object that passes through the solar system but is not orbiting another object is on a hyperbolic path. The path of a comet as it passes Earth is a hyperbola.

In this chapter we will explore these conic sections and the relationships between them. At the end of the chapter, you will find a more in-depth activity involving orbiting objects.

CHAPTER 9 OUTLINE

9 pretest

Name ____________________

Section ________ Date ________

This pretest provides a preview of the types of exercises you will encounter in each section of this chapter. The answers for these exercises can be found in the back of the text. If you are working on your own, or ahead of the class, this pretest can help you identify the sections in which you should focus more of your time.

Answers

1. See exercise
2. See exercise
3. (0, 0); $r = 3$
4. See exercise
5. See exercise
6. (4, 5) and (−1, 5)

Graph each of the equations.

9.1 **1.** $y = x^2 - 2$

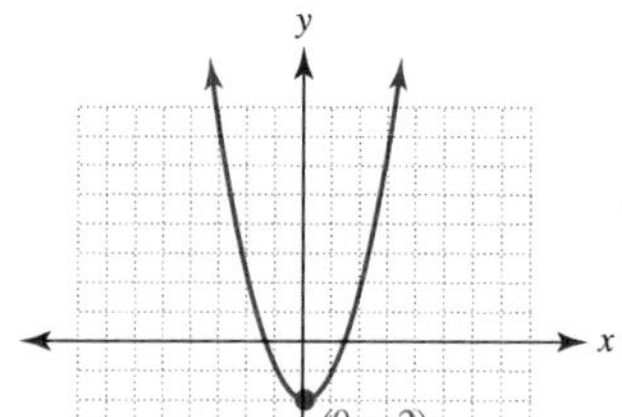

2. $y = -x^2 + 3x + 4$

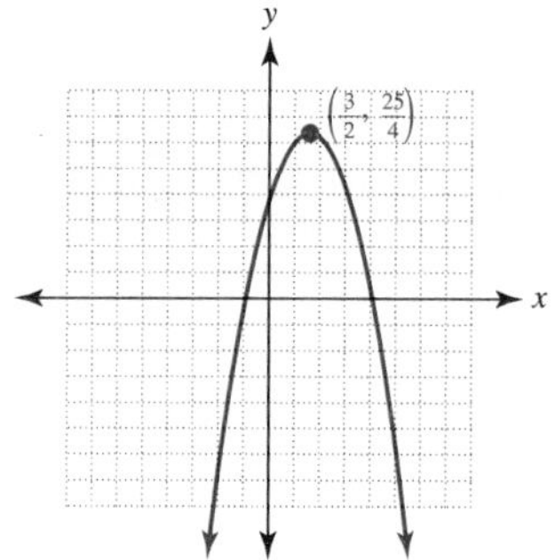

9.2 **3.** Find the coordinates of the center and the radius of the graph of the equation $3x^2 + 3y^2 = 27$.

Sketch the graph of each of the equations.

9.3 **4.** $\frac{x^2}{4} + \frac{y^2}{9} = 1$

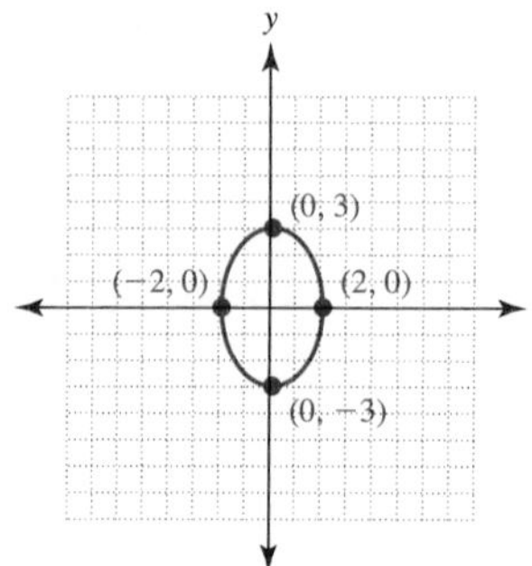

5. $\frac{y^2}{9} - \frac{x^2}{4} = 1$

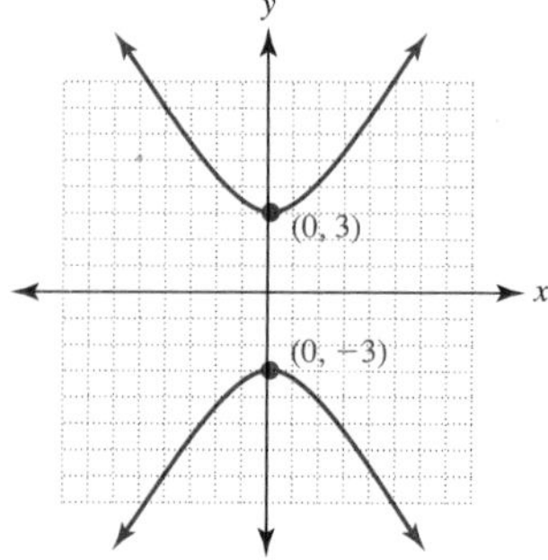

9.4 **6.** Solve the system algebraically.

$y = x^2 - 3x + 1$

$y = 5$

7. Solve the system of inequalities.

$y \geq x^2 - 3x + 1$
$y \geq 5$

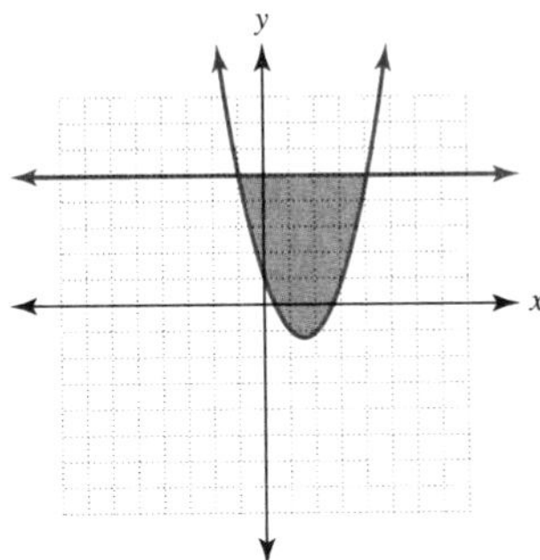

Identify each of the following as a line, circle, parabola, ellipse, or hyperbola.

8. $(x - 2)^2 + y^2 = 4$

9. $5x + 5y = 60$

10. $x = y^2 + 2y + 2$

Answers

7. See exercise

8. Circle

9. Line

10. Parabola

9.1 Parabolas

< 9.1 Objectives >

1 > Find the axis of symmetry and the vertex of a parabola

2 > Graph a parabola

3 > Application of a quadratic function

In Chapter 3 we discussed the graphs of linear equations in two variables of the form

$ax + by = c$ in which a and b cannot both be 0

The graphs of all linear equations are straight lines. Suppose that we now allow the terms in x or y to be quadratic; that is, we will allow squares in one or both of those terms. The graphs of such equations will form a family of curves called the **conic sections.** Conic sections are curves formed when a plane cuts through, or forms a section of, a cone. The conic sections include four curves—the **parabola, circle, ellipse,** and **hyperbola.** Examples of how these curves are formed are shown here.

NOTE

The inclination of the plane determines which of the sections is formed. We saw some parabolas in Chapter 8.

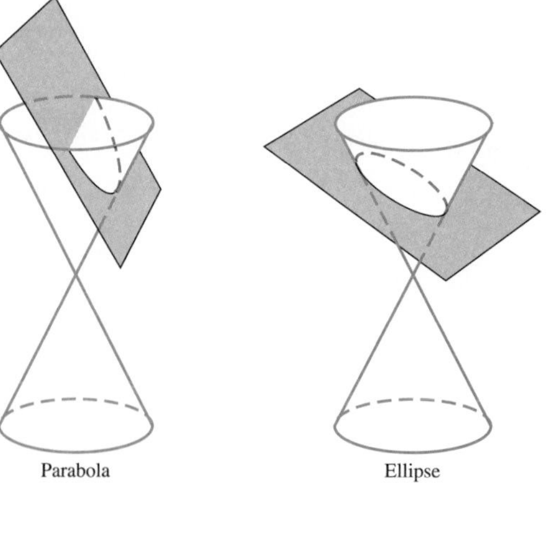

NOTE

The names *ellipse, parabola,* and *hyperbola* are attributed to Apollonius, a third-century B.C.E. Greek mathematician and astronomer.

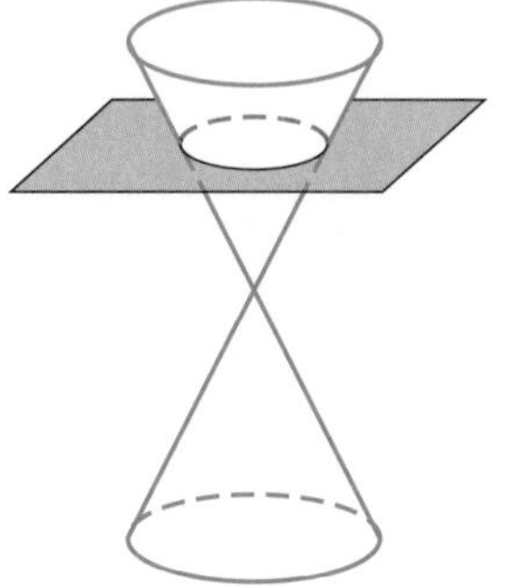

Circle

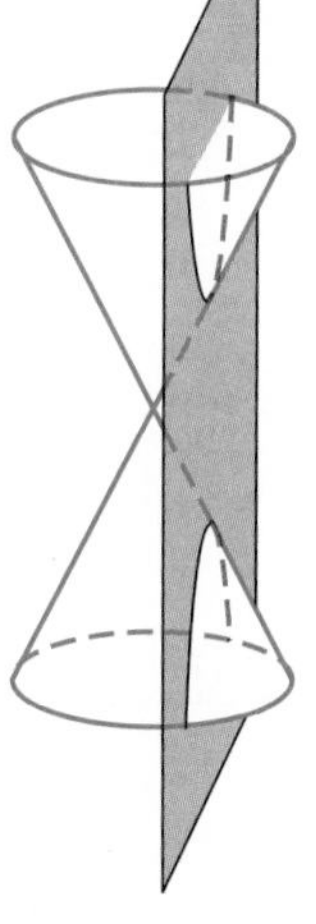

Hyperbola

We will examine the first of these sections, the parabola. Consider the equation $y = x^2$. This equation is quadratic in x and linear in y. Its graph is a parabola.

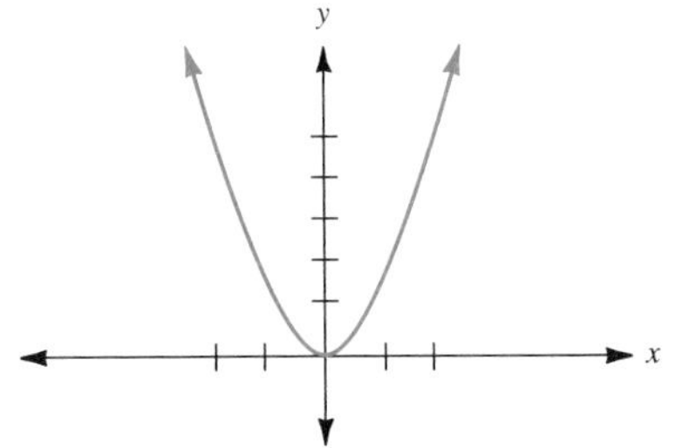

x	y
−2	4
−1	1
0	0
1	1
2	4

We could plot points, and then connect them.

NOTE

The parabola is rounded and not pointed at the bottom.

RECALL

In Section 8.1 we graphed quadratic functions, which were parabolas.

There are three elements of the graph that should be noted.

1. The graph opens upward.
2. The y-axis cuts the graph into two equal parts. A line that does this is called an **axis of symmetry.**
3. The graph has a minimum point, called the **vertex.**

Compare that graph to the graph of the equation $y = -x^2$.

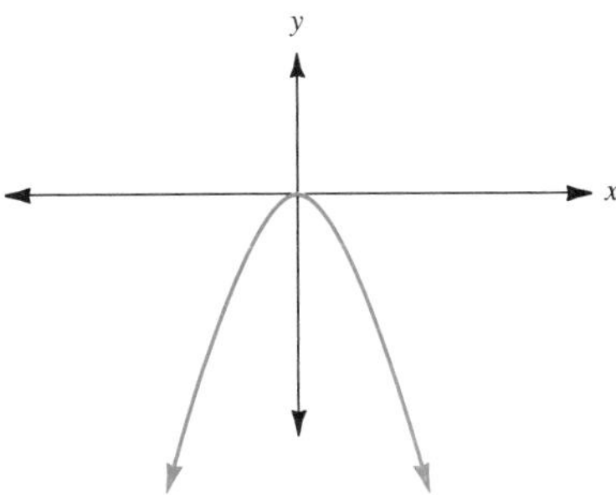

Looking at the three elements we just examined, we make these observations:

1. The graph opens downward.
2. The y-axis is the *axis of symmetry.*
3. The graph has a maximum point, called the *vertex.*

It will always be the case that the sign of the coefficient of the x^2-term will determine which way the parabola opens. It will also be the case that a parabola opening upward has a minimum, and one opening downward has a maximum.

For every equation that is quadratic in x and linear in y, we will look for three things:

1. Does the graph open upward or downward?
2. Where is the axis of symmetry?
3. What are the coordinates of the vertex?

Example 1 Graphing with a Vertical Translation

< Objective 1 >

Graph the equation $y = x^2 - 3$.

The difference between this graph and that of equation $y = x^2$ is that each y-value has been decreased by 3. This results in a **translation** of 3 units in the negative direction on the y-axis.

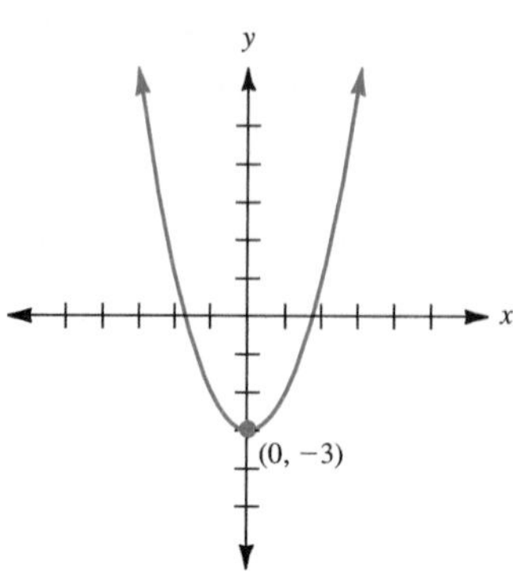

Note that the curve opens upward, the axis of symmetry is $x = 0$ (the y-axis), and the vertex is $(0, -3)$.

Check Yourself 1

Graph the equation $y = -x^2 + 2$.

An equation of the form $y = (x - h)^2$ will be translated along the x-axis with the axis of symmetry at $x = h$.

Example 2 Graphing with a Horizontal Translation

> CAUTION

When you enter the equation in your graphing calculator, be certain that the negative is *in front of* the parentheses.

Graph the equation $y = -(x - 3)^2$.

Because the coefficient of the x^2-term is negative, the parabola opens downward and has a maximum point. Notice that when $x = 3$, y is 0. If x is more than 3, y will be negative. Try substituting values for x in the equation, and then evaluate y. When x is less than 3, y is also negative. Thus, the vertex is at $(3, 0)$, and the axis of symmetry has the equation $x = 3$.

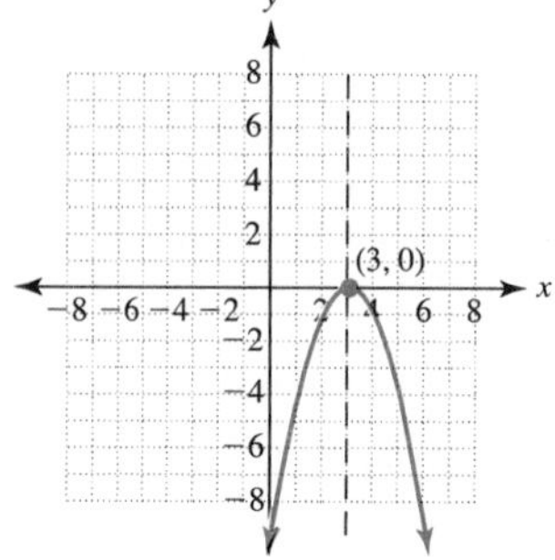

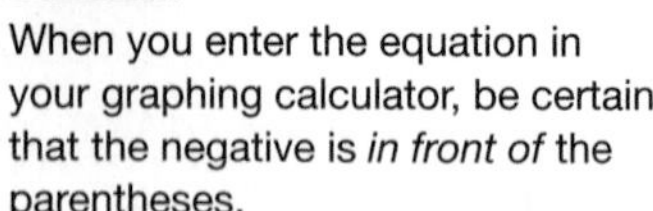

RECALL

The graph of an absolute value equation of the form $y = |x - a| + b$ is the graph of $y = |x|$ translated horizontally a units and vertically b units.

Check Yourself 2

Graph the equation $y = (x + 2)^2$.

Combining the lessons of Examples 1 and 2, we see that the graph of an equation of the form $y = (x - h)^2 + k$ is the parabola $y = x^2$ translated horizontally h units and vertically k units. The axis of symmetry is $x = h$, and the vertex is at (h, k).

Example 3 Graphing a Parabola

< Objective 2 >

Graph the equation $y = (x + 3)^2 + 1$.

The parabola will be translated to the left 3 units and up 1 unit. The parabola opens upward, with an axis of symmetry at $x = -3$ and a vertex at $(-3, 1)$.

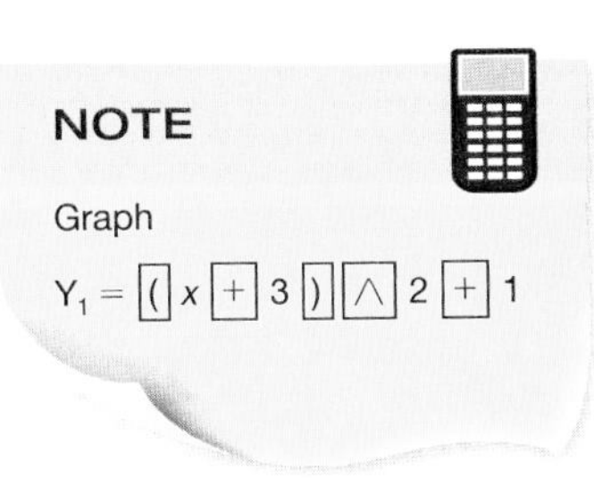

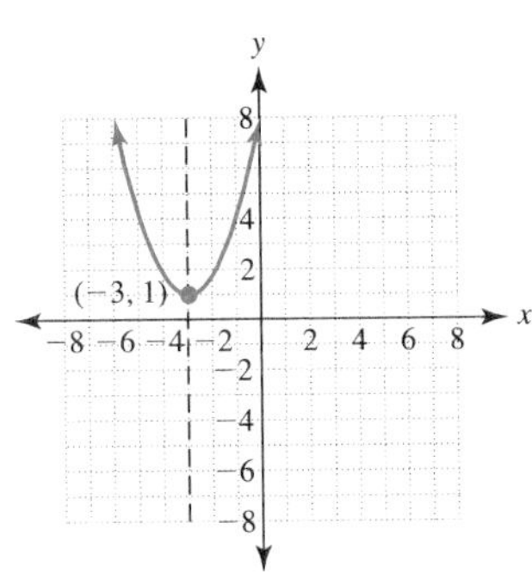

$$y = (x + 3)^2 + 1$$

No negative, so parabola opens upward

Translated to left 3 units

Translated up 1 unit

$x + 3 = x - (-3)$

Check Yourself 3

Graph the equation $y = -(x - 2)^2 - 3$.

The rate at which the sides of a parabola rise (or fall) is determined by the coefficient of the x^2-term.

Example 4 Graphing Parabolas

Graph the parabolas $y = 2x^2$, $y = x^2$, and $y = \frac{1}{2}x^2$ on the same axes.

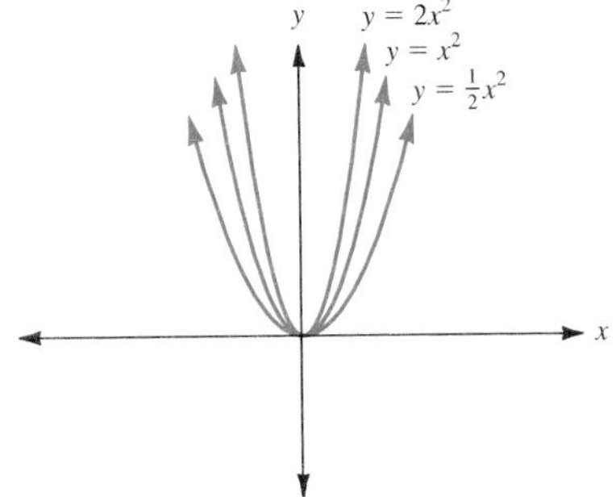

Compare the tables

x	x^2
−2	4
−1	1
0	0
1	1
2	4

x	$2x^2$
−2	8
−1	2
0	0
1	2
2	8

x	$\frac{1}{2}x^2$
−2	2
−1	$\frac{1}{2}$
0	0
1	$\frac{1}{2}$
2	2

Notice that the larger the coefficient of x^2, the faster the parabola rises, and thus the thinner the parabola appears.

Check Yourself 4

Graph the parabolas $y = -2x^2$, $y = -x^2$, and $y = -\frac{1}{2}x^2$ on the same axes.

We can now graph any equation of the form $y = a(x - h)^2 + k$.

Example 5 Graphing a Parabola

Graph the equation $y = -2(x - 3)^2 - 4$.

This parabola will open downward, the axis of symmetry is at $x = 3$, the vertex is at $(3, -4)$, and the parabola has the shape of $y = 2x^2$, which is slightly narrower than $y = x^2$.

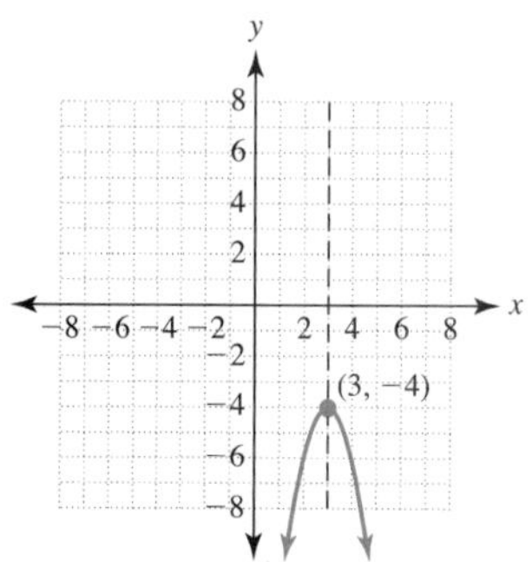

Check Yourself 5

Graph the equation $y = \frac{1}{4}(x + 3)^2 - 1$.

The standard form for a quadratic equation in two variables is $y = ax^2 + bx + c$. Any quadratic equation can be written in either this form or as $y = a(x - h)^2 + k$. Example 6 illustrates.

Example 6 Graphing an Equation of the Form $y = x^2 + bx + c$

RECALL

One-half the middle term squared will complete the square.

Graph the equation

$y = x^2 - 2x - 3$

Using the techniques of Section 8.2, we will first complete the square.

$$\begin{aligned} y &= x^2 - 2x - 3 \\ &= x^2 - 2x + 1 - 3 - 1 \\ &= (x - 1)^2 - 4 \end{aligned}$$

We can do this because $+1 - 1 = 0$.

NOTE

We could also use the original form and factor

$x^2 - 2x - 3 = 0$
$(x - 3)(x + 1) = 0$

The intercepts are (3, 0) and (−1, 0).

We know the parabola opens upward, the axis of symmetry is $x = 1$, and the vertex is at $(1, -4)$.

To improve the sketch, we can find the x-intercepts. These are the x-values for which $y = 0$, so

$$0 = (x - 1)^2 - 4$$
$$4 = (x - 1)^2$$
$$\pm 2 = x - 1$$
$$x = 1 + 2 \quad \text{or} \quad x = 1 - 2$$
$$= 3 \qquad\qquad = -1$$

The x-intercepts are $(3, 0)$ and $(-1, 0)$.

Now draw a smooth curve connecting the vertex and the x-intercepts.

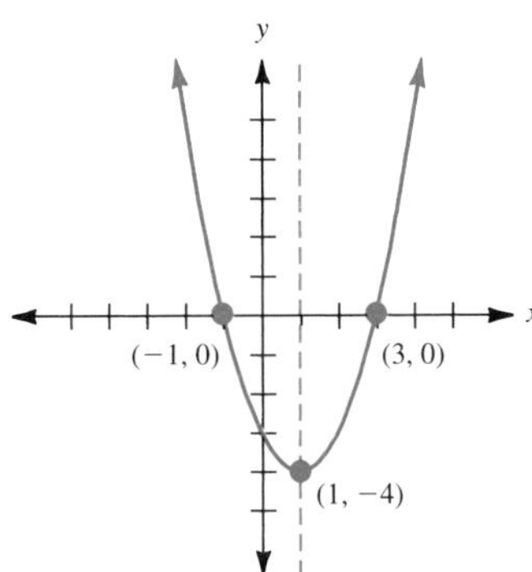

Again, look at the table

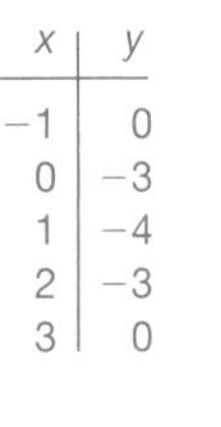

x	y
−1	0
0	−3
1	−4
2	−3
3	0

Check Yourself 6

Graph the equation

$y = -x^2 + 6x - 5$

Hint: Rewrite this as $y = -(x^2 - 6x + 9) - 5 + 9$.

A similar process will work if the quadratic member of the given equation is *not* factorable. In that case, one of two things happens:

1. The x-intercepts are irrational. In this case, a calculator can be used to estimate the intercepts.
2. The x-intercepts do not exist.

Consider Example 7.

Example 7 Graphing an Equation of the Form $y = x^2 + bx + c$

NOTE

To keep the equation balanced, we both add and subtract 4.

Graph the equation

$$y = x^2 - 4x + 2$$
$$= x^2 - 4x + 2$$
$$= x^2 - 4x + 4 + 2 - 4$$
$$= (x - 2)^2 - 2$$

The parabola opens upward, the axis of symmetry is $x = 2$, and the vertex is $(2, -2)$.

Again, we can improve the sketch if we find two symmetric points. Here the quadratic member is not factorable, and the x-intercepts are irrational, so we would prefer to find another pair of symmetric points.

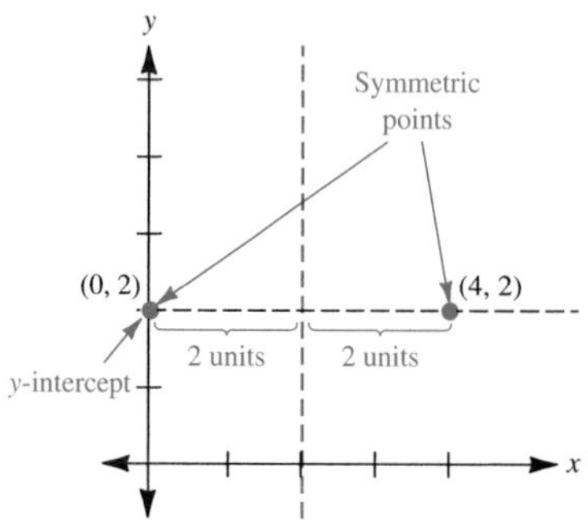

Note that (0, 2) is the y-intercept of the parabola. We found the axis of symmetry at $x = 2$ earlier. The symmetric point to (0, 2) lies along the horizontal line through the y-intercept at the same distance (2 units) from the axis of symmetry, or at $x = 4$. Hence, (4, 2) is our symmetric point.

Draw a smooth curve connecting the points found to form the parabola.

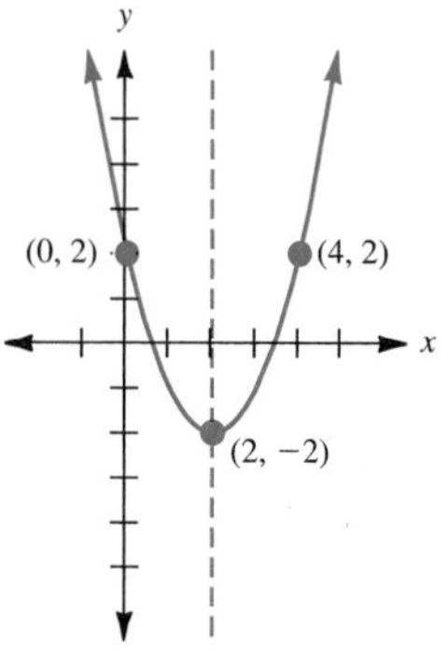

Check Yourself 7

Graph the equation $y = x^2 + 2x + 3$.

The coefficient of x^2 was 1 or -1 in Example 7. Example 8 shows the effect of different coefficients of the x^2-term.

Example 8 Graphing an Equation of the Form $y = ax^2 + bx + c$

NOTE

We have added 2 times 1 or 2, so we must also subtract 2.

Graph the equation

$$y = 2x^2 - 4x + 3$$

Step 1 Complete the square.

$$\begin{aligned} y &= 2(x^2 - 2x) + 3 \\ &= 2(x^2 - 2x + 1) + 3 - 2 \\ &= 2(x - 1)^2 + 1 \end{aligned}$$

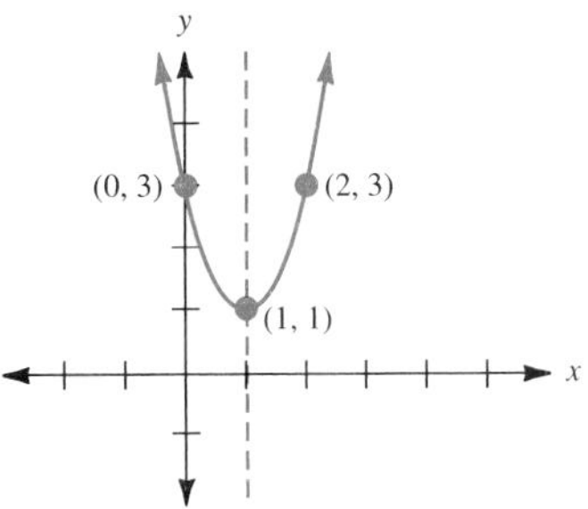

Step 2 The axis of symmetry is $x = 1$; the vertex is $(1, 1)$.

Step 3 Find symmetric points. Again the quadratic member is not factorable, and we use the y-intercept $(0, 3)$ and its symmetric point $(2, 3)$.

Step 4 Connect the points with a smooth curve to form the parabola.

Compare this curve to those in Examples 1 to 7. Note that the parabola is "tighter" about the axis of symmetry. That is the effect of the larger x^2-coefficient.

Check Yourself 8

Graph the equation $y = \frac{1}{2}x^2 - 2x - 2$.

The following algorithm summarizes our work thus far in this section.

Step by Step

Graphing a Quadratic Equation

Step 1 Complete the square for the quadratic variable.

Step 2 Find the axis of symmetry and the vertex.

Step 3 Determine two symmetric points.
Note: You can use the x-intercepts if the quadratic member of the given equation is factorable. Otherwise it may be easier to use the y-intercept and its symmetric point.

Step 4 Draw a smooth curve connecting the points found to form the parabola. You may choose to find additional pairs of symmetric points at this time.

If we use the algorithm to find the vertex of the equation $y = ax^2 + bx + c$, we get useful results. The axis of symmetry will always have the equation $x = \frac{-b}{2a}$ and the vertex will always be at $\left(\frac{-b}{2a}, f\left(\frac{-b}{2a}\right)\right)$.

To see why this is so, we first assume that the quadratic function has two x-intercepts. We have seen this means the graph is a parabola that crosses the x-axis in two distinct points. Since the parabola is symmetric with respect to a vertical line through its vertex (the axis of symmetry) the x-coordinate of the vertex is always halfway between the two x-intercepts. By the quadratic formula, the two x-intercepts are

$$x_1 = \frac{-b + \sqrt{b^2 - 4ac}}{2a} = \frac{-b}{2a} + \frac{\sqrt{b^2 - 4ac}}{2a}$$

and

$$x_2 = \frac{-b - \sqrt{b^2 - 4ac}}{2a} = \frac{-b}{2a} - \frac{\sqrt{b^2 - 4ac}}{2a}$$

Notice that the same number, $\frac{\sqrt{b^2 - 4ac}}{2a}$, is being added to and subtracted from $\frac{-b}{2a}$. It follows that the number $\frac{-b}{2a}$ is halfway between x_1 and x_2. It means that the x-coordinate of the vertex is $x = \frac{-b}{2a}$. We can then find the y-coordinate of the vertex by evaluating $f\left(\frac{-b}{2a}\right)$. Notice that we have also found the axis of symmetry to be at $x = \frac{-b}{2a}$.

Although we assumed that the quadratic function had two x-intercepts when we derived our vertex formula, it also holds in the other two cases, where the parabola has one or no x-intercepts.

So far we have dealt with equations of the form

$$y = ax^2 + bx + c$$

Suppose we reverse the role of x and y. We then have

$$x = ay^2 + by + c$$

which is quadratic in y but not in x. The graph of such an equation is once again a parabola, but this time the parabola will be horizontally oriented—opening to the right or left as a is positive or negative, respectively.

For $x = ay^2 + by + c$,

NOTE

The vertical line test shows us these are not functions.

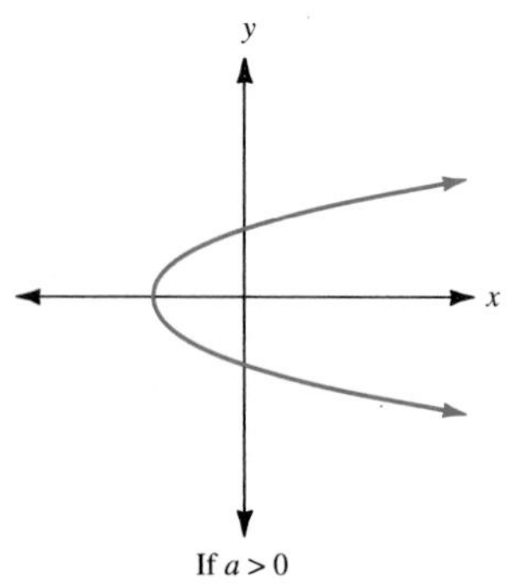

If $a > 0$

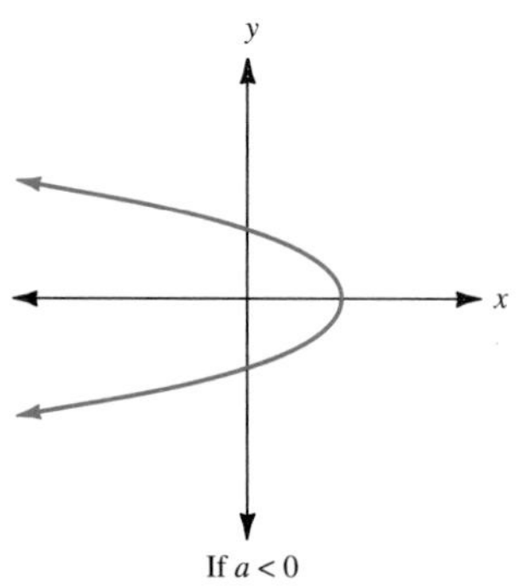

If $a < 0$

Much of what we did earlier is easily extended to this new case. Example 9 will illustrate the changes in the process.

Example 9 Graphing an Equation of the Form $x = ay^2 + by + c$

Graph the equation

$$x = y^2 + 2y - 3$$

Step 1 Complete the square.

$$x = y^2 + 2y + 1 - 3 - 1$$
$$x = (y + 1)^2 - 4$$

Step 2 Find the axis of symmetry and the vertex. Because the y-term is squared, the axis of symmetry is a horizontal line. Here, it is $y = -1$. Substituting -1 for y in the original equation, shows us that $(-4, -1)$ is the vertex.

Step 3 Sketch the parabola.

NOTE

To find the y-intercepts we let $x = 0$.

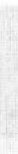

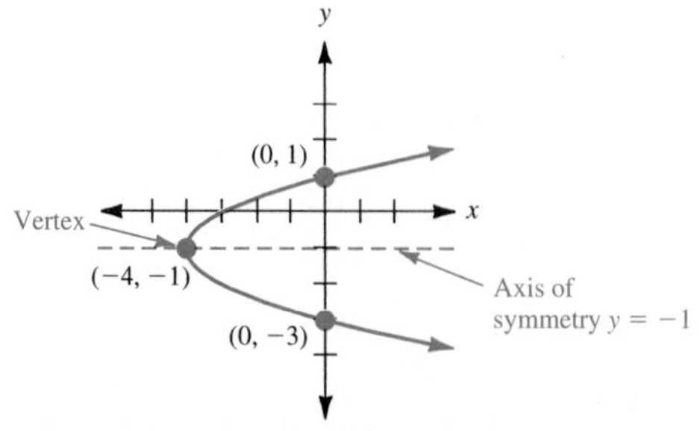

Check Yourself 9

Graph the equation $x = y^2 - 5y + 4$.

NOTE

When graphed, the equations produced when solving for y are the half-parabolas determined by the axis of symmetry, which is horizontal.

There are several ways to make a graphing calculator produce a parabola when there is a y^2-term. One such method involves solving the equation for y and graphing the top and bottom portions of the parabola as individual functions. We will use a graphing calculator to graph an equation of the form $x = a(y - k)^2 + h$. In this case, the vertex is still given by (h, k) but their roles are reversed in the given equation. The axis of symmetry is still $y = k$.

Example 10 Using a Graphing Calculator with a y^2-Term

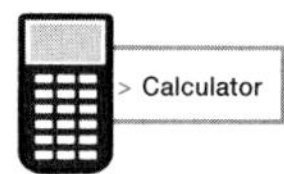

Use a graphing calculator to graph the equation $x = (y + 1)^2 + 2$.

First, we solve the equation for y, using the techniques we learned in Chapter 7.

$$x = (y + 1)^2 + 2$$
$$x - 2 = (y + 1)^2$$
$$\pm\sqrt{x - 2} = y + 1 \qquad \text{Take the square root of both sides.}$$
$$-1 \pm \sqrt{x - 2} = y$$
$$y = -1 \pm \sqrt{x - 2} \qquad \text{Solve for } y \text{, writing } y \text{ on the left.}$$

RECALL

When you take a square root, you need to include both the positive and the negative square roots.

This leaves us with two distinct functions, which we enter into the graphing calculator and graph.

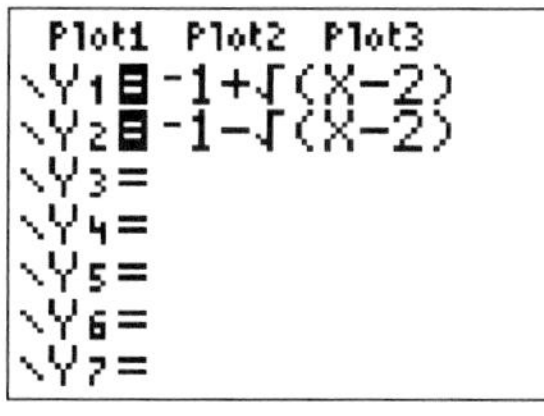

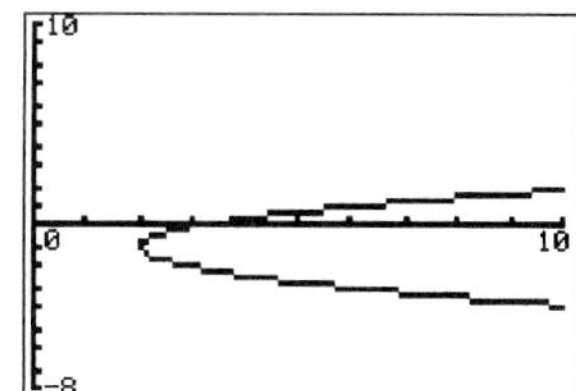

As we expect, the vertex is at $(2, -1)$, and the axis of symmetry is given by the line $y = -1$.

Check Yourself 10

Graph the equation $x = (y - 3)^2 - 1$ using a graphing calculator.

As we saw earlier, the vertex of a parabola can be found directly from the function

$$f(x) = ax^2 + bx + c$$

as the coordinates

$$\left(\frac{-b}{2a}, f\left(\frac{-b}{2a}\right)\right)$$

That technique will be used in Example 11.

Given equations of the form $y = ax^2 + bx + c$, we know that if $a > 0$, then the vertex is the lowest point on the graph (the minimum value). Also, if $a < 0$, then the vertex is the highest point on the graph (the maximum value). We can use this result to solve a variety of problems in which we want to find the maximum or minimum value of a variable.

Example 11 An Application of a Quadratic Function

< Objective 3 >

A software company sells a word processing program for personal computers. It has found that its monthly profit in dollars, P, from selling x copies of the program is approximated by

$$P(x) = -0.2x^2 + 80x - 1{,}200$$

Find the number of copies of the program that should be sold to maximize the profit.

Because the function is quadratic, the graph must be a parabola. Also because the coefficient of x^2 is negative, the parabola must open downward, and thus the vertex will give the maximum value for the profit, P. To find the vertex,

$$x = \frac{-b}{2a} = \frac{-80}{2(-0.2)} = \frac{-80}{-0.4} = 200$$

The maximum profit must then occur when $x = 200$. We substitute that value into the original equation:

$$P(x) = -0.2(200)^2 + (80)(200) - 1{,}200$$
$$= \$6{,}800$$

The maximum profit will occur when 200 copies are sold per month, and that profit will be \$6,800.

Check Yourself 11

A company that sells portable radios finds that its weekly profit in dollars, P, and the number of radios sold, x, are related by

$$P(x) = -0.1x^2 + 20x - 200$$

Find the number of radios that should be sold to have the largest weekly profit and the amount of that profit.

Example 12 An Application of a Quadratic Function

A farmer has 1,000 ft of fence and wishes to enclose the largest possible rectangular area with that fencing. Find the length and width of the largest possible area that can be enclosed.

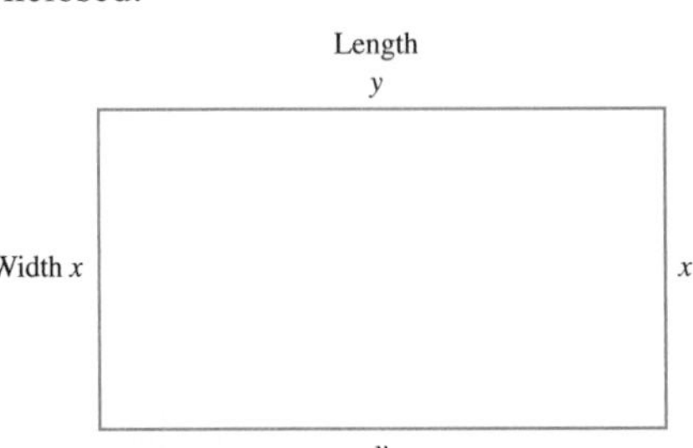

> **NOTE**
>
> As usual, when dealing with geometric figures, we began by drawing a sketch of the problem.

> **RECALL**
>
> Area = length × width
>
> The perimeter of the region is $2x + 2y$

> **NOTE**
>
> The width x is 250 ft. So
>
> $y = 500 - 250$
> $= 250$ ft
>
> which means the length is also 250 ft. The desired region is a square.

First, we can write the area A as

$$A = xy$$

Also because 1,000 ft of fence is to be used, we know that

$$2x + 2y = 1{,}000$$
$$2y = 1{,}000 - 2x$$
$$y = 500 - x$$

Substituting for y in the area equation, we have

$$A = x(500 - x) = 500x - x^2$$
$$= -x^2 + 500x$$

Again, the graph for A is a parabola opening downward, and the largest possible area will occur at the vertex. As before,

$$x = \frac{-500}{2(-1)} = \frac{-500}{-2} = 250$$

and the largest possible area is

$$A = -(250)^2 + 500(250) = 62{,}500 \text{ ft}^2$$

Check Yourself 12

We want to enclose the largest possible rectangular area by using 400 ft of fence. The fence will be connected to the house, so only three sides of fence will be needed. What should be the dimensions of the rectangle, and what is the largest possible area?

There are many physical models involving a parabolic path or design. The fact that a projectile follows a parabolic path was known in the time of Galileo. The reflective properties of the parabola are also important. If light rays enter a parabola along lines parallel to the axis of symmetry, the rays will reflect off the parabola and pass through what is called the *focus* of the parabola. That fact accounts for the design of parabolic radar antennas and solar collectors.

The reflective surface of an automobile headlight is also a parabolic surface. The light source in the headlight is placed approximately at the focus so that the light rays will reflect off the surface as nearly parallel rays.

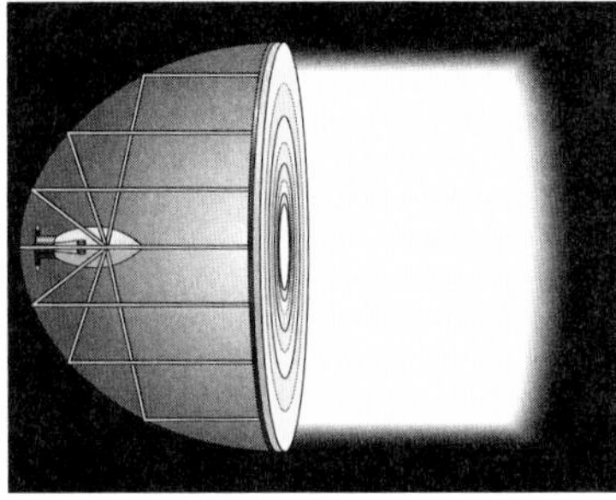

Check Yourself ANSWERS

1. $y = -x^2 + 2$

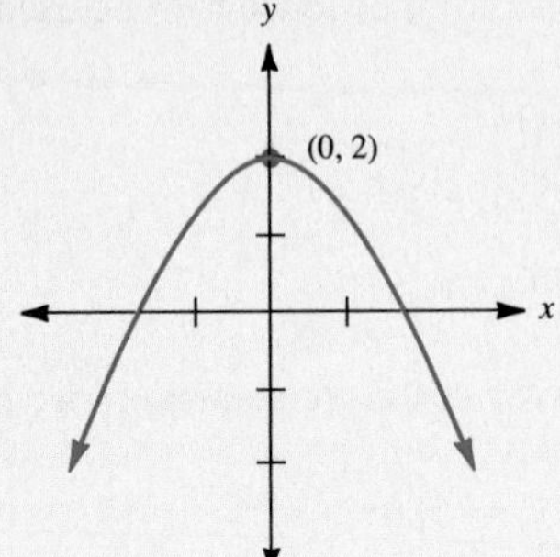

2. $y = (x + 2)^2$

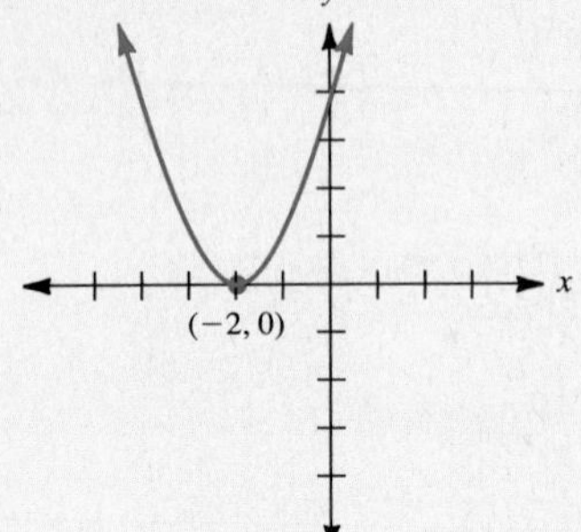

3. $y = -(x - 2)^2 - 3$

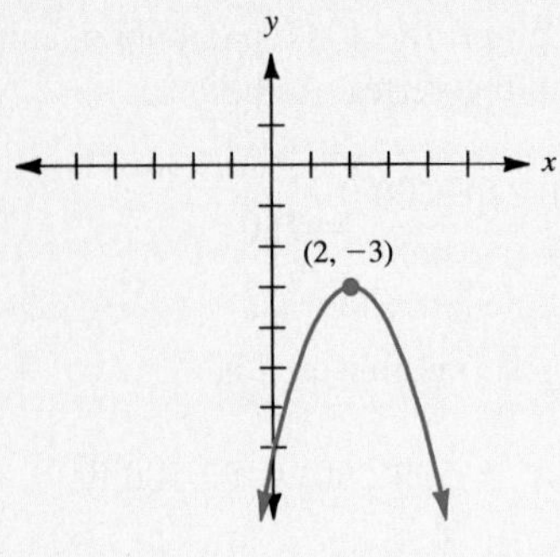

4.

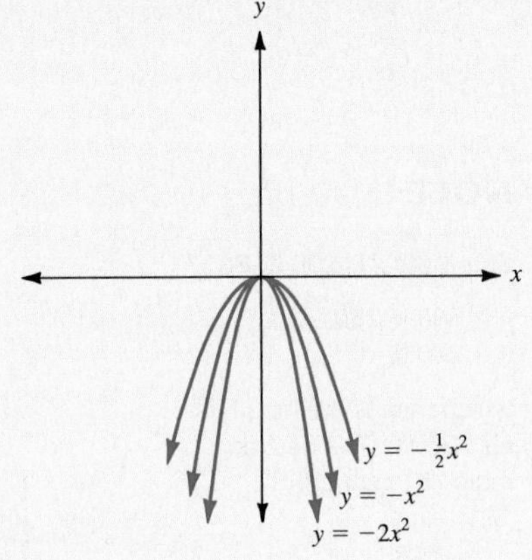

5. $y = \dfrac{1}{4}(x + 3)^2 - 1$

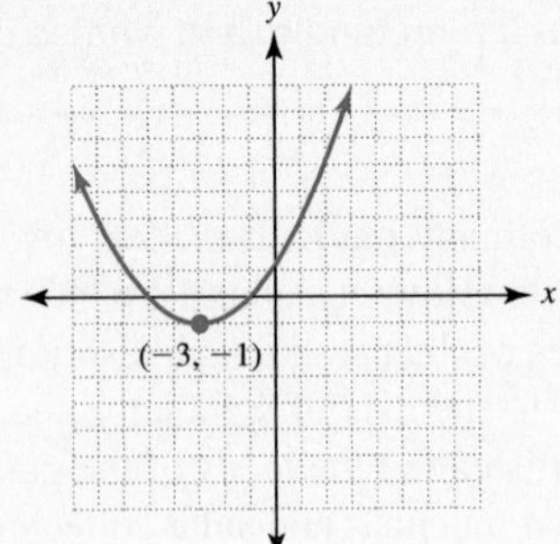

6. $y = -x^2 + 6x - 5$

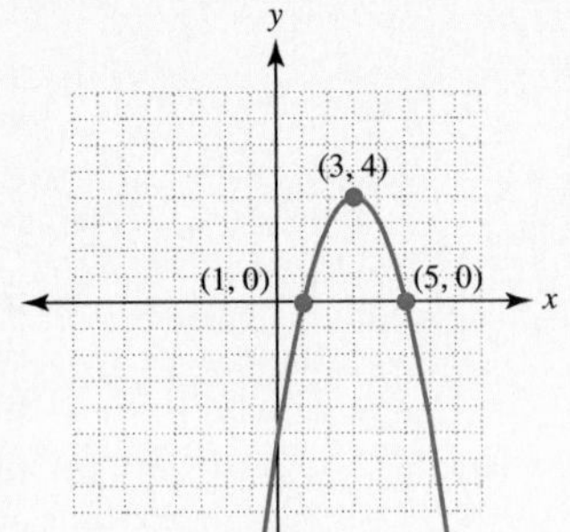

7. $y = x^2 + 2x + 3$

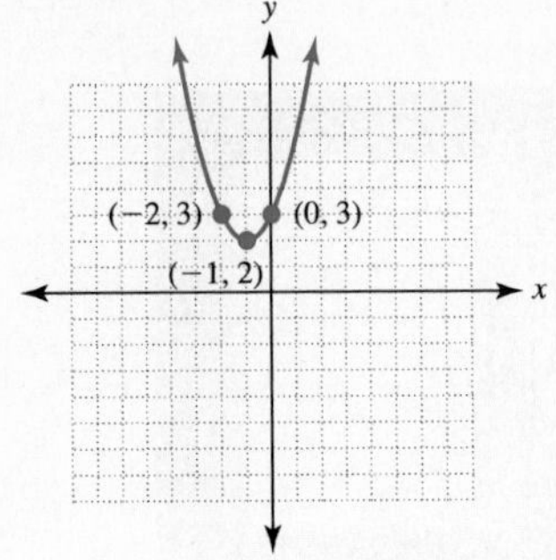

8. $y = \dfrac{1}{2}x^2 - 2x - 2$

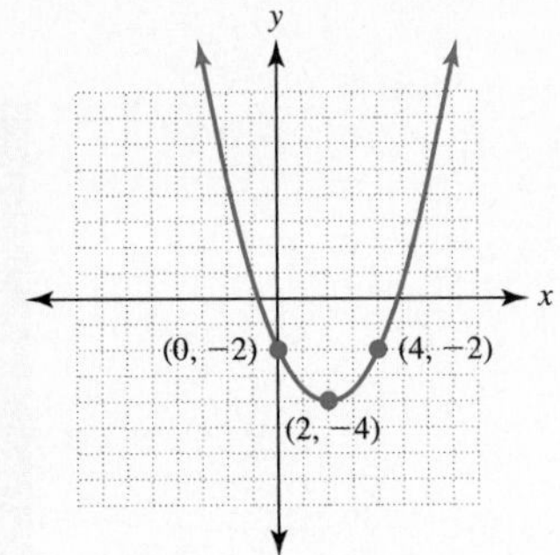

9. $x = y^2 - 5y + 4$

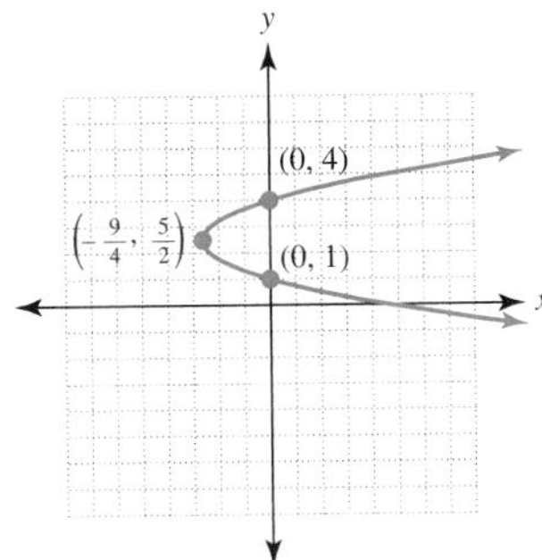

10. $x = (y - 3)^2 - 1$

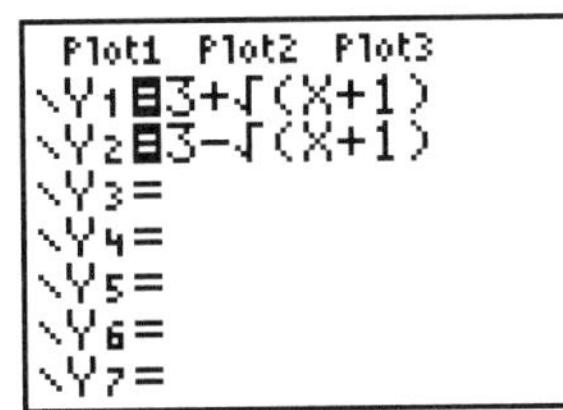

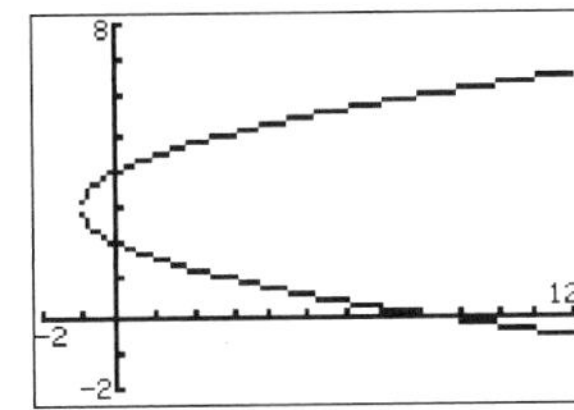

11. 100 radios; $800 **12.** Width: 100 ft; length: 200 ft; area: 20,000 ft^2

Reading Your Text

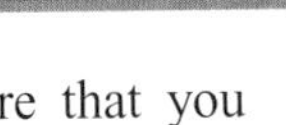

The following fill-in-the-blank exercises are designed to ensure that you understand some of the key vocabulary used in this section.

SECTION 9.1

(a) ______________ are curves formed when a plane cuts through, or forms a section of, a cone.

(b) The conic sections include four curves: the ______________, ______________, ______________, and ______________.

(c) A line that cuts the graph of a parabola into two equal parts is called an ______________.

(d) The ______________ is the maximum or minimum point of a parabola.

9.1 exercises

Basic Skills | Advanced Skills | Vocational-Technical Applications | Calculator/Computer | Above and Beyond

Name ______________

Section ______ Date ______

Answers

1. (d)
2. (f)
3. (b)
4. (g)
5. (a)
6. (c)
7. (e)
8. (h)

In exercises 1 to 10, match each graph with one of the equations.

(a) $y = x^2 + 2$ **(b)** $y = 2x^2 - 1$

(c) $y = 2x + 1$ **(d)** $y = \left(x - \frac{3}{2}\right)^2 - \frac{9}{4}$

(e) $y = -(x + 2)^2 + 4$ **(f)** $y = -2x + 1$

(g) $y = (x + 1)^2 - 4$ **(h)** $y = -(x - 3)^2 + 1$

(i) $y = \left(x - \frac{1}{2}\right)^2 - \frac{9}{4}$ **(j)** $x = -(y - 1)^2 + 4$

1.

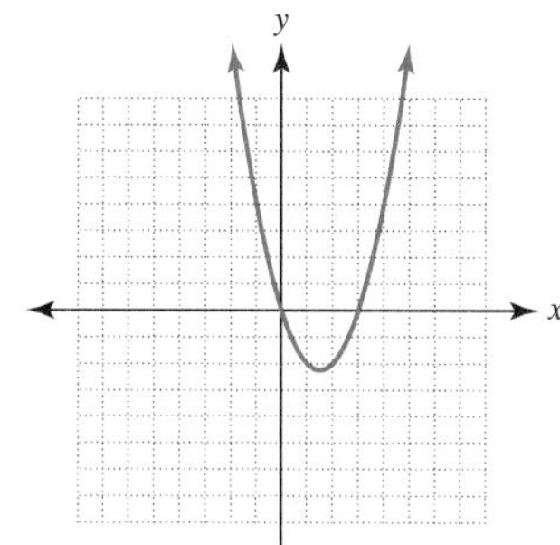

2.

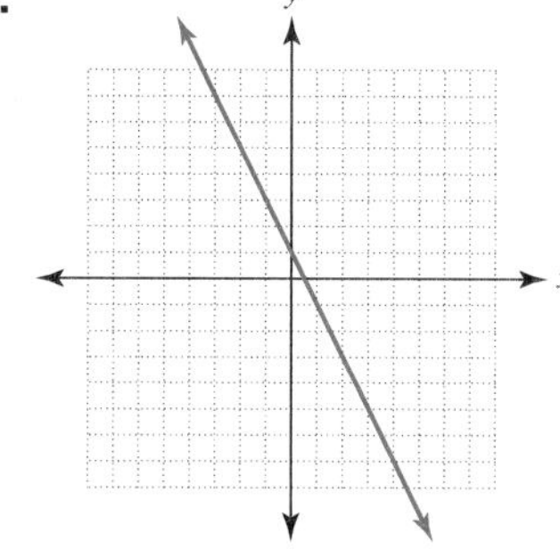

3.

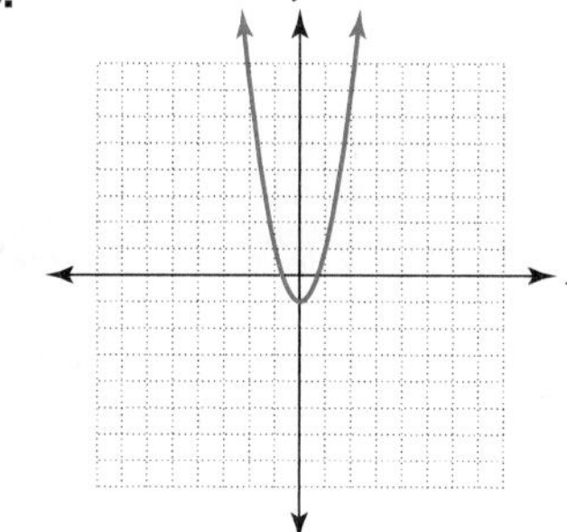

4.

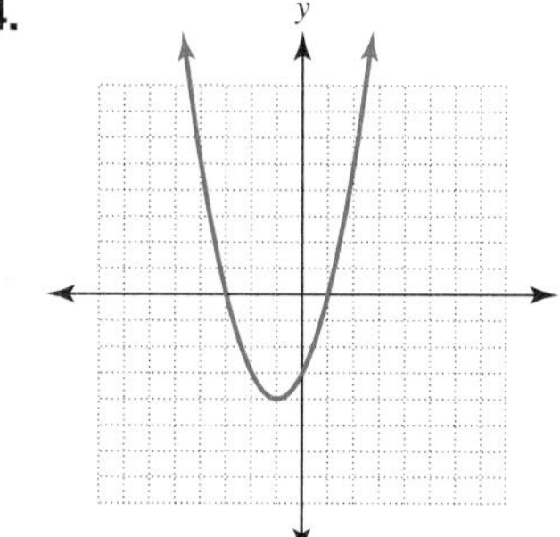

5.

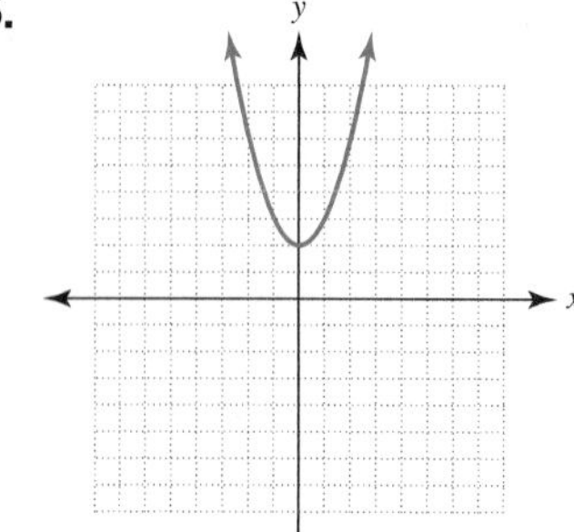

6.

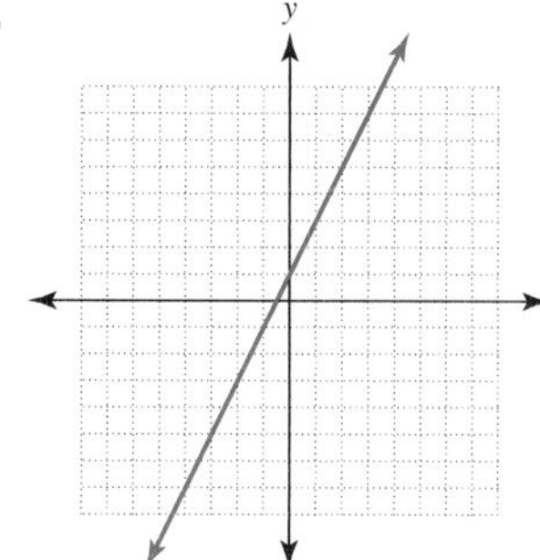

7.

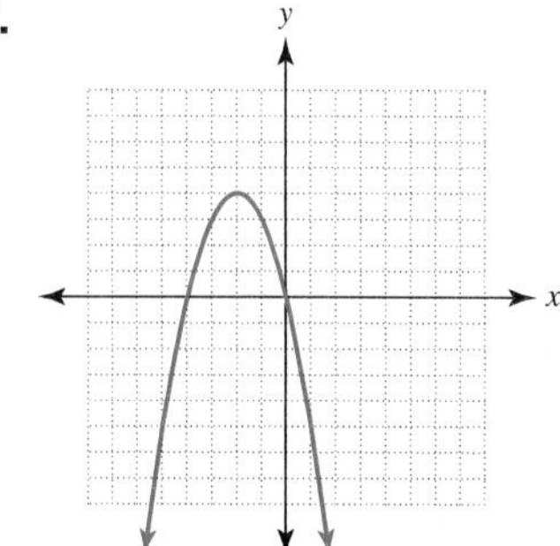

8.

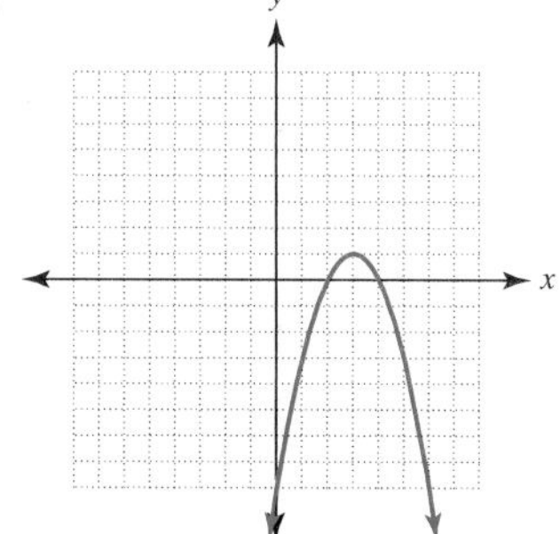

9.

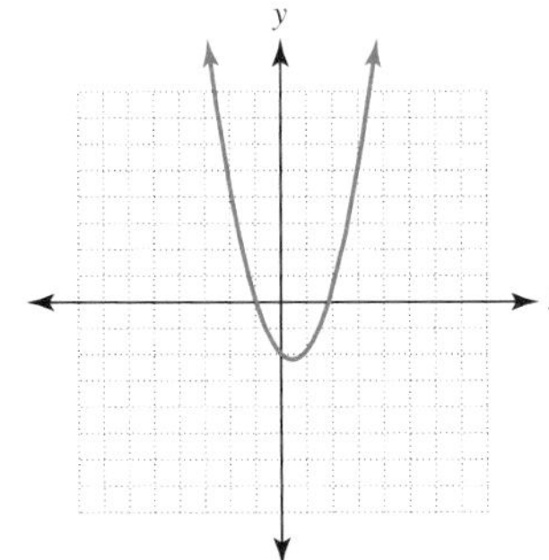

10.

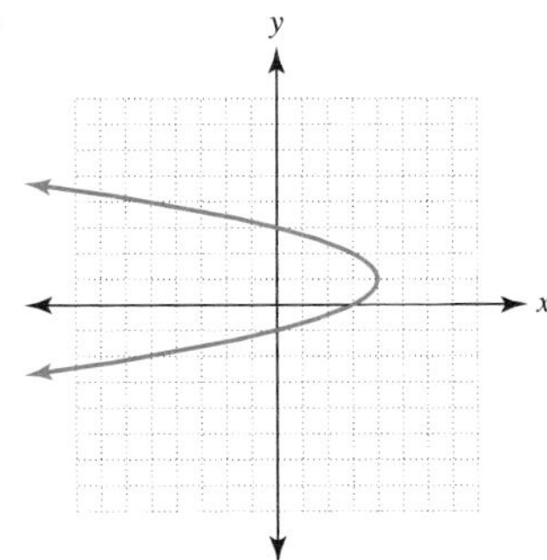

Determine whether each parabola is translated from the origin to the left, to the right, upward, or downward.

11. $y = (x + 5)^2$

12. $y = x^2 + 7$

13. $y = (x - 2)^2$

14. $y = (x - 5)^2$

15. $x = y^2 - 4$

16. $x = (y + 2)^2$

< Objective 1 >

Find the equation of the axis of symmetry and the coordinates for the vertex of each function.

17. $f(x) = x^2$

18. $f(x) = x^2 + 2$

19. $f(x) = x^2 - 5$

20. $f(x) = (x - 3)^2$

21. $f(x) = (x + 3)^2 + 1$

22. $f(x) = -(x + 2)^2 - 3$

23. $f(x) = -x^2 + 2x$

24. $f(x) = x^2 + 4x + 5$

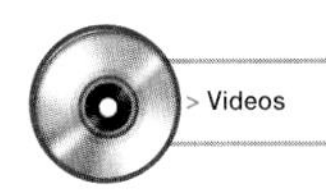

< Objective 2 >

Graph each equation.

25. $y = -\frac{1}{2}(x + 3)^2$

26. $y = (x - 3)^2 + 2$

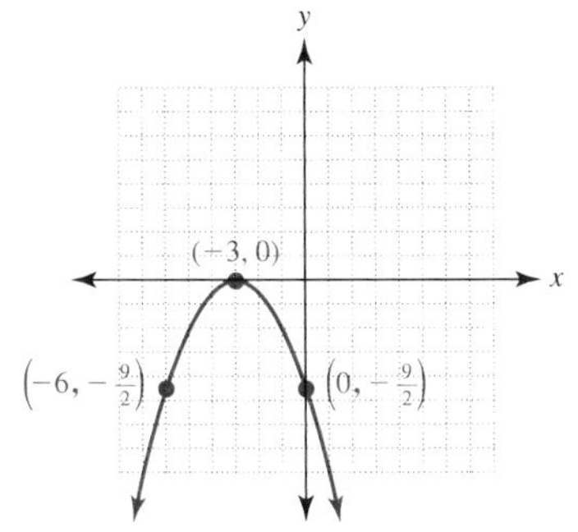

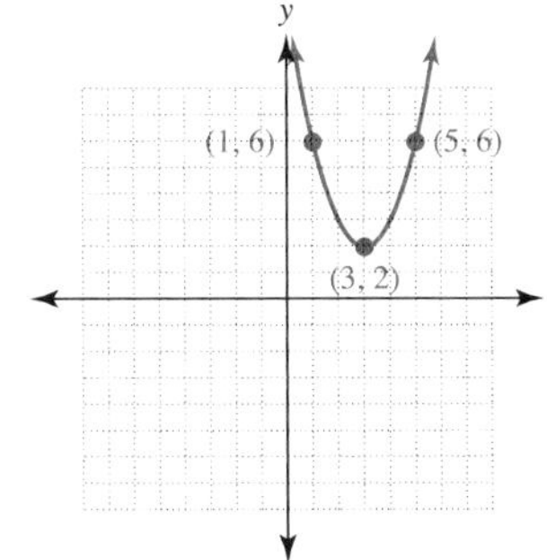

Answers

9. (i)
10. (j)
11. Left
12. Up
13. Right
14. Right
15. Left
16. Down
17. $x = 0$, $(0, 0)$
18. $x = 0$, $(0, 2)$
19. $x = 0$, $(0, -5)$
20. $x = 3$, $(3, 0)$
21. $x = -3$, $(-3, 1)$
22. $x = -2$, $(-2, -3)$
23. $x = 1$, $(1, 1)$
24. $x = -2$, $(-2, 1)$
25. See exercise
26. See exercise

Answers

27. See exercise

28. See exercise

29. See exercise

30. See exercise

31. See exercise

32. See exercise

33. See exercise

34. See exercise

27. $y = -(x + 2)^2 - 1$

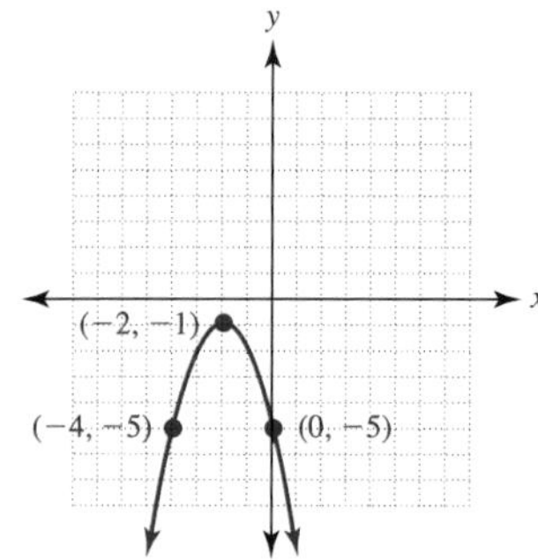

28. $y = 2(x + 3)^2 - 3$

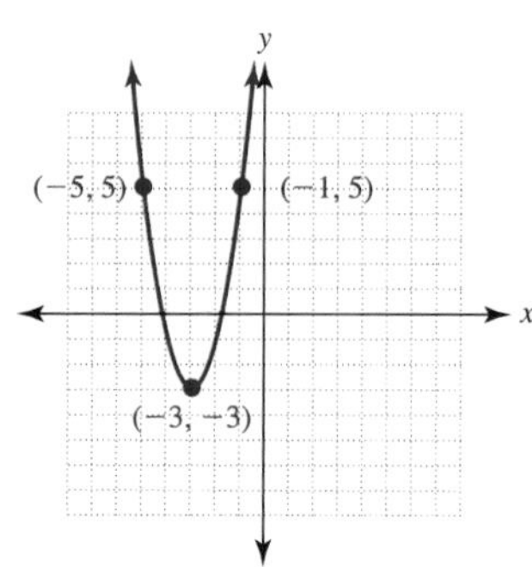

29. $y = x^2 - 2x$

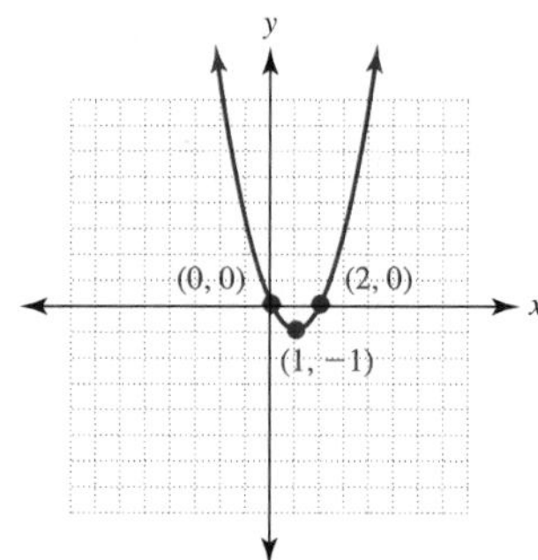

30. $y = x^2 - 4$

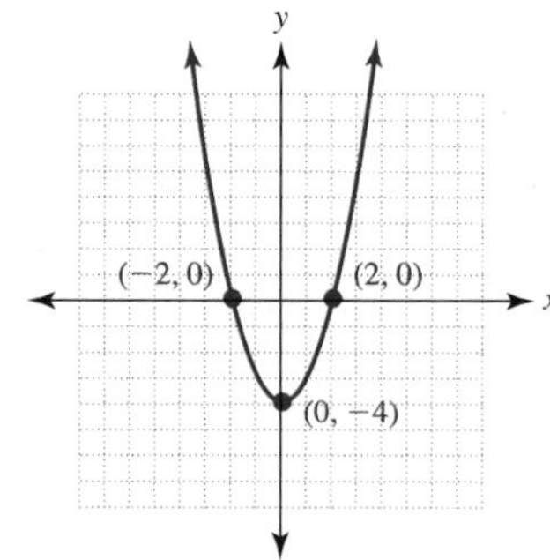

31. $y = -x^2 + 1$

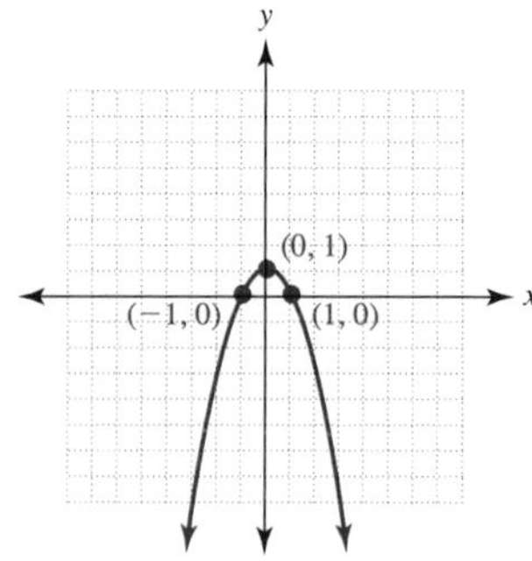

32. $y = x^2 + 4x$

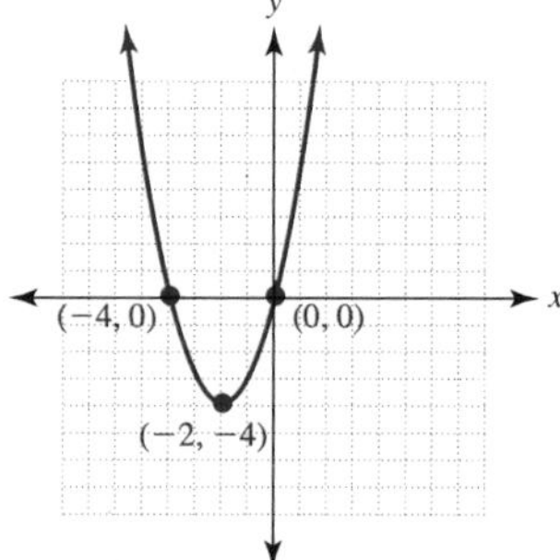

33. $y = x^2 - 2x - 3$

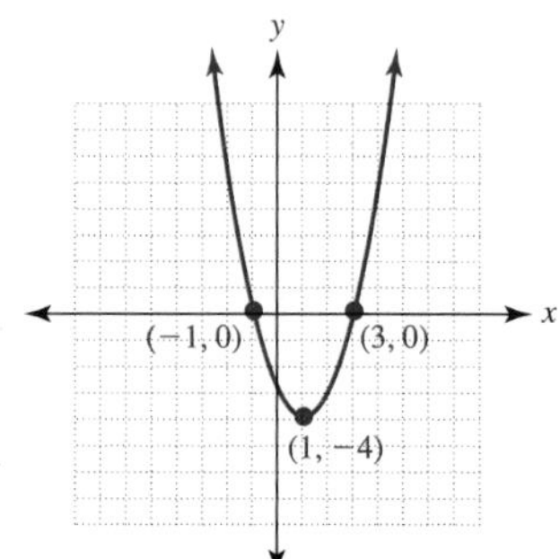

34. $y = x^2 - x - 6$

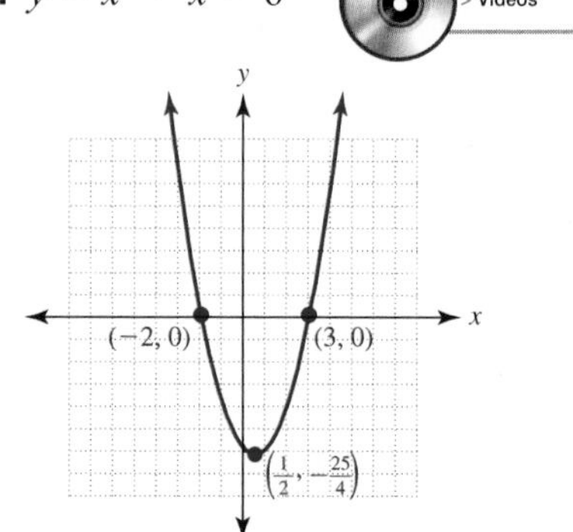

35. $y = 2x^2 - 4x + 1$

36. $y = \frac{1}{2}x^2 + x - 2$

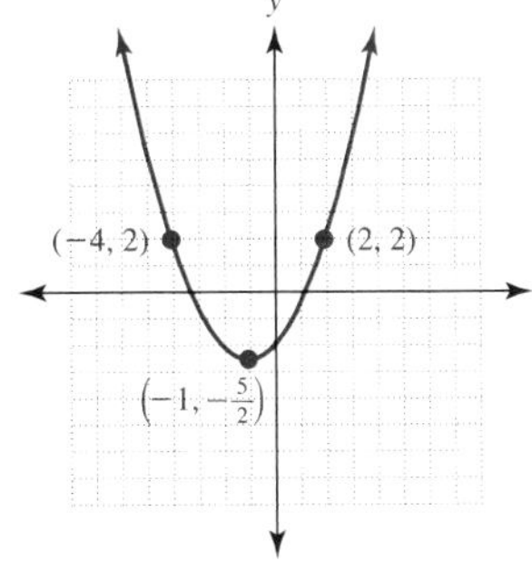

37. $y = -\frac{1}{3}x^2 + x - 2$

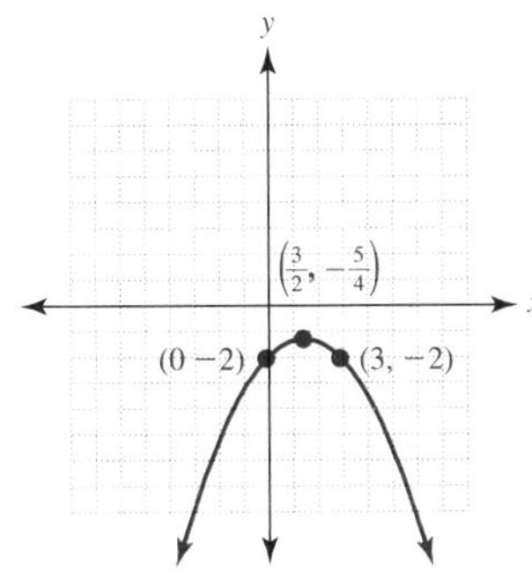

38. $y = -2x^2 + 4x - 3$

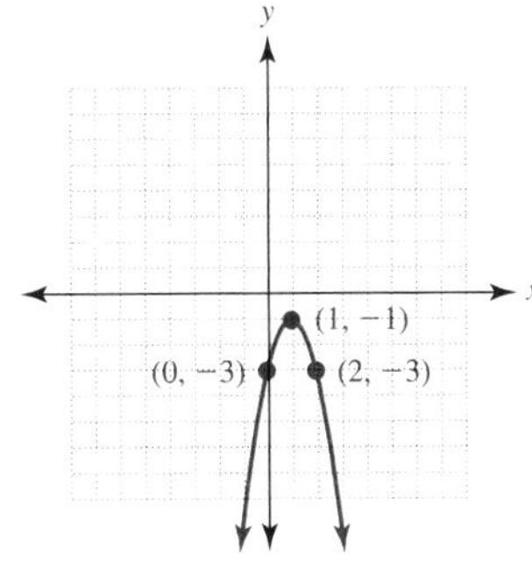

39. $y = 3x^2 + 6x - 1$

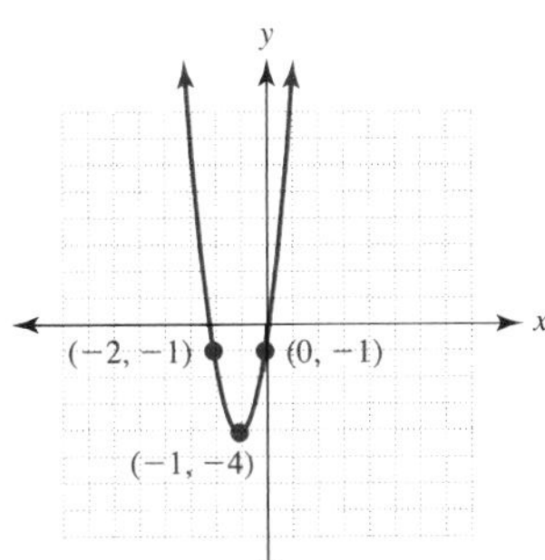

40. $y = -3x^2 + 12x - 5$

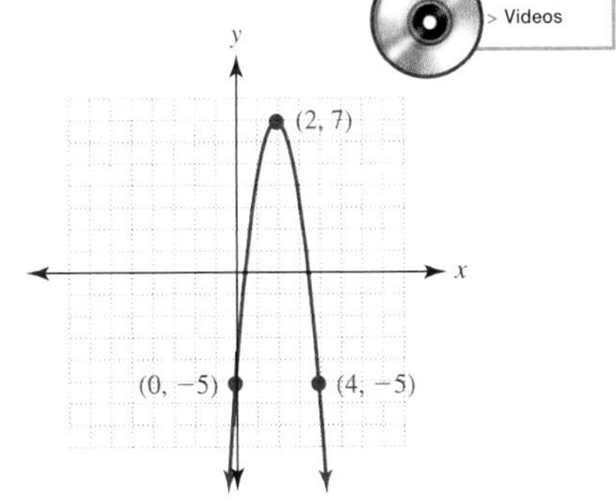

41. $x = y^2 - 4y$

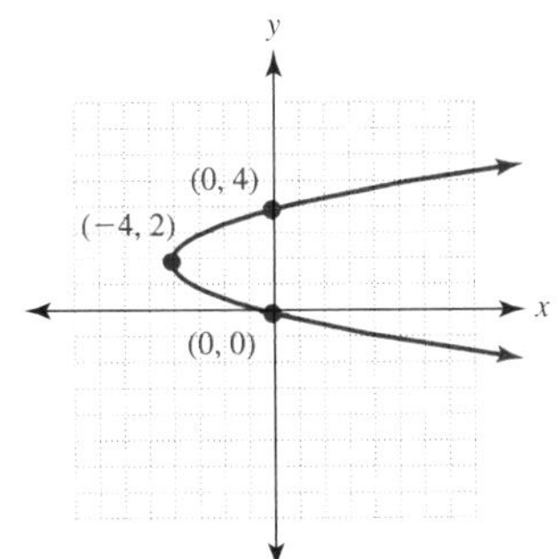

42. $x = y^2 + 3y$

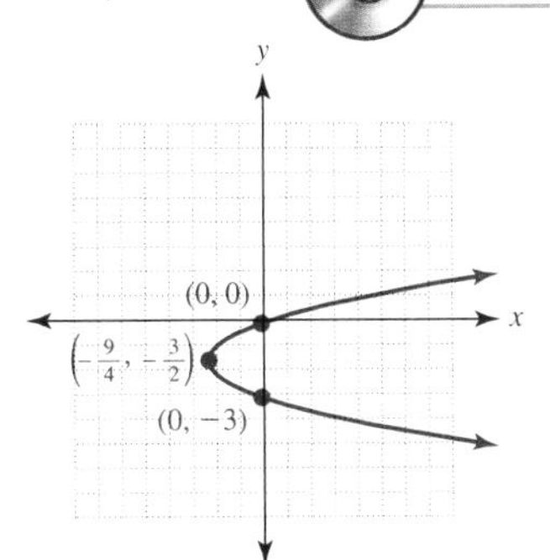

Answers

35. See exercise
36. See exercise
37. See exercise
38. See exercise
39. See exercise
40. See exercise
41. See exercise
42. See exercise

Answers

43. See exercise

44. See exercise

45. 100 items, \$1,500

46. 150 items, \$1,250

47. 400 ft by 400 ft, 160,000 ft^2

48. 600 ft by 300 ft, 180,000 ft^2

49. 64 ft

43. $x = y^2 - 3y - 4$

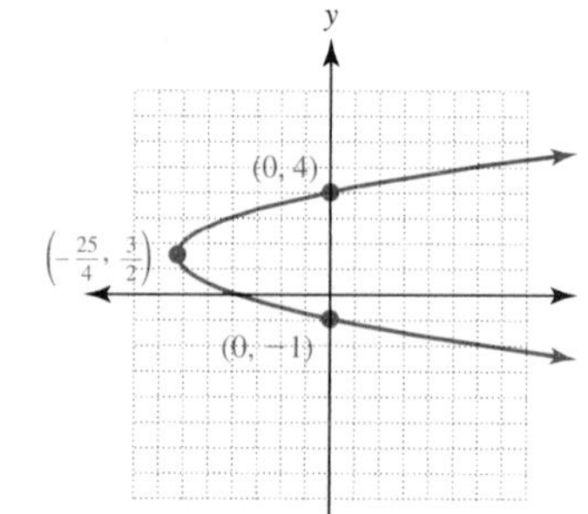

44. $x = -y^2 - y + 6$

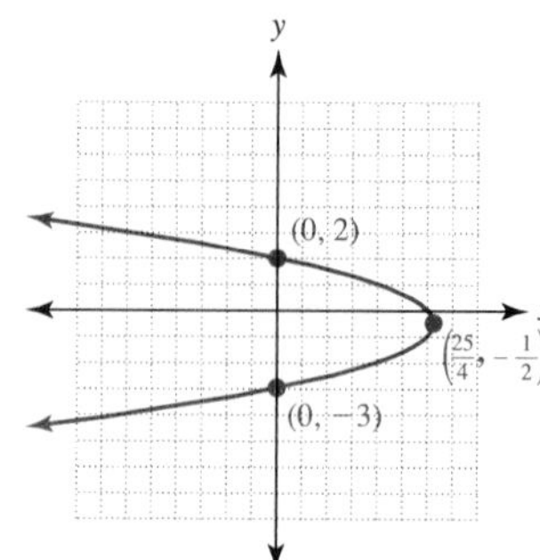

Recall from Example 10 that if you wish to check your work on exercises 43 and 44, you can use a graphing utility. For example, to graph $x = y^2 - 3y - 4$, first, we rewrite the equation as a quadratic in y, set equal to zero.

$$y^2 - 3y - (x + 4) = 0$$

Then, use the quadratic formula to solve for y and enter the resulting equations into our graphing utility.

$$Y_1 = \frac{3 + \sqrt{9 + 4(x + 4)}}{2}$$

$$Y_2 = \frac{3 - \sqrt{9 + 4(x + 4)}}{2}$$

We enter this as two equations because they are each functions, separately. However, they are not a single function.

< Objective 3 >

45. **Business and Finance** A company's weekly profit, P, is related to the number of items sold by $P(x) = -0.2x^2 + 40x - 500$. Find the number of items that should be sold each week to maximize the profit. Then find the amount of that weekly profit.

> Videos

46. **Business and Finance** A company's monthly profit, P, is related to the number of items sold by $P(x) = -0.1x^2 + 30x - 1{,}000$. How many items should be sold each month to obtain the largest possible profit? What is that profit?

47. **Construction Technology** A builder wants to enclose the largest possible rectangular area with 1,600 ft of fencing. What should be the dimensions of the rectangle, and what will its area be?

48. **Construction Technology** A farmer wants to enclose a field along a river on three sides. If 1,200 ft of fencing is to be used, what dimensions will give the maximum enclosed area? Find that maximum area.

49. **Science and Medicine** A ball is thrown upward into the air with an initial velocity of 64 ft/sec. If h gives the height of the ball at time t, then the equation relating h and t is

$$h(t) = -16t^2 + 64t$$

Find the maximum height that the ball will attain.

50. **Science and Medicine** A ball is thrown upward into the air with an initial velocity of 32 ft/sec. If h gives the height of the ball at time t, then the equation relating h and t is

$$h(t) = -16t^2 + 32t$$

Find the maximum height that the ball will attain.

In each of the following statements, fill in the blank with **always, sometimes,** *or* **never.**

51. The axis of symmetry for a parabola is _________ a vertical line.

52. The vertex for a parabola is _________ a maximum.

53. The equation of a parabola function is _________ quadratic in x and linear in y.

Consider the general form for a parabola: $y = a(x - h)^2 + k$. *Match each letter of the formula with what it indicates.*

(a) Width of sides of parabola
(b) Translated along x-axis with axis of symmetry at $x = h$
(c) Translated vertically k units and has vertex at (h, k)

54. h indicates

55. k indicates

56. a indicates

Basic Skills | **Advanced Skills** | Vocational-Technical Applications | Calculator/Computer | Above and Beyond

Each equation in exercises 57 to 60 defines a relation. Write the domain of each relation. (Hint: Determine the vertex and whether the parabola opens to the left or to the right.)

57. $x = y^2 + 6y$

58. $x = y^2 - 8y$

59. $x = -y^2 + 6y - 7$

60. $x = -y^2 - 4y + 3$

Answers

50. 16 ft
51. sometimes
52. sometimes
53. sometimes
54. (b)
55. (c)
56. (a)
57. $\{x \mid x \geq -9\}$
58. $\{x \mid x \geq -16\}$
59. $\{x \mid x \leq 2\}$
60. $\{x \mid x \leq 7\}$

Answers

61. D: $\mathbb{R}$; R: $\{y \mid y \geq 1\}$

62. D: $\mathbb{R}$; R: $\{y \mid y \geq -2\}$

63. D: $\{x \mid x \geq -1\}$; R: $\mathbb{R}$

64. D: $\{x \mid x \geq 4\}$; R: $\mathbb{R}$

65. $a > 0$ and $h > 0$ or $a < 0$ and $h < 0$

66. Above and Beyond

Write the domain and range of each relation.

61. $y = 3(x - 2)^2 + 1$

62. $y = (x + 1)^2 - 2$

63. $x = (y - 1)^2 - 1$

64. $x = (y + 2)^2 + 4$

Basic Skills | Advanced Skills | Vocational-Technical Applications | Calculator/Computer | **Above and Beyond**

65. Under what conditions will the graph of $x = a(y - k)^2 + h$ have no y-intercepts?

66. Discuss similarities and differences between the graphs of $y = x^2 + 3x + 4$ and $x = y^2 + 3y + 4$. Use both graphs in your discussion.

Answers

1. (d) **3.** (b) **5.** (a) **7.** (e) **9.** (i) **11.** Left **13.** Right **15.** Left **17.** $x = 0, (0, 0)$ **19.** $x = 0, (0, -5)$ **21.** $x = -3, (-3, 1)$ **23.** $x = 1, (1, 1)$

25.

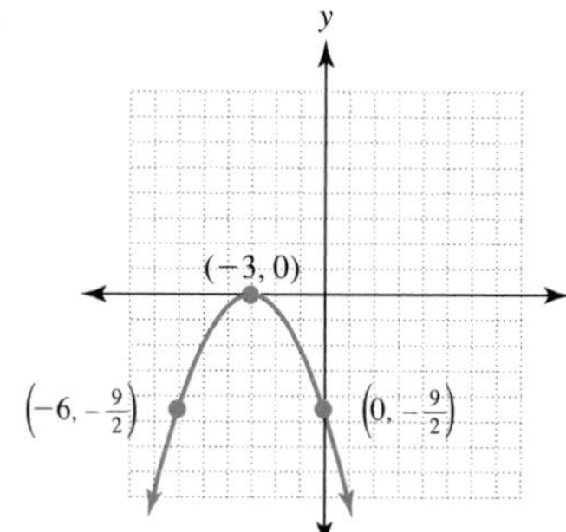

27.

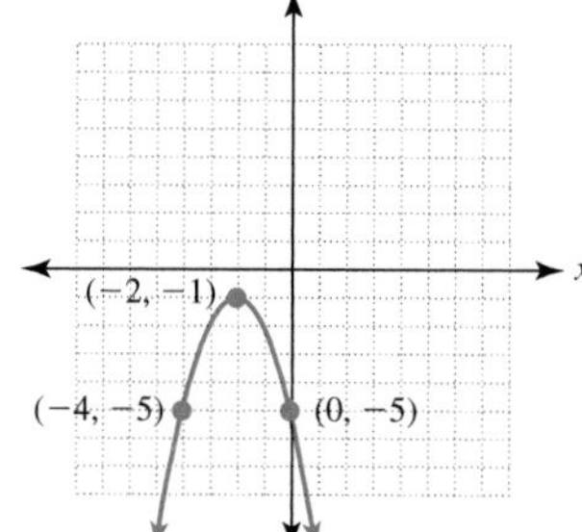

29.

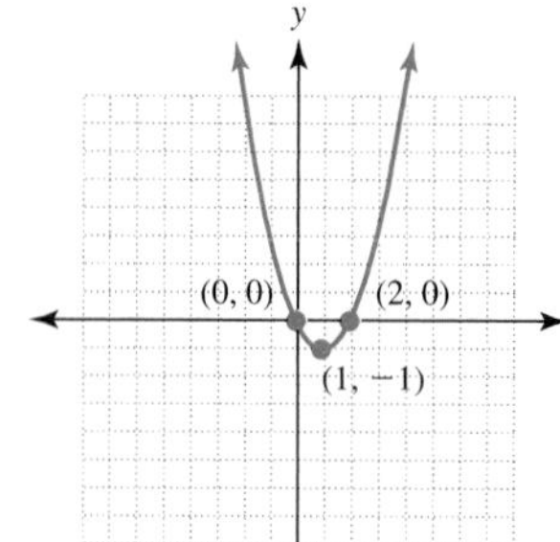

31.

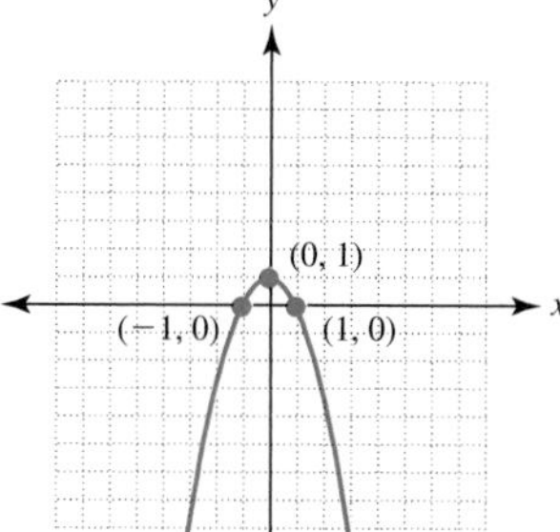

33.

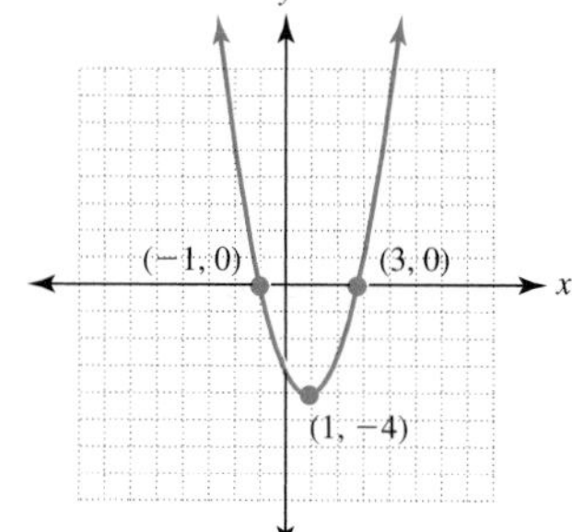

35.

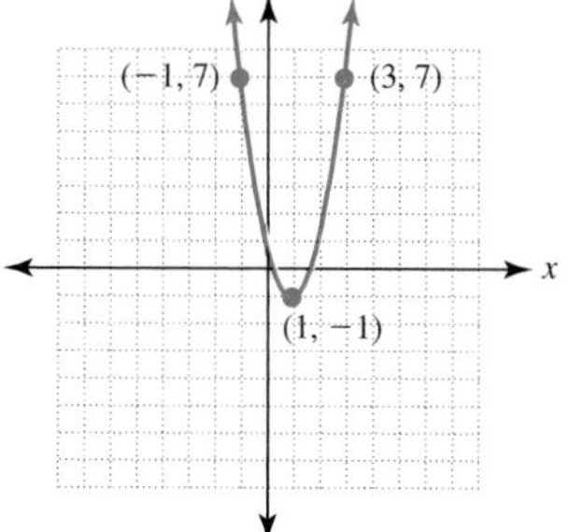

37.

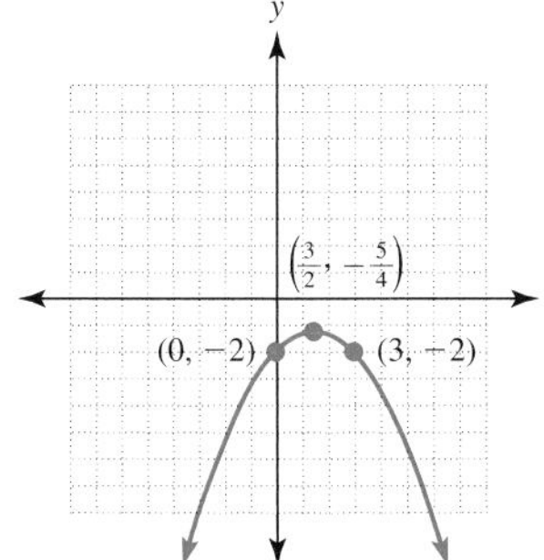

39.

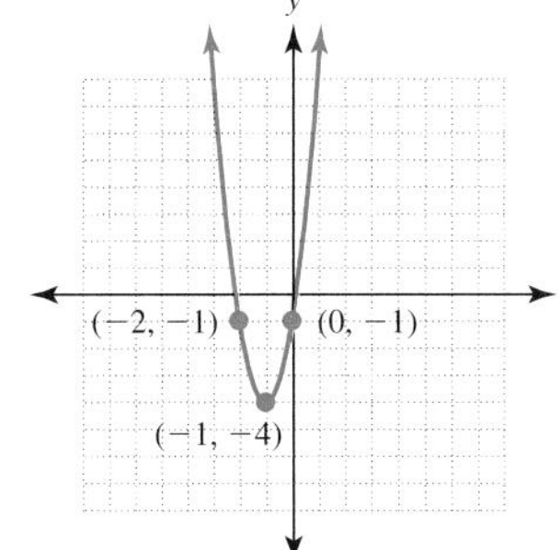

41.

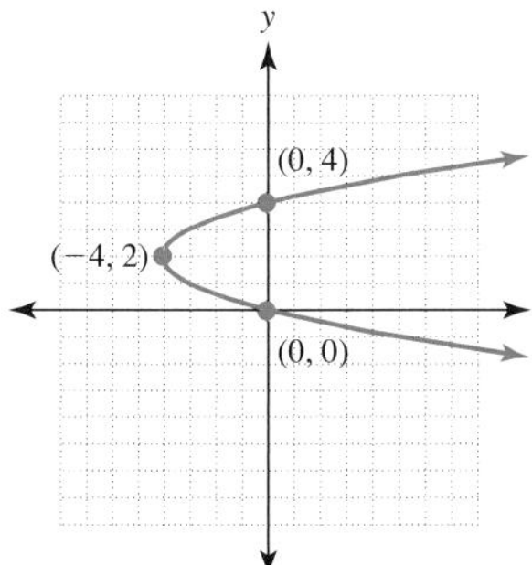

43.

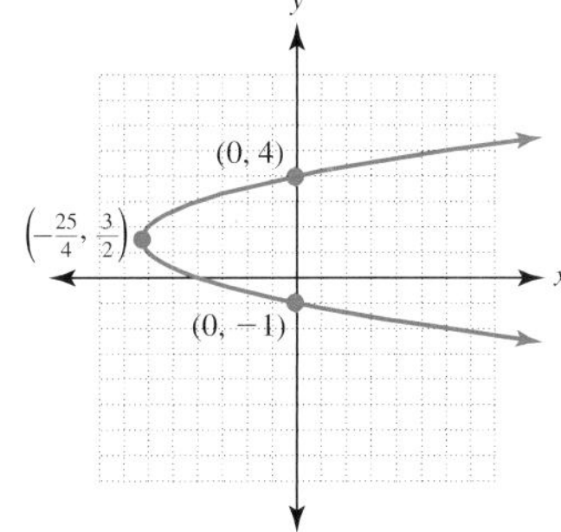

45. 100 items, \$1,500 **47.** 400 ft by 400 ft, 160,000 ft^2 **49.** 64 ft
51. sometimes **53.** sometimes **55.** (c) **57.** $\{x \mid x \geq -9\}$
59. $\{x \mid x \leq 2\}$ **61.** D: $\mathbb{R}$; R: $\{y \mid y \geq 1\}$ **63.** D: $\{x \mid x \geq -1\}$; R: $\mathbb{R}$
65. $a > 0$ and $h > 0$ or $a < 0$ and $h < 0$

9.2 Circles

< 9.2 Objectives >

1 > Given a center and radius, find the equation of a circle

2 > Given an equation for a circle, find the center and radius

3 > Given an equation, sketch the graph of a circle

In Section 9.1, we examined the parabola. In this section, we turn our attention to another conic section, the circle.

Definition

Circle

A **circle** is the set of all points in the plane equidistant from a fixed point, called the **center** of the circle. The distance between the center of the circle and any point on the circle is called the **radius** of the circle.

The distance formula is central to any discussion of conic sections.

Property

The Distance Formula

The distance, d, between any two points (x_1, y_1) and (x_2, y_2) is given by

$$d = \sqrt{(x_2 - x_1)^2 + (y_2 - y_1)^2}$$

Although this formula may seem complicated, it is actually just a restatement of the Pythagorean theorem. Consider two points, (x_1, y_1) and (x_2, y_2).

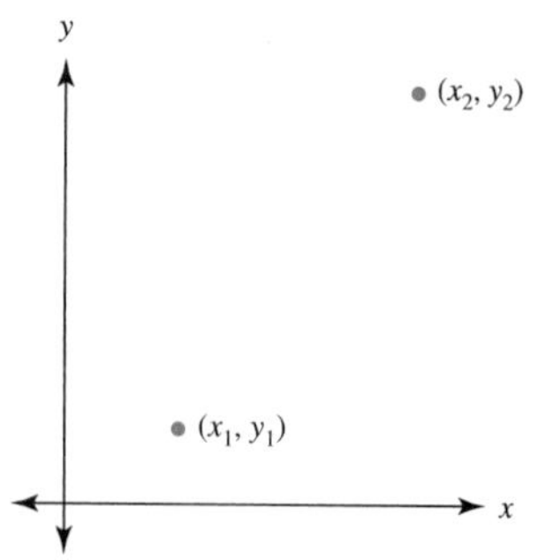

From these two points, we can create a right triangle by introducing a new point.

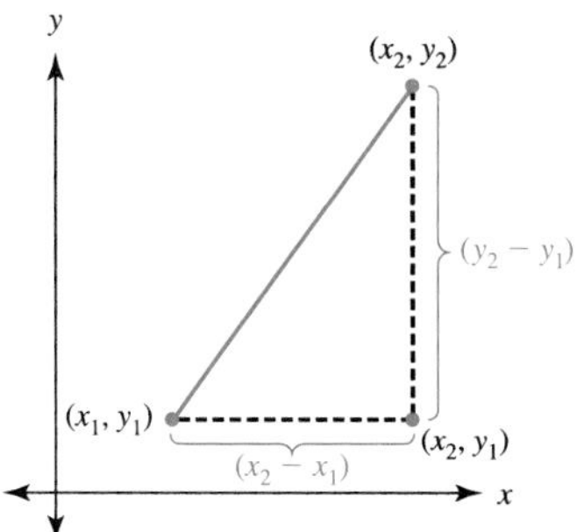

We are trying to find the distance between (x_1, y_1) and (x_2, y_2). Notice that this is the hypotenuse of our triangle. Using the Pythagorean theorem,

$$c^2 = a^2 + b^2$$

So we want to know,

$$c = \sqrt{a^2 + b^2}$$

However, the length of the base of the triangle is $x_2 - x_1$ and the length of the other leg of the triangle is $y_2 - y_1$. Let $a = x_2 - x_1$ and $b = y_2 - y_1$. Then from the last equation, we see that

$$c = \sqrt{(x_2 - x_1)^2 + (y_2 - y_1)^2}$$

Using d for distance (instead of c) we have the distance formula.

To verify the distance formula with numbers, consider (1, 4) and (4, 0). Then

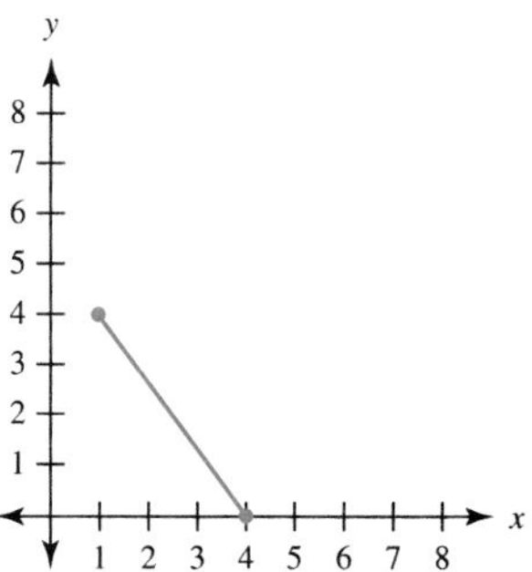

Creating our right triangle we see

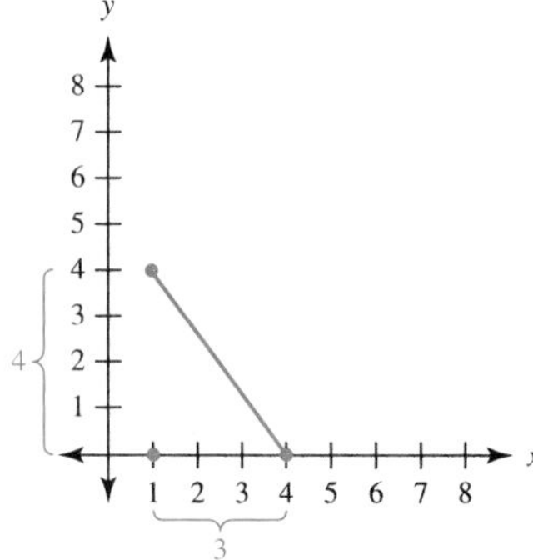

The length of the base of the triangle is $4 - 1 = 3$. The length of the other leg of the triangle is $4 - 0 = 4$. Therefore, using the Pythagorean theorem,

$$\begin{aligned} c^2 &= a^2 + b^2 \\ &= 3^2 + 4^2 \\ c &= \sqrt{3^2 + 4^2} \\ &= \sqrt{9 + 16} \\ &= \sqrt{25} = 5 \end{aligned}$$

Using the distance formula with $(x_1, y_1) = (1, 4)$ and $(x_2, y_2) = (4, 0)$, we have

$$\begin{aligned} d &= \sqrt{(x_2 - x_1)^2 + (y_2 - y_1)^2} \\ &= \sqrt{(4 - 1)^2 + (0 - 4)^2} \\ &= \sqrt{3^2 + (-4)^2} \\ &= \sqrt{9 + 16} \\ &= \sqrt{25} = 5 \end{aligned}$$

The same as the preceding answer.

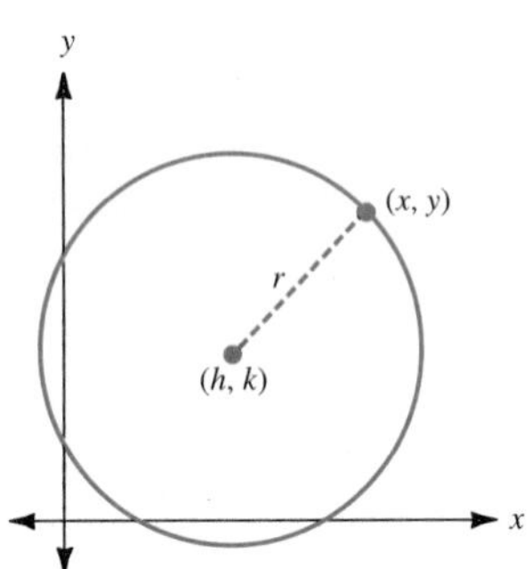

Therefore, we have shown the distance between (1, 4) and (4, 0) is 5 units.

We can use the distance formula to derive the algebraic equation of a circle, given its center and its radius.

Suppose a circle has its center at a point with coordinates (h, k) and radius r. If (x, y) represents any point on the circle, then, by its definition, the distance from (h, k) to (x, y) is r. Applying the distance formula, we have

$$r = \sqrt{(x - h)^2 + (y - k)^2}$$

Squaring both sides of the equation gives the equation of the circle.

$$r^2 = (x - h)^2 + (y - k)^2$$

We state this now as a property.

NOTE

A special case is the circle centered at the origin with radius r. Then $(h, k) = (0, 0)$, and its equation is $x^2 + y^2 = r^2$

Property

Equation of a Circle

The equation of a circle with center (h, k) and radius r is

$$(x - h)^2 + (y - k)^2 = r^2$$

The circle equation can be used in two ways. Given the center and radius of the circle, we can write its equation; or given its equation, we can find the center and radius of a circle.

Example 1 Finding the Equation of a Circle

< Objective 1 >

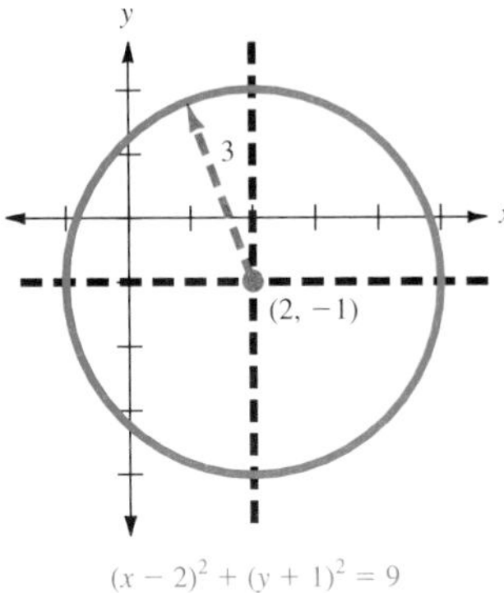

$(x-2)^2+(y+1)^2=9$

Find the equation of a circle with center at $(2, -1)$ and radius 3. Sketch the circle.

Let $(h, k) = (2, -1)$ and $r = 3$. Applying the circle equation yields

$$(x-2)^2+[y-(-1)]^2=3^2$$
$$(x-2)^2+(y+1)^2=9$$

To sketch the circle, we locate the center of the circle. Then we determine four points 3 units to the right and left and up and down from the center of the circle. Drawing a smooth curve through those four points completes the graph.

Check Yourself 1

Find the equation of the circle with center at $(-2, 1)$ and radius 5. Sketch the circle.

Now, given an equation for a circle, we can also find the radius and center and then sketch the circle. We start with the circle equation.

Example 2 Finding the Center and Radius of a Circle

< Objective 2 >

Find the center and radius of the circle with equation

$$(x-1)^2+(y+2)^2=9$$

Remember, the general form is

$$(x-h)^2+(y-k)^2=r^2$$

Our equation "fits" this form when it is written as

Note: $y+2=y-(-2)$

$$(x-1)^2+[y-(-2)]^2=3^2$$

So the center is at $(1, -2)$, and the radius is 3. The graph is shown.

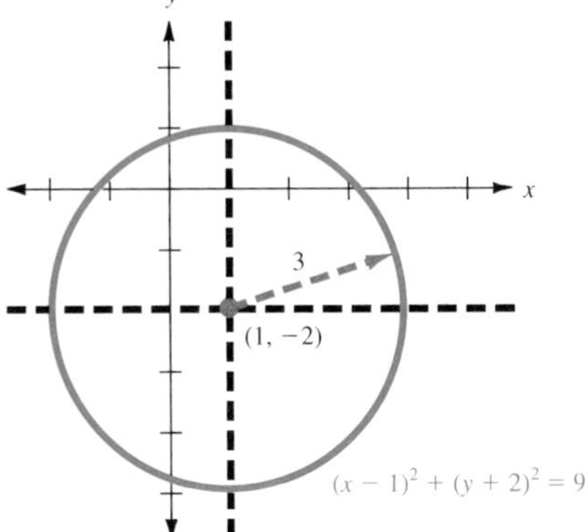

$(x-1)^2+(y+2)^2=9$

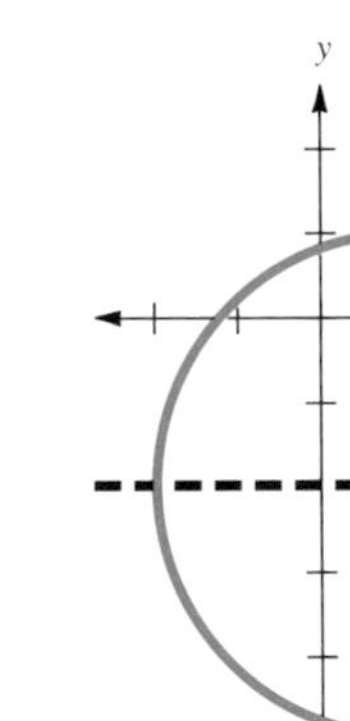

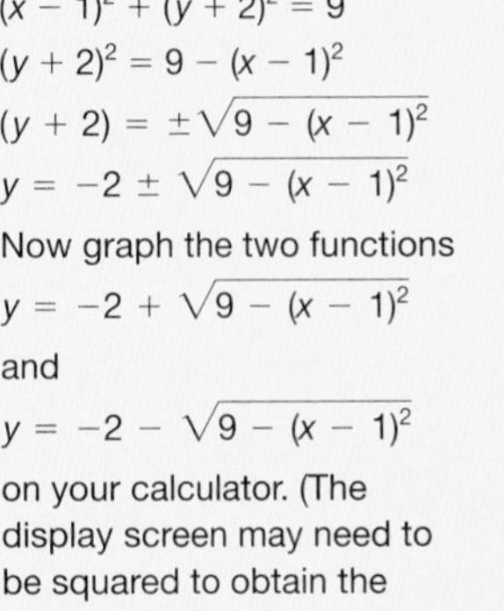

NOTE

The circle can be graphed on the calculator by solving for y, and then graphing both the upper half and lower half of the circle. In this case,

$$(x-1)^2+(y+2)^2=9$$
$$(y+2)^2=9-(x-1)^2$$
$$(y+2)=\pm\sqrt{9-(x-1)^2}$$
$$y=-2\pm\sqrt{9-(x-1)^2}$$

Now graph the two functions

$$y=-2+\sqrt{9-(x-1)^2}$$

and

$$y=-2-\sqrt{9-(x-1)^2}$$

on your calculator. (The display screen may need to be squared to obtain the shape of a circle.)

Check Yourself 2

Find the center and radius of the circle with equation

$(x + 3)^2 + (y - 2)^2 = 16$

Sketch the circle.

To graph the equation of a circle that is not in standard form, we *complete the square.* We will see how completing the square can be used in graphing the equation of a circle.

Example 3 Graphing the Equation of a Circle

< Objective 3 >

NOTES

To recognize the equation as having the form of a circle, note that the coefficients of x^2 and y^2 are equal.

The linear terms in x and y show a translation of the center away from the origin.

Find the center and radius of the circle with equation

$$x^2 + 2x + y^2 - 6y = -1$$

Then sketch the circle.

We could, of course, simply substitute values of x and try to find the corresponding values for y. A much better approach is to rewrite the original equation so that it matches the standard form.

First, add 1 to both sides to complete the square in x.

$$x^2 + 2x + 1 + y^2 - 6y = -1 + 1$$

Then add 9 to both sides to complete the square in y.

$$x^2 + 2x + 1 + y^2 - 6y + 9 = -1 + 1 + 9$$

We factor the two trinomials on the left (they are both perfect squares) and simplify on the right.

$$(x + 1)^2 + (y - 3)^2 = 9$$

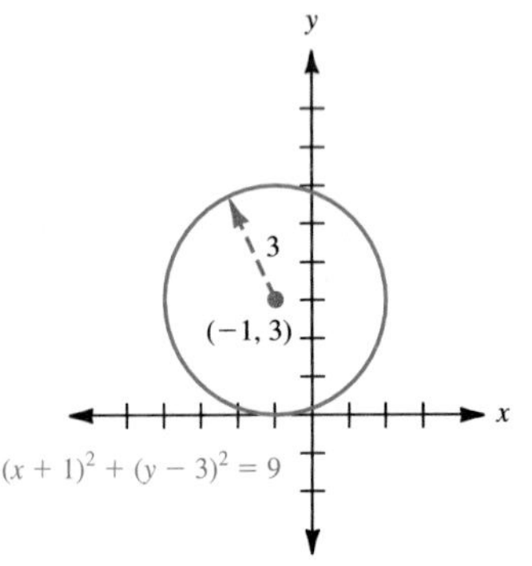

The equation is now in standard form, and we see that the center is at $(-1, 3)$ and the radius is 3. The sketch of the circle is shown in the margin. Note the "translation" of the center to $(-1, 3)$.

Check Yourself 3

Find the center and radius of the circle with equation

$x^2 - 4x + y^2 + 2y = -1$

Sketch the circle.

Check Yourself ANSWERS

1. $(x + 2)^2 + (y - 1)^2 = 25$

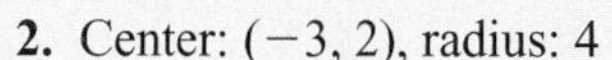

2. Center: $(-3, 2)$, radius: 4

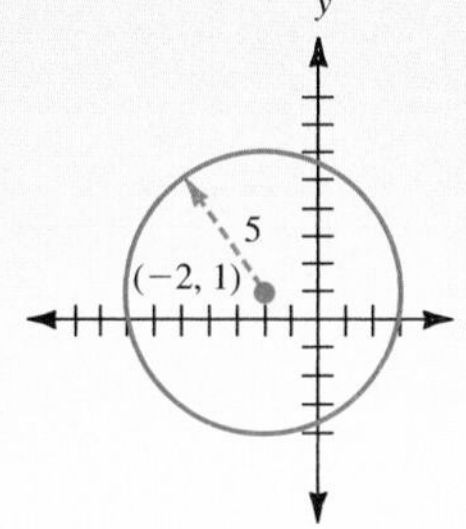

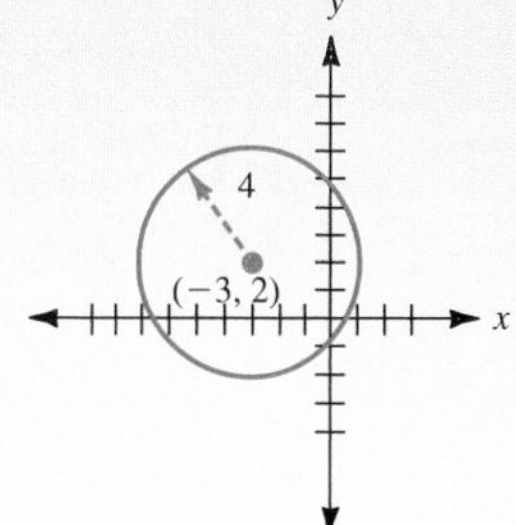

3. $(x - 2)^2 + (y + 1)^2 = 4$, center: $(2, -1)$, radius: 2

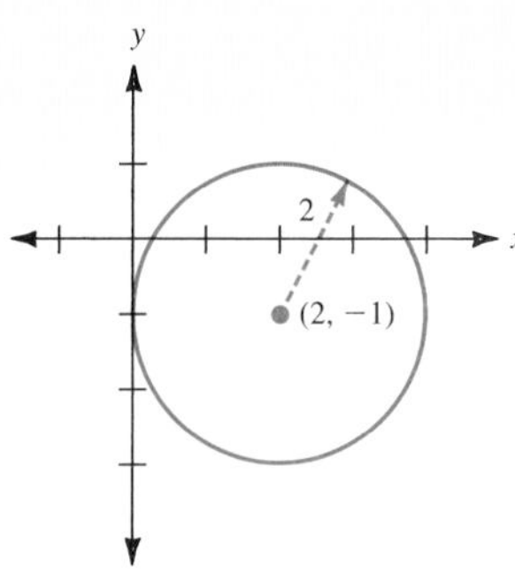

Reading Your Text

The following fill-in-the-blank exercises are designed to ensure that you understand some of the key vocabulary used in this section.

SECTION 9.2

(a) A ______________ is the set of all points in the plane equidistant from a fixed point.

(b) The distance between the center of a circle and any point on the circle is called the ______________ of the circle.

(c) The distance between any two points (x_1, y_1) and (x_2, y_2) is given by the equation ______________.

(d) Given the standard form for the equation of a circle, $(x - h)^2 + (y - k)^2 = r^2$, the circle has radius r and center ______________.

9.2 exercises

Basic Skills | Advanced Skills | Vocational-Technical Applications | Calculator/Computer | Above and Beyond

MathZone

Boost your grade at mathzone.com!
> Practice Problems
> NetTutor
> Self-Tests
> e-Professors
> Videos

Name ____________

Section ________ Date ________

In exercises 1 to 12, decide whether each equation has as its graph a line, a parabola, a circle, or none of these.

1. $y = x^2 - 2x + 5$

2. $y^2 + x^2 = 64$

3. $y = 3x - 2$

4. $2y - 3x = 12$

5. $(x - 3)^2 + (y + 2)^2 = 10$

6. $y + 2(x - 3)^2 = 5$

7. $x^2 + 4x + y^2 - 6y = 3$

8. $4x = 3$

9. $y^2 - 4x^2 = 36$

10. $x^2 + (y - 3)^2 = 9$

11. $y = -2x^2 + 8x - 3$

12. $2x^2 - 3y^2 + 6y = 13$

< Objective 1 >

Find the equation of the circle with the given center and radius.

13. Center at (0, 0) and radius 5

14. Center at (0, 0) and radius $6\sqrt{2}$

15. Center at (3, −1) and radius 4

16. Center at (−3, 0) and radius 9

< Objective 2 >

Find the center and the radius for each circle.

17. $x^2 + y^2 = 4$

18. $(x + 3)^2 + (y - 1)^2 = 16$

19. $x^2 + 2x + y^2 = 15$

20. $x^2 - 6x + y^2 + 8y = 16$

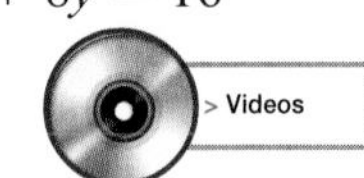

< Objective 3 >

Graph each circle by finding the center and the radius.

21. $x^2 + y^2 = 4$

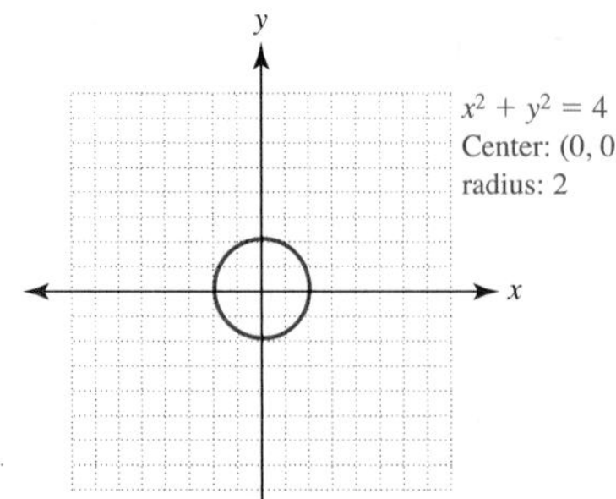

22. $x^2 + y^2 = 25$

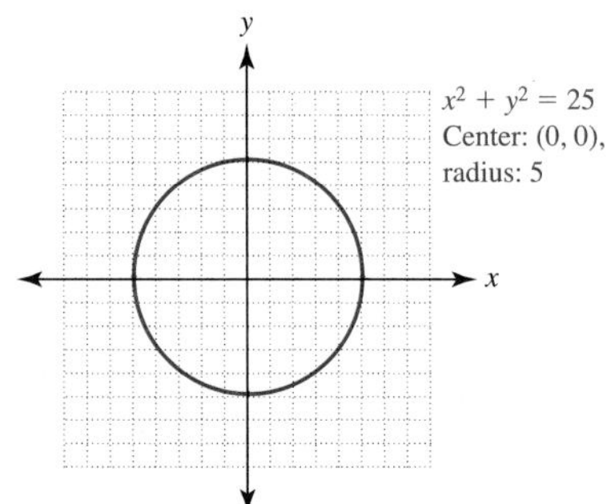

Answers

1.	Parabola	2.	Circle
3.	Line	4.	Line
5.	Circle	6.	Parabola
7.	Circle	8.	Line
9.	None of these		
10.	Circle	11.	Parabola
12.	None of these		
13.	$x^2 + y^2 = 25$		
14.	$x^2 + y^2 = 72$		
15.	$(x - 3)^2 + (y + 1)^2 = 16$		
16.	$(x + 3)^2 + y^2 = 81$		
17.	Center: (0, 0), radius: 2		
18.	Center: (−3, 1), radius: 4		
19.	Center: (−1, 0), radius: 4		
20.	Center: (3, −4), radius: $\sqrt{41}$		
21.	See exercise		
22.	See exercise		

23. $4x^2 + 4y^2 = 36$

$4x^2 + 4y^2 = 36$
$x^2 + y^2 = 9$
Center: (0, 0),
radius: 3

24. $9x^2 + 9y^2 = 144$

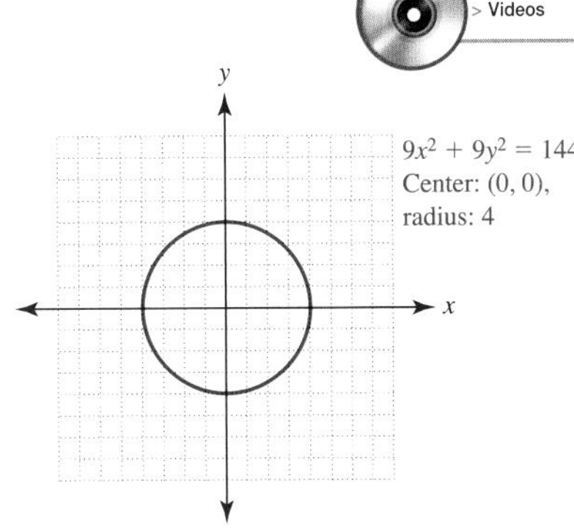

25. $(x - 1)^2 + y^2 = 9$

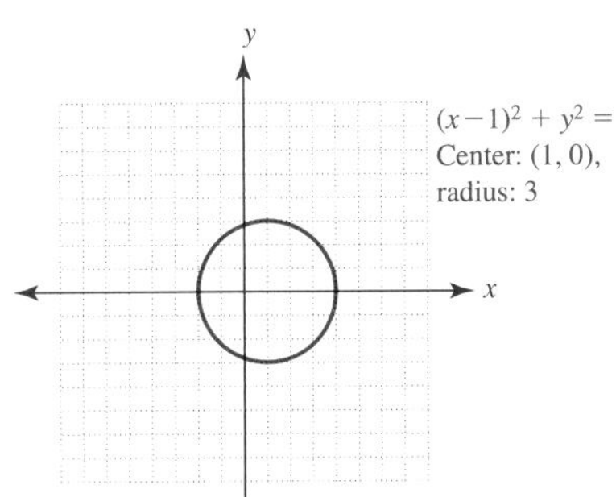

26. $x^2 + (y + 2)^2 = 16$

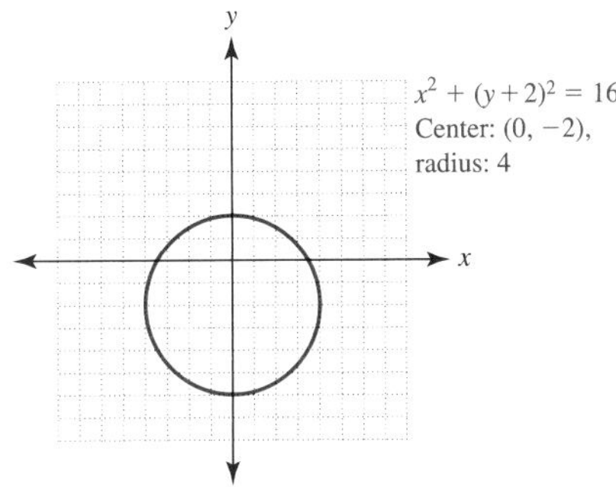

27. $(x - 4)^2 + (y + 1)^2 = 16$

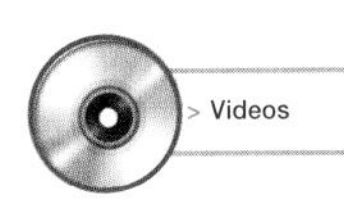

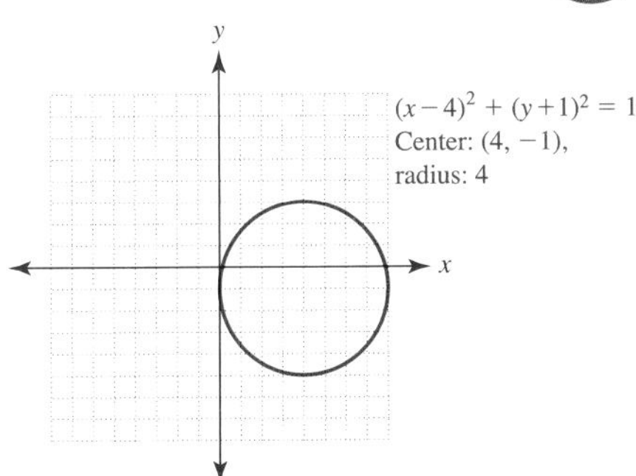

28. $(x + 3)^2 + (y + 2)^2 = 25$

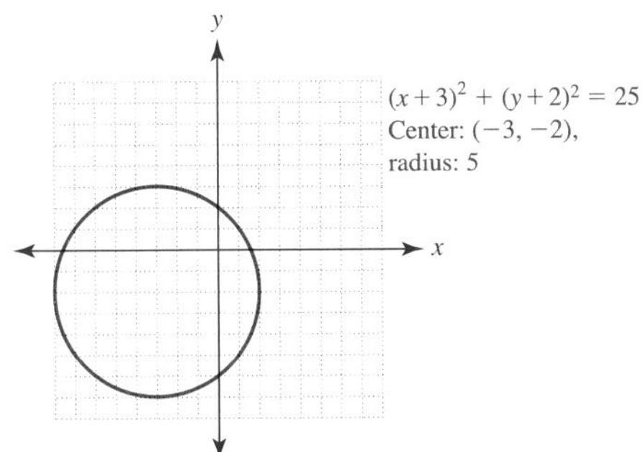

Answers

23. See exercise

24. See exercise

25. See exercise

26. See exercise

27. See exercise

28. See exercise

Answers

29. See exercise
30. See exercise
31. See exercise
32. See exercise
33. False
34. True
35. $\sqrt{500} = 10\sqrt{5}$ cm ≈ 22.4 cm

29. $x^2 + y^2 - 4y = 12$

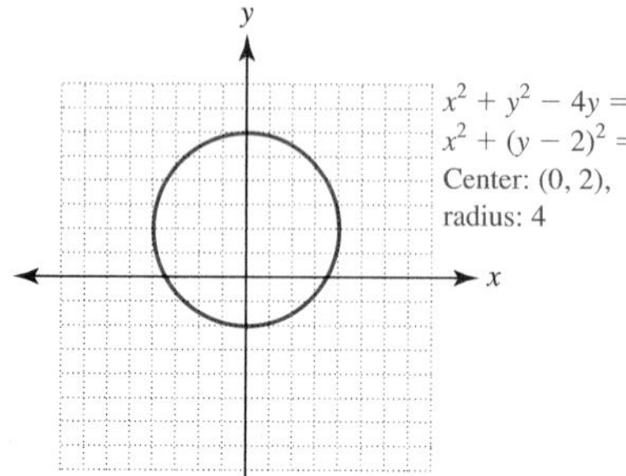

30. $x^2 - 6x + y^2 = 0$

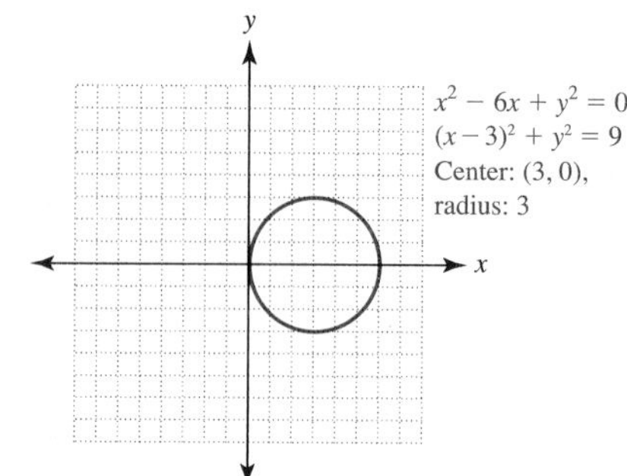

31. $x^2 - 4x + y^2 + 2y = -1$

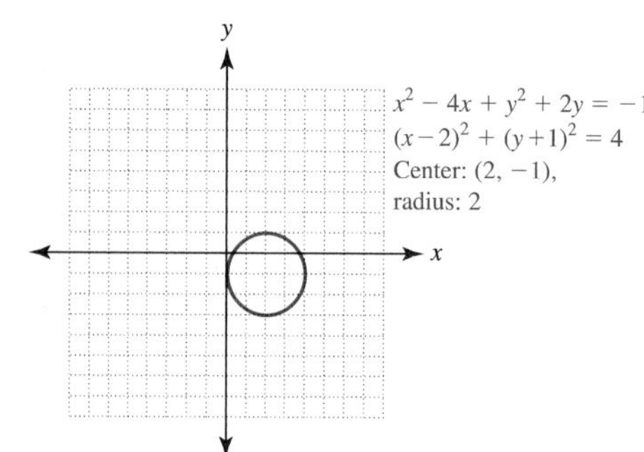

32. $x^2 - 2x + y^2 - 6y = 6$

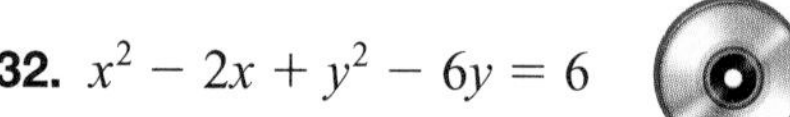

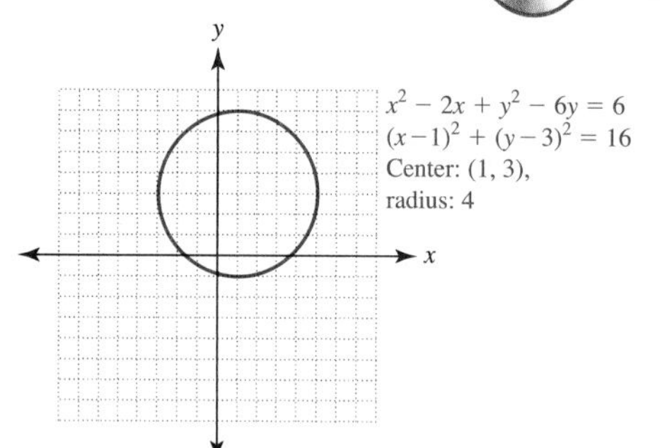

Label each of the following statements as **true** *or* **false.**

33. The distance between two points (x_1, y_1) and (x_2, y_2) is given by $d = (x_2 - x_1)^2 + (y_2 - y_1)^2$.

34. The equation of a circle with center (h, k) and radius r is given by $(x - h)^2 + (y - k)^2 = r^2$.

Basic Skills | **Advanced Skills** | Vocational-Technical Applications | Calculator/Computer | Above and Beyond

35. **Construction Technology** A solar oven is constructed in the shape of a hemisphere. If the equation

$x^2 + y^2 + 500 = 1{,}000$

describes the outer edge of the oven in centimeters, what is its radius?

36. **Construction Technology** A solar oven in the shape of a hemisphere is to have a diameter of 80 cm. Write the equation that describes the outer edge of this oven.

37. **Construction Technology** A solar water heater is constructed in the shape of a half-cylinder, with the water supply pipe at its center. If the water heater has a diameter of $\frac{4}{3}$ meters, what is the equation that describes its outer edge?

38. **Construction Technology** A solar water heater is constructed in the shape of a half-cylinder with a circumference described by the equation

$$9x^2 + 9y^2 - 16 = 0$$

What is the diameter if the units for the equation are in meters?

Each of the equations in exercises 39 to 42 defines a relation. Write the domain and the range of each relation.

39. $(x + 3)^2 + (y - 2)^2 = 16$

40. $(x - 1)^2 + (y - 5)^2 = 9$

41. $x^2 + (y - 3)^2 = 25$

42. $(x + 2)^2 + y^2 = 36$

Basic Skills | Advanced Skills | Vocational-Technical Applications | **Calculator/Computer** | Above and Beyond

A circle can be graphed on a calculator by plotting the upper and lower semicircles on the same axes. For example, to graph $x^2 + y^2 = 16$, we solve for y:

$$y = \pm\sqrt{16 - x^2}$$

This is then graphed as two separate functions,

$$Y_1 = \sqrt{16 - x^2} \quad \text{and} \quad Y_2 = -\sqrt{16 - x^2}$$

In exercises 43 to 46, use that technique to graph each circle.

43. $x^2 + y^2 = 36$

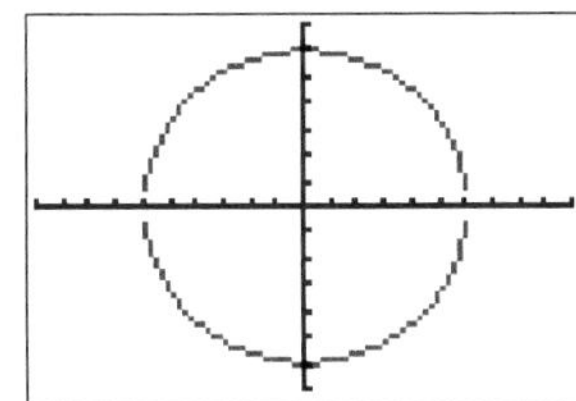

$y = \sqrt{36 - x^2}$
$y = -\sqrt{36 - x^2}$

44. $(x - 3)^2 + y^2 = 9$

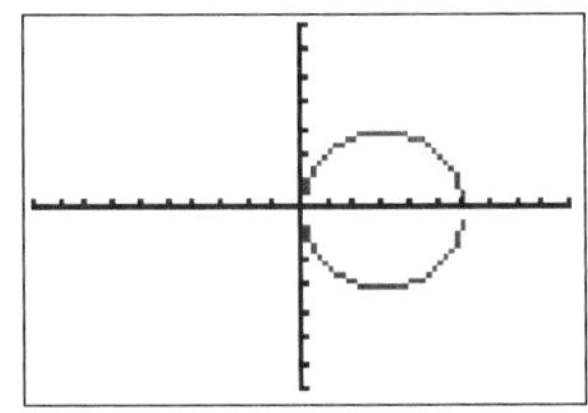

$y = \sqrt{9 - (x - 3)^2}$
$y = -\sqrt{9 - (x - 3)^2}$

Answers

36. $x^2 + y^2 = 1{,}600$

37. $x^2 + y^2 = \frac{4}{9}$

38. $\frac{8}{3}$ m

39. D: $\{x \mid -7 \le x \le 1\}$; R: $\{y \mid -2 \le y \le 6\}$

40. D: $\{x \mid -2 \le x \le 4\}$; R: $\{y \mid 2 \le y \le 8\}$

41. D: $\{x \mid -5 \le x \le 5\}$; R: $\{y \mid -2 \le y \le 8\}$

42. D: $\{x \mid -8 \le x \le 4\}$; R: $\{y \mid -6 \le y \le 6\}$

43. See exercise

44. See exercise

Answers

45. See exercise

46. See exercise

47. Circle with radius of 0 and center at (1, 2)

48. Above and Beyond

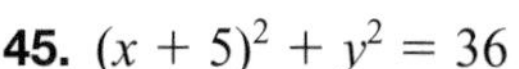

45. $(x + 5)^2 + y^2 = 36$

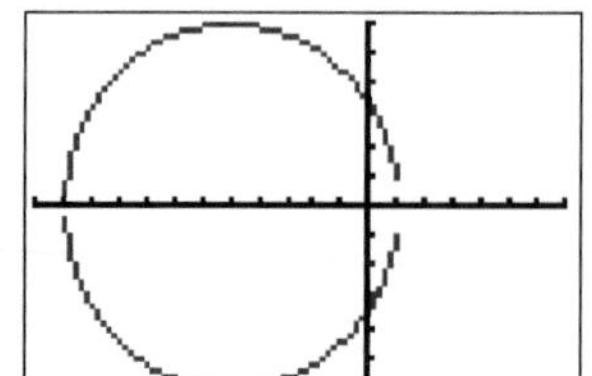

$y = \sqrt{36 - (x + 5)^2}$
$y = -\sqrt{36 - (x + 5)^2}$

46. $(x - 2)^2 + (y + 1)^2 = 25$

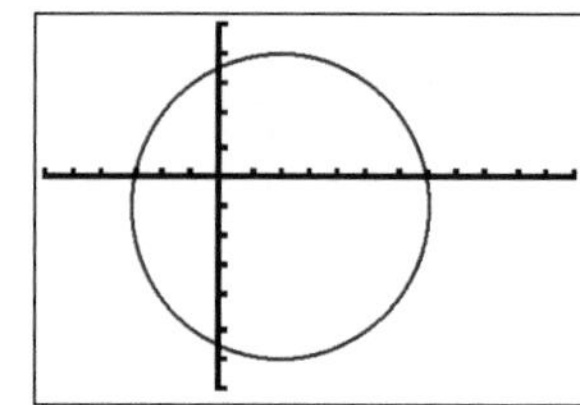

$y = -1 + \sqrt{25 - (x - 2)^2}$
$y = -1 - \sqrt{25 - (x - 2)^2}$

Basic Skills | Advanced Skills | Vocational-Technical Applications | Calculator/Computer | **Above and Beyond**

47. Describe the graph of $x^2 + y^2 - 2x - 4y + 5 = 0$.

48. Describe how completing the square is used in graphing circles.

Answers

1. Parabola **3.** Line **5.** Circle **7.** Circle **9.** None of these
11. Parabola **13.** $x^2 + y^2 = 25$ **15.** $(x - 3)^2 + (y + 1)^2 = 16$
17. Center: (0, 0), radius: 2 **19.** Center: $(-1, 0)$, radius: 4

21.

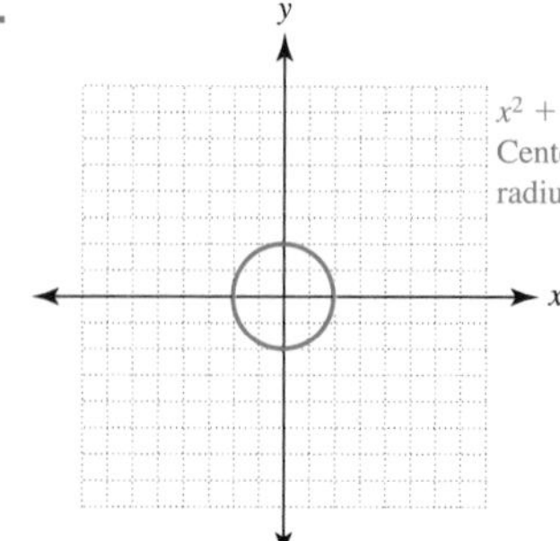

23.

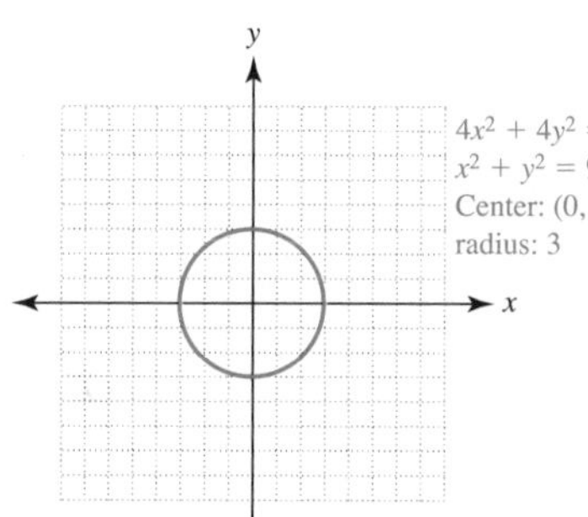

25.

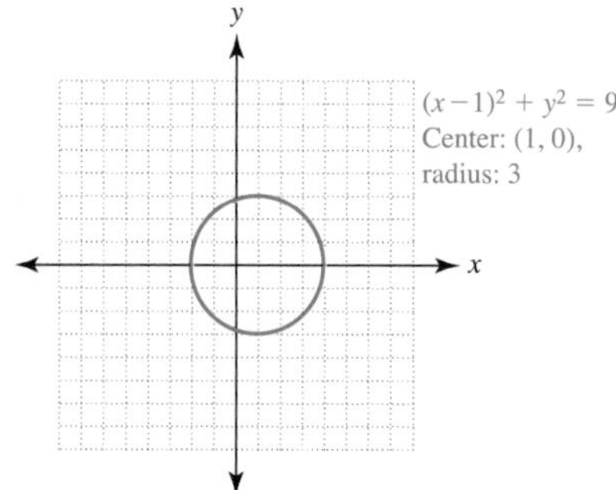

27.

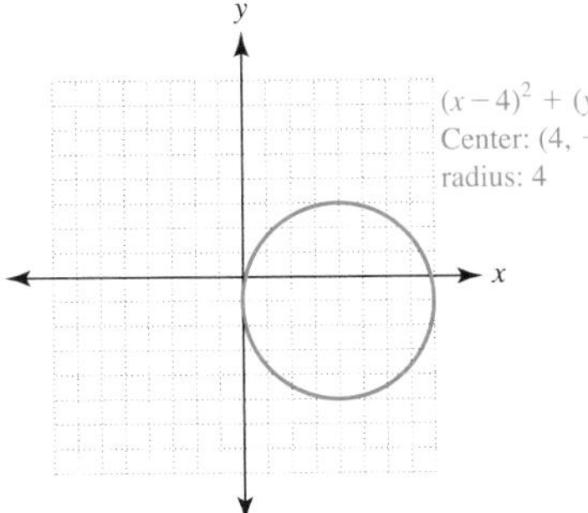

$(x-4)^2 + (y+1)^2 = 16$
Center: $(4, -1)$,
radius: 4

29.

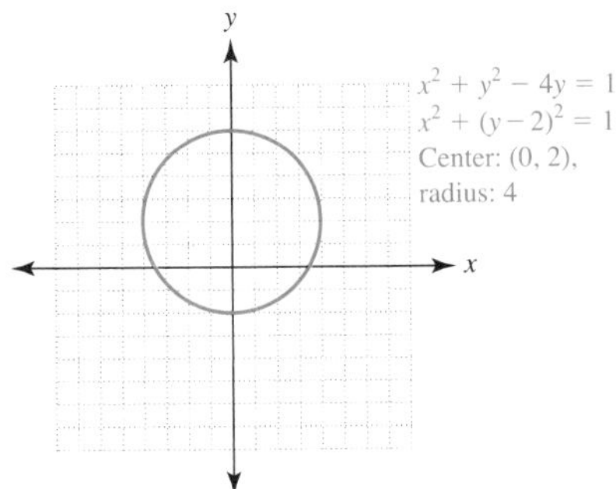

$x^2 + y^2 - 4y = 12$
$x^2 + (y-2)^2 = 16$
Center: $(0, 2)$,
radius: 4

31.

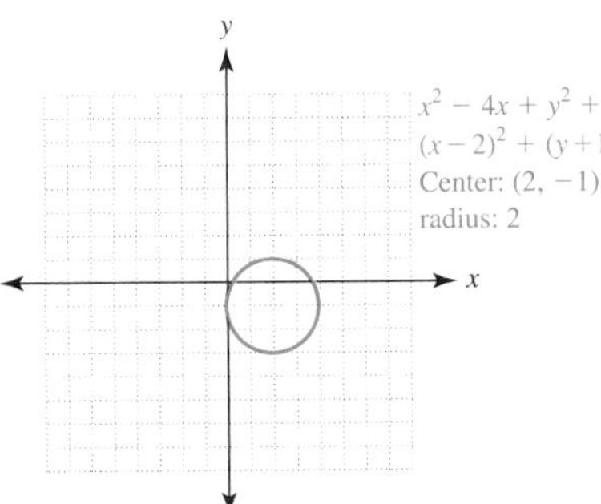

$x^2 - 4x + y^2 + 2y = -1$
$(x-2)^2 + (y+1)^2 = 4$
Center: $(2, -1)$,
radius: 2

33. False 35. $\sqrt{500} = 10\sqrt{5}$ cm ≈ 22.4 cm 37. $x^2 + y^2 = \frac{4}{9}$

39. D: $\{x \mid -7 \le x \le 1\}$; R: $\{y \mid -2 \le y \le 6\}$

41. D: $\{x \mid -5 \le x \le 5\}$; R: $\{y \mid -2 \le y \le 8\}$

43. $x^2 + y^2 = 36$

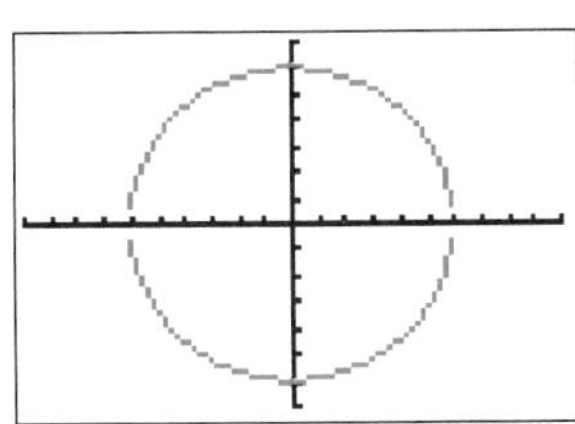

$y = \sqrt{36 - x^2}$
$y = -\sqrt{36 - x^2}$

45. $(x + 5)^2 + y^2 = 36$

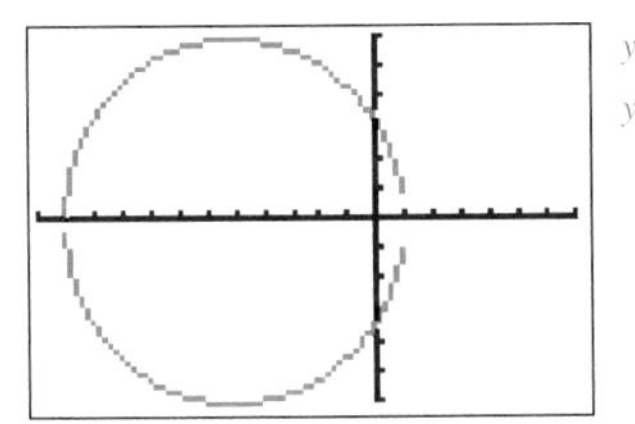

$y = \sqrt{36 - (x + 5)^2}$
$y = -\sqrt{36 - (x + 5)^2}$

47. Circle with radius of 0 and center at (1, 2)

9.3 Ellipses and Hyperbolas

< 9.3 Objectives >

1 > Given an equation, graph an ellipse

2 > Given an equation, graph a hyperbola

We now turn to the third conic section, the ellipse. It can be described as an "oval-shaped" curve and has the following geometric description.

Definition

Ellipse

An **ellipse** is the set of all points (x, y) such that the sum of the distances from (x, y) to two fixed points, called the *foci* of the ellipse, is constant.

Ellipses occur frequently in nature. The planets have elliptical orbits with the sun at one focus. The reflecting properties of the ellipse are also interesting. Rays from one focus are reflected by the ellipse in such a way that they always pass through the other focus.

The following property illustrates the definition in two particular cases:

1. When the foci are located on the x-axis and are symmetric about the origin.
2. When the foci are located on the y-axis and are symmetric about the origin.

Property

The Equation of an Ellipse

The **equation** of an **ellipse** is written

$$\frac{x^2}{a^2} + \frac{y^2}{b^2} = 1$$

The x-intercepts are $(a, 0)$ and $(-a, 0)$.

The y-intercepts are $(0, b)$ and $(0, -b)$.

NOTE

From the equation we can also find the x-intercepts, by letting $y = 0$ and solving for x. To find the y-intercepts, let $x = 0$ and solve for y.

We can sketch ellipses of these forms quickly by determining the *four points* where the ellipse intersects the coordinate axes. This is illustrated in Example 1.

Example 1 Graphing an Ellipse

< Objective 1 >

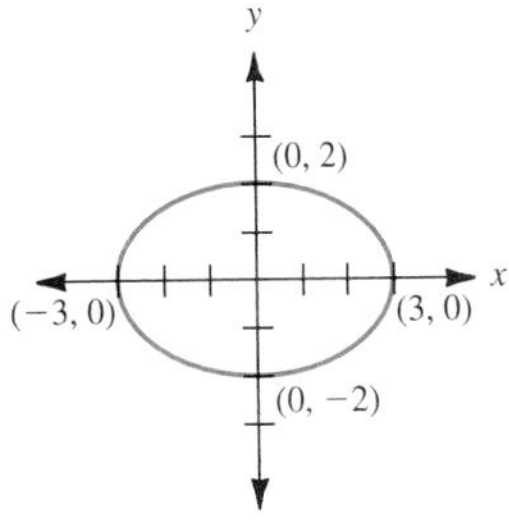

Sketch the ellipse.

$$\frac{x^2}{9} + \frac{y^2}{4} = 1$$

Step 1 The equation is in standard form.

Step 2 From the ellipse equation, $a^2 = 9$, the x-intercepts are $(3, 0)$ and $(-3, 0)$.

Step 3 From the ellipse equation, $b^2 = 4$, the y-intercepts are $(0, 2)$ and $(0, -2)$.

Step 4 Plot the intercepts found in steps 2 and 3, and draw a smooth curve to form the desired ellipse.

Check Yourself 1

Sketch the ellipse.

$$\frac{x^2}{16} + \frac{y^2}{9} = 1$$

Example 2 Graphing an Ellipse

NOTE

To recognize the equation as an ellipse in this form, note that the equation has both x^2- and y^2-terms. The coefficients of those terms are different, but have the same sign.

Sketch the ellipse with equation

$$9x^2 + 4y^2 = 36$$

Step 1 Because this equation is *not* in standard form (the right side is *not* 1), we divide both sides of the equation by the constant 36:

$$\frac{9x^2}{36} + \frac{4y^2}{36} = \frac{36}{36}$$

$$\frac{x^2}{4} + \frac{y^2}{9} = 1$$

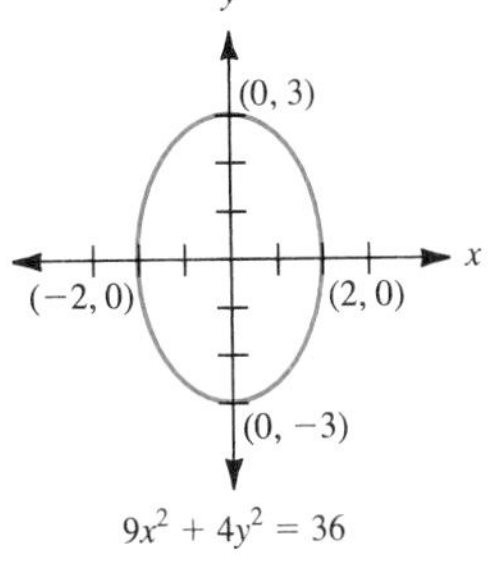

$9x^2 + 4y^2 = 36$

We can now proceed as before. Comparing the derived equation with that in standard form, we complete steps 2 and 3.

Step 2 The x-intercepts are $(2, 0)$ and $(-2, 0)$.

Step 3 The y-intercepts are $(0, 3)$ and $(0, -3)$.

Step 4 We connect the intercepts with a smooth curve to complete the sketch of the ellipse.

Check Yourself 2

Sketch the ellipse.

$$25x^2 + 4y^2 = 100$$

The following algorithm summarizes our work so far with graphing ellipses.

Step by Step

Graphing the Ellipse

Step 1 Write the given equation in standard form.
Step 2 From standard form, determine the x-intercepts.
Step 3 Determine the y-intercepts.
Step 4 Plot the four intercepts and connect the points with a smooth curve to complete the sketch.

So far we have only considered ellipses that are centered at the origin. You may be wondering what happens to the equation if the center of the ellipse is not (0, 0). This actually relates to what we have done earlier. If the center of the ellipse is (h, k), then the equation of the ellipse becomes

$$\frac{(x - h)^2}{a^2} + \frac{(y - k)^2}{b^2} = 1$$

The four points needed for graphing can then be found, but we must remember the translation. As before, h indicates the number of horizontal units and k indicates the number of vertical units. When centered at the origin, our horizontal points were found at $(a, 0)$ and $(-a, 0)$. The zero indicated the y-value of the center. Since we have now moved h units horizontally, our new x-values can be found at $a + h$ and $-a + h$. These can be also written as $h \pm a$. Our corresponding y-value will be k since the center is at (h, k). Similarly, when centered at the origin, our vertical points were found at $(0, b)$ and $(0, -b)$, where 0 indicated the x-value of the center. Since we have moved k units vertically, our new y-values are $b + k$ and $-b + k$ (or $k \pm b$), with a corresponding x-value of h. Putting all this together our four points are found at $(h + a, k)$, $(h - a, k)$, $(h, k + b)$, $(h, k - b)$.

Example 3 Graphing an Ellipse

Sketch the graph of the ellipse with equation

$$\frac{(x - 2)^2}{25} + \frac{(y + 1)^2}{16} = 1$$

Using the preceding formula for an ellipse, $h = 2$ and $k = -1$, so the center is at $(2, -1)$. The formula also tells us that $a = 5$ and $b = 4$. Since we are centered at the point $(2, -1)$, we have shifted to the right two places, so our x-values are $2 \pm a$. In other words, our points are $(2 + 5, -1)$ and $(2 - 5, -1)$, or $(7, -1)$ and $(-3, -1)$. Similarly, we have shifted down one unit, so our y-values are $-1 \pm b$. In other words, our points are $(2, -1 + 4)$ and $(2, -1 - 4)$, or $(2, 3)$ and $(2, -5)$. We now have four points with which to sketch a graph.

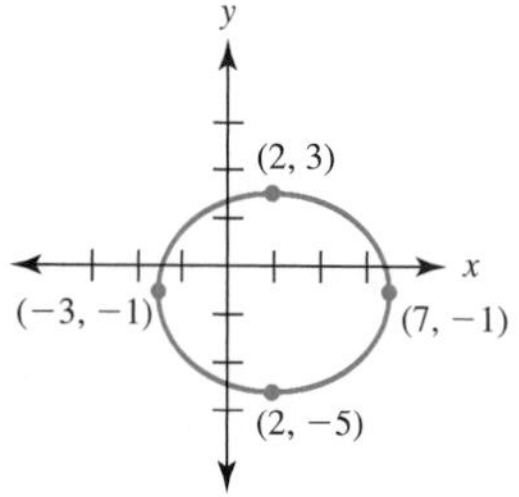

Check Yourself 3

Sketch the graph of the ellipse with equation

$$\frac{(x+3)^2}{4} + \frac{(y-4)^2}{25} = 1$$

Our discussion now turns to the last of the conic sections, the hyperbola. As you will see, the geometric description of the hyperbola (and hence the corresponding standard form) is quite similar to that of the ellipse.

Definition

Hyperbola

A **hyperbola** is the set of all points (x, y) such that the absolute value of the difference of the distance from (x, y) to each of two fixed points, called the *foci* of the hyperbola, is constant.

The following sketch illustrates the definition in the case in which the foci are located on the x-axis and are symmetric about the origin. This is the first of two special cases we will investigate in this section.

Property

The Equation of a Hyperbola

The **equation** of a **hyperbola** that intersects the x-axis is

$$\frac{x^2}{a^2} - \frac{y^2}{b^2} = 1$$

The **vertices** are $(a, 0)$ and $(-a, 0)$. The **asymptotes** are given by the equations

$$y = \pm\frac{b}{a}x$$

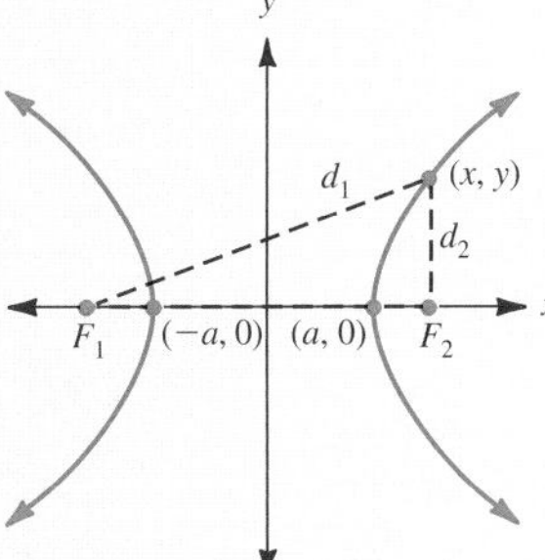

$$\frac{x^2}{a^2} - \frac{y^2}{b^2} = 1$$

The difference $|d_1 - d_2|$ remains constant for any point on the hyperbola, where F_1 and F_2 are the foci.

NOTE

Although we show these asymptote equations, you will see an easier method for finding the asymptotes in Example 4.

The points where the hyperbola intersects the x-axis are called the *vertices* of the hyperbola. The graph of a hyperbola with an equation like the one given opens to the left and right (as shown in the figure) and is symmetric about the x-axis. As we move away from the center of the hyperbola, the **branches** of the hyperbola approach two straight lines called the *asymptotes* of the hyperbola.

These asymptotes will prove to be extremely useful aids in sketching the hyperbola. In fact, for most purposes, the vertices and the asymptotes will be the only tools that we will need. Example 4 illustrates.

Example 4 Graphing a Hyperbola

< Objective 2 >

NOTE

The equation of the hyperbola also has both x^2- and y^2-terms. Here the coefficients of those terms have *opposite* signs. If the x^2-coefficient is *positive,* the hyperbola will open *horizontally.*

Sketch the hyperbola.

$$\frac{x^2}{9} - \frac{y^2}{4} = 1$$

Step 1 The equation is in standard form.

Step 2 Find and plot the vertices.

From the standard form we can see that $a^2 = 9$ and $a = 3$ or $a = -3$. The vertices of the hyperbola then occur at (3, 0) and (−3, 0).

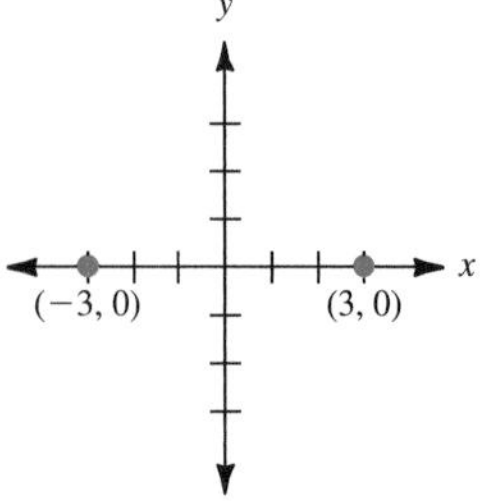

NOTE

From the equation of a hyperbola, we could also sketch the asymptotes by graphing the equations $y = \pm\frac{b}{a}x$. Here the asymptotes are the lines $y = \frac{2}{3}x$ and $y = -\frac{2}{3}x$.

Step 3 Sketch the asymptotes.

Here is an easy way to sketch the asymptotes. Note from the standard form that $b^2 = 4$, so $b = 2$ or $b = -2$. Plot the points (0, 2) and (0, −2) on the y-axis.

Draw (using dashed lines) the rectangle whose sides are parallel to the x- and y-axes and that passes through the points determined in steps 2 and 3.

Draw the diagonals of the rectangle (again using dashed lines), and then extend those diagonals to form the desired asymptotes.

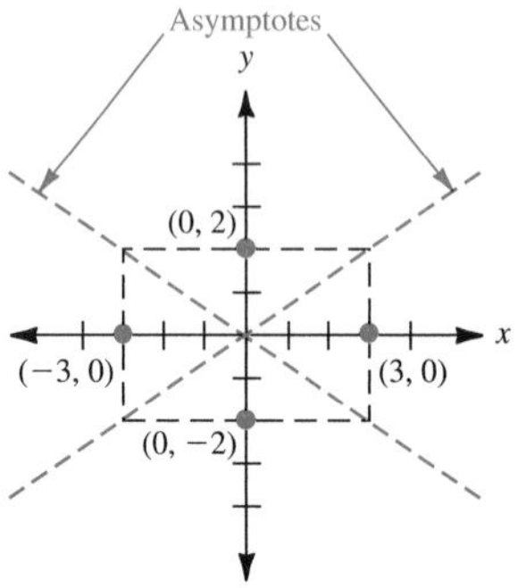

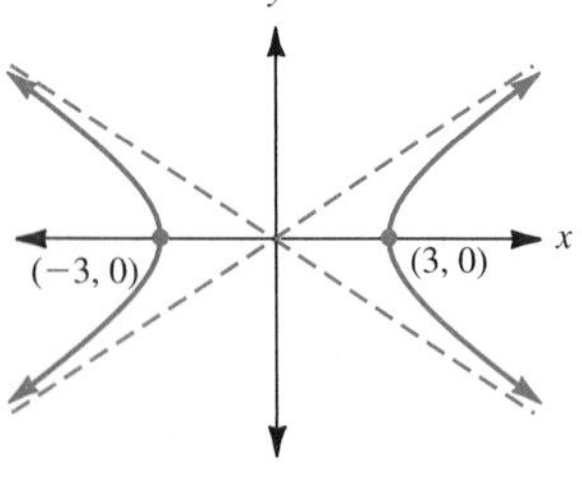

Step 4 Sketch the hyperbola.

We now complete our task by sketching the hyperbola as two smooth curves, passing through the vertices and approaching the asymptotes.

It is important to remember that the asymptotes are *not* a part of the graph. They are simply used as aids in sketching the graph as the branches get "closer and closer" to the lines.

Check Yourself 4

Sketch the hyperbola.

$$\frac{x^2}{16} - \frac{y^2}{9} = 1$$

Property

The Equation of a Hyperbola

The **equation** of a **hyperbola** that intersects the y-axis is

$$\frac{y^2}{b^2} - \frac{x^2}{a^2} = 1$$

The **vertices** are $(0, b)$ and $(0, -b)$. The **asymptotes** are given by the equations

$$y = \pm\frac{b}{a}x$$

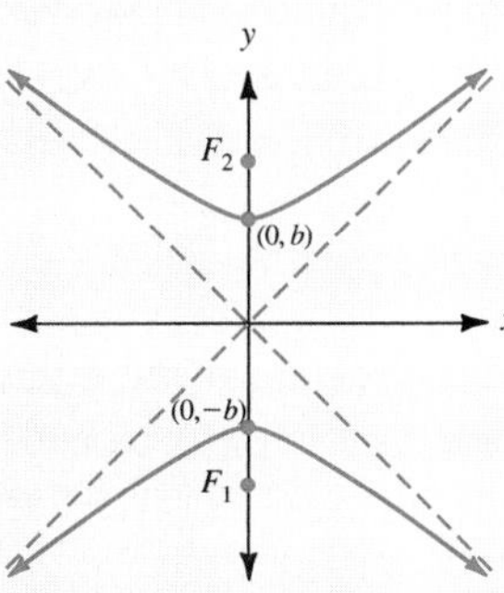

$$\frac{y^2}{b^2} - \frac{x^2}{a^2} = 1$$

F_1 and F_2 are the foci.

The graph of a hyperbola with an equation like the one given opens up and down (as shown in the figure) and is symmetric about the y-axis.

Example 5 illustrates sketching a hyperbola in this case.

Example 5 Graphing a Hyperbola

NOTE

You can recognize this equation as corresponding to a hyperbola because the coefficients of the squared terms are *opposite* in sign. Because the y^2-coefficient is *positive,* the hyperbola will open *vertically.*

Sketch the hyperbola.

$$4y^2 - 25x^2 = 100$$

Step 1 Write the equation in the standard form by dividing both sides by 100:

$$\frac{4y^2}{100} - \frac{25x^2}{100} = \frac{100}{100}$$

$$\frac{y^2}{25} - \frac{x^2}{4} = 1$$

Step 2 Find the vertices.

From the standard form, we see that because $b^2 = 25$, $b = 5$ or $b = -5$, so the vertices are at $(0, 5)$ and $(0, -5)$.

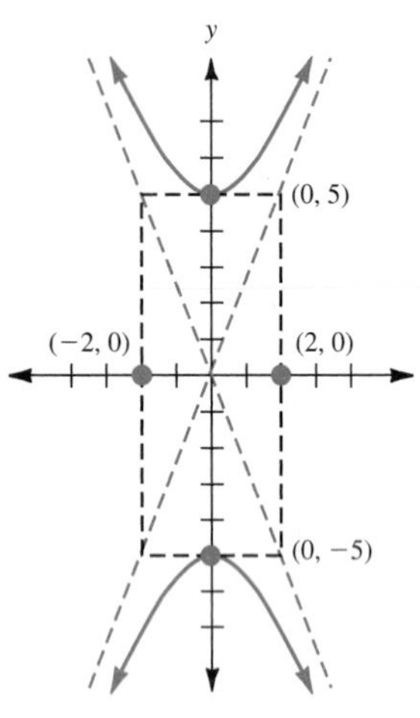

Step 3 Sketch the asymptotes.

Also from the standard form, we see that because $a^2 = 4$, $a = 2$ or $a = -2$.

Plot (2, 0) and (−2, 0) on the x-axis, and complete the dashed rectangle as before. The diagonals once again extend to form the asymptotes.

Step 4 Sketch the hyperbola.

Draw smooth curves, through the vertices, that approach the asymptotes to complete the graph.

Check Yourself 5

Sketch the hyperbola $9y^2 - 4x^2 = 36$.

The following algorithm summarizes our work so far with sketching hyperbolas.

Step by Step

Graphing the Hyperbola

Step 1 Write the given equation in standard form.

Step 2 Determine the vertices of the hyperbola.
If the x^2-coefficient is positive, the vertices are at $(a, 0)$ and $(-a, 0)$ on the x-axis.
If the y^2-coefficient is positive, the vertices are at $(0, b)$ and $(0, -b)$ on the y-axis.

Step 3 Sketch the asymptotes of the hyperbola.
Plot points $(a, 0)$, $(-a, 0)$, $(0, b)$, and $(0, -b)$. Form a rectangle from these points. The diagonals (extended) are the asymptotes of the hyperbola.

Step 4 Sketch the hyperbola.
Draw smooth curves through the vertices and approaching the asymptotes.

We have only considered hyperbolas that are centered at the origin up to this point. As we did with ellipses, let us now consider what happens to the equation if the center of the hyperbola is not (0, 0). This again relates to what we have done earlier. If the center of the hyperbola is (h, k), then the equation of the hyperbola becomes

$$\frac{(x-h)^2}{a^2} - \frac{(y-k)^2}{b^2} = 1$$

or

$$\frac{(y-k)^2}{b^2} - \frac{(x-h)^2}{a^2} = 1$$

Recall that when a hyperbola is centered at the origin, the asymptotes have equations

$$y = \pm\frac{b}{a}x$$

Thinking about how our center has shifted h units horizontally and k units vertically, the asymptotes for any translated hyperbola equation will be

$$y - k = \pm\frac{b}{a}(x - h)$$

We now must consider the vertices. We have seen that the equation of a hyperbola that is centered at the origin and intersects the x-axis is given by

$$\frac{x^2}{a^2} - \frac{y^2}{b^2} = 1$$

The vertices of this hyperbola are then at $(a, 0)$ and $(-a, 0)$.

Consider our new equation of a hyperbola that opens left and right but is centered at (h, k),

$$\frac{(x - h)^2}{a^2} - \frac{(y - k)^2}{b^2} = 1$$

Relating back to our work with ellipses, we can see that this hyperbola has vertices at $(h + a, k)$ and $(h - a, k)$.

Similarly, we can consider the equation of a hyperbola that opens up and down but is centered at (h, k),

$$\frac{(y - k)^2}{b^2} - \frac{(x - h)^2}{a^2} = 1$$

Again relating back to our work with ellipses, we can see that this hyperbola has vertices at $(h, k + b)$ and $(h, k - b)$.

Example 6 Graphing a Hyperbola

Sketch the graph of the hyperbola with equation

$$\frac{(x - 2)^2}{9} - \frac{(y + 1)^2}{16} = 1$$

Since the x-term is positive, this hyperbola will intersect the x-axis. Using the preceding formula for a hyperbola, $h = 2$ and $k = -1$, so the center is at $(2, -1)$. The formula also tells us that $a = 3$ and $b = 4$. We are centered at the point $(2, -1)$, which means we have shifted to the right two units, so our x-values are $2 \pm a$. In other words, our vertices are $(2 + 3, -1)$ and $(2 - 3, -1)$, or $(5, -1)$ and $(-1, -1)$. The asymptotes are given by

$$y - k = \pm\frac{b}{a}(x - h)$$

NOTE

We also could have sketched the asymptotes by finding the rectangle, as in Example 5. Here, the rectangle is determined by $(2 \pm a, k)$ and $(h, -1 \pm b)$ or vertices at $(5, -1), (-1, -1), (2, 3), (2, -5)$.

So plugging in the values from this problem we have

$$y - (-1) = \pm\frac{4}{3}(x - 2)$$

$$y = -1 \pm \frac{4}{3}(x - 2)$$

$$y = -1 + \frac{4}{3}(x - 2) \quad \text{and} \quad y = -1 - \frac{4}{3}(x - 2)$$

$$y = -1 + \frac{4}{3}x - \frac{8}{3} \qquad y = -1 - \frac{4}{3}x + \frac{8}{3}$$

$$y = \frac{4}{3}x - \frac{11}{3} \qquad y = -\frac{4}{3}x + \frac{5}{3}$$

We now have enough information to sketch a graph.

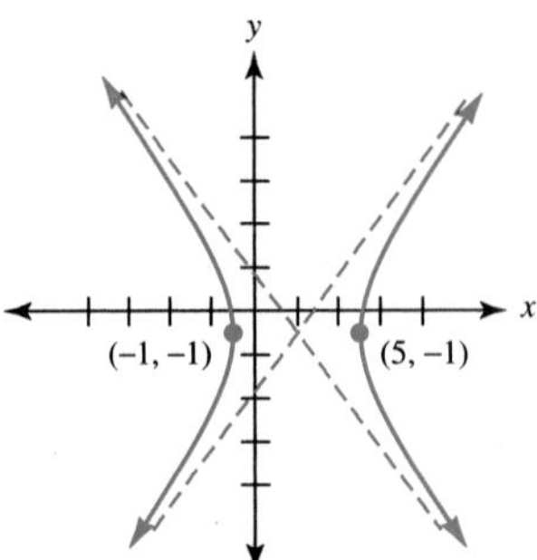

Check Yourself 6

Sketch the graph of the hyperbola with equation

$$\frac{(y-4)^2}{25} - \frac{(x+3)^2}{4} = 1$$

The given chart shows all of the conic section equation forms.

Curve	Example	Recognizing the Curve
Line	$4x - 3y = 12$	The equation involves x and y to the first power only.
Parabola	$y = x^2 - 3x$ or $x = y^2 - 2y + 3$	Only one term, in x or in y, may be squared. The other variable appears to the first power.
Circle	$x^2 + 4x + y^2 = 5$	The equation has both x^2- and y^2-terms. The coefficients of those terms are equal.
Ellipse	$4x^2 + 9y^2 = 36$	The equation has both x^2- and y^2-terms. The coefficients of those terms have the same sign but different values.
Hyperbola	$4x^2 - 9y^2 = 36$ or $9y^2 - 16x^2 = 144$	The equation has both x^2- and y^2-terms. The coefficients of those terms have different signs.

Check Yourself ANSWERS

1. $\frac{x^2}{16} + \frac{y^2}{9} = 1$

2. $\frac{x^2}{4} + \frac{y^2}{25} = 1$

3. $\dfrac{(x+3)^2}{4} + \dfrac{(y-4)^2}{25} = 1$

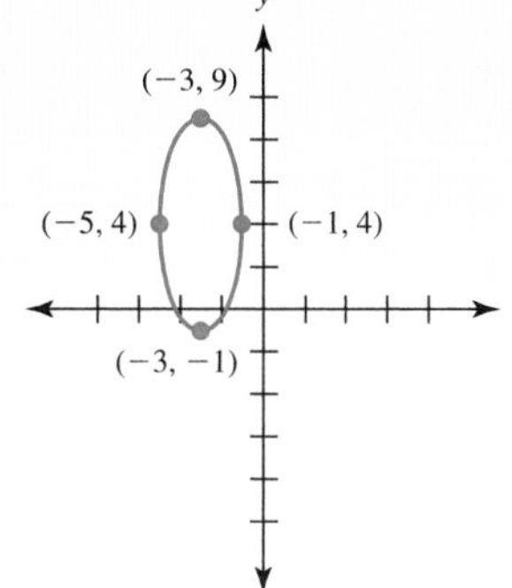

4. $\dfrac{x^2}{16} - \dfrac{y^2}{9} = 1$

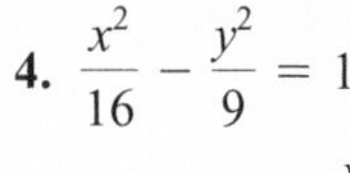

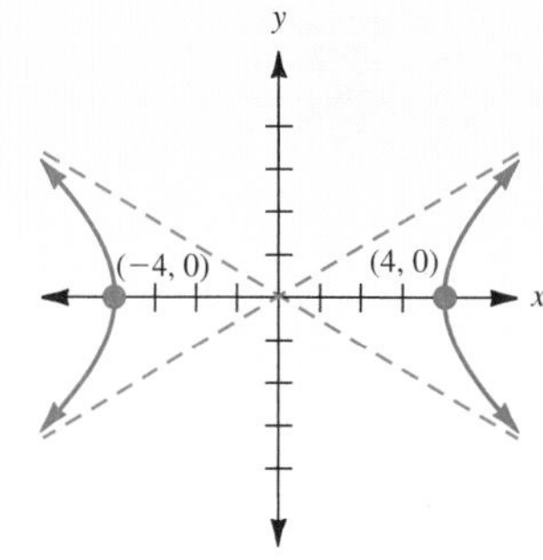

5. $\dfrac{y^2}{4} - \dfrac{x^2}{9} = 1$

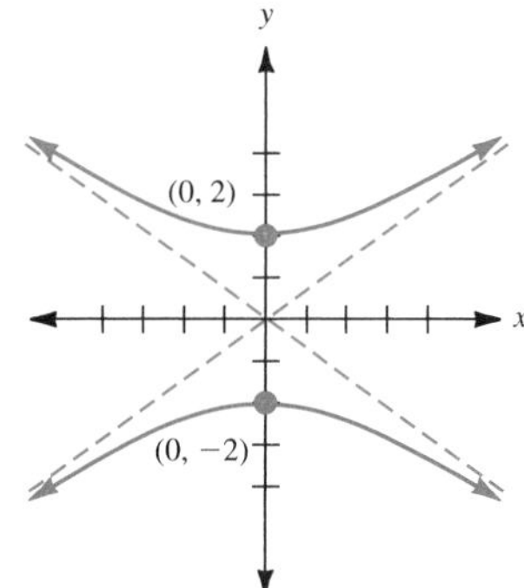

6. $\dfrac{(y-4)^2}{25} - \dfrac{(x+3)^2}{4} = 1$

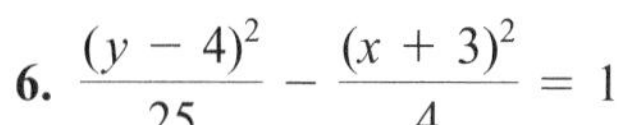

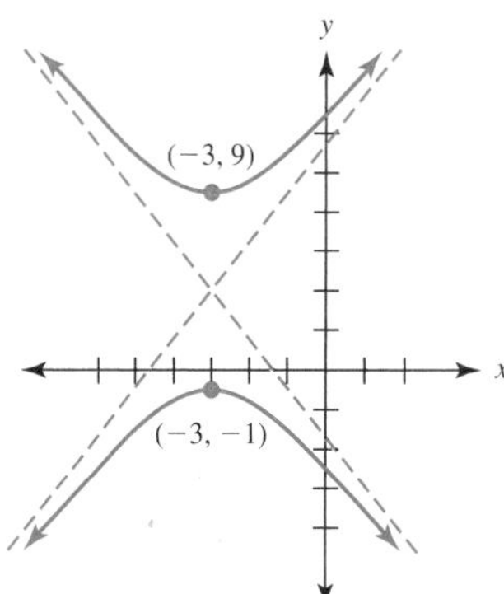

Reading Your Text

The following fill-in-the-blank exercises are designed to ensure that you understand some of the key vocabulary used in this section.

SECTION 9.3

(a) A(n) ______________ is the set of all points (x, y) such that the sum of the distances from (x, y) to two fixed points is constant.

(b) A(n) ______________ is the set of all points (x, y) such that the absolute value of the difference of the distances from (x, y) to each of two fixed points is constant.

(c) The ______________ are given by the equations $y = \pm\frac{b}{a}x$.

(d) The conic section equation forms can be recognized by counting the number of squared terms and, if there are two squared terms (both x^2- and y^2-terms), by looking at the ______________ of those squared terms.

9.3 exercises

Basic Skills | Advanced Skills | Vocational-Technical Applications | Calculator/Computer | Above and Beyond

MathZone

Boost your grade at mathzone.com!
- Practice Problems
- NetTutor
- Self-Tests
- e-Professors
- Videos

Name ______________

Section ________ Date ________

Answers

1. (d)
2. (f)
3. (h)
4. (a)
5. (b)
6. (g)
7. (c)
8. (e)

In exercises 1 to 8, match each of the curves shown with the appropriate equation.

(a) $4x^2 + 25y^2 = 100$ **(b)** $y = x^2 - 2x - 3$

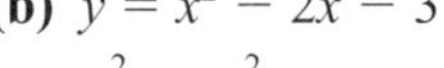

(c) $x = \frac{1}{2}y^2 - 2y$ **(d)** $\frac{x^2}{9} + \frac{y^2}{16} = 1$

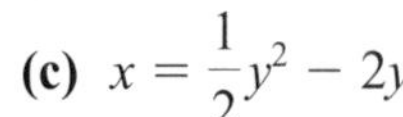

(e) $\frac{y^2}{25} - \frac{x^2}{4} = 1$ **(f)** $16x^2 - 9y^2 = 144$

(g) $(x - 2)^2 + (y - 2)^2 = 9$ **(h)** $x^2 + y^2 = 16$

1.

2.

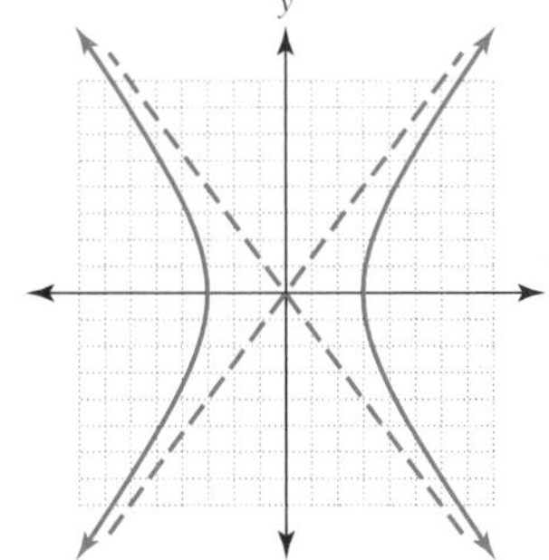

3.

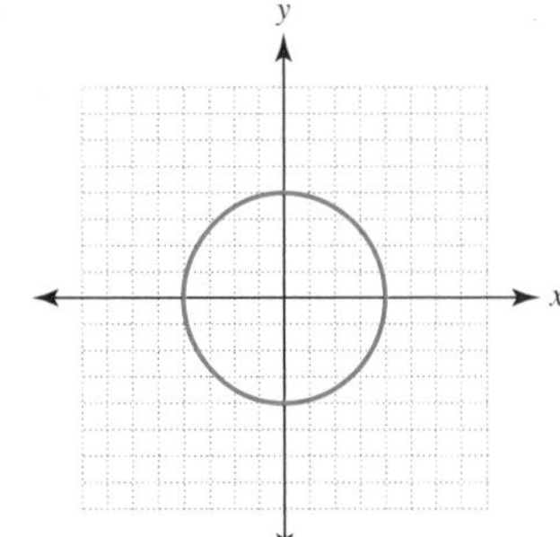

4.

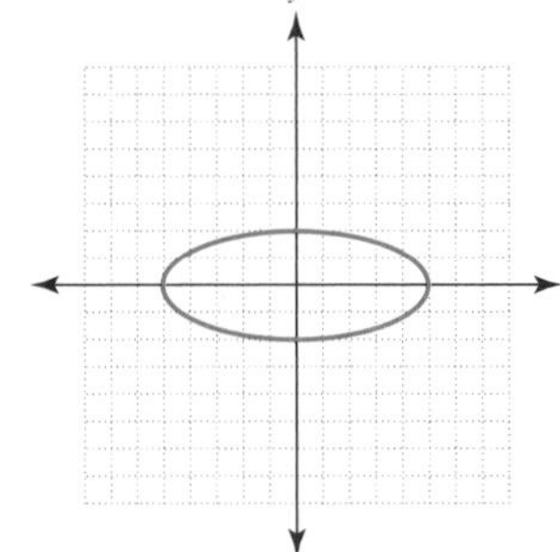

5.

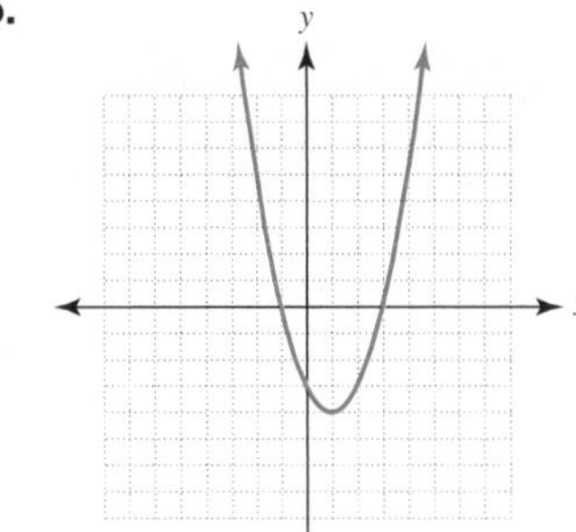

6.

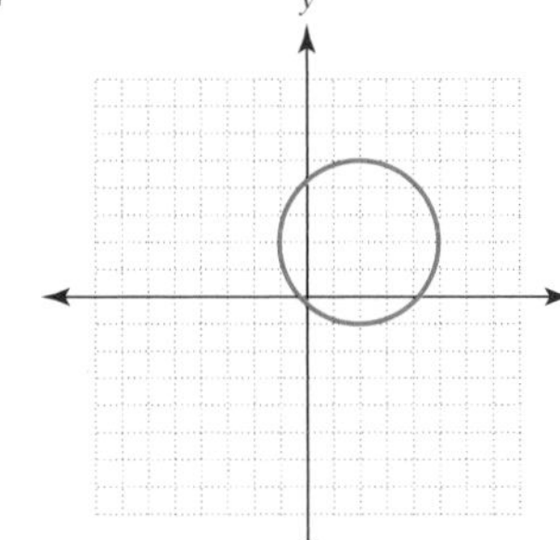

7.

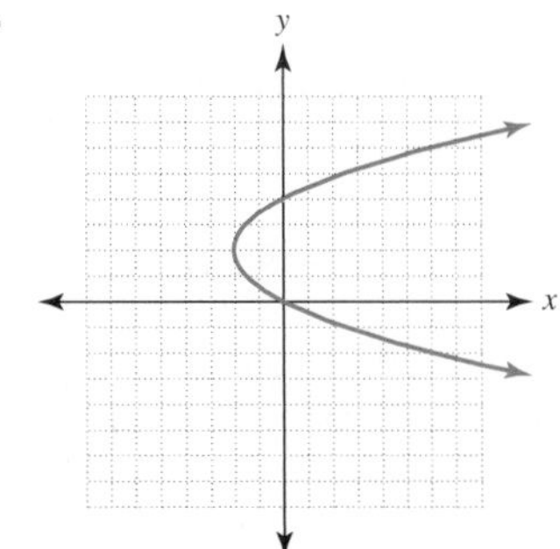

8.

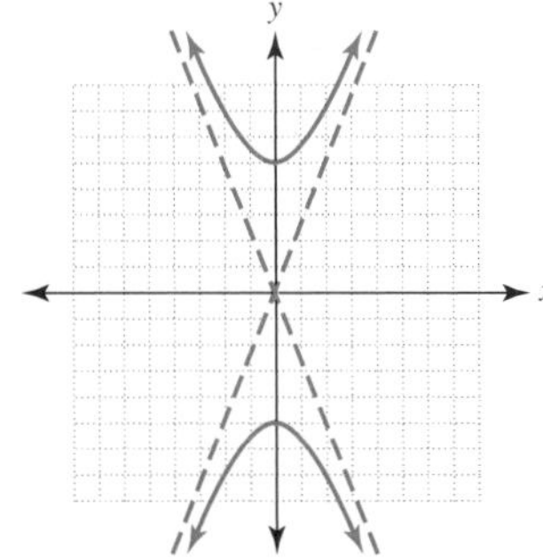

Identify the graph of each of the following equations as one of the conic sections (parabola, circle, ellipse, or hyperbola).

9. $x^2 + y^2 = 16$

10. $\frac{x^2}{4} - \frac{y^2}{16} = 1$

11. $y = x^2 - 4$

12. $\frac{x^2}{16} + \frac{y^2}{9} = 1$

13. $9x^2 - 4y^2 = 36$

14. $x^2 = 4y$

15. $y^2 - 4x^2 = 4$

16. $x = y^2 - 2y + 1$

17. $x^2 - 6x + y^2 + 2x = 2$

18. $4x^2 + 25y^2 = 100$

19. $9y^2 - 16x^2 = 144$

20. $y = x^2 - 6x + 8$

< Objective 1 >

Graph the following ellipses by finding the x- and y-intercepts. If necessary, write the equation in standard form.

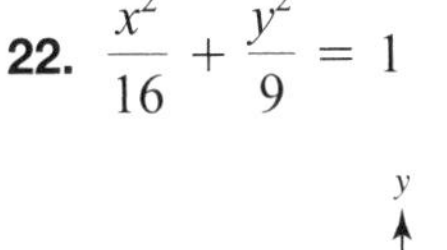

21. $\frac{x^2}{4} + \frac{y^2}{9} = 1$

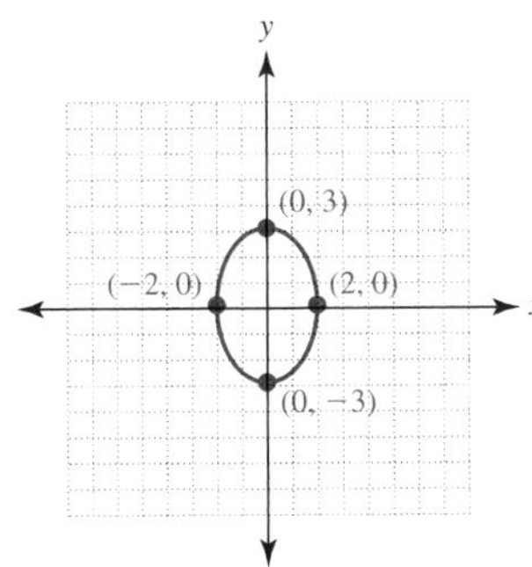

22. $\frac{x^2}{16} + \frac{y^2}{9} = 1$

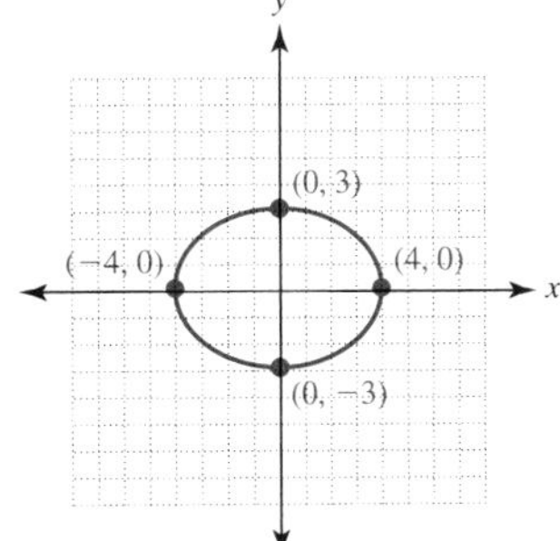

23. $\frac{x^2}{9} + \frac{y^2}{25} = 1$

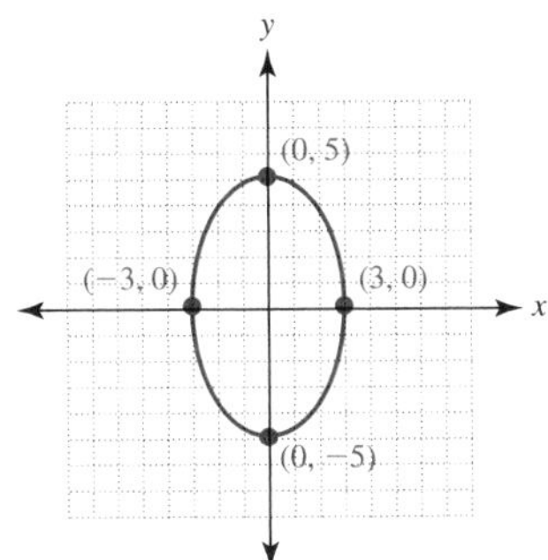

24. $\frac{x^2}{36} + \frac{y^2}{16} = 1$

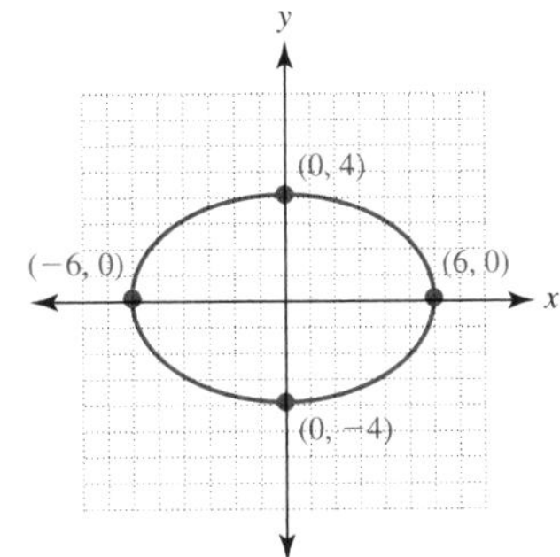

Answers

9. Circle
10. Hyperbola
11. Parabola
12. Ellipse
13. Hyperbola
14. Parabola
15. Hyperbola
16. Parabola
17. Circle
18. Ellipse
19. Hyperbola
20. Parabola
21. See exercise
22. See exercise
23. See exercise
24. See exercise

Answers

25. See exercise

26. See exercise

27. See exercise

28. See exercise

29. See exercise

30. See exercise

31. See exercise

32. See exercise

25. $x^2 + 9y^2 = 36$

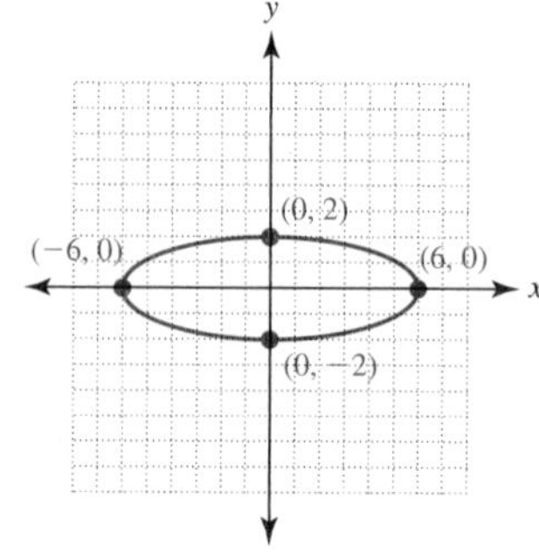

26. $4x^2 + y^2 = 16$

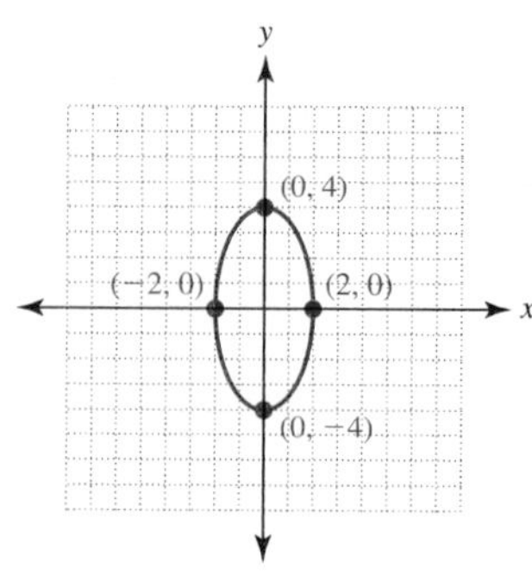

27. $4x^2 + 9y^2 = 36$

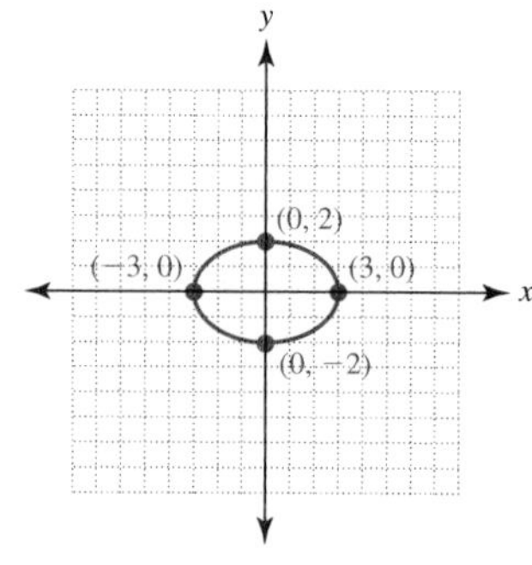

28. $25x^2 + 4y^2 = 100$

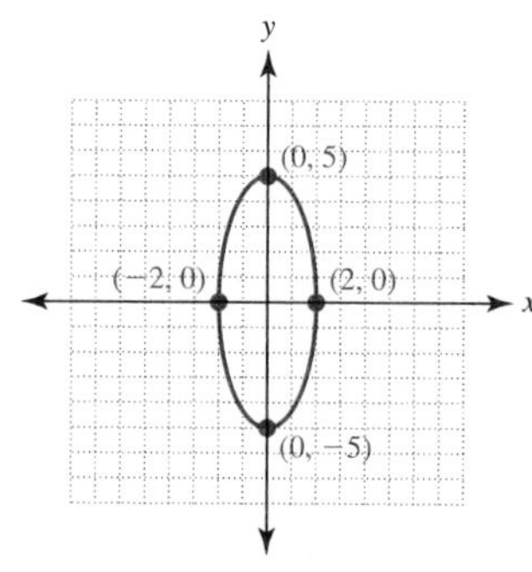

29. $4x^2 + 25y^2 = 100$

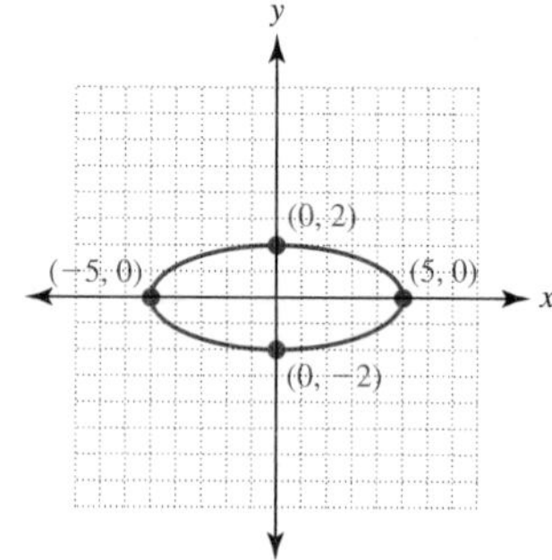

30. $9x^2 + 16y^2 = 144$

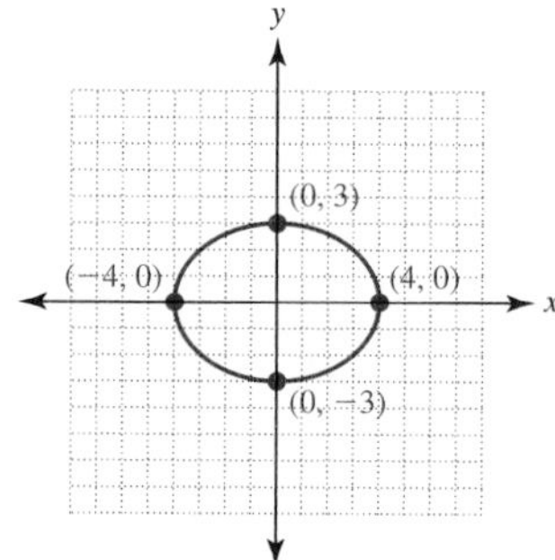

31. $25x^2 + 9y^2 = 225$ > Videos

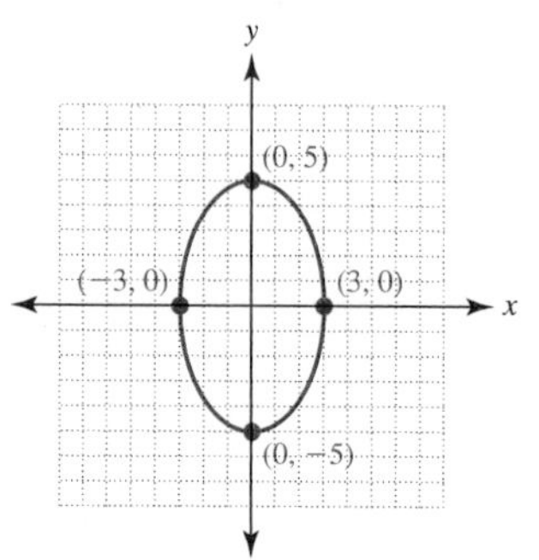

32. $16x^2 + 9y^2 = 144$

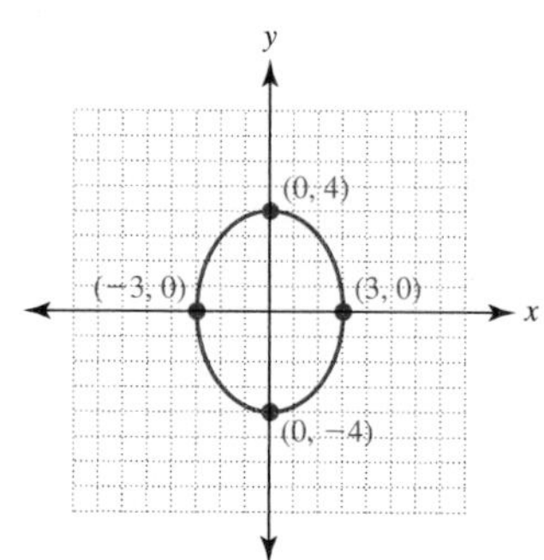

Graph the following ellipses not centered at the origin.

33. $\dfrac{(x+4)^2}{36} + \dfrac{(y+5)^2}{49} = 1$

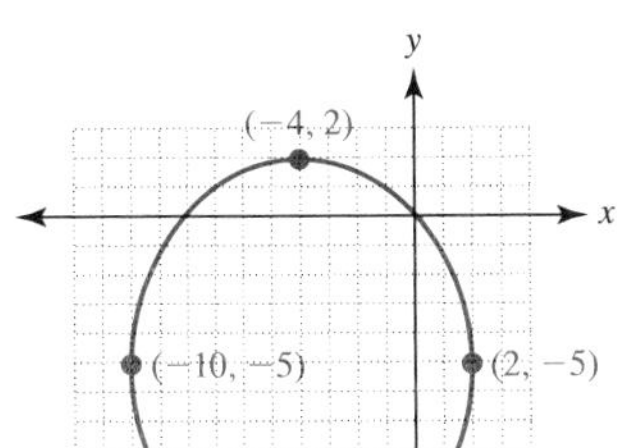

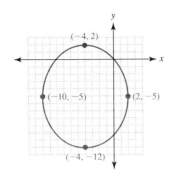

34. $\dfrac{(x-2)^2}{4} + \dfrac{(y-1)^2}{9} = 1$

> Videos

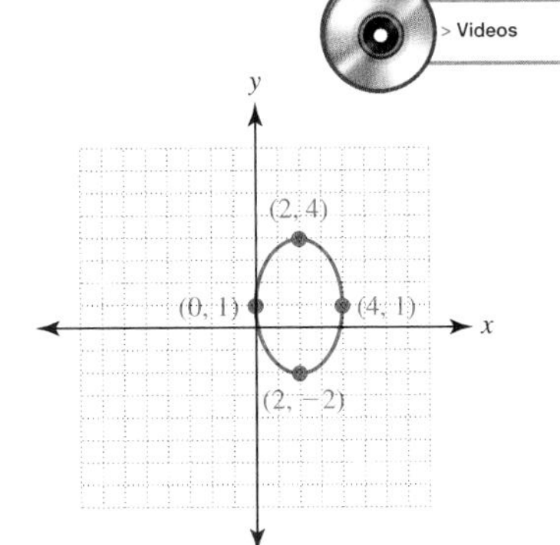

35. $4(x+2)^2 + 9(y-1)^2 = 36$

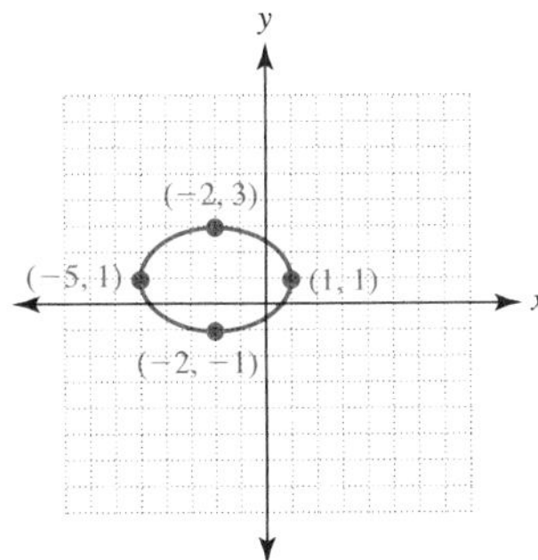

36. $4(x-2)^2 + 25(y+1)^2 = 100$

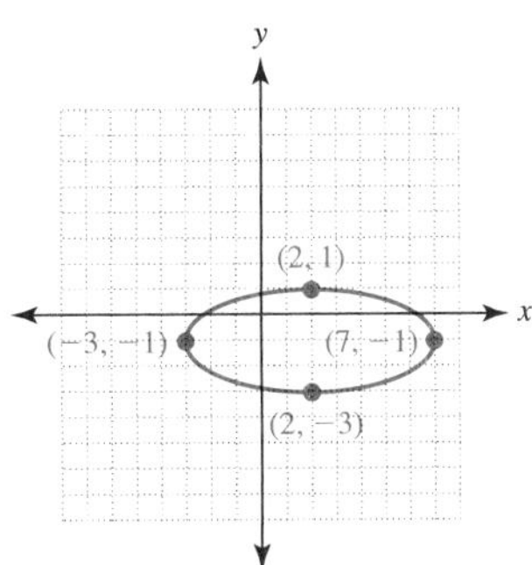

< Objective 2 >

Graph the following hyperbolas by finding the vertices and asymptotes. If necessary, write the equation in standard form.

chapter 9 > Make the Connection

37. $\dfrac{x^2}{9} - \dfrac{y^2}{9} = 1$

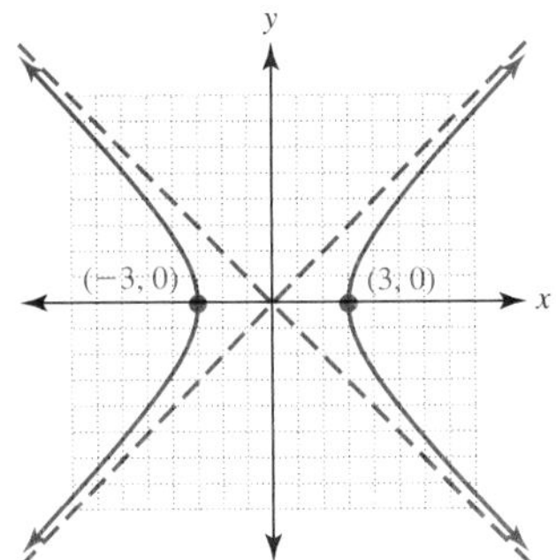

38. $\dfrac{y^2}{9} - \dfrac{x^2}{4} = 1$

> Videos

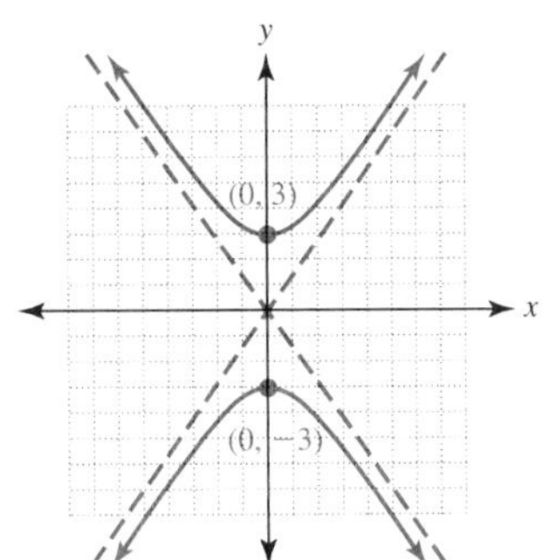

Answers

33. See exercise

34. See exercise

35. See exercise

36. See exercise

37. See exercise

38. See exercise

Answers

39. See exercise

40. See exercise

41. See exercise

42. See exercise

43. See exercise

44. See exercise

45. See exercise

46. See exercise

39. $\frac{y^2}{16} - \frac{x^2}{9} = 1$

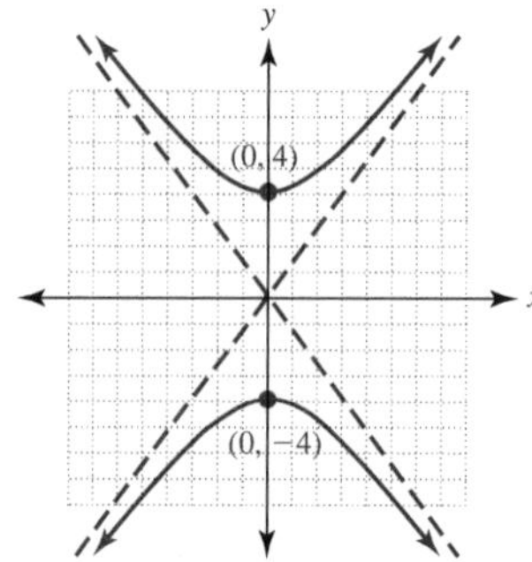

40. $\frac{x^2}{25} - \frac{y^2}{16} = 1$

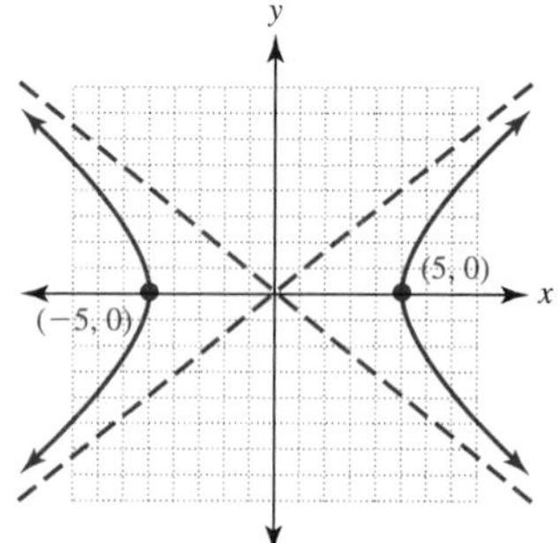

41. $\frac{x^2}{36} - \frac{y^2}{9} = 1$

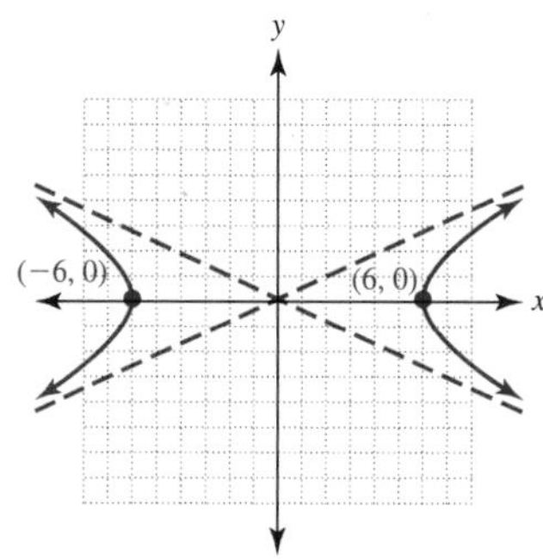

42. $\frac{y^2}{25} - \frac{x^2}{9} = 1$

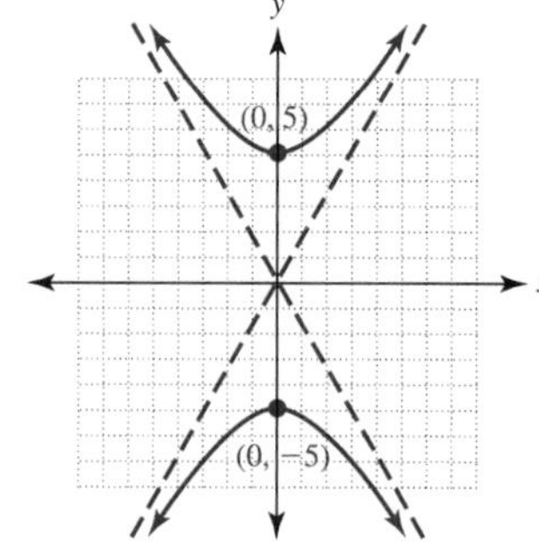

43. $x^2 - 9y^2 = 36$

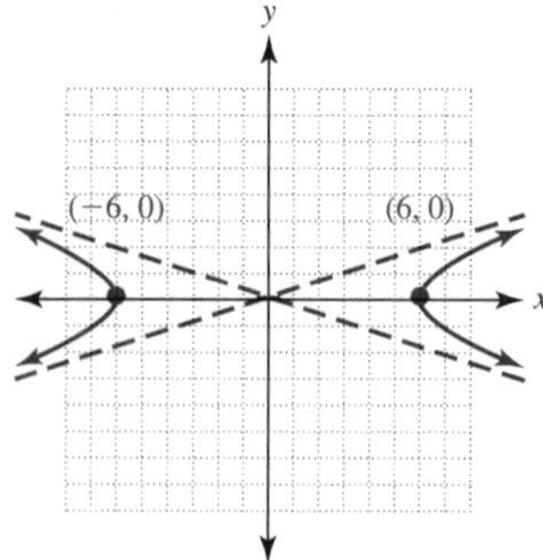

44. $y^2 - 4x^2 = 36$

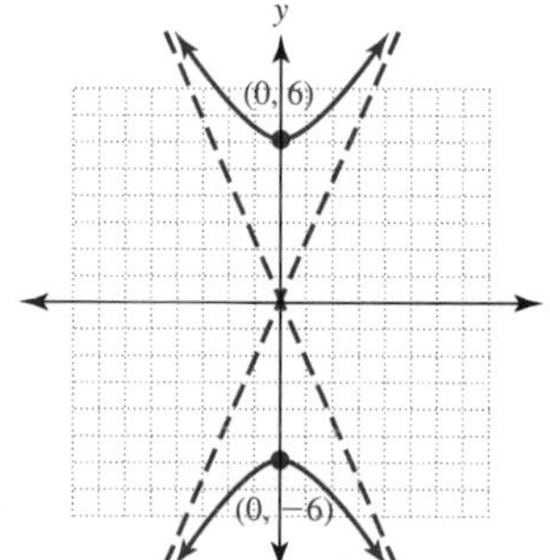

45. $9x^2 - 4y^2 = 36$

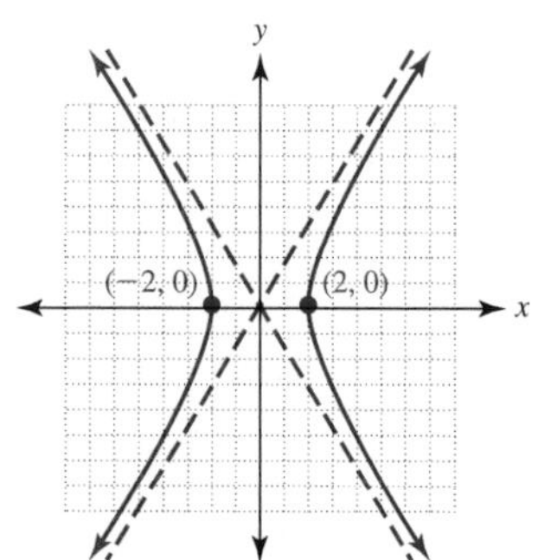

46. $9y^2 - 4x^2 = 36$

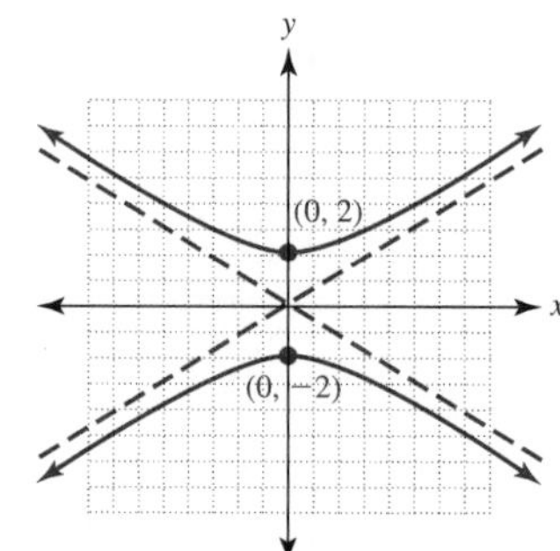

47. $25y^2 - 9x^2 = 225$

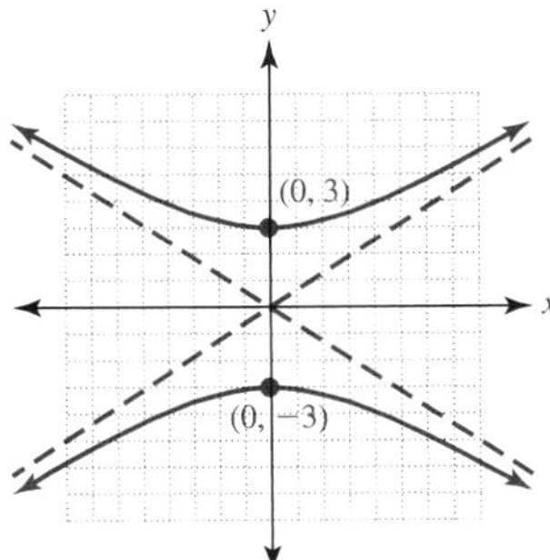

48. $4x^2 - 9y^2 = 36$

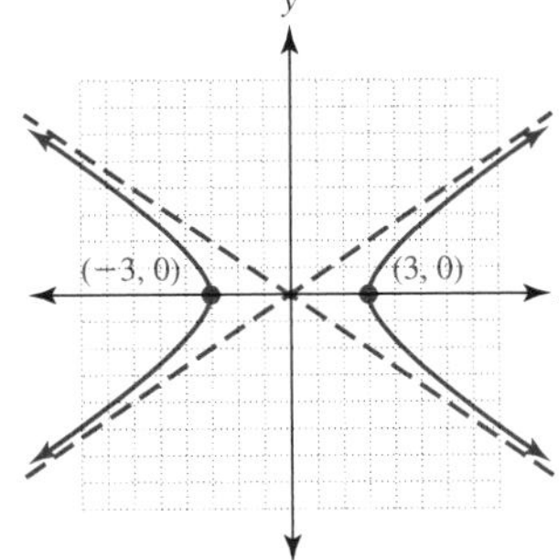

49. $25y^2 - 4x^2 = 100$

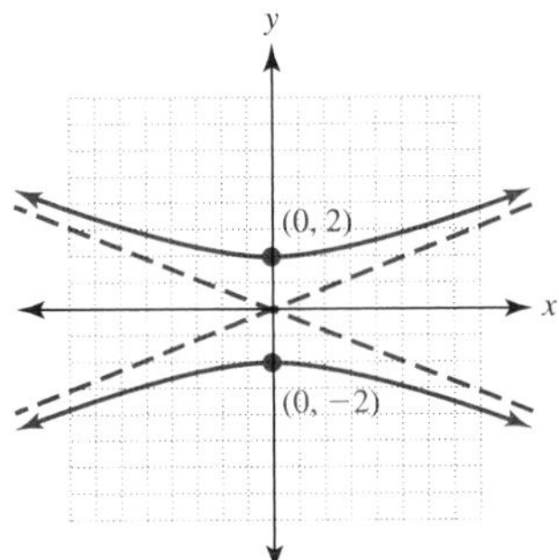

50. $9x^2 - 25y^2 = 225$ > Videos

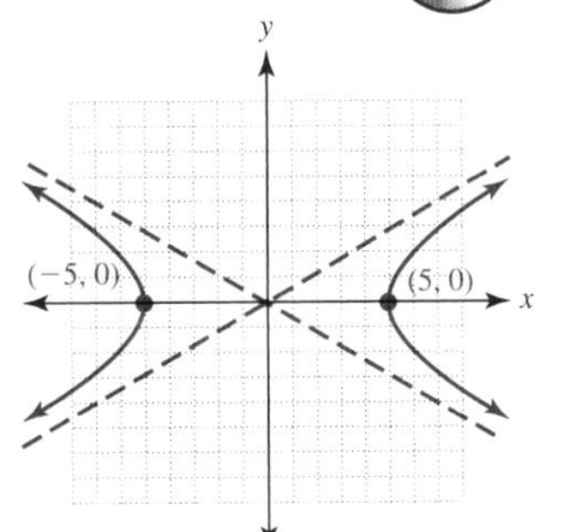

51. $\dfrac{(x-2)^2}{25} - \dfrac{(y-2)^2}{9} = 1$

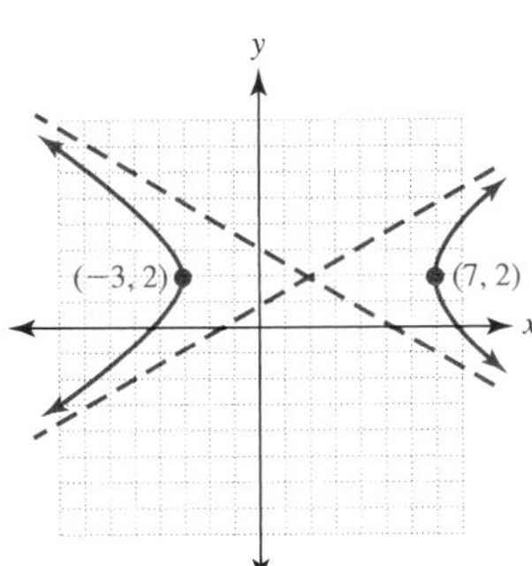

52. $\dfrac{(y+4)^2}{36} - \dfrac{(x+5)^2}{49} = 1$

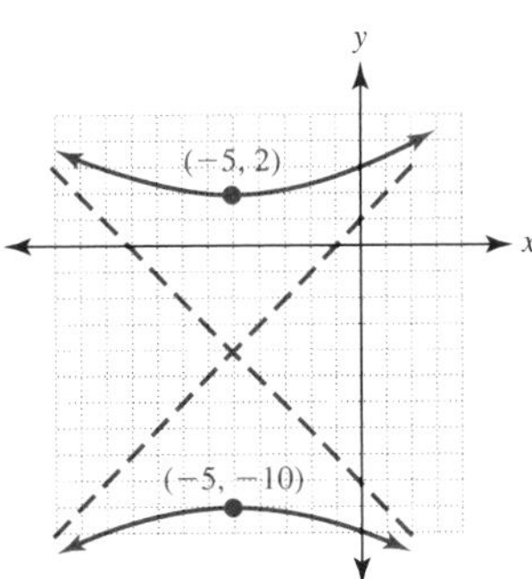

53. $16(x-2)^2 - 9(y+1)^2 = 144$

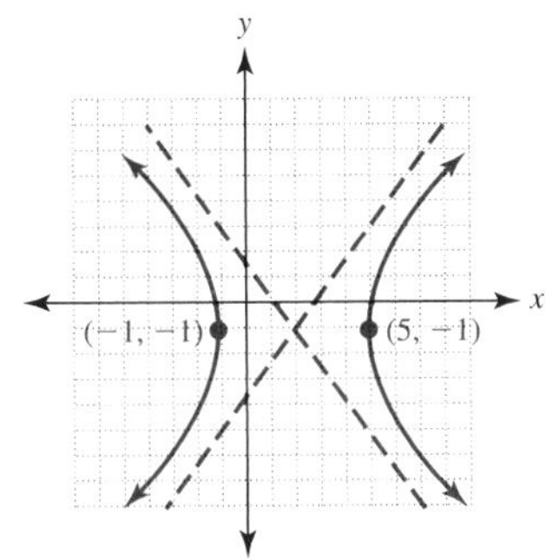

54. $4(y+2)^2 - 25(x-1)^2 = 100$ > Videos

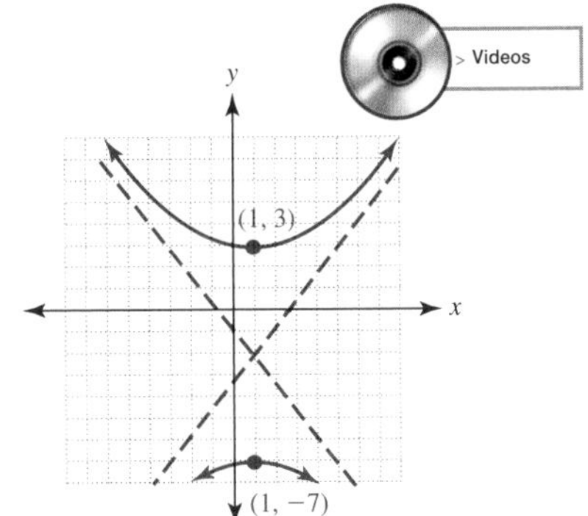

Answers

47. See exercise
48. See exercise
49. See exercise
50. See exercise
51. See exercise
52. See exercise
53. See exercise
54. See exercise

Answers

55. sometimes

56. never

57. never

58. sometimes

59. Yes

60. Yes

61. See exercise

62. See exercise

63. See exercise

64. See exercise

In each of the following statements, fill in the blank with **always, sometimes,** *or* **never.**

55. An ellipse ________ has x-intercepts.

56. The asymptotes of a hyperbola are ________ part of the graph.

57. In the equation of a hyperbola, the coefficients of x^2 and y^2 ________ have the same sign.

58. A hyperbola ________ has y-intercepts.

Basic Skills | **Advanced Skills** | Vocational-Technical Applications | Calculator/Computer | Above and Beyond

59. CONSTRUCTION TECHNOLOGY A semielliptical archway over a one-way road has a height of 10 ft and a width of 40 ft (see the figure). Will a truck that is 10 ft wide and 9 ft high clear the opening of the highway?

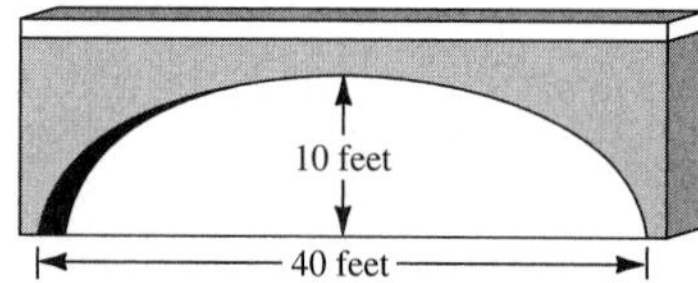

60. CONSTRUCTION TECHNOLOGY A truck that is 8 ft wide is carrying a load that reaches 7 ft above the ground. Will the truck clear a semielliptical arch that is 10 ft high and 30 ft wide?

Basic Skills | Advanced Skills | Vocational-Technical Applications | **Calculator/Computer** | Above and Beyond

An ellipse can be graphed on a calculator by plotting the upper and lower halves on the same axes. For example, to graph $9x^2 + 16y^2 = 144$, we solve for y:

$$Y_1 = \frac{\sqrt{144 - 9x^2}}{4} \quad \text{and} \quad Y_2 = -\frac{\sqrt{144 - 9x^2}}{4}$$

Then graph each equation as a separate function.

Use this technique to graph each ellipse.

61. $4x^2 + 16y^2 = 64$

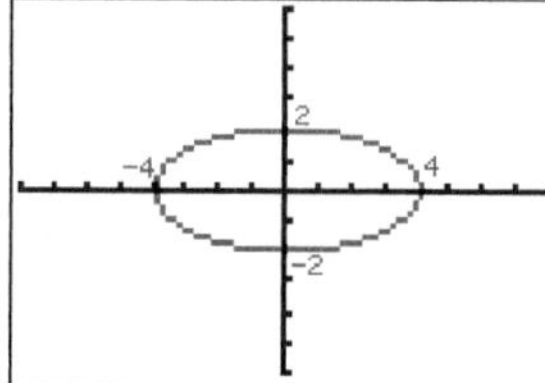

62. $9x^2 + 36y^2 = 324$

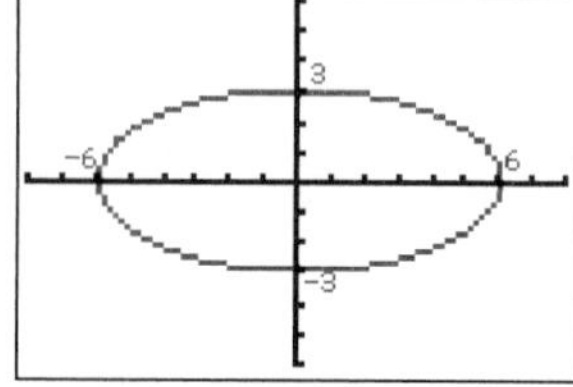

63. $25x^2 + 9y^2 = 225$

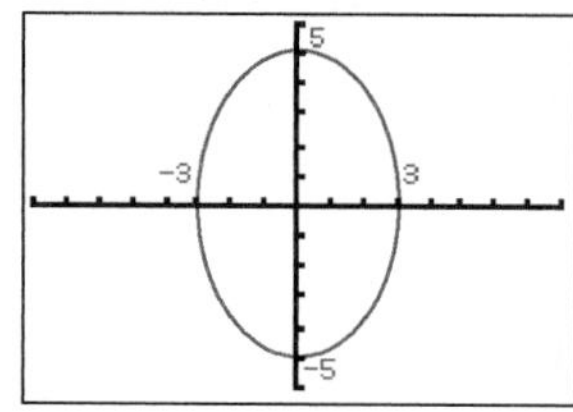

64. $4x^2 + 9y^2 = 36$

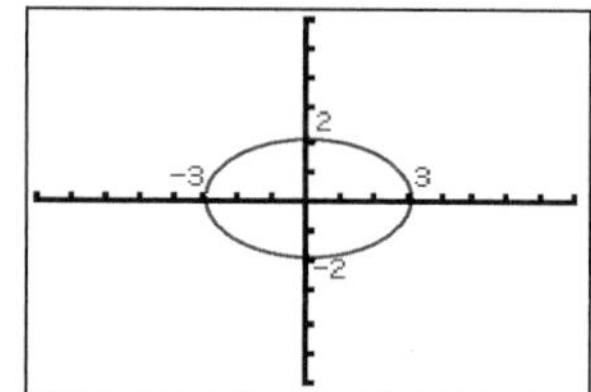

Use a graphing utility to graph each equation.

65. $y^2 - 16x^2 = 16$

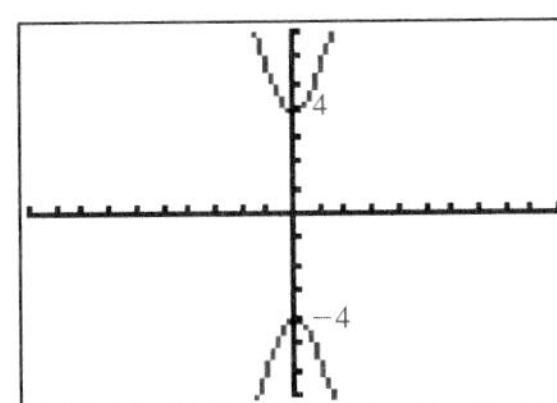

66. $y^2 - 25x^2 = 25$

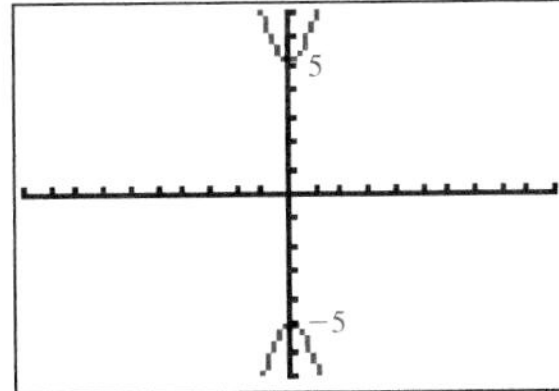

67. $16x^2 - 9y^2 = 144$

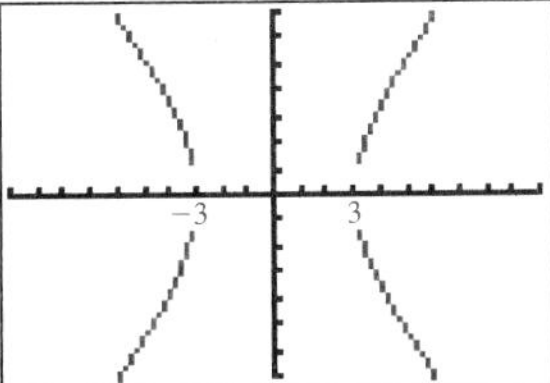

68. $25x^2 - 16y^2 = 400$

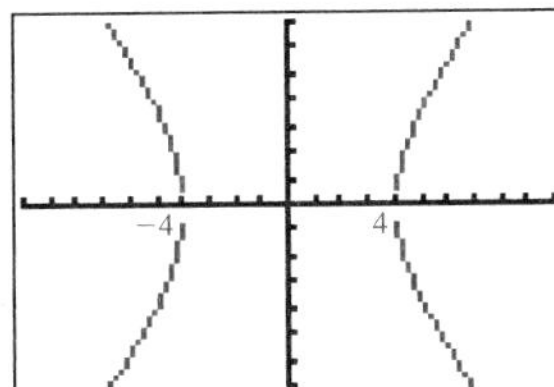

Answers

65. See exercise

66. See exercise

67. See exercise

68. See exercise

Answers

1. (d) **3.** (h) **5.** (b) **7.** (c) **9.** Circle **11.** Parabola
13. Hyperbola **15.** Hyperbola **17.** Circle **19.** Hyperbola

21. $\frac{x^2}{4} + \frac{y^2}{9} = 1$

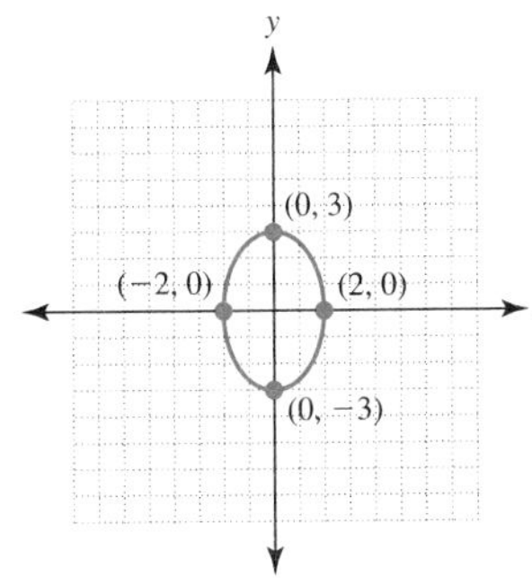

23. $\frac{x^2}{9} + \frac{y^2}{25} = 1$

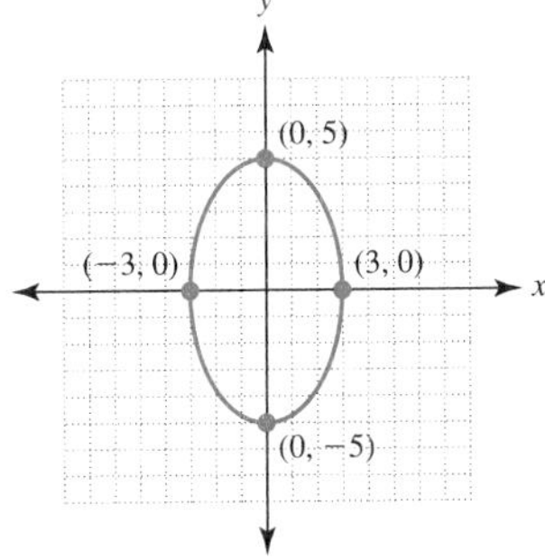

25. $x^2 + 9y^2 = 36$

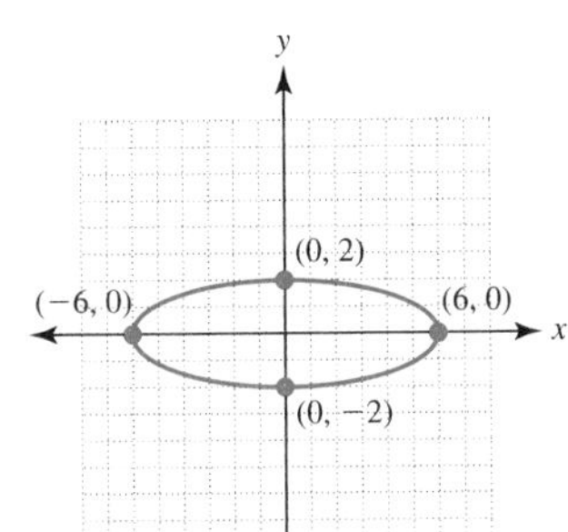

27. $4x^2 + 9y^2 = 36$

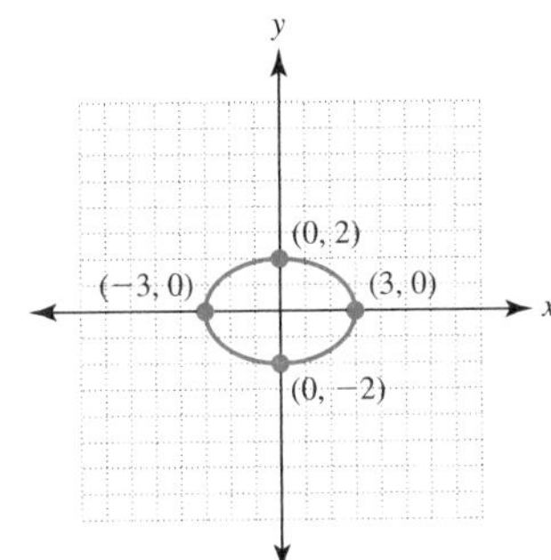

29. $4x^2 + 25y^2 = 100$

31. $25x^2 + 9y^2 = 225$

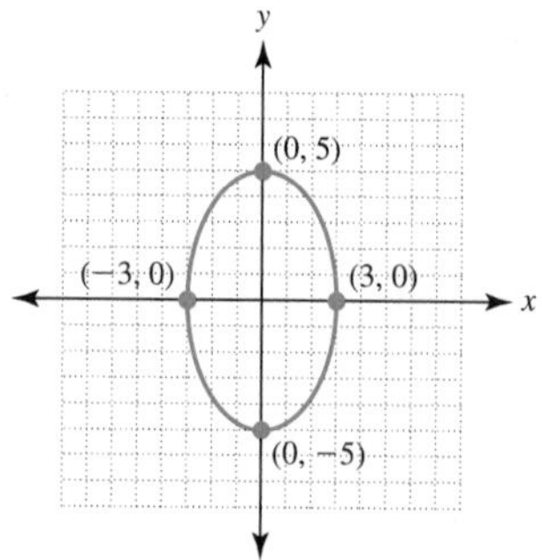

33. $\dfrac{(x + 4)^2}{36} + \dfrac{(y + 5)^2}{49} = 1$

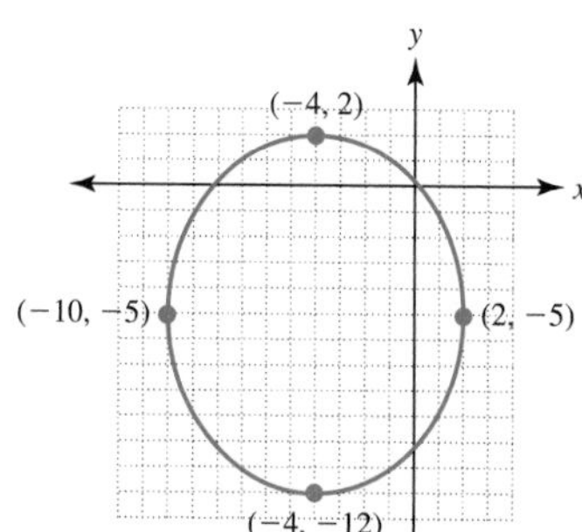

35. $4(x + 2)^2 + 9(y - 1)^2 = 36$

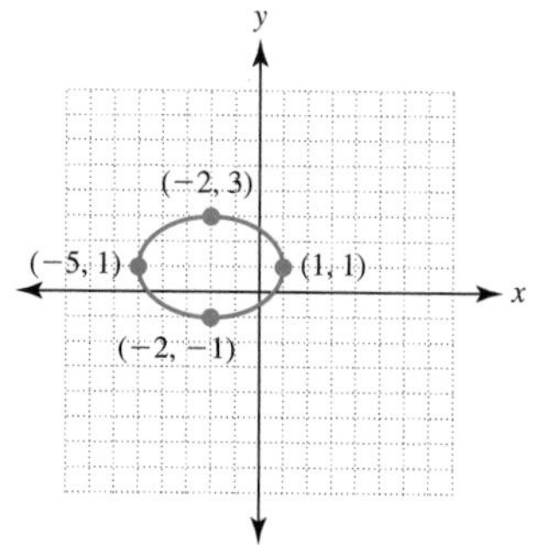

37. $\dfrac{x^2}{9} - \dfrac{y^2}{9} = 1$

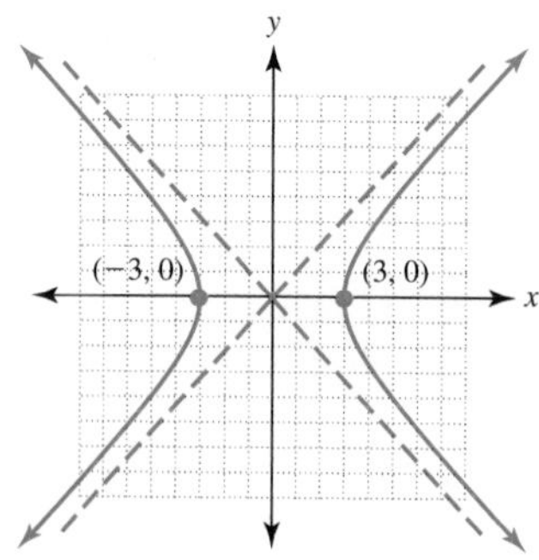

39. $\dfrac{y^2}{16} - \dfrac{x^2}{9} = 1$

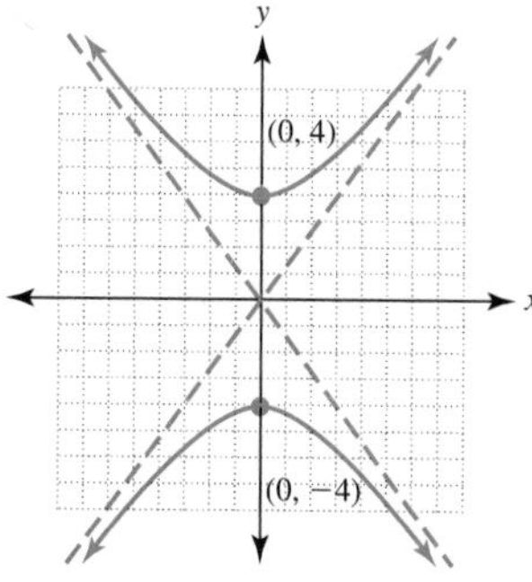

41. $\dfrac{x^2}{36} - \dfrac{y^2}{9} = 1$

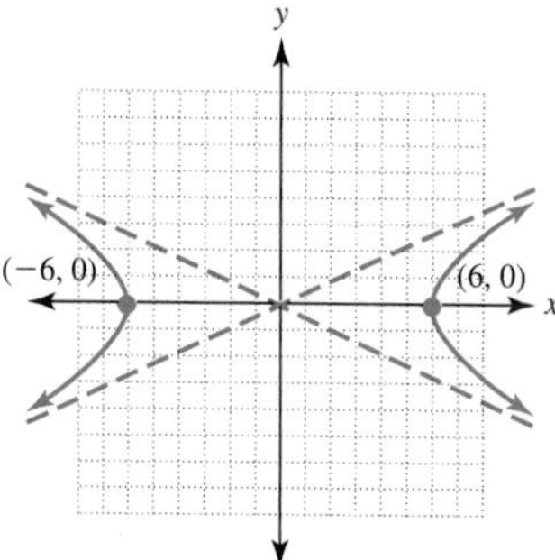

43. $x^2 - 9y^2 = 36$

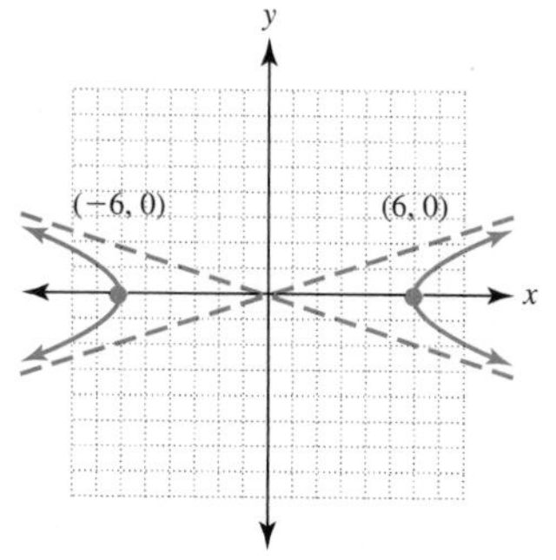

45. $9x^2 - 4y^2 = 36$

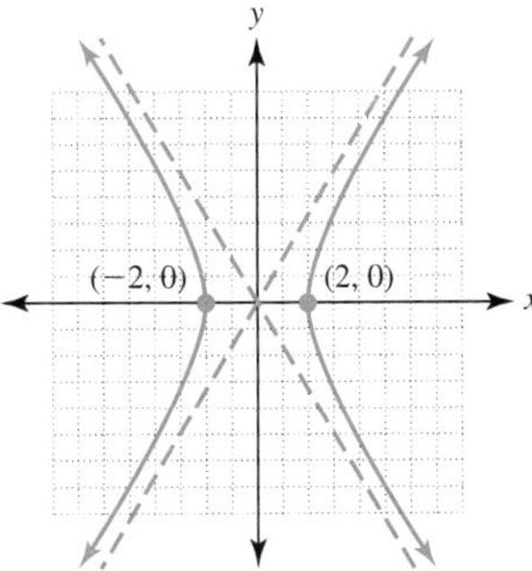

47. $25y^2 - 9x^2 = 225$

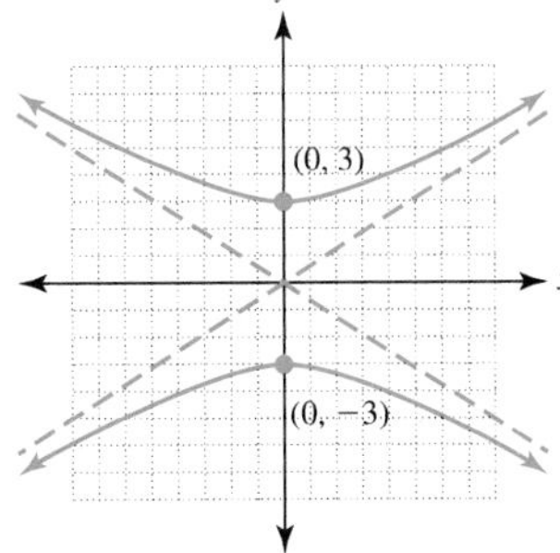

49. $25y^2 - 4x^2 = 100$

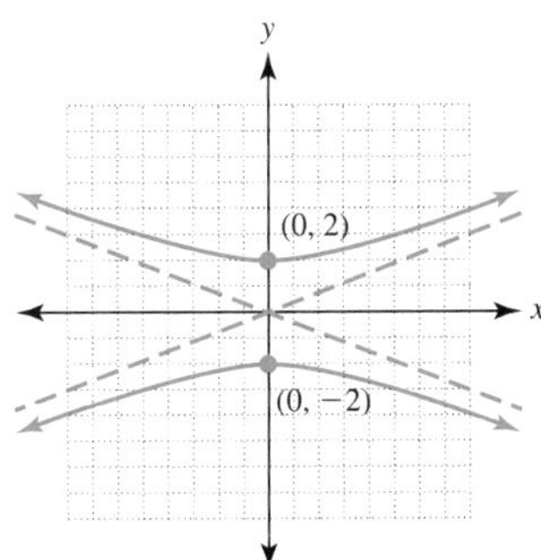

51. $\frac{(x-2)^2}{25} - \frac{(y-2)^2}{9} = 1$

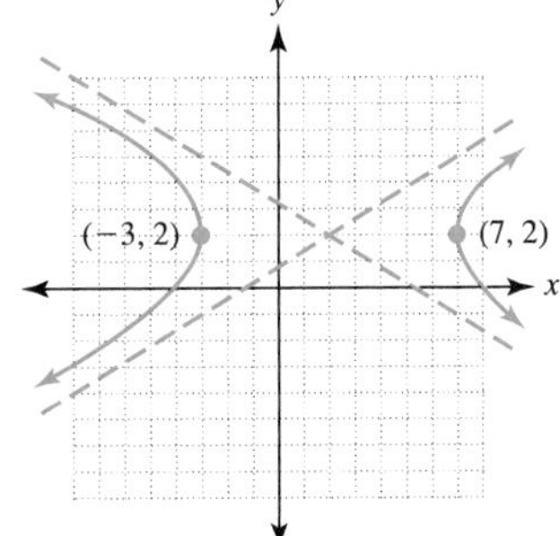

53. $16(x-2)^2 - 9(y+1)^2 = 144$

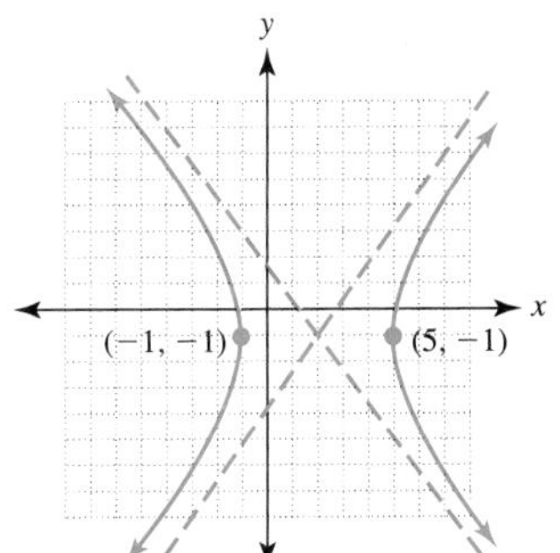

55. sometimes 57. never 59. Yes

61. $4x^2 + 16y^2 = 64$

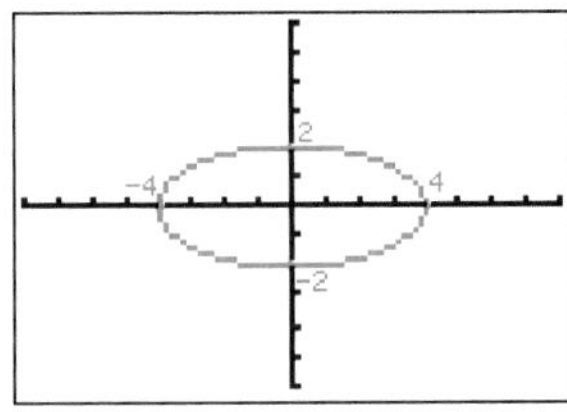

63. $25x^2 + 9y^2 = 225$

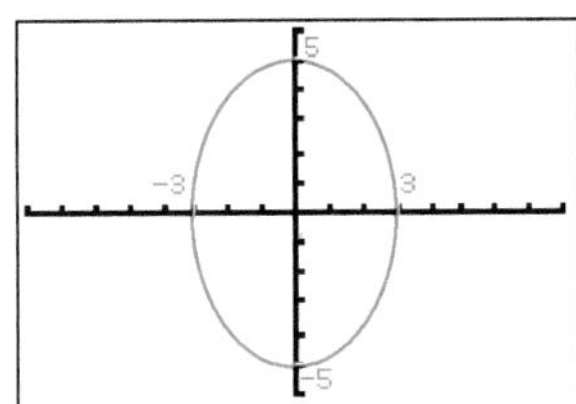

65. $y^2 - 16x^2 = 16$

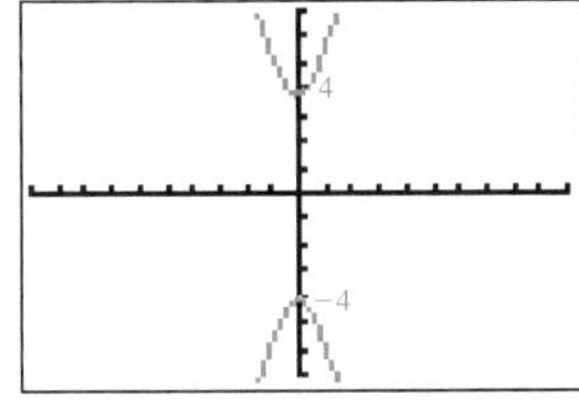

67. $16x^2 - 9y^2 = 144$

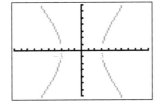

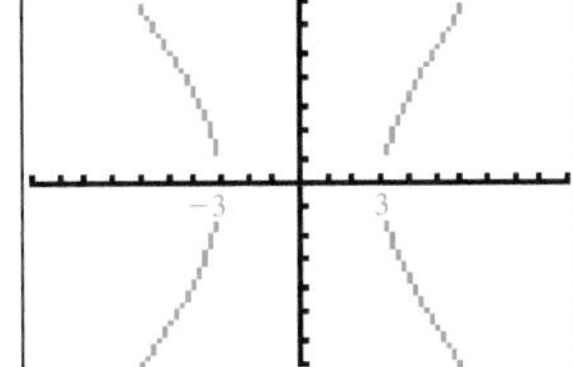

9.4 Nonlinear Systems

< 9.4 Objectives >

1 > Solve a system of nonlinear equations by graphing

2 > Solve a system of nonlinear equations algebraically

3 > Solve a system of nonlinear inequalities by graphing

In Section 4.1, we solved a system of linear equations by graphing the lines corresponding to those equations, and then recording the point of intersection. That point represented the solution to the system of equations. We will use a similar method to find the solutions for a nonlinear system. A system with two or more conic curves can have zero, one, two, three, four, or an infinite number of solutions. The following graphs represent each of the finite possibilities.

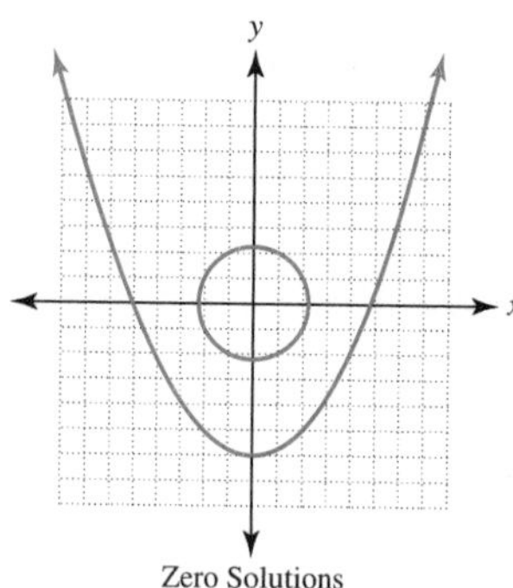

Zero Solutions

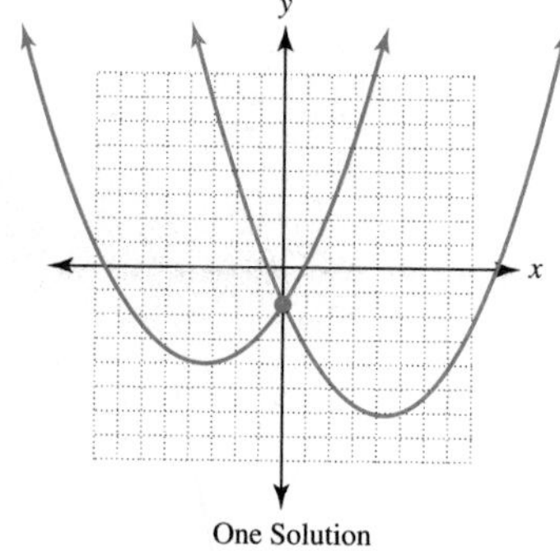

One Solution

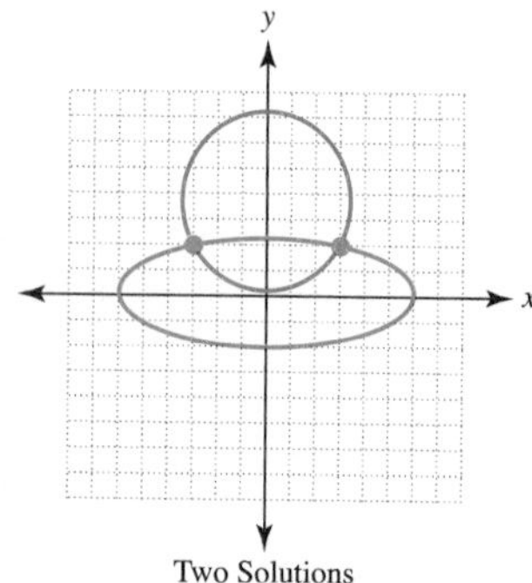

Two Solutions

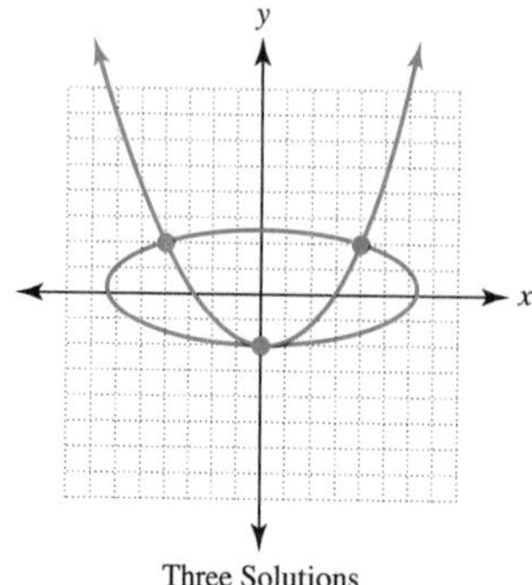

Three Solutions

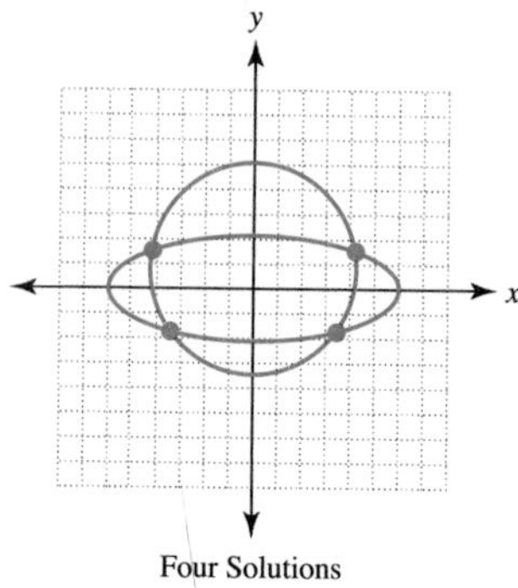

Four Solutions

In Example 1, we will look at a system that has as its graph a line and a parabola. Such a system has either zero, one, or two solutions.

Example 1 Solving a System of Nonlinear Equations

< Objective 1 >

Solve the system of equations.

$y = x^2 - 3x + 2$

$y = 6$

First, we graph the system. From this graph we will be able to see the number of solutions. The graph will also give us a way to check the reasonableness of our algebraic results.

NOTE

Use your calculator to approximate the solutions for the system.

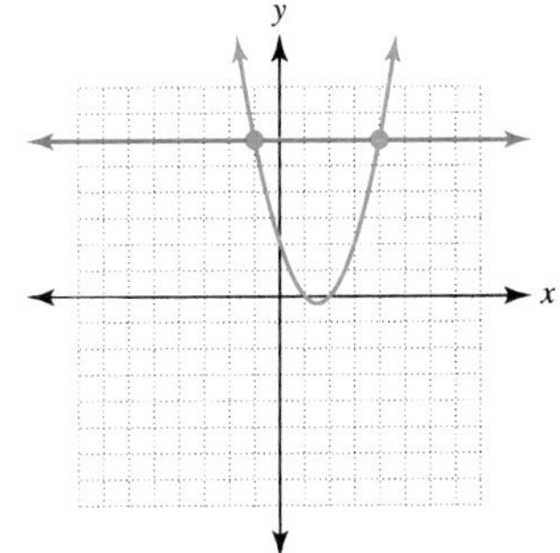

We will use the method of substitution to solve the system. Substituting 6, from the second equation, for y in the first equation, we get

$6 = x^2 - 3x + 2$

$0 = x^2 - 3x - 4$

$0 = (x - 4)(x + 1)$

The x-values for the solutions are -1 and 4. We can substitute these values for x in either equation to solve for y, but we know from the second equation that $y = 6$. The solutions are $(-1, 6)$ and $(4, 6)$. Looking at the graph, we see that this is a reasonable solution for the system.

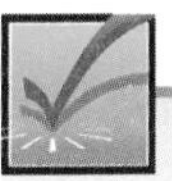

Check Yourself 1

Solve the system of equations.

$y = x^2 - 5x + 4$

$y = 10$

Of course, not every quadratic expression is factorable. In Example 2, we must use the quadratic formula.

Example 2 Solving a Nonlinear System

Solve the system of equations.

$y = x^2 + x + 3$

$y = 7$

First, we look at the graph of the system.

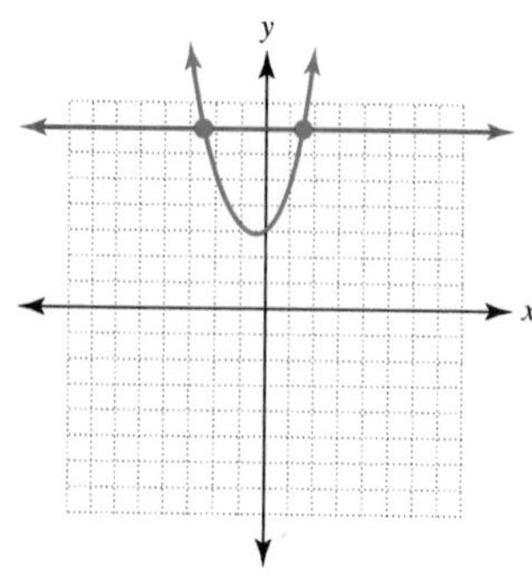

We see two points of intersection, but neither seems to be an integer value for x. We will solve the system algebraically. Using the method of substitution, we find

$$7 = x^2 + x + 3$$
$$0 = x^2 + x - 4$$

The result is not factorable, so we use the quadratic formula to find the solutions.

$$x = \frac{-1 \pm \sqrt{1 + 16}}{2} = \frac{-1 \pm \sqrt{17}}{2}$$

The two points of intersection are $\left(\frac{-1 - \sqrt{17}}{2}, 7\right)$ and $\left(\frac{-1 + \sqrt{17}}{2}, 7\right)$. It is difficult to check these points against the graph, so we will approximate them. The approximate solutions (to the nearest tenth) are $(-2.6, 7)$ and $(1.6, 7)$. The graph indicates that these are reasonable answers.

Check Yourself 2

Solve the system of equations.

$y = x^2 + x + 5$
$y = 8$

As was stated earlier, not every system has two solutions. In Example 3, we will see a system with no real solution.

Example 3 **Solving a System of Nonlinear Equations**

Solve the system of equations.

$y = x^2 - 2x + 1$
$y = -2$

As we did with the previous systems, we will first look at the graph of the system.

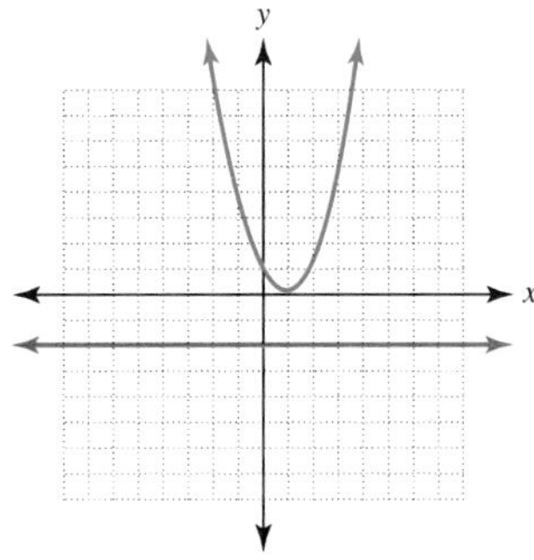

NOTE

The discriminant of this quadratic is -8 and $\sqrt{-8}$ is not a real number.

Using the method of substitution, we get

$$-2 = x^2 - 2x + 1$$
$$0 = x^2 - 2x + 3$$

Using the quadratic formula, we can confirm that there are no real solutions to this system.

$$\frac{-(-2) \pm \sqrt{(-2)^2 - 4(1)(3)}}{2(1)} = \frac{2 \pm \sqrt{-8}}{2}$$

Check Yourself 3

Solve the system of equations.

$y = x^2 + 3x + 5$
$y = 2$

Consider the system consisting of the following two equations:

$$x^2 + y^2 = 25$$
$$3x^2 - y^2 = 11$$

The graph of the system indicates there are four solutions.

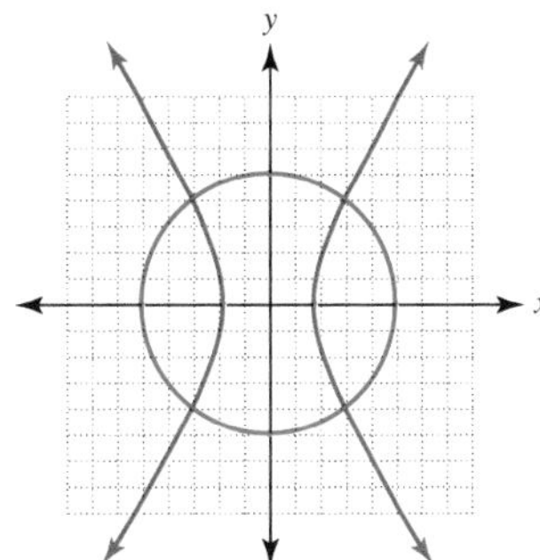

We could approximate the solutions, and then check those approximations by substitution. But how could we find the solutions algebraically? Example 4 illustrates the elimination method.

Example 4 Solving a Nonlinear System by Elimination

< Objective 2 >

Solve the system algebraically.

$$x^2 + y^2 = 25$$
$$3x^2 - y^2 = 11$$

As was the case with linear systems, we can eliminate one of the variables. In this case, adding the equations eliminates the y-variable.

$$\begin{array}{r} x^2 + y^2 = 25 \\ \underline{3x^2 - y^2 = 11} \\ 4x^2 \quad\quad = 36 \end{array}$$

Dividing by 4, we have

$$x^2 = 9$$
$$x = \pm 3$$

Substituting the value 3 into the first equation

$$(3)^2 + y^2 = 25$$
$$9 + y^2 = 25$$
$$y^2 = 16$$
$$y = \pm 4$$

Two of the ordered pairs in the solution are $(3, -4)$ and $(3, 4)$.

Substituting the value -3 into the first equation

$$(-3)^2 + y^2 = 25$$
$$9 + y^2 = 25$$
$$y^2 = 16$$
$$y = \pm 4$$

The other two pairs in the solution are $(-3, -4)$ and $(-3, 4)$.

The solutions are $(-3, -4)$, $(-3, 4)$, $(3, -4)$, and $(3, 4)$.

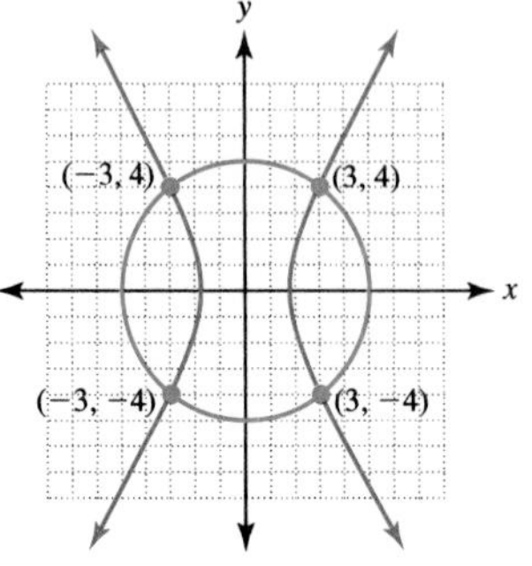

Check Yourself 4

Solve by the elimination method.

$$x^2 + y^2 = 5$$
$$2x^2 + 3y^2 = 14$$

Recall that a system of inequalities has as its solutions the set of all ordered pairs that make every inequality in the system a true statement. We almost always express the solutions to a system of inequalities graphically. We will do the same thing with nonlinear systems.

Example 5 Solving a System of Nonlinear Inequalities

< Objective 3 >

Solve the following system.

$$y \geq x^2 - 3x + 2$$
$$y \leq 6$$

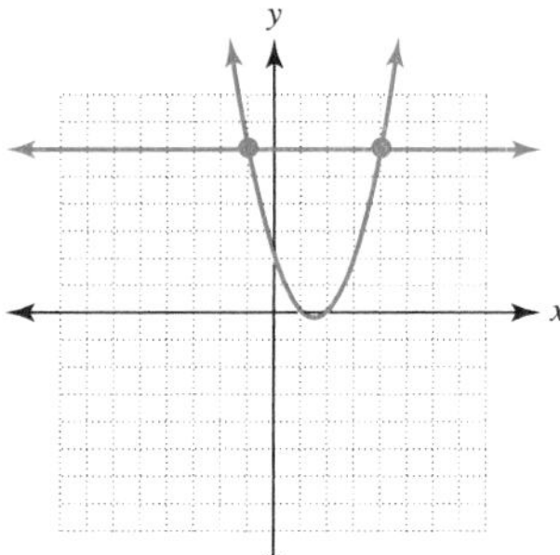

From Example 1, we have the graph of the related system of equations.

The first inequality has as its solution every ordered pair with a y-value that is greater than (above) the graph of the parabola. The second statement has as its solution every ordered pair with a y-value that is less than (below) the graph of the line. The solutions to the system are the ordered pairs that meet both of those criteria. Here is the graph of the solution.

NOTE

The solution is the shaded area above the parabola and below the line.

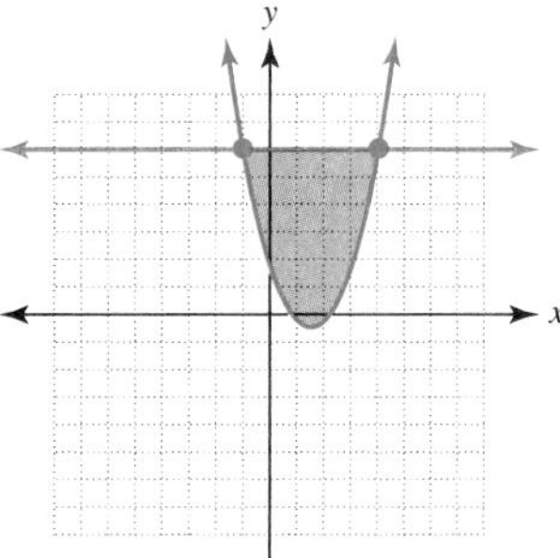

Check Yourself 5

Solve the system.

$y \geq x^2 - 5x + 4$

$y \leq 10$

Example 6 demonstrates that, even if the related system of equations has no solution, the system of inequalities could have a solution.

Example 6 Solving a System of Nonlinear Inequalities

Solve the system.

$y \leq x^2 - 2x + 1$

$y \geq -2$

As we did with the previous systems, we will first look at the graph of the related system of equations (from Example 3).

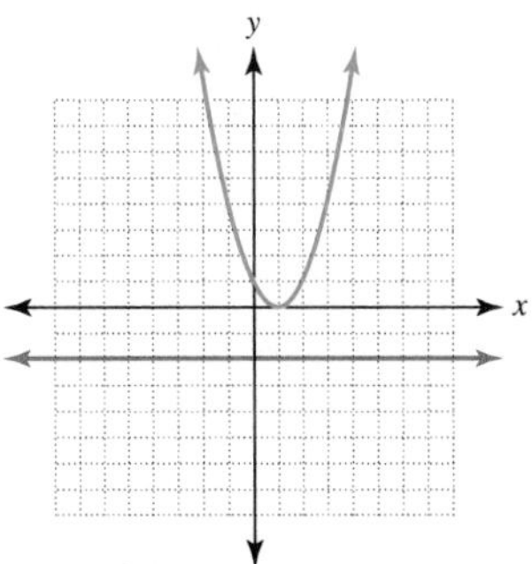

The solution is now all ordered pairs *below* the parabola ($y \leq x^2 - 2x + 1$) and *above* the line ($y \geq -2$). Here is the graph of the solution.

NOTE

The solution continues beyond the borders of the grid.

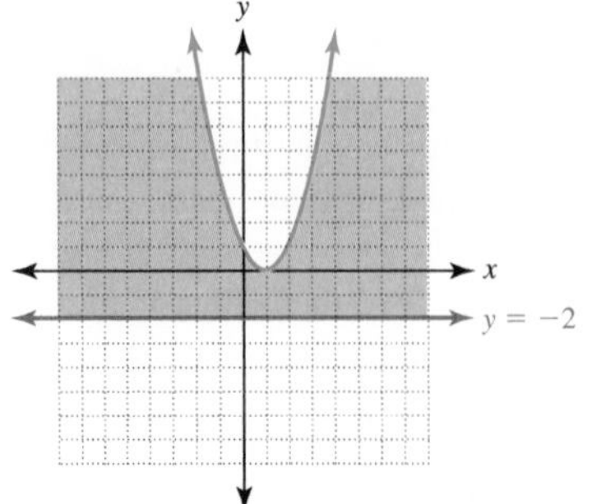

Check Yourself 6

Solve the system.

$y \leq x^2 + 3x + 5$

$y \geq 2$

Check Yourself ANSWERS

1. $(-1, 10), (6, 10)$ **2.** $\left(\frac{-1 \pm \sqrt{13}}{2}, 8\right) \approx (1.3, 8), (-2.3, 8)$

3. No real solutions **4.** $(1, 2), (1, -2), (-1, 2), (-1, -2)$

5.

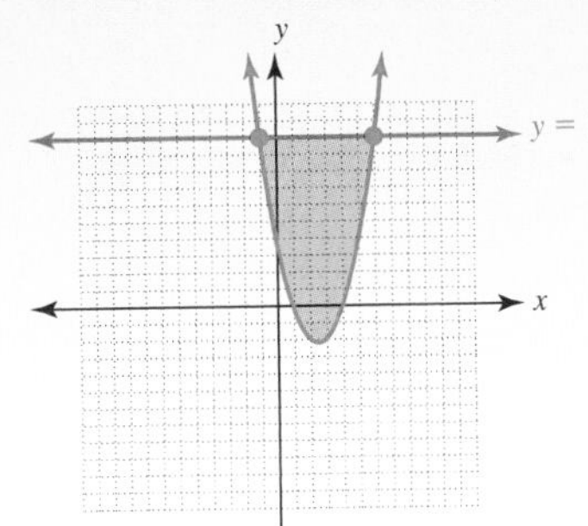

6.

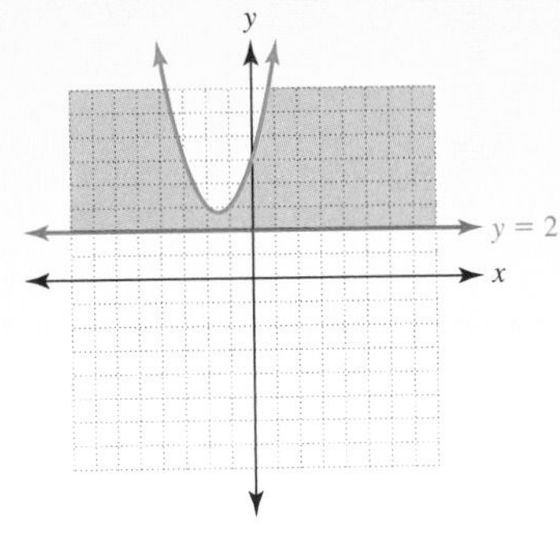

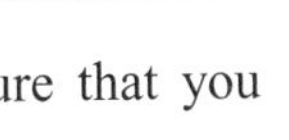

Reading Your Text

The following fill-in-the-blank exercises are designed to ensure that you understand some of the key vocabulary used in this section.

SECTION 9.4

(a) A system with two or more ______________ can have zero, one, two, three, four, or an infinite number of solutions.

(b) Systems of nonlinear ______________ are usually solved graphically or algebraically.

(c) A system that has as its graph a circle and a hyperbola has ______________ solutions.

(d) A system of ______________ has as its solutions all ordered pairs that make every inequality in the system a true statement.

9.4 exercises

Basic Skills | Advanced Skills | Vocational-Technical Applications | Calculator/Computer | Above and Beyond

MathZone

Boost your grade at mathzone.com!

- Practice Problems
- NetTutor
- Self-Tests
- e-Professors
- Videos

Name ______________

Section ________ Date ________

In exercises 1 to 8, the graph of a system of equations is given. Determine how many real solutions each system has.

1.

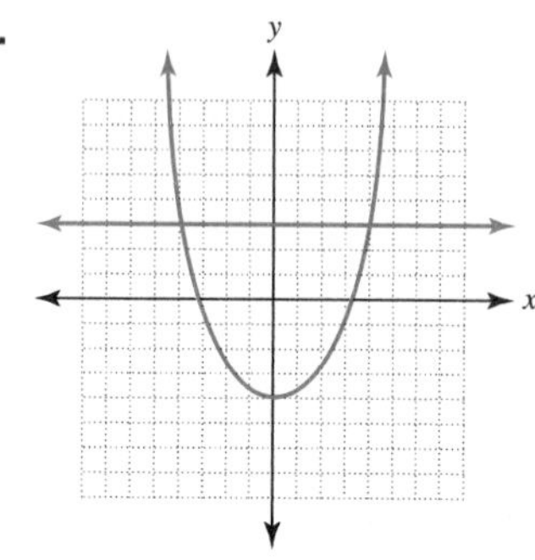

2.

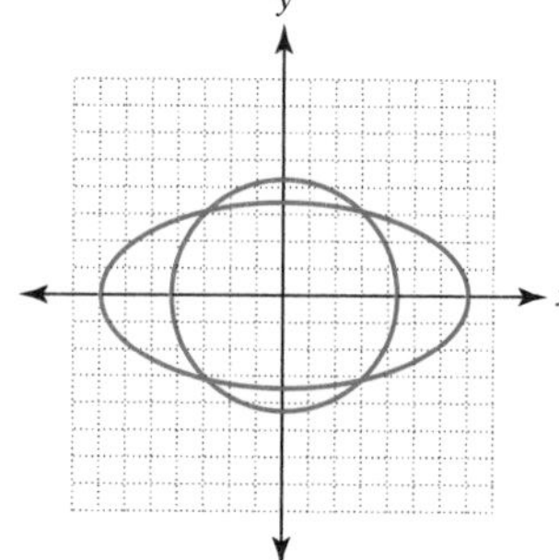

3.

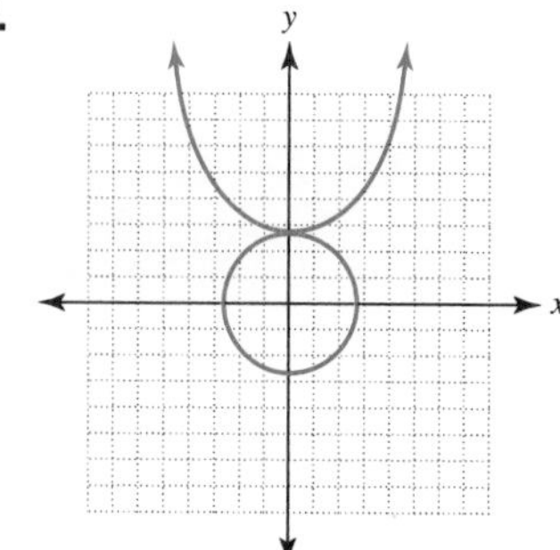

4.

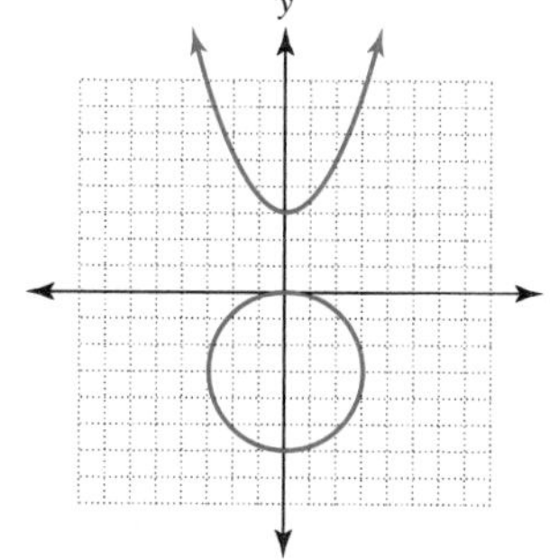

5.

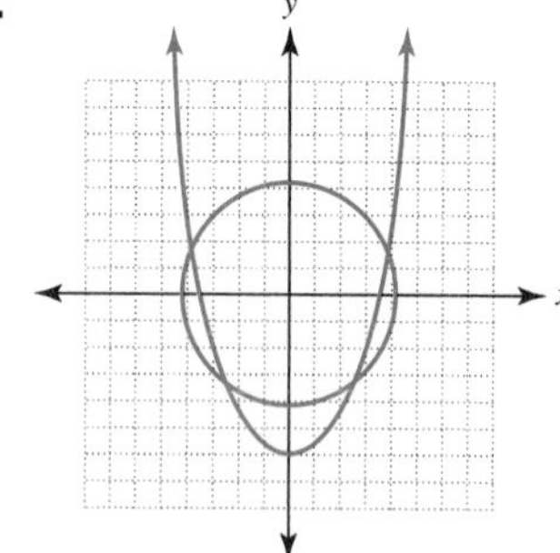

6.

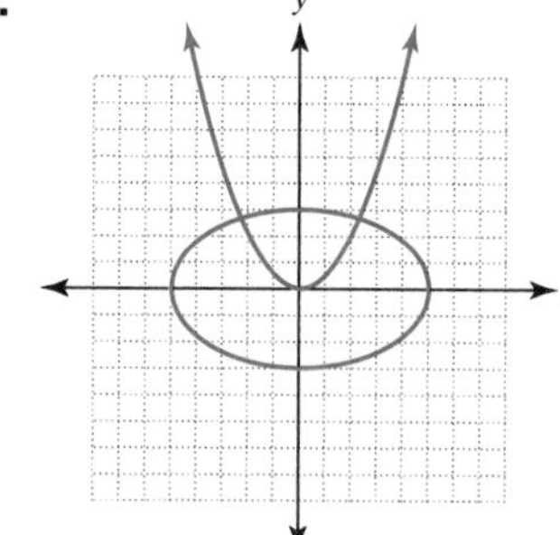

7.

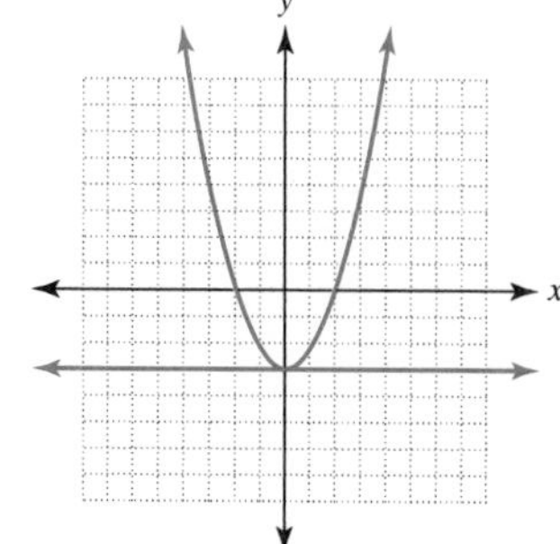

8.

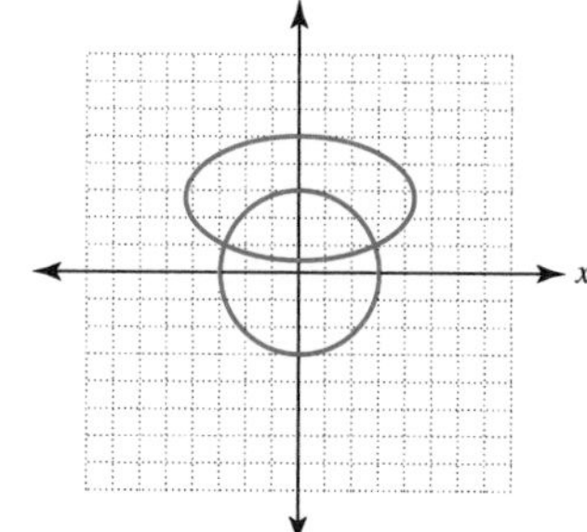

Answers

1. 2
2. 4
3. 1
4. 0
5. 4
6. 2
7. 1
8. 2

In exercises 9 to 12, draw the graph of a system that has the indicated number of solutions. Use the conic sections indicated.

9. 0 solutions: **(a)** use a circle and an ellipse, and **(b)** use a parabola and a line.

(a)

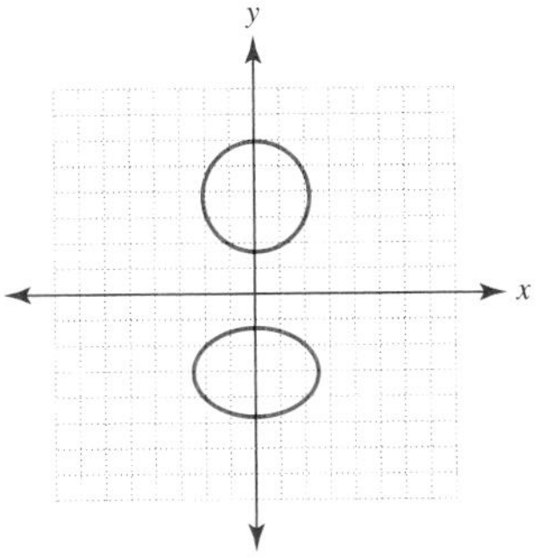

(b)

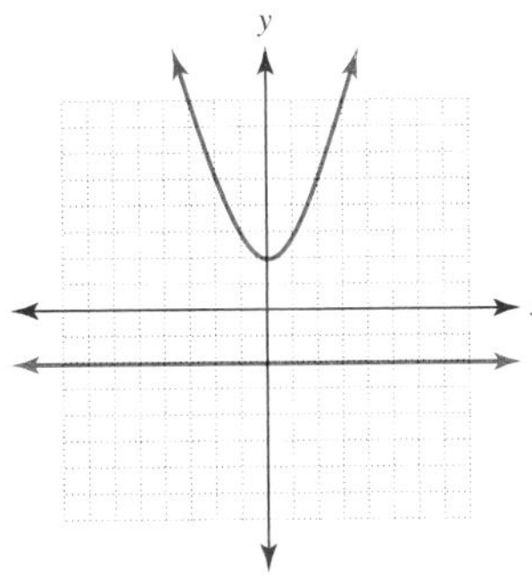

10. 1 solution: **(a)** use a parabola and a circle, and **(b)** use a line and an ellipse.

(a)

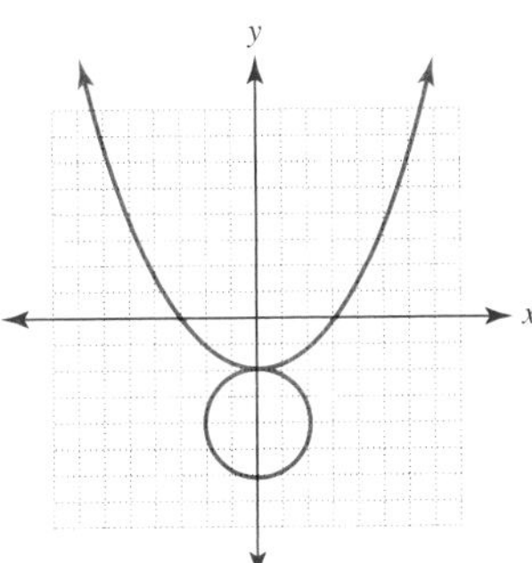

(b)

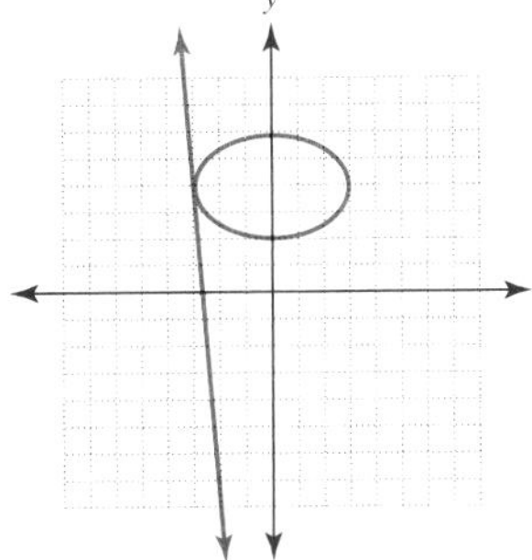

11. 2 solutions: **(a)** use a parabola and a circle, and **(b)** use an ellipse and a parabola.

(a)

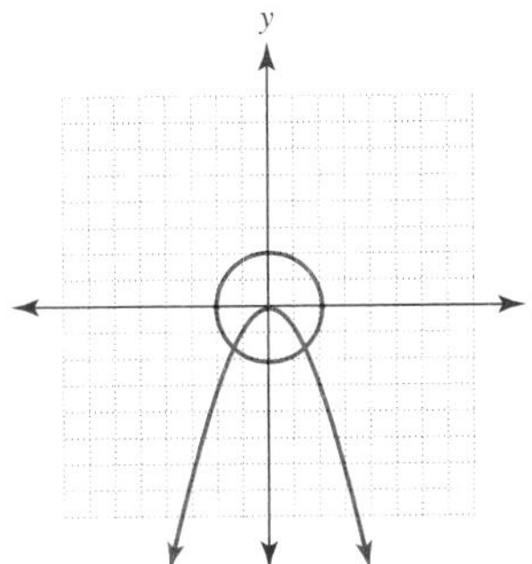

(b)

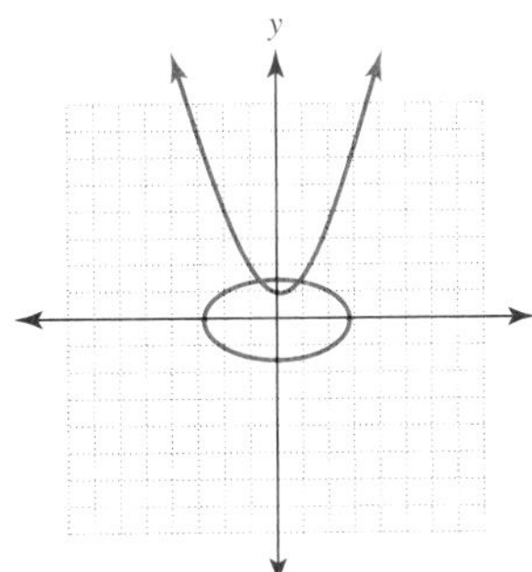

12. 4 solutions: **(a)** use a circle and an ellipse, and **(b)** use a parabola and a circle.

(a)

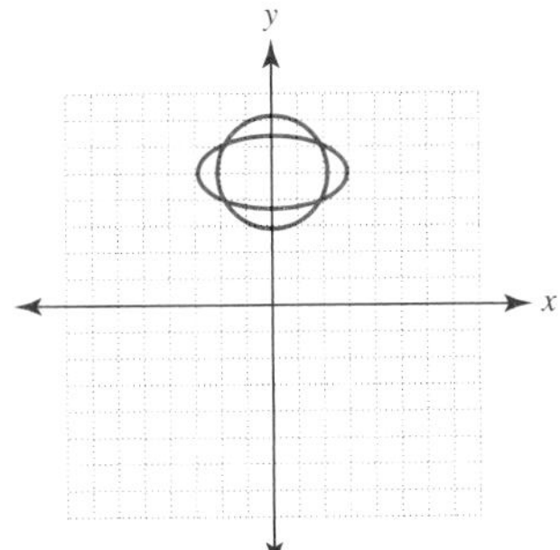

(b)

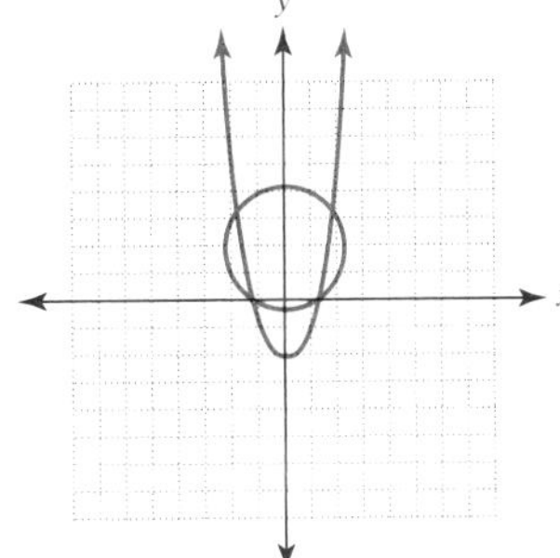

Answers

9. See exercise

10. See exercise

11. See exercise

12. See exercise

Answers

13. See exercise

14. See exercise

15. See exercise

16. See exercise

17. See exercise

18. See exercise

19. See exercise

20. See exercise

< Objective 1 >

Graph each system and estimate the solutions.

13. $y = x^2 - x - 2$
$y = 4$

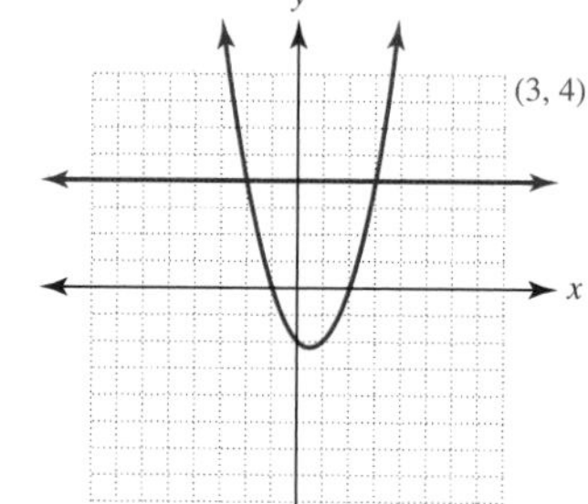

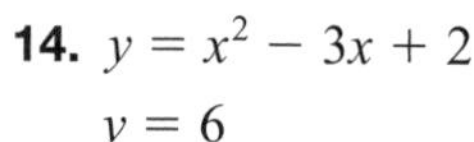

14. $y = x^2 - 3x + 2$
$y = 6$

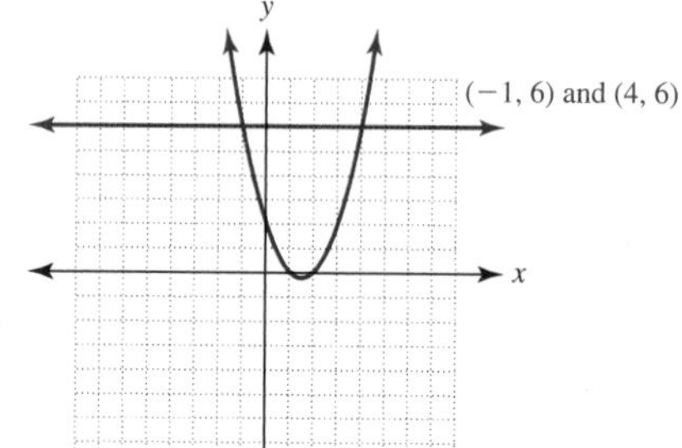

15. $y = x^2 - 5x + 7$
$y = 3$

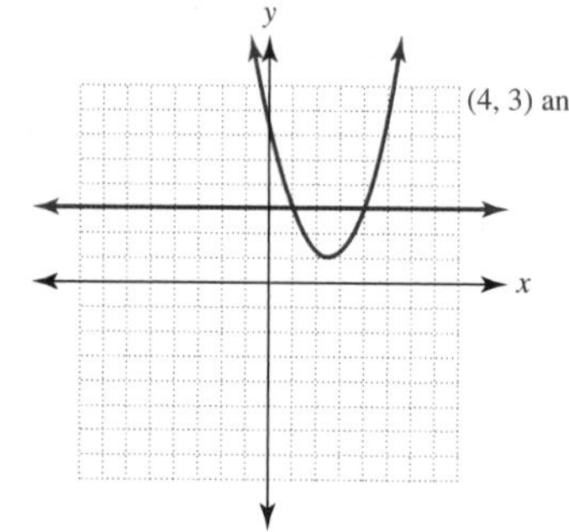

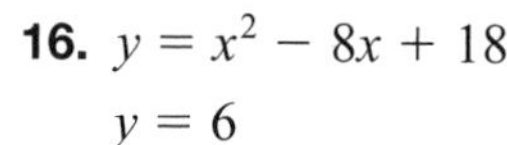

16. $y = x^2 - 8x + 18$
$y = 6$

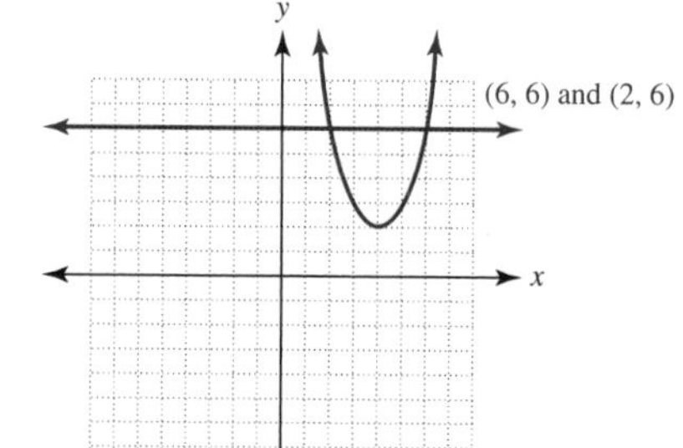

17. $y = x^2 + 4x + 7$
$y = 4$

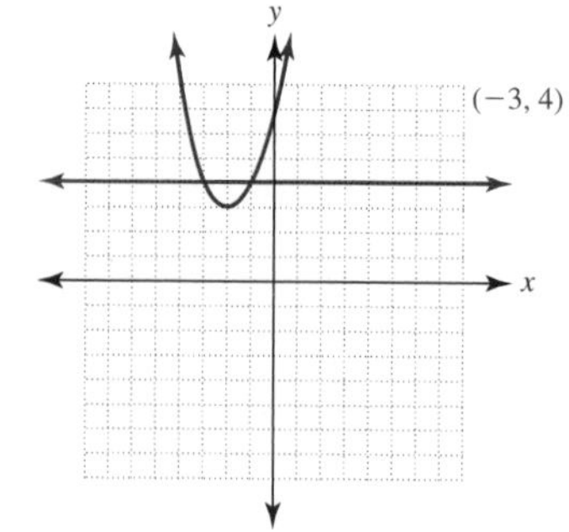

18. $y = x^2 - 6x + 7$
$y = 2$

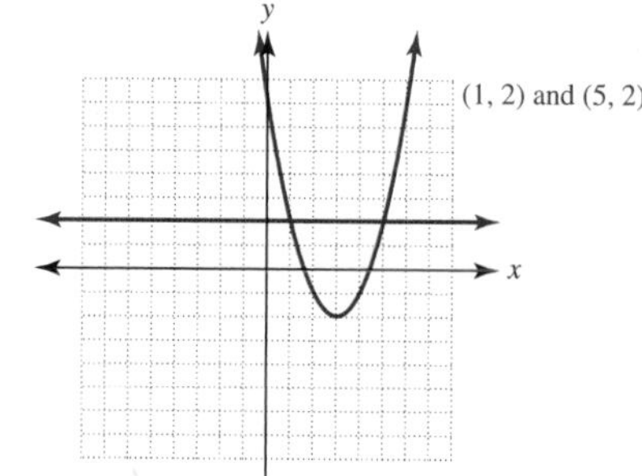

19. $y = x^2 + x + 5$
$y = 6$

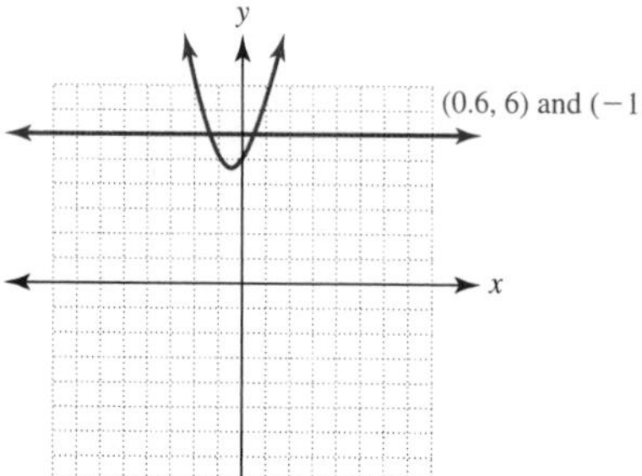

20. $y = x^2 + 8x + 17$
$y = 5$

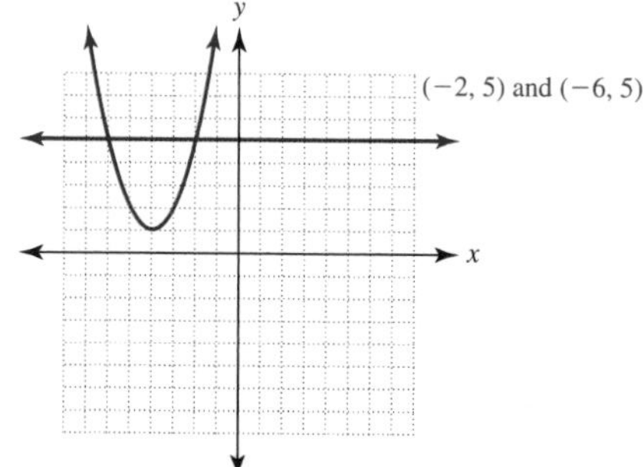

21. $y = x^2 - 7x + 11$
$y = 6$

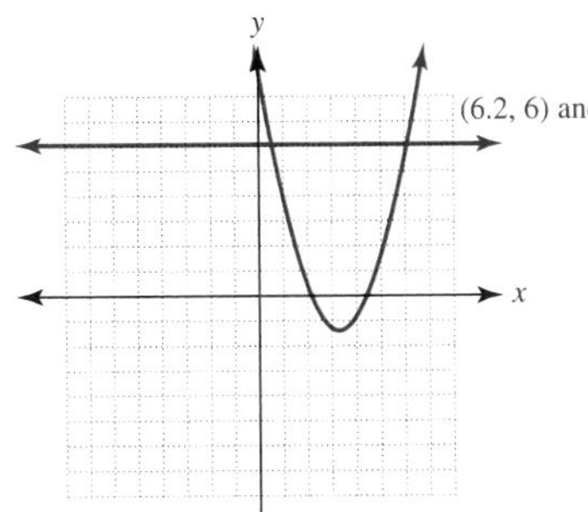

22. $y = x^2 - 2x + 2$
$y = 6$

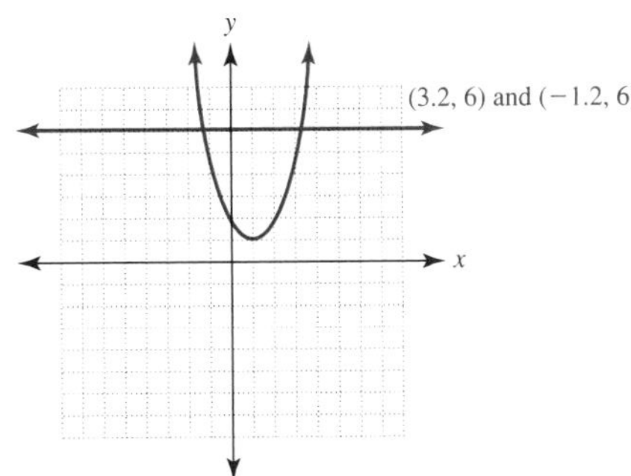

23. $y = x^2 + 5$
$y = 4$

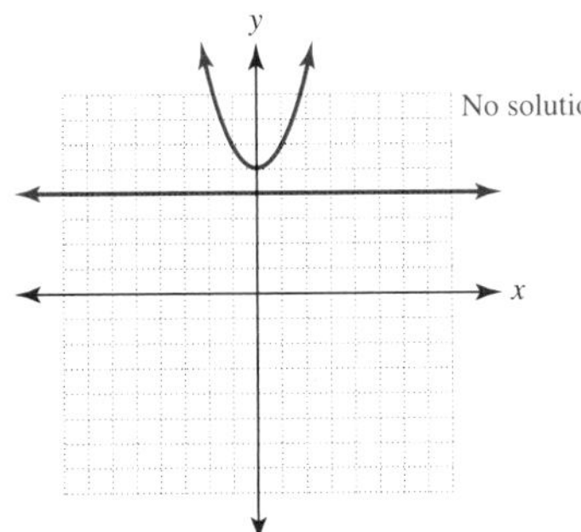

24. $y = x^2 - 4x + 9$
$y = 2$

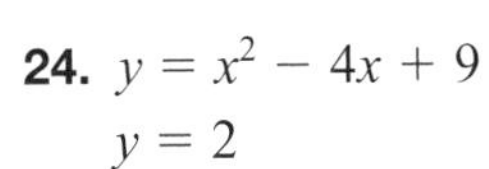

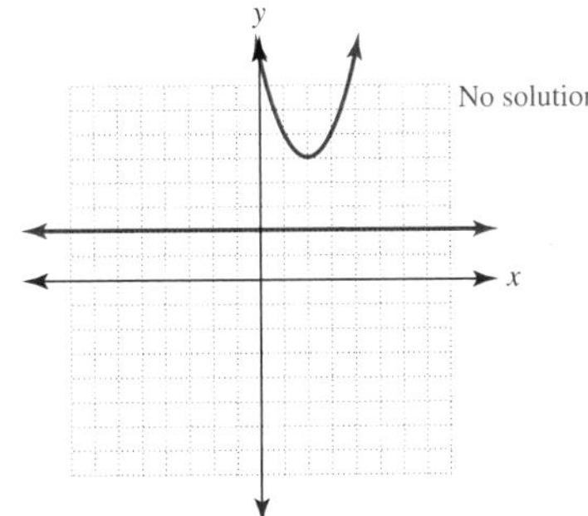

< Objective 2 >

Solve using algebraic methods. (Note: *These exercises have been solved graphically in exercises 13 to 24.*)

25. $y = x^2 - x - 2$
$y = 4$
(See exercise 13.)

26. $y = x^2 - 3x + 2$
$y = 6$
(See exercise 14.)

27. $y = x^2 - 5x + 7$
$y = 3$
(See exercise 15.)

28. $y = x^2 - 8x + 18$
$y = 6$
(See exercise 16.)

29. $y = x^2 + x + 5$
$y = 6$
(See exercise 19.)

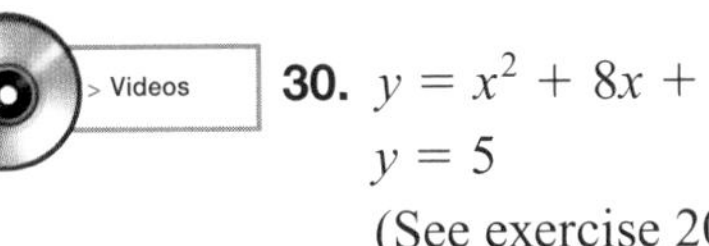

30. $y = x^2 + 8x + 17$
$y = 5$
(See exercise 20.)

31. $y = x^2 + 5$
$y = 4$
(See exercise 23.)

32. $y = x^2 - 4x + 9$
$y = 2$
(See exercise 24.)

Answers

21. See exercise
22. See exercise
23. See exercise
24. See exercise
25. (3, 4), (−2, 4)
26. (−1, 6), (4, 6)
27. (4, 3), (1, 3)
28. (6, 6), (2, 6)
29. $\left(\frac{-1 + \sqrt{5}}{2}, 6\right)$, $\left(\frac{-1 - \sqrt{5}}{2}, 6\right)$, or (0.62, 6), (−1.62, 6)
30. (−2, 5), (−6, 5)
31. No solution
32. No solution

Answers

33. See exercise

34. See exercise

35. See exercise

36. See exercise

37. See exercise

38. See exercise

< Objective 3 >

Solve the systems of inequalities graphically. (Note: *These have already been graphed as systems of equations in exercises 13 to 24.*)

33. $y \geq x^2 - x - 2$
$y \leq 4$
(See exercise 13.)

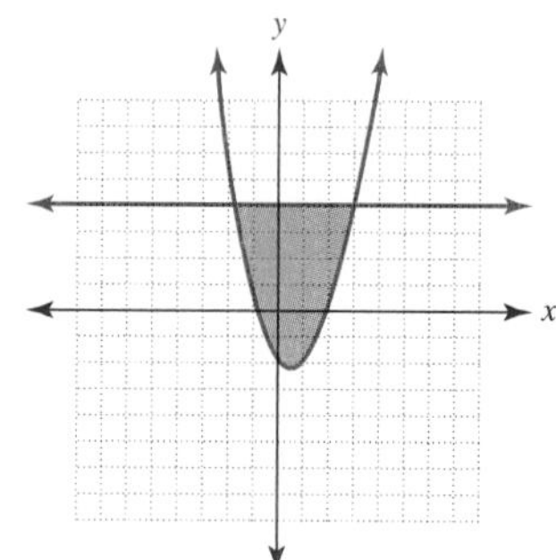

34. $y \geq x^2 - 3x + 2$
$y \leq 6$
(See exercise 14.)

> Videos

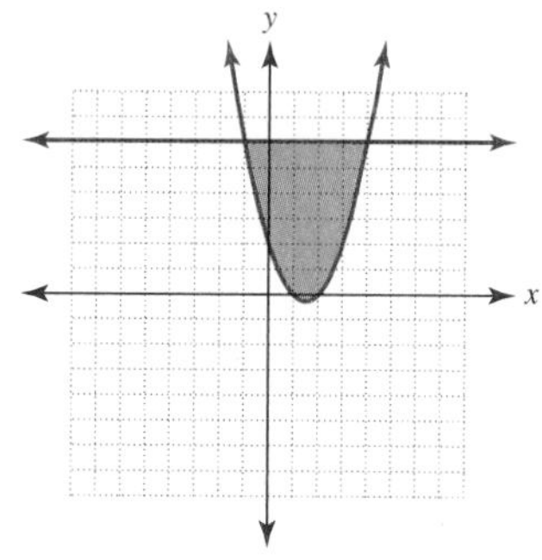

35. $y \geq x^2 - 5x + 7$
$y \leq 3$
(See exercise 15.)

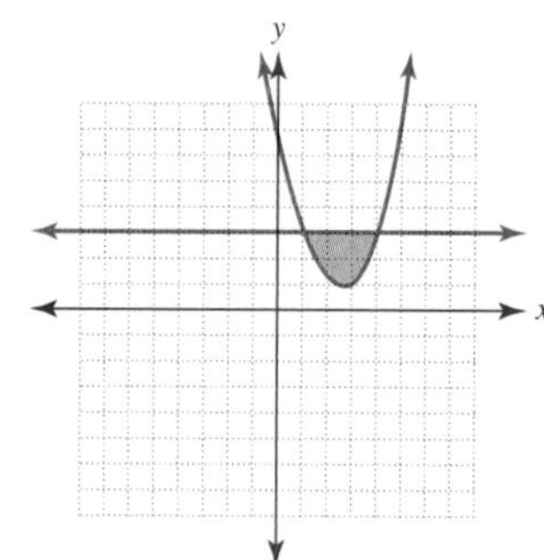

36. $y \geq x^2 - 8x + 18$
$y \leq 6$
(See exercise 16.)

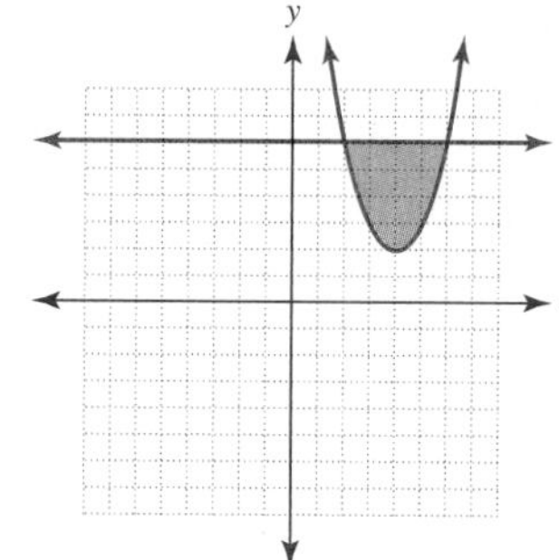

37. $y \geq x^2 + 4x + 7$
$y \geq 4$
(See exercise 17.)

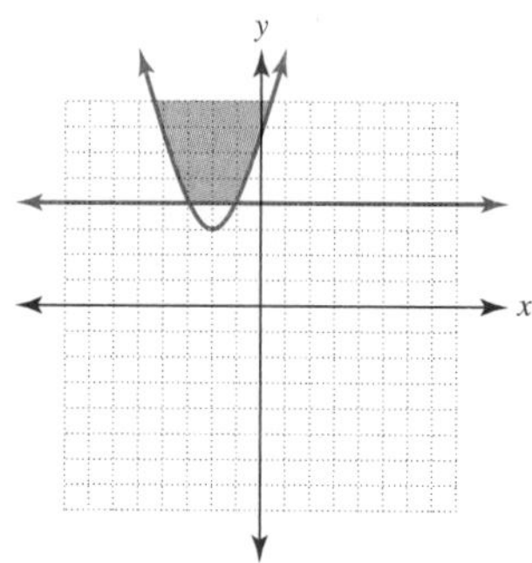

38. $y \geq x^2 - 6x + 7$
$y \geq 2$
(See exercise 18.)

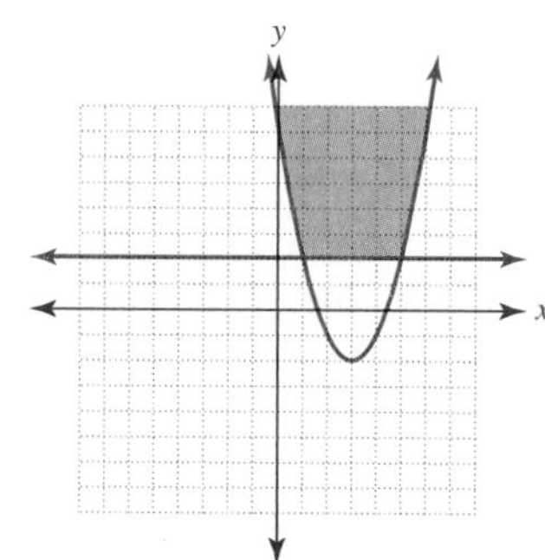

39. $y \le x^2 + 5$
$y \ge 4$
(See exercise 23.)

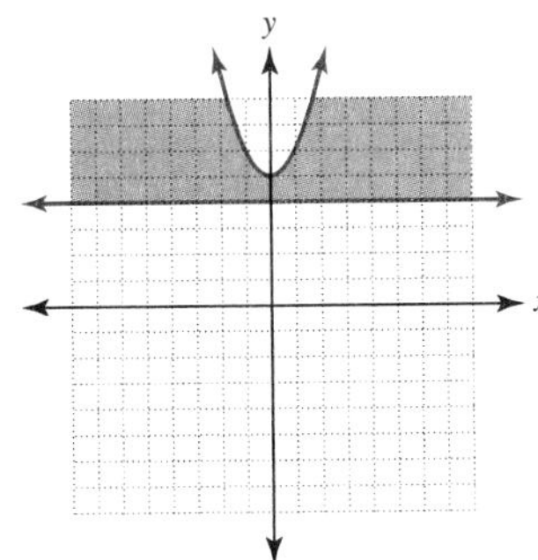

40. $y \le x^2 - 4x + 9$
$y \ge 2$
(See exercise 24.)

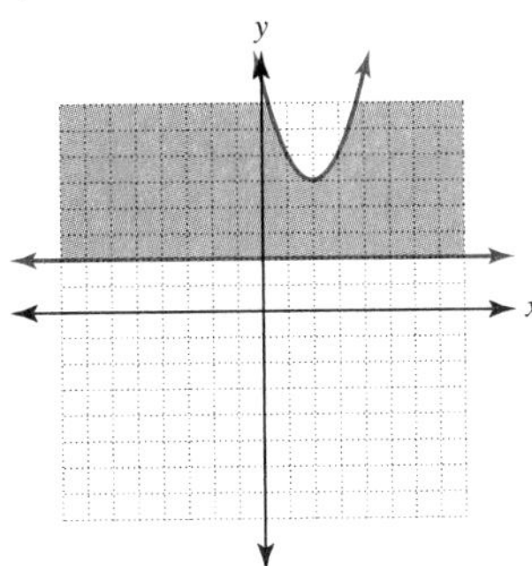

Label each of the following statements as **true** *or* **false.**

41. A system consisting of equations of a line and a parabola can have four solutions.

42. A system consisting of nonlinear inequalities could have a solution, even if the related system of equations has no solution.

Basic Skills | **Advanced Skills** | Vocational-Technical Applications | Calculator/Computer | Above and Beyond

In exercises 43 to 46, **(a)** *graph each system and estimate the solution, and* **(b)** *use algebraic methods to solve each system.*

43. $y = x^2$
$x + y = 2$

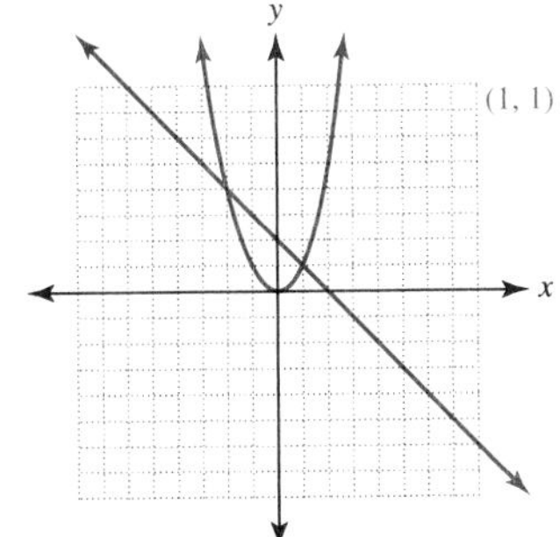

44. $y = x^2 - 6x$
$3x + y = 4$

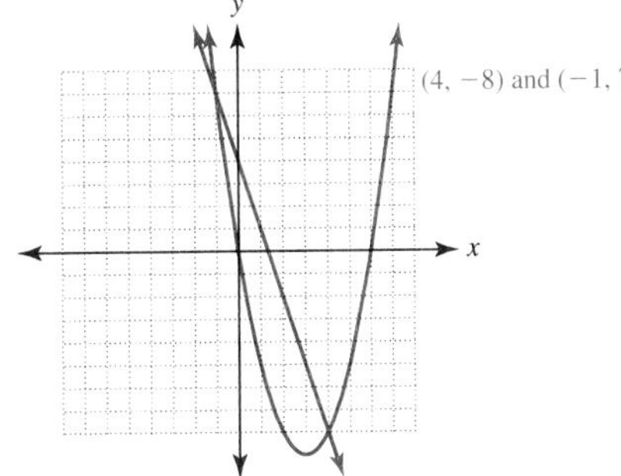

45. $x^2 + y^2 = 5$
$-3x + 4y = 2$

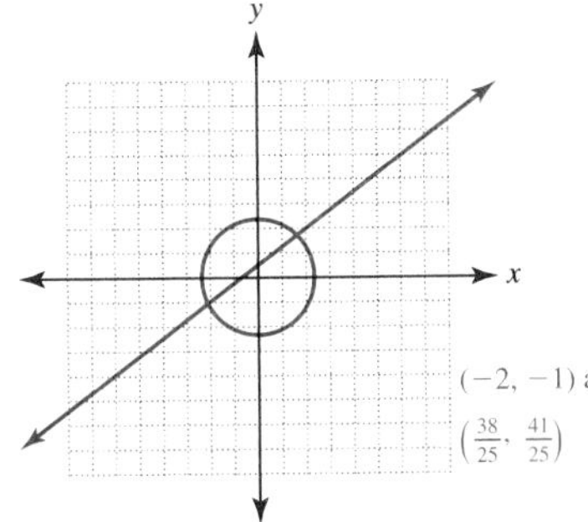

46. $x^2 + y^2 = 9$
$x + y = -3$

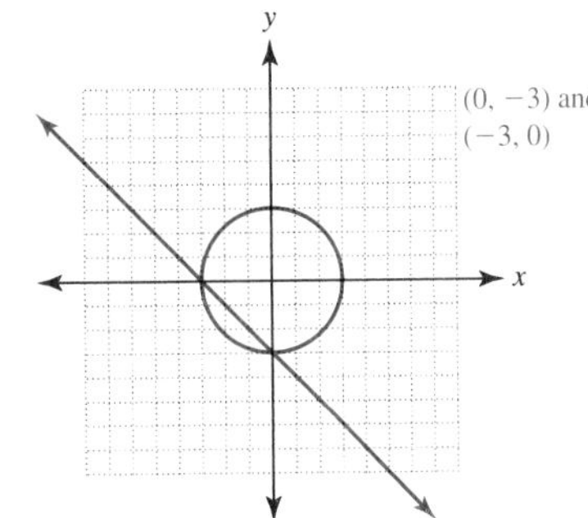

Answers

39. See exercise
40. See exercise
41. False
42. True
43. See exercise
44. See exercise
45. See exercise
46. See exercise

Answers

47. 60 apartments

48. 250 bicycles

49. (−4, −1), (−4, 1), (4, −1), (4, 1)

50. (−5, −2), (−5, 2), (5, −2), (5, 2)

51. (−2, −2), (−2, 2), (2, −2), (2, 2)

52. (−1, −1), (−1, 1), (1, −1), (1, 1)

53. $y = 9$

54. $x^2 + y^2 \le 16$
$y > 2$

55. Above and Beyond

56. Above and Beyond

Solve the applications.

47. Business and Finance The manager of a large apartment complex has found that the profit, in dollars, is given by the equation

$$P = 120x - x^2$$

in which x is the number of apartments rented. How many apartments must be rented to produce a profit of \$3,600?

48. Business and Finance The manager of a bicycle shop has found that the revenue (in dollars) from the sale of x bicycles is given by the following equation.

$$R = x^2 - 200x$$

How many bicycles must be sold to produce a revenue of \$12,500?

Solve the systems algebraically.

49. $x^2 + y^2 = 17$
$x^2 - y^2 = 15$

50. $x^2 + y^2 = 29$
$2x^2 - y^2 = 46$

51. $x^2 + y^2 = 8$
$2x^2 + 3y^2 = 20$

52. $2x^2 + y^2 = 3$
$3x^2 + 4y^2 = 7$

Basic Skills | Advanced Skills | Vocational-Technical Applications | Calculator/Computer | **Above and Beyond**

53. Find the equation of the line passing through the points of intersection of the graphs $y = x^2$ and $x^2 + y^2 = 90$.

54. Write a system of inequalities to describe the following set of points: The points are in the interior of a circle whose center is the origin with a radius of 4, and above the line $y = 2$.

55. We are asked to solve the system of equations.

$x^2 - y = 5$
$x + y = -3$

Explain how we can determine, before doing any work, that this system cannot have more than two solutions.

56. Without graphing, how can you tell that the following system of inequalities has no solution?

$x^2 + y^2 < 9$
$y > 4$

Answers

1. 2 **3.** 1 **5.** 4 **7.** 1

9. (a)

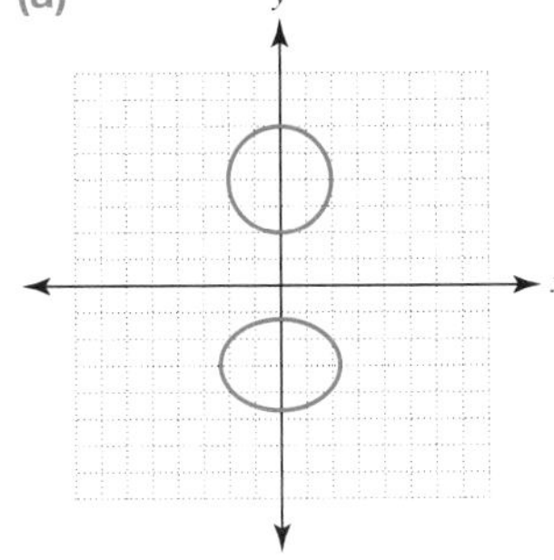

(b)

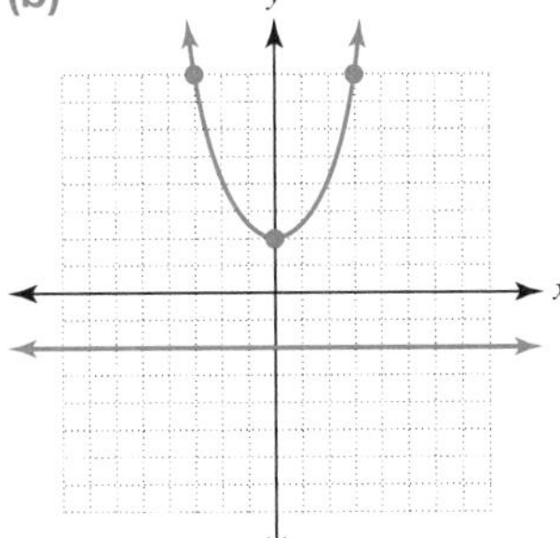

11. (a)

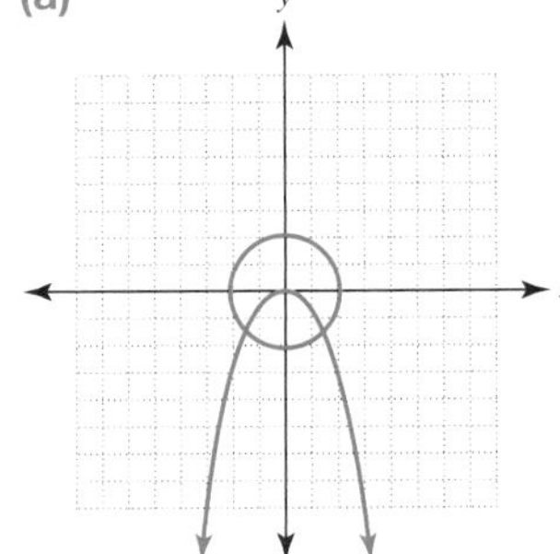

(b)

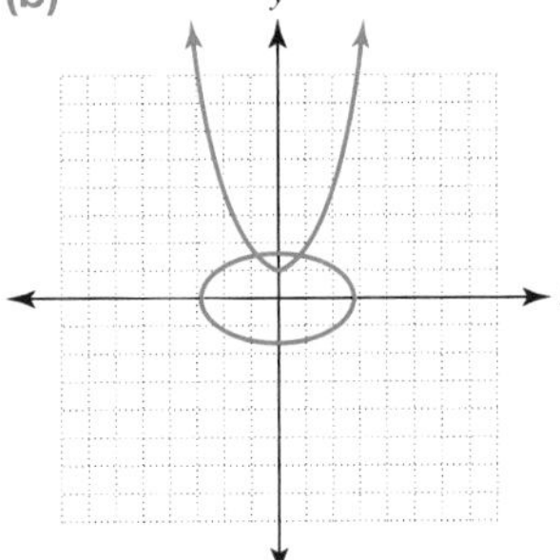

13. (3, 4) and (−2, 4)

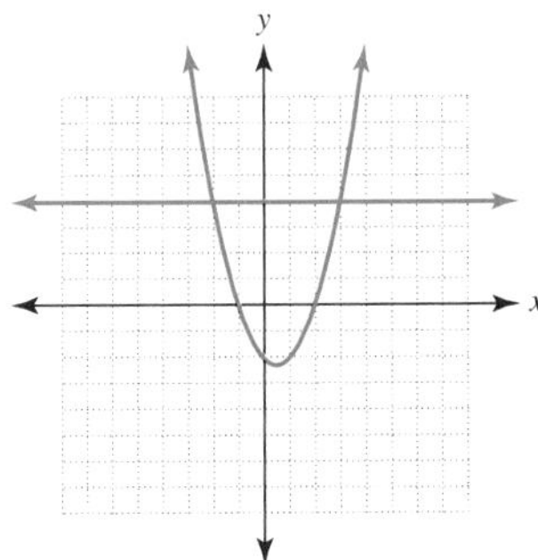

15. (4, 3) and (1, 3)

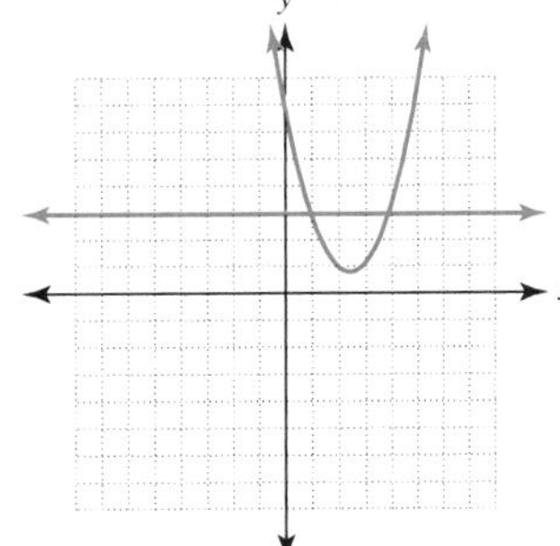

17. (−3, 4) and (−1, 4)

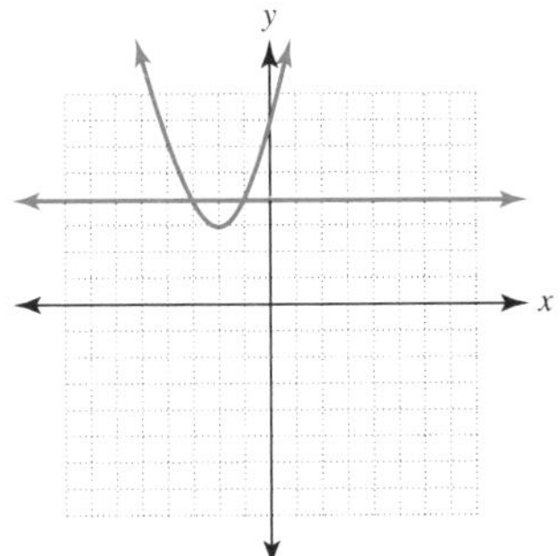

19. (0.6, 6) and (−1.6, 6)

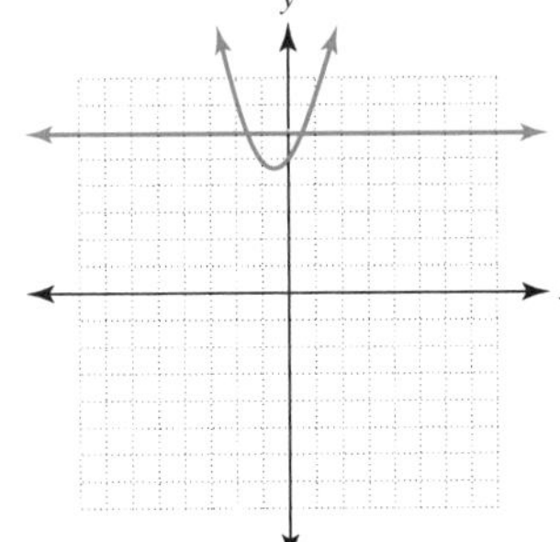

21. (6.2, 6) and (0.8, 6)

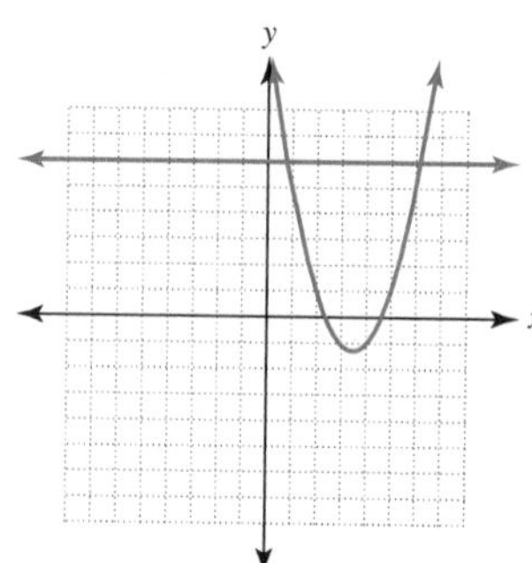

23. No solution

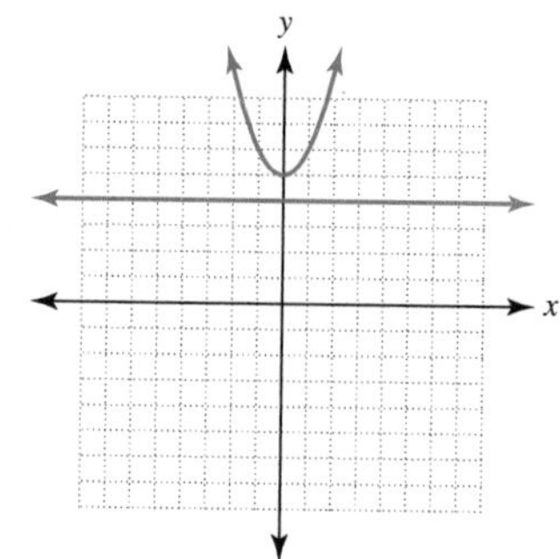

25. (3, 4), (−2, 4) **27.** (4, 3), (1, 3)

29. $\left(\frac{-1+\sqrt{5}}{2}, 6\right), \left(\frac{-1-\sqrt{5}}{2}, 6\right)$ or (0.62, 6), (−1.62, 6)

31. No solution

33.

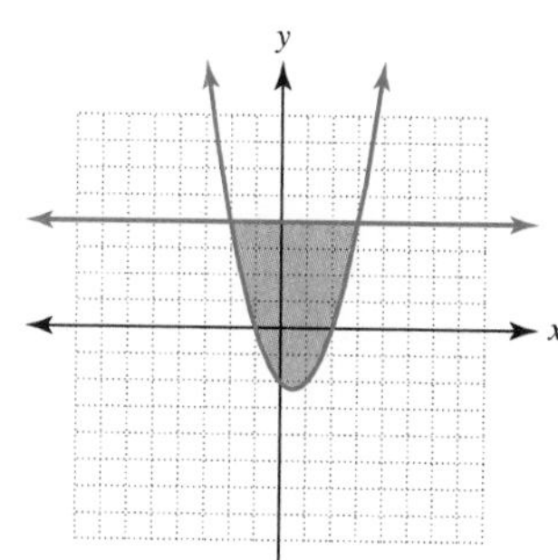

35.

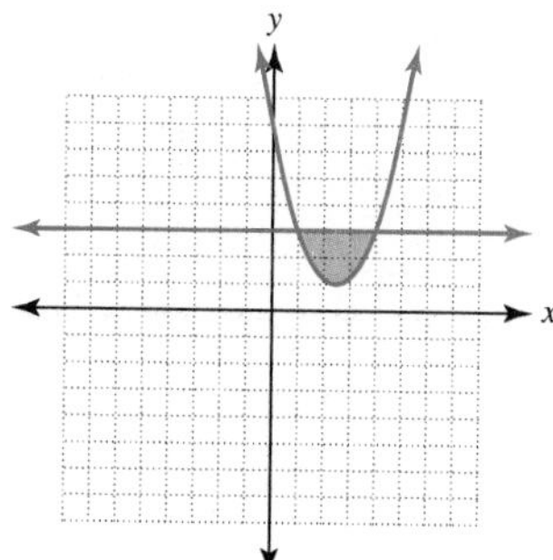

37.

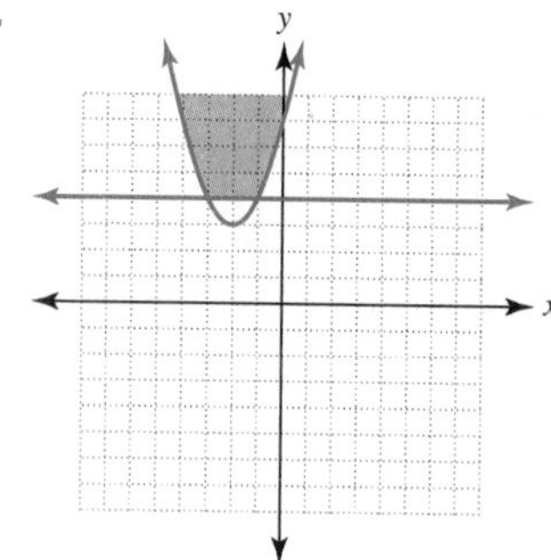

39.

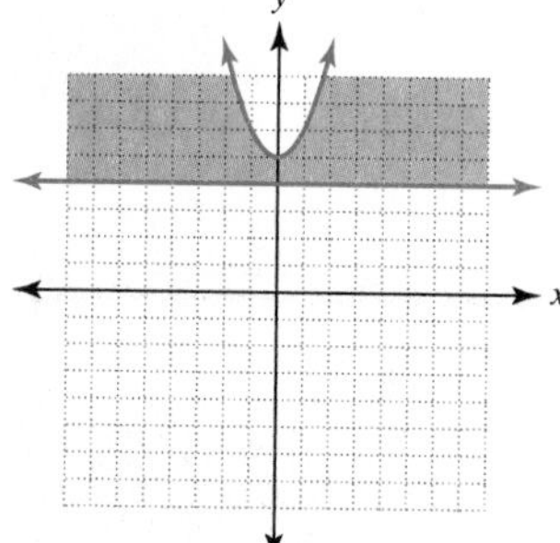

41. False

43. (1, 1) and (−2, 4)

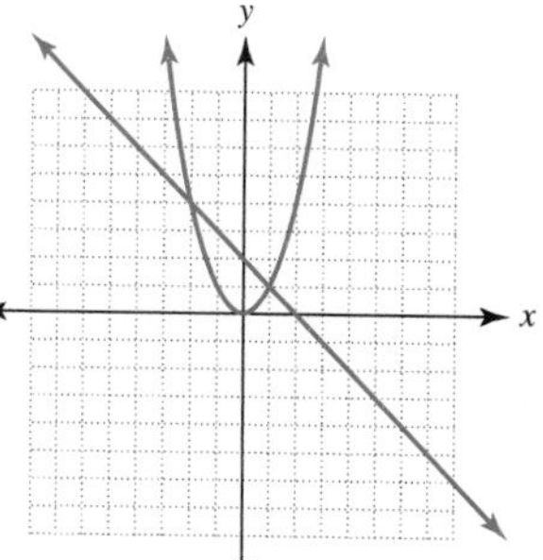

45. (−2, −1) and $\left(\frac{38}{25}, \frac{41}{25}\right)$

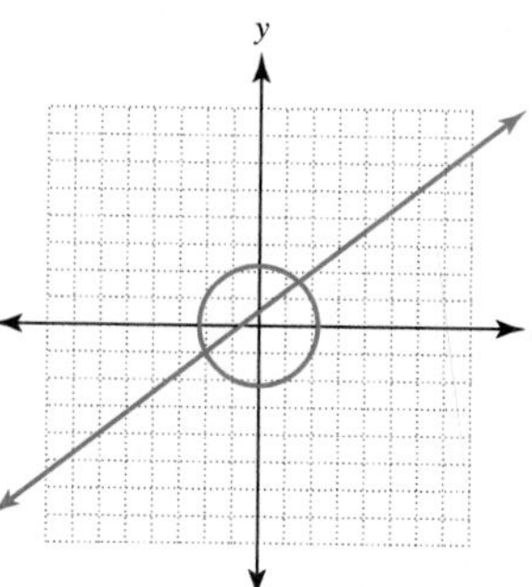

47. 60 apartments **49.** (−4, −1), (−4, 1), (4, −1), (4, 1)

51. (−2, −2), (−2, 2), (2, −2), (2, 2) **53.** $y = 9$ **55.** Above and Beyond

Definition/Procedure	Example	Reference
Parabolas		**Section 9.1**
The *conic sections* are the curves formed when a plane cuts through a cone. These include the *parabola, circle, ellipse,* and *hyperbola.* 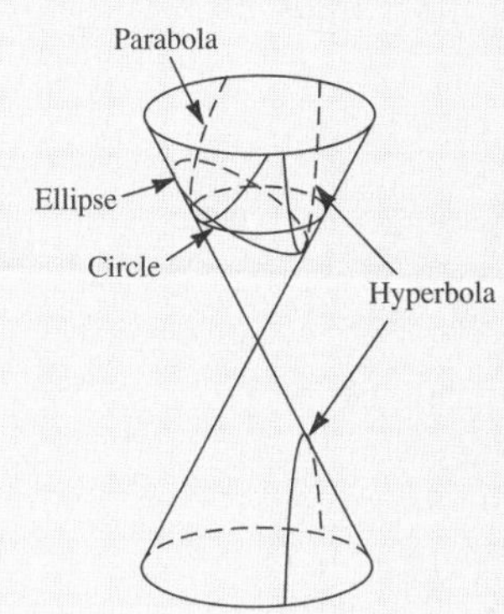		*p.* 842
The graph of an equation quadratic in one variable and linear in the other is a parabola.	$y = x^2$ is linear in y and quadratic in x. 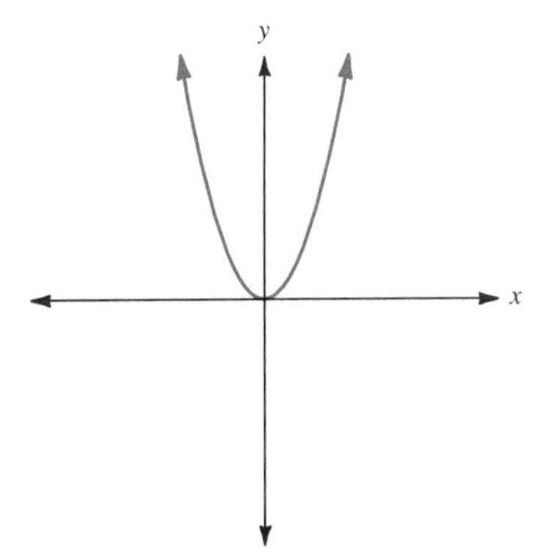	*p.* 843
If the equation is in the form $y = a(x - h)^2 + k$ the vertex of the parabola is at (h, k).	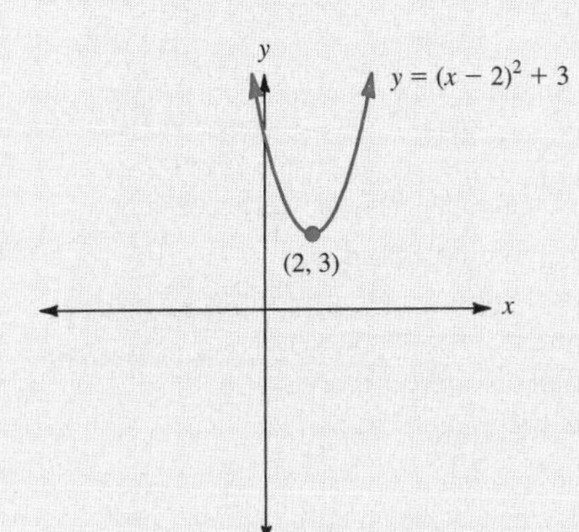	*pp.* 845–846

Continued

Definition/Procedure	Example	Reference

The graph of

$y = ax^2 + bx + c \qquad a \neq 0$

is a parabola.

The parabola opens *upward* if $a > 0$.

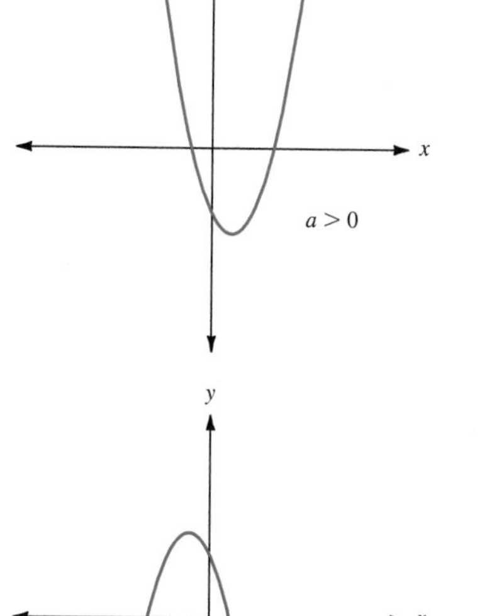

p. 843

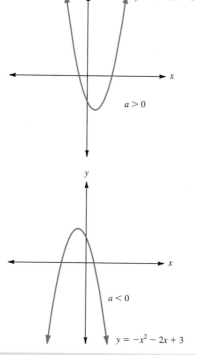

The parabola opens *downward* if $a < 0$.

y
x
$a < 0$
$y = -x^2 - 2x + 3$

The *vertex* of the parabola (either the highest or the lowest point on the graph) is on the *axis of symmetry* with the equation

$$x = -\frac{b}{2a}$$

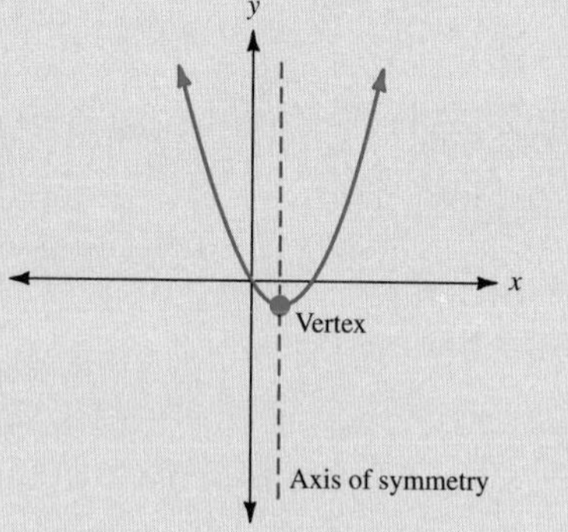

pp. 846–847

To graph a quadratic equation:

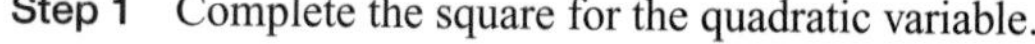

Step 1 Complete the square for the quadratic variable.

Step 2 Find the axis of symmetry and the vertex.

Step 3 Determine two symmetric points.
Note: You can use the x-intercepts if the quadratic member of the given equation is factorable and the x-intercepts are distinct. Otherwise, use the y-intercept and its symmetric point.

Step 4 Draw a smooth curve connecting the points found in steps 2 and 3, to form the parabola. You may choose to find additional pairs of symmetric points at this time.

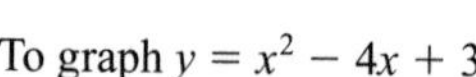

To graph $y = x^2 - 4x + 3$

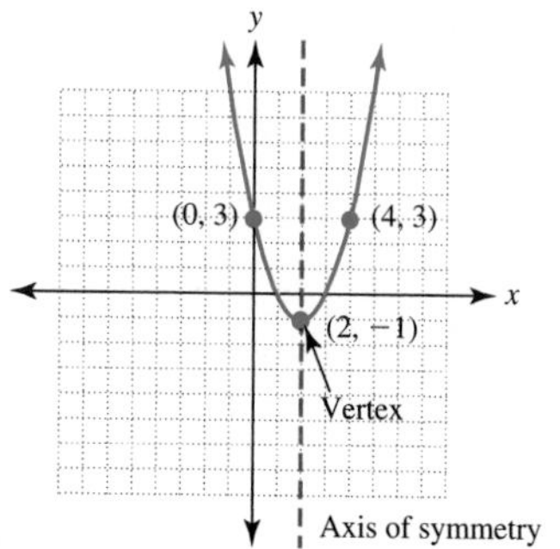

p. 849

Definition/Procedure	Example	Reference
Circles		**Section 9.2**
The standard form for the circle with center (h, k) and radius r is $(x - h)^2 + (y - k)^2 = r^2$ Determining the center and radius of the circle from its equation allows us to easily graph the circle. **Note:** Completing the square may be used to derive an equivalent equation in standard form if the original equation is not in this form.	Given the equation $(x - 2)^2 + (y + 3)^2 = 4$ we see that the center is at $(2, -3)$ and the radius is 2. 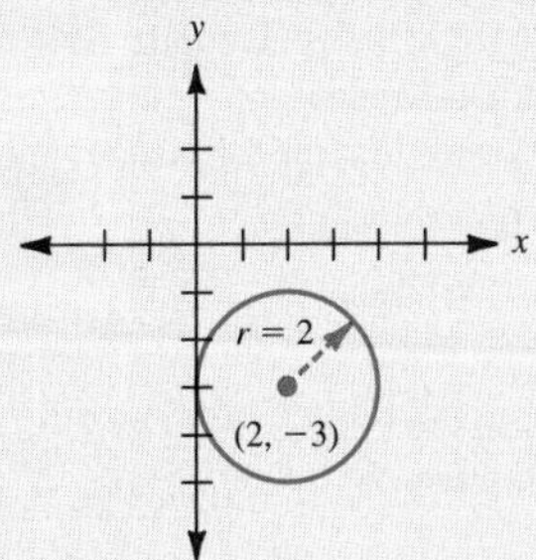	*p.* 866
Ellipses and Hyperbolas		**Section 9.3**
Ellipse		
The standard form for the *ellipse,* whose foci are located on either the x- or y-axis and are symmetric about the origin, is $\frac{x^2}{a^2} + \frac{y^2}{b^2} = 1$ The x-intercepts for the ellipse are $(a, 0)$ and $(-a, 0)$. The y-intercepts for the ellipse are $(0, b)$ and $(0, -b)$. Determining the four intercepts of an ellipse allows us to sketch its graph. **Note:** If the given equation is not in standard form, we can divide both sides of the equation by the appropriate constant to derive the standard form.	Graph the equation $\frac{x^2}{9} + \frac{y^2}{4} = 1$ 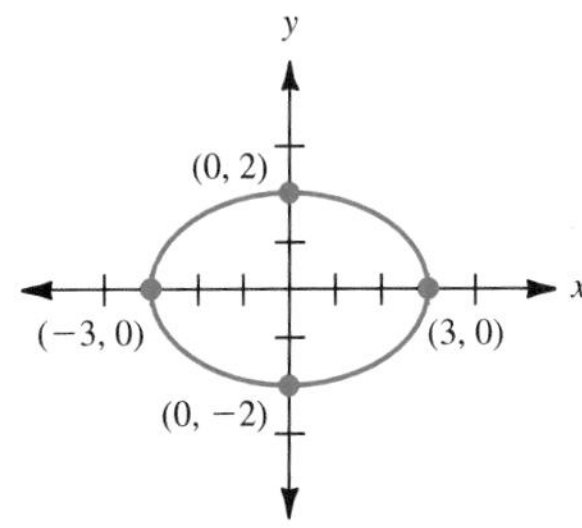	*p.* 876
If the center of the ellipse is (h, k), then the equation of the ellipse becomes $\frac{(x - h)^2}{a^2} + \frac{(y - k)^2}{b^2} = 1$ and the four points needed for graphing are $(h + a, k)$, $(h - a, k)$, $(h, k + b)$, and $(h, k - b)$.		*p.* 878
Hyperbola		
The standard form for the *hyperbola* whose foci are located on the x-axis and are symmetric about the origin is $\frac{x^2}{a^2} - \frac{y^2}{b^2} = 1$	Sketch the hyperbola $\frac{x^2}{4} - \frac{y^2}{9} = 1$ The vertices are at $(2, 0)$ and $(-2, 0)$.	*pp.* 879, 881

Continued

Definition/Procedure	Example	Reference
The vertices for this hyperbola are on the x-axis, $(a, 0)$ and $(-a, 0)$. The asymptotes of the hyperbola have the equations $y = \pm\frac{b}{a}x$ Determining and sketching the vertices and asymptotes of a hyperbola will allow us to sketch its graph quickly. **Note:** Again divide both sides of the given equation by the appropriate constant if the equation is not in standard form. If the foci of the hyperbola are located on the y-axis and are symmetric about the origin, the standard form is $\frac{y^2}{b^2} - \frac{x^2}{a^2} = 1$ The vertices for this hyperbola are on the y-axis, $(0, b)$ and $(0, -b)$. The equations for the asymptotes of the hyperbola remain the same as before.	The asymptotes are $y = \frac{3}{2}x$ and $y = -\frac{3}{2}x$. 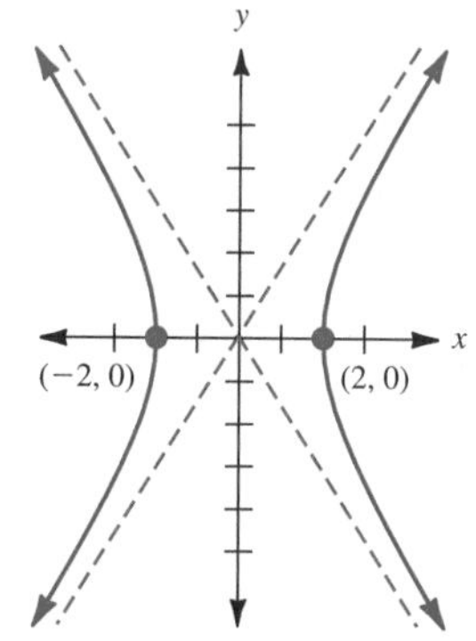 	
A hyperbola that opens left and right but is centered at (h, k) will have the equation $\frac{(x-h)^2}{a^2} - \frac{(y-k)^2}{b^2} = 1$ with vertices at $(h + a, k)$ and $(h - a, k)$. The asymptotes are given by $y - k = \pm\frac{b}{a}(x - h)$		*pp.* 882–883
A hyperbola that opens up and down but is centered at (h, k) will have the equation $\frac{(y-k)^2}{b^2} - \frac{(x-h)^2}{a^2} = 1$ with vertices at $(h, k + b)$ and $(h, k - b)$. The asymptotes are again given by $y - k = \pm\frac{b}{a}(x - h)$		*pp.* 882–883
Nonlinear Systems		**Section 9.4**
A system with two conic curves can have zero, one, two, three, four, or an infinite number of solutions. 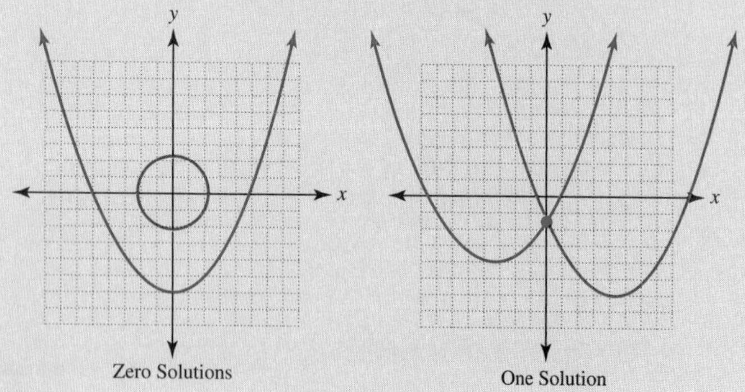 Zero Solutions One Solution	To solve: $y = x^2 + x - 5$ $y = 7$ let $7 = x^2 + x - 5$ $0 = x^2 + x - 12$ $0 = (x + 4)(x - 3)$ $x = 3, -4$ $(x, y) = (3, 7)$ or $(-4, 7)$	*p.* 896

Definition/Procedure	Example	Reference

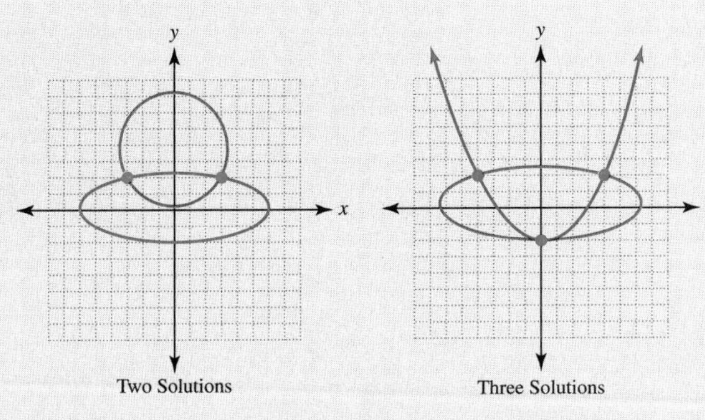

Two Solutions

Three Solutions

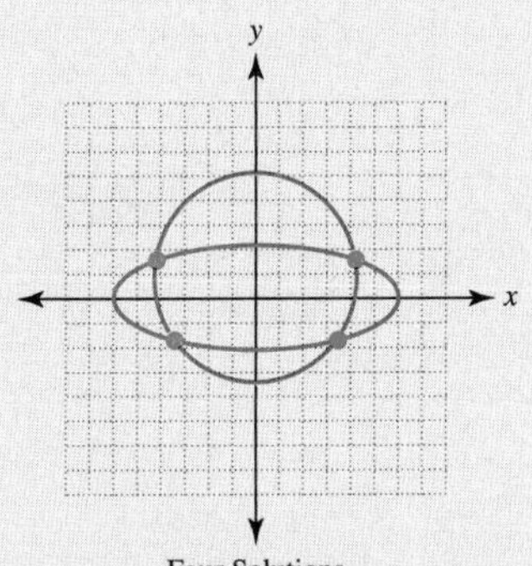

Four Solutions

A system that has as its graph a line and a parabola has, at most, two solutions. To solve such a system, use the following steps:

1. Solve both equations for y.
2. Create a new equation by setting the two right-hand expressions equal to each other.
3. Solve the equation for x.
4. Find the associated ordered pair(s).

Solving a Nonlinear System Algebraically

To solve a nonlinear system of equations, use the following steps:

1. Add or subtract the equations to eliminate one of the variables.
2. Solve the resulting equation for the remaining variable.
3. Substitute the value(s) from step 2 into one of the original equations to find the ordered pairs in the solution.

Solve the given system:

$$x + y^2 = 12$$
$$-x + 2y^2 = 15$$

Add the equations to get

$$3y^2 = 27$$
$$y^2 = 9$$
$$y = \pm 3$$

Substituting, we get the solutions $(3, -3)$ and $(3, 3)$.

p. 900

summary exercises :: chapter 9

This summary exercise set is provided to give you practice with each of the objectives of this chapter. Each exercise is keyed to the appropriate chapter section. When you are finished, you can check your answers to the odd-numbered exercises against those presented in the back of the text. If you have difficulty with any of these questions, go back and reread the examples from that section. The answers to the even-numbered exercises appear in the *Instructor's Solutions Manual.* Your instructor will give you guidelines on how best to use these exercises in your instructional setting.

9.1 *Graph each of the following.*

1. $y = x^2$

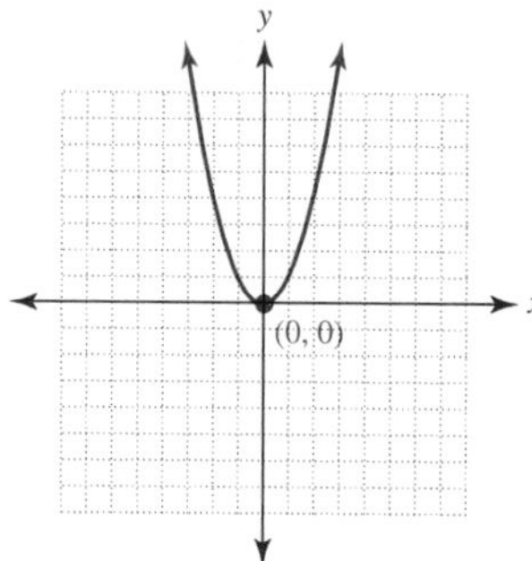

2. $y = x^2 + 2$

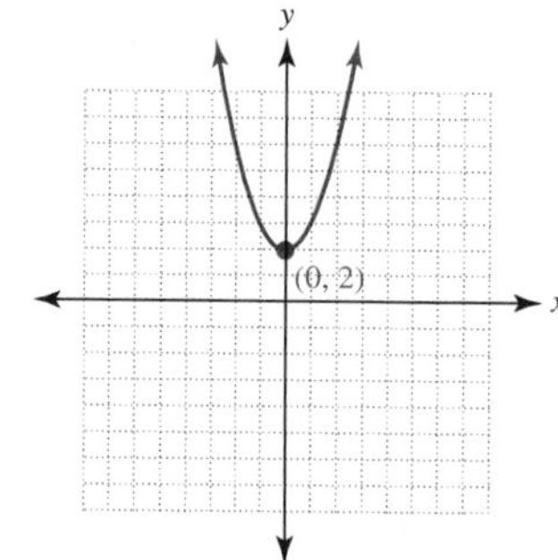

3. $y = x^2 - 5$

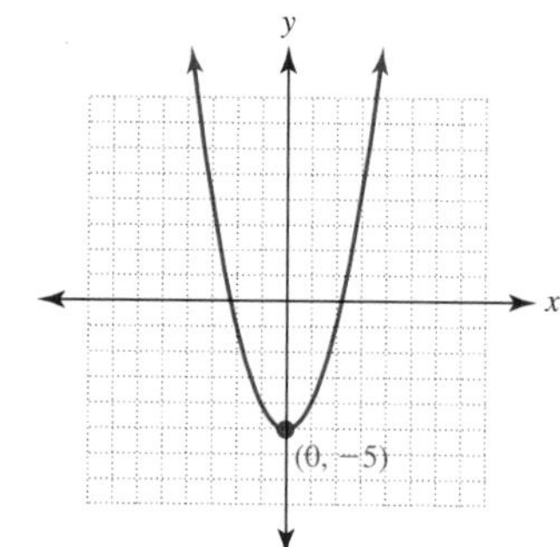

4. $y = (x - 3)^2$

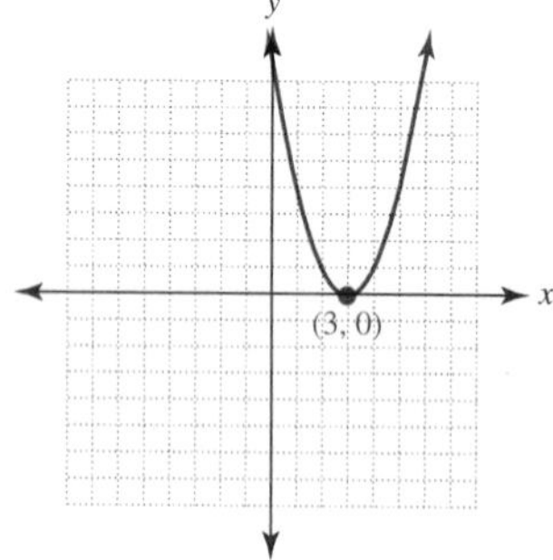

5. $y = (x + 2)^2$

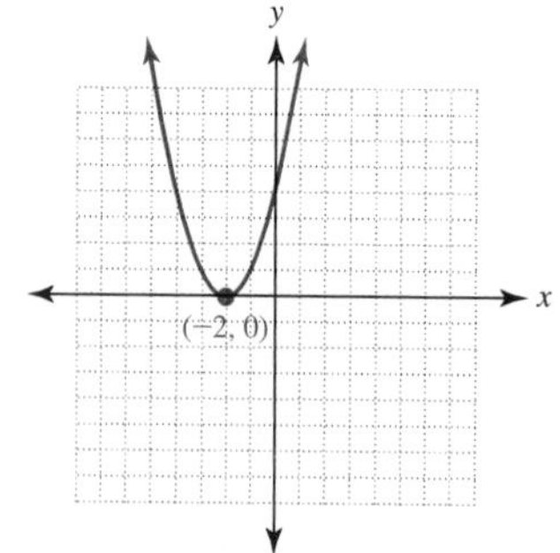

6. $y = -(x - 3)^2$

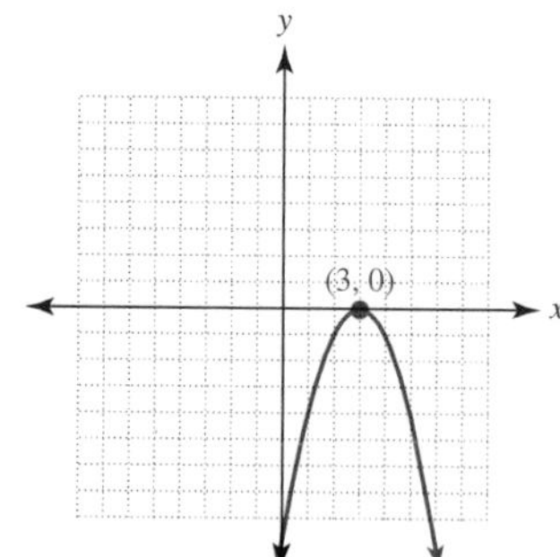

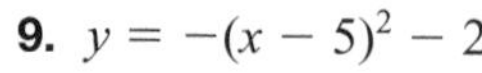

7. $y = (x + 3)^2 + 1$

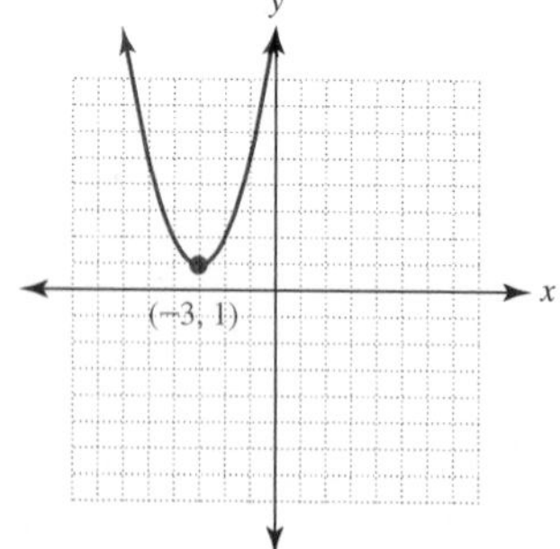

8. $y = -(x + 2)^2 - 3$

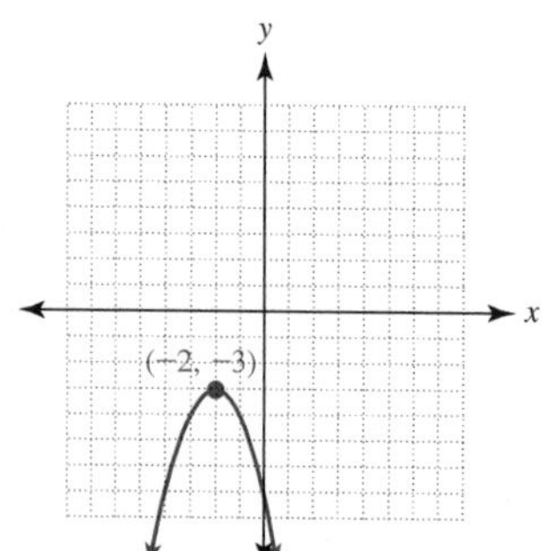

9. $y = -(x - 5)^2 - 2$

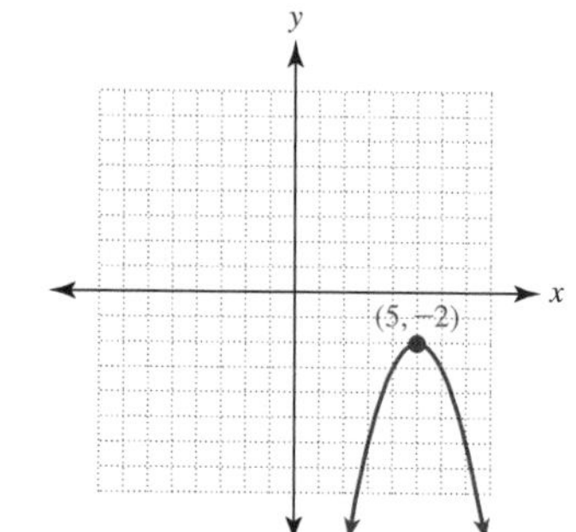

10. $y = 2(x - 2)^2 - 5$

11. $y = x^2 + 2x - 3$

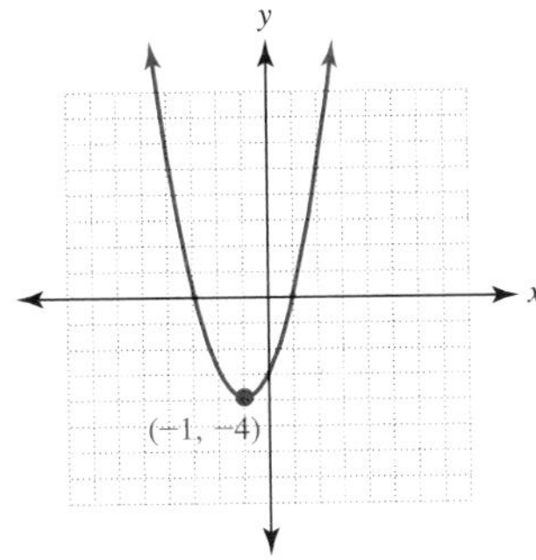

12. $y = x^2 - 4x + 3$

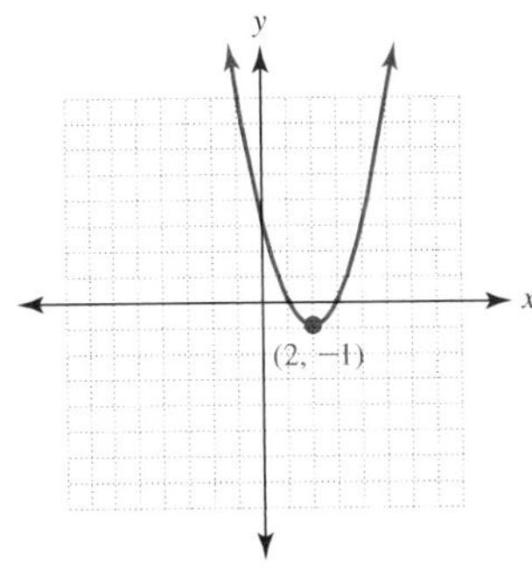

13. $y = -x^2 - x + 6$

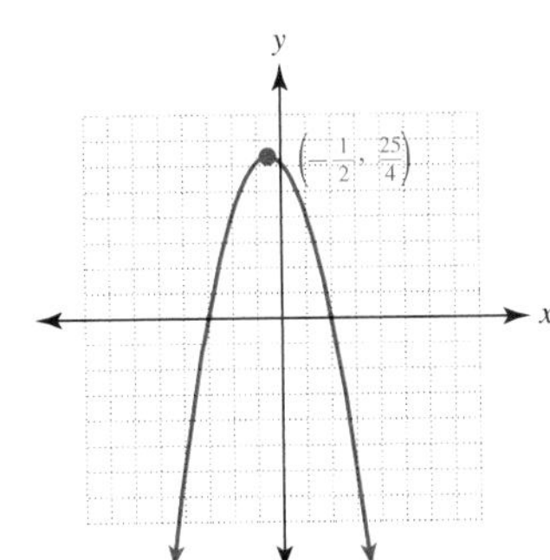

14. $y = -x^2 + 3x + 4$

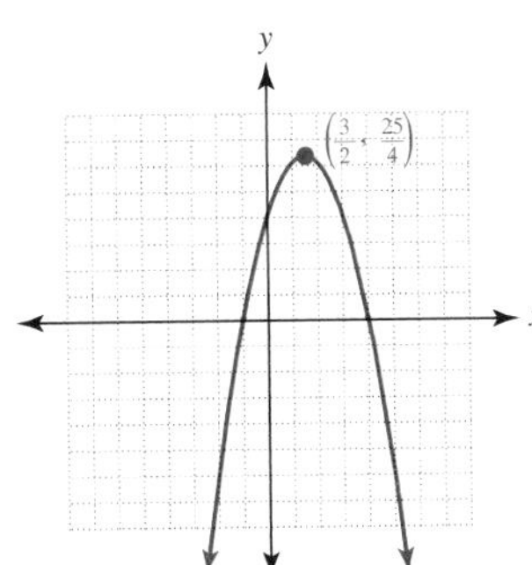

15. $y = x^2 + 4x + 5$

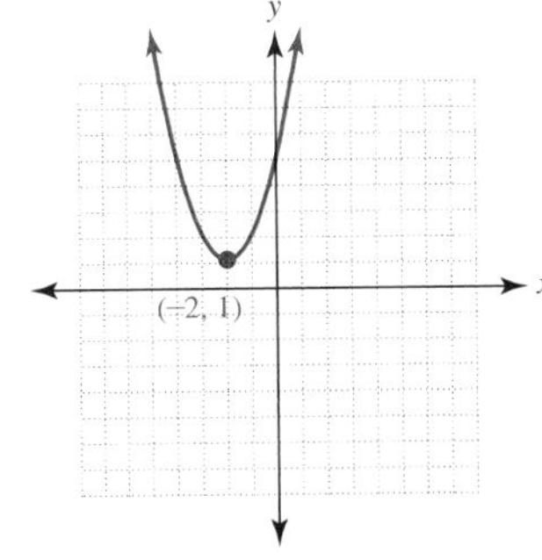

16. $y = x^2 - 6x + 4$

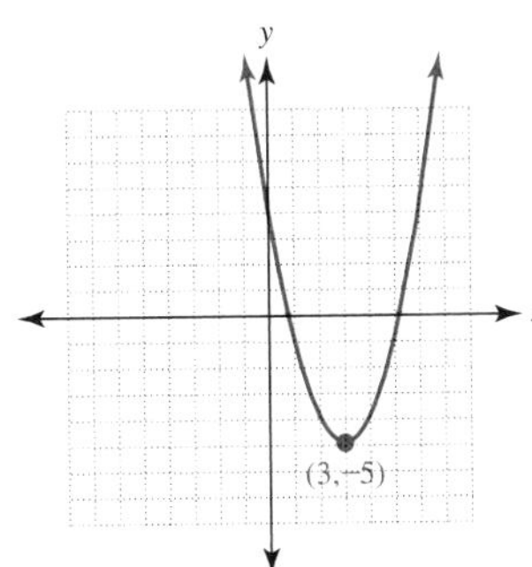

17. $y = x^2 - 2x + 4$

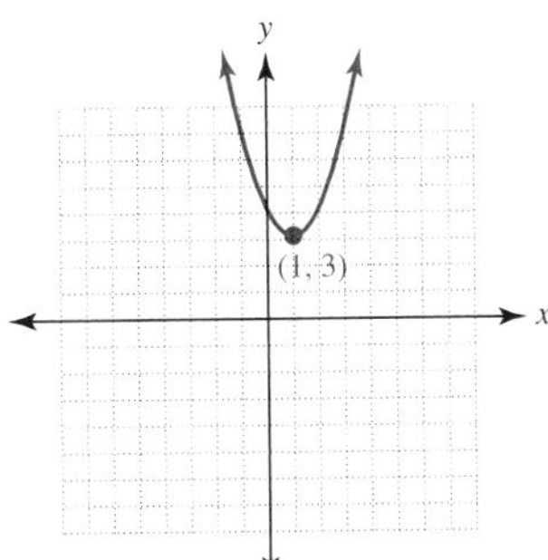

18. $y = -x^2 + 2x - 2$

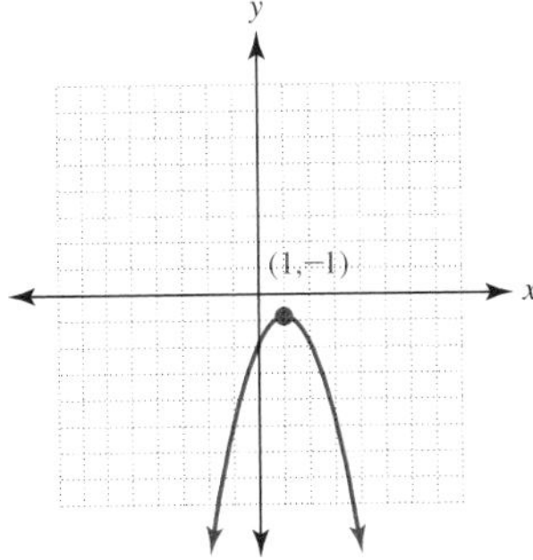

19. $y = 2x^2 - 4x + 1$

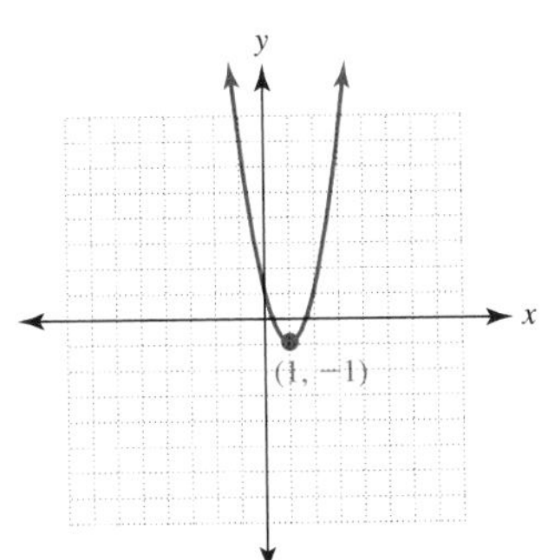

20. $y = \frac{1}{2}x^2 - 4x$

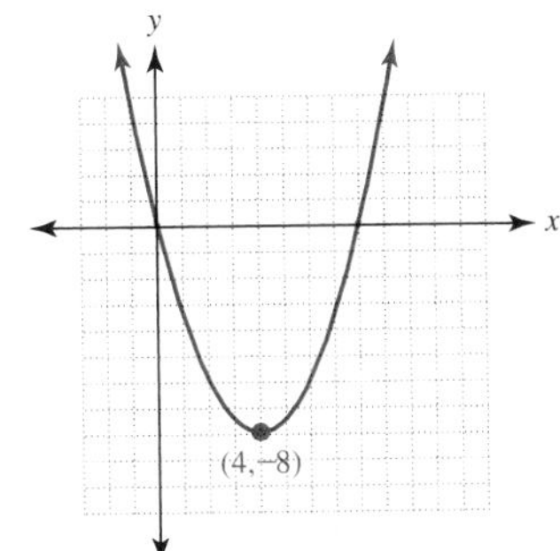

21. $x = y^2 - 4y$

22. $x = -y^2 + 4y$

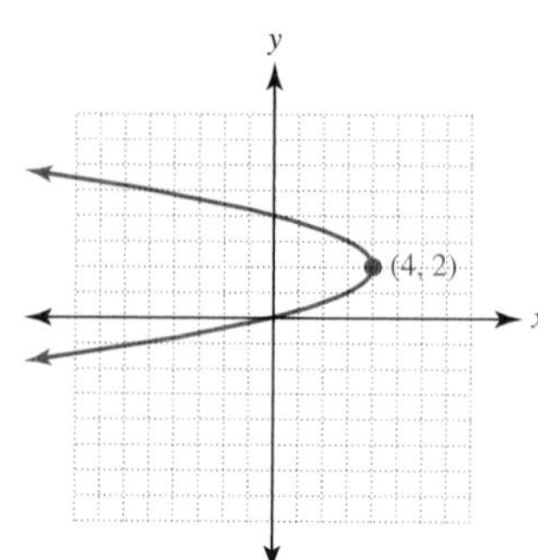

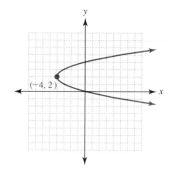

9.2 Find the center and the radius of the graph of each equation.

23. $x^2 + y^2 = 16$ $(0, 0), r = 4$

24. $x^2 + y^2 = 50$ $(0, 0), r = 5\sqrt{2}$

25. $4x^2 + 4y^2 = 36$ $(0, 0), r = 3$

26. $3x^2 + 3y^2 = 36$ $(0, 0), r = 2\sqrt{3}$

27. $(x - 3)^2 + y^2 = 36$ $(3, 0), r = 6$

28. $(x - 2)^2 + y^2 = 9$ $(2, 0), r = 3$

29. $(x - 1)^2 + (y - 2)^2 = 16$ $(1, 2), r = 4$

30. $x^2 + 6x + y^2 + 4y = 12$ $(-3, -2), r = 5$

31. $x^2 + 8x + y^2 + 10y = 23$ $(-4, -5), r = 8$

32. $x^2 - 6x + y^2 + 6y = 18$ $(3, -3), r = 6$

33. $x^2 + y^2 - 4y - 5 = 0$ $(0, 2), r = 3$

34. $x^2 - 2x + y^2 - 6y = 6$ $(1, 3), r = 4$

Graph each of the following.

35. $x^2 + y^2 = 16$

Center: (0, 0),
radius: 4

36. $4x^2 + 4y^2 = 36$

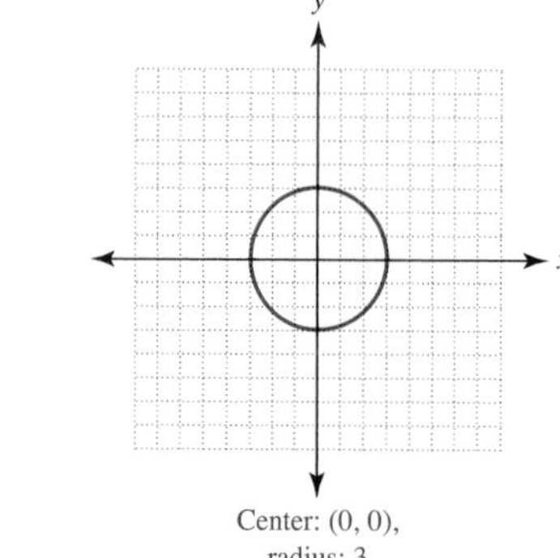

Center: (0, 0),
radius: 3

37. $x^2 + (y + 3)^2 = 25$

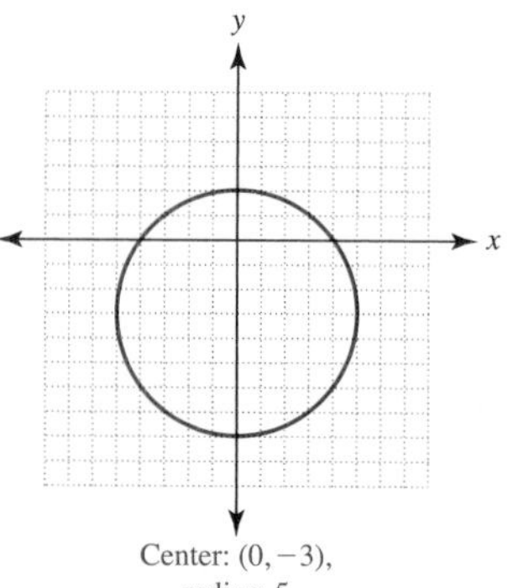

Center: (0, −3),
radius: 5

38. $(x - 2)^2 + y^2 = 9$

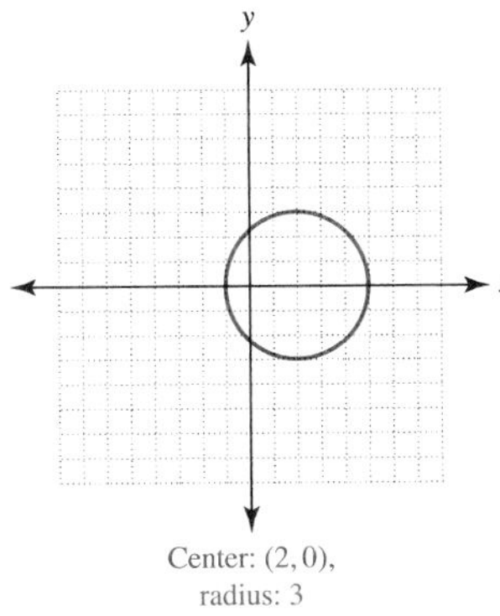

Center: (2, 0),
radius: 3

39. $(x - 1)^2 + (y - 2)^2 = 16$

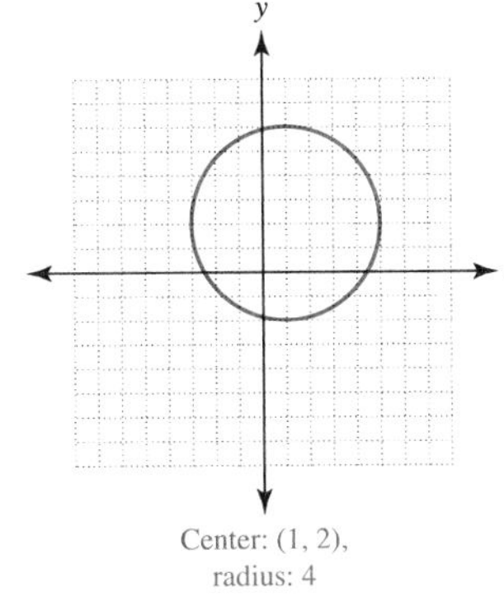

Center: (1, 2),
radius: 4

40. $(x + 3)^2 + (y + 2)^2 = 25$

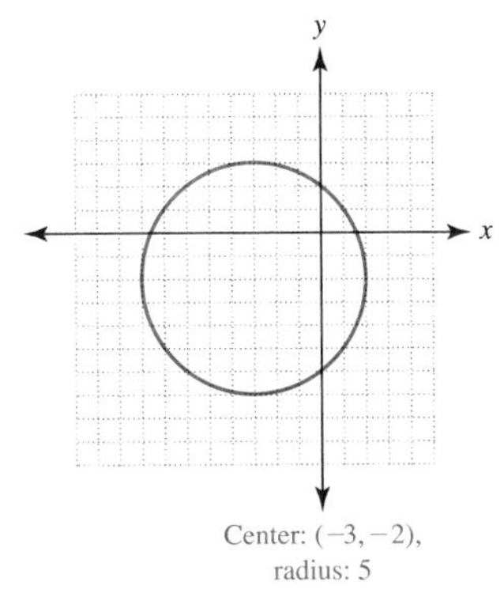

Center: (−3, −2),
radius: 5

41. $x^2 + y^2 - 4y - 5 = 0$

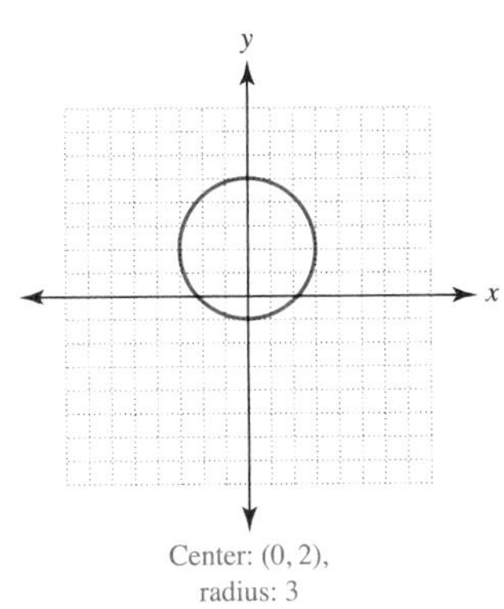

Center: (0, 2),
radius: 3

42. $x^2 - 2x + y^2 - 6y = 6$

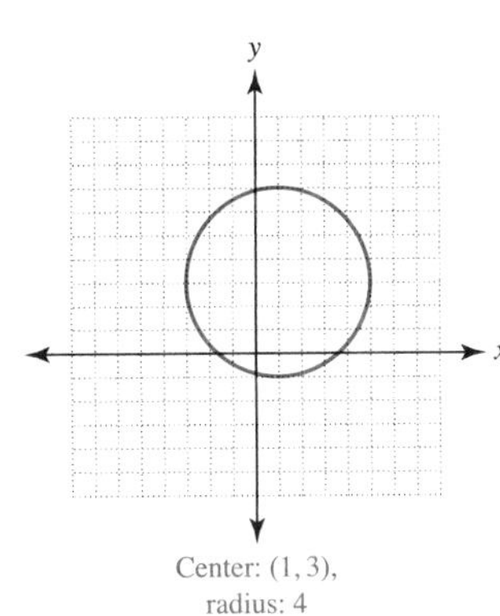

Center: (1, 3),
radius: 4

9.1–9.3 *For each of the following equations decide whether its graph is a line, a parabola, a circle, an ellipse, or a hyperbola.*

43. $x + y = 16$ Line

44. $x + y^2 = 5$ Parabola

45. $4x^2 + 4y^2 = 36$ Circle

46. $3x + 3y = 36$ Line

47. $y = (x - 3)^2$ Parabola

48. $(x - 2)^2 + y^2 = 9$ Circle

49. $y = (x - 1)^2 + 1$ Parabola

50. $x = y^2 + 4y + 4$ Parabola

9.3 *Graph each of the following.*

51. $\dfrac{x^2}{25} + \dfrac{y^2}{9} = 1$

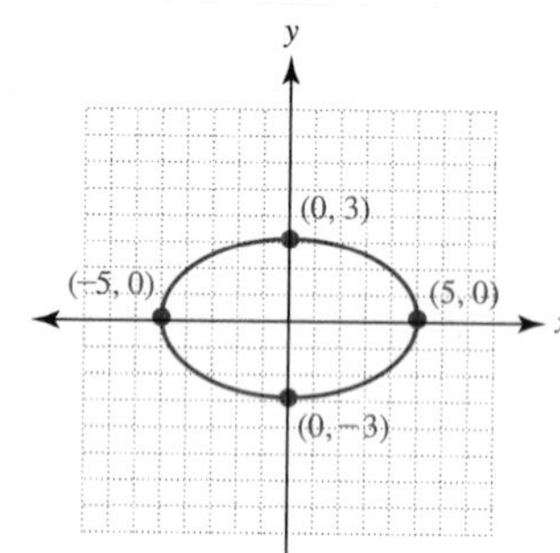

52. $\dfrac{x^2}{4} + \dfrac{y^2}{16} = 1$

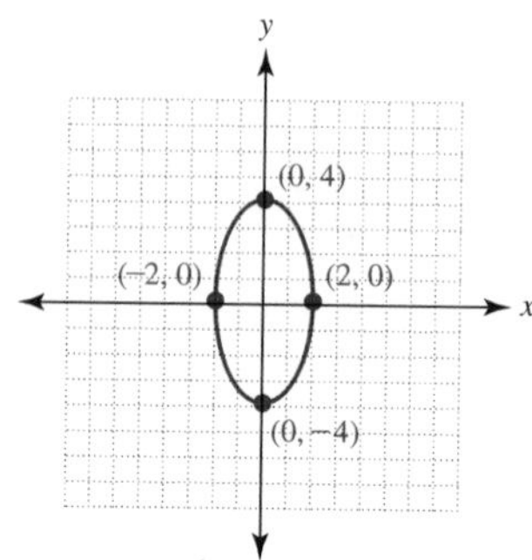

53. $9x^2 + 4y^2 = 36$

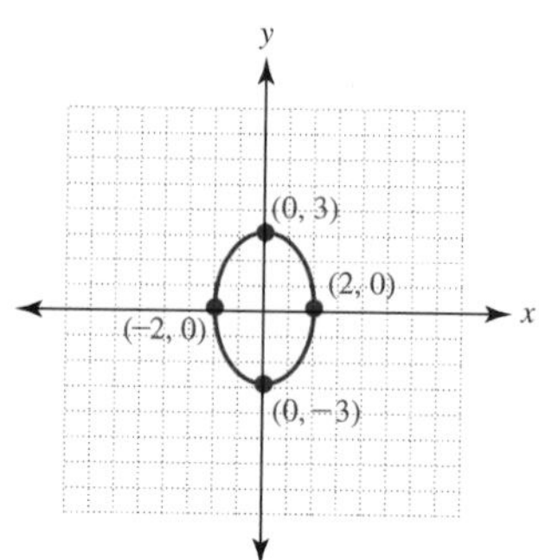

54. $16x^2 + 9y^2 = 144$

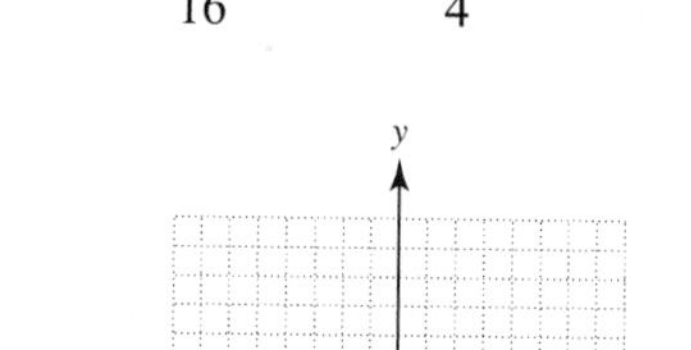

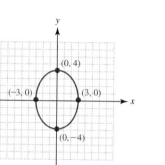

55. $\dfrac{(x-2)^2}{16} + \dfrac{(y+1)^2}{4} = 1$

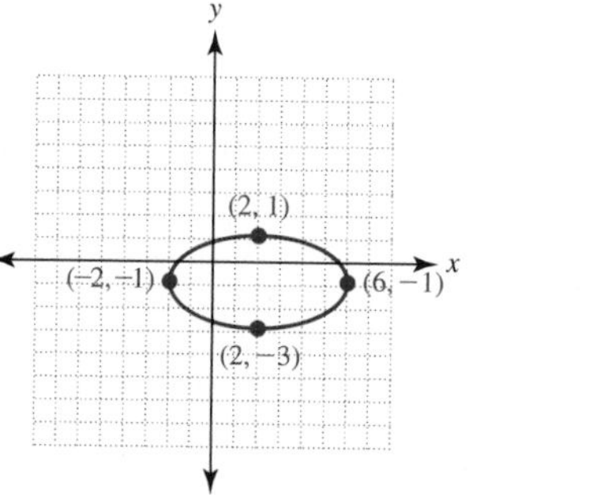

56. $\dfrac{x^2}{9} - \dfrac{y^2}{4} = 1$

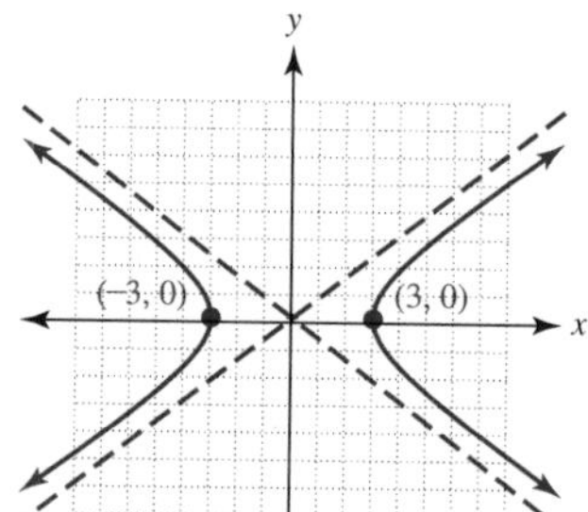

57. $\dfrac{y^2}{16} - \dfrac{x^2}{4} = 1$

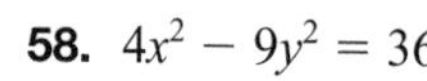

58. $4x^2 - 9y^2 = 36$

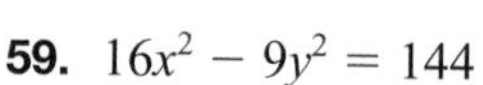

59. $16x^2 - 9y^2 = 144$

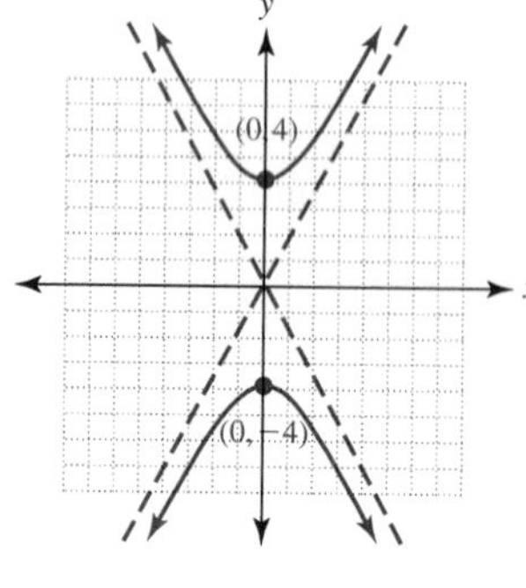

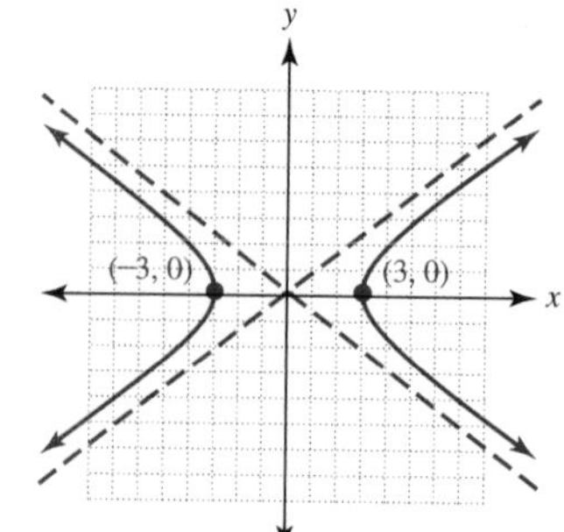

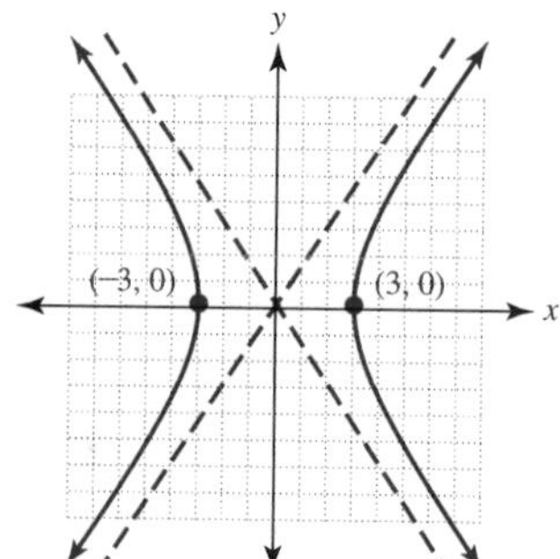

60. $\dfrac{(y+1)^2}{4} - \dfrac{(x-2)^2}{16} = 1$

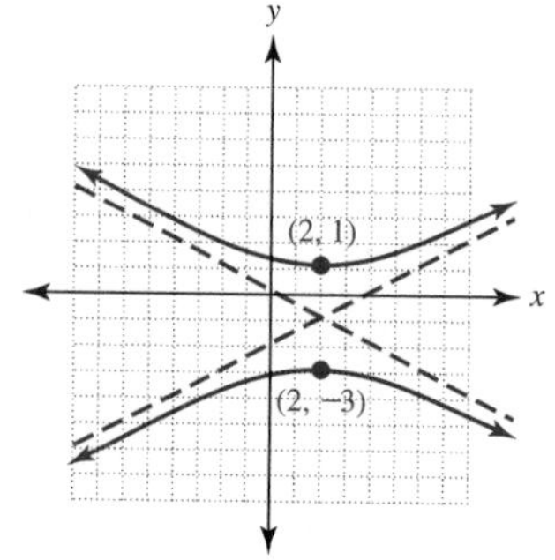

9.4 Solve each of the following systems graphically.

61. $y = x^2 - x + 4$
$y = 4$

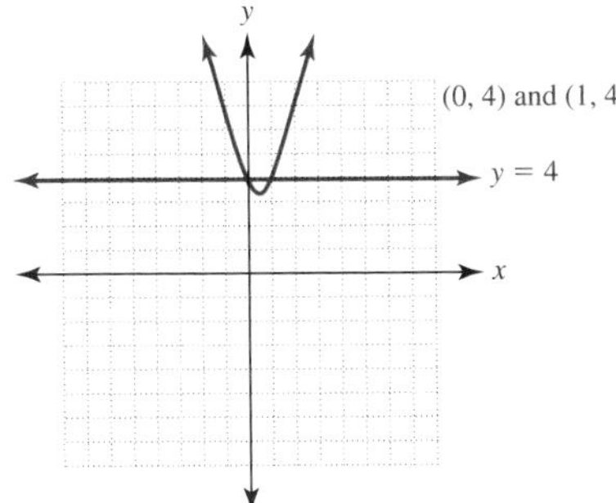

62. $y = x^2 + x - 9$
$y = 3$

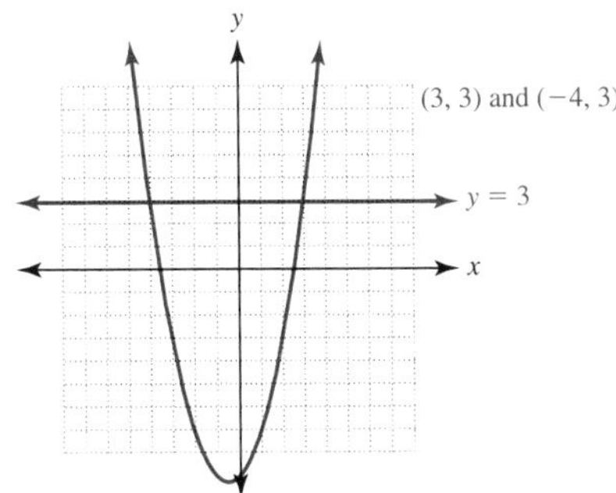

63. $y = x^2 - 3x + 1$
$y = 5$

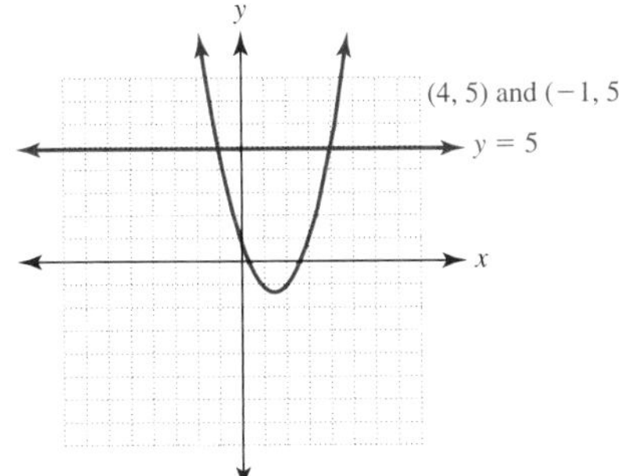

64. $y = x^2 + 12x + 40$
$y = 5$

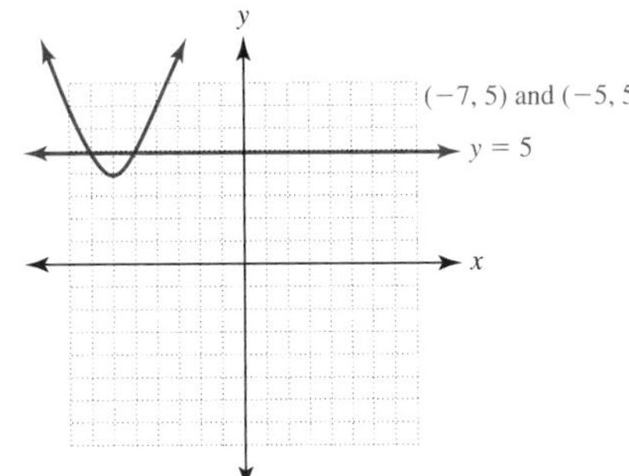

65. $y = x^2 + x - 6$
$y = 6$

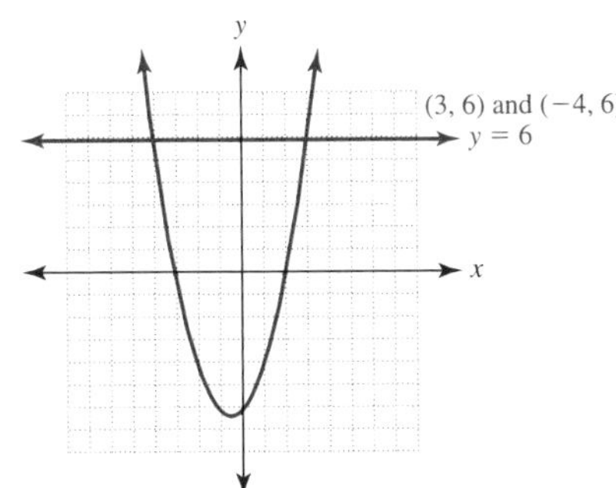

Solve the following systems algebraically.

66. $y = x^2 - x + 4$ (0, 4) and (1, 4)
$y = 4$
(See exercise 61.)

67. $y = x^2 + x - 9$ (3, 3) and (−4, 3)
$y = 3$
(See exercise 62.)

68. $y = x^2 - 3x + 1$ (4, 5) and (−1, 5)
$y = 5$
(See exercise 63.)

69. $y = x^2 + 12x + 40$ (−7, 5) and (−5, 5)
$y = 5$
(See exercise 64.)

70. $y = x^2 + x - 6$ (3, 6) and (−4, 6)
$y = 6$
(See exercise 65.)

Solve each of the following systems of inequalities.

71. $y \geq x^2 - x + 4$
$y \geq 4$
(See exercise 61.)

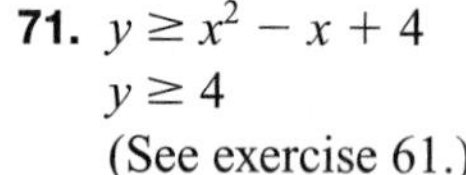

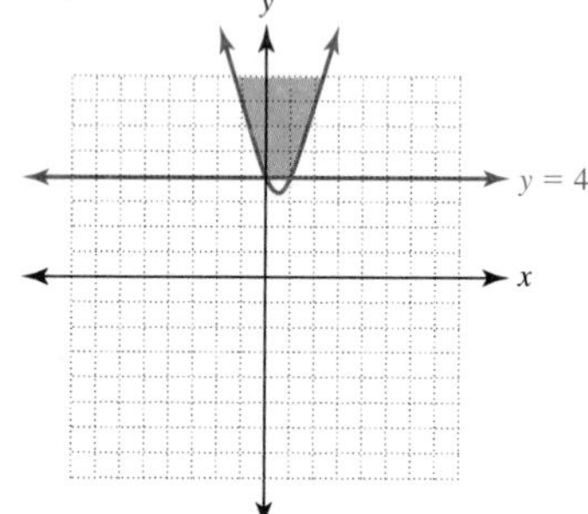

72. $y \geq x^2 + x - 9$
$y \leq 3$
(See exercise 62.)

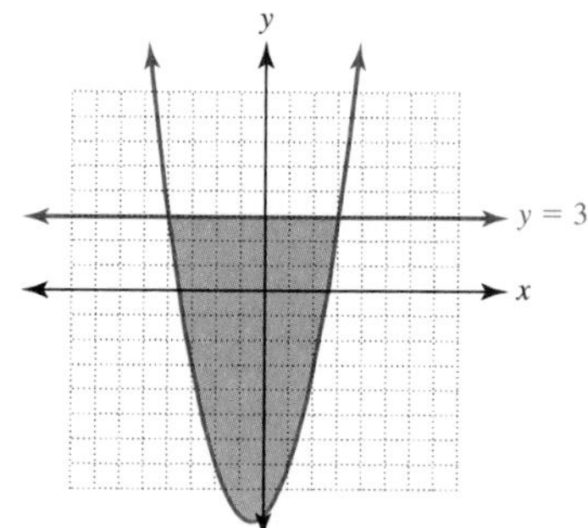

73. $y \geq x^2 - 3x + 1$
$y \leq 5$
(See exercise 63.)

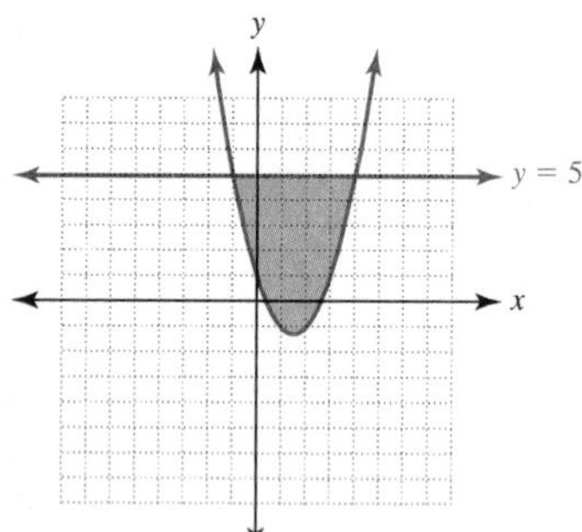

74. $y \geq x^2 + 12x + 40$
$y \leq 5$
(See exercise 64.)

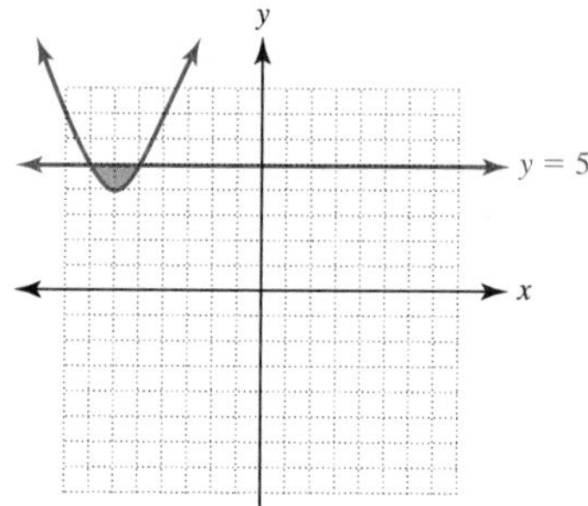

75. $y \leq x^2 + x - 6$
$y \leq 6$
(See exercise 65.)

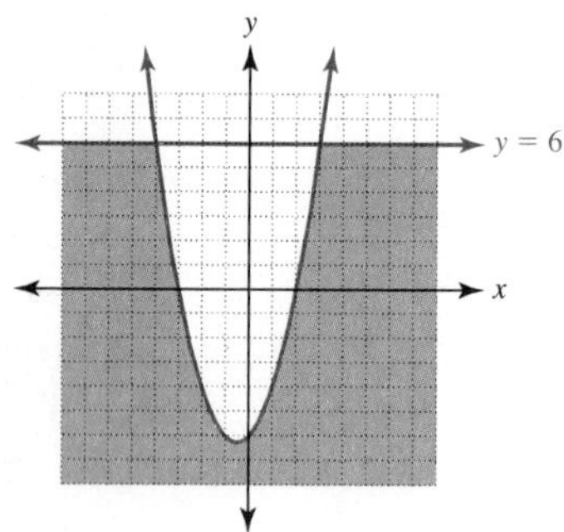

self-test 9

Name ______________________

Section ________ Date ________

The purpose of this chapter test is to help you check your progress so that you can find sections and concepts that you need to review before the next exam. Allow yourself about an hour to take this test. At the end of that hour, check your answers against those given in the back of this text. If you missed any, note the section reference that accompanies the answer. Go back to that section and reread the examples until you have mastered that particular concept.

Answers

1. See exercise
2. See exercise
3. See exercise
4. See exercise
5. See exercise
6. See exercise

9.1

Graph each of the following equations.

1. $y = (x - 5)^2$

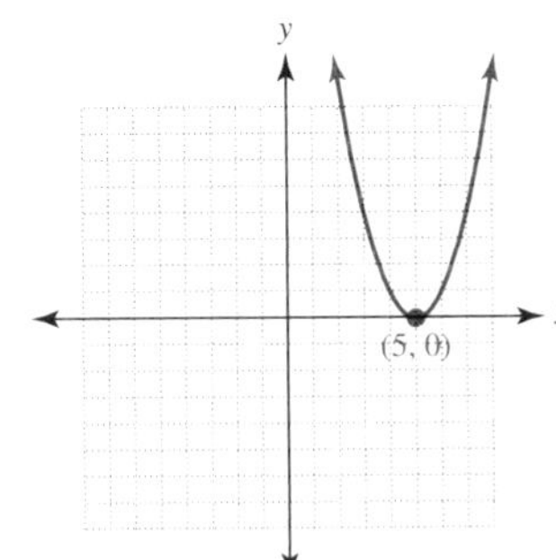

2. $y = (x + 2)^2 - 3$

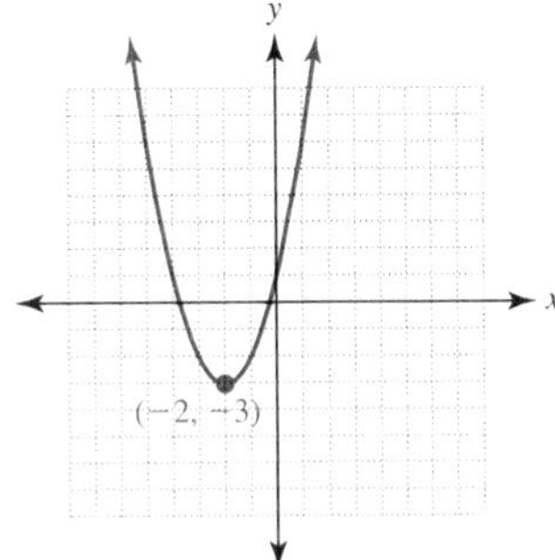

3. $y = -2(x - 3)^2 - 1$

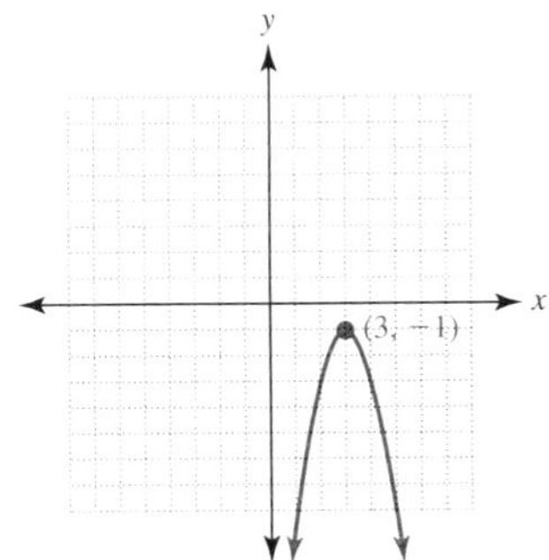

4. $y = 3x^2 + 9x + 2$

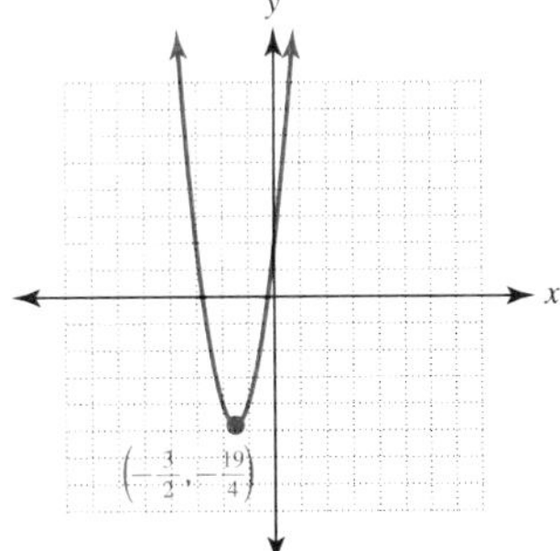

5. $x = \frac{1}{2}(y - 4)^2 + 2$

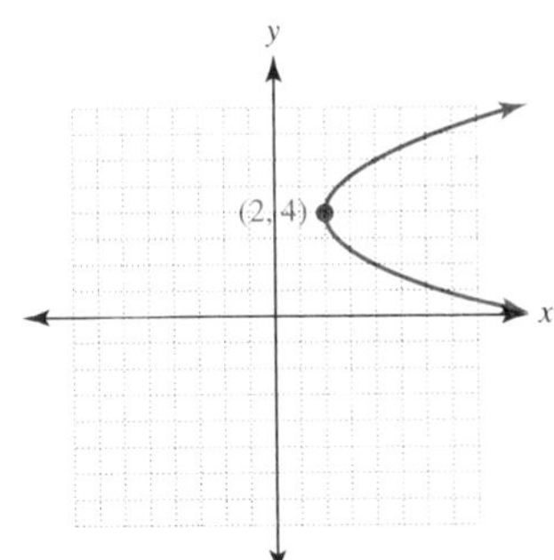

6. $x = y^2 + 4y - 3$

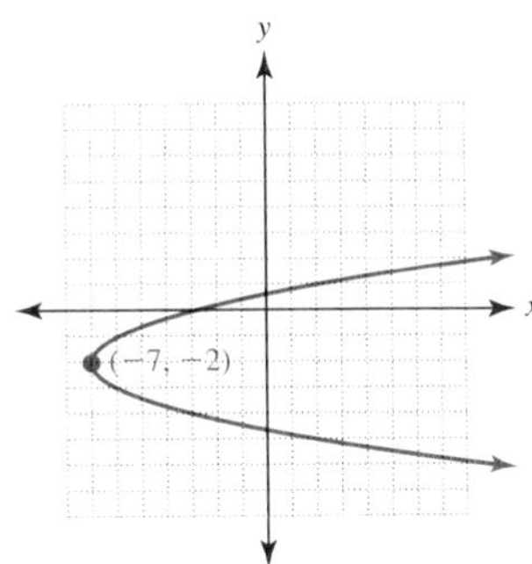

Answers

7. (3, −2); $r = 6$

8. (−1, 2); $r = \sqrt{26}$

9. See exercise

10. See exercise

11. See exercise

12. See exercise

13. See exercise

14. See exercise

9.2

Find the coordinates for the center and the radius of the graph of each equation.

7. $(x - 3)^2 + (y + 2)^2 = 36$

8. $x^2 + 2x + y^2 - 4y - 21 = 0$

Sketch the graph of each of the following equations.

9. $(x - 2)^2 + (y + 3)^2 = 9$

9.3

10. 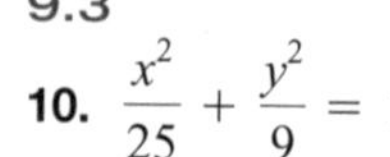
$\dfrac{x^2}{25} + \dfrac{y^2}{9} = 1$

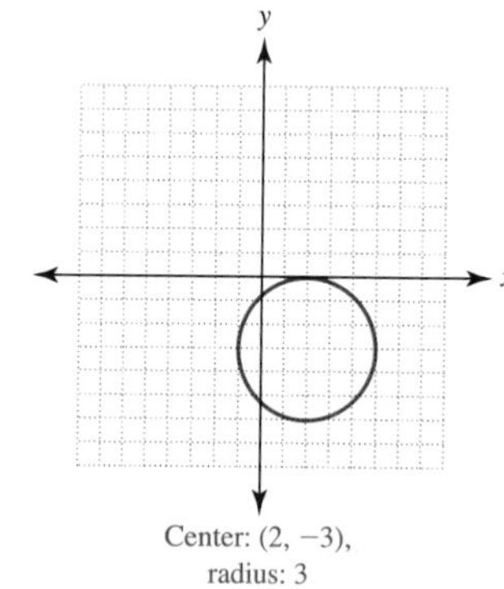

Center: (2, −3),
radius: 3

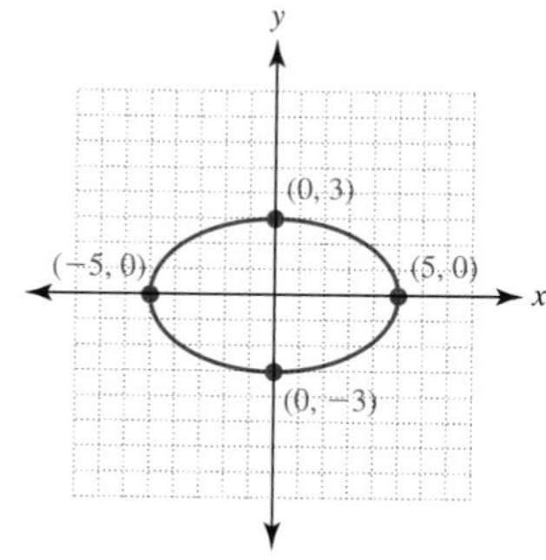

11. $\dfrac{(x + 2)^2}{4} + \dfrac{(y - 1)^2}{16} = 1$

12. 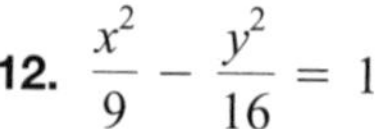
$\dfrac{x^2}{9} - \dfrac{y^2}{16} = 1$

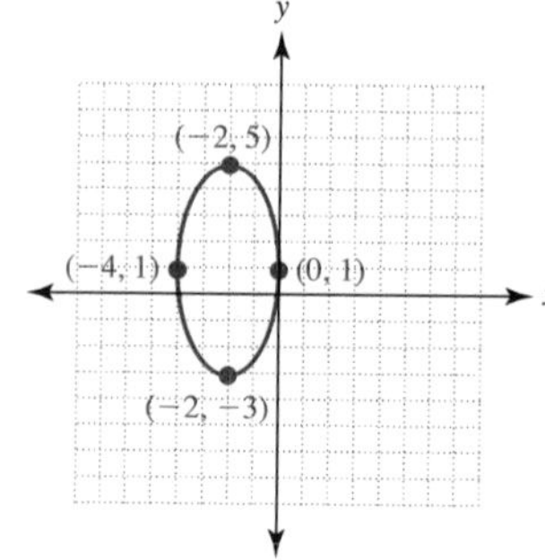

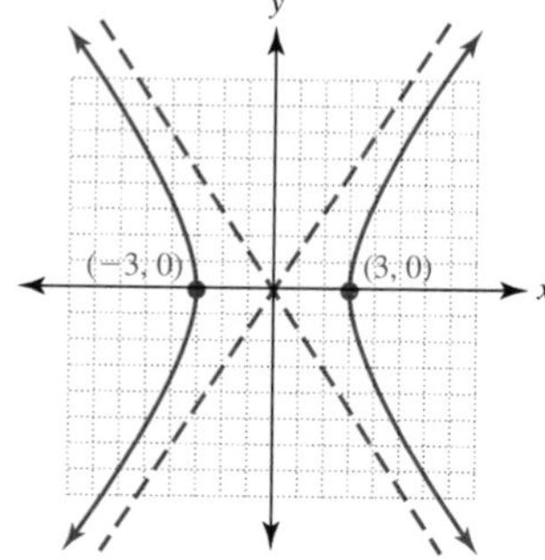

13. $4y^2 - 25x^2 = 100$

14. 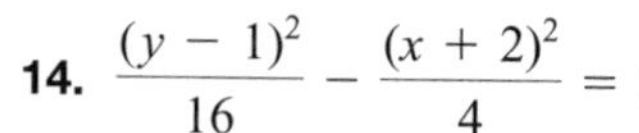
$\dfrac{(y - 1)^2}{16} - \dfrac{(x + 2)^2}{4} = 1$

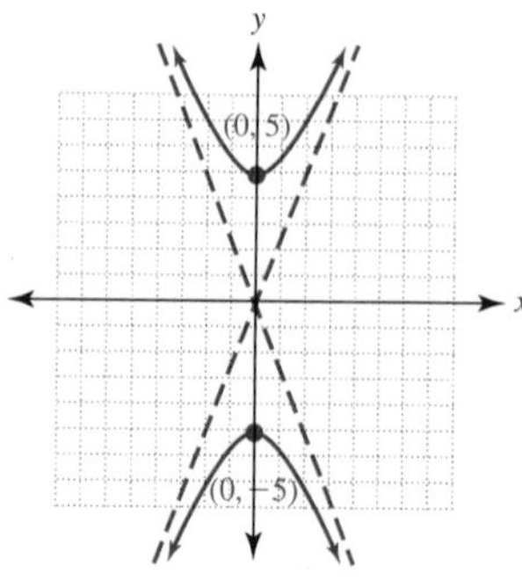

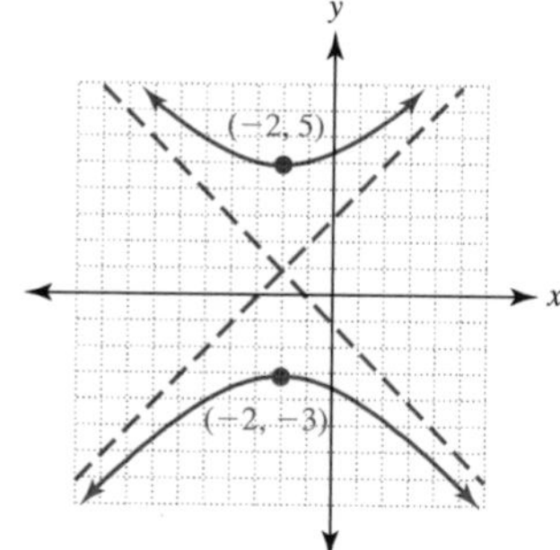

9.4

Solve each of the following systems graphically.

15. $y = x^2 + 3x - 5$
$y = 5$

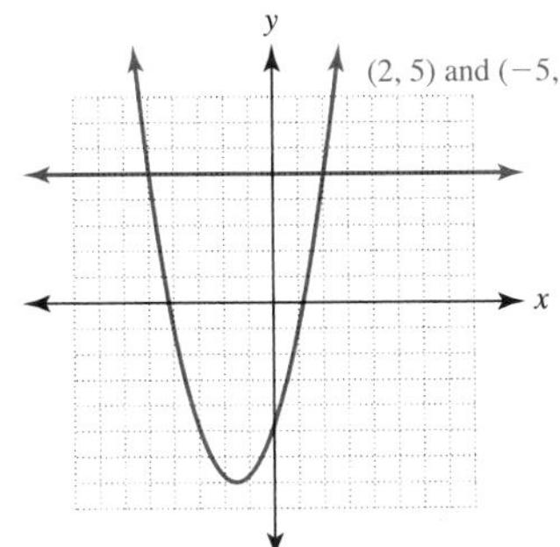

16. $y = x^2 - x - 8$
$y = 4$

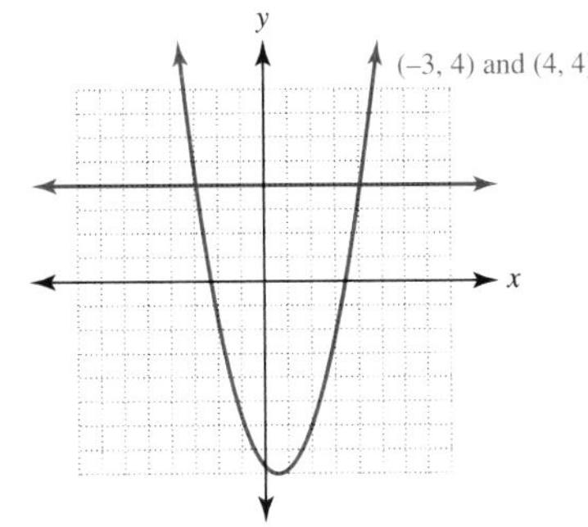

Solve each of the following systems algebraically.

17. $y = x^2 + 3x - 5$
$y = 5$
(See exercise 15.)

18. $y = x^2 - x - 8$
$y = 4$
(See exercise 16.)

Solve each of the following systems of inequalities.

19. $y \geq x^2 + 3x - 5$
$y \leq 5$
(See exercise 15.)

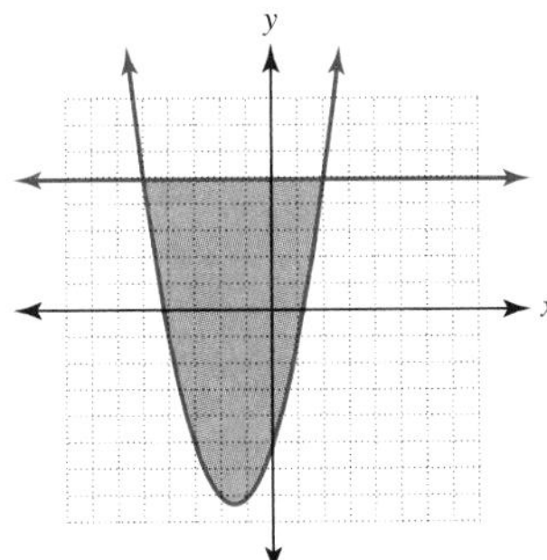

20. $y \geq x^2 - x - 8$
$y \geq 4$
(See exercise 16.)

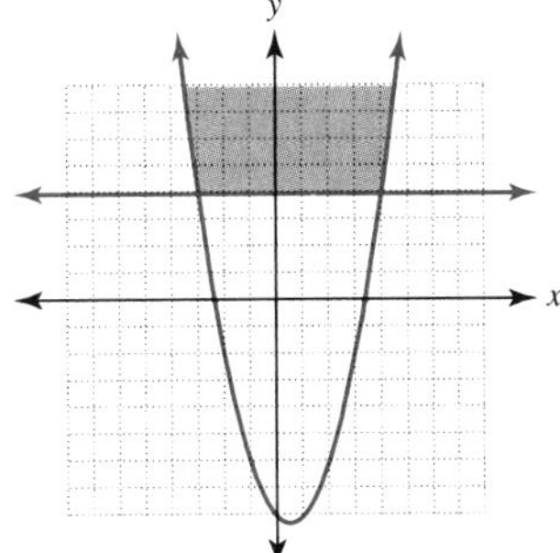

9.1–9.3

Identify the following as a line, a circle, a parabola, an ellipse, or a hyperbola.

21. $x^2 - 4x + y^2 + 6y - 3 = 0$

22. $9x^2 - 4y^2 = 36$

Answers

15. See exercise

16. See exercise

17. (2, 5) and (−5, 5)

18. (−3, 4) and (4, 4)

19. See exercise

20. See exercise

21. Circle

22. Hyperbola

Activity 9 ::
Orbiting Objects

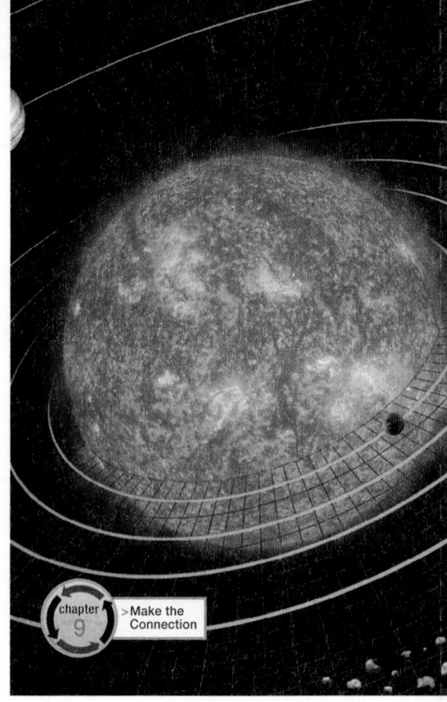

Each chapter in this text concludes with a chapter activity such as this one. These activities provide you with the opportunity to apply the math you studied in that chapter to a relevant topic. Your instructor will determine how best to use these activities in your instructional setting. You may find yourself working in class or outside of class; you may find yourself working alone or in small groups; you may even be asked to perform research in a library or on the Internet.

In this activity we will explore the different conic sections produced by orbiting objects. You will need a pencil, a string, two pins (or thumbtacks), and a surface in which to insert the thumbtacks, such as a drawing board.

1. When people first began looking at the skies, they believed that Earth was the center of the universe. Let us model this situation. Tie the ends of a length of string to one pin (or thumbtack) stuck in a sheet of paper on a drawing board. Then, keeping the string taut with the point of a pencil, allow the pencil to trace a path around the pin.

(a) What figure is produced?

(b) What is true about the distance from the pin to the pencil?

(c) Does this distance remain the same for any position of the pencil?

(d) Is this an accurate model of the solar system?

2. Suppose we had two pins (or thumbtacks) instead of one. Tie the ends of a length of string to two pins stuck in a sheet of paper on a drawing board. Then, keeping the string taut with the point of a pencil, allow the pencil to trace a path around the pins.

(a) What shape is produced?

(b) What is true about the sum of the distances from the pins to the pencil?

(c) Does this sum remain the same for any position of the pencil?

(d) Is this an accurate model of the solar system?

3. How might you model a parabola?

4. How might you model a hyperbola?

cumulative review chapters 1-9

Name ______________

Section ________ Date ________

The following exercises are presented to help you review concepts from earlier chapters. This is meant as review material and not as a comprehensive exam. The answers are presented in the back of the text. Beside each answer is a section reference for the concept. If you have difficulty with any of these exercises, be certain to at least read through the summary related to that section.

Solve each of the following.

2.1

1. $3x - 2(x + 5) = 12 - 3x$

2.4

2. $2x - 7 < 3x - 5$

2.5

3. $|2x - 3| = 5$

4. $|3x + 5| \leq 7$

5. $|5x - 4| > 21$

5.9

6. $x^2 - 5x - 24 = 0$

7.4

7. $\sqrt{x} = \sqrt{10x - 9}$

6.5

8. $\frac{5y}{y + 1} - \frac{y}{3y + 3} = \frac{-56}{6y + 6}$

8.2

9. $2x^2 = 2x + 1$

Graph each of the following.

3.3

10. $5x + 7y = 35$

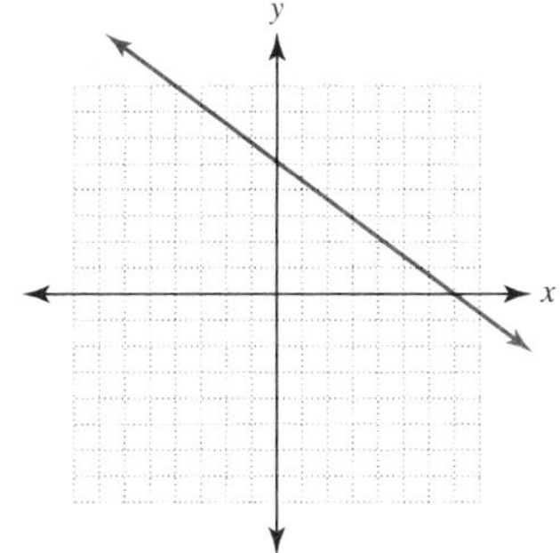

3.6

11. $2x + 3y < 6$

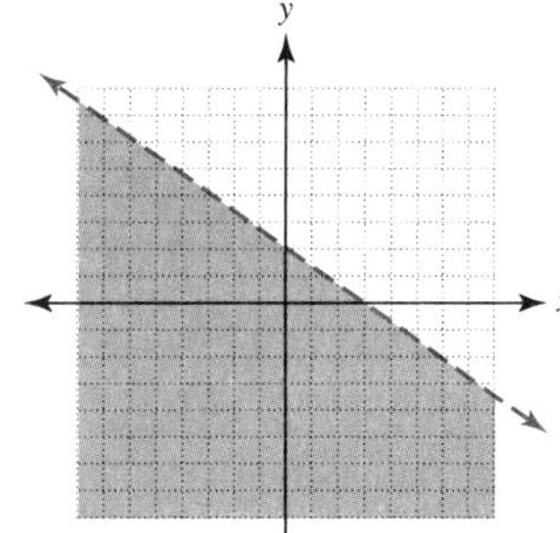

9.2

12. Find the distance between the points $(-1, 2)$ and $(4, -22)$.

3.4

13. Find the slope of the line connecting $(4, 6)$ and $(3, -1)$.

3.5

14. Write the equation of the line that passes through the points $(-1, 4)$ and $(5, -2)$.

Simplify the following polynomials.

5.2

15. $(2x + 1)(x - 3)$

16. $(3x - 2)^2$

5.4

17. Completely factor the function $f(x) = x^3 - 3x^2 - 5x + 15$.

Answers

1. $\frac{11}{2}$
2. $x > -2$
3. $-1, 4$
4. $-4 \leq x \leq \frac{2}{3}$
5. $x < -\frac{17}{5}$ or $x > 5$
6. 8, −3
7. 1
8. −2
9. $\frac{1 \pm \sqrt{3}}{2}$
10. See exercise
11. See exercise
12. $\sqrt{601} \approx 24.5$
13. 7
14. $y = -x + 3$
15. $2x^2 - 5x - 3$
16. $9x^2 - 12x + 4$
17. $f(x) = (x - 3)(x^2 - 5)$

Answers

18. See exercise

19. See exercise

20. See exercise

21. 2

22. $w\sqrt{3w}$

23. $\left(-10, \frac{26}{3}\right)$

24. 8 cm by 19 cm

25. 73

Graph the following:

9.1

18. $y = x^2 - 6x + 5$

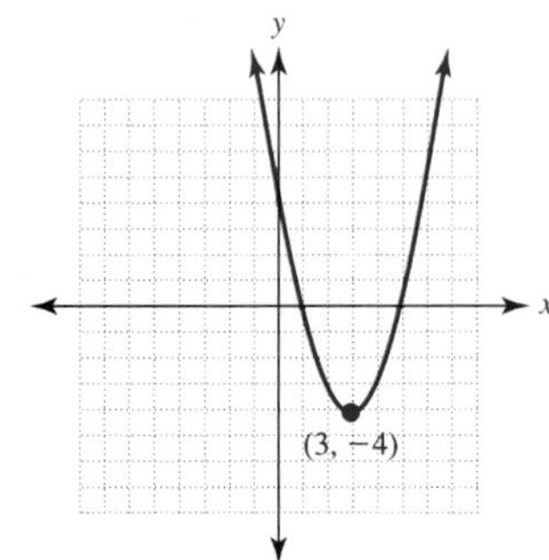

9.2

19. $(x + 1)^2 + (y - 2)^2 = 25$

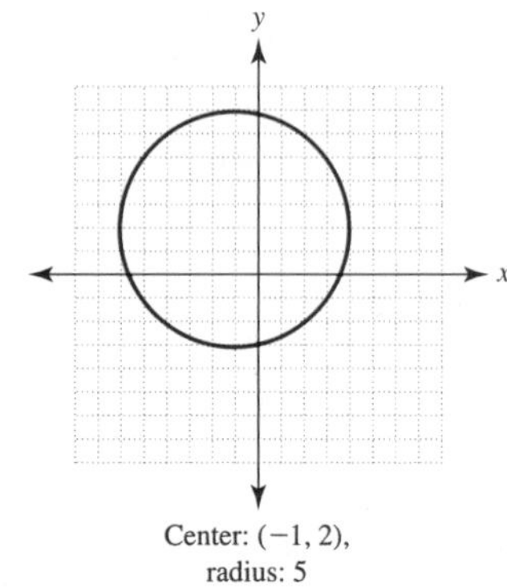

Center: $(-1, 2)$,
radius: 5

9.3

20. $\dfrac{x^2}{64} + \dfrac{y^2}{9} = 1$

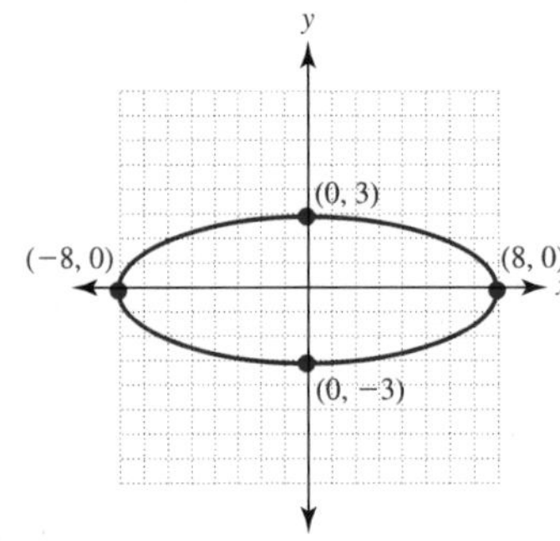

6.3

21. Simplify the expression $\dfrac{7x}{3x + 1} - \dfrac{x - 2}{3x + 1}$.

7.3

22. Simplify the expression $\sqrt{75w^3} - w\sqrt{48w}$.

Solve the following system of equations.

4.1

23. $2x + 3y = 6$
$5x + 3y = -24$

Solve each of the following applications.

24. **Geometry** The length of a rectangle is 3 cm more than twice its width. If the perimeter of the rectangle is 54 cm, find the dimensions of the rectangle.

25. **Number Problem** The sum of the digits of a two-digit number is 10. If the digits are reversed, the new number is 36 less than the original number. What was the original number?

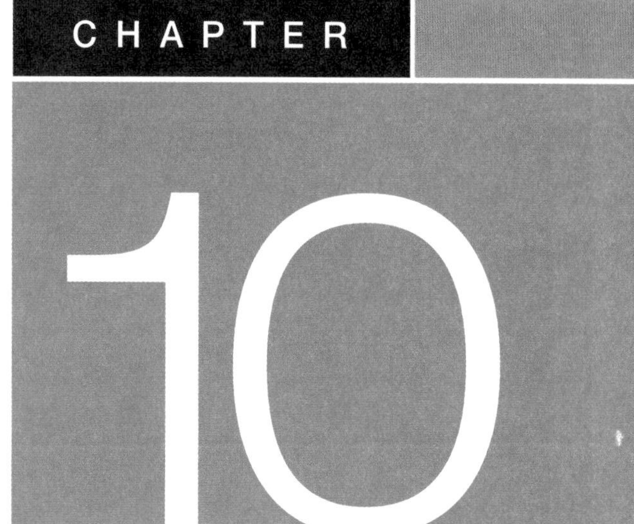

Additional Properties of Functions

INTRODUCTION

Economists are among the many professionals who use graphs to show connections between two sets of data. For example, an economist may use a graph to look for a connection between two different measures for the standard of living in various countries.

One way of measuring the standard of living in a country is the per capita gross domestic product (GDP). The GDP is the total value of all goods and services produced by all businesses and individuals over the course of 1 year. To find the per capita GDP, we divide that total value by the population of the country.

Other economists, including some who wrote an article in *Scientific American* in May 1993, question this method. Rather than comparing GDP among countries, they use survival rate (life expectancy) to measure the quality of life.

In this chapter we will further explore functions. We will also see how functions can be used to help us answer questions about business and the economy. At the end of the chapter, you will find a more in-depth activity involving the relationship between GDP and life expectancy.

CHAPTER 10 OUTLINE

10 pretest

Name ______________

Section ________ Date ________

This pretest will provide a preview of the types of exercises you will encounter in each section of this chapter. The answers for these exercises can be found in the back of the text. If you are working on your own, or ahead of the class, this pretest can help you identify the sections in which you should focus more of your time.

10.1 For exercises 1 and 2 use the functions $f(x) = x^2 - 2$ and $g(x) = 2x + 3$.

1. Find $f(x) + g(x)$.

2. Find $f(x) - g(x)$.

For exercises 3 to 6 use the functions $f(x) = x^2 - 1$ and $g(x) = 3x - 1$.

3. Find $(f \cdot g)(x)$.

4. Find $\left(\frac{f}{g}\right)(x)$.

5. Find $(f \cdot g)(-1)$.

6. Find $\left(\frac{f}{g}\right)(2)$.

For exercises 7 and 8 use the functions $f(x) = x^3 - 1$ and $g(x) = x - 1$.

7. Find $\left(\frac{f}{g}\right)(x)$.

8. Find $\left(\frac{g}{f}\right)(x)$.

9. What is the domain of the result of exercise 3?

10. What is the domain of the result of exercise 4?

10.2 For exercises 11 to 14 use the functions $f(x) = x^2 - 3$ and $g(x) = -2x + 1$.

11. Find $(f \circ g)(x)$.

12. Find $(g \circ f)(x)$.

13. Find $(f \circ g)(2)$.

14. Find $(g \circ f)(2)$.

10.3 For exercises 15 and 16 use the function $f(x) = 2x - 4$.

15. Find the inverse of f. Is the inverse also a function?

16. Graph f and its inverse on the same set of axes.

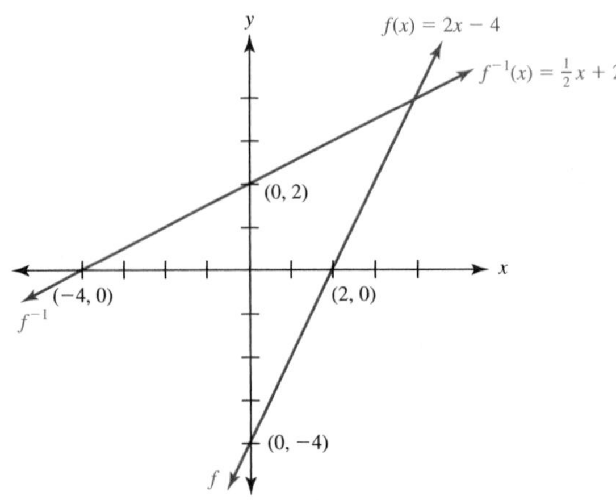

Answers

1. $x^2 + 2x + 1$
2. $x^2 - 2x - 5$
3. $3x^3 - x^2 - 3x + 1$
4. $\frac{x^2 - 1}{3x - 1}$
5. 0
6. $\frac{3}{5}$
7. $x^2 + x + 1$
8. $\frac{1}{x^2 + x + 1}$
9. D: $\mathbb{R}$
10. D: $\left\{x \mid x \neq \frac{1}{3}\right\}$
11. $4x^2 - 4x - 2$
12. $-2x^2 + 7$
13. 6
14. -1
15. $f^{-1}(x) = \frac{1}{2}x + 2$, yes
16. See exercise

10.1 Algebra of Functions

< 10.1 Objectives >

1 > Find the sum or difference of two functions

2 > Find the domain of the sum or difference of two functions

3 > Find the product and domain of two functions

4 > Find the quotient and domain of two functions

The profit that a company makes on an item is determined by subtracting the cost of making the item from the total revenue the company receives from selling the item. This is an example of **combining functions.** It can be written as

$P(x) = R(x) - C(x)$

Many applications of functions involve the combining of two or more component functions. In this section, we will look at several properties that allow for the addition, subtraction, multiplication, and division of functions.

One way in which we combine functions is to find their sum.

Definition

Sum of Two Functions

The **sum of two functions** f and g is written as $f + g$ and defined as

$(f + g)(x) = f(x) + g(x)$

for every value of x that is in the domain of both functions f and g.

We are also combining functions when we find their difference.

Definition

Difference of Two Functions

The **difference of two functions** f and g is written as $f - g$ and defined as

$(f - g)(x) = f(x) - g(x)$

for every value of x that is in the domain of both functions f and g.

Example 1 **Finding the Sum or Difference of Two Functions**

< Objective 1 >

Given the functions $f(x) = 2x - 1$ and $g(x) = -3x + 4$,

(a) Find $(f + g)(x)$.

$$(f + g)(x) = f(x) + g(x)$$
$$= (2x - 1) + (-3x + 4) = -x + 3$$

(b) Find $(f - g)(x)$.

$$(f - g)(x) = f(x) - g(x) = (2x - 1) - (-3x + 4) = 5x - 5$$

(c) Find $(f + g)(2)$.

If we use the definition of the sum of two functions, we find that

$$(f + g)(2) = f(2) + g(2) \qquad f(2) = 2(2) - 1 = 3$$
$$= 3 + (-2) = 1 \qquad g(2) = -3(2) + 4 = -2$$

As an alternative, we could use part **(a)**

$$(f + g)(x) = -x + 3$$

Therefore,

$$(f + g)(2) = -2 + 3 = 1$$

Check Yourself 1

Given the functions $f(x) = -2x - 3$ and $g(x) = 5x - 1$,

(a) Find $(f + g)(x)$. **(b)** Find $(f - g)(x)$. **(c)** Find $(f + g)(2)$.

In defining the sum of two functions, we indicated that the domain was determined by the domain of both functions. We will find the domain in Example 2.

Example 2 Finding the Domain of the Sum or Difference of Functions

< Objective 2 >

Given $f(x) = 2x - 4$ and $g(x) = \frac{1}{x}$,

(a) Find $(f + g)(x)$.

$$(f + g)(x) = (2x - 4) + \frac{1}{x} = 2x - 4 + \frac{1}{x}$$

(b) Find the domain of $f + g$.

The domain of $f + g$ is the set of all numbers in the domain of f and also in the domain of g. The domain of f consists of all real numbers. The domain of g consists of all real numbers except 0 because we cannot divide by 0. The domain of $f + g$ is the set of all real numbers except 0. We write D: $\{x | x \neq 0\}$.

Check Yourself 2

Given $f(x) = -3x + 1$ and $g(x) = \frac{1}{x - 2}$,

(a) Find $(f + g)(x)$. **(b)** Find the domain of $f + g$.

Definition

Product of Two Functions

The **product of two functions** f and g is written as $f \cdot g$ and defined as

$$(f \cdot g)(x) = f(x) \cdot g(x)$$

for every value of x that is in the domain of both functions f and g.

Example 3 Finding the Product and Domain of Two Functions

< Objective 3 >

RECALL

The product of two binomials, $(x + a)(x + b)$ is

$x^2 + bx + ax + ab$

Given $f(x) = x - 1$ and $g(x) = x + 5$.

(a) Find $(f \cdot g)(x)$.

$(f \cdot g)(x) = f(x) \cdot g(x) = (x - 1)(x + 5) = x^2 + 5x - x - 5 = x^2 + 4x - 5$

(b) Find the domain of $f \cdot g$.

The domain of f is the set of all real numbers and the domain of g is the set of all real numbers. The domain of their product is the set of all real numbers. We write D: $\mathbb{R}$.

Check Yourself 3

Given $f(x) = x - 3$ and $g(x) = x + 2$, find $(f \cdot g)(x)$.

The final operation on functions that we will look at involves the quotient of two functions.

Definition

Quotient of Two Functions

The **quotient of two functions** f and g is written as $f \div g$ and defined as

$$(f \div g)(x) = f(x) \div g(x)$$

for every value of x that is in the domain of both functions f and g, such that $g(x) \neq 0$.

As an alternative, we could write

$$(f \div g)(x) = \frac{f(x)}{g(x)}$$

Example 4 Finding the Quotient and Domain of Two Functions

< Objective 4 >

Given $f(x) = x - 1$ and $g(x) = x + 5$,

(a) Find $(f \div g)(x)$.

$$(f \div g)(x) = f(x) \div g(x) = (x - 1) \div (x + 5) = \frac{x - 1}{x + 5}$$

(b) Find the domain of $f \div g$.

The domain is the set of all real numbers except -5 because $g(-5) = 0$, and division by 0 is undefined. We write D: $\{x | x \neq -5\}$.

Check Yourself 4

Given $f(x) = x - 3$ and $g(x) = x + 2$,

(a) Find $(f \div g)(x)$.

(b) Find the domain of $f \div g$.

Check Yourself ANSWERS

1. (a) $3x - 4$; **(b)** $-7x - 2$; **(c)** 2

2. (a) $-3x + 1 + \frac{1}{x - 2}$; **(b)** D: $\{x | x \neq 2\}$

3. $(x - 3)(x + 2) = x^2 - x - 6$

4. (a) $\frac{x - 3}{x + 2}$; **(b)** D: $\{x | x \neq -2\}$

Reading Your Text

The following fill-in-the-blank exercises are designed to ensure that you understand some of the key vocabulary used in this section.

SECTION 10.1

(a) Many applications of functions involve the combining of two or more component ______________.

(b) The sum of two functions f and g is written as $f + g$ and defined as $(f + g)(x) =$ ______________.

(c) In defining the sum of two functions, we indicated that the domain was determined by the ______________ of both functions.

(d) The product of two functions f and g is written as $f \cdot g$ and defined as $(f \cdot g)(x) =$ ______________.

< Objective 1 >

In exercises 1 to 8, find **(a)** $(f+g)(x)$, **(b)** $(f-g)(x)$, **(c)** $(f+g)(3)$, *and* **(d)** $(f-g)(2)$.

1. $f(x) = -4x + 5, \quad g(x) = 7x - 4$

2. $f(x) = 9x - 3, \quad g(x) = -3x + 5$

3. $f(x) = 8x - 2, \quad g(x) = -5x + 6$

4. $f(x) = -7x + 9, \quad g(x) = 2x - 1$

5. $f(x) = x^2 + x - 1, \quad g(x) = -3x^2 - 2x + 5$

6. $f(x) = -3x^2 - 2x + 5, \quad g(x) = 5x^2 + 3x - 6$

7. $f(x) = -x^3 - 5x + 8, \quad g(x) = 2x^2 + 3x - 4$

8. $f(x) = 2x^3 + 3x^2 - 5, \quad g(x) = -4x^2 + 5x - 7$

< Objective 2 >

In exercises 9 to 14, find **(a)** $(f+g)(x)$ *and* **(b)** *the domain of* $f+g$.

9. $f(x) = -9x + 11, \quad g(x) = 15x - 7$

10. $f(x) = -11x + 3, \quad g(x) = 8x - 5$

11. $f(x) = 3x + 2, \quad g(x) = \dfrac{1}{x - 2}$

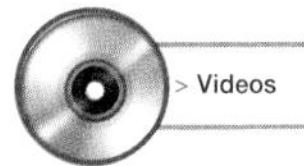

12. $f(x) = -2x + 5, \quad g(x) = \dfrac{3}{x + 1}$

MathZone

Boost your grade at mathzone.com!
- Practice Problems
- NetTutor
- Self-Tests
- e-Professors
- Videos

Name ____________

Section ________ Date ________

Answers

1. (a) $3x + 1$; (b) $-11x + 9$; (c) 10; (d) -13
2. (a) $6x + 2$; (b) $12x - 8$; (c) 20; (d) 16
3. (a) $3x + 4$; (b) $13x - 8$; (c) 13; (d) 18
4. (a) $-5x + 8$; (b) $-9x + 10$; (c) -7; (d) -8
5. (a) $-2x^2 - x + 4$; (b) $4x^2 + 3x - 6$; (c) -17; (d) 16
6. (a) $2x^2 + x - 1$; (b) $-8x^2 - 5x + 11$; (c) 20; (d) -31
7. (a) $-x^3 + 2x^2 - 2x + 4$; (b) $-x^3 - 2x^2 - 8x + 12$; (c) -11; (d) -20
8. (a) $2x^3 - x^2 + 5x - 12$; (b) $2x^3 + 7x^2 - 5x + 2$; (c) 48; (d) 36
9. (a) $6x + 4$; (b) $\mathbb{R}$
10. (a) $-3x - 2$; (b) $\mathbb{R}$
11. (a) $3x + 2 + \dfrac{1}{x - 2}$; (b) $\{x \mid x \neq 2\}$
12. (a) $-2x + 5 + \dfrac{3}{x + 1}$; (b) $\{x \mid x \neq -1\}$

Answers

13. (a) $x^2 + x - 5 + \frac{2}{3x + 1}$; (b) $\left\{x \mid x \neq -\frac{1}{3}\right\}$

14. (a) $3x^2 - 5x + 1 + \frac{-2}{2x - 3}$; (b) $\left\{x \mid x \neq \frac{3}{2}\right\}$

15. (a) $2x^2 - 7x + 3$; (b) $\frac{2x - 1}{x - 3}$; (c) $\{x \mid x \neq 3\}$

16. (a) $-x^2 - x + 12$; (b) $\frac{-x + 3}{x + 4}$; (c) $\{x \mid x \neq -4\}$

17. (a) $6x^2 + x - 2$; (b) $\frac{3x + 2}{2x - 1}$; (c) $\left\{x \mid x \neq \frac{1}{2}\right\}$

18. (a) $3x^2 - 11x + 10$; (b) $\frac{-3x + 5}{-x + 2}$; (c) $\{x \mid x \neq 2\}$

19. (a) $-2x^2 - x + 10$; (b) $\frac{2 - x}{5 + 2x}$; (c) $\left\{x \mid x \neq -\frac{5}{2}\right\}$

20. (a) $-3x^2 - 14x + 5$; (b) $\frac{x + 5}{1 - 3x}$; (c) $\left\{x \mid x \neq \frac{1}{3}\right\}$

21. $P(x) = -x^2 + 21x - 50$

22. $P(x) = -x^2 + 18x - 30$

23. $V(t) = 10 - 9.8t$

24. $V(t) = 64 - 32t$

25. $R(x) = 119x - 6x^2$

26. $R(x) = 1{,}190x - 36x^2$

13. $f(x) = x^2 + x - 5, \quad g(x) = \frac{2}{3x + 1}$

14. $f(x) = 3x^2 - 5x + 1, \quad g(x) = \frac{-2}{2x - 3}$

< Objectives 3–4 >

In exercises 15 to 20, find **(a)** $(f \cdot g)(x)$, **(b)** $(f \div g)(x)$, *and* **(c)** *the domain of* $f \div g$.

15. $f(x) = 2x - 1, \quad g(x) = x - 3$

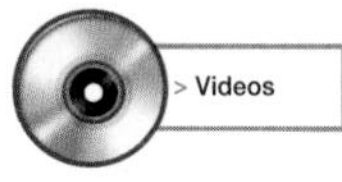

16. $f(x) = -x + 3, \quad g(x) = x + 4$

17. $f(x) = 3x + 2, \quad g(x) = 2x - 1$

18. $f(x) = -3x + 5,$
$g(x) = -x + 2$

19. $f(x) = 2 - x, \quad g(x) = 5 + 2x$

20. $f(x) = x + 5, \quad g(x) = 1 - 3x$

Basic Skills | **Advanced Skills** | Vocational-Technical Applications | Calculator/Computer | Above and Beyond

In business, the profit, $P(x)$, obtained from selling x units of a product is equal to the revenue, $R(x)$, minus the cost, $C(x)$. In exercises 21 and 22, find the profit, $P(x)$, for selling x units.

21. $R(x) = 25x,$
$C(x) = x^2 + 4x + 50$

22. $R(x) = 20x,$
$C(x) = x^2 + 2x + 30$

Let $V(t)$ be the velocity of an object that has been thrown in the air. It can be shown that $V(t)$ is the combination of three functions: the initial velocity, V_0 (this is a constant); the acceleration due to gravity, g (this is also a constant); and the time that has elapsed, t. We have

$$V(t) = V_0 + g \cdot t$$

In exercises 23 and 24, find the velocity as a function of time t.

23. $V_0 = 10$ m/sec, $g = -9.8$ m/sec^2

24. $V_0 = 64$ ft/sec, $g = -32$ ft/sec^2

The revenue, $R(x)$, produced from the sale of an item can be found by multiplying the price, $p(x)$, by the quantity sold, x. In exercises 25 and 26, find the revenue produced from selling x items.

25. $p(x) = 119 - 6x$

26. $p(x) = 1{,}190 - 36x$

Answers

1. **(a)** $3x + 1$; **(b)** $-11x + 9$; **(c)** 10; **(d)** -13 **3.** **(a)** $3x + 4$; **(b)** $13x - 8$; **(c)** 13; **(d)** 18 **5.** **(a)** $-2x^2 - x + 4$; **(b)** $4x^2 + 3x - 6$; **(c)** -17; **(d)** 16 **7.** **(a)** $-x^3 + 2x^2 - 2x + 4$; **(b)** $-x^3 - 2x^2 - 8x + 12$; **(c)** -11; **(d)** -20 **9.** **(a)** $6x + 4$; **(b)** $\mathbb{R}$ **11.** **(a)** $3x + 2 + \frac{1}{x - 2}$; **(b)** $\{x|x \neq 2\}$ **13.** **(a)** $x^2 + x - 5 + \frac{2}{3x + 1}$; **(b)** $\left\{x|x \neq -\frac{1}{3}\right\}$ **15.** **(a)** $2x^2 - 7x + 3$; **(b)** $\frac{2x - 1}{x - 3}$; **(c)** $\{x|x \neq 3\}$ **17.** **(a)** $6x^2 + x - 2$; **(b)** $\frac{3x + 2}{2x - 1}$; **(c)** $\left\{x|x \neq \frac{1}{2}\right\}$ **19.** **(a)** $-2x^2 - x + 10$; **(b)** $\frac{2 - x}{5 + 2x}$; **(c)** $\left\{x|x \neq -\frac{5}{2}\right\}$ **21.** $P(x) = -x^2 + 21x - 50$ **23.** $V(t) = 10 - 9.8t$ **25.** $R(x) = 119x - 6x^2$

10.2 Composition of Functions

< 10.2 Objectives >

1 > Evaluate the composition of two functions given in table form

2 > Evaluate the composition of two functions given in equation form

3 > Write a function as a composition of two simpler functions

4 > Solve an application involving function composition

In Section 10.1, we learned that two functions could be combined using any of the standard operations of arithmetic. In this section we examine another way to combine two functions called **composition.**

Definition

Composition of Functions

The **composition** of functions f and g is the function $f \circ g$ where

$(f \circ g)(x) = f(g(x))$

The domain of the composition is the set of all elements x in the domain of g for which $g(x)$ is in the domain of f.

Composition may be thought of as a chaining together of functions. To understand the meaning of $(f \circ g)(x)$, note that first the function g acts on x, producing $g(x)$, and then the function f acts on $g(x)$.

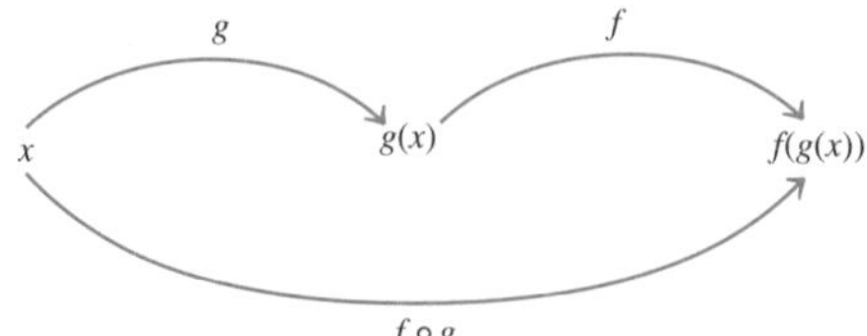

Step by Step

Finding the Composition $f \circ g$

Step 1 Find $g(x)$.

Step 2 Find the value of f at $g(x)$.

Consider Example 1 involving functions given in table form.

Example 1 Composing Two Functions

< Objective 1 >

Suppose we have the functions f and g:

x	$g(x)$
−2	5
1	0
3	−4
8	2

x	$f(x)$
−4	8
0	6
2	5
1	−2

(a) Find $(f \circ g)(1)$.

Because $(f \circ g)(1) = f(g(1))$, we first find $g(1)$. In the table for g we see that $g(1) = 0$. We then find $f(0)$. In the table for f we see that $f(0) = 6$. We then have

$(f \circ g)(1) = f(g(1)) = f(0) = 6$

or $(f \circ g)(1) = 6$.

NOTE

Think. What does g do to 1? And then, what does f do to the result?

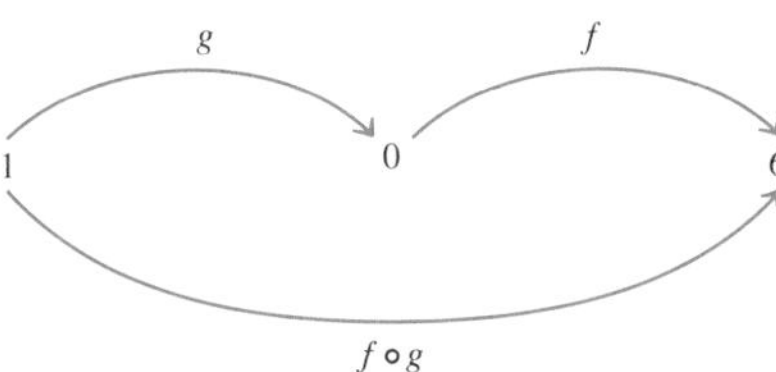

(b) Find $(f \circ g)(8)$.

Because $(f \circ g)(8) = f(g(8))$, we first note that $g(8) = 2$. Next we note that $f(2) = 5$. So we have

$(f \circ g)(8) = f(g(8)) = f(2) = 5$

or $(f \circ g)(8) = 5$.

> CAUTION

When evaluating $(f \circ g)(x)$, the first function to act is g, not f.

(c) Find $(f \circ g)(-2)$.

Because $(f \circ g)(-2) = f(g(-2))$, we see that $g(-2) = 5$. But we cannot compute $f(5)$ because 5 is not in the domain of f. So $(f \circ g)(-2)$ does not exist.

NOTE

−2 is not in the domain of $f \circ g$.

(d) Find $(f \circ g)(3)$.

Because $(f \circ g)(3) = f(g(3))$, we first find $g(3) = -4$. We then find that $f(-4) = 8$. Altogether we have

$(f \circ g)(3) = f(g(3)) = f(-4) = 8$

or $(f \circ g)(3) = 8$.

Check Yourself 1

Using the functions given in Example 1, find

(a) $(g \circ f)(-4)$ **(b)** $(g \circ f)(1)$ **(c)** $(g \circ f)(2)$

Typically, we encounter the composition of functions given in equation form. Example 2 again demonstrates how f and g are chained together to form the new function $f \circ g$.

Example 2 Composing Two Functions

< Objective 2 >

NOTE

The function g turns 0 into 3. The function f then turns 3 into 7.

Suppose we have the functions $f(x) = x^2 - 2$ and $g(x) = x + 3$.

(a) Find $(f \circ g)(0)$.

Because $(f \circ g)(0) = f(g(0))$, we first find $g(0)$:

$g(0) = 0 + 3 = 3$

Then,

$f(3) = 3^2 - 2 = 7$

Altogether,

$f(g(0)) = f(3) = 7$

So,

$(f \circ g)(0) = 7$

(b) Find $(f \circ g)(4)$.

Because $(f \circ g)(4) = f(g(4))$, we first find $g(4)$:

$g(4) = 4 + 3 = 7$

Then,

$f(7) = 7^2 - 2 = 47$

So,

$(f \circ g)(4) = f(g(4)) = f(7) = 47$

or $(f \circ g)(4) = 47$

(c) Find $(f \circ g)(x)$.

Because $(f \circ g)(x) = f(g(x))$, we first note that $g(x) = x + 3$. Then,

$$\begin{aligned} f(g(x)) &= f(x + 3) = (x + 3)^2 - 2 \\ &= x^2 + 6x + 9 - 2 = x^2 + 6x + 7 \end{aligned}$$

So,

$(f \circ g)(x) = x^2 + 6x + 7$

Check Yourself 2

Suppose that $f(x) = x^2 + x$ and $g(x) = x - 1$. Find each of the compositions.

(a) $(f \circ g)(0)$ **(b)** $(f \circ g)(-2)$ **(c)** $(f \circ g)(x)$

In Example 3, we will need to pay attention to the domains of the functions involved.

Example 3 Composing Two Functions

Suppose we have the functions $f(x) = \sqrt{x}$ and $g(x) = 3 - x$. Find each of the compositions.

(a) $(f \circ g)(1) = f(g(1))$ Note that $g(1) = 2$.

$= f(2)$

$= \sqrt{2}$

(b) $(f \circ g)(-1) = f(g(-1))$ Note that $g(-1) = 4$.

$= f(4)$

$= \sqrt{4}$

$= 2$

(c) $(f \circ g)(7) = f(g(7))$ Note that $g(7) = -4$.

$= f(-4)$

$= \sqrt{-4}$

Because this is not a real number, we say that $(f \circ g)(7)$ does not exist. 7 is not in the domain of $f \circ g$.

NOTE

Graph the function $y = \sqrt{3 - x}$ in your graphing calculator. Observe that the graph only exists for $x \leq 3$.

(d) $(f \circ g)(x) = f(g(x))$

$= f(3 - x)$

$= \sqrt{3 - x}$

This function produces real number values only if $3 - x \geq 0$. That is, only if $x \leq 3$. This is in fact the domain of $f \circ g$.

Check Yourself 3

Suppose that $f(x) = \frac{1}{x}$ and $g(x) = x^2 - 4$. Find each of the compositions.

(a) $(f \circ g)(0)$ **(b)** $(f \circ g)(-2)$ **(c)** $(f \circ g)(x)$

The order of composition is important. In general, $(f \circ g)(x) \neq (g \circ f)(x)$. Using the functions given in Example 2, we saw that $(f \circ g)(x) = x^2 + 6x + 7$. Whereas,

$$(g \circ f)(x) = g(f(x)) = g(x^2 - 2) = x^2 - 2 + 3 = x^2 + 1$$

Often it is convenient to write a given function as the composition of two simpler functions. While the choice of simpler functions is not unique, a good choice makes many applications easier to solve.

Example 4 Writing a Function as the Composition of Two Functions

< Objective 3 >

Use the functions $f(x) = x + 3$ and $g(x) = x^2$ to express the given function h as a composition of f and g.

(a) $h(x) = (x + 3)^2$

Note that when a value is substituted for x, the first action that occurs is that 3 is added to the input. The function f does exactly that. The second action that occurs is that of squaring. The function g does this.

Since f acts first, and then g (to carry out the total action of h), we propose:

NOTE

Can you see how we are using the order of operations here?

$h(x) = g(f(x)) = (g \circ f)(x)$

It is easily checked that $(g \circ f)(x) = h(x)$.

$(g \circ f)(x) = g(f(x)) = g(x + 3) = (x + 3)^2 = h(x)$

(b) $k(x) = x^2 + 3$

Now when a value is substituted for x, the first action that occurs is a squaring action (which is what g does). The second action is that of adding 3 (which is what f does). We propose:

$k(x) = f(g(x)) = (f \circ g)(x)$

Check.

$(f \circ g)(x) = f(g(x)) = f(x^2) = x^2 + 3 = k(x)$

Check Yourself 4

Use the functions $f(x) = \sqrt{x}$ and $g(x) = x + 2$ to express the given function as a composition of f and g.

(a) $h(x) = \sqrt{x + 2}$ **(b)** $k(x) = \sqrt{x} + 2$

There are many examples that involve the composition of functions as illustrated in Example 5.

Example 5 Solving an Application Involving Function Composition

< Objective 4 >

At Kinky's Duplication Salon, customers pay \$2 plus 4¢ per page copied. Duplication consultant, Vinny, makes a commission of 5% of the bill for each job he sends to Kinky's.

(a) Express a customer's bill, B, as a function of the number of pages copied, p.

$B(p) = 0.04p + 2$

(b) Express Vinny's commission, V, as a function of each customer's bill, B.

$V(B) = 0.05B$

(c) Use function composition to express Vinny's commission, V, as a function of the number of pages a customer has copied, p.

$V(B(p)) = 0.05(0.04p + 2) = 0.002p + 0.1$

(d) Use the function in part **(c)** to find Vinny's commission on a job consisting of 2,000 pages.

$V(2{,}000) = 0.002(2{,}000) + 0.1 = 4 + 0.1 = 4.1$

Therefore, Vinny's commission is \$4.10.

Check Yourself 5

On his regular route, Gonzalo averages 62 mi/h between Charlottesville and Lawrenceville. His van averages 24 mi/gal, and his gas tank holds 12 gal of fuel.
Assume that his tank is full when he starts the trip from Charlottesville to Lawrenceville.

(a) Express the fuel left in the tank as a function of n, the number of gallons used.
(b) Express the number of gallons used as a function of m, the number of miles driven.
(c) Express the fuel left in the tank as a function of m, the number of miles driven.

Check Yourself ANSWERS

1. (a) 2; **(b)** 5; **(c)** does not exist **2. (a)** 0; **(b)** 6; **(c)** $x^2 - x$
3. (a) $-\frac{1}{4}$; **(b)** does not exist; **(c)** $\frac{1}{x^2 - 4}$ **4. (a)** $(f \circ g)(x)$; **(b)** $(g \circ f)(x)$
5. (a) $f(n) = 12 - n$; **(b)** $g(m) = \frac{m}{24}$; **(c)** $(f \circ g)(m) = 12 - \frac{m}{24}$

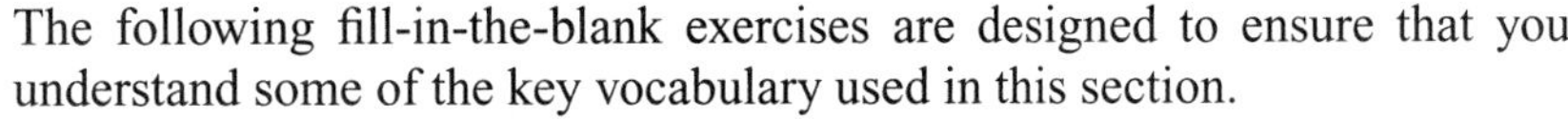

Reading Your Text

The following fill-in-the-blank exercises are designed to ensure that you understand some of the key vocabulary used in this section.

SECTION 10.2

(a) The composition of functions f and g is the function $f \circ g$ where $(f \circ g)(x) =$ ______________.

(b) Composition may be thought of as a ______________ together of functions.

(c) To understand the meaning of $(f \circ g)(x)$, we note that the first function g acts on x, producing $g(x)$, and then the function f acts on ______________.

(d) In general, $(f \circ g)(x)$ ______________ $(g \circ f)(x)$.

10.2 exercises

Basic Skills | Advanced Skills | Vocational-Technical Applications | Calculator/Computer | Above and Beyond

Name ____________

Section ________ Date ________

Answers

1. −3
2. 5
3. 5
4. −3
5. Does not exist
6. −4
7. 3
8. Does not exist
9. 4
10. 5
11. 5
12. 3
13. (a) −2; (b) −6; (c) 4; (d) $2x - 2$
14. (a) 3; (b) −3; (c) 12; (d) $3x + 3$
15. (a) 9; (b) −3; (c) 20; (d) $6x + 2$
16. (a) 18; (b) 34; (c) −15; (d) $-8x + 9$

< Objective 1 >

Use the tables to find the desired values.

x	$f(x)$
−3	−8
−1	2
2	4
5	−3

x	$g(x)$
−6	1
0	3
1	3
4	5

x	$h(x)$
−4	3
−2	7
3	5
7	−4

x	$k(x)$
−5	2
−3	−4
0	2
6	−4

1. $(f \circ g)(4)$

2. $(g \circ f)(2)$

3. $(h \circ g)(1)$

4. $(f \circ h)(3)$

5. $(g \circ h)(3)$

6. $(k \circ f)(5)$

7. $(h \circ k)(-3)$

8. $(h \circ k)(0)$

9. $(f \circ k)(-5)$

10. $(h \circ g)(0)$

11. $(h \circ h)(-4)$

12. $(g \circ g)(-6)$

< Objective 2 >

In Exercises 13 to 20, f and g are given. Evaluate the composite functions in each part.

13. $f(x) = x - 3, \quad g(x) = 2x + 1$

(a) $(f \circ g)(0)$ **(b)** $(f \circ g)(-2)$ **(c)** $(f \circ g)(3)$ **(d)** $(f \circ g)(x)$

14. $f(x) = x - 1, \quad g(x) = 3x + 4$

(a) $(f \circ g)(0)$ **(b)** $(f \circ g)(-2)$ **(c)** $(f \circ g)(3)$ **(d)** $(f \circ g)(x)$

15. $f(x) = 2x - 1, \quad g(x) = 3x + 5$

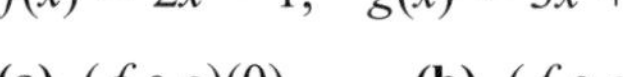

(a) $(f \circ g)(0)$ **(b)** $(f \circ g)(-2)$ **(c)** $(g \circ f)(3)$ **(d)** $(g \circ f)(x)$

16. $f(x) = 4x - 2, \quad g(x) = -2x + 5$

(a) $(f \circ g)(0)$ **(b)** $(f \circ g)(-2)$ **(c)** $(g \circ f)(3)$ **(d)** $(g \circ f)(x)$

17. $f(x) = x^2, \quad g(x) = x + 3$

(a) $(f \circ g)(0)$ (b) $(f \circ g)(-2)$ (c) $(g \circ f)(3)$ (d) $(g \circ f)(x)$

18. $f(x) = x^2 + 3, \quad g(x) = 3x$

(a) $(f \circ g)(0)$ (b) $(f \circ g)(-2)$ (c) $(g \circ f)(3)$ (d) $(g \circ f)(x)$

19. $f(x) = x^2, \quad g(x) = x + 3$

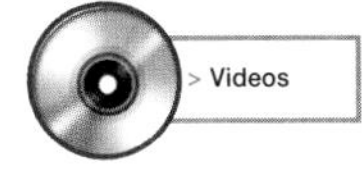

(a) $(g \circ f)(0)$ (b) $(g \circ f)(-2)$ (c) $(f \circ g)(3)$ (d) $(f \circ g)(x)$

20. $f(x) = x^2 + 3, \quad g(x) = 3x$

(a) $(g \circ f)(0)$ (b) $(g \circ f)(-2)$ (c) $(f \circ g)(3)$ (d) $(f \circ g)(x)$

< Objective 3 >

Rewrite the function h as a composite of functions f and g.

21. $f(x) = 3x, \quad g(x) = x + 2, \quad h(x) = 3x + 2$

22. $f(x) = x - 4, \quad g(x) = 7x, \quad h(x) = 7x - 4$

23. $f(x) = x + 5, \quad g(x) = \sqrt{x}, \quad h(x) = \sqrt{x + 5}$

24. $f(x) = x + 5, \quad g(x) = \sqrt{x}, \quad h(x) = \sqrt{x} + 5$

25. $f(x) = x^2, \quad g(x) = x - 5, \quad h(x) = x^2 - 5$

26. $f(x) = x^2, \quad g(x) = x - 5, \quad h(x) = (x - 5)^2$

27. $f(x) = x - 3, \quad g(x) = \dfrac{2}{x}, \quad h(x) = \dfrac{2}{x - 3}$

28. $f(x) = x - 3, \quad g(x) = \dfrac{2}{x}, \quad h(x) = \dfrac{2}{x} - 3$

29. $f(x) = x - 1, \quad g(x) = x^2 + 2, \quad h(x) = x^2 + 1$

30. $f(x) = x - 1, \quad g(x) = x^2 + 2, \quad h(x) = x^2 - 2x + 3$

Answers

17. (a) 9; (b) 1; (c) 12; (d) $x^2 + 3$
18. (a) 3; (b) 39; (c) 36; (d) $3x^2 + 9$
19. (a) 3; (b) 7; (c) 36; (d) $x^2 + 6x + 9$
20. (a) 9; (b) 21; (c) 84; (d) $9x^2 + 3$
21. $h(x) = (g \circ f)(x)$
22. $h(x) = (f \circ g)(x)$
23. $h(x) = (g \circ f)(x)$
24. $h(x) = (f \circ g)(x)$
25. $h(x) = (g \circ f)(x)$
26. $h(x) = (f \circ g)(x)$
27. $h(x) = (g \circ f)(x)$
28. $h(x) = (f \circ g)(x)$
29. $h(x) = (f \circ g)(x)$
30. $h(x) = (g \circ f)(x)$

Answers

31. (a) $N(v) = 0.8v$;
(b) $C(N) = 40N + 1,000$;
(c) $C(v) = 32v + 1,000$

32. 0.3800

< Objective 4 >

Solve the following applications.

31. Carine and Jacob are getting married at East Fork Estates. The wedding will cost \$1,000 plus \$40 per guest. They have read that, typically, 80% of the people invited actually attend a wedding.

(a) Write a function to represent the number of people, N, expected to attend if v are invited.

(b) Write a function to represent the cost, C, of the wedding for N guests.

(c) Write a function to represent the cost, C, of the wedding if v people are invited.

32. If the exchange rate for Japanese yen is 127.3 and the exchange rate for Indian rupees is 48.37 (both from U.S. dollars), then what is the exchange rate from Japanese yen to Indian rupees?

Answers

1. -3 **3.** 5 **5.** Does not exist **7.** 3 **9.** 4 **11.** 5
13. **(a)** -2; **(b)** -6; **(c)** 4; **(d)** $2x - 2$ **15.** **(a)** 9; **(b)** -3; **(c)** 20; **(d)** $6x + 2$
17. **(a)** 9; **(b)** 1; **(c)** 12; **(d)** $x^2 + 3$ **19.** **(a)** 3; **(b)** 7; **(c)** 36; **(d)** $x^2 + 6x + 9$
21. $h(x) = (g \circ f)(x)$ **23.** $h(x) = (g \circ f)(x)$ **25.** $h(x) = (g \circ f)(x)$
27. $h(x) = (g \circ f)(x)$ **29.** $h(x) = (f \circ g)(x)$
31. **(a)** $N(v) = 0.8v$; **(b)** $C(N) = 40N + 1,000$; **(c)** $C(v) = 32v + 1,000$

10.3 One-to-One and Inverse Functions

< 10.3 Objectives >

1 > Find the inverse of a function given in equation form

2 > Find the inverse of a function given in table form

3 > Graph a relation and its inverse

4 > Identify a one-to-one function

5 > Determine if the inverse of a function is also a function

The use of composition introduced in Section 10.2 leads us to the question: Can we chain together (i.e., compose) two functions in such a way that one function "undoes" the other? Suppose, for example, that $f(x) = \frac{x - 5}{3}$ and $g(x) = 3x + 5$. We will pick a convenient x value for f, say $x = 8$. Then $f(8) = \frac{8 - 5}{3} = \frac{3}{3} = 1$. The function f turns 8 into 1. Now let g act on this result: $g(1) = 3(1) + 5 = 8$. The function g turns 1 back into 8.

When we view the composition of g and f, acting on 8, we see this effect of g "undoing" f's actions:

$$(g \circ f)(8) = g(f(8)) = g(1) = 8$$

In general, a function g that undoes the action of f is called the **inverse** of f.

Definition

Inverse Functions

f and g are said to be **inverse functions** if

$(g \circ f)(x) = x$ for all x in the domain of f

and

$(f \circ g)(x) = x$ for all x in the domain of g

NOTE

The notation f^{-1} has a different meaning from the negative exponent, as in x^{-1} or $\frac{1}{x}$.

If g is the inverse of f, we denote the function g as f^{-1}.

A natural question now is: Given a function f, how do we find the inverse function f^{-1}? One way to find such a function f^{-1} is to first analyze the actions of f, noting the order of operations involved, and then to define f^{-1} using the *opposite* operations *in the reverse order.*

Example 1 Finding the Inverse of a Function

< Objective 1 >

Given $f(x) = \dfrac{x - 5}{3}$, find its inverse function f^{-1}.

When we substitute a value for x into f, two actions occur in the following order:

Step 1 5 is subtracted.

Step 2 Division by 3 occurs.

To design an inverse function f^{-1}, we use the *opposite* operations *in the reverse order:*

Step 1 Multiplication by 3 occurs.

Step 2 5 is added.

So we conclude: $f^{-1}(x) = 3x + 5$.

To verify, we must check that $(f^{-1} \circ f)(x) = x$ and $(f \circ f^{-1})(x) = x$:

$$(f^{-1} \circ f)(x) = f^{-1}(f(x)) = f^{-1}\left(\frac{x - 5}{3}\right) = 3\left(\frac{x - 5}{3}\right) + 5 = x - 5 + 5 = x$$

$$(f \circ f^{-1})(x) = f(f^{-1}(x)) = f(3x + 5) = \frac{3x + 5 - 5}{3} = \frac{3x}{3} = x$$

Check Yourself 1

Given $f(x) = \dfrac{x + 1}{4}$, find f^{-1}.

To develop another technique for finding inverses, let us revisit functions defined by tables.

Example 2 Finding the Inverse of a Function

< Objective 2 >

Find the inverse of the function f:

x	$f(x)$
−4	8
0	6
2	5
1	−2

The inverse of f is easily found by reversing the order of the input values and output values:

x	$f^{-1}(x)$	As ordered pairs:
8	−4	(8, −4)
6	0	(6, 0)
5	2	(5, 2)
−2	1	(−2, 1)

NOTE

The domain of $f(x)$ becomes the range of $f^{-1}(x)$ and the range of $f(x)$ becomes the domain of $f^{-1}(x)$.

Note that while f turns −4 into 8, for example, f^{-1} turns 8 back into −4.

Check Yourself 2

Find the inverse of the function f:

x	$f(x)$
−2	5
1	0
4	−4
8	2

In Example 2, if we write y in place of $f(x)$, we see that we are just interchanging the roles of x and y in order to create the inverse f^{-1}. This suggests a technique for finding the inverse of a function given in equation form.

Step by Step

Finding the Inverse of a Function

Step 1 Given a function $f(x)$ in equation form, write y in place of $f(x)$.
Step 2 Interchange the variables x and y.
Step 3 Solve for y.
Step 4 Write $f^{-1}(x)$ in place of y.

Example 3 Finding the Inverse of a Function

Find the inverse of $f(x) = 2x - 4$.

Begin by writing y in place of $f(x)$:

$$y = 2x - 4 \qquad \text{Interchange } x \text{ and } y.$$

$$x = 2y - 4 \qquad \text{Solve for } y. \text{ Add 4 to both sides.}$$

$$x + 4 = 2y \qquad \text{Divide both sides by 2.}$$

$$\frac{x + 4}{2} = y \qquad \text{Write } f^{-1}(x) \text{ in place of } y.$$

So,

$$f^{-1}(x) = \frac{x + 4}{2}$$

You should verify this result by checking that $(f^{-1} \circ f)(x) = x$ and $(f \circ f^{-1})(x) = x$.

Check Yourself 3

Find the inverse of $f(x) = \dfrac{x - 7}{5}$.

The graphs of relations and their inverses are connected in an interesting way. First, note that the graphs of the ordered pairs (a, b) and (b, a) always have symmetry about the line $y = x$.

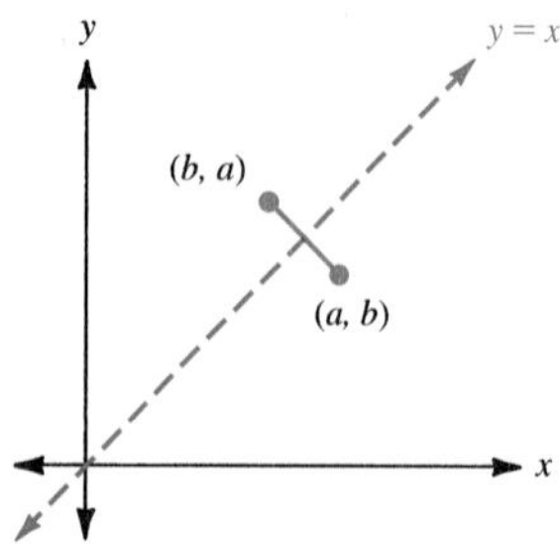

Now, with this symmetry in mind, we will consider Example 4.

Example 4 Graphing a Relation and Its Inverse

< Objective 3 >

Graph the function f from Example 3 along with its inverse.

Recall that

$$f(x) = 2x - 4$$

and

$$f^{-1}(x) = \frac{1}{2}x + 2$$

NOTE

We write $f^{-1}(x)$ in slope-intercept form $y = mx + b$ to graph it.

$$f^{-1}(x) = \frac{x + 4}{2} = \frac{x}{2} + \frac{4}{2} = \frac{1}{2}x + 2$$

The graphs of f and f^{-1} are shown here.

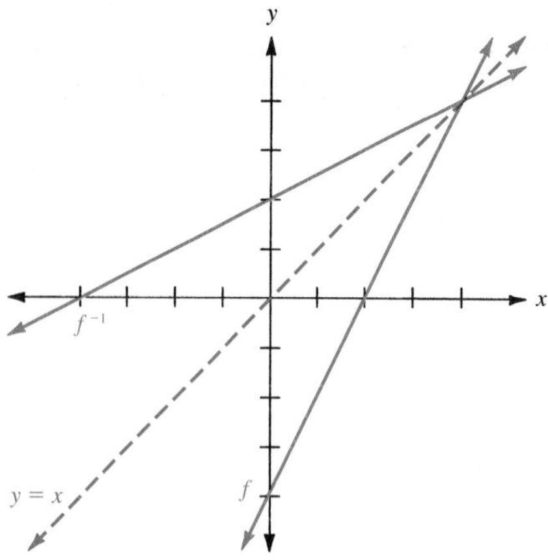

Now we can see the graphs of f and f^{-1} are symmetric about the line $y = x$. That symmetry follows from our earlier observation about the pairs (a, b) and (b, a) because we simply reversed the roles of x and y in forming the inverse relation.

Check Yourself 4

Graph the function $g(x) = 3x + 6$ along with its inverse.

From our work thus far, we have seen techniques for finding the inverse of a function. However, it is quite possible that the inverse obtained may not be a function.

Example 5 Finding the Inverse of a Function

NOTE

The elements of the ordered pairs have been interchanged.

Find the inverses of the functions.

(a) $f = \{(1, 3), (2, 4), (3, 9)\}$

Its inverse is

$\{(3, 1), (4, 2), (9, 3)\}$

which is also a function.

(b) $g = \{(1, 3), (2, 6), (3, 6)\}$

NOTE

It is not a function because 6 is mapped to both 2 and 3.

Its inverse is

$\{(3, 1), (6, 2), (6, 3)\}$

which is *not* a function.

Check Yourself 5

Write the inverses for each of the functions. Which of the inverses are also functions?

(a) $\{(-1, 2), (0, 3), (1, 4)\}$ **(b)** $\{(2, 5), (3, 7), (4, 5)\}$

Can we predict in advance whether the inverse of a function will also be a function? The answer is yes. We already know that, for a relation to be a function, no element in its domain can be associated with more than one element in its range. Because, in creating an inverse, the x-values and y-values are interchanged, the inverse of a function f will also be a function only if *no element in the range of f can be associated with more than one element in its domain.* That is, no two ordered pairs of f can have the same y-coordinate. This leads us to the following definition.

Definition

One-to-One Function

A function f is **one-to-one** if no two distinct domain elements are paired with the same range element.

We then have the following property.

Property

Inverse of a Function

The inverse of a function f is also a function if f is one-to-one.

NOTE

g is not one-to-one because both 2 and 3 are paired with 6.

Note that in Example 5(a)

$f = \{(1, 3), (2, 4), (3, 9)\}$

is a one-to-one function and its inverse is also a function. However, the function in Example 5(b)

$g = \{(1, 3), (2, 6), (3, 6)\}$

is *not* a one-to-one function, and its inverse is *not* a function.

Our result regarding a one-to-one function and its inverse also has a convenient graphical interpretation. Here we graph the function g from Example 5:

$g = \{(1, 3), (2, 6), (3, 6)\}$

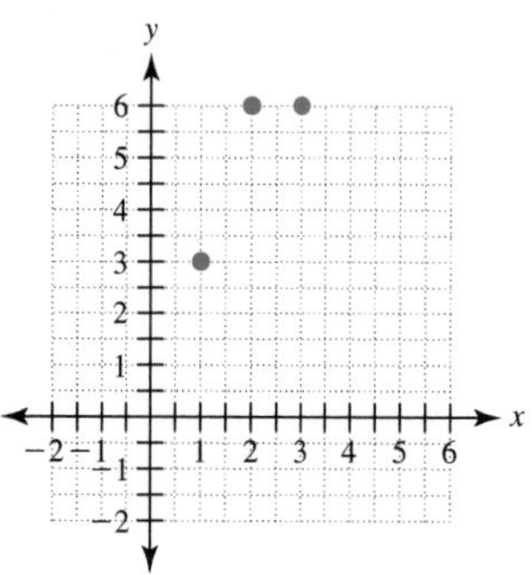

Again, g is *not* a one-to-one function, since two pairs, namely, (2, 6) and (3, 6), have the same range element. As a result, a horizontal line may be drawn that passes through two points.

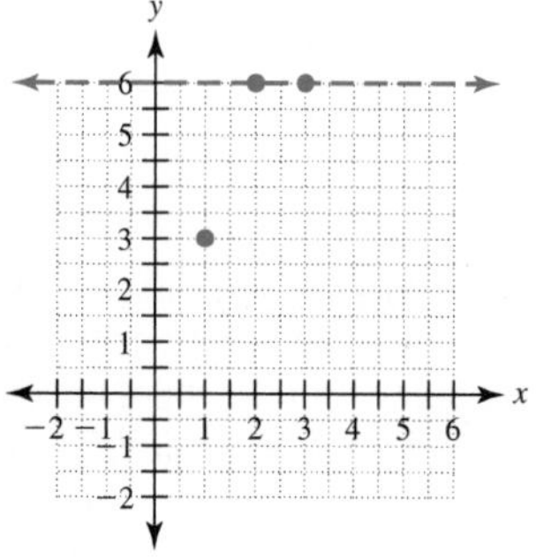

This means that when we form the inverse by reversing the coordinates, the resulting relation will *not* be a function. The pairs (6, 2) and (6, 3) are part of the inverse, and the resulting graph fails the vertical line test.

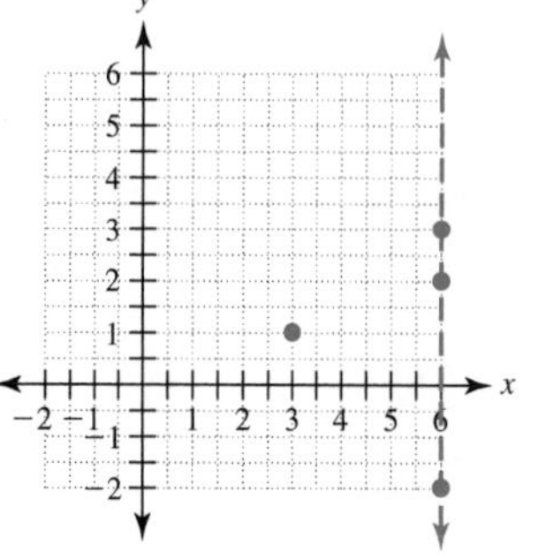

NOTE

In Section 3.2, we referred to the *vertical-line test* to determine whether a relation was a function. The *horizontal-line test* determines whether a function is one-to-one.

This leads us to the **horizontal-line test.**

Definition

Horizontal-Line Test

A function is one-to-one if no horizontal line can pass through two or more points on its graph.

Now we have a graphical way to determine whether the inverse of a function *f* will also be a function.

Property

Inverse of a Function

The inverse of a function *f* is also a function if the graph of *f* passes the horizontal-line test.

This is a very useful property, as Example 6 illustrates.

Example 6 Identifying One-to-One Functions

< Objectives 4 and 5 >

For each function, determine (i) whether the function is one-to-one, and (ii) whether the inverse is also a function.

(a)

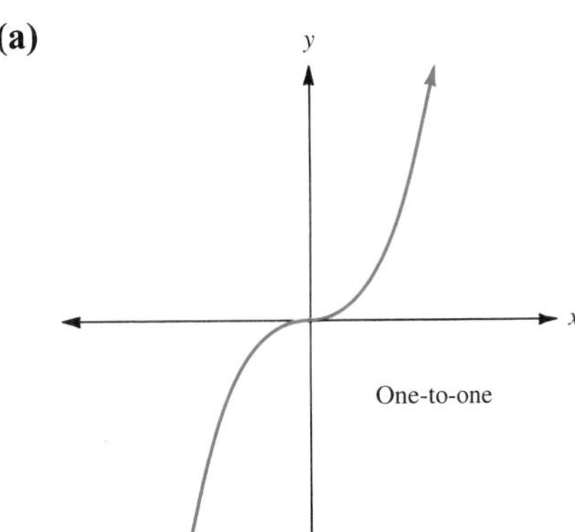

(i) Because no horizontal line passes through two or more points of the graph, *f* is one-to-one.

(ii) Because *f* is one-to-one, the inverse is also a function.

(b)

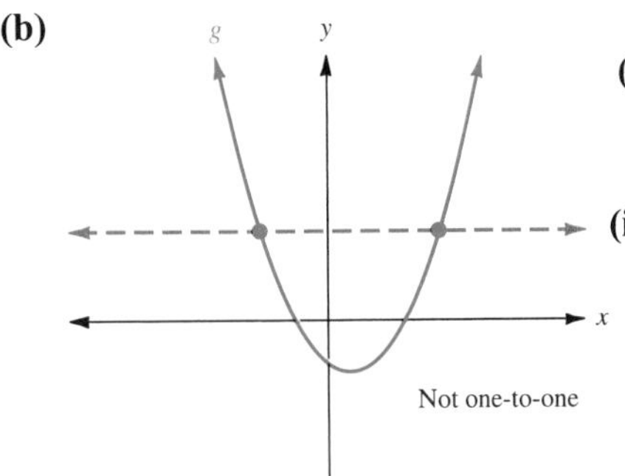

(i) Because a horizontal line can meet the graph of *g* at two points, *g* is *not* a one-to-one function.

(ii) Because *g* is not one-to-one, the inverse is not a function.

Check Yourself 6

For each function, determine (i) whether the function is one-to-one, and (ii) whether the inverse is also a function.

(a)

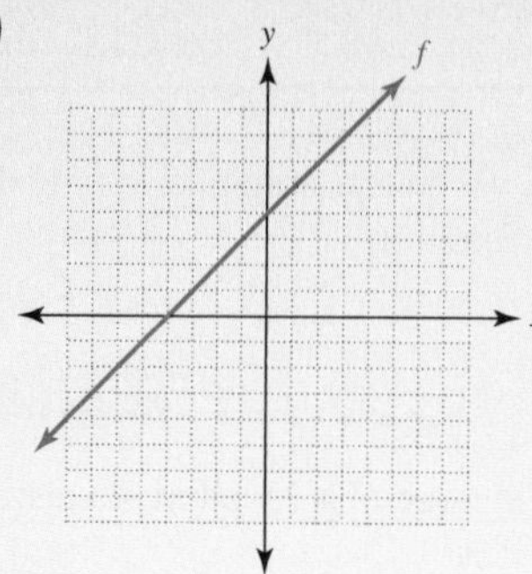

(b)

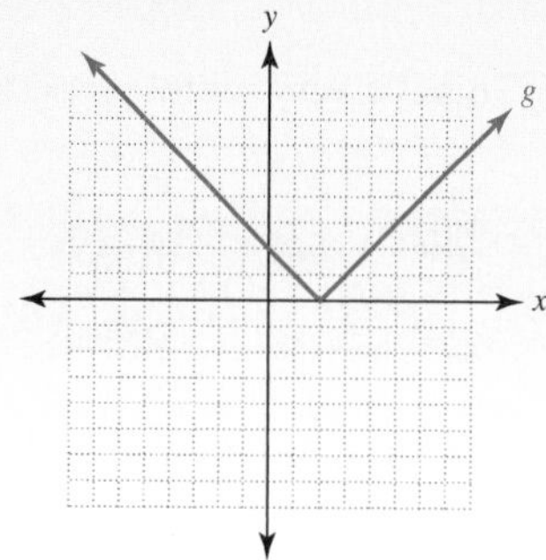

Check Yourself ANSWERS

1. $f^{-1}(x) = 4x - 1$

2.

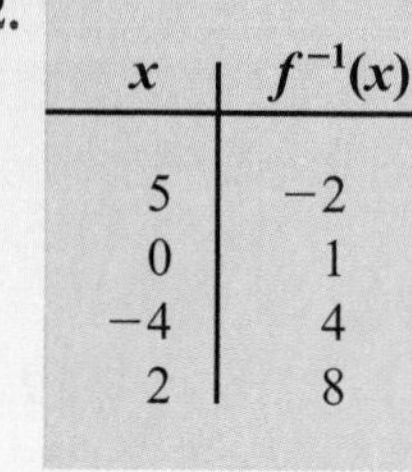

x	$f^{-1}(x)$
5	−2
0	1
−4	4
2	8

As ordered pairs: $(5, -2), (0, 1), (-4, 4), (2, 8)$

3. $f^{-1}(x) = 5x + 7$

4.

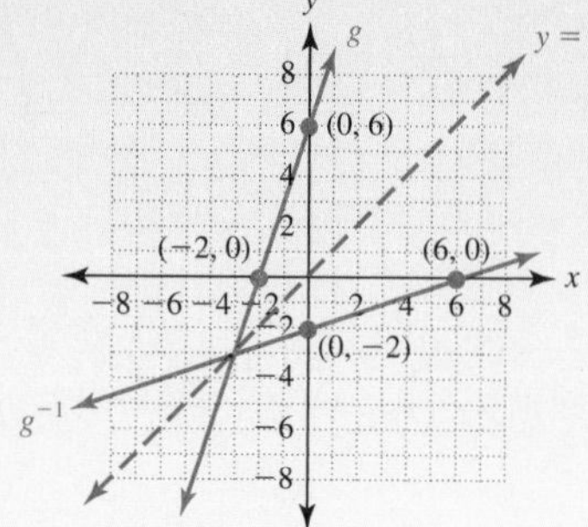

5. (a) $\{(2, -1), (3, 0), (4, 1)\}$; function

(b) $\{(5, 2), (7, 3), (5, 4)\}$; not a function

6. (a) One-to-one; inverse is a function

(b) Not one-to-one; inverse is not a function

Reading Your Text

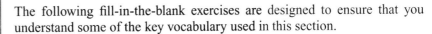

The following fill-in-the-blank exercises are designed to ensure that you understand some of the key vocabulary used in this section.

SECTION 10.3

(a) In general a function g that undoes the action of f is called the ________________ of f.

(b) To find the inverse of a function in equation form, write y in place of $f(x)$, ________________ x and y in the equation, and solve for y.

(c) The graphs of a function and its inverse are ________________ about the line $y = x$.

(d) A function f is one-to-one if no two distinct domain elements are paired with the ________________ range element.

10.3 exercises

Basic Skills | Advanced Skills | Vocational-Technical Applications | Calculator/Computer | Above and Beyond

Name ______________

Section ________ Date ________

< Objective 1 >

Find the inverse function f^{-1} for the given function f.

1. $f(x) = 2x - 8$

2. $f(x) = -2x - 4$

3. $f(x) = \dfrac{x - 1}{2}$

4. $f(x) = \dfrac{x + 1}{3}$

5. $f(x) = 4x + 5$

6. $f(x) = -3x + 7$

7. $f(x) = \dfrac{x + 2}{6}$

8. $f(x) = \dfrac{x - 3}{9}$

< Objective 2 >

In exercises 9 to 18, find the inverse of each function. In each case, determine whether the inverse is also a function.

9.

x	f(x)
−3	−8
−1	2
2	4
5	−3

10.

x	g(x)
−6	1
0	3
1	3
4	5

11.

x	h(x)
−4	3
−2	7
3	5
7	−4

12.

x	k(x)
−5	2
−3	−4
0	2
6	−4

13. $f = \{(2, 3), (3, 4), (4, 5)\}$

14. $g = \{(2, 3), (3, 4), (4, 3)\}$

Answers

1. $f^{-1}(x) = \dfrac{x + 8}{2}$
2. $f^{-1}(x) = \dfrac{x + 4}{-2} = \dfrac{-x - 4}{2}$
3. $f^{-1}(x) = 2x + 1$
4. $f^{-1}(x) = 3x - 1$
5. $f^{-1}(x) = \dfrac{x - 5}{4}$
6. $f^{-1}(x) = \dfrac{x - 7}{-3} = \dfrac{-x + 7}{3}$
7. $f^{-1}(x) = 6x - 2$
8. $f^{-1}(x) = 9x + 3$
9. {(−8, −3), (2, −1), (4, 2), (−3, 5)}; function
10. {(1, −6), (3, 0), (3, 1), (5, 4)}; not a function
11. {(3, −4), (7, −2), (5, 3), (−4, 7)}; function
12. {(2, −5), (−4, −3), (2, 0), (−4, 6)}; not a function
13. {(3, 2), (4, 3), (5, 4)}; function
14. {(3, 2), (4, 3), (3, 4)}; not a function

15. $f = \{(1, 2), (2, 2), (3, 2)\}$

16. $g = \{(5, 9), (3, 7), (7, 5)\}$

17. $f = \{(2, 4), (3, 9), (4, 16)\}$

18. $g = \{(-1, 2), (0, 3), (1, 2)\}$

In exercises 19 to 22, find the inverse function f^{-1} for the given function f. (Hint: *Use the method demonstrated in Example* 3.)

19. $f(x) = \dfrac{3 - 2x}{5}$

20. $f(x) = \dfrac{7 - 4x}{6}$

21. $f(x) = \dfrac{8x}{5} - 1$

22. $f(x) = 6 - \dfrac{2x}{7}$

< Objective 3 >

For each function f, find its inverse f^{-1}. Then graph both on the same set of axes.

23. $f(x) = 3x - 6$

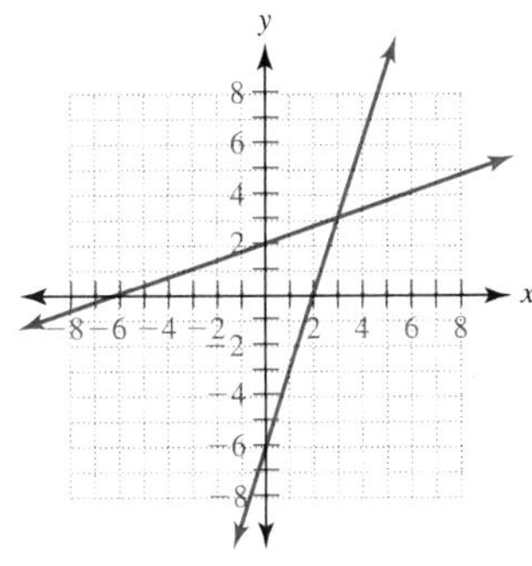

24. $f(x) = 4x + 8$

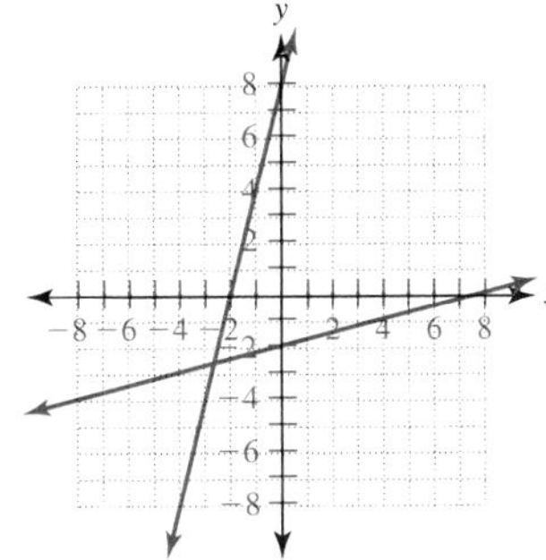

25. $f(x) = -2x + 6$

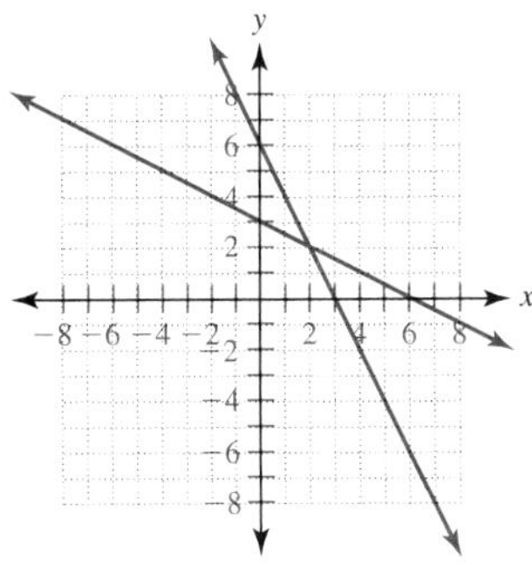

26. $f(x) = -3x - 6$

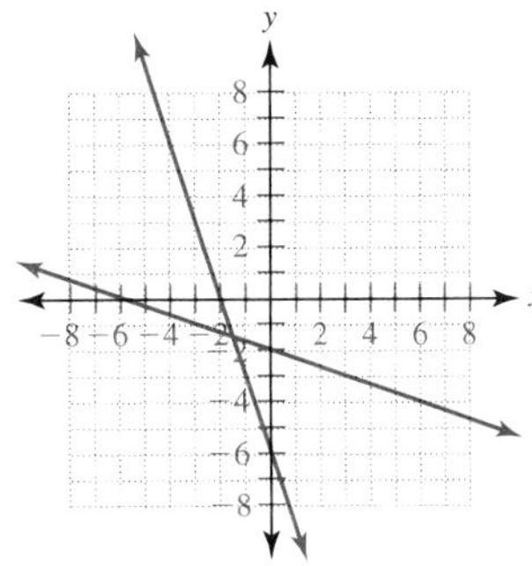

< Objectives 4 and 5 >

In exercises 27 to 34, determine whether the given function is one-to-one. In each case decide whether the inverse is a function.

27. $f = \{(-3, 5), (-2, 3), (0, 2), (1, 4), (6, 5)\}$

28. $g = \{(-3, 7), (0, 4), (2, 5), (4, 1)\}$

Answers

15. $\{(2, 1), (2, 2), (2, 3)\}$; not a function

16. $\{(9, 5), (7, 3), (5, 7)\}$; function

17. $\{(4, 2), (9, 3), (16, 4)\}$; function

18. $\{(2, -1), (3, 0), (2, 1)\}$; not a function

19. $f^{-1}(x) = \dfrac{3 - 5x}{2}$

20. $f^{-1}(x) = \dfrac{7 - 6x}{4}$

21. $f^{-1}(x) = \dfrac{5x + 5}{8}$

22. $f^{-1}(x) = \dfrac{42 - 7x}{2}$

23. $f^{-1}(x) = \dfrac{x + 6}{3} = \dfrac{1}{3}x + 2$; see exercise

24. $f^{-1}(x) = \dfrac{x - 8}{4} = \dfrac{1}{4}x - 2$; see exercise

25. $f^{-1}(x) = \dfrac{6 - x}{2} = -\dfrac{1}{2}x + 3$; see exercise

26. $f^{-1}(x) = \dfrac{-x - 6}{3} = -\dfrac{1}{3}x - 2$; see exercise

27. Not one-to-one; not a function

28. One-to-one; function

Answers

29. One-to-one; function
30. Not one-to-one; not a function
31. Not one-to-one; not a function
32. Not one-to-one; not a function
33. One-to-one; function
34. One-to-one; function
35. Answers may vary
36. Answers may vary

29.

x	$f(x)$
−3	4
0	−3
2	1
6	2
8	0

30.

x	$g(x)$
−2	−6
−1	2
3	0
4	2

31.

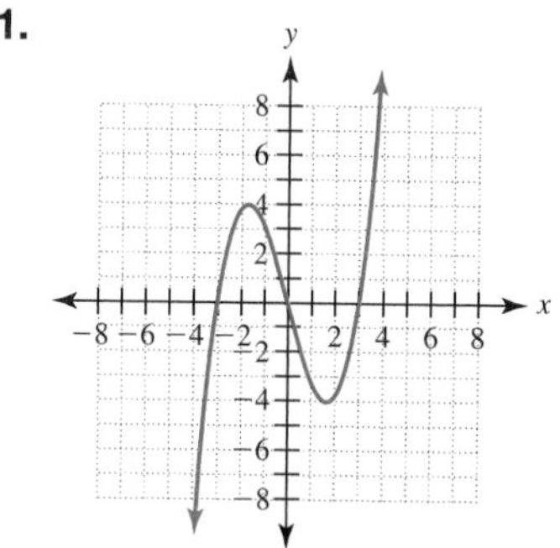

32.

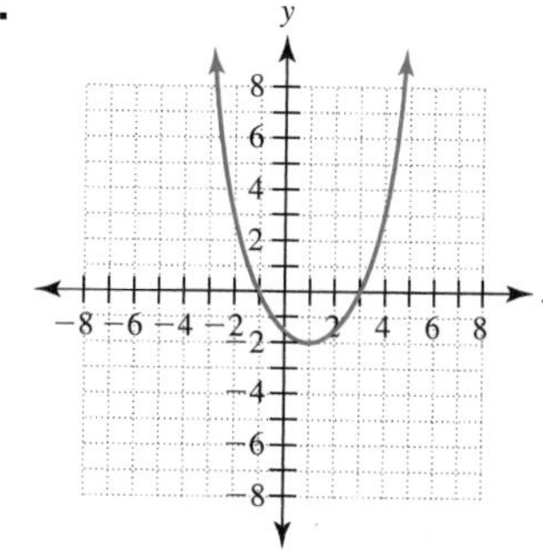

> Videos

33.

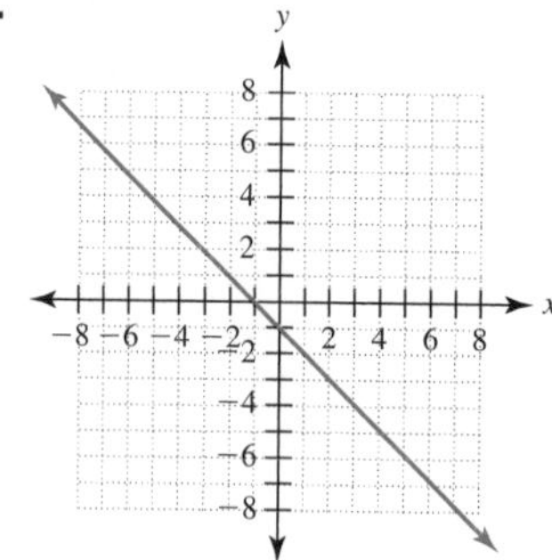

34.

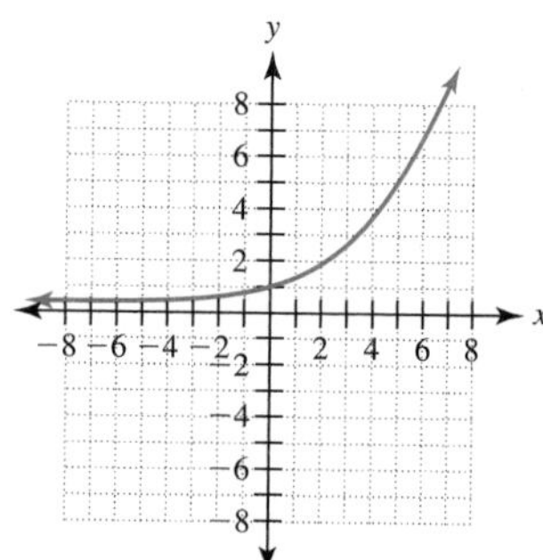

Basic Skills | **Advanced Skills** | Vocational-Technical Applications | Calculator/Computer | Above and Beyond

35. An inverse process is an operation that undoes a procedure. If the procedure is wrapping a present, describe in detail the inverse process.

36. If the procedure is the series of steps that take you from home to your classroom, describe the inverse process.

If $f(x) = 3x - 6$, *then* $f^{-1}(x) = \frac{1}{3}x + 2$. *Given these two functions, in exercises 37 to 42, find each of the following.*

37. $f(6)$

38. $f^{-1}(6)$

39. $f(f^{-1}(6))$

40. $f^{-1}(f(6))$

41. $f(f^{-1}(x))$

42. $f^{-1}(f(x))$

If $g(x) = \frac{x + 1}{2}$, *then* $g^{-1}(x) = 2x - 1$. *Given these two functions, in exercises 43 to 48, find each of the following.*

43. $g(3)$

44. $g^{-1}(3)$

45. $g(g^{-1}(3))$

46. $g^{-1}(g(3))$

47. $g(g^{-1}(x))$

48. $g^{-1}(g(x))$

Given $h(x) = 2x + 8$, *then* $h^{-1}(x) = \frac{x - 8}{2}$ *in exercises 49 to 54, find each of the following.*

49. $h(4)$

50. $h^{-1}(4)$

51. $h(h^{-1}(4))$

52. $h^{-1}(h(4))$

53. $h(h^{-1}(x))$

54. $h^{-1}(h(x))$

Answers

1. $f^{-1}(x) = \frac{x + 8}{2}$ **3.** $f^{-1}(x) = 2x + 1$ **5.** $f^{-1}(x) = \frac{x - 5}{4}$
7. $f^{-1}(x) = 6x - 2$ **9.** $\{(-8, -3), (2, -1), (4, 2), (-3, 5)\}$; function
11. $\{(3, -4), (7, -2), (5, 3), (-4, 7)\}$; function
13. $\{(3, 2), (4, 3), (5, 4)\}$; function **15.** $\{(2, 1), (2, 2), (2, 3)\}$; not a function
17. $\{(4, 2), (9, 3), (16, 4)\}$; function
19. $f^{-1}(x) = \frac{3 - 5x}{2}$ **21.** $f^{-1}(x) = \frac{5x + 5}{8}$

Answers

37. 12
38. 4
39. 6
40. 6
41. x
42. x
43. 2
44. 5
45. 3
46. 3
47. x
48. x
49. 16
50. −2
51. 4
52. 4
53. x
54. x

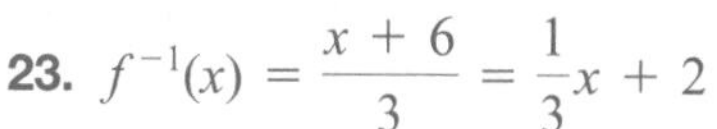
23. $f^{-1}(x) = \dfrac{x+6}{3} = \dfrac{1}{3}x + 2$

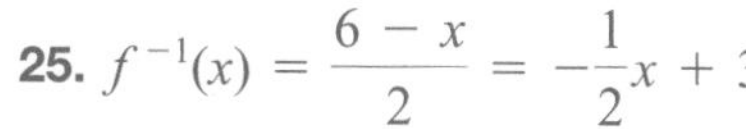
25. $f^{-1}(x) = \dfrac{6-x}{2} = -\dfrac{1}{2}x + 3$

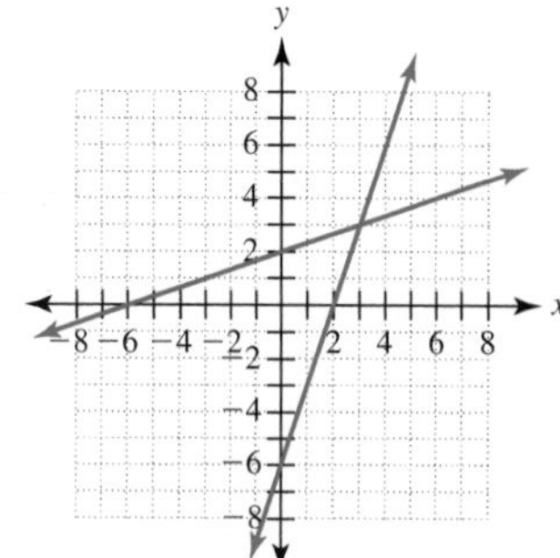

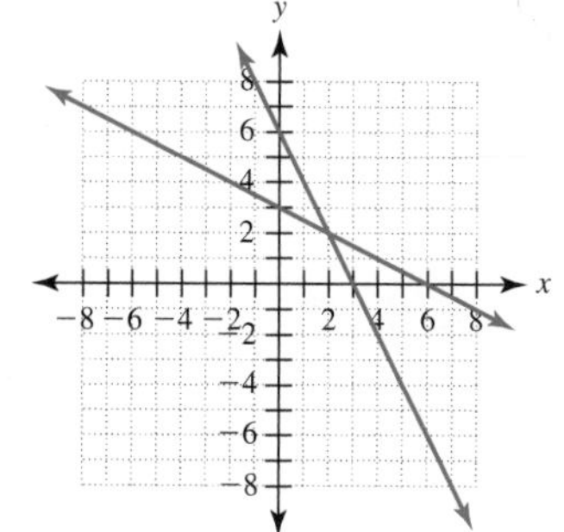

27. Not one-to-one; not a function **29.** One-to-one; function
31. Not one-to-one; not a function **33.** One-to-one; function
35. Answers may vary **37.** 12 **39.** 6 **41.** x **43.** 2
45. 3 **47.** x **49.** 16 **51.** 4 **53.** x

Definition/Procedure	Example	Reference
Algebra of Functions		Section 10.1
The **sum of two functions** f and g is written $f + g$. It is defined as $(f + g)(x) = f(x) + g(x)$. The **difference of two functions** f and g is written $f - g$. It is defined as $(f - g)(x) = f(x) - g(x)$. The **product of two functions** f and g is written $f \cdot g$. It is defined as $(f \cdot g)(x) = f(x) \cdot g(x)$. The **quotient of two functions** f and g is written $f \div g$. It is defined as $(f \div g)(x) = f(x) \div g(x)$.	If $f(x) = x + 3$ and $g(x) = 2x^2$, $(f \cdot g)(x) = (x + 3)(2x^2)$ $= 2x^3 + 6x^2$	*pp.* 933, 935
Composition of Functions		Section 10.2
The **composition** of functions f and g is the function $f \circ g$ where $(f \circ g)(x) = f(g(x))$. The **domain** of the composition is the set of all elements x in the domain of g for which $g(x)$ is in the domain of f.	From $f(x)$ and $g(x)$ above, $f \circ g = f(g(x))$ $= f(2x^2)$ $= 2x^2 + 3$	*p.* 940
One-to-One and Inverse Functions		Section 10.3
The **inverse** of a relation is formed by interchanging the components of each ordered pair in the given relation. If a relation (or function) is specified by an equation, interchange the roles of x and y in the defining equation to form the inverse. 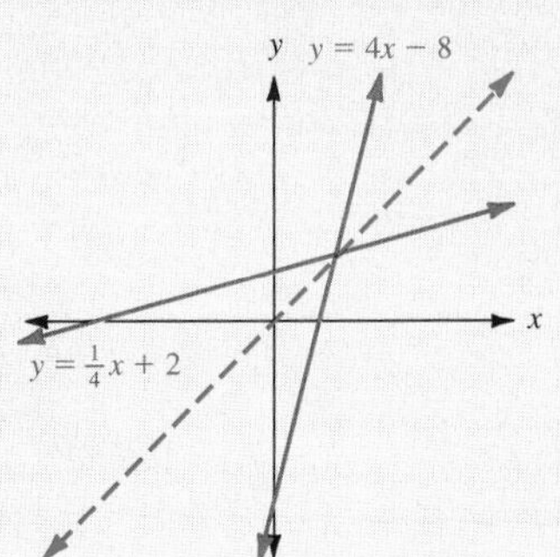 	The inverse of the relation $\{(1, 2), (2, 3), (4, 3)\}$ is $\{(2, 1), (3, 2), (3, 4)\}$. To find the inverse of $f(x) = 4x - 8$, $y = 4x - 8$ change y to x and x to y $x = 4y - 8$ so $4y = x + 8$ $y = \frac{1}{4}(x + 8)$ $y = \frac{1}{4}x + 2$	*pp.* 949, 951
The inverse of a function f may or may not be a function. If the inverse *is* also a function, we denote that inverse as f^{-1}, read "the inverse of f."	If $f(x) = 4x - 8$, then $f^{-1}(x) = \frac{1}{4}x + 2$	*pp.* 951, 953
A function f has an inverse f^{-1}, which is also a function, if and only if f is a **one-to-one** function. That is, no two ordered pairs in the function have the same second component. The **horizontal-line test** can be used to determine whether a function is one-to-one.	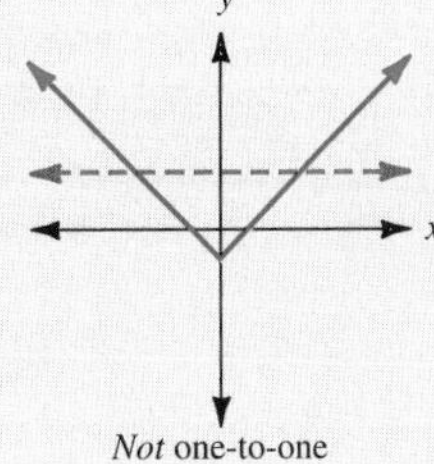 *Not* one-to-one	*pp.* 953, 955

summary exercises :: chapter 10

This summary exercise set is provided to give you practice with each of the objectives of this chapter. Each exercise is keyed to the appropriate chapter section. When you are finished, you can check your answers to the odd-numbered exercises against those presented in the back of the text. If you have difficulty with any of these questions, go back and reread the examples from that section. The answers to the even-numbered exercises appear in the *Instructor's Solutions Manual.* Your instructor will give you guidelines on how best to use these exercises in your instructional setting.

10.1 *In exercises 1 and 2, $f(x)$ and $g(x)$ are given. Let $h(x) = f(x) + g(x)$. Find* **(a)** $h(x)$, **(b)** $f(1) + g(1)$, *and* **(c)** $h(1)$.

1. $f(x) = 2x^4 + 4x^2 + 5, \quad g(x) = x^3 - 5x^2 + 6x$ (a) $2x^4 + x^3 - x^2 + 6x + 5$; (b) 13; (c) 13

2. $f(x) = 3x^3 + 5x - 5, \quad g(x) = -2x^3 + 2x^2 + 5x$ (a) $x^3 + 2x^2 + 10x - 5$; (b) 8; (c) 8

In exercises 3 to 6, $f(x)$ and $g(x)$ are given. Let $h(x) = f(x) - g(x)$. Find **(a)** $h(x)$, **(b)** $f(1) - g(1)$, *and* **(c)** $h(1)$.

3. $f(x) = 7x^2 - 2x + 3, \quad g(x) = 2x^2 - 5x - 7$ (a) $5x^2 + 3x + 10$; (b) 18; (c) 18

4. $f(x) = 9x^2 - 4x, \quad g(x) = 5x^2 + 3$ (a) $4x^2 - 4x - 3$; (b) -3; (c) -3

5. $f(x) = 8x^2 + 5x, \quad g(x) = 4x^2 - 3x$ (a) $4x^2 + 8x$; (b) 12; (c) 12

6. $f(x) = -2x^2 - 3x, \quad g(x) = -3x^2 + 4x - 5$ (a) $x^2 - 7x + 5$; (b) -1; (c) -1

Find the product $f(x) \cdot g(x)$.

7. $f(x) = 2x, \quad g(x) = 3x - 5$ $6x^2 - 10x$

8. $f(x) = x + 1, \quad g(x) = 4x - 3$ $4x^2 + x - 3$

9. $f(x) = 3x, \quad g(x) = x^2$ $3x^3$

10. $f(x) = 2x, \quad g(x) = x^2 - 5$ $2x^3 - 10x$

Find the quotient $f(x) \div g(x)$ and state the domain of the resulting function.

11. $f(x) = 2x, \quad g(x) = 3x - 5$ $\dfrac{2x}{3x - 5}, \left\{x \middle| x \neq \dfrac{5}{3}\right\}$

12. $f(x) = x + 1, \quad g(x) = 4x - 3$ $\dfrac{x + 1}{4x - 3}, \left\{x \middle| x \neq \dfrac{3}{4}\right\}$

13. $f(x) = 3x, \quad g(x) = x^2$ $\dfrac{3x}{x^2}, \{x | x \neq 0\}$

14. $f(x) = 2x^2, \quad g(x) = x - 5$ $\dfrac{2x^2}{x - 5}, \{x | x \neq 5\}$

10.2 *Evaluate the indicated composite functions in each part.*

15. $f(x) = x - 3, \quad g(x) = 3x + 1$

(a) $(f \circ g)(0)$ -2

(b) $(f \circ g)(-2)$ -8

(c) $(f \circ g)(3)$ 7

(d) $(f \circ g)(x)$ $3x - 2$

16. $f(x) = 5x - 1, \quad g(x) = -4x + 5$

(a) $(f \circ g)(0)$ 24

(b) $(f \circ g)(-2)$ 64

(c) $(g \circ f)(3)$ -51

(d) $(g \circ f)(x)$ $-20x + 9$

17. $f(x) = x^2, \quad g(x) = x - 5$

(a) $(f \circ g)(0)$ 25

(b) $(f \circ g)(-2)$ 49

(c) $(g \circ f)(3)$ 4

(d) $(g \circ f)(x)$ $x^2 - 5$

18. $f(x) = x^2 + 3, \quad g(x) = -2x$

(a) $(g \circ f)(0)$ -6

(b) $(g \circ f)(-2)$ -14

(c) $(f \circ g)(3)$ 39

(d) $(f \circ g)(x)$ $4x^2 + 3$

Rewrite the function h as a composite of functions f and g.

19. $f(x) = -2x, \quad g(x) = x + 2, \quad h(x) = -2x - 4$ $h(x) = (f \circ g)(x)$

20. $f(x) = x - 3, \quad g(x) = x^2 + 2, \quad h(x) = x^2 - 6x + 11$ $h(x) = (g \circ f)(x)$

10.3 *Write the inverse relation for each of the functions. Which inverses are also functions?*

21. $\{(1, 5), (2, 7), (3, 9)\}$ $\{(5, 1), (7, 2), (9, 3)\}$; function

22. $\{(3, 1), (5, 1), (7, 1)\}$ $\{(1, 3), (1, 5), (1, 7)\}$; not a function

23. $\{(2, 4), (4, 3), (6, 4)\}$ $\{(4, 2), (3, 4), (4, 6)\}$; not a function

Write an equation for the inverse of the relation defined by each of the equations.

24. $y = 3x - 6$ $y = \frac{1}{3}x + 2$

25. $y = \dfrac{x + 1}{2}$ $y = 2x - 1$

26. $y = x^2 - 2$ $y = \pm\sqrt{x + 2}$

27. $y = 3x + 6$ $y = \frac{1}{3}x - 2$

self-test 10

CHAPTER 10

Name ____________________

Section ________ Date ________

The purpose of this chapter test is to help you check your progress so that you can find sections and concepts that you need to review before the next exam. Allow yourself about an hour to take this test. At the end of that hour, check your answers against those given in the back of this text. If you missed any, note the section reference that accompanies the answer. Go back to that section and reread the examples until you have mastered that particular concept.

10.1

In exercises 1 and 2, use the functions $f(x) = x^2 + 1$ and $g(x) = 3x - 4$.

1. Find $f(x) + g(x)$.

2. Find $f(x) - g(x)$.

In the following, $f(x)$ and $g(x)$ are given. Find **(a)** $h(x) = f(x) + g(x)$, **(b)** $p(x) = f(x) - g(x)$, **(c)** $f(1) + g(1)$, **(d)** $f(1) - g(1)$, **(e)** $h(1)$, *and* **(f)** $p(1)$.

3. $f(x) = 4x^2 - 3x + 7, \quad g(x) = 2x^2$

4. $f(x) = -3x^3 + 5x^2 - 2x - 7, \quad g(x) = -2x^2 + 7x - 2$

In exercises 5 to 12, use $f(x) = x^2 - 1$ and $g(x) = 3x - 2$.

5. Find $(f + g)(x)$ and state the domain of the resulting function.

6. Find $(g - f)(x)$ and state the domain of the resulting function.

7. Find $(g \cdot f)(x)$ and state the domain of the resulting function.

8. Find $\left(\dfrac{f}{g}\right)(x)$ and state the domain of the resulting function.

10.2

9. Find $(f \circ g)(x)$.

10. Find $(g \circ f)(x)$.

11. Find $(f \circ g)(3)$.

12. Find $(g \circ f)(3)$.

10.3

13. Use $f(x) = 4x - 2$ in parts **(a)** and **(b)**.

(a) Find the inverse of f. Is the inverse also a function?

(b) Graph f and its inverse on the same set of axes.

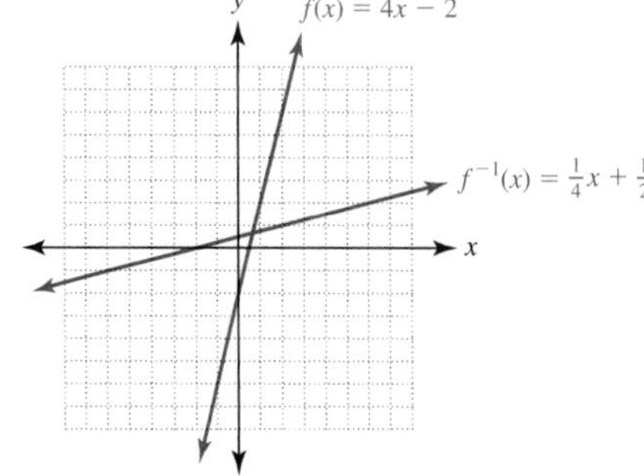

Answers

1. $x^2 + 3x - 3$

2. $x^2 - 3x + 5$

3. (a) $6x^2 - 3x + 7$; (b) $2x^2 - 3x + 7$; (c) 10; (d) 6; (e) 10; (f) 6

4. (a) $-3x^3 + 3x^2 + 5x - 9$; (b) $-3x^3 + 7x^2 - 9x - 5$; (c) -4; (d) -10; (e) -4; (f) -10

5. $(f + g)(x) = x^2 + 3x - 3$, D: $\mathbb{R}$

6. $(g - f)(x) = -x^2 + 3x - 1$, D: $\mathbb{R}$

7. $(g \cdot f)(x) = 3x^3 - 2x^2 - 3x + 2$, D: $\mathbb{R}$

8. $\left(\dfrac{f}{g}\right)(x) = \dfrac{x^2 - 1}{3x - 2}$, D: $\left\{x \mid x \neq \dfrac{2}{3}\right\}$

9. $9x^2 - 12x + 3$

10. $3x^2 - 5$

11. 48

12. 22

13. (a) $f^{-1}(x) = \dfrac{1}{4}x + \dfrac{1}{2}$, function; (b) see exercise

Activity 10 :: GDP and Life Expectancy

Each chapter in this text concludes with a chapter activity such as this one. These activities provide you with the opportunity to apply the math you studied in that chapter to a relevant topic. Your instructor will determine how best to use these activities in your instructional setting. You may find yourself working in class or outside of class; you may find yourself working alone or in small groups; you may even be asked to perform research in a library or on the Internet.

The introduction to this chapter referred to economists who use graphs to show connections between two sets of data, namely the per capita gross domestic product (GDP) of a country and life expectancy to measure the quality of life.

Activity

1. Connect to the Internet and do a search.

- **(a)** Find the current GDP for the five richest countries and the five poorest countries.
- **(b)** Find the population for each of these countries.
- **(c)** Compute the per capita GDP (divide that total by the current population) for each country.
- **(d)** Set up a table showing the per capita GDP.
- **(e)** Next do a search for the population life expectancy for these same countries.
- **(f)** Set up a table on the life expectancy for each country.

2. Create two different sets of ordered pairs from the data you have collected.

- **(a)** (GDP, life expectancy)
- **(b)** Plot the points on a graph.
- **(c)** Does this relation appear to be a function or not?
- **(d)** (life expectancy, GDP)
- **(e)** Plot the points on a graph.
- **(f)** Does this relation appear to be a function or not?
- **(g)** How do the graphs compare?

3. If part 2**(a)** were a function, what would part 2**(d)** be in relation to part 2**(a)**?

4. What conclusion (if any) can you reach regarding the relation between a country's GDP and its life expectancy?

cumulative review chapters 1-10

Name ______________________

Section __________ Date __________

Answers

1. $-\frac{1}{24}$

2. $-\frac{2}{3} < x < \frac{10}{3}$

3. 29 cm

4. $x = -2$

5. See exercise

6. (7, −2)

7. Inconsistent

8. −2, 5, and 7

9. $5x^3 - x^2 - 4x + 1$

The following exercises are presented to help you review concepts from earlier chapters. This is meant as review material and not as a comprehensive exam. The answers are presented in the back of the text. Beside each answer is a section reference for the concept. If you have difficulty with any of these exercises, be certain to at least read through the summary related to that section.

Solve each of the following.

2.1

1. $2x + \frac{3}{4} = \frac{2}{3}$

2.5

2. $|4 - 3x| < 6$

2.3

3. **Geometry** The length of a rectangle is 5 cm less than twice the width. If the perimeter of the rectangle is 92 cm, find the length.

3.4

4. Write the equation of the line that passes through $(-2, -3)$ and is perpendicular to the line with equation $y = 5$.

Graph the following inequality.

3.5

5. $x < y - 2$

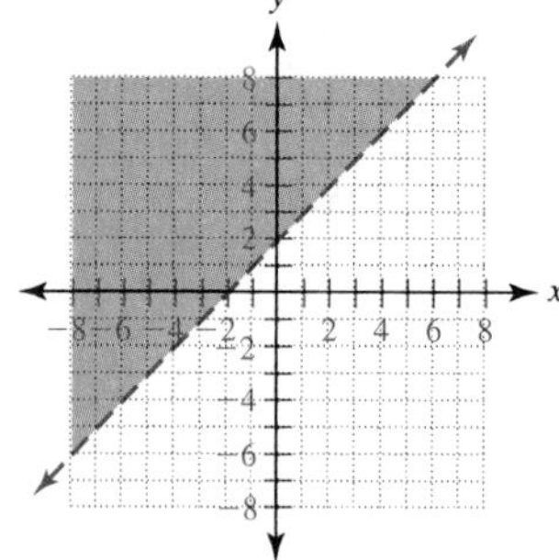

4.1

Solve each of the following systems. If a unique solution does not exist, state whether the given system is inconsistent or dependent.

6. $2x + 5y = 4$
$x = 1 - 3y$

7. $6x - 4y = 7$
$y = \frac{3}{2}x + 5$

4.2

8. **Number Problem** The sum of three integers is 10. The largest integer is 1 more than twice the sum of the other two integers. The difference between the middle integer and the smallest is equal to the largest integer. Find the three integers.

5.1

9. Subtract the sum of $x^3 + 5x - 7$ and $x^2 - 2x^3 + 5$ from $4x^3 + x - 1$.

5.3

10. Divide: $(3x^2 - 5x + 4) \div (x - 2)$

Completely factor the following.

5.4

11. $6m^2n^2 - 9mn^2 - 3mn$

12. $2x(x - 3) - 5(x - 3)$

5.5

13. $2a^3 + 54$

5.9

14. Solve: $15 - x = 2x^2$

Simplify.

6.2

15. $\dfrac{x^2 - 4x - 5}{x^2 + 3x - 10} \div \dfrac{x^2 - 2x - 3}{x^2 + 2x - 15}$

6.5

16. Solve $\dfrac{1}{A} + \dfrac{1}{B} = \dfrac{1}{C}$ for C.

Simplify each of the following. Assume that all variables represent positive real numbers.

7.2

17. $\sqrt{12p^5r^9}$

18. $\dfrac{6a}{\sqrt{2a}}$

7.3

19. $(5 - \sqrt{5})^2$

7.6

20. $(m^{-3/2})^4$

7.4

21. Solve: $\sqrt{5x - 2} = 3$

7.7

22. Simplify: $\dfrac{2 - 3i}{3 + 5i}$

Answers

10. $3x + 1 + \dfrac{6}{x - 2}$

11. $3mn(2mn - 3n - 1)$

12. $(x - 3)(2x - 5)$

13. $2(a + 3)(a^2 - 3a + 9)$

14. $-3, \dfrac{5}{2}$

15. $\dfrac{x - 5}{x - 2}$

16. $C = \dfrac{AB}{A + B}$

17. $2p^2r^4\sqrt{3pr}$

18. $3\sqrt{2a}$

19. $30 - 10\sqrt{5}$

20. $\dfrac{1}{m^6}$

21. $\dfrac{11}{5}$

22. $-\dfrac{9}{34} - \dfrac{19}{34}i$

Answers

23. $\frac{5 \pm \sqrt{17}}{2}$

24. $x = \frac{3}{5}, -4$

25. (1, 3)

26. $18\frac{3}{4}$ h

27. D: {−4, −2, 6}, R: {−1, 3, 5}

28. $\{x \mid x \neq \pm 1\}$

29. $4x^2 - 12x + 8$

30. $y = 5x + 4$

Solve the following equation.

8.3

23. $x^2 - 5x + 2 = 0$

8.1

24. Find the zeros of the function: $f(x) = 5x^2 + 17x - 12$

9.1

25. Find the coordinates of the vertex of the graph of f: $f(x) = 2x^2 - 4x + 5$

6.5

26. **Work Problem** If Carlos builds a certain fence alone, it would take him 30 hours. His friend, Santiago, would require 50 hours to do the same job. How long would it take them if they worked together?

3.1

27. Find the domain and the range of the relation $\{(-4, 3), (-2, -1), (-2, 5), (6, 5)\}$.

10.1

28. If $f(x) = x^2 - 1$ and $g(x) = 2x - 3$, find the domain of $(g \div f)(x)$.

10.2

29. If $f(x) = x^2 - 1$ and $g(x) = 2x - 3$, find $(f \circ g)(x)$.

10.3

30. Write an equation for the inverse of the relation $y = \frac{x - 4}{5}$.

CHAPTER

11

Exponential and Logarithmic Functions

INTRODUCTION

Pharmacologists researching the effects of drugs use exponential and logarithmic functions to model drug absorption and elimination. After a drug is taken orally, it is distributed throughout the body via the circulatory system. Once in the bloodstream, the drug is carried to the body's organs, where it is first absorbed and then eliminated again into the bloodstream. For a medicine or drug to be effective, there must be enough of the substance in the body to achieve the desired effect but not enough to cause harm. This therapeutic level is maintained by taking the proper dosage at timed intervals determined by the rate the body absorbs or eliminates the medicine.

The rate at which the body eliminates the drug is proportional to the amount of the drug present. That is, the more drug there is, the faster the drug is eliminated. The amount of a drug dosage, P, still left after a number of hours, t, is affected by the **half-life** of the drug. In this case, the half-life is how many hours it takes for the body to use up or eliminate half the drug dosage.

CHAPTER 11 OUTLINE

If P is the amount of an initial dose, and H is the time it takes the body to eliminate half a dose of a drug, then the amount of the drug still remaining in the system after t units of time is

$$A(t) = Pe^{t(-\ln 2)/H}$$

If the amount of an initial dose of a drug is 30 mg and if the half-life of the drug in the body is 4 hours, the amount in milligrams of the drug still in the body t hours after one dose is given by the following formula:

$$A(t) = 30e^{-0.173t}$$

In this chapter, we develop many of the skills needed in handling exponential and logarithmic functions found in applications such as this one. At the end of the chapter, you will find a more in-depth activity involving half-life and decay.

Name ________________

Section ________ Date ________

This pretest provides a preview of the types of exercises you will encounter in each section of this chapter. The answers for these exercises can be found in the back of the text. If you are working on your own, or ahead of the class, this pretest can help you identify the sections in which you should focus more of your time.

11.1 **1.** Graph the exponential function defined by $y = \left(\frac{1}{2}\right)^x$.

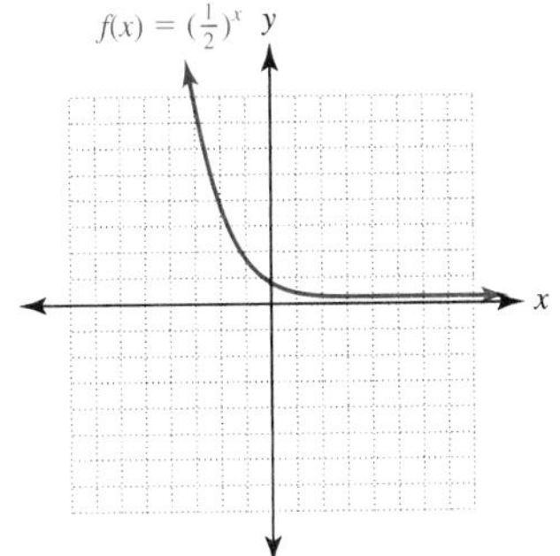

11.2 **2.** Solve the following exponential equation for x: $4^{x-1} = 16$.

3. Graph the logarithmic function defined by $y = \log_2 x$.

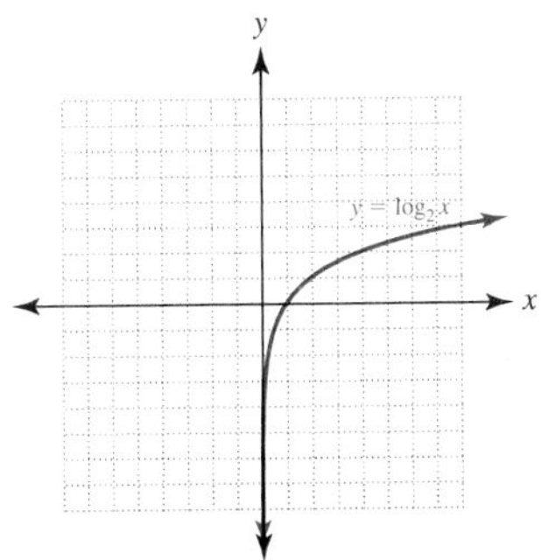

4. Convert to logarithmic form: $64^{2/3} = 16$.

5. Solve for the unknown variable: $\log_9 x = 2$.

11.3 **6.** Use the properties of logarithms to expand: $\log_5 \frac{x^2y}{z}$.

Solve for x.

11.4 **7.** $\log_2 (x + 3) - \log_2 (x - 1) = \log_2 3$

8. $9^{x-1} = 27$

Answers

1. See exercise
2. 3
3. See exercise
4. $\log_{64} 16 = \frac{2}{3}$
5. 81
6. $2 \log_5 x + \log_5 y - \log_5 z$
7. 3
8. $\frac{5}{2}$

11.1 Exponential Functions

< 11.1 Objectives >

1 > Graph an exponential function

2 > Solve an application of exponential functions

3 > Solve an elementary exponential equation

Up to this point in the text, we have worked with polynomial functions and other functions in which the variable was used as a base. We now want to turn to a new classification of functions, the **exponential function.**

Exponential functions are functions whose defining equations involve the variable as an *exponent*. The introduction of these functions will allow us to consider many further applications, including population growth and radioactive decay.

Definition

Exponential Functions

An **exponential function** is a function that can be expressed in the form

$f(x) = b^x$

in which $b > 0$ and $b \neq 1$. We call b the **base** of the exponential function.

The following are examples of exponential functions.

$$f(x) = 2^x \qquad g(x) = 3^x \qquad h(x) = \left(\frac{1}{2}\right)^x$$

As we have done with other new functions, we begin by finding some function values. We then use that information to graph the function.

Example 1 — Graphing an Exponential Function

< Objective 1 >

Graph the exponential function

$f(x) = 2^x$

First, choose convenient values for x.

RECALL

$2^{-2} = \frac{1}{2^2} = \frac{1}{4}$

$$f(0) = 2^0 = 1 \qquad f(-1) = 2^{-1} = \frac{1}{2} \qquad f(1) = 2^1 = 2$$

$$f(-2) = 2^{-2} = \frac{1}{4} \qquad f(2) = 2^2 = 4 \qquad f(-3) = 2^{-3} = \frac{1}{8}$$

Next, form a table from these values. Then, plot the corresponding points, and connect them with a smooth curve for the desired graph.

NOTE

There is no value for x such that

$2^x = 0$

so the graph never touches the x-axis.

x	$f(x)$
−3	0.125
−2	0.25
−1	0.5
0	1
1	2
2	4
3	8

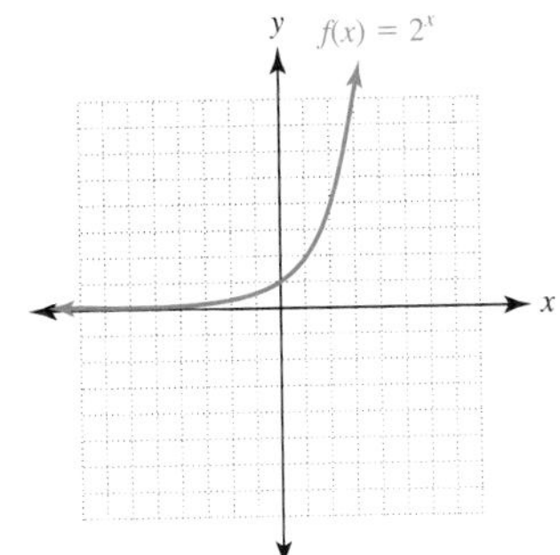

NOTE

We call $y = 0$ (or the x-axis) the **horizontal asymptote.**

Let us examine some characteristics of the graph of the exponential function. First, the vertical-line test shows that this is indeed the graph of a function. Also note that the horizontal-line test shows that the function is one-to-one.

The graph *approaches* the x-axis on the left, but it does *not intersect* the x-axis. The y-intercept is $(0, 1)$ (because $2^0 = 1$). To the right the functional values get larger. We say that the values *grow without bound.*

Check Yourself 1

Sketch the graph of the exponential function

$g(x) = 3^x$

Let us look at an example in which the base of the function is less than 1.

Example 2 Graphing an Exponential Function

RECALL

$\left(\frac{1}{2}\right)^x = 2^{-x}$

Graph the exponential function

$$f(x) = \left(\frac{1}{2}\right)^x$$

First, choose convenient values for x.

$$f(0) = \left(\frac{1}{2}\right)^0 = 1 \qquad f(-1) = \left(\frac{1}{2}\right)^{-1} = 2 \qquad f(1) = \left(\frac{1}{2}\right)^1 = \frac{1}{2}$$

$$f(-2) = \left(\frac{1}{2}\right)^{-2} = 4 \qquad f(2) = \left(\frac{1}{2}\right)^2 = \frac{1}{4} \qquad f(-3) = \left(\frac{1}{2}\right)^{-3} = 8$$

$$f(3) = \left(\frac{1}{2}\right)^3 = \frac{1}{8}$$

Again, form a table of values and graph the desired function.

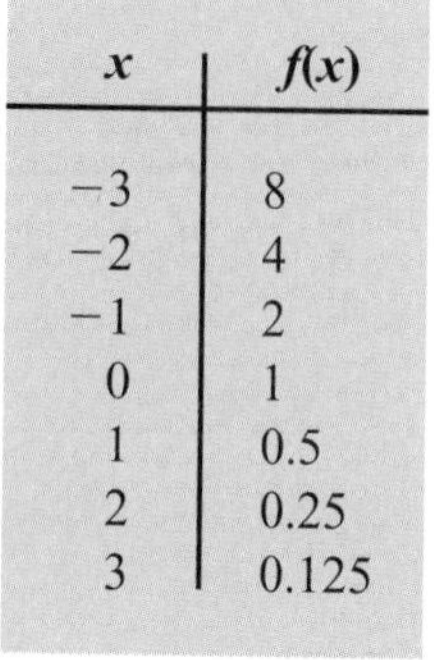

x	$f(x)$
−3	8
−2	4
−1	2
0	1
1	0.5
2	0.25
3	0.125

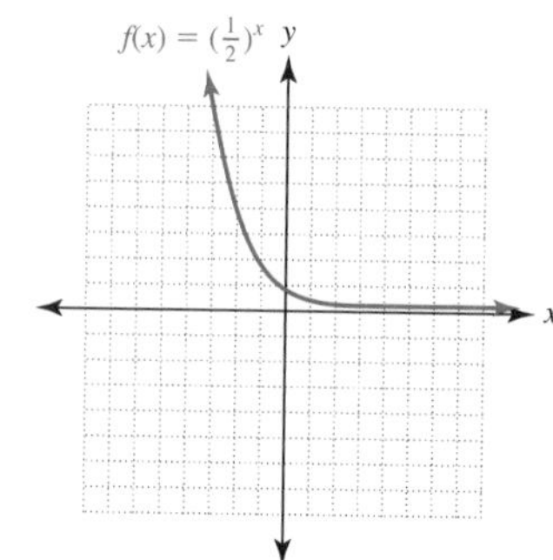

NOTE

Again, by the vertical- and horizontal-line tests, this is the graph of a one-to-one function.

Let us compare this graph and that in Example 1. Clearly, the graph also represents a one-to-one function. As was true in Example 1, the graph does not intersect the x-axis but approaches that axis, here on the right. The values for the function again grow without bound, but this time on the left. The y-intercept for both graphs occurs at 1.

Note that the graph of Example 1 was *increasing* (going up) as we moved from left to right. That function is an example of a **growth function.**

The graph of Example 2 is *decreasing* (going down) as we move from left to right. It is an example of a **decay function.**

NOTES

The base of a *growth function* is *greater than* 1.

The base of a *decay function* is *less than* 1 but greater than 0.

Check Yourself 2

Sketch the graph of the exponential function

$$g(x) = \left(\frac{1}{3}\right)^x$$

The following algorithm summarizes our work thus far in this section.

Step by Step

Graphing an Exponential Function

Step 1 Establish a table of values by considering the function in the form $y = b^x$.

Step 2 Plot points from that table of values and connect them with a smooth curve to form the graph.

Step 3 If $b > 1$, the graph increases from left to right. If $0 < b < 1$, the graph decreases from left to right.

Step 4 All graphs will have the following in common:
(a) The y-intercept will be (0, 1).
(b) The graphs will approach, but not touch, the x-axis.
(c) The graphs will represent one-to-one functions.

We used bases of 2 and $\frac{1}{2}$ for the exponential functions of our examples because they provided convenient computations. A far more important base for an exponential

NOTE

The use of the letter *e* as a base originated with Leonhard Euler (1707–1783) and *e* is sometimes called *Euler's number* for that reason.

function is an irrational number named *e*. In fact, when *e* is used as a base, the function defined by

$$f(x) = e^x$$

is called *the* exponential function.

The significance of this number will be made clear in later courses, particularly calculus. For our purposes, *e* can be approximated as

$$e \approx 2.71828$$

The graph of $f(x) = e^x$ is shown here. Of course, it is very similar to the graphs seen earlier in this section.

NOTE

Graph $y = e^x$ on your calculator. You may find the e^x key to be the 2nd (or inverse) function to the ln *x* key. Note that e^1 is approximately 2.71828.

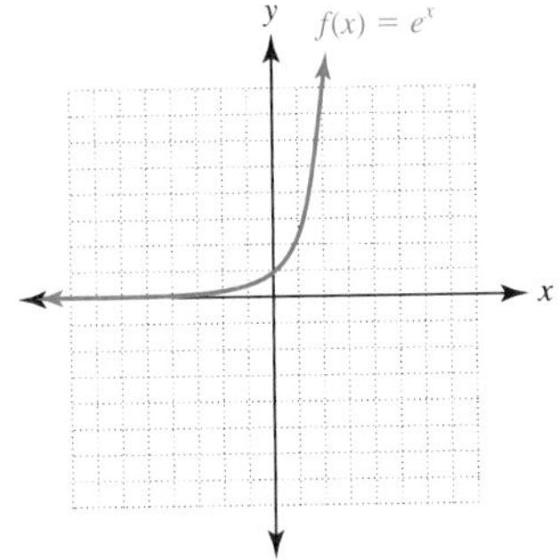

Exponential expressions involving base *e* occur frequently in real-world applications. Example 3 illustrates this approach.

Example 3 **A Population Application**

< Objective 2 >

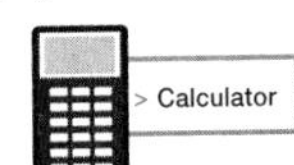

NOTES

Be certain that you enclose the multiplication (0.05 × 5) in parentheses or the calculator will misinterpret your intended order of operation.

Continuous compounding will give the highest accumulation of interest at any rate. However, daily compounding will result in an amount of interest that is only slightly less.

In 9 years the amount in the account is a little more than *double* the original principal.

(a) Suppose that the population of a city is presently 20,000 and that the population is expected to grow at a rate of 5% per year. The equation

$$P(t) = 20{,}000e^{(0.05)t}$$

gives the town's population after *t* years. Find the population in 5 years.

Let $t = 5$ in the original equation to obtain

$$P(5) = 20{,}000e^{(0.05)(5)} \approx 25{,}681$$

which is the population expected 5 years from now.

(b) Suppose $1,000 is invested at an annual rate of 8%, compounded continuously. The equation

$$A(t) = 1{,}000e^{0.08t}$$

gives the amount in the account after *t* years. Find the amount in the account after 9 years.

Let $t = 9$ in the original equation to obtain

$$A(9) = 1{,}000e^{(0.08)(9)} \approx 2{,}054$$

which is the amount in the account after 9 years.

Check Yourself 3

If \$1,000 is invested at an annual rate of 6%, compounded continuously, then the equation for the amount in the account after t years is

$$A(t) = 1{,}000e^{0.06t}$$

Use your calculator to find the amount in the account after 12 years.

As we observed in this section, the exponential function is always one-to-one. This yields an important property that can be used to solve certain types of equations involving exponents.

Property

Exponential Property

If $b > 0$ and $b \neq 1$, then

$b^m = b^n$ if and only if $m = n$

in which m and n are any real numbers.

The usefulness of this property is illustrated in Example 4.

Example 4 Solving an Exponential Equation

< Objective 3 >

(a) Solve $2^x = 8$ for x.

We recognize that 8 is a power of 2, and we can write the equation as

$2^x = 2^3$ Write with equal bases.

Applying the exponential property, we have

$x = 3$ Set exponents equal.

and 3 is the solution.

NOTE

The answer can easily be checked by substitution. Letting $x = 2$ gives

$3^{2(2)} = 3^4 = 81$

(b) Solve $3^{2x} = 81$ for x.

Because $81 = 3^4$, we can write

$3^{2x} = 3^4$

$2x = 4$

$x = 2$

We see that 2 is the solution for the equation.

RECALL

$\frac{1}{16} = \frac{1}{2^4} = 2^{-4}$

(c) Solve $2^{x+1} = \frac{1}{16}$ for x.

Again, we write $\frac{1}{16}$ as a power of 2, so that

$2^{x+1} = 2^{-4}$

> **NOTE**
>
> To verify the solution.
>
> $2^{-5+1} \stackrel{?}{=} 2^{-4}$
>
> $2^{-4} \stackrel{?}{=} 2^{-4}$
>
> $\frac{1}{16} = \frac{1}{16}$

Then

$$x + 1 = -4$$
$$x = -5$$

The solution is -5.

Check Yourself 4

Solve each of the following equations for x.

(a) $2^x = 16$ **(b)** $4^{x+1} = 64$ **(c)** $3^{2x} = \frac{1}{81}$

Check Yourself ANSWERS

1. $g(x) = 3^x$ **2.** $g(x) = \left(\frac{1}{3}\right)^x$ 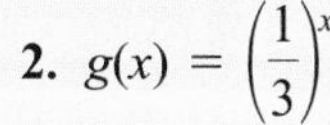

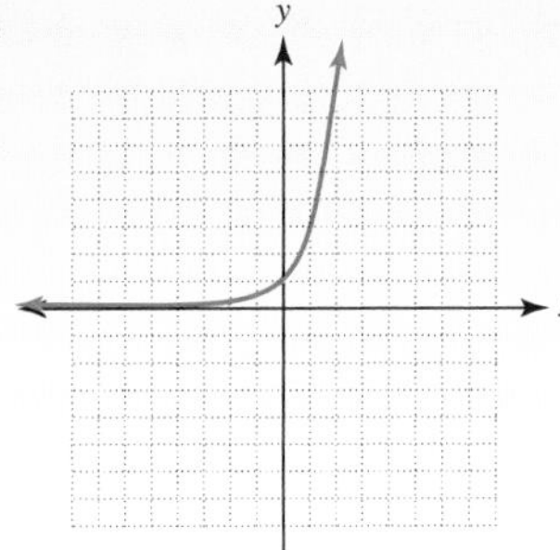

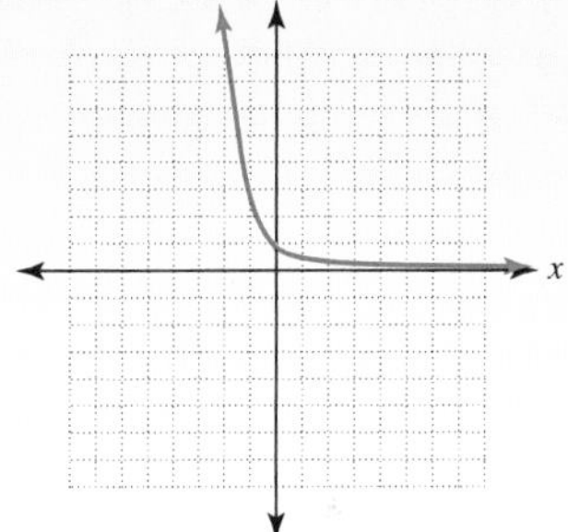

3. \$2,054.43 **4.** **(a)** 4; **(b)** 2; **(c)** -2

Reading Your Text

The following fill-in-the-blank exercises are designed to ensure that you understand some of the key vocabulary used in this section.

SECTION 11.1

(a) ______________ are functions whose defining equations involve the variable as an exponent.

(b) An exponential function is a function that can be expressed in the form ______________ in which ______________ and ______________.

(c) A graph that increases as we move from left to right is a graph of a ______________ function.

(d) A ______________ function has a graph that is decreasing as we move from left to right.

11.1 exercises

Basic Skills | Advanced Skills | Vocational-Technical Applications | Calculator/Computer | Above and Beyond

Name ____________

Section ________ Date ________

Answers

1. (c)
2. (d)
3. (b)
4. (a)
5. (h)
6. (e)
7. (f)
8. (g)

Match the graphs in exercises 1 to 8 with the appropriate equation.

(a) $y = \left(\frac{1}{2}\right)^x$ **(b)** $y = 2x - 1$ **(c)** $y = 2^x$ **(d)** $y = x^2$

(e) $y = 1^x$ **(f)** $y = 5^x$ **(g)** $x = 2^y$ **(h)** $x = y^2$

1.

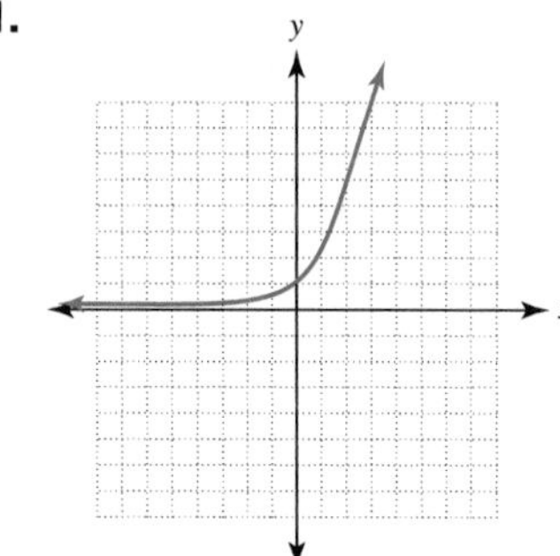

2.

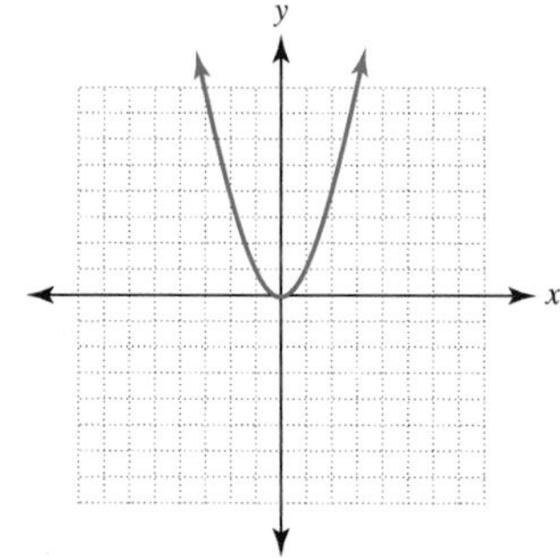

3.

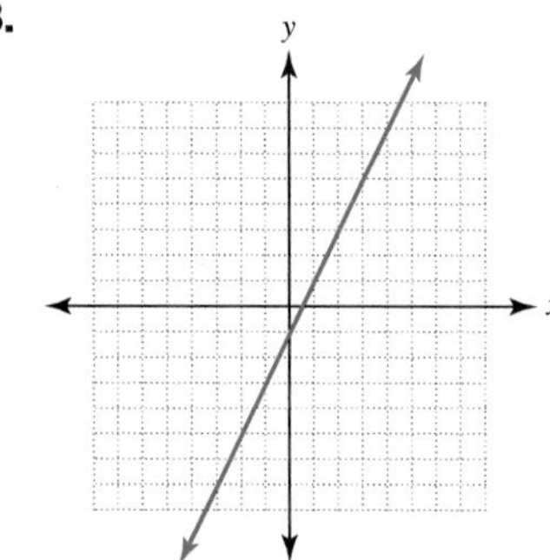

4.

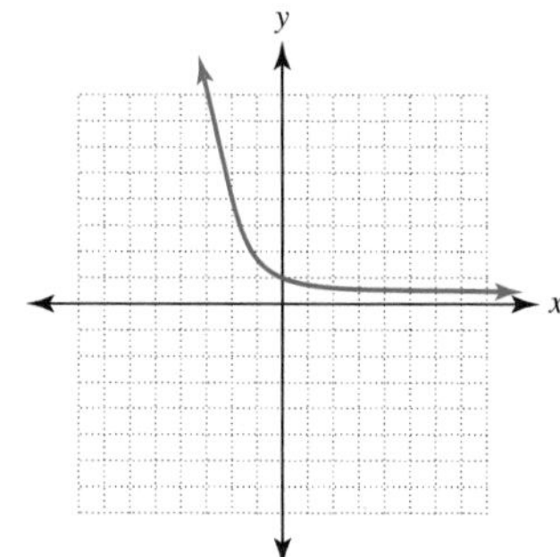

5.

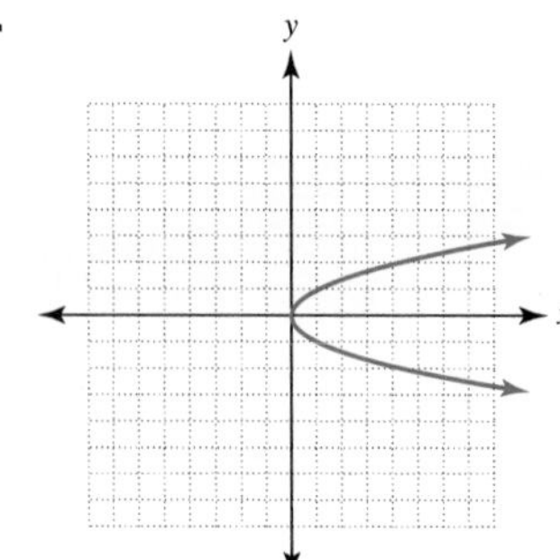

6.

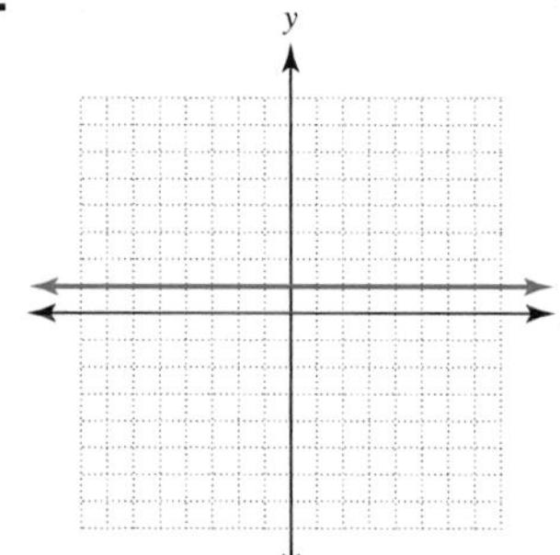

7.

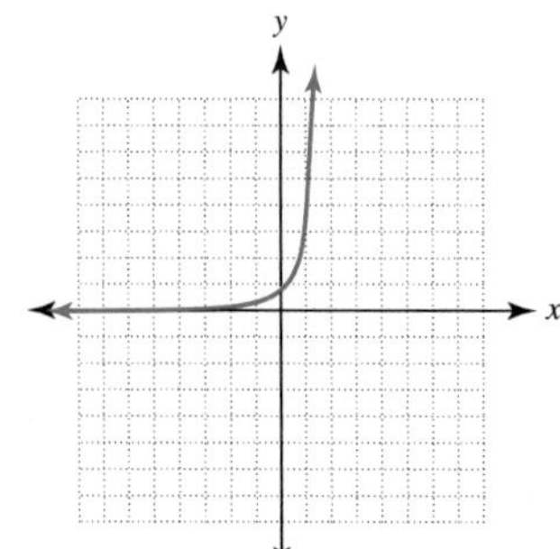

8.

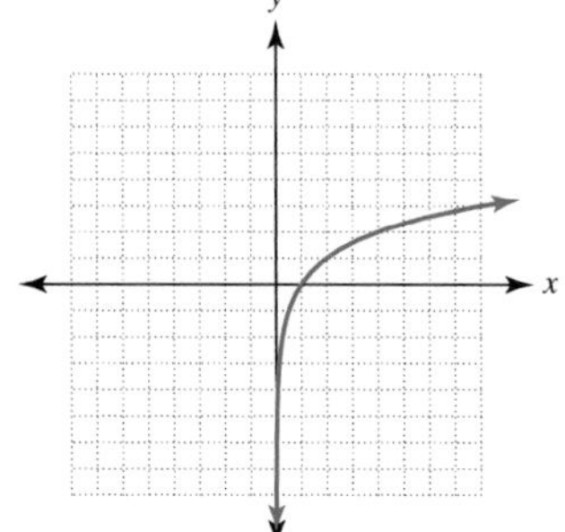

In exercises 9 to 12, let $f(x) = 4^x$ and find each of the following.

9. $f(0)$

10. $f(1)$

11. $f(2)$

12. $f(-2)$

In exercises 13 to 16, let $g(x) = 4^{x+1}$ and find each of the following.

13. $g(0)$

14. $g(1)$

15. $g(2)$

16. $g(-2)$

In exercises 17 to 20, let $h(x) = 4^x + 1$ and find each of the following.

17. $h(0)$

18. $h(1)$

19. $h(2)$

20. $h(-2)$

In exercises 21 to 24, let $f(x) = \left(\frac{1}{4}\right)^x$ and find each of the following.

21. $f(1)$

22. $f(-1)$

23. $f(-2)$

24. $f(2)$

< Objective 1 >

Graph each exponential function.

25. $y = 4^x$

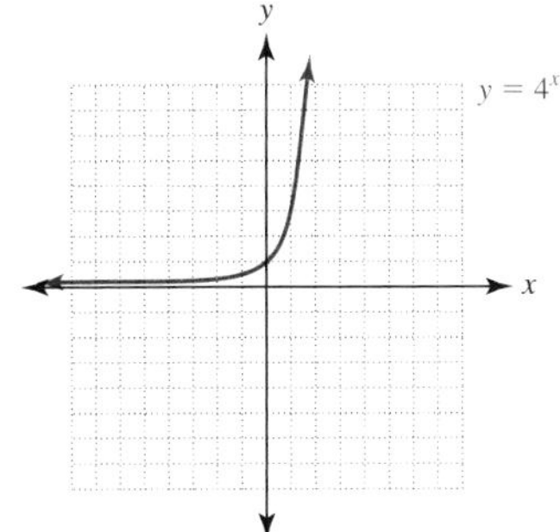

26. $y = \left(\frac{1}{4}\right)^x$

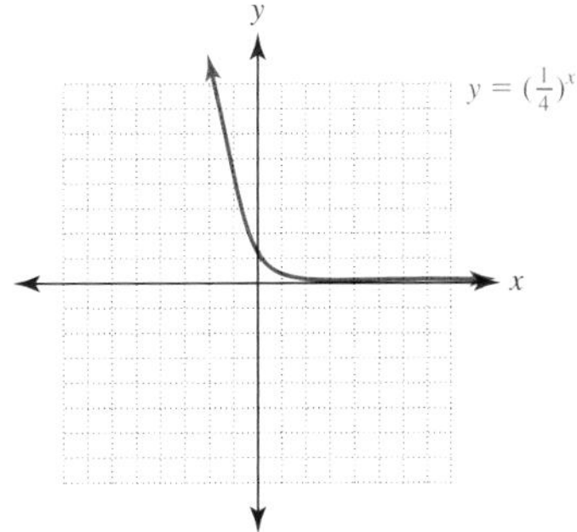

Answers

9. 1
10. 4
11. 16
12. $\frac{1}{16}$
13. 4
14. 16
15. 64
16. $\frac{1}{4}$
17. 2
18. 5
19. 17
20. $\frac{17}{16}$
21. $\frac{1}{4}$
22. 4
23. 16
24. $\frac{1}{16}$
25. See exercise
26. See exercise

Answers

27. See exercise

28. See exercise

29. See exercise

30. See exercise

31. See exercise

32. See exercise

27. $y = \left(\frac{2}{3}\right)^x$

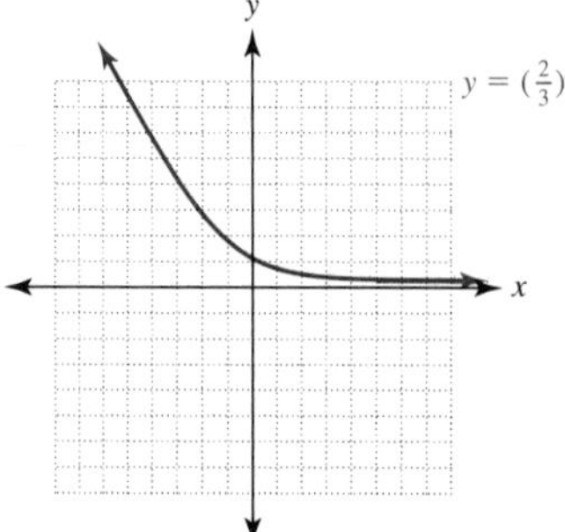

28. $y = \left(\frac{3}{2}\right)^x$

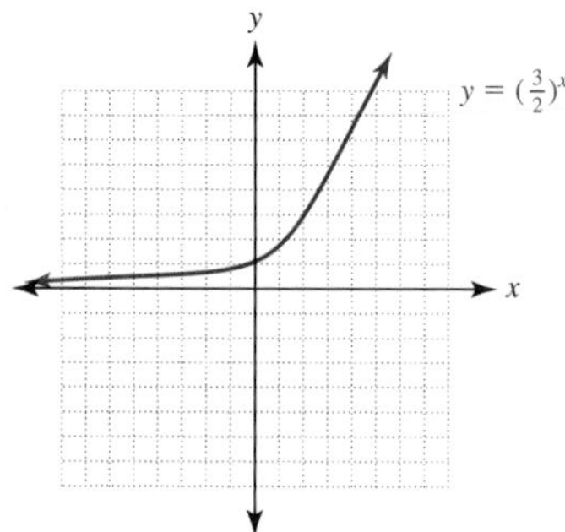

29. $y = 3 \cdot 2^x$

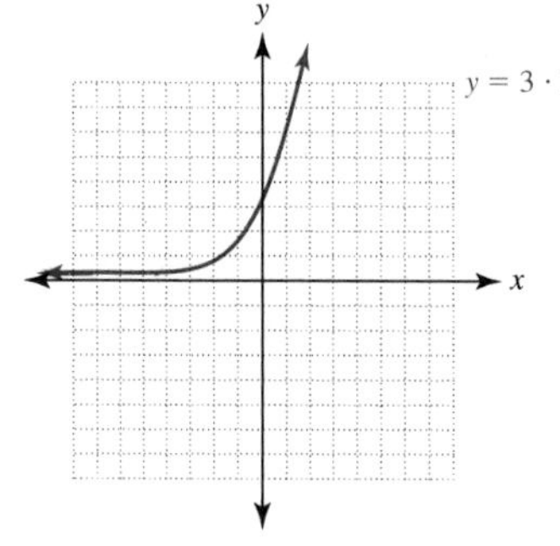

30. $y = 2 \cdot 3^x$

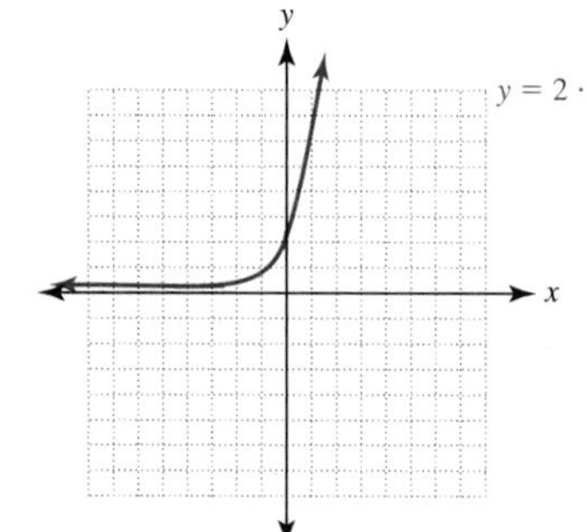

31. $y = 3^x$

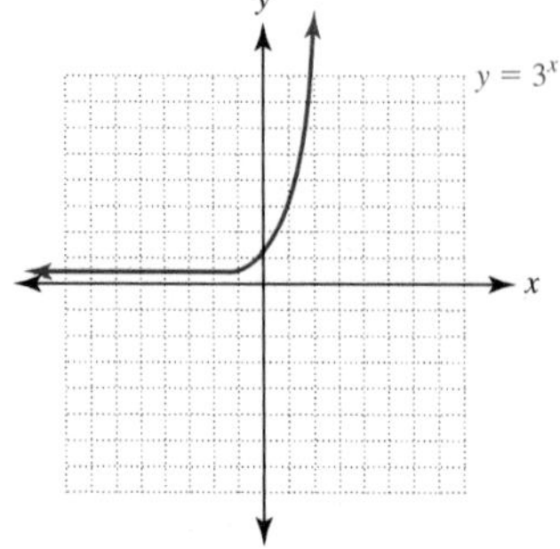

32. $y = 2^{x-1}$

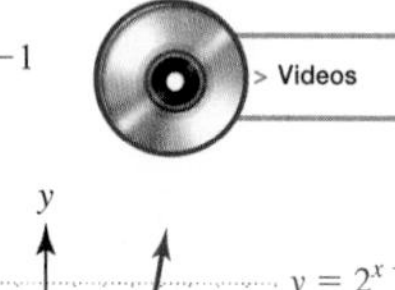

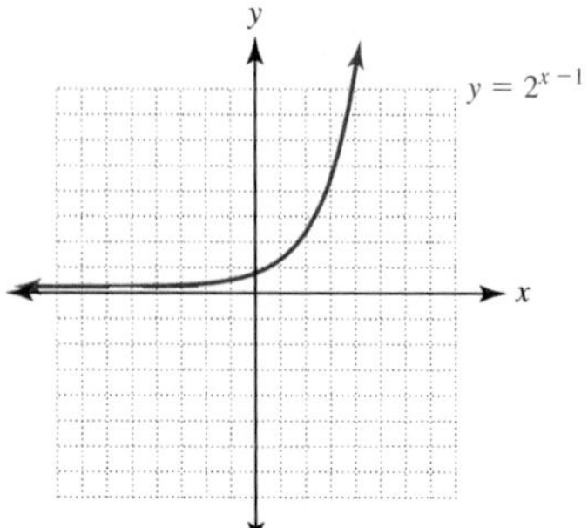

33. $y = 2^{2x}$

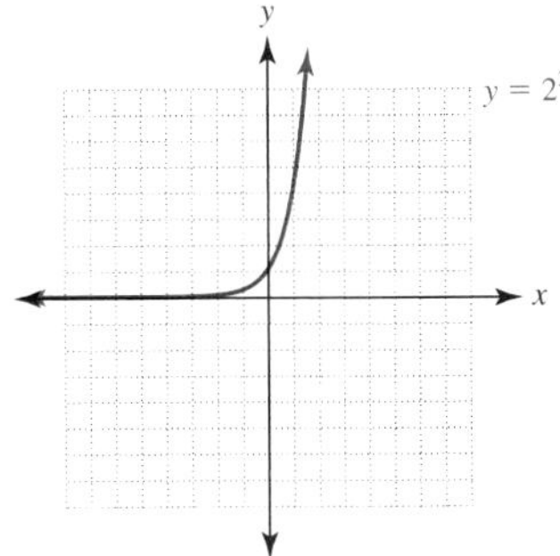

34. $y = \left(\frac{1}{2}\right)^{2x}$

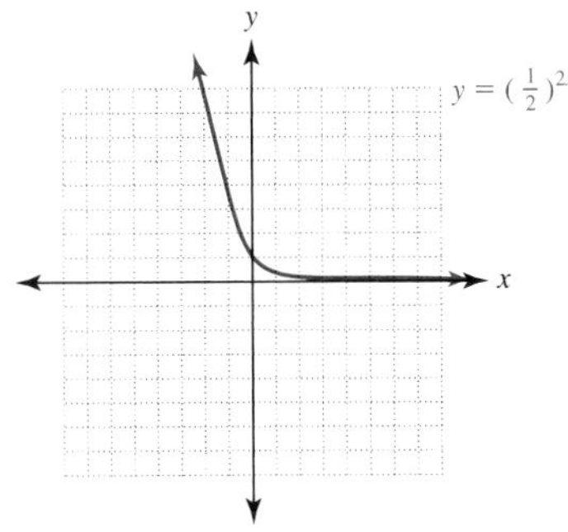

35. $y = e^{-x}$

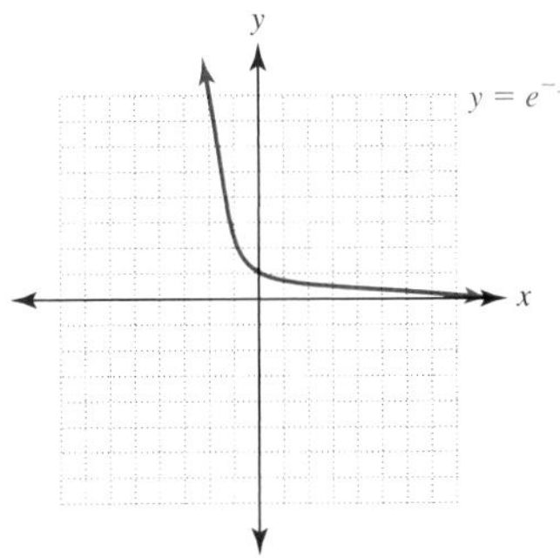

36. $y = e^{2x}$

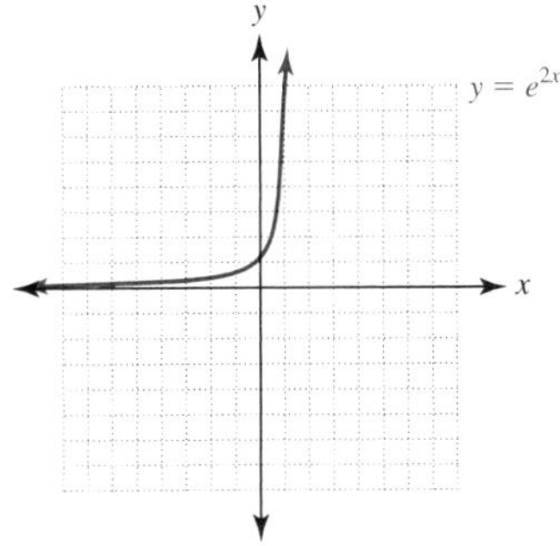

< Objective 3 >

Solve each exponential equation for x.

37. $2^x = 32$

38. $4^x = 64$

39. $10^x = 10{,}000$

40. $5^x = 125$

41. $3^x = \dfrac{1}{9}$

42. $2^x = \dfrac{1}{16}$

43. $2^{2x} = 64$

44. $3^{2x} = 81$

45. $2^{x+1} = 64$

46. $4^{x-1} = 16$

47. $3^{x-1} = \dfrac{1}{27}$

48. $2^{x+2} = \dfrac{1}{8}$

Answers

33. See exercise

34. See exercise

35. See exercise

36. See exercise

37. 5

38. 3

39. 4

40. 3

41. −2

42. −4

43. 3

44. 2

45. 5

46. 3

47. −2

48. −5

Answers

49. never

50. (a), (b), (c)

51. 400 bacteria

52. 800 bacteria

53. 3,200 bacteria

54. See exercise

55. 32 g

56. 16 g

57. 8 g

In the following statement, fill in the blank with **always, sometimes,** *or* **never.**

49. In the exponential function $f(x) = b^x$, the base is __________ equal to 1.

50. All graphs of exponential functions of the form $f(x) = b^x$ will have the following in common (choose all that apply):

(a) The y-intercept will be (0, 1).

(b) The graphs will approach, but not touch, the x-axis.

(c) The graphs will represent one-to-one functions.

< Objective 2 >

SCIENCE AND MEDICINE *Suppose it takes* 1 h *for a certain bacterial culture to double by dividing in half. If there are* 100 *bacteria in the culture to start, then the number of bacteria in the culture after x hours is given by* $N(x) = 100 \cdot 2^x$. *Use this function to solve exercises 51 to 54.*

51. Find the number of bacteria in the culture after 2 h.

52. Find the number of bacteria in the culture after 3 h.

53. Find the number of bacteria in the culture after 5 h.

54. Graph the relationship between the number of bacteria in the culture and the number of hours. Be sure to choose an appropriate scale for the N-axis.

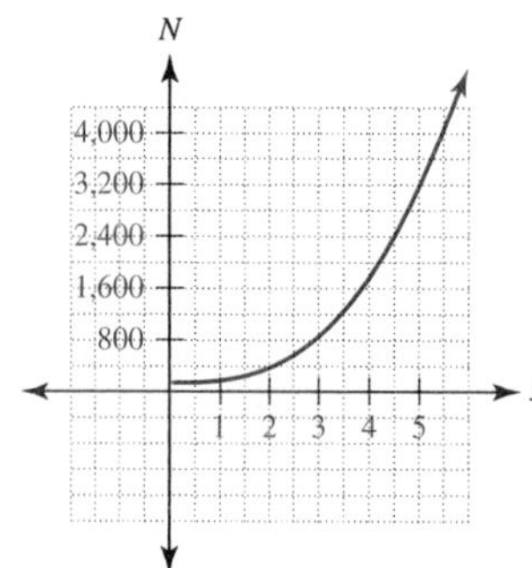

SCIENCE AND MEDICINE *The half-life of radium is* 1,690 *years. That is, after a* 1,690-*year period, one-half of the original amount of radium will have decayed into another substance. If the original amount of radium is* 64 *grams* (g), *the formula relating the amount of radium left after time t is given by* $R(t) = 64 \cdot 2^{-t/1,690}$. *Use this function to solve exercises 55 to 58.*

chapter 11 > Make the Connection

55. Find the amount of radium left after 1,690 years.

56. Find the amount of radium left after 3,380 years.

57. Find the amount of radium left after 5,070 years.

58. Graph the relationship between the amount of radium remaining and time. Be sure to use appropriate scales for the R- and t-axes.

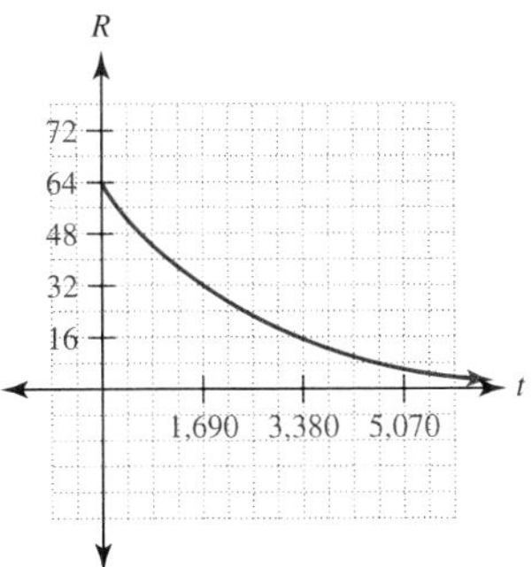

Basic Skills | Advanced Skills | **Vocational-Technical Applications** | Calculator/Computer | Above and Beyond

59. **Allied Health** The activity, A [in millicuries (mCi)] of a vial of sodium chromate (Cr51) originally containing 4.2 mCi is given by the function $A = 4.2e^{-0.025t}$, where the time, t, is measured in days since the vial was created. Determine the activity remaining in the vial at each of the following times:

(a) After 2 days
(b) After 1 week
(c) After 2 weeks
(d) After 1 month

60. **Manufacturing Technology** The intensity of light transmitted through a certain material is reduced by 6% per millimeter of thickness. The percentage of light transmitted can be found using the formula $P = (1 - 0.06)^T$, where T is the thickness of the material in millimeters. Find the percentage of light transmitted if the thickness of the material is 34 mm.

61. **Construction Technology** Many construction materials swell up when they are exposed to moisture. For a given material, the thickness is given by the formula

$$t(m) = t_{\text{initial}} + (1 - e^{-\text{moisture\%}/300})$$

where t_{initial} is the thickness of the material when it is dry.

(a) What is the thickness of a material that has a dry thickness of $\frac{3}{4}$ inch when it has a moisture level of 40%?

(b) What is the thickness of the material at 65% humidity if the dry thickness is $\frac{1}{2}$ inch?

62. **Agricultural Technology** The biomass per acre of a cornfield over time grows exponentially. The amount of biomass is given by the equation $b = 1.132^d$, where b is the biomass per acre in pounds and d is the growing time in days.

(a) How much biomass is in a 1-acre field after 80 days of growth?
(b) How much will the biomass increase in the next 10 days after day 80?

Answers

58. See exercise

59. (a) 4.00 mCi; (b) 3.53 mCi; (c) 2.96 mCi; (d) 1.98 mCi

60. 12.2%

61. (a) 0.875 in.; (b) 0.695 in.

62. (a) 20,310.2 lb; (b) 49,864.2 lb

Basic Skills | Advanced Skills | Vocational-Technical Applications | **Calculator/Computer** | Above and Beyond

Answers

63. $1,166.40

64. $1,469.33

65. $1,999

66. See exercise

67. (a) 36 words per minute; (b) 56 words per minute; (c) 67 words per minute

68. See exercise

69. Answers will vary

Business and Finance *If $1,000 is invested in a savings account with an interest rate of 8%, compounded annually, the amount in the account after t years is given by* $A(t) = 1{,}000(1 + 0.08)^t$. *Use a calculator and this function to solve exercises 63 to 66.*

63. Find the amount in the account after 2 years.

64. Find the amount in the account after 5 years.

65. Find the amount in the account after 9 years.

66. Graph the relationship between the amount in the account and time. Be sure to choose appropriate scales for the A- and t-axes.

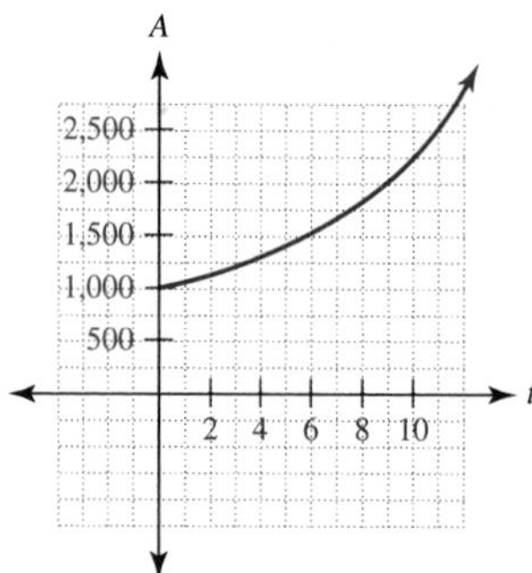

Science and Medicine *The so-called learning curve in psychology applies to learning a skill, such as typing, in which the performance level progresses rapidly at first and then levels off with time. You can approximate N, the number of words per minute that a person can type after t weeks of training, with the equation* $N = 80(1 - e^{-0.06t})$. *Use a calculator and this function to solve exercises 67 and 68.*

67. Find the following: **(a)** N after 10 weeks, **(b)** N after 20 weeks, **(c)** N after 30 weeks.

68. Graph the relationship between the number of words per minute N and the number of weeks of training t.

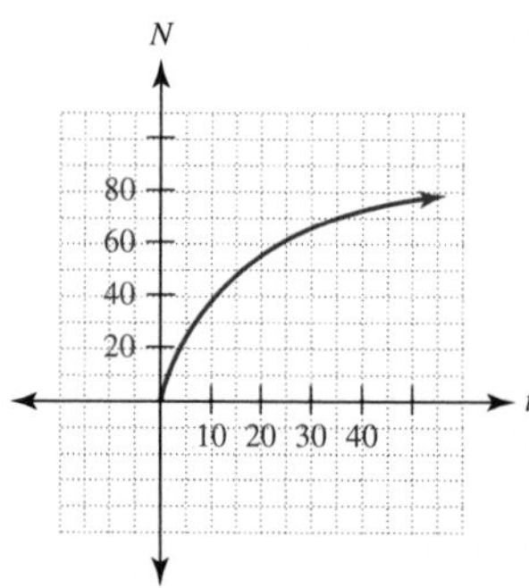

69. Find two different calculators that have $\boxed{e^x}$ keys. Describe how to use the function on each of the calculators.

70. Are there any values of x for which e^x produces an exact answer on the calculator? Why are other answers not exact?

A possible calculator sequence for evaluating the expression

$$\left(1 + \frac{1}{n}\right)^n$$

in which $n = 10$ is

[(] 1 [+] 1 [÷] 10 [)] [∧] 10 [=]

In exercises 71 to 75, use this sequence to find $\left(1 + \frac{1}{n}\right)^n$ *for the following values of n.*

71. $n = 100$ **72.** $n = 1{,}000$ **73.** $n = 10{,}000$

74. $n = 100{,}000$ **75.** $n = 1{,}000{,}000$

76. What did you observe from the experiment in exercises 71 to 75?

Basic Skills | Advanced Skills | Vocational-Technical Applications | Calculator/Computer | **Above and Beyond**

77. Graph the exponential function defined by $y = 2^x$.

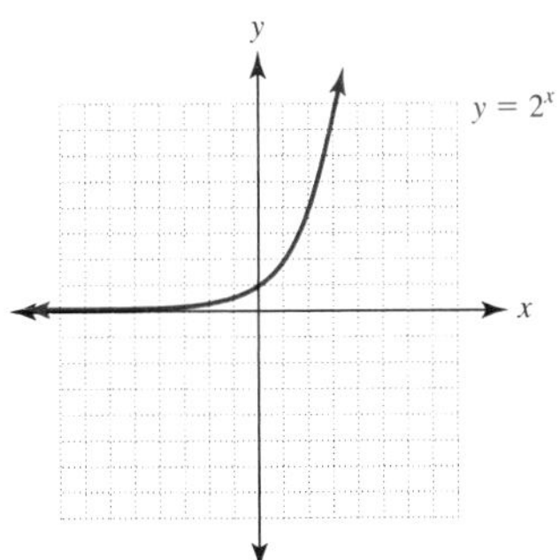

78. Graph the function defined by $x = 2^y$ on the same set of axes as that of the graph in exercise 77. What do you observe? (*Hint:* To graph $x = 2^y$, choose convenient values for y and then find the corresponding values for x.)

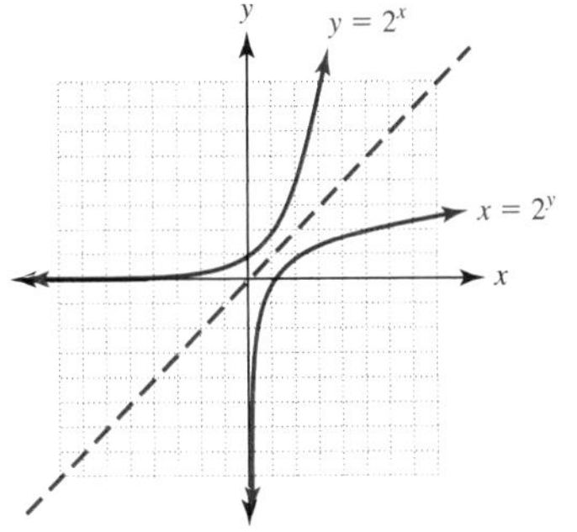

Answers

70. 0; Answers will vary

71. 2.70481

72. 2.71692

73. 2.71815

74. 2.71827

75. 2.71828

76. As n gets larger, the value approaches e.

77. See exercise

78. See exercise; the graphs are symmetric about the line $y = x$.

Answers

1. (c) **3.** (b) **5.** (h) **7.** (f) **9.** 1 **11.** 16 **13.** 4
15. 64 **17.** 2 **19.** 17 **21.** $\frac{1}{4}$ **23.** 16

25. $y = 4^x$

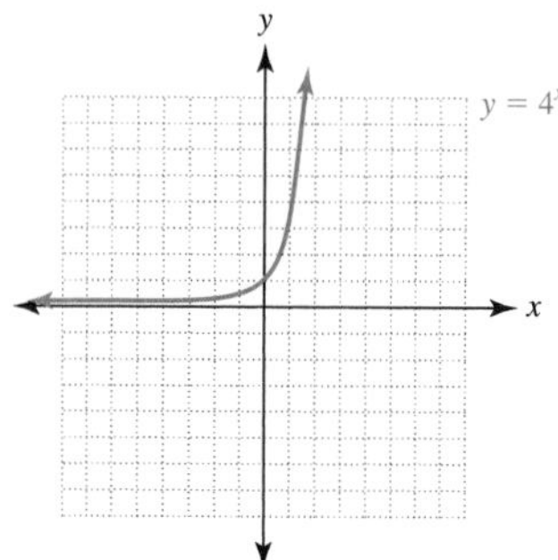

27. $y = \left(\frac{2}{3}\right)^x$

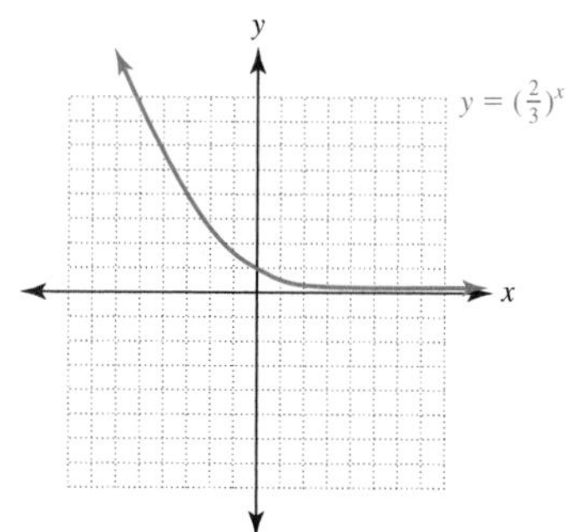

29. $y = 3 \cdot 2^x$

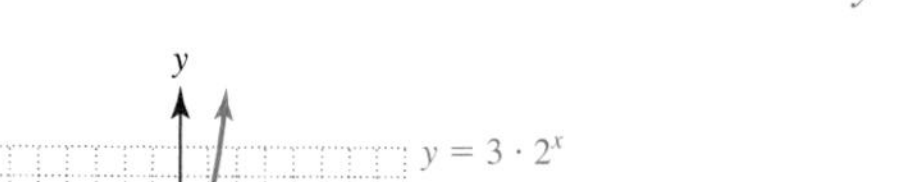

31. $y = 3^x$

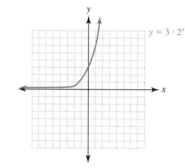

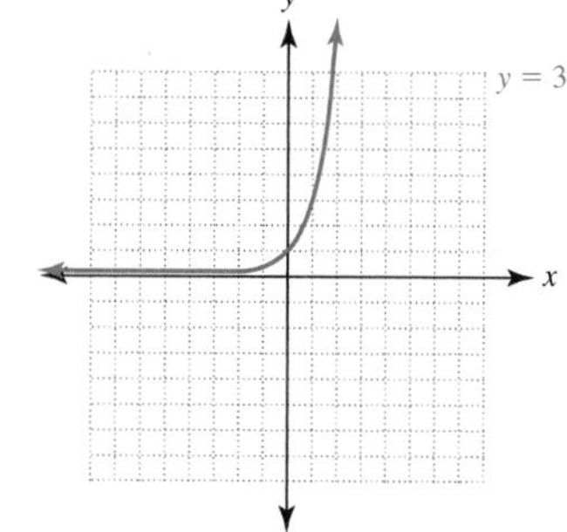

33. $y = 2^{2x}$

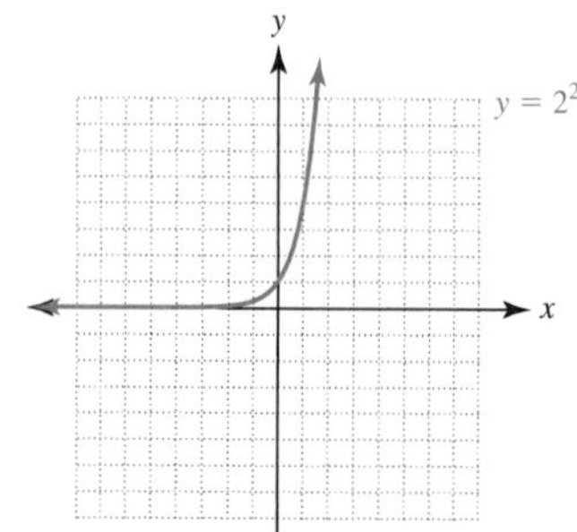

35. $y = e^{-x}$

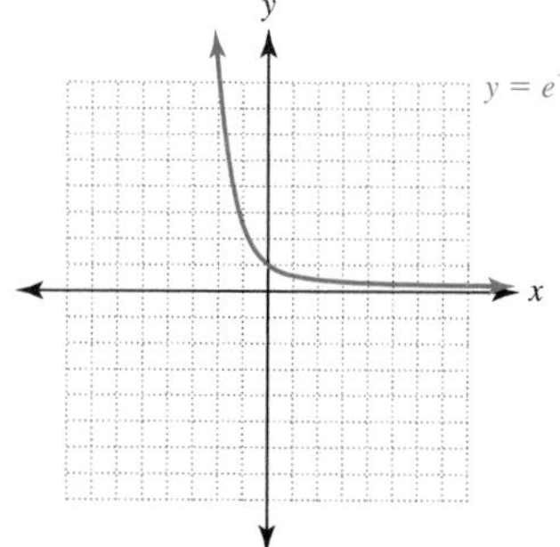

37. 5 **39.** 4 **41.** -2 **43.** 3 **45.** 5 **47.** -2 **49.** never
51. 400 bacteria **53.** 3,200 bacteria **55.** 32 g **57.** 8 g
59. **(a)** 4.00 mCi; **(b)** 3.53 mCi; **(c)** 2.96 mCi; **(d)** 1.98 mCi

61. **(a)** 0.875 in.; **(b)** 0.695 in. **63.** \$1,166.40 **65.** \$1,999

67. **(a)** 36 words per minute; **(b)** 56 words per minute; **(c)** 67 words per minute

69. Answers will vary **71.** 2.70481 **73.** 2.71815 **75.** 2.71828

77.

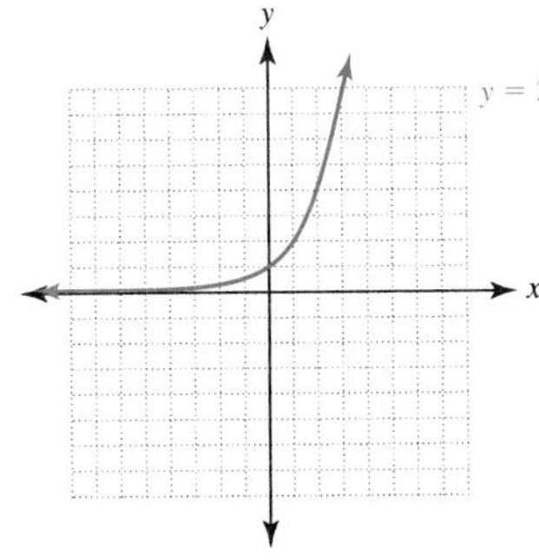

11.2 Logarithmic Functions

< 11.2 Objectives >

1 > Graph a logarithmic function

2 > Convert between logarithmic and exponential expressions

3 > Evaluate a logarithmic expression

4 > Solve an elementary logarithmic equation

NOTE

Napier also coined the word *logarithm* from the Greek words *logos*—a ratio—and *arithmos*—a number.

Given our experience with the exponential function in Section 11.1 and our earlier work with the inverse of a function, we now can introduce the logarithmic function.

John Napier (1550–1617), a Scotsman, is credited with the invention of logarithms. The development of the logarithm grew out of a desire to ease the work involved in numerical computations, particularly in the field of astronomy. Today the availability of inexpensive scientific calculators has made the use of logarithms as a computational tool unnecessary.

However, the concept of the logarithm and the properties of the logarithmic function that we will describe in Section 11.3 still are very important in the solutions of particular equations, in calculus, and in the applied sciences.

Again, the applications for this new function are numerous. The Richter scale for measuring the intensity of an earthquake and the decibel scale for measuring the intensity of sound both make use of logarithms.

RECALL

The exponential function f is a one-to-one function, so its inverse is also a function.

To develop the idea of a logarithmic function, we must return to the exponential function $f(x) = b^x$, $b > 0, b \neq 1$. We can also write this as $y = b^x, b > 0, b \neq 1$. Then interchanging the roles of x and y, we have the inverse function

$$x = b^y$$

Presently, we have no way to solve the equation $x = b^y$ for y. So, to write the inverse function in a more useful form, we offer the following definition.

Definition

Logarithm

The **logarithm of x to base b** is denoted

$\log_b x$

and

$y = \log_b x$ if and only if $x = b^y$

NOTE

The restrictions on the base are the same as those used for the exponential function.

We can now write our inverse function, using this new notation, as

$f(x) = log_b x, b > 0, b \neq 1$

In general, any function defined in this form is called a **logarithmic function.**

At this point we should stress the meaning of this new relationship. Consider the equivalent forms illustrated here.

Definition

Logarithm

Power or exponent

$y = \log_b x$ means the same as $x = b^y$

Base

The **logarithm** y is the power to which we must raise b to get x. In other words, *a logarithm is simply a power or an exponent.* We return to this thought later when using the exponential and logarithmic forms of equivalent equations.

We begin our work by graphing a typical logarithmic function.

Example 1 Graphing a Logarithmic Function

< Objective 1 >

NOTES

The base is 2, and the logarithm or power is y.

What do the vertical- and horizontal-line tests tell you about this graph?

Graph the logarithmic function

$y = \log_2 x$

Because $y = \log_2 x$ is equivalent to the exponential form

$x = 2^y$

we can find ordered pairs satisfying this equation by choosing convenient values for y and calculating the corresponding values for x.

Letting y take on values from -3 to 3 yields the following table of values. As before, we plot points from the ordered pairs and connect them with a smooth curve to form the graph of the function.

x	y
$\frac{1}{8}$	-3
$\frac{1}{4}$	-2
$\frac{1}{2}$	-1
1	0
2	1
4	2
8	3

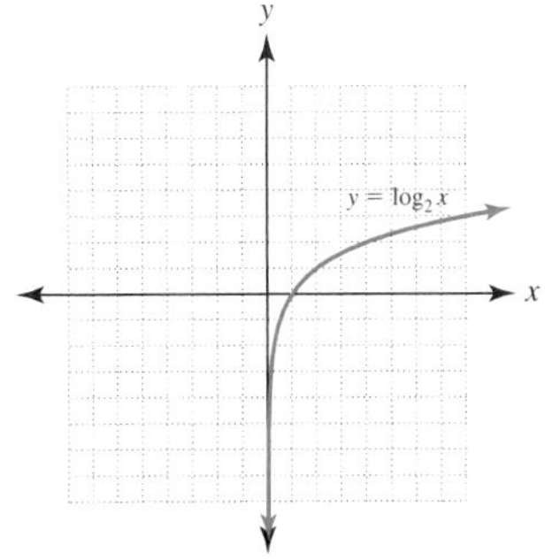

NOTE

Use your calculator to compare the graphs of $y = 10^x$ and $y = \log_{10} x$. Are they inverse functions? How can you tell?

We observe that the graph represents a one-to-one function whose domain is $\{x|x > 0\}$ and whose range is the set of all real numbers.

For base 2 (or for any base greater than 1) the function will always be increasing over its domain.

Recall from Section 10.3 that the graphs of a function and its inverse are always reflections of each other using the line $y = x$. Because we have defined the logarithmic function as the inverse of an exponential function, we can anticipate the same relationship.

The graphs of

$$f(x) = 2^x \quad \text{and} \quad f^{-1}(x) = \log_2 x$$

are shown here.

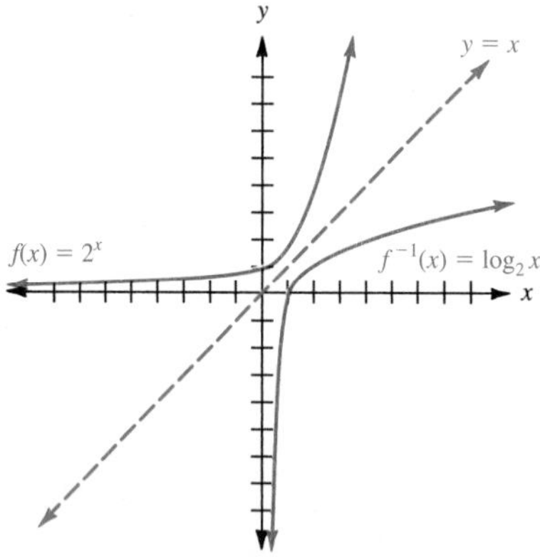

We see that the graphs of f and f^{-1} are indeed reflections of each other about the line $y = x$. In fact, this relationship provides an alternate method of sketching $y = \log_b x$. We can sketch the graph of $y = b^x$ and then reflect that graph using the line $y = x$ to form the graph of the logarithmic function.

Check Yourself 1

Graph the logarithmic function defined by

$y = \log_3 x$

***Hint*: Consider the equivalent form $x = 3^y$.**

> **NOTE**
>
> Again, this tells us that a logarithm is an exponent or a power.

For our later work in this chapter, it will be necessary for us to be able to convert back and forth between exponential and logarithmic forms. The conversion is straightforward. You need only keep in mind the basic relationship

$$y = \log_b x \quad \text{means the same as} \quad x = b^y$$

Look at Example 2.

Example 2 Writing Equations in Logarithmic Form

< Objective 2 >

Convert to logarithmic form.

(a) $3^4 = 81$ is equivalent to $\log_3 81 = 4$.

(b) $10^3 = 1{,}000$ is equivalent to $\log_{10} 1{,}000 = 3$.

NOTE

In part **(a)**: the base is 3; the exponent or power is 4.

(c) $2^{-3} = \frac{1}{8}$ is equivalent to $\log_2 \frac{1}{8} = -3$.

(d) $9^{1/2} = 3$ is equivalent to $\log_9 3 = \frac{1}{2}$.

Check Yourself 2

Convert each statement to logarithmic form.

(a) $4^3 = 64$ **(b)** $10^{-2} = 0.01$ **(c)** $3^{-3} = \frac{1}{27}$ **(d)** $27^{1/3} = 3$

Example 3 shows how to write a logarithmic expression in exponential form.

Example 3 Writing Equations in Exponential Form

NOTE

In part **(a)**: the base is 2; the logarithm, which is the power, is 3.

Convert to exponential form.

(a) $\log_2 8 = 3$ is equivalent to $2^3 = 8$.

(b) $\log_{10} 100 = 2$ is equivalent to $10^2 = 100$.

(c) $\log_3 \frac{1}{9} = -2$ is equivalent to $3^{-2} = \frac{1}{9}$.

(d) $\log_{25} 5 = \frac{1}{2}$ is equivalent to $25^{1/2} = 5$.

Check Yourself 3

Convert to exponential form.

(a) $\log_2 32 = 5$ **(b)** $\log_{10} 1{,}000 = 3$

(c) $\log_4 \frac{1}{16} = -2$ **(d)** $\log_{27} 3 = \frac{1}{3}$

Certain logarithms can be directly calculated by changing an expression to the equivalent exponential form, as Example 4 illustrates.

Example 4 Evaluating Logarithmic Expressions

< Objective 3 >

RECALL

$b^m = b^n$ if and only if $m = n$.

(a) Evaluate $\log_3 27$.

If $x = \log_3 27$, in exponential form we have

$$3^x = 27$$
$$3^x = 3^3$$
$$x = 3$$

We then have $\log_3 27 = 3$.

NOTE

Rewrite each side as a power of the same base.

(b) Evaluate $\log_{10} \frac{1}{10}$.

If $x = \log_{10} \frac{1}{10}$, we can write

$$10^x = \frac{1}{10}$$
$$= 10^{-1}$$

We then have $x = -1$ and

$$\log_{10} \frac{1}{10} = -1$$

Check Yourself 4

Evaluate each logarithm.

(a) $\log_2 64$ **(b)** $\log_3 \frac{1}{27}$

The relationship between exponents and logarithms also allows us to solve certain equations involving logarithms in which two of the quantities in the equation $y = \log_b x$ are known, as Example 5 illustrates.

Example 5 Solving Logarithmic Equations

< Objective 4 >

(a) Solve $\log_5 x = 3$ for x.

Because $\log_5 x = 3$, in exponential form we have

$$x = 5^3$$
$$= 125$$

(b) Solve $y = \log_4 \frac{1}{16}$ for y.

The original equation is equivalent to

$$4^y = \frac{1}{16}$$
$$= 4^{-2}$$

We then have $y = -2$ as the solution.

NOTE

Keep in mind that the base must be *positive*, so we do not consider the possible solution $b = -3$.

(c) Solve $\log_b 81 = 4$ for b.

In exponential form the equation becomes

$$b^4 = 81$$
$$b = 3$$

Check Yourself 5

Solve each of the following equations for the variable cited.

(a) $\log_4 x = 4$ for x **(b)** $\log_b \frac{1}{8} = -3$ for b **(c)** $y = \log_9 3$ for y

To conclude this section, we turn to two common applications of the logarithmic function. The **decibel scale** is used in measuring the loudness of various sounds.

If I represents the intensity of a given sound and I_0 represents the intensity of a "threshold sound," then the decibel (dB) rating of the given sound is given by

$$L = 10 \log_{10} \frac{I}{I_0}$$

in which $I_0 = 10^{-16}$ watts per square centimeter (W/cm^2). Consider Example 6.

NOTES

Loudness can be measured in **bels (B),** a unit named for Alexander Graham Bell. This unit is rather large, so a more practical unit is the **decibel (dB),** a unit one-tenth as large.

Variable I_0 is the intensity of the minimum sound level detectable by the human ear.

Example 6 A Decibel Application

(a) A whisper has intensity $I = 10^{-14}$ W/cm^2. Its decibel rating is

$$\begin{aligned} L &= 10 \log_{10} \frac{10^{-14}}{10^{-16}} \\ &= 10 \log_{10} 10^2 \\ &= 10 \cdot 2 \\ &= 20 \end{aligned}$$

(b) A rock concert has intensity $I = 10^{-4}$ W/cm^2. Its decibel rating is

$$\begin{aligned} L &= 10 \log_{10} \frac{10^{-4}}{10^{-16}} \\ &= 10 \log_{10} 10^{12} \\ &= 10 \cdot 12 \\ &= 120 \end{aligned}$$

Check Yourself 6

Ordinary conversation has intensity $I = 10^{-12}$. Find its rating on the decibel scale.

NOTES

The scale was named after Charles Richter, a U.S. geologist.

A "zero-level" earthquake is the quake of least intensity that is measurable by a seismograph.

Another commonly used logarithmic scale is the **Richter scale.** Geologists use that scale to convert seismographic readings, which give the intensity of the shock waves of an earthquake, to a measure of the magnitude of the earthquake.

The magnitude M of an earthquake is given by

$$M = \log_{10} \frac{a}{a_0}$$

in which a is the intensity of its shock waves and a_0 is the intensity of the shock wave of a zero-level earthquake.

Example 7 A Richter Scale Application

How many times stronger is an earthquake measuring 5 on the Richter scale than one measuring 4 on the Richter scale?

Suppose a_1 is the intensity of the earthquake with magnitude 5 and a_2 is the intensity of the earthquake with magnitude 4. Then

NOTE

On your calculator, the log key is actually $\log_{10} x$.

$$5 = \log_{10} \frac{a_1}{a_0} \quad \text{and} \quad 4 = \log_{10} \frac{a_2}{a_0}$$

We convert these logarithmic expressions to exponential form.

$$10^5 = \frac{a_1}{a_0} \quad \text{and} \quad 10^4 = \frac{a_2}{a_0}$$

or

$$a_1 = a_0 \cdot 10^5 \quad \text{and} \quad a_2 = a_0 \cdot 10^4$$

NOTE

The ratio of a_1 to a_2 is $\frac{a_1}{a_2}$

We want the ratio of the intensities of the two earthquakes, so

$$\frac{a_1}{a_2} = \frac{a_0 \cdot 10^5}{a_0 \cdot 10^4} = 10^1 = 10$$

The earthquake of magnitude 5 is *10 times stronger* than the earthquake of magnitude 4.

Check Yourself 7

How many times stronger is an earthquake of magnitude 6 than one of magnitude 4?

Check Yourself ANSWERS

1. $y = \log_3 x$

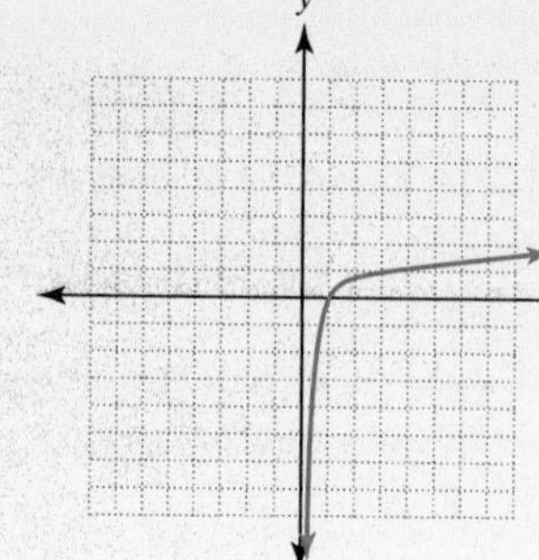

2. **(a)** $\log_4 64 = 3$; **(b)** $\log_{10} 0.01 = -2$; **(c)** $\log_3 \frac{1}{27} = -3$; **(d)** $\log_{27} 3 = \frac{1}{3}$

3. **(a)** $2^5 = 32$; **(b)** $10^3 = 1{,}000$; **(c)** $4^{-2} = \frac{1}{16}$; **(d)** $27^{1/3} = 3$

4. **(a)** $\log_2 64 = 6$; **(b)** $\log_3 \frac{1}{27} = -3$ **5.** **(a)** $x = 256$; **(b)** $b = 2$; **(c)** $y = \frac{1}{2}$

6. 40 dB **7.** 100 times

Reading Your Text

The following fill-in-the-blank exercises are designed to ensure that you understand some of the key vocabulary used in this section.

SECTION 11.2

(a) The ______________ is denoted $\log_b x$.

(b) Any function defined as $f(x) = \log_b x$ (for $b > 0$, $b \neq 1$) is called a ______________.

(c) The ______________ y is the power to which we must raise b to get x.

(d) A ______________ is simply a power or an exponent.

11.2 exercises

Basic Skills | Advanced Skills | Vocational-Technical Applications | Calculator/Computer | Above and Beyond

MathZone

Boost your grade at mathzone.com!

- Practice Problems
- NetTutor
- Self-Tests
- e-Professors
- Videos

Name ________________

Section ________ Date ________

< Objective 1 >

Sketch the graph of the function defined by each equation.

1. $y = \log_4 x$

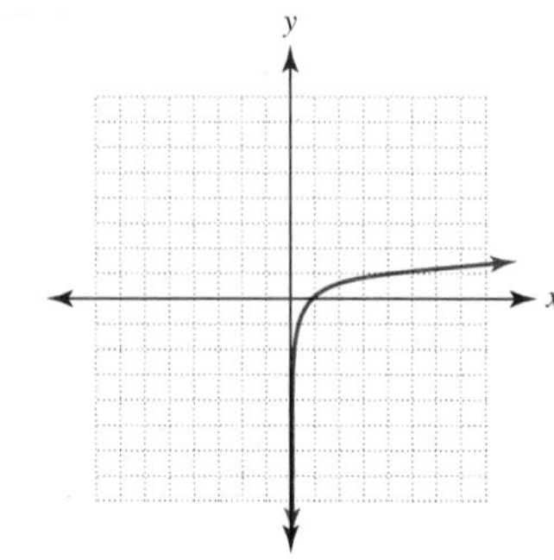

2. $y = \log_{10} x$

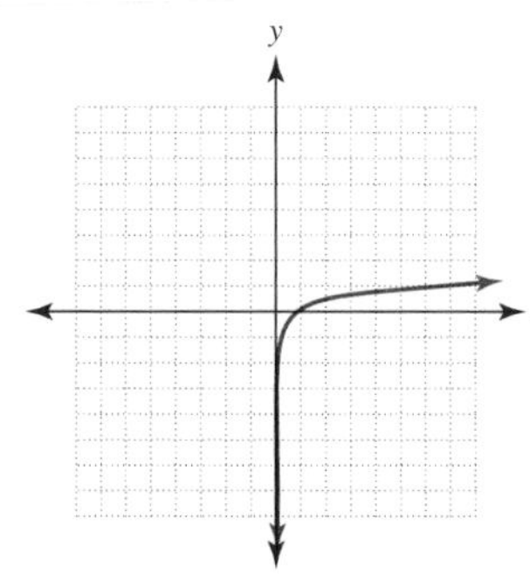

3. $y = \log_2 (x - 1)$

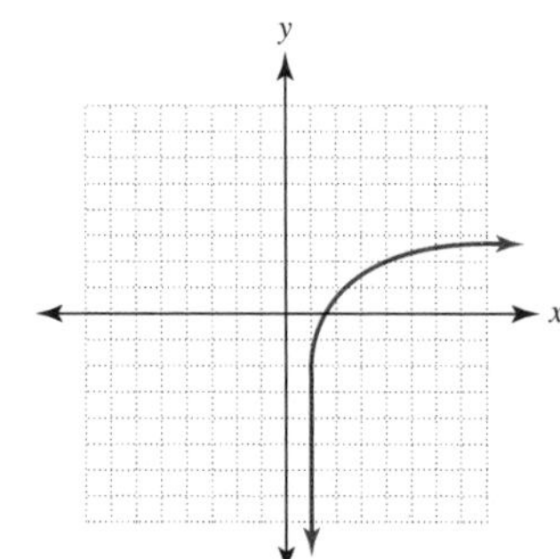

4. $y = \log_3 (x + 1)$

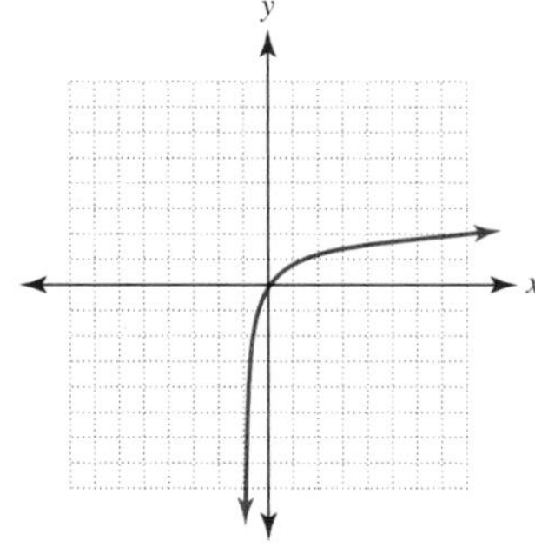

5. $y = \log_8 x$

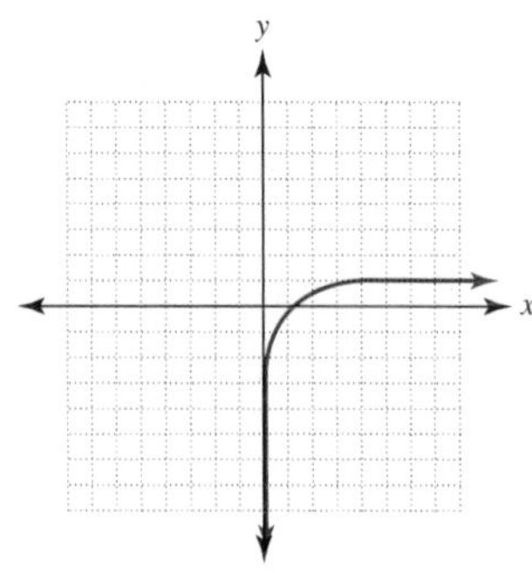

6. $y = \log_3 x + 1$ > Videos

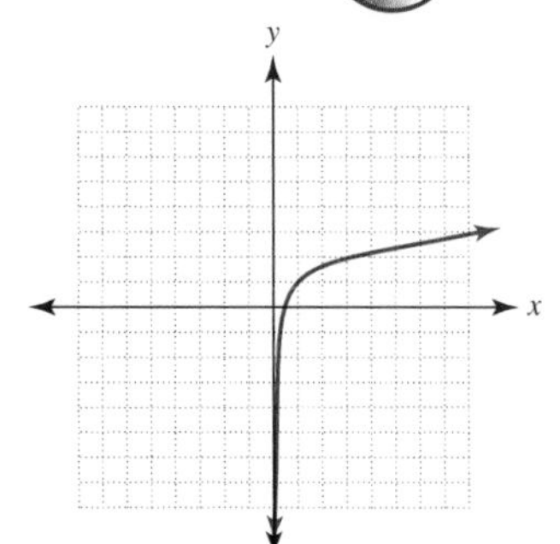

< Objective 2 >

Convert each statement to logarithmic form.

7. $2^4 = 16$

8. $3^5 = 243$

9. $10^2 = 100$

10. $4^3 = 64$

11. $3^0 = 1$

12. $10^0 = 1$

Answers

1. See exercise
2. See exercise
3. See exercise
4. See exercise
5. See exercise
6. See exercise
7. $\log_2 16 = 4$
8. $\log_3 243 = 5$
9. $\log_{10} 100 = 2$
10. $\log_4 64 = 3$
11. $\log_3 1 = 0$
12. $\log_{10} 1 = 0$

13. $4^{-2} = \frac{1}{16}$

14. $3^{-4} = \frac{1}{81}$

15. $10^{-3} = \frac{1}{1,000}$

16. $2^{-5} = \frac{1}{32}$

17. $16^{1/2} = 4$

18. $125^{1/3} = 5$

19. $64^{-1/3} = \frac{1}{4}$

20. $36^{-1/2} = \frac{1}{6}$

21. $8^{2/3} = 4$

22. $9^{3/2} = 27$

23. $27^{-2/3} = \frac{1}{9}$

24. $16^{-3/2} = \frac{1}{64}$

Convert each statement to exponential form.

25. $\log_2 16 = 4$

26. $\log_3 3 = 1$

27. $\log_5 1 = 0$

28. $\log_3 27 = 3$

29. $\log_{10} 10 = 1$

30. $\log_2 32 = 5$

31. $\log_5 125 = 3$

32. $\log_{10} 1 = 0$

33. $\log_3 \frac{1}{27} = -3$

34. $\log_5 \frac{1}{25} = -2$

35. $\log_{10} 0.01 = -2$

36. $\log_{10} \frac{1}{1,000} = -3$

Answers

13. $\log_4 \frac{1}{16} = -2$

14. $\log_3 \frac{1}{81} = -4$

15. $\log_{10} \frac{1}{1,000} = -3$

16. $\log_2 \frac{1}{32} = -5$

17. $\log_{16} 4 = \frac{1}{2}$

18. $\log_{125} 5 = \frac{1}{3}$

19. $\log_{64} \frac{1}{4} = -\frac{1}{3}$

20. $\log_{36} \frac{1}{6} = -\frac{1}{2}$

21. $\log_8 4 = \frac{2}{3}$

22. $\log_9 27 = \frac{3}{2}$

23. $\log_{27} \frac{1}{9} = -\frac{2}{3}$

24. $\log_{16} \frac{1}{64} = -\frac{3}{2}$

25. $2^4 = 16$

26. $3^1 = 3$

27. $5^0 = 1$

28. $3^3 = 27$

29. $10^1 = 10$

30. $2^5 = 32$

31. $5^3 = 125$

32. $10^0 = 1$

33. $3^{-3} = \frac{1}{27}$

34. $5^{-2} = \frac{1}{25}$

35. $10^{-2} = 0.01$

36. $10^{-3} = \frac{1}{1,000}$

37. $\log_{16} 4 = \frac{1}{2}$

38. $\log_{125} 5 = \frac{1}{3}$

39. $\log_8 4 = \frac{2}{3}$

40. $\log_9 27 = \frac{3}{2}$

41. $\log_{25} \frac{1}{5} = -\frac{1}{2}$

42. $\log_{64} \frac{1}{16} = -\frac{2}{3}$

< Objective 3 >

Evaluate each logarithm.

43. $\log_2 32$

44. $\log_3 81$

45. $\log_4 64$

46. $\log_{10} 1{,}000$

47. $\log_3 \frac{1}{81}$

48. $\log_4 \frac{1}{64}$

49. $\log_{10} \frac{1}{100}$

50. $\log_5 \frac{1}{25}$

51. $\log_{25} 5$

52. $\log_{27} 3$

< Objective 4 >

Solve each equation for the unknown variable.

53. $y = \log_5 25$

54. $\log_2 x = 4$

55. $\log_b 64 = 3$

56. $y = \log_3 1$

57. $\log_{10} x = 2$

58. $\log_b 125 = 3$

59. $y = \log_5 5$

60. $y = \log_3 81$

61. $\log_{3/2} x = 3$

62. $\log_b \frac{4}{9} = 2$

63. $\log_b \frac{1}{25} = -2$

64. $\log_3 x = -3$

Answers

37. $16^{1/2} = 4$

38. $125^{1/3} = 5$

39. $8^{2/3} = 4$

40. $9^{3/2} = 27$

41. $25^{-1/2} = \frac{1}{5}$

42. $64^{-2/3} = \frac{1}{16}$

43. 5 | 44. 4

45. 3 | 46. 3

47. −4 | 48. −3

49. −2 | 50. −2

51. $\frac{1}{2}$ | 52. $\frac{1}{3}$

53. 2 | 54. 16

55. 4 | 56. 0

57. 100 | 58. 5

59. 1 | 60. 4

61. $\frac{27}{8}$ | 62. $\frac{2}{3}$

63. 5 | 64. $\frac{1}{27}$

65. $\log_{10} x = -3$

66. $y = \log_2 \frac{1}{16}$

67. $y = \log_8 \frac{1}{64}$

68. $\log_b \frac{1}{100} = -2$

69. $\log_{27} x = \frac{1}{3}$

70. $y = \log_{100} 10$

71. $\log_b 5 = \frac{1}{2}$

72. $\log_{64} x = \frac{2}{3}$

73. $y = \log_{27} \frac{1}{9}$

74. $\log_b \frac{1}{8} = -\frac{3}{4}$

Label the following statements as **true** *or* **false.**

75. $y = \log_b x$ means the same as $b^y = x$.

76. The inverse of $f(x) = b^x$ (for $b > 0, b \neq 1$) is $f^{-1}(x) = \log_b x$ (for $b > 0, b \neq 1$).

SCIENCE AND MEDICINE *Use the decibel formula*

$$L = 10 \log_{10} \frac{I}{I_0}$$

in which $I_0 = 10^{-16}$ W/cm², *to solve exercises 77 to 80.*

77. A television commercial has a volume with intensity $I = 10^{-11}$ W/cm². Find its rating in decibels.

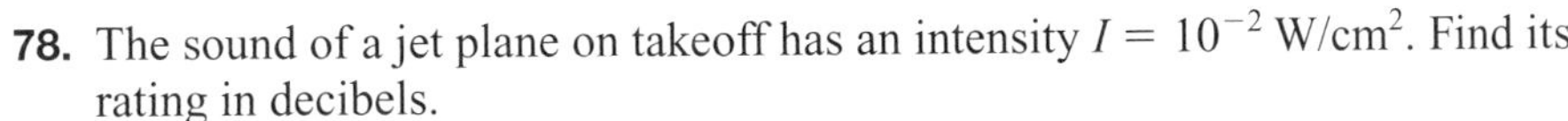

78. The sound of a jet plane on takeoff has an intensity $I = 10^{-2}$ W/cm². Find its rating in decibels.

79. The sound of a vacuum cleaner has an intensity $I = 10^{-9}$ W/cm². Find its rating in decibels.

80. The sound of a busy street has an intensity $I = 10^{-8}$ W/cm². Find its rating in decibels.

Answers

65. $\frac{1}{1,000}$

66. −4

67. −2

68. 10

69. 3

70. $\frac{1}{2}$

71. 25

72. 16

73. $-\frac{2}{3}$

74. 16

75. True

76. True

77. 50 dB

78. 140 dB

79. 70 dB

80. 80 dB

Answers

81. 10^{-8} W/cm^2

82. 10^{-9} W/cm^2

83. 10

84. 100

85. 1,000

86. $I = I_0 10^{L/10}$

87. 6

88. 8.3

89. $10^5 \cdot a_0$

Science and Medicine *The formula for the decibel rating L can be solved for the intensity of the sound as $I = I_0 \cdot 10^{L/10}$. Use this formula in exercises 81 to 85.*

81. Find the intensity of the sound in an airport waiting area if the decibel rating is 80.

82. Find the intensity of the sound of conversation in a crowded room if the decibel rating is 70.

83. What is the ratio of intensity of the sound of 80 dB to that of 70 dB?

84. What is the ratio of intensity of a sound of 60 dB to one measuring 40 dB?

85. What is the ratio of intensity of a sound of 70 dB to one measuring 40 dB?

86. Derive the formula for intensity provided above. (*Hint:* First divide both sides of the decibel formula by 10. Then write the equation in exponential form.)

Science and Medicine *Use the earthquake formula*

$$M = \log_{10} \frac{a}{a_0}$$

to solve exercises 87 to 90.

87. An earthquake has an intensity a of $10^6 \cdot a_0$, in which a_0 is the intensity of the zero-level earthquake. What is its magnitude? > Videos

88. The great San Francisco earthquake of 1906 had an intensity $10^{8.3} \cdot a_0$. What was its magnitude?

89. An earthquake can begin causing damage to buildings with a magnitude of 5 on the Richter scale. Find its intensity in terms of a_0.

90. An earthquake may cause moderate building damage with a magnitude of 6 on the Richter scale. Find its intensity in terms of a_0.

91. The **learning curve** describes the relationship between learning and time. Its graph is a logarithmic curve in the first quadrant. Describe that curve as it relates to learning.

92. In which scientific fields would you expect to again encounter a discussion of logarithms?

Basic Skills | **Advanced Skills** | Vocational-Technical Applications | Calculator/Computer | Above and Beyond

SCIENCE AND MEDICINE The *half-life* of a radioactive substance is the time it takes for half the original amount of the substance to decay to a nonradioactive element. The half-life of radioactive waste is very important in figuring out how long the waste must be kept isolated from the environment in some sort of storage facility. Half-lives of various radioactive waste products vary from a few seconds to millions of years. It usually takes at least 10 half-lives for a radioactive waste product to be considered safe.

The half-life of a radioactive substance can be determined by the following formula.

chapter 11 > Make the Connection

$$\ln \frac{1}{2} = -\lambda x$$

in which λ = radioactive decay constant, x = half-life and $\ln x$ represents $\log_e x$

In exercises 93 to 97, find the half-lives (in years) of the following important radioactive waste products given the radioactive decay constant (RDC).

93. Plutonium 239, RDC = 0.000029

94. Strontium 90, RDC = 0.024755

95. Thorium 230, RDC = 0.000009

96. Cesium 135, RDC = 0.00000035

97. How many years will it be before each waste product will be considered safe?

Basic Skills | Advanced Skills | **Vocational-Technical Applications** | Calculator/Computer | Above and Beyond

98. **ALLIED HEALTH** The molar concentration of hydrogen ions, $[H^+]$, in an aqueous solution is equal to the normality, N, times the percent ionization. The acidity or pH level of a solution is a function of the molar concentration given by the formula $\text{pH} = -\log_{10}[H^+]$. Determine the pH of a 0.15 N acid solution that is 65% ionized.

Answers

90. $10^6 \cdot a_0$

91. Answers will vary

92. Answers will vary

93. 23,901 yr

94. 28 yr

95. 77,016 yr

96. 1,980,421 yr

97. Pu239: 239,010 yr; Sr90: 280 yr; Th230: 770,160 yr; Cs135: 19,804,210 yr

98. pH = 1.01

Answers

99. 34 h

99. **Construction Technology** The strength of concrete depends on the curing time. The longer it takes to cure, the stronger the concrete will be. If the desired strength (up to the maximum of 3,000 lb/in.^{2}) of the concrete is known, the required curing time (concrete reaches its maximum strength after 48 hours) is found from the formula

$$t = 48 \log_e \left(\frac{s}{3{,}000}\right) + 48$$

Find the required curing time if we need concrete with a strength of 2,241 lb/in.^{2}.

Answers

1.

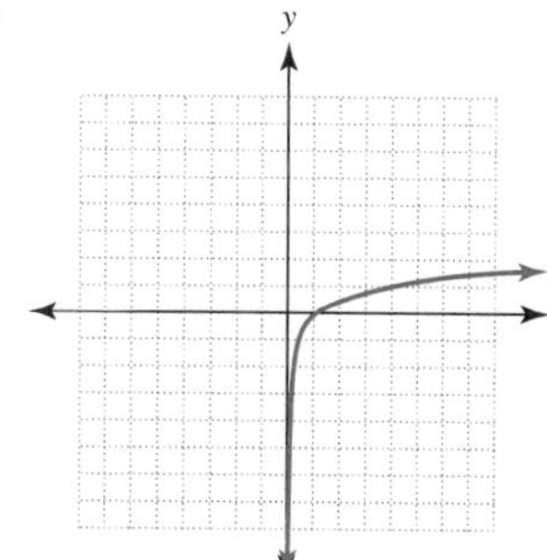

3.

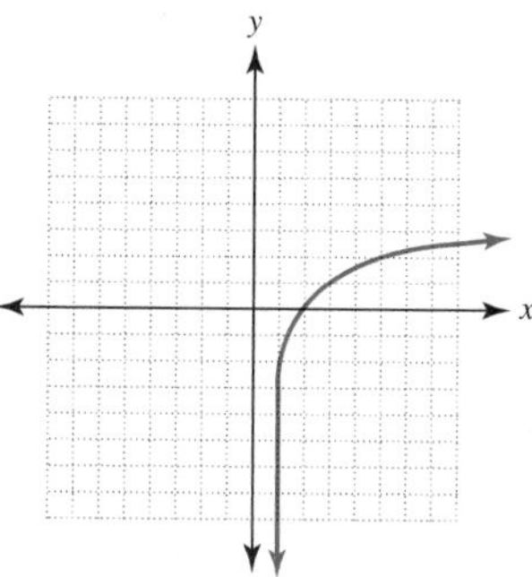

5.

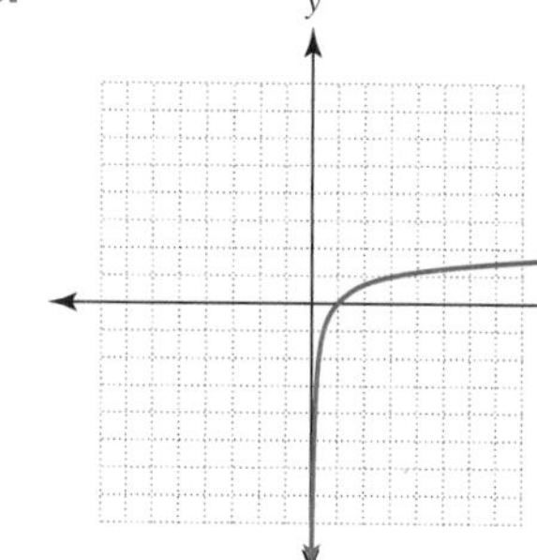

7. $\log_2 16 = 4$ **9.** $\log_{10} 100 = 2$ **11.** $\log_3 1 = 0$ **13.** $\log_4 \frac{1}{16} = -2$ **15.** $\log_{10} \frac{1}{1{,}000} = -3$ **17.** $\log_{16} 4 = \frac{1}{2}$ **19.** $\log_{64} \frac{1}{4} = -\frac{1}{3}$ **21.** $\log_8 4 = \frac{2}{3}$ **23.** $\log_{27} \frac{1}{9} = -\frac{2}{3}$ **25.** $2^4 = 16$ **27.** $5^0 = 1$ **29.** $10^1 = 10$ **31.** $5^3 = 125$ **33.** $3^{-3} = \frac{1}{27}$ **35.** $10^{-2} = 0.01$ **37.** $16^{1/2} = 4$ **39.** $8^{2/3} = 4$ **41.** $25^{-1/2} = \frac{1}{5}$ **43.** 5 **45.** 3 **47.** -4 **49.** -2 **51.** $\frac{1}{2}$ **53.** 2 **55.** 4 **57.** 100 **59.** 1 **61.** $\frac{27}{8}$ **63.** 5 **65.** $\frac{1}{1{,}000}$ **67.** -2 **69.** 3 **71.** 25 **73.** $-\frac{2}{3}$ **75.** True **77.** 50 dB **79.** 70 dB **81.** 10^{-8} W/cm^2 **83.** 10 **85.** 1,000 **87.** 6 **89.** $10^5 \cdot a_0$ **91.** Answers will vary **93.** 23,901 yr **95.** 77,016 yr **97.** Pu239: 239,010 yr; Sr90: 280 yr; Th230: 770,160 yr; Cs135: 19,804,210 yr **99.** 34 h

11.3 Properties of Logarithms

< 11.3 Objectives >

1 > Apply the properties of logarithms

2 > Evaluate logarithmic expressions with any base

3 > Solve applications involving logarithms

4 > Estimate the value of an antilogarithm

As we mentioned earlier, logarithms were developed as aids to numerical computations. The early utility of the logarithm was due to the properties that we will discuss in this section. Even with the advent of the scientific calculator, that utility remains important today. We can apply these same properties to applications in a variety of areas that lead to exponential or logarithmic equations.

Because a logarithm is, by definition, an exponent, it seems reasonable that our knowledge of the properties of exponents should lead to useful properties for logarithms. That is, in fact, the case.

We start with two basic facts that follow immediately from the definition of the logarithm.

NOTE

The properties follow from the facts that

$b^1 = b$ and $b^0 = 1$

Property

Properties 1 and 2 of Logarithms

For $b > 0$ and $b \neq 1$,

Property 1. $\log_b b = 1$

Property 2. $\log_b 1 = 0$

We know that the logarithmic function $y = \log_b x$ and the exponential function $y = b^x$ are inverses of each other. So, for $f(x) = b^x$, we have $f^{-1}(x) = \log_b x$.

It is important to note that for any one-to-one function f,

$f^{-1}(f(x)) = x$ for any x in the domain of f

and

$f(f^{-1}(x)) = x$ for any x in the domain of f^{-1}

NOTE

The inverse has "undone" whatever f did to x.

Because $f(x) = b^x$ is a one-to-one function, we can apply the preceding to the case in which

$f(x) = b^x$ and $f^{-1}(x) = \log_b x$

to derive the following.

Property

Properties 3 and 4 of Logarithms

Property 3. $\log_b b^x = x$

Property 4. $b^{\log_b x} = x$ for $x > 0$

NOTE

For property 3,

$f^{-1}(f(x)) = f^{-1}(b^x) = \log_b b^x$

But in general, for any one-to-one function f,

$f^{-1}(f(x)) = x$

Because logarithms are exponents, we can again turn to the familiar exponent rules to derive some further properties of logarithms. Consider the following.

We know that

$$\log_b M = x \quad \text{if and only if} \quad M = b^x$$

and

$$\log_b N = y \quad \text{if and only if} \quad N = b^y$$

Then

$$M \cdot N = b^x \cdot b^y = b^{x+y}$$

From this equation we see that $x + y$ is the power to which we must raise b to get the product MN. In logarithmic form, that becomes

$$\log_b MN = x + y$$

Now, because $x = \log_b M$ and $y = \log_b N$, we can substitute in the preceding equation to write

$$\log_b MN = \log_b M + \log_b N$$

NOTE

In all cases, $M, N > 0$, $b > 0$, $b \neq 1$, and p is any real number.

This is the first of the basic logarithmic properties presented here. The remaining properties may all be proved by arguments similar to those presented in the three preceding equations.

Property

Properties of Logarithms

Product property

$$\log_b MN = \log_b M + \log_b N$$

Quotient property

$$\log_b \frac{M}{N} = \log_b M - \log_b N$$

Power property

$$\log_b M^p = p \log_b M$$

Many applications of logarithms require using these properties to write a single logarithmic expression as the sum or difference of simpler expressions, as Example 1 illustrates.

Example 1 Using the Properties of Logarithms

< Objective 1 >

Expand, using the properties of logarithms.

(a) $\log_b xy = \log_b x + \log_b y$ Product property

(b) $\log_b \frac{xy}{z} = \log_b xy - \log_b z$ Quotient property

$= \log_b x + \log_b y - \log_b z$ Product property

(c) $\log_{10} x^2y^3 = \log_{10} x^2 + \log_{10} y^3$ Product property

$= 2 \log_{10} x + 3 \log_{10} y$ Power property

RECALL

$\sqrt{a} = a^{1/2}$.

(d) $\log_b \sqrt{\frac{x}{y}} = \log_b \left(\frac{x}{y}\right)^{1/2}$ Definition of rational exponent

$= \frac{1}{2} \log_b \frac{x}{y}$ Power property

$= \frac{1}{2} (\log_b x - \log_b y)$ Quotient property

$= \frac{1}{2} \log_b x - \frac{1}{2} \log_b y$

Check Yourself 1

Expand each expression, using the properties of logarithms.

(a) $\log_b x^2y^3z$ **(b)** $\log_{10} \sqrt{\frac{xy}{z}}$

In some cases, we will reverse the process and use the properties to write a single logarithm, given a sum or difference of logarithmic expressions.

Example 2 Rewriting Logarithmic Expressions

Write each expression as a single logarithm with coefficient 1.

(a) $2 \log_b x + 3 \log_b y$

$= \log_b x^2 + \log_b y^3$ Power property

$= \log_b x^2y^3$ Product property

(b) $\frac{1}{2}(\log_2 x - \log_2 y)$

$= \frac{1}{2}\left(\log_2 \frac{x}{y}\right)$ Quotient property

$= \log_2 \left(\frac{x}{y}\right)^{1/2}$ Power property

$= \log_2 \sqrt{\frac{x}{y}}$

Check Yourself 2

Write each expression as a single logarithm with coefficient 1.

(a) $3 \log_b x + 2 \log_b y - 2 \log_b z$ **(b)** $\frac{1}{3}(2 \log_2 x - \log_2 y)$

Example 3 illustrates the basic concept of the use of logarithms as a computational aid.

Example 3 Evaluating Logarithmic Expressions

< Objective 2 >

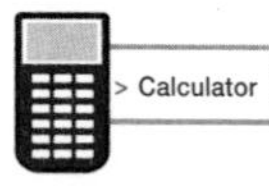

Suppose $\log_{10} 2 = 0.301$ and $\log_{10} 3 = 0.447$. Given these values, find the following.

(a) $\log_{10} 6$ Because $6 = 2 \cdot 3$

$= \log_{10} (2 \cdot 3)$

$= \log_{10} 2 + \log_{10} 3$

$= 0.301 + 0.477$

$= 0.778$

> **NOTE**
>
> We have written the logarithms correct to three decimal places and will follow this practice throughout the remainder of this chapter. Keep in mind, however, that this is an approximation and that $10^{0.301}$ will only approximate 2. Verify this with your calculator.

(b) $\log_{10} 18$ Because $18 = 2 \cdot 3 \cdot 3$

$= \log_{10} (2 \cdot 3 \cdot 3)$

$= \log_{10} 2 + \log_{10} 3 + \log_{10} 3$

$= 1.195$

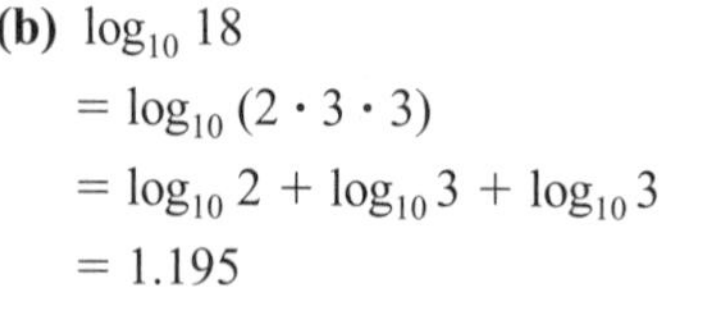

(c) $\log_{10} \frac{1}{9}$ Because $\frac{1}{9} = \frac{1}{3^2}$

$= \log_{10} \frac{1}{3^2}$

$= \log_{10} 1 - \log_{10} 3^2$

$= 0 - 2 \log_{10} 3$

$= -0.894$

> **RECALL**
>
> $\log_b 1 = 0$ for any base b.

(d) $\log_{10} 16$ Because $16 = 2^4$

$= \log_{10} 2^4 = 4 \log_{10} 2$

$= 1.204$

(e) $\log_{10} \sqrt{3}$ Because $\sqrt{3} = 3^{1/2}$

$= \log_{10} 3^{1/2} = \frac{1}{2} \log_{10} 3$

$= 0.224$

> **NOTE**
>
> Verify each answer with your calculator.

Check Yourself 3

Given the preceding values for $\log_{10} 2$ and $\log_{10} 3$, find each of the following.

(a) $\log_{10} 12$ **(b)** $\log_{10} 27$ **(c)** $\log_{10} \sqrt[3]{2}$

There are two types of logarithms used most frequently in mathematics:

Logarithms to base 10

Logarithms to base e

NOTE

When no base for "log" is written, it is assumed to be 10.

Of course, the use of logarithms to base 10 is convenient because our number system has base 10. We call logarithms to base 10 **common logarithms,** and it is customary to omit the base in writing a common (or base-10) logarithm. So

$$\log N \quad \text{means} \quad \log_{10} N$$

The following table shows the common logarithms for various powers of 10.

Exponential Form	Logarithmic Form
$10^3 = 1{,}000$	$\log 1{,}000 = 3$
$10^2 = 100$	$\log 100 = 2$
$10^1 = 10$	$\log 10 = 1$
$10^0 = 1$	$\log 1 = 0$
$10^{-1} = 0.1$	$\log 0.1 = -1$
$10^{-2} = 0.01$	$\log 0.01 = -2$
$10^{-3} = 0.001$	$\log 0.001 = -3$

Example 4 Approximating Logarithms with a Calculator

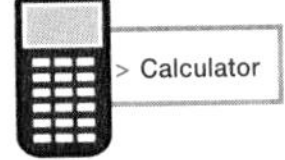

Verify each of the following with a calculator.

(a) $\log 4.8 = 0.681$

(b) $\log 48 = 1.681$

(c) $\log 480 = 2.681$

(d) $\log 4{,}800 = 3.681$

(e) $\log 0.48 = -0.319$

NOTES

The number 4.8 lies between 1 and 10, so log 4.8 lies between 0 and 1.

$480 = 4.8 \times 10^2$
and
$\log (4.8 \times 10^2)$
$= \log 4.8 + \log 10^2$
$= \log 4.8 + 2$
$= 2 + \log 4.8$

The value of log 0.48 is really $-1 + 0.681$. Your calculator will combine the signed numbers.

Check Yourself 4

Use your calculator to find each of the following logarithms, correct to three decimal places.

(a) log 2.3 **(b)** log 23 **(c)** log 230
(d) log 2,300 **(e)** log 0.23 **(f)** log 0.023

Let us look at an application of common logarithms from chemistry. Common logarithms are used to define the pH of a solution. This is a scale that measures whether the solution is acidic or basic.

The pH of a solution is defined as

$$\text{pH} = -\log [\text{H}^+]$$

in which $[\text{H}^+]$ is the hydrogen ion concentration, in moles per liter (mol/L), in the solution.

NOTE

A solution is **neutral** with pH = 7, **acidic** if the pH is less than 7, and **basic** if the pH is greater than 7.

Example 5 A pH Application

< Objective 3 >

Find the pH of each of the following. Determine whether each is a base or an acid.

NOTES

The product rule is used here.

Also, in general, $\log_b b^x = x$, so $\log 10^{-7} = -7$.

(a) Rainwater: $[H^+] = 1.6 \times 10^{-7}$

From the definition,

$$\begin{aligned} pH &= -\log [H^+] \\ &= -\log (1.6 \times 10^{-7}) \\ &= -(\log 1.6 + \log 10^{-7}) \\ &= -[0.204 + (-7)] \\ &= -(-6.796) = 6.796 \end{aligned}$$

The rain is just slightly acidic.

(b) Household ammonia: $[H^+] = 2.3 \times 10^{-8}$

$$\begin{aligned} pH &= -\log (2.3 \times 10^{-8}) \\ &= -(\log 2.3 + \log 10^{-8}) \\ &= -[0.362 + (-8)] \\ &= 7.638 \end{aligned}$$

The ammonia is slightly basic.

(c) Vinegar: $[H^+] = 2.9 \times 10^{-3}$

$$\begin{aligned} pH &= -\log (2.9 \times 10^{-3}) \\ &= -(\log 2.9 + \log 10^{-3}) \\ &= 2.538 \end{aligned}$$

The vinegar is very acidic.

Check Yourself 5

Find the pH for the following solutions. Are they acidic or basic?

(a) Orange juice: $[H^+] = 6.8 \times 10^{-5}$

(b) Drain cleaner: $[H^+] = 5.2 \times 10^{-13}$

Many applications require reversing the process. That is, given the logarithm of a number, we must be able to find that number. The process is straightforward.

Example 6 Using a Calculator to Estimate Antilogarithms

< Objective 4 >

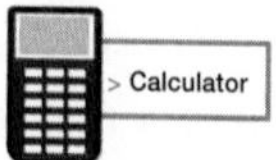

Suppose that $\log x = 2.1567$. We want to find a number x whose logarithm is 2.1567. Using a calculator requires one of the following sequences:

2.1567 [10^x] or 2.1567 [INV] [log] or [2nd] [log] 2.1567

Each gives the result 143.45, often called the **antilogarithm** of 2.1567.

RECALL

Because it is a one-to-one function, the logarithmic function has an inverse.

Check Yourself 6

Find the value of the antilogarithm of x.

(a) $\log x = 0.828$ **(b)** $\log x = 1.828$
(c) $\log x = 2.828$ **(d)** $\log x = -0.172$

Let us return to the application from chemistry for an example requiring the use of the antilogarithm.

Example 7 A pH Application

Suppose that the pH for tomato juice is 6.2. Find the hydrogen ion concentration $[H^+]$.

Recall from our earlier formula that

$$\text{pH} = -\log [H^+]$$

In this case, we have

$$6.2 = -\log [H^+] \quad \text{or} \quad \log [H^+] = -6.2$$

The desired value for $[H^+]$ is then the antilogarithm of -6.2.

The result is 0.00000063, and we can write

$$[H^+] = 6.3 \times 10^{-7}$$

NOTE

Natural logarithms are also called **napierian logarithms** after Napier. The importance of this system of logarithms was not fully understood until later developments in calculus.

Check Yourself 7

The pH for eggs is 7.8. Find $[H^+]$ for eggs.

As we mentioned, there are two systems of logarithms in common use. The second type of logarithm uses the number e as a base, and we call logarithms to base e the **natural logarithms.** As with common logarithms, a convenient notation has developed, as the following definition shows.

Definition

Natural Logarithm

The **natural logarithm** is a logarithm to base e, and it is denoted $\ln x$, as

$$\ln x = \log_e x$$

NOTES

The restrictions on the domain of the natural logarithmic function are the same as before. The function is defined only if $x > 0$.

In general

$\log_b b^x = x \qquad b \neq 1$

By the general definition of a logarithm,

$$y = \ln x \quad \text{means the same as} \quad x = e^y$$

and this leads us directly to the following.

$$\ln 1 = 0 \quad \text{because} \quad e^0 = 1$$

$$\ln e = 1 \quad \text{because} \quad e^1 = e$$

$$\ln e^2 = 2 \quad \text{and} \quad \ln e^{-3} = -3$$

Example 8 Estimating Natural Logarithms

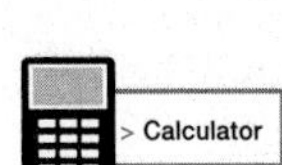

To find other natural logarithms, we can again turn to a calculator. To find the value of ln 2, use the sequence

[ln] 2 or [ln(] 2 [)]

The result is 0.693 (to three decimal places).

Check Yourself 8

Use a calculator to find each of the following.

(a) ln 3 **(b)** ln 6 **(c)** ln 4 **(d)** ln $\sqrt{3}$

Of course, the properties of logarithms are applied in an identical fashion, no matter what the base.

Example 9 Evaluating Logarithms

RECALL

$\log_b MN = \log_b M + \log_b N$
$\log_b M^p = p \log_b M$

If $\ln 2 = 0.693$ and $\ln 3 = 1.099$, find the following.

(a) $\ln 6 = \ln (2 \cdot 3) = \ln 2 + \ln 3 = 1.792$

(b) $\ln 4 = \ln 2^2 = 2 \ln 2 = 1.386$

(c) $\ln \sqrt{3} = \ln 3^{1/2} = \dfrac{1}{2} \ln 3 = 0.550$

Again, verify these results with your calculator.

Check Yourself 9

Use ln 2 = 0.693 and ln 3 = 1.099 to find the following.

(a) ln 12 **(b)** ln 27

The natural logarithm function plays an important role in both theoretical and applied mathematics. Example 10 illustrates just one of the many applications of this function.

Example 10 A Learning Curve Application

A class of students took a final mathematics examination and received an average score of 76. In a psychological experiment, the students are retested at weekly intervals over the same material. If t is measured in weeks, then the new average score after t weeks is given by

RECALL

We read $S(t)$ as "S of t," which means that S is a function of t.

$S(t) = 76 - 5 \ln (t + 1)$

Complete the following.

(a) Find the score after 10 weeks.

$$S(t) = 76 - 5 \ln (10 + 1)$$
$$= 76 - 5 \ln 11 \approx 64$$

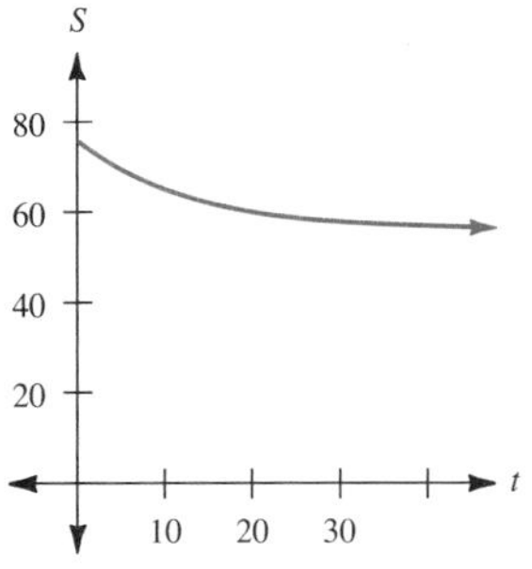

(b) Find the score after 20 weeks.

$$S(t) = 76 - 5 \ln (20 + 1) \approx 61$$

(c) Find the score after 30 weeks.

$$S(t) = 76 - 5 \ln (30 + 1) \approx 59$$

NOTE

This is an example of a **forgetting curve.** Note how it drops more rapidly at first. Compare this curve to the learning curve drawn in Section 11.1, exercise 68.

Check Yourself 10

The average score for a group of biology students, retested after time t (in months), is given by

$$S(t) = 83 - 9 \ln (t + 1)$$

Find the average score after

(a) 3 months **(b) 6 months**

We conclude this section with one final property of logarithms. This property will allow us to quickly find the logarithm of a number to any base. Although work with logarithms with bases other than 10 or e is relatively infrequent, the relationship between logarithms of different bases is interesting in itself. Consider the following argument.

Suppose that

$$x = \log_2 5$$

or

$$2^x = 5$$

Taking the logarithm to base 10 of both sides of this equation yields

$$\log 2^x = \log 5$$

or

$$x \log 2 = \log 5 \quad \text{Use the power property of logarithms.}$$

(Note that we omit the 10 for the base and write log 2, for example.) Now, dividing both sides of the preceding equation by log 2, we have

$$x = \frac{\log 5}{\log 2}$$

We can now find a value for x with the calculator. Dividing with the calculator log 5 by log 2, we get an approximate answer of 2.322.

Because $x = \log_2 5$ and $x = \dfrac{\log 5}{\log 2}$, then

$$\log_2 5 = \frac{\log 5}{\log 2}$$

Generalizing our result, we find the following.

Property

Change-of-Base Formula

For the positive real numbers a and x,

$$\log_a x = \frac{\log x}{\log a}$$

Note that the logarithm on the left side has base a whereas the logarithms on the right side have base 10. This allows us to calculate the logarithm to base a of any positive number, given the corresponding logarithms to base 10 (or any other base), as Example 11 illustrates.

Example 11 Evaluating Logarithms

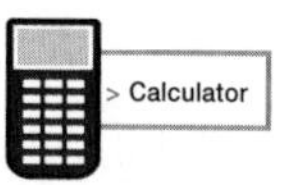
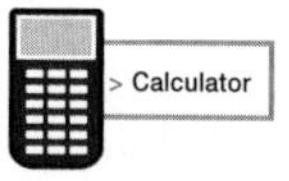

Find $\log_5 15$.

From the change-of-base formula with $a = 5$ and $b = 10$,

$$\log_5 15 = \frac{\log 15}{\log 5}$$
$$= 1.683$$

The calculator sequence for this computation is

NOTES

We have written $\log_5 15$ rather than log 15 to emphasize the change-of-base formula.

$\log_5 5 = 1$ and $\log_5 25 = 2$, so the result for $\log_5 15$ must be between 1 and 2.

Check Yourself 11

Use the change-of-base formula to find $\log_8 32$.

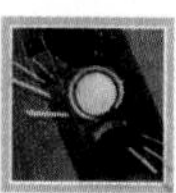

> CAUTION

A *common error* is to write

$$\frac{\log 15}{\log 5} = \log 15 - \log 5$$

This is *not* a logarithmic property. A true statement would be

$$\log \frac{15}{5} = \log 15 - \log 5$$

but

$$\log \frac{15}{5} \quad \text{and} \quad \frac{\log 15}{\log 5}$$

are *not* the same.

Remember that the $\log_e x$ is called the **natural log** of x. We use "ln x" to designate the natural log of x. A special case of the change-of-base formula allows us to find natural logarithms in terms of common logarithms:

$$\ln x = \frac{\log x}{\log e}$$

so

$$\ln x \approx \frac{\log x}{0.434} \quad \text{or, because } \frac{1}{0.434} \approx 2.304\text{, then} \quad \ln x \approx 2.304 \log x$$

Of course, because all modern calculators have both the log function key and the ln function key, this conversion formula is now rarely used.

Check Yourself ANSWERS

1. **(a)** $2 \log_b x + 3 \log_b y + \log_b z$; **(b)** $\frac{1}{2}\log_{10} x + \frac{1}{2}\log_{10} y - \frac{1}{2}\log_{10} z$

2. **(a)** $\log_b \frac{x^3y^2}{z^2}$; **(b)** $\log_2 \sqrt[3]{\frac{x^2}{y}}$ **3.** **(a)** 1.049; **(b)** 1.341; **(c)** 0.100

4. **(a)** 0.362; **(b)** 1.362; **(c)** 2.362; **(d)** 3.362; **(e)** -0.638; **(f)** -1.638

5. **(a)** 4.167, acidic; **(b)** 12.284, basic **6.** **(a)** 6.73; **(b)** 67.3; **(c)** 673; **(d)** 0.673

7. $[H^+] = 1.6 \times 10^{-8}$ **8.** **(a)** 1.099; **(b)** 1.792; **(c)** 1.386; **(d)** 0.549

9. **(a)** 2.485; **(b)** 3.297 **10.** **(a)** 71; **(b)** 65

11. $\log_8 32 = \frac{\log 32}{\log 8} \approx 1.667$

Reading Your Text

The following fill-in-the-blank exercises are designed to ensure that you understand some of the key vocabulary used in this section.

SECTION 11.3

(a) We call logarithms to base 10 ____________ logarithms.

(b) The inverse of a logarithm is often called the ____________.

(c) We call logarithms to base *e* ____________ logarithms.

(d) ln *x* is called the ____________ of *x*.

11.3 exercises

Basic Skills | Advanced Skills | Vocational-Technical Applications | Calculator/Computer | Above and Beyond

MathZone

Boost your grade at mathzone.com!
> Practice Problems
> NetTutor
> Self-Tests
> e-Professors
> Videos

Name ______

Section ______ Date ______

Answers

1. $\log_b 5 + \log_b x$
2. $\log_3 7 + \log_3 x$
3. $\log_4 x - \log_4 3$
4. $\log_b 2 - \log_b y$
5. $2 \log_3 a$
6. $4 \log_5 y$
7. $\frac{1}{2} \log_5 x$
8. $\frac{1}{3} \log z$
9. $3 \log_b x + 2 \log_b y$
10. $2 \log_5 x + 4 \log_5 z$
11. $2 \log_4 y + \frac{1}{2} \log_4 x$
12. $3 \log_b x + \frac{1}{3} \log_b z$
13. $2 \log_b x + \log_b y - \log_b z$
14. $\log_5 3 - \log_5 x - \log_5 y$
15. $\log x + 2 \log y - \frac{1}{2} \log z$
16. $3 \log_4 x + \frac{1}{2} \log_4 y - 2 \log_4 z$
17. $\frac{1}{3} \log_5 x + \frac{1}{3} \log_5 y - \frac{2}{3} \log_5 z$
18. $\frac{1}{2} \log_b x + \frac{1}{4} \log_b y - \frac{3}{4} \log_b z$

< Objective 1 >

Use the properties of logarithms to expand each expression.

1. $\log_b 5x$

2. $\log_3 7x$

3. $\log_4 \frac{x}{3}$

4. $\log_b \frac{2}{y}$

5. $\log_3 a^2$

6. $\log_5 y^4$

7. $\log_5 \sqrt{x}$

8. $\log \sqrt[3]{z}$

9. $\log_b x^3y^2$

10. $\log_5 x^2z^4$

11. $\log_4 y^2 \sqrt{x}$

12. $\log_b x^3 \sqrt[3]{z}$

13. $\log_b \frac{x^2y}{z}$

14. $\log_5 \frac{3}{xy}$

15. $\log \frac{xy^2}{\sqrt{z}}$

16. $\log_4 \frac{x^3\sqrt{y}}{z^2}$

17. $\log_5 \sqrt[3]{\frac{xy}{z^2}}$

18. $\log_b \sqrt[4]{\frac{x^2y}{z^3}}$

Write each expression as a single logarithm.

19. $\log_b x + \log_b y$

20. $\log_5 x - \log_5 y$

21. $2 \log_2 x - \log_2 y$

22. $3 \log_b x + \log_b z$

23. $\log_b x + \frac{1}{2} \log_b y$

24. $\frac{1}{3} \log_b x - 2 \log_b z$

25. $\log_b x + 2 \log_b y - \log_b z$

26. $2 \log_5 x - (3 \log_5 y + \log_5 z)$

27. $\frac{1}{2} \log_6 y - 3 \log_6 z$

28. $\log_b x - \frac{1}{3} \log_b y - 4 \log_b z$

29. $\frac{1}{3}(2 \log_b x + \log_b y - \log_b z)$

30. $\frac{1}{5}(2 \log_4 x - \log_4 y + 3 \log_4 z)$

< Objective 2 >

Given that $\log 2 = 0.301$ *and* $\log 3 = 0.477$, *find each logarithm.*

31. $\log 24$

32. $\log 36$

33. $\log 8$

34. $\log 81$

35. $\log \sqrt{2}$

36. $\log \sqrt[3]{3}$

37. $\log \frac{1}{4}$

38. $\log \frac{1}{27}$

In exercises 39 to 44, choose the best answer for each question. (**Note:** *Some answers may be used more than once.*)

(a) 0 **(b)** 1 **(c)** x **(d)** 10 **(e)** e

39. $\log_b b =$ _______ for $b > 0, \quad b \neq 1$

40. $\log_b b^x =$ _______

Answers

19. $\log_b xy$
20. $\log_5 \frac{x}{y}$
21. $\log_2 \frac{x^2}{y}$
22. $\log_b x^3 z$
23. $\log_b x\sqrt{y}$
24. $\log_b \frac{\sqrt[3]{x}}{z^2}$
25. $\log_b \frac{xy^2}{z}$
26. $\log_5 \frac{x^2}{y^3 z}$
27. $\log_6 \frac{\sqrt{y}}{z^3}$
28. $\log_b \frac{x}{z^4 \sqrt[3]{y}}$
29. $\log_b \sqrt[3]{\frac{x^2 y}{z}}$
30. $\log_4 \sqrt[5]{\frac{x^2 z^3}{y}}$
31. 1.380
32. 1.556
33. 0.903
34. 1.908
35. 0.151
36. 0.159
37. −0.602
38. −1.431
39. (b)
40. (c)

41. log N means the base of the logarithm is ______

42. $b^{\log_b x} =$ ______ for $x > 0$

43. $\log_b 1 =$ ______ for $b > 0, b \neq 1$

44. ln x means the base of the logarithm is ______

In exercises 45 to 48, choose the appropriate letter to correctly complete each property.

(a) $p\log_b M$ **(b)** $\log_b M - \log_b N$ **(c)** $\log_b M + \log_b N$ **(d)** $\dfrac{\log x}{\log a}$

45. $\log_b \dfrac{M}{N} =$

46. $\log_a x =$

47. $\log_b M^p =$

48. $\log_b MN =$

Basic Skills | Advanced Skills | Vocational-Technical Applications | **Calculator/Computer** | Above and Beyond

Use your calculator to find each logarithm.

49. log 6.8

50. log 68

51. log 680

52. log 6,800

53. log 0.68

54. log 0.068

< Objective 3 >

In exercises 55 and 56, find the pH, given the hydrogen ion concentration $[H^+]$ for each solution. Use the formula

$$\text{pH} = -\log [H^+]$$

Are the solutions acidic or basic?

55. Blood: $[H^+] = 3.8 \times 10^{-8}$

56. Lemon juice: $[H^+] = 6.4 \times 10^{-3}$

Answers

41. (d)
42. (c)
43. (a)
44. (e)
45. (b)
46. (d)
47. (a)
48. (c)
49. 0.833
50. 1.833
51. 2.833
52. 3.833
53. −0.167
54. −1.167
55. 7.42, basic
56. 2.19, acidic

< Objective 4 >

Use your calculator to find the antilogarithm for each logarithm.

57. $\log x = 0.749$

58. $\log x = 1.749$

59. $\log x = 3.749$

60. $\log x = -0.251$

In exercises 61 and 62, given the pH of the solutions, find the hydrogen ion concentration $[H^+]$.

61. Wine: pH = 4.7

62. Household ammonia: pH = 7.8

Use your calculator to find each logarithm.

63. ln 2

64. ln 3

65. ln 10

66. ln 30

Basic Skills | Advanced Skills | Vocational-Technical Applications | Calculator/Computer | **Above and Beyond**

SCIENCE AND MEDICINE *The average score on a final examination for a group of psychology students, retested after time t (in weeks), is given by*

$S = 85 - 8 \ln (t + 1)$

Find the average score on the retests.

67. After 3 weeks

68. After 12 weeks

Use the change-of-base formula to find each logarithm.

69. $\log_3 25$

70. $\log_5 30$

SCIENCE AND MEDICINE *The amount of a radioactive substance remaining after a given amount of time t is given by the following formula:*

chapter 11 > Make the Connection

$A = e^{\lambda t + \ln A_0}$

in which A is the amount remaining after time t, variable A_0 is the original amount of the substance, and λ is the radioactive decay constant. Use this formula to solve exercises 71 to 74. Assume t is in years.

71. How much plutonium 239 will remain after 50,000 years if 24 kg was originally stored? Plutonium 239 has a radioactive decay constant of −0.000029.

Answers

57. 5.61

58. 56.1

59. 5,610

60. 0.561

61. 2×10^{-5}

62. 1.6×10^{-8}

63. 0.693

64. 1.099

65. 2.303

66. 3.401

67. 74

68. 64

69. 2.930

70. 2.113

71. 5.6 kg

72. How much plutonium 241 will remain after 100 years if 52 kg was originally stored? Plutonium 241 has a radioactive decay constant of -0.053319.

73. How much strontium 90 was originally stored if after 56 years it is discovered that 15 kg still remains? Strontium 90 has a radioactive decay constant of -0.024755.

74. How much cesium 137 was originally stored if after 90 years it is discovered that 20 kg still remains? Cesium 137 has a radioactive decay constant of -0.023105.

75. Which keys on your calculator are function keys and which are operation keys? What is the difference?

76. How is the pH factor relevant to your selection of a hair care product?

Answers

72. 0.25 kg

73. 60 kg

74. 160 kg

75. Above and Beyond

76. Above and Beyond

Answers

1. $\log_b 5 + \log_b x$ **3.** $\log_4 x - \log_4 3$ **5.** $2 \log_3 a$ **7.** $\frac{1}{2} \log_5 x$

9. $3 \log_b x + 2 \log_b y$ **11.** $2 \log_4 y + \frac{1}{2} \log_4 x$ **13.** $2 \log_b x + \log_b y - \log_b z$

15. $\log x + 2 \log y - \frac{1}{2} \log z$ **17.** $\frac{1}{3}\log_5 x + \frac{1}{3}\log_5 y - \frac{2}{3}\log_5 z$

19. $\log_b xy$ **21.** $\log_2 \frac{x^2}{y}$ **23.** $\log_b x\sqrt{y}$ **25.** $\log_b \frac{xy^2}{z}$

27. $\log_6 \frac{\sqrt{y}}{z^3}$ **29.** $\log_b \sqrt[3]{\frac{x^2y}{z}}$ **31.** 1.380 **33.** 0.903 **35.** 0.151

37. -0.602 **39.** (b) **41.** (d) **43.** (a) **45.** (b) **47.** (a)

49. 0.833 **51.** 2.833 **53.** -0.167 **55.** 7.42, basic **57.** 5.61

59. 5,610 **61.** 2×10^{-5} **63.** 0.693 **65.** 2.303 **67.** 74

69. 2.930 **71.** 5.6 kg **73.** 60 kg **75.** Above and Beyond

11.4 Solving Logarithmic and Exponential Equations

< 11.4 Objectives >

1 > Solve a logarithmic equation

2 > Solve an exponential equation

3 > Solve an application involving an exponential equation

Much of the importance of the properties of logarithms developed in Section 11.3 lies in the application of those properties to the solution of equations involving logarithms and exponentials. Our work in this section will consider solution techniques for both types of equations. Let us start with a definition.

Definition

Logarithmic Equation

A **logarithmic equation** is an equation that contains a logarithmic expression.

We solved some simple examples in Section 11.2. Let us review for a moment. To solve $\log_3 x = 4$ for x, recall that we simply convert the logarithmic equation to exponential form. Here,

$$x = 3^4$$

so

$$x = 81$$

and 81 is the solution to the given equation.

Now, what if the logarithmic equation involves more than one logarithmic term? Example 1 illustrates how the properties of logarithms must then be applied.

Example 1 Solving a Logarithmic Equation

< Objective 1 >

Solve each logarithmic equation.

(a) $\log_5 x + \log_5 3 = 2$

The original equation can be written as

$$\log_5 3x = 2$$

Now, because only a single logarithm is involved, we can write the equation in the equivalent exponential form:

$$3x = 5^2$$

$$3x = 25$$

$$x = \frac{25}{3}$$

RECALL

We apply the product rule for logarithms:

$\log_b M + \log_b N = \log_b MN$

RECALL

Because no base is written, it is assumed to be 10.

(b) $\log x + \log (x - 3) = 1$

Write the equation as

$\log x(x - 3) = 1$

or

$x(x - 3) = 10^1$

NOTES

Given the base of 10, this is the equivalent exponential form.

Checking possible solutions is particularly important here.

We now have

$$x^2 - 3x = 10$$
$$x^2 - 3x - 10 = 0$$
$$(x - 5)(x + 2) = 0$$

Possible solutions are $x = 5$ or $x = -2$.

Note that substitution of -2 into the original equation gives

$\log (-2) + \log (-5) = 1$

Because logarithms of negative numbers are *not* defined, -2 is an extraneous solution and we must reject it. The only solution for the original equation is 5.

Check Yourself 1

Solve $\log_2 x + \log_2 (x + 2) = 3$ for x.

The quotient property is used in a similar fashion for solving logarithmic equations. Consider Example 2.

Example 2 Solving a Logarithmic Equation

RECALL

We apply the quotient rule for logarithms:

$\log_b M - \log_b N = \log_b \frac{M}{N}$

Solve each equation for x.

(a) $\log_5 x - \log_5 2 = 2$

Rewrite the original equation as

$$\log_5 \frac{x}{2} = 2$$

Now,

$$\frac{x}{2} = 5^2$$

$$\frac{x}{2} = 25$$

$$x = 50$$

(b) $\log_3 (x + 1) - \log_3 x = 3$

$$\log_3 \frac{x + 1}{x} = 3$$

$$\frac{x + 1}{x} = 27$$

NOTE

Again, you should verify that substituting $\frac{1}{26}$ for x leads to a positive value in each of the original logarithms.

$$x + 1 = 27x$$
$$1 = 26x$$
$$x = \frac{1}{26}$$

Check Yourself 2

Solve $\log_5 (x + 3) - \log_5 x = 2$ for x.

The solution of certain types of logarithmic equations calls for the one-to-one property of the logarithmic function.

Property

One-to-One Property of Logarithmic Functions

If $\log_b M = \log_b N$

then $M = N$

Example 3 **Solving a Logarithmic Equation**

Solve the following equation for x.

$\log (x + 2) - \log 2 = \log x$

Again, we rewrite the left-hand side of the equation. So

$$\log \frac{x + 2}{2} = \log x$$

Because the logarithmic function is one-to-one, this is equivalent to

$$\frac{x + 2}{2} = x$$

or

$x = 2$

Check Yourself 3

Solve for x.

$\log (x + 3) - \log 3 = \log x$

The following algorithm summarizes our work in solving logarithmic equations.

Step by Step

Solving Logarithmic Equations

Step 1 Use the properties of logarithms to combine terms containing logarithmic expressions into a single term.

Step 2 Write the equation formed in step 1 in exponential form.

Step 3 Solve for the indicated variable.

Step 4 Check your solutions to make sure that possible solutions do not result in the logarithms of negative numbers or zero.

Let us look now at **exponential equations,** which are equations in which the variable appears as an exponent.

We solved some particular exponential equations in Section 11.1. In solving an equation such as

$$3^x = 81$$

we wrote the right-hand member as a power of 3, so that

$$3^x = 3^4$$

or

$$x = 4$$

NOTE

Again, we want to write both sides as a power of the same base, here 3.

The technique here will work only when both sides of the equation can be conveniently expressed as powers of the same base. If that is not the case, we must use logarithms for the solution of the equation, as illustrated in Example 4.

Example 4 Solving an Exponential Equation

< Objective 2 >

Solve $3^x = 5$ for x.

We begin by taking the common logarithm of both sides of the original equation.

$$\log 3^x = \log 5$$

RECALL

If $M = N$, then $\log_b M = \log_b N$

Now we apply the power property so that the variable becomes a coefficient on the left.

$$x \log 3 = \log 5$$

Dividing both sides of the equation by log 3 will isolate x, and we have

$$x = \frac{\log 5}{\log 3}$$

$$= 1.465 \quad \text{(to three decimal places)}$$

> CAUTION

This is *not* log 5 − log 3, a common error.

Note: You can verify the approximate solution by using the $\boxed{y^x}$ key on your calculator. Raise 3 to power 1.465.

Check Yourself 4

Solve $2^x = 10$ for x.

Example 5 shows how to solve an equation with a more complicated exponent.

Example 5 Solving an Exponential Equation

Solve $5^{2x+1} = 8$ for x.

The solution begins as in Example 4.

$$\log 5^{2x+1} = \log 8$$

$$(2x + 1) \log 5 = \log 8$$

RECALL

On the left, we apply $\log_b M^p = p \log_b M$

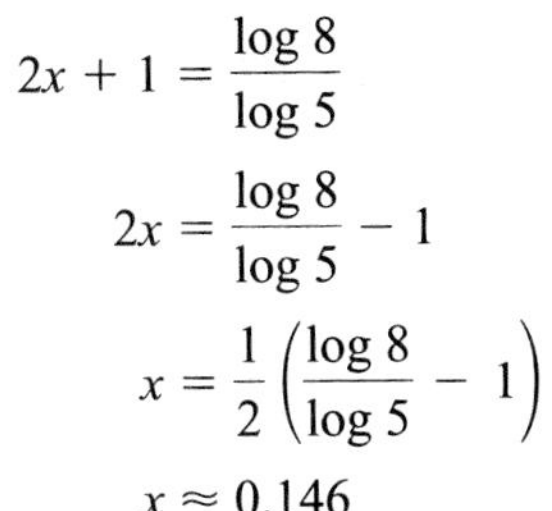

$$2x + 1 = \frac{\log 8}{\log 5}$$

$$2x = \frac{\log 8}{\log 5} - 1$$

$$x = \frac{1}{2}\left(\frac{\log 8}{\log 5} - 1\right)$$

$$x \approx 0.146$$

NOTE

On a graphing calculator, the sequence would be (log (8) ÷ log (5) − 1) ÷ 2

Check Yourself 5

Solve $3^{2x-1} = 7$ for x.

The procedure is similar if the variable appears as an exponent in more than one term of the equation.

Example 6 Solving an Exponential Equation

RECALL

Use the power property to write the variables as coefficients.

Solve $3^x = 2^{x+1}$ for x.

$$\log 3^x = \log 2^{x+1}$$

$$x \log 3 = (x + 1) \log 2$$

$$x \log 3 = x \log 2 + \log 2$$

$$x \log 3 - x \log 2 = \log 2$$

$$x(\log 3 - \log 2) = \log 2$$

$$x = \frac{\log 2}{\log 3 - \log 2}$$

$$\approx 1.710$$

NOTES

We now isolate x on the left.

To check the reasonableness of this result, use your calculator to verify that $3^{1.710} = 2^{2.710}$

Check Yourself 6

Solve $5^{x+1} = 3^{x+2}$ for x.

The following algorithm summarizes our work with solving exponential equations.

Step by Step

Solving Exponential Equations

Step 1 Try to write each side of the equation as a power of the same base. Then equate the exponents to form an equation.

Step 2 If the procedure in step 1 is not applicable, take the common logarithm of both sides of the original equation.

Step 3 Use the power rule for logarithms to write an equivalent equation with the variables as coefficients.

Step 4 Solve the resulting equation.

There are many applications of our work with exponential equations. Consider the following.

Example 7 An Interest Application

< Objective 3 >

If an investment of P dollars earns interest at an annual interest rate r and the interest is compounded n times per year, then the amount in the account after t years is given by

> Calculator

$$A = P\left(1 + \frac{r}{n}\right)^{nt}$$

If \$1,000 is placed in an account with an annual interest rate of 6%, find out how long it will take the money to double when interest is compounded annually and quarterly.

NOTE

Because the interest is compounded *once* a year, $n = 1$.

(a) Compounding interest annually.

Using the given equation with $A = 2{,}000$ (we want the original 1,000 to double), $P = 1{,}000$, $r = 0.06$, and $n = 1$, we have

$$2{,}000 = 1{,}000(1 + 0.06)^t$$

Dividing both sides by 1,000 yields

$$2 = (1.06)^t$$

NOTE

From accounting, we have the **rule of 72**, which states that the doubling time is approximately 72 divided by the interest rate as a percentage. Here $\frac{72}{6} = 12$ years.

We now have an exponential equation that can be solved by our earlier techniques.

$$\begin{aligned}\log 2 &= \log (1.06)^t \\ &= t \log 1.06\end{aligned}$$

or

$$\begin{aligned}t &= \frac{\log 2}{\log 1.06} \\ &\approx 11.9 \text{ years}\end{aligned}$$

It takes just a little less than 12 years for the money to double.

NOTE

Because the interest is compounded four times per year, $n = 4$.

(b) Compounding interest quarterly.

Now $n = 4$ in the given equation, so

$$\begin{aligned}2{,}000 &= 1{,}000\left(1 + \frac{0.06}{4}\right)^{4t} \\ 2 &= (1.015)^{4t} \\ \log 2 &= \log (1.015)^{4t} \\ \log 2 &= 4t \log 1.015 \\ \frac{\log 2}{4 \log 1.015} &= t \\ t &\approx 11.6 \text{ years}\end{aligned}$$

Note that the doubling time is reduced by approximately 3 months by the more frequent compounding.

Check Yourself 7

Find the doubling time in Example 7 if the interest is compounded monthly.

Problems involving rates of growth or decay can also be solved by using exponential equations.

Example 8 A Population Application

A town's population is presently 10,000. Given a projected growth rate of 7% per year, t years from now the population P will be given by

$$P = 10{,}000e^{0.07t}$$

In how many years will the town's population double?

We want the time t when P will be 20,000 (doubled in size). So

NOTE

Divide both sides by 10,000.

$$20{,}000 = 10{,}000e^{0.07t}$$

or

$$2 = e^{0.07t}$$

In this case, we take the *natural logarithm* of both sides of the equation. This is because e is involved in the equation.

RECALL

Apply the power property.

$\ln e = 1$

$$\ln 2 = \ln e^{0.07t}$$
$$\ln 2 = 0.07t \ln e$$
$$\ln 2 = 0.07t$$
$$\frac{\ln 2}{0.07} = t$$
$$t \approx 9.9 \text{ years}$$

The population will double in approximately 9.9 years.

Check Yourself 8

If $1,000 is invested in an account with an annual interest rate of 6%, compounded continuously, the amount A in the account after t years is given by

$$A = 1{,}000e^{0.06t}$$

Find the time t that it will take for the amount to double ($A = 2{,}000$). Compare this time with the result of the Check Yourself 7 exercise. Which is shorter? Why?

Check Yourself ANSWERS

1. 2 **2.** $\frac{1}{8}$ **3.** $\frac{3}{2}$ **4.** 3.322 **5.** 1.386 **6.** 1.151
7. 11.58 years **8.** 11.55 years; the doubling time is shorter, because interest is compounded more frequently

Reading Your Text

The following fill-in-the-blank exercises are designed to ensure that you understand some of the key vocabulary used in this section.

SECTION 11.4

(a) A ______________ is an equation that contains a logarithmic expression.

(b) If no base is written for a logarithm, it is assumed to be ______________.

(c) If $\log_b M = \log_b N$, then ______________.

(d) ______________ are equations in which the variable appears as an exponent.

Basic Skills | Advanced Skills | Vocational-Technical Applications | Calculator/Computer | Above and Beyond

11.4 exercises

< Objective 1 >

Solve each logarithmic equation for x.

1. $\log_4 x = 3$

2. $\log_3 x = -2$

3. $\log (x + 1) = 2$

4. $\log_5 (2x - 1) = 2$

5. $\log_2 x + \log_2 8 = 6$

6. $\log 5 + \log x = 2$

7. $\log_3 x - \log_3 6 = 3$

8. $\log_4 x - \log_4 8 = 3$

9. $\log_2 x + \log_2 (x + 2) = 3$

10. $\log_3 x + \log_3 (2x + 3) = 2$

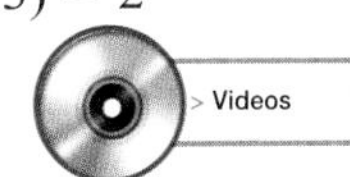

11. $\log_7 (x + 1) + \log_7 (x - 5) = 1$

12. $\log_2 (x + 2) + \log_2 (x - 5) = 3$

13. $\log x - \log (x - 2) = 1$

14. $\log_5 (x + 5) - \log_5 x = 2$

15. $\log_3 (x + 1) - \log_3 (x - 2) = 2$

16. $\log (x + 2) - \log (2x - 1) = 1$

17. $\log (x + 5) - \log (x - 2) = \log 5$

18. $\log_3 (x + 12) - \log_3 (x - 3) = \log_3 6$

19. $\log_2 (x^2 - 1) - \log_2 (x - 2) = 3$

20. $\log (x^2 + 1) - \log (x - 2) = 1$

< Objective 2 >

Solve each exponential equation for x. Give your solutions in decimal form, correct to three decimal places.

21. $5^x = 625$

22. $4^x = 64$

23. $2^{x+1} = \dfrac{1}{8}$

24. $9^x = 3$

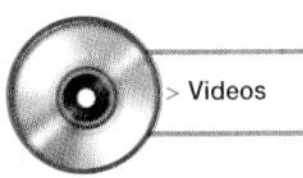

25. $8^x = 2$

26. $3^{2x-1} = 27$

27. $3^x = 7$

28. $5^x = 30$

29. $4^{x+1} = 12$

30. $3^{2x} = 5$

MathZone

Boost your grade at mathzone.com!

> Practice Problems
> NetTutor
> Self-Tests
> e-Professors
> Videos

Name ____________

Section ________ Date ________

Answers

1. 64 **2.** $\frac{1}{9}$

3. 99 **4.** 13

5. 8 **6.** 20

7. 162 **8.** 512

9. 2 **10.** $\frac{3}{2}$

11. 6 **12.** 6

13. $\frac{20}{9}$ **14.** $\frac{5}{24}$

15. $\frac{19}{8}$ **16.** $\frac{12}{19}$

17. $\frac{15}{4}$ **18.** 6

19. 5, 3 **20.** 3, 7

21. 4 **22.** 3

23. −4 **24.** $\frac{1}{2}$

25. $\frac{1}{3}$ **26.** 2

27. 1.771 **28.** 2.113

29. 0.792 **30.** 0.732

31. $7^{3x} = 50$

32. $6^{x-3} = 21$

33. $5^{3x-1} = 15$

34. $8^{2x+1} = 20$

35. $4^x = 3^{x+1}$

36. $5^x = 2^{x+2}$ > Videos

37. $2^{x+1} = 3^{x-1}$

38. $3^{2x+1} = 5^{x+1}$

< Objective 3 >

Business and Finance *Use the formula*

$$A = P\left(1 + \frac{r}{n}\right)^{nt}$$

to solve exercises 39 to 42.

39. If $5,000 is placed in an account with an annual interest rate of 9%, how long will it take the amount to double if the interest is compounded annually?

40. Repeat exercise 39 if the interest is compounded semiannually.

41. Repeat exercise 39 if the interest is compounded quarterly.

42. Repeat exercise 39 if the interest is compounded monthly.

Science and Medicine *Suppose the number of bacteria present in a culture after t hours is given by $N(t) = N_0 \cdot 2^{t/2}$, in which N_0 is the initial number of bacteria. Use the formula to solve exercises 43 to 46.*

43. How long will it take the bacteria to increase from 12,000 to 20,000?

44. How long will it take the bacteria to increase from 12,000 to 50,000?

45. How long will it take the bacteria to triple? (*Hint:* Let $N(t) = 3N_0$.)

46. How long will it take the culture to increase to 5 times its original size? (*Hint:* Let $N(t) = 5N_0$.)

Science and Medicine *The radioactive element strontium 90 has a half-life of approximately 28 years. That is, in a 28-year period, one-half of the initial amount will have decayed into another substance. If A_0 is the initial amount of the element, then the amount A remaining after t years is given by*

chapter 11 > Make the Connection

$$A(t) = A_0\left(\frac{1}{2}\right)^{t/28}$$

Use the formula to solve exercises 47 to 50.

47. If the initial amount of the element is 100 g, in how many years will 60 g remain?

48. If the initial amount of the element is 100 g, in how many years will 20 g remain?

Answers

31. 0.670
32. 4.699
33. 0.894
34. 0.220
35. 3.819
36. 1.513
37. 4.419
38. 0.869
39. 8 yr
40. 7.9 yr
41. 7.8 yr
42. 7.7 yr
43. 1.47 h
44. 4.12 h
45. 3.17 h
46. 4.64 h
47. 20.6 yr
48. 65 yr

49. In how many years will 75% of the original amount remain? (*Hint:* Let $A(t) = 0.75A_0$.)

50. In how many years will 10% of the original amount remain? (*Hint:* Let $A(t) = 0.1A_0$.)

SOCIAL SCIENCE *Given projected growth, t years from now a city's population P can be approximated by* $P(t) = 25{,}000e^{0.045t}$. *Use the formula to solve exercises 51 and 52.*

51. How long will it take the city's population to reach 35,000?

52. How long will it take the population to double?

SCIENCE AND MEDICINE *The number of bacteria in a culture after t hours can be given by* $N(t) = N_0e^{0.03t}$, *in which* N_0 *is the initial number of bacteria in the culture. Use the formula to solve exercises 53 and 54.*

53. In how many hours will the size of the culture double?

54. In how many hours will the culture grow to four times its original population?

SCIENCE AND MEDICINE *The atmospheric pressure P, in inches of mercury (in. Hg), at an altitude h feet above sea level is approximated by* $P(t) = 30e^{-0.00004h}$. *Use the formula to solve exercises 55 and 56.*

55. Find the altitude if the pressure at that altitude is 25 in. Hg.

56. Find the altitude if the pressure at that altitude is 20 in. Hg.

SCIENCE AND MEDICINE *Carbon 14 dating is used to measure the age of specimens and is based on the radioactive decay of the element carbon 14. If* A_0 *is the initial amount of carbon 14, then the amount remaining after t years is* $A(t) = A_0e^{-0.000124t}$. *Use the formula to solve exercises 57 and 58.*

chapter 11 > Make the Connection

57. Estimate the age of a specimen if 70% of the original amount of carbon 14 remains.

58. Estimate the age of a specimen if 20% of the original amount of carbon 14 remains.

Basic Skills | Advanced Skills | **Vocational-Technical Applications** | Calculator/Computer | Above and Beyond

59. **ALLIED HEALTH** The acidity or pH level of an aqueous solution is a function of the molar concentration of the hydrogen ions, $[H^+]$, given by the formula $pH = -\log [H^+]$. Determine the molar concentration that will yield a pH of 9.5.

60. **AUTOMOTIVE TECHNOLOGY** The sound level, in decibels, is given by the formula

$$N = 10 \log\left(\frac{I}{10^{-12}\ \text{W/m}^2}\right)$$

If the sound level of car exhaust is required by city ordinance to be below 100 dB, what is the maximum sound level (in W/m^2) that the exhaust can be?

Answers

49. 11.6 yr
50. 93 yr
51. 7.5 yr
52. 15.4 yr
53. 23.1 h
54. 46.2 h
55. 4,558 ft
56. 10,137 ft
57. 2,876 yr
58. 12,979 yr
59. 3.16×10^{-10}
60. 0.01 W/m^2

Answers

61. See exercise

62. See exercise

63. See exercise

64. See exercise

65. Above and Beyond

66. Above and Beyond

Basic Skills | Advanced Skills | Vocational-Technical Applications | **Calculator/Computer** | Above and Beyond

In exercises 61 to 64, use your calculator to find the graph for each equation, and then explain the result.

61. $y = \log 10^x$

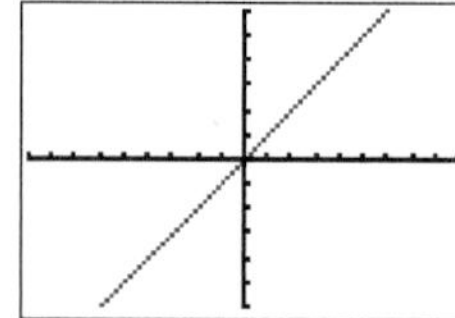

The graph is that of $y = x$. The two operations cancel each other.

62. $y = 10^{\log x}$

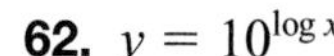

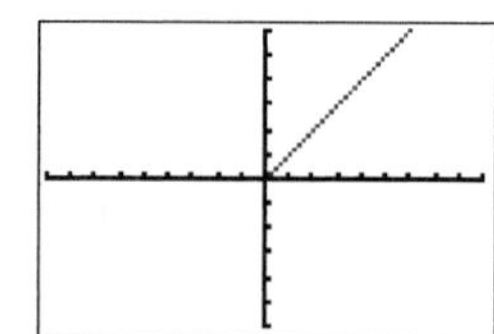

The graph is that of $y = x$. The two operations cancel each other. Only positive values of x show since $\log x$ is only defined for $x > 0$.

63. $y = \ln e^x$

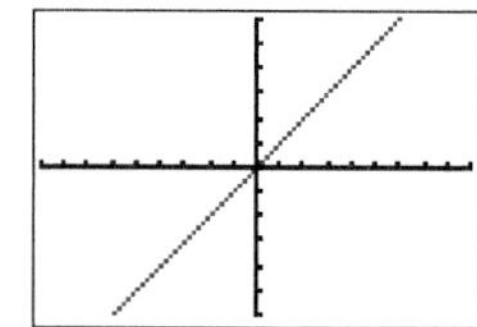

The graph is that of $y = x$. The two operations cancel each other.

64. $y = e^{\ln x}$

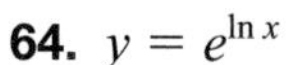

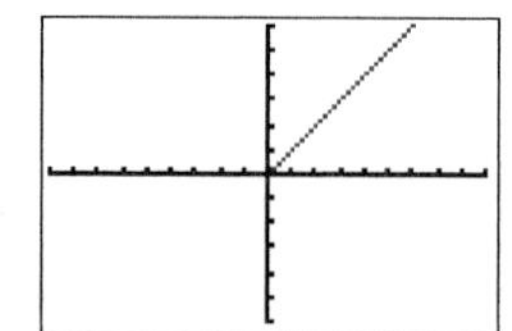

The graph is that of $y = x$. The two operations cancel each other. Only positive values of x show since $\ln x$ is only defined for $x > 0$.

Basic Skills | Advanced Skills | Vocational-Technical Applications | Calculator/Computer | **Above and Beyond**

65. In some of the earlier exercises, we talked about bacteria cultures that double in size every few minutes. Can this go on forever? Explain.

66. The population of the United States has been doubling every 45 years. Is it reasonable to assume that this rate will continue? What factors will start to limit that growth?

Answers

1. 64 **3.** 99 **5.** 8 **7.** 162 **9.** 2 **11.** 6 **13.** $\frac{20}{9}$
15. $\frac{19}{8}$ **17.** $\frac{15}{4}$ **19.** 5, 3 **21.** 4 **23.** -4 **25.** $\frac{1}{3}$
27. 1.771 **29.** 0.792 **31.** 0.670 **33.** 0.894 **35.** 3.819
37. 4.419 **39.** 8 yr **41.** 7.8 yr **43.** 1.47 h **45.** 3.17 h
47. 20.6 yr **49.** 11.6 yr **51.** 7.5 yr **53.** 23.1 h **55.** 4,558 ft
57. 2,876 yr **59.** 3.16×10^{-10}

61.

The graph is that of $y = x$. The two operations cancel each other.

63.

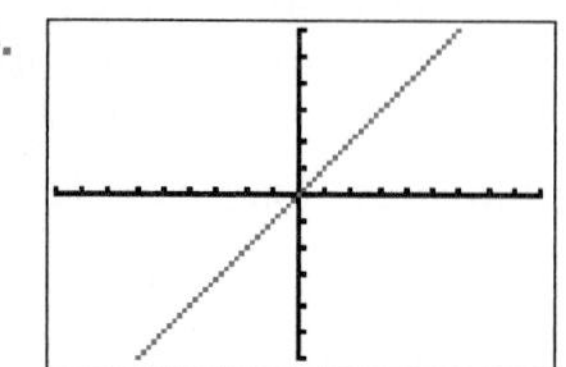

The graph is that of $y = x$. The two operations cancel each other.

65. Above and Beyond

Definition/Procedure	Example	Reference
Exponential Functions		Section 11.1
An **exponential function** is any function defined by an equation of the form $y = f(x) = b^x \qquad b > 0, b \neq 1$ If b is greater than 1, the function is always increasing (a **growth function**). If b is less than 1, the function is always decreasing (a **decay function**). In both cases, the exponential function is one-to-one. The domain is the set of all real numbers, and the range is the set of positive real numbers. The function defined by $f(x) = e^x$, in which e is an irrational number (approximately 2.71828), is called *the* exponential function.	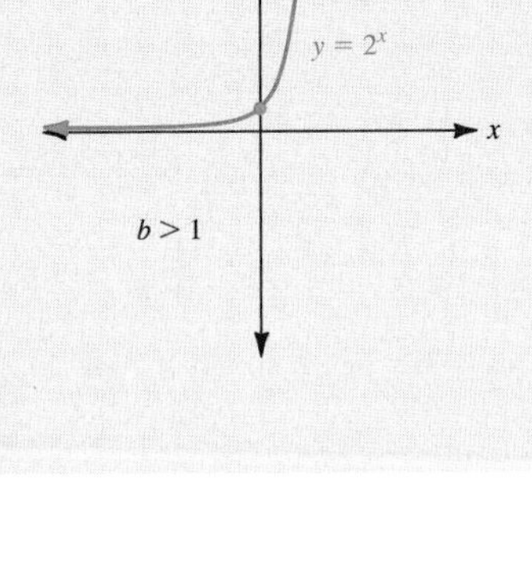	p. 974
Graphing an Exponential Function **Step 1** Establish a table of values by considering the function in the form $y = b^x$. **Step 2** Plot points from that table of values and connect them with a smooth curve to form the graph. **Step 3** If $b > 1$, the graph increases from left to right. If $0 < b < 1$, the graph decreases from left to right. **Step 4** All graphs will have the following in common: **(a)** The y-intercept will be (0, 1). **(b)** The graphs will approach, but not touch, the x-axis. **(c)** The graphs will represent one-to-one functions.	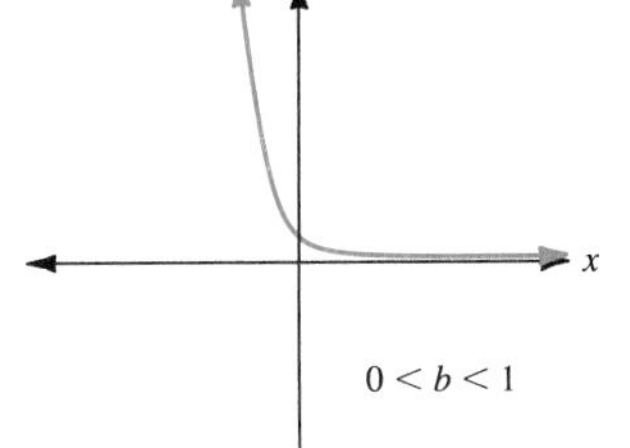	p. 976
Logarithmic Functions		Section 11.2
In the expression $y = \log_b x$ y is called the *logarithm of* x *to base* b, when $b > 0$ and $b \neq 1$. An expression such as $y = \log_b x$ is said to be in **logarithmic form.** An expression such as $x = b^y$ is said to be in **exponential form.** $y = \log_b x \quad$ means the same as $\quad x = b^y$ A logarithm is an exponent or a power. The logarithm of x to base b is the power to which we must raise b to get x. A **logarithmic function** is any function defined by an equation of the form $y = f(x) = \log_b x \qquad b > 0, b \neq 1$ The logarithm function is the inverse of the corresponding exponential function. The function is one-to-one with the domain $\{x \mid x > 0\}$ and the range composed of the set of all real numbers.	$\log_3 9 = 2$ is in logarithmic form. $3^2 = 9$ is in exponential form. $\log_3 9 = 2$ is equivalent to $3^2 = 9$. 2 is the power to which we must raise 3 to get 9. 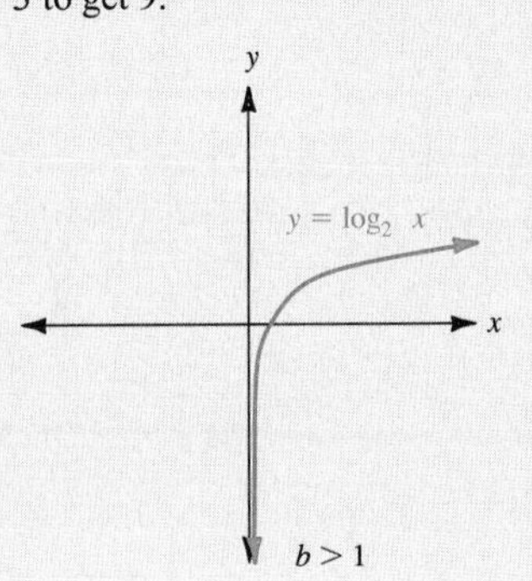	p. 990

Continued

Definition/Procedure	Example	Reference
Properties of Logarithms		**Section 11.3**
If M, N, and b are positive real numbers with $b \neq 1$ and if p is any real number, then we can state the following properties of logarithms:		*pp.* 1005–1006
1. $\log_b b = 1$	$\log 10 = 1$	
2. $\log_b 1 = 0$	$\log_2 1 = 0$	
3. $b^{\log_b x} = x$	$3^{\log_3 2} = 2$	
4. $\log_b b^x = x$	$\log_5 5^x = x$	
Product Property		
$\log_b MN = \log_b M + \log_b N$	$\log_3 x + \log_3 y = \log_3 xy$	*p.* 1006
Quotient Property		
$\log_b \dfrac{M}{N} = \log_b M - \log_b N$	$\log_5 8 - \log_5 3 = \log_5 \dfrac{8}{3}$	*p.* 1006
Power Property		
$\log_b M^p = p \log_b M$	$\log 3^2 = 2 \log 3$	*p.* 1006
Common logarithms are logarithms to base 10. For convenience, we omit the base in writing common logarithms: $\log M = \log_{10} M$	$\log_{10} 1{,}000 = \log 1{,}000$ $= \log 10^3 = 3$	*p.* 1009
Natural logarithms are logarithms to base e. By custom we also omit the base in writing natural logarithms: $\ln M = \log_e M$	$\ln 3 = \log_e 3$	*p.* 1011
Solving Logarithmic and Exponential Equations		**Section 11.4**
A **logarithmic equation** is an equation that contains a logarithmic expression. $\log_2 x = 5$ is a logarithmic equation.	To solve $\log_2 x = 5$: Write the equation in the equivalent exponential form to solve $x = 2^5$ or $x = 32$	*p.* 1021

Definition/Procedure	Example	Reference
Solving Logarithmic Equations **Step 1** Use the properties of logarithms to combine terms containing logarithmic expressions into a single term. **Step 2** Write the equation formed in step 1 in exponential form. **Step 3** Solve for the indicated variable. **Step 4** Check your solutions to make sure that possible solutions do not result in the logarithms of negative numbers or zero.	To solve $\log_4 x + \log_4 (x - 6) = 2$ $\log_4 x(x - 6) = 2$ $x(x - 6) = 4^2$ $x^2 - 6x - 16 = 0$ $(x - 8)(x + 2) = 0$ $x = 8$ or $x = -2$ Because substituting -2 for x in the original equation results in the logarithm of a negative number, we reject that answer. The only solution is 8.	*p.* 1023
An **exponential equation** is an equation in which the variable appears as an exponent. The following algorithm summarizes the steps in solving any exponential equation.	To solve $4^x = 64$: Because $64 = 4^3$, write $4^x = 4^3$ or $x = 3$	*p.* 1024
Solving Exponential Equations **Step 1** Try to write each side of the equation as a power of the same base. Then, equate the exponents to form an equation. **Step 2** If the procedure in step 1 is not applicable, take the common logarithm of both sides of the original equation. **Step 3** Use the power rule for logarithms to write an equivalent equation with the variables as coefficients. **Step 4** Solve the resulting equation.	$2^{x+3} = 5^x$ $\log 2^{x+3} = \log 5^x$ $(x + 3) \log 2 = x \log 5$ $x \log 2 + 3 \log 2 = x \log 5$ $x \log 2 - x \log 5 = -3 \log 2$ $x (\log 2 - \log 5) = -3 \log 2$ $x = \dfrac{-3 \log 2}{\log 2 - \log 5} \approx 2.269$	*p.* 1025

summary exercises :: chapter 11

This summary exercise set is provided to give you practice with each of the objectives of this chapter. Each exercise is keyed to the appropriate chapter section. When you are finished, you can check your answers to the odd-numbered exercises against those presented in the back of the text. If you have difficulty with any of these questions, go back and reread the examples from that section. The answers to the even-numbered exercises appear in the *Instructor's Solutions Manual.* Your instructor will give you guidelines on how best to use these exercises in your instructional setting.

11.1 *Graph the exponential functions defined by each of the following equations.*

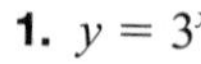

1. $y = 3^x$

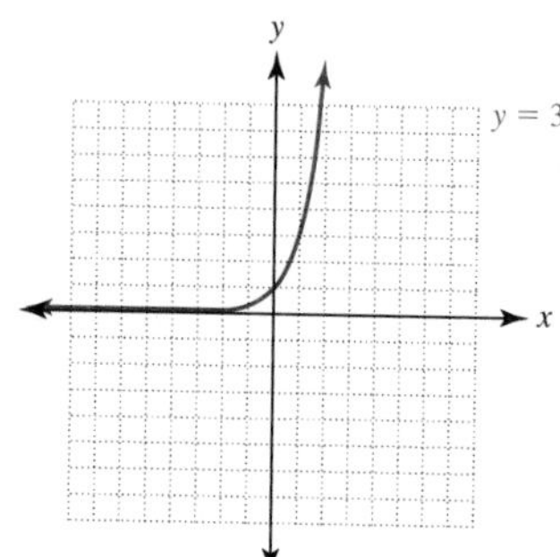

2. $y = \left(\frac{3}{4}\right)^x$

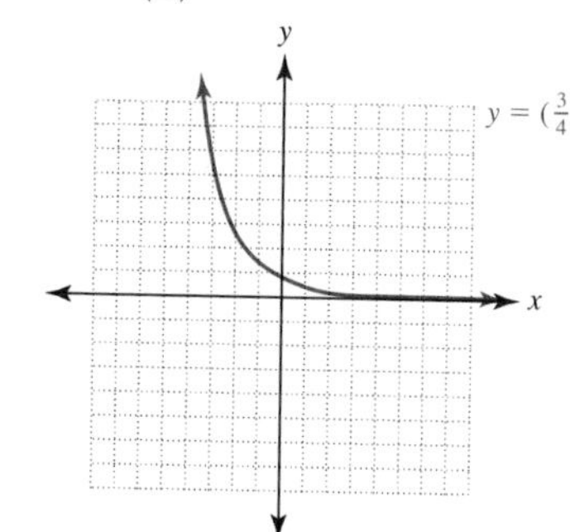

11.2 *Solve each of the following exponential equations for x.*

3. $5^x = 125$ 3

4. $2^{2x+1} = 32$ 2

5. $3^{x-1} = \frac{1}{9}$ −1

If it takes 2 h for the population of a certain bacteria culture to double (by dividing in half), then the number N of bacteria in the culture after t hours is given by $N = 1{,}000 \cdot 2^{t/2}$, *when the initial population of the culture was* 1,000. *Using this formula, find the number in the culture:*

6. After 4 h 4,000 bacteria

7. After 12 h 64,000 bacteria

8. After 15 h 181,019 bacteria

Graph the logarithmic functions defined by each of the following equations.

9. $y = \log_3 x$

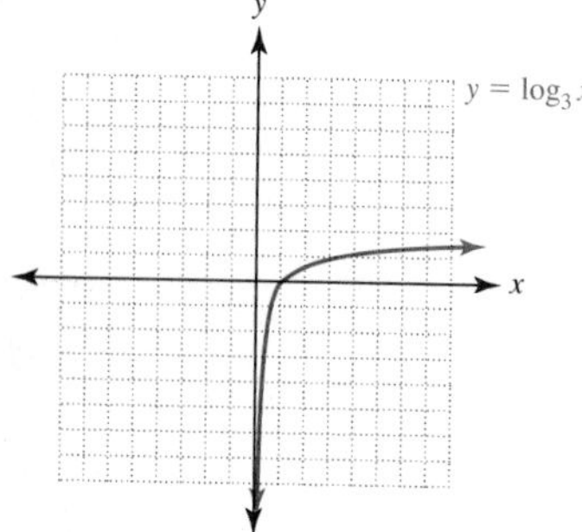

10. $y = \log_2 (x - 1)$

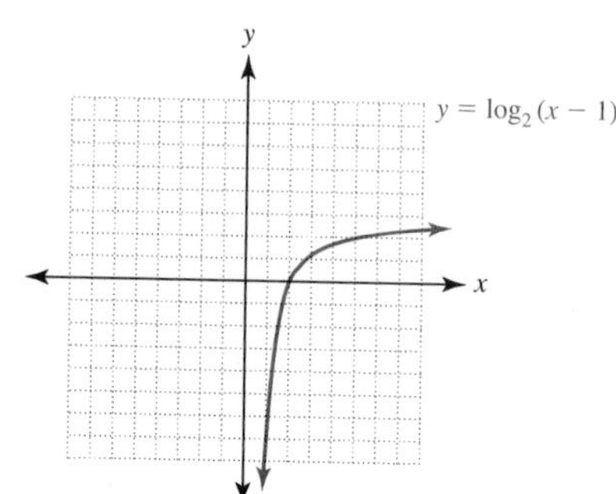

Convert each of the following statements to logarithmic form.

11. $3^4 = 81$ $\log_3 81 = 4$

12. $10^3 = 1{,}000$ $\log 1{,}000 = 3$

13. $5^0 = 1$ $\log_5 1 = 0$

14. $5^{-2} = \frac{1}{25}$ $\log_5\left(\frac{1}{25}\right) = -2$

15. $25^{1/2} = 5$ $\log_{25} 5 = \frac{1}{2}$

16. $16^{3/4} = 8$ $\log_{16} 8 = \frac{3}{4}$

Convert each of the following statements to exponential form.

17. $\log_3 81 = 4$ $3^4 = 81$

18. $\log 1 = 0$ $10^0 = 1$

19. $\log_{81} 9 = \frac{1}{2}$ $81^{1/2} = 9$

20. $\log_5 25 = 2$ $5^2 = 25$

21. $\log 0.001 = -3$ $10^{-3} = 0.001$

22. $\log_{32} \frac{1}{2} = -\frac{1}{5}$ $32^{-1/5} = \frac{1}{2}$

Solve each of the following equations for the unknown variable.

23. $y = \log_5 125$ 3

24. $\log_b \frac{1}{9} = -2$ 3

25. $\log_8 x = 2$ 64

26. $y = \log_5 1$ 0

27. $\log_b 3 = \frac{1}{2}$ 9

28. $y = \log_{16} 2$ $\frac{1}{4}$

29. $y = \log_8 2$ $\frac{1}{3}$

The decibel (dB) rating for the loudness of a sound is given by

$$L = 10 \log \frac{I}{I_0}$$

in which I is the intensity of that sound in watts per square centimeter and I_0 is the intensity of the "threshold" sound, $I_0 = 10^{-16}$ W/cm². Find the decibel rating of each of the given sounds in exercises 30 and 31.

30. A table saw in operation with intensity $I = 10^{-6}\ \text{W/cm}^2$ 100 dB

31. The sound of a passing car horn with intensity $I = 10^{-8}\ \text{W/cm}^2$ 80 dB

The formula for the decibel rating of a sound can be solved for the intensity of the sound as

$I = I_0 \cdot 10^{L/10}$

in which L is the decibel rating of the given sound. Use this formula to solve exercises 32 and 33.

32. What is the ratio of intensity of a 60-dB sound to one of 50 dB? 10

33. What is the ratio of intensity of a 60-dB sound to one of 40 dB? 100

The magnitude of an earthquake on the Richter scale is given by

$M = \log \frac{a}{a_0}$

in which a is the intensity of the shock wave of the given earthquake and a_0 is the intensity of the shock wave of a zero-level earthquake. Use this formula to solve exercises 34 and 35.

34. The Alaskan earthquake of 1964 had an intensity of $10^{8.4}\, a_0$. What was its magnitude on the Richter scale? 8.4

35. Find the ratio of intensity of an earthquake of magnitude 7 to an earthquake of magnitude 6. 10

11.3 *Use the properties of logarithms to expand each of the following expressions.*

36. $\log_b x^2y$ $\quad 2 \log_b x + \log_b y$

37. $\log_4 \frac{y^3}{5}$ $\quad 3 \log_4 y - \log_4 5$

38. $\log_3 \frac{xy^2}{z}$ $\quad \log_3 x + 2 \log_3 y - \log_3 z$

39. $\log_5 x^3yz^2$ $\quad 3 \log_5 x + \log_5 y + 2 \log_5 z$

40. $\log \frac{xy}{\sqrt{z}}$ $\quad \log x + \log y - \frac{1}{2} \log z$

41. $\log_b \sqrt[3]{\frac{x^2y}{z}}$ $\quad \frac{2}{3} \log_b x + \frac{1}{3} \log_b y - \frac{1}{3} \log_b z$

Use the properties of logarithms to write each of the following expressions as a single logarithm.

42. $\log x + 2 \log y$ $\quad \log xy^2$

43. $3 \log_b x - 2 \log_b z$ $\quad \log_b \frac{x^3}{z^2}$

44. $\log_b x + \log_b y - \log_b z$ $\quad \log_b \frac{xy}{z}$

45. $2 \log_5 x - 3 \log_5 y - \log_5 z$ $\quad \log_5 \frac{x^2}{y^3z}$

46. $\log x - \frac{1}{2} \log y$ $\quad \log \frac{x}{\sqrt{y}}$

47. $\frac{1}{3} (\log_b x - 2 \log_b y)$ $\quad \log_b \sqrt[3]{\frac{x}{y^2}}$

Given that $\log 2 = 0.301$ *and* $\log 3 = 0.477$, *find each of the following logarithms. Verify your results with a calculator.*

48. $\log 18$ $\quad 1.255$

49. $\log 16$ $\quad 1.204$

50. $\log \frac{1}{8}$ $\quad -0.903$

51. $\log \sqrt{3}$ $\quad 0.239$

Use your calculator to find the pH of each of the following solutions, given the hydrogen ion concentration $[H^+]$ for each solution, when

$$pH = -\log [H^+]$$

Are the solutions acidic or basic?

52. Coffee: $[H^+] = 5 \times 10^{-6}$ 5.301, acidic

53. Household detergent: $[H^+] = 3.2 \times 10^{-10}$ 9.495, basic

Given the pH of the following solutions, find the hydrogen ion concentration $[H^+]$.

54. Lemonade: pH = 3.5 3.2×10^{-4}

55. Ammonia: pH = 10.2 6.3×10^{-11}

The average score on a final examination for a group of chemistry students, retested after time t (in weeks), is given by

$$S(t) = 81 - 6 \ln (t + 1)$$

Find the average score on the retests after the given times.

56. After 5 weeks 70.2

57. After 10 weeks 66.6

58. After 15 weeks 64.4

59. Graph the results from exercises 56 to 58.

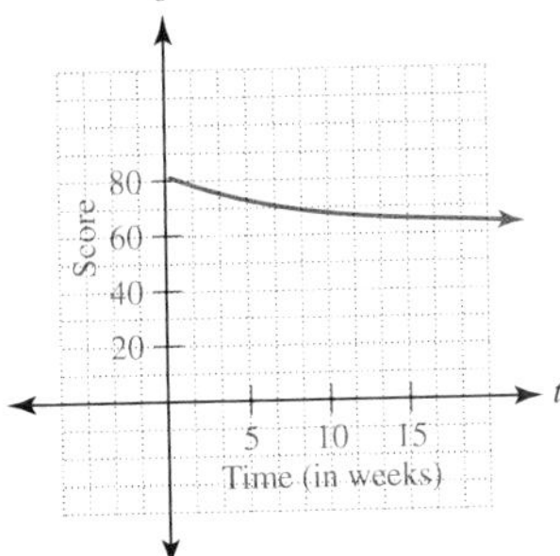

The formula for converting from a logarithm with base a to a logarithmic expression with base 10 is

$$\log_a x = \frac{\log x}{\log a}$$

Use that formula to find each of the following logarithms.

60. $\log_4 20$ 2.161

61. $\log_8 60$ 1.969

11.4 *Solve each of the following logarithmic equations for x.*

62. $\log_3 x + \log_3 5 = 3$ $\frac{27}{5}$

63. $\log_5 x - \log_5 10 = 2$ 250

64. $\log_3 x + \log_3 (x + 6) = 3$ 3

65. $\log_5 (x + 3) + \log_5 (x - 1) = 1$ 2

66. $\log x - \log (x - 1) = 1$ $\frac{10}{9}$

67. $\log_2 (x + 3) - \log_2 (x - 1) = \log_2 3$ 3

Solve each of the following exponential equations for x. Give your results correct to three decimal places.

68. $3^x = 243$ 5

69. $5^x = \frac{1}{25}$ −2

70. $5^x = 10$ 1.431

71. $4^{x-1} = 8$ 2.500

72. $6^x = 2^{2x+1}$ 1.710

73. $2^{x+1} = 3^{x-1}$ 4.419

If an investment of P dollars earns interest at an annual rate of 12% and the interest is compounded n times per year, then the amount A in the account after t years is

$$A(t) = P\left(1 + \frac{0.12}{n}\right)^{nt}$$

Use that formula to solve each of the following.

74. If \$1,000 is invested and the interest is compounded quarterly, how long will it take the amount in the account to double? 5.9 yr

75. If \$3,000 is invested and the interest is compounded monthly, how long will it take the amount in the account to reach \$8,000? 8.2 yr

A certain radioactive element has a half-life of 50 years. The amount A of the substance remaining after t years is given by

$$A(t) = A_0 \cdot 2^{-t/50}$$

when A_0 is the initial amount of the substance. Use this formula to solve each of the following.

76. If the initial amount of the substance is 100 milligrams (mg), after how long will 40 mg remain? 66.1 yr

77. After how long will only 10% of the original amount of the substance remain? 166.1 yr

A city's population is presently 50,000. Given the projected growth, t years from now the population P will be given by $P(t) = 50{,}000e^{0.08t}$. Use this formula to solve each of the following.

78. How long will it take the population to reach 70,000? 4.2 yr

79. How long will it take the population to double? 8.7 yr

The atmospheric pressure, in inches of mercury, at an altitude h miles above the surface of Earth, is approximated by $P(h) = 30e^{-0.021h}$. Use this formula to solve the following exercises.

80. Find the altitude at the top of Mt. McKinley in Alaska if the pressure is 27.7 in. Hg. 3.8 mi

81. Find the altitude outside an airliner in flight if the pressure is 26.1 in. Hg. 6.6 mi

self-test 11

Name ______________

Section ________ Date ________

The purpose of this chapter test is to help you check your progress so that you can find sections and concepts that you need to review before the next exam. Allow yourself about an hour to take this test. At the end of that hour, check your answers against those given in the back of this text. If you missed any, note the section reference that accompanies the answer. Go back to that section and reread the examples until you have mastered that particular concept.

11.1

Graph the exponential functions defined by each of the following equations.

1. $y = 4^x$

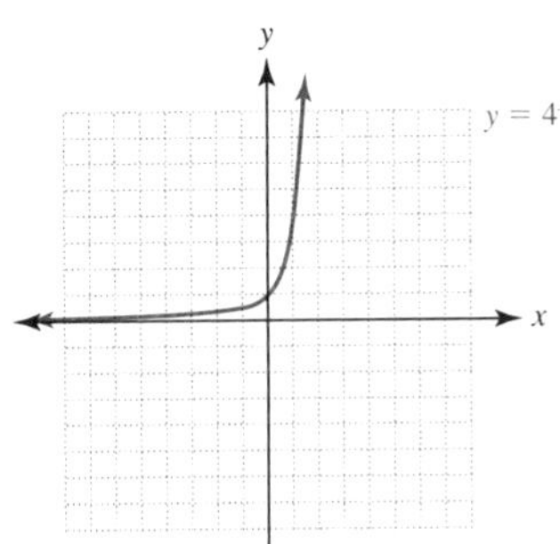

2. $y = \left(\frac{2}{3}\right)^x$

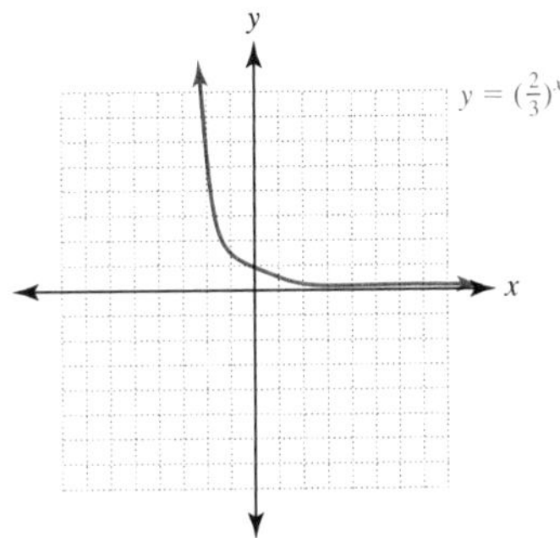

11.2

3. Solve each of the following exponential equations for x.

(a) $5^x = \frac{1}{25}$ **(b)** $3^{2x-1} = 81$

4. Graph the logarithmic function defined by the following equation.

$y = \log_4 x$

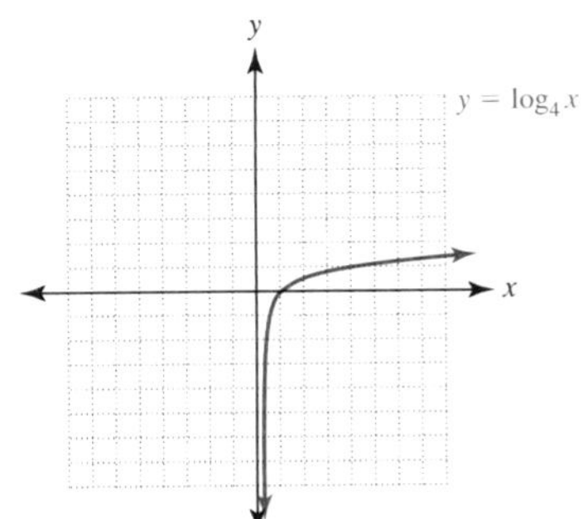

Convert each of the following statements to logarithmic form.

5. $10^4 = 10{,}000$ **6.** $27^{2/3} = 9$

Answers

1. See exercise
2. See exercise
3. (a) -2; (b) $\frac{5}{2}$
4. See exercise
5. $\log 10{,}000 = 4$
6. $\log_{27} 9 = \frac{2}{3}$

Answers

7. $5^3 = 125$

8. $10^{-2} = 0.01$

9. 6

10. 4

11. 5

12. $2 \log_b x + \log_b y + 3 \log_b z$

13. $\frac{1}{2}\log_5 x + \log_5 y - \frac{1}{2}\log_5 z$

14. $\log (xy^3)$

15. $\log_b \sqrt[3]{\frac{x}{z^2}}$

16. 8

17. $\frac{11}{8}$

18. 0.262

19. 2.151

Convert each of the following statements to exponential form.

7. $\log_5 125 = 3$

8. $\log 0.01 = -2$

Solve each of the following equations for the unknown variable.

9. $y = \log_2 64$

10. $\log_b \frac{1}{16} = -2$

11. $\log_{25} x = \frac{1}{2}$

11.3

Use the properties of logarithms to expand each of the following expressions.

12. $\log_b x^2yz^3$

13. $\log_5 \sqrt{\frac{xy^2}{z}}$

Use the properties of logarithms to write each of the following expressions as a single logarithm.

14. $\log x + 3 \log y$

15. $\frac{1}{3}(\log_b x - 2 \log_b z)$

11.4

Solve each of the following logarithmic equations for x.

16. $\log_6 (x + 1) + \log_6 (x - 4) = 2$

17. $\log (2x + 1) - \log (x - 1) = 1$

Solve each of the following exponential equations for x. Give your results correct to three decimal places.

18. $3^{x+1} = 4$

19. $5^x = 3^{x+1}$

Activity 11 :: Half-Life and Decay

Each chapter in this text concludes with a chapter activity such as this one. These activities provide you with the opportunity to apply the math you studied in that chapter to a relevant topic. Your instructor will determine how best to use these activities in your instructional setting. You may find yourself working in class or outside of class; you may find yourself working alone or in small groups; you may even be asked to perform research in a library or on the Internet.

The concept of half-life as described in the introduction to this chapter is probably familiar to you. You may have encountered this idea in connection with radioactive substances. Given an initial amount of radioactive material, half of that material will still be radioactive after an amount of time known as the **half-life** of the material. As the material continues to decay, the amount that is still radioactive may be modeled by an **exponential** function. We studied this type of function in this chapter.

To simulate the decay of radioactive material, do the following: Working with two or three partners, obtain approximately 20 wooden cubes, and place a marker on just one side of each cube. (Dice may be used: simply choose one number to be the marked side.)

1. Count the number of cubes you have. This is your *initial amount of radioactive material.* Record this number.
2. Roll the entire set of cubes. The cube(s) that show the marked side up have decayed. Remove these, and record the number that are still active.
3. Roll the remaining radioactive cubes, remove those that have decayed, and record the amount remaining.
4. Continue in this manner, filling out a table like that shown, until all cubes have decayed. Note that the variable x represents the number of rolls, and y represents the number of cubes still active.

x	y	x	y
0			
1		11	
2		12	
3		13	
4		14	
5		15	
6		16	
7		17	
8		18	
9		19	
10		20	

5. Plot the ordered pairs from your table on graph paper, after drawing appropriately scaled and labeled axes.
6. Repeat the entire procedure (with the same set of cubes), completing a new table. Plot this set of ordered pairs on the *same* coordinate system you made in step 5.

7. Do this yet a third time, again adding the points to your scatter plot.

8. Now, draw a smooth curve that seems (to you) to fit the points best.

9. Use your graph to determine the approximate half-life for your cubes. For example, if you began with 22 cubes, see how many rolls it took for 11 to remain. Confirm your estimate of the half-life by checking elsewhere on the graph. For example, estimate the number of rolls corresponding to 16 cubes, and see about how many rolls it took, from that point, for 8 to remain.

Sample Data

x	0	1	2	3	4	5	6	7	8	9	10	11	12	13	14	15	16	17	18	19	20
y	22	19	16	14	10	8	6	5	4	4	4	3	3	3	3	3	3	3	2	2	0

x	0	1	2	3	4	5	6	7	8	9	10	11	12	13	14	15	16	17	18
y	22	20	15	13	10	9	9	7	5	1	1	1	1	1	1	0			

x	0	1	2	3	4	5	6	7	8	9	10	11	12	13	14	15	16	17	18
y	22	15	12	8	7	7	5	5	5	4	4	4	3	2	2	0			

Name ________________

Section ________ Date ________

The following exercises are presented to help you review concepts from earlier chapters. This is meant as review material and not as a comprehensive exam. The answers are presented in the back of the text. Beside each answer is a section reference for the concept. If you have difficulty with any of these exercises, be certain to at least read through the summary related to that section.

Solve each of the following.

2.1

1. $2x - 3(x + 2) = 4(5 - x) + 7$

2.5

2. $|3x - 7| > 5$

11.4

3. $\log x - \log (x - 1) = 1$

Graph each of the following.

3.3

4. $5x - 3y = 15$

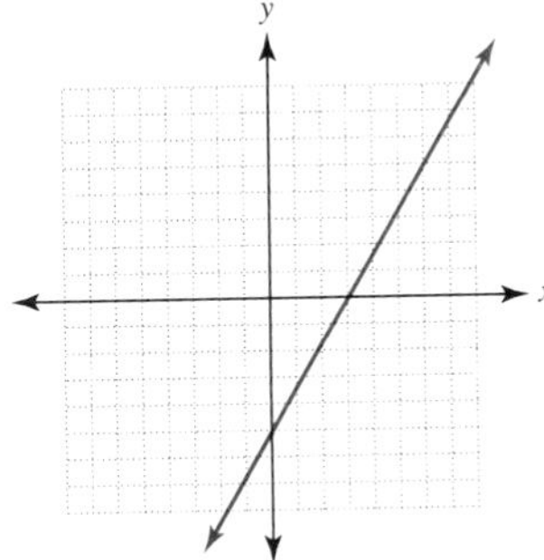

3.6

5. $-8(2 - x) \geq y$

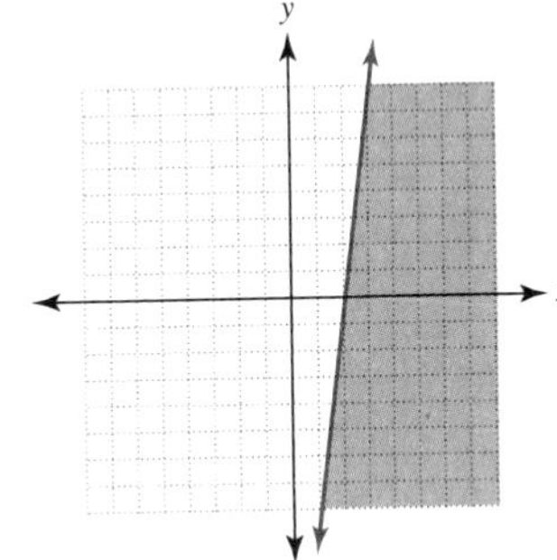

3.5

6. Find the equation of the line that passes through the points $(2, -1)$ and $(-3, 5)$.

2.4

7. Solve the linear inequality.

$3x - 2(x - 5) \geq 20$

Simplify each of the following expressions.

1.4

8. $4x^2 - 3x + 8 - 2(x^2 + 5) - 3(x - 1)$

5.3

9. $(3x + 1)(2x - 5)$

Factor each of the following completely.

5.7

10. $2x^2 - x - 10$

5.5

11. $25x^3 - 16xy^2$

Perform the indicated operations.

6.3

12. $\dfrac{2}{x - 4} - \dfrac{3}{x - 5}$

6.2

13. $\dfrac{x^2 - x - 6}{x^2 + 2x - 15} \div \dfrac{x - 2}{x + 5}$

Answers

1. 11
2. $x < \dfrac{2}{3}$ or $x > 4$
3. $\dfrac{10}{9}$
4. See exercise
5. See exercise
6. $6x + 5y = 7$
7. $x \geq 10$
8. $2x^2 - 6x + 1$
9. $6x^2 - 13x - 5$
10. $(2x - 5)(x + 2)$
11. $x(5x + 4y)(5x - 4y)$
12. $\dfrac{-x + 2}{(x - 4)(x - 5)}$
13. $\dfrac{x + 2}{x - 2}$

Answers

14. $-4\sqrt{2}$

15. $22 + 12\sqrt{2}$

16. $\frac{5}{3}(\sqrt{5} + \sqrt{2})$

17. 77, 79, 81

18. $-2, 1$

19. $\frac{3 \pm \sqrt{19}}{2}$

20. $-\frac{3}{2} \le x \le 1$

21. 3

22. $1 \le x \le 4$

23. $(x - 1)^2 + (y + 2)^2 = 9$

24. x^3w^{12}

25. 6

Simplify each of the following radical expressions.

7.3

14. $\sqrt{18} + \sqrt{50} - 3\sqrt{32}$

15. $(3\sqrt{2} + 2)(3\sqrt{2} + 2)$

16. $\dfrac{5}{\sqrt{5} - \sqrt{2}}$

2.3

17. Find three consecutive odd integers whose sum is 237.

Solve each of the following equations.

5.9

18. $x^2 + x - 2 = 0$

8.3

19. $2x^2 - 6x - 5 = 0$

8.5

20. Solve the inequality.

$2x^2 + x - 3 \le 0$

5.1

21. If $f(x) = -x^3 + 3x + 5$, evaluate $f(-1)$.

2.5

22. Solve the inequality.

$|2x - 5| \le 3$

9.2

23. Write the equation of the circle with center $(1, -2)$ and radius 3.

1.5

24. Simplify the expression.

$$\left(\frac{x^{-2}w^3}{x^{-3}w^{-1}}\right)^3$$

6.5

25. Solve the equation.

$$\frac{2}{x-2} - \frac{3}{x+2} = \frac{4}{x^2-4}$$

Appendix: Determinants and Cramer's Rule

< A Objectives >

1 > Find the determinant of a matrix

2 > Use Cramer's rule to solve a system

Thus far, we have seen four different algebraic methods for solving systems of linear equations. We have solved these systems by substitution, by addition (sometimes called elimination), by graphing, and by using elementary row operations on a matrix that represented the system. In this section, we will examine determinants to see how they are used in solving systems of equations.

Definition

Determinant

A **determinant** is an operation on a square matrix of numbers written as shown here. The symbol | | is used to denote the determinant.

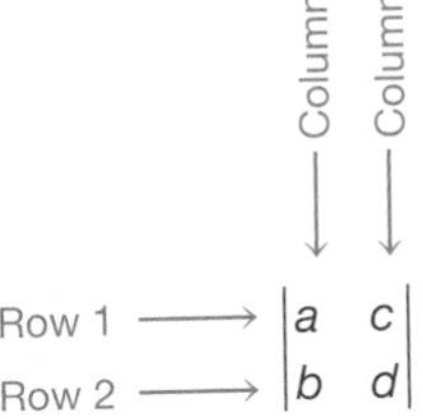

A determinant, by this definition, will be a number whenever all the matrix entries are numbers. The idea of a determinant dates back to Seki Kowa in Japan (1683) and Gottfried Leibniz (one of the inventors of calculus) in Europe (1693). The name "determinant" came from the French mathematician Augustin Cauchy and was not used until 1812.

The *order* of a square matrix is the number of rows (or columns). The matrix in the definition is said to be of order 2. It is sometimes called a 2×2 matrix for convenience. (In general, a matrix of *order n* has *n* rows and *n* columns.) The *value* of the determinant of a second-order matrix is defined as follows:

$$\begin{vmatrix} a & c \\ b & d \end{vmatrix} = ad - bc$$

Example 1 Evaluating a Determinant

< Objective 1 >

Find the value of each determinant.

(a) $\begin{vmatrix} 2 & 3 \\ -1 & 4 \end{vmatrix} = 2(4) - (-1)(3)$

$= 8 + 3 = 11$

(b) $\begin{vmatrix} 4 & -3 \\ 5 & 0 \end{vmatrix} = 4(0) - 5(-3)$

$= 15$

Check Yourself 1

Find the value for each determinant.

(a) $\begin{vmatrix} 5 & -4 \\ 1 & 3 \end{vmatrix}$ **(b)** $\begin{vmatrix} -3 & -2 \\ -2 & -1 \end{vmatrix}$

The use of determinants to solve linear systems is called **Cramer's rule.** To develop that rule, consider the system of two linear equations in two unknowns:

$$a_1x + b_1y = c_1$$
$$a_2x + b_2y = c_2$$

To solve for x, we multiply both sides of the first equation by b_2 and both sides of the second equation by $-b_1$. We then have

$$a_1b_2x + b_1b_2y = c_1b_2$$
$$-a_2b_1x - b_1b_2y = -c_2b_1$$

Adding these new equations will eliminate the variable y from the system.

$$(a_1b_2 - a_2b_1)x = c_1b_2 - c_2b_1$$

or

$$x = \frac{c_1b_2 - c_2b_1}{a_1b_2 - a_2b_1}$$

We can solve for y in a similar fashion:

$$y = \frac{a_1c_2 - a_2c_1}{a_1b_2 - a_2b_1}$$

NOTE

To verify this, return to the original system. Multiply the first equation by a_2 and the second equation by $-a_1$. Then add to eliminate the variable x.

To see how determinants are used, we will rewrite the equations for x and y in a determinant form.

$$x = \frac{\begin{vmatrix} c_1 & b_1 \\ c_2 & b_2 \end{vmatrix}}{\begin{vmatrix} a_1 & b_1 \\ a_2 & b_2 \end{vmatrix}} \qquad y = \frac{\begin{vmatrix} a_1 & c_1 \\ a_2 & c_2 \end{vmatrix}}{\begin{vmatrix} a_1 & b_1 \\ a_2 & b_2 \end{vmatrix}}$$

NOTE

This rule was named for the Swiss mathematician Gabriel Cramer, who invented the idea of determinants independently of Kowa and Leibniz and published the rule for solving linear systems of equations in 1750.

Using the determinant definition, you should verify that these are simply restatements of the original equations for x and y. In determinant form this result is called Cramer's rule.

You do not need to "memorize" the result. It is better if you observe the following patterns. We will look at our original system again.

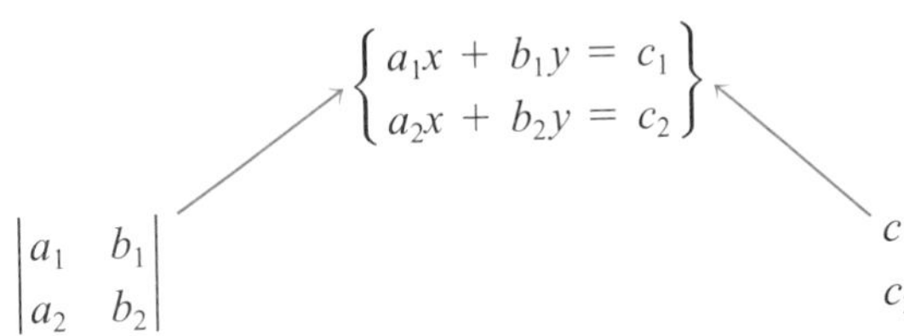

$$\begin{cases} a_1x + b_1y = c_1 \\ a_2x + b_2y = c_2 \end{cases}$$

$$\begin{vmatrix} a_1 & b_1 \\ a_2 & b_2 \end{vmatrix} \qquad\qquad \begin{matrix} c_1 \\ c_2 \end{matrix}$$

The determinant of the coefficients — The column of constants

Returning to our statement of Cramer's rule, we note that

1. The denominator for each variable is simply the determinant of the coefficients.
2. The numerator for x is formed from the determinant of the coefficients by replacing the x-coefficients with the column of constants.
3. The numerator for y is found by replacing the y-coefficients with the column of constants.

We will denote the determinant of the coefficients as D, the determinant in the numerator for x as D_x, and the determinant in the numerator for y as D_y. The following summarizes our discussion.

Property

Cramer's Rule

To solve the linear system

$$a_1x + b_1y = c_1$$
$$a_2x + b_2y = c_2$$

write

$$D = \begin{vmatrix} a_1 & b_1 \\ a_2 & b_2 \end{vmatrix}$$ The determinant of the coefficients.

$$D_x = \begin{vmatrix} c_1 & b_1 \\ c_2 & b_2 \end{vmatrix}$$ The x-coefficients have been replaced by the constants.

$$D_y = \begin{vmatrix} a_1 & c_1 \\ a_2 & c_2 \end{vmatrix}$$ The y-coefficients have been replaced by the constants.

Then

$$x = \frac{D_x}{D} \quad \text{and} \quad y = \frac{D_y}{D} \quad \text{when } D \neq 0$$

Example 2 — **Solving a Two-Variable System**

< Objective 2 >

Use Cramer's rule to solve the system.

$$2x - 3y = 12$$
$$4x + 3y = 6$$

$$x = \frac{D_x}{D} = \frac{\begin{vmatrix} 12 & -3 \\ 6 & 3 \end{vmatrix}}{\begin{vmatrix} 2 & -3 \\ 4 & 3 \end{vmatrix}} = \frac{54}{18} = 3$$

$$y = \frac{D_y}{D} = \frac{\begin{vmatrix} 2 & 12 \\ 4 & 6 \end{vmatrix}}{\begin{vmatrix} 2 & -3 \\ 4 & 3 \end{vmatrix}} = \frac{-36}{18} = -2$$

NOTE

You should check the solution by substituting these values for x and y in the original system.

The solution for the system is $(3, -2)$.

Check Yourself 2

Use Cramer's rule to solve the system.

$$2x - 3y = 10$$
$$-x + 5y = -19$$

From our earlier work with systems we know that there are three possibilities for the solution of a linear system.

1. The system is *consistent* and has a unique solution.
2. The system is *inconsistent* and has no solutions.
3. The system is *dependent* and has an infinite number of solutions.

We will see how these cases are identified when using Cramer's rule.

1. If $D \neq 0$, the system is consistent.
2. If $D = 0$ and either $D_x \neq 0$ or $D_y \neq 0$, the system is inconsistent.
3. If $D = 0$ and both $D_x = 0$ and $D_y = 0$, the system is dependent.

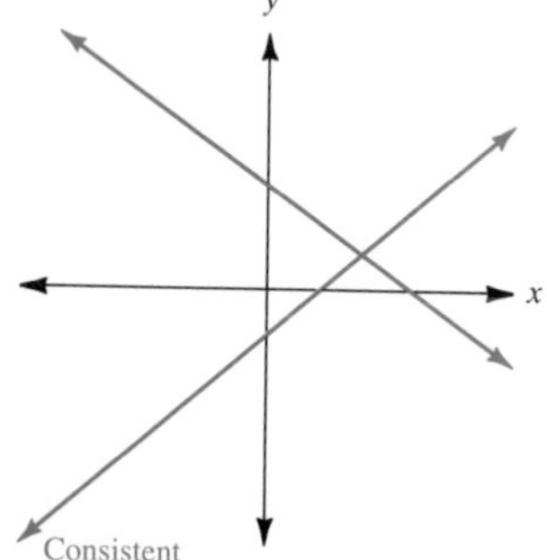

Consistent

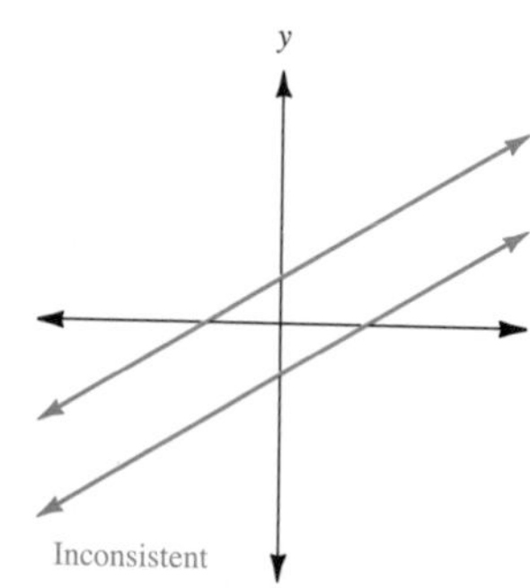

Inconsistent

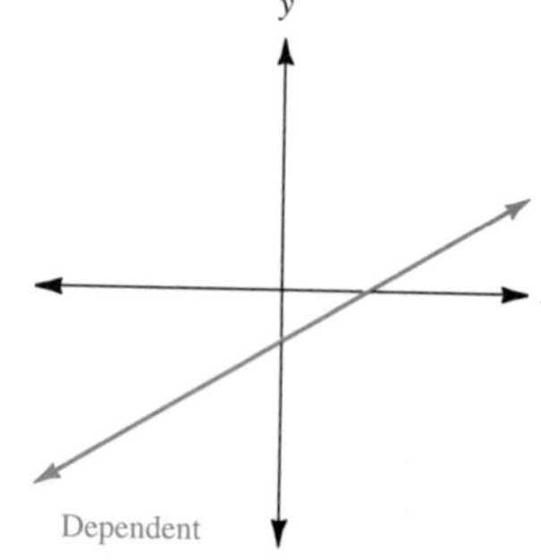

Dependent

Example 3 — Solving a Two-Variable System

Use Cramer's rule to solve the system.

$$2x - 3y = 4$$
$$-4x + 6y = 3$$

$$D = \begin{vmatrix} 2 & -3 \\ -4 & 6 \end{vmatrix} = 12 - 12 = 0$$

$$D_x = \begin{vmatrix} 4 & -3 \\ 3 & 6 \end{vmatrix} = 24 + 9 = 33$$

$$D_y = \begin{vmatrix} 2 & 4 \\ -4 & 3 \end{vmatrix} = 6 + 16 = 22$$

In applying Cramer's rule, we have

$$x = \frac{33}{0} \quad \text{and} \quad y = \frac{22}{0}$$

Because these values are undefined, no solution for the system exists and the system is inconsistent.

Check Yourself 3

Solve, using Cramer's rule.

$$\begin{aligned} x - 3y &= 5 \\ -2x + 6y &= 8 \end{aligned}$$

Example 4 Solving a Two-Variable System

Solve, using Cramer's rule.

$$\begin{aligned} x - 2y &= 4 \\ -2x + 4y &= -8 \end{aligned}$$

$$D = \begin{vmatrix} 1 & -2 \\ -2 & 4 \end{vmatrix} = 4 - 4 = 0$$

$$D_x = \begin{vmatrix} 4 & -2 \\ -8 & 4 \end{vmatrix} = 16 - 16 = 0$$

$$D_y = \begin{vmatrix} 1 & 4 \\ -2 & -8 \end{vmatrix} = -8 - (-8) = 0$$

Because $D = D_x = D_y = 0$, the system is dependent and has an infinite number of solutions, in this case all ordered pairs (x, y) satisfying the equation $x - 2y = 4$.

Check Yourself 4

Solve, using Cramer's rule.

$$\begin{aligned} 3x - y &= 2 \\ -6x + 2y &= -4 \end{aligned}$$

The use of second-order determinants to solve systems of equations is easily extendable to systems involving three unknowns, as we will now see.

To solve systems of three linear equations by determinants, we must first be able to evaluate a third-order determinant. To start, a third-order determinant is written in a similar fashion to that which we saw earlier and can be evaluated as follows:

$$\begin{vmatrix} a_1 & b_1 & c_1 \\ a_2 & b_2 & c_2 \\ a_3 & b_3 & c_3 \end{vmatrix} = a_1b_2c_3 + a_2b_3c_1 + a_3b_1c_2 - a_1b_3c_2 - a_2b_1c_3 - a_3b_2c_1$$

Even though this formula can always be used, it is rather awkward and difficult to remember. Fortunately, a more convenient pattern is available that allows us to evaluate a 3×3 determinant in terms of 2×2 determinants. This is called *expansion of the determinant by minors.*

Definition

Minor

The **minor** of an element in a 3×3 determinant is the 2×2 determinant remaining when the row and column to which the element belongs have been deleted. The diagram here will help you picture the definition.

NOTES

Delete the first row and the first column.

Delete the second row and the first column.

Delete the third row and the first column.

For a_1: $\begin{vmatrix} a_1 & b_1 & c_1 \\ a_2 & b_2 & c_2 \\ a_3 & b_3 & c_3 \end{vmatrix}$ The minor for a_1 is $\begin{vmatrix} b_2 & c_2 \\ b_3 & c_3 \end{vmatrix}$.

For a_2: $\begin{vmatrix} a_1 & b_1 & c_1 \\ a_2 & b_2 & c_2 \\ a_3 & b_3 & c_3 \end{vmatrix}$ The minor for a_2 is $\begin{vmatrix} b_1 & c_1 \\ b_3 & c_3 \end{vmatrix}$.

For a_3: $\begin{vmatrix} a_1 & b_1 & c_1 \\ a_2 & b_2 & c_2 \\ a_3 & b_3 & c_3 \end{vmatrix}$ The minor for a_3 is $\begin{vmatrix} b_1 & c_1 \\ b_2 & c_2 \end{vmatrix}$.

We can now evaluate a 3×3 determinant by using the three minors just defined. To expand about the first column:

1. Write the product of each element with its minor.
2. Connect those products with a $+ - +$ sign pattern.

NOTE

We will come back to this sign pattern later.

From these steps we have

$$\begin{vmatrix} a_1 & b_1 & c_1 \\ a_2 & b_2 & c_2 \\ a_3 & b_3 & c_3 \end{vmatrix} = a_1\begin{vmatrix} b_2 & c_2 \\ b_3 & c_3 \end{vmatrix} - a_2\begin{vmatrix} b_1 & c_1 \\ b_3 & c_3 \end{vmatrix} + a_3\begin{vmatrix} b_1 & c_1 \\ b_2 & c_2 \end{vmatrix}$$

This is called the *expansion* of a 3×3 determinant about the first column. Using our earlier definition of a 2×2 determinant, you can verify that this equation and our earlier equation for a third-order determinant are the same. However, the pattern of this equation is much easier to remember and is the most commonly used.

We will look at the evaluation of a 3×3 determinant, using this definition.

Example 5 Evaluating a 3 × 3 Determinant

Evaluate the determinant by expanding about the first column.

$$\downarrow$$
$$\begin{vmatrix} 1 & -3 & 2 \\ -4 & 0 & 3 \\ 2 & -1 & 3 \end{vmatrix}$$

First we write the three minors.

Element	Minor
1	$\begin{vmatrix} 0 & 3 \\ -1 & 3 \end{vmatrix}$
-4	$\begin{vmatrix} -3 & 2 \\ -1 & 3 \end{vmatrix}$
2	$\begin{vmatrix} -3 & 2 \\ 0 & 3 \end{vmatrix}$

Now we write the product of each element and its minor, and connect those products with the $+ - +$ sign pattern.

$$+\ 1\begin{vmatrix} 0 & 3 \\ -1 & 3 \end{vmatrix} - (-4)\begin{vmatrix} -3 & 2 \\ -1 & 3 \end{vmatrix} + 2\begin{vmatrix} -3 & 2 \\ 0 & 3 \end{vmatrix}$$

$+ - +$ pattern

$$= 1(3) + 4(-7) + 2(-9)$$
$$= 3 - 28 - 18$$
$$= -43$$

The value of the determinant is -43.

Check Yourself 5

Evaluate the determinant by expanding about the first column.

$$\begin{vmatrix} 1 & 3 & -2 \\ 2 & 0 & 1 \\ 4 & -1 & 1 \end{vmatrix}$$

NOTE

We simply place a + sign in the upper left-hand corner and then alternate signs in a checkerboard pattern.

A 3×3 determinant can actually be expanded in a similar fashion about *any row or column.* But first we need the following.

The *sign array* for a 3×3 determinant is given by

$$\begin{vmatrix} + & - & + \\ - & + & - \\ + & - & + \end{vmatrix}$$

Now to generalize our earlier approach:

1. Choose *any* row or column for the expansion.
2. Write the product of each element, in the row or column chosen, with its minor.
3. Connect those products with the appropriate sign pattern from the sign array.

How do we pick a row or column for the expansion? The value of the determinant will be the same in any case. However, the computation will be much easier if you can choose a row or column with one or more zeros.

We now will return to Example 5, expanded in a different manner in Example 6.

Example 6 Evaluating a 3 × 3 Determinant

Evaluate the determinant by expanding about the second row.

$$\rightarrow \begin{vmatrix} 1 & -3 & 2 \\ -4 & 0 & 3 \\ 2 & -1 & 3 \end{vmatrix}$$

The expansion is now

$$-(-4)\begin{vmatrix} -3 & 2 \\ -1 & 3 \end{vmatrix} + 0\begin{vmatrix} 1 & 2 \\ 2 & 3 \end{vmatrix} - 3\begin{vmatrix} 1 & -3 \\ 2 & -1 \end{vmatrix}$$

NOTE

Notice the − + − from the sign array for the second row.

$$= 4(-7) + 0(-1) - 3(5)$$
$$= -28 + 0 - 15 = -43$$

Of course, the result is the same as before. Note that in practice, the 0 makes it unnecessary to evaluate (or even write) the second minor. That is why the choice of the second row for the expansion is more efficient in this case.

Check Yourself 6

Evaluate the determinant by expanding about the second row.

$$\begin{vmatrix} 2 & 1 & 1 \\ 3 & 4 & 5 \\ -2 & 1 & -1 \end{vmatrix}$$

We are now ready to apply our work with 3 × 3 determinants to solving linear systems in three unknowns. Given the system

$$a_1x + b_1y + c_1z = d_1$$
$$a_2x + b_2y + c_2z = d_2$$
$$a_3x + b_3y + c_3z = d_3$$

let D be the determinant of the coefficients.

$$D = \begin{vmatrix} a_1 & b_1 & c_1 \\ a_2 & b_2 & c_2 \\ a_3 & b_3 & c_3 \end{vmatrix}$$

We form D_x by replacing the first column of D with the constants d_1, d_2, and d_3. Similarly D_y is formed by replacing the second column with the constants and D_z by replacing the third column with the constants. Then

$$D_x = \begin{vmatrix} d_1 & b_1 & c_1 \\ d_2 & b_2 & c_2 \\ d_3 & b_3 & c_3 \end{vmatrix} \qquad D_y = \begin{vmatrix} a_1 & d_1 & c_1 \\ a_2 & d_2 & c_2 \\ a_3 & d_3 & c_3 \end{vmatrix} \qquad \text{and} \qquad D_z = \begin{vmatrix} a_1 & b_1 & d_1 \\ a_2 & b_2 & d_2 \\ a_3 & b_3 & d_3 \end{vmatrix}$$

With these definitions, we can now extend Cramer's rule to the case of a system of three linear equations in three unknowns.

Property

Cramer's Rule

Given the system

$$a_1x + b_1y + c_1z = d_1$$
$$a_2x + b_2y + c_2z = d_2$$
$$a_3x + b_3y + c_3z = d_3$$

If $D \neq 0$, the solution for the system is given by

$$x = \frac{D_x}{D} \qquad y = \frac{D_y}{D} \qquad \text{and} \qquad z = \frac{D_z}{D}$$

If $D = 0$, the system will have either an infinite number of solutions or no solutions.

Example 7 Solving a Three-Variable System

Use Cramer's rule to solve the system.

$$\begin{aligned} x - 2y - 3z &= -8 \\ 2x + 3y + 2z &= 9 \\ -3x \qquad + 2z &= 2 \end{aligned}$$

We first calculate D, D_x, D_y, and D_z.

NOTE

We expand about row 3. Do you see why?

$$D = \begin{vmatrix} 1 & -2 & -3 \\ 2 & 3 & 2 \\ -3 & 0 & 2 \end{vmatrix}$$

$$= -3\begin{vmatrix} -2 & -3 \\ 3 & 2 \end{vmatrix} + 2\begin{vmatrix} 1 & -2 \\ 2 & 3 \end{vmatrix}$$

$$= (-3)(5) + 2(7)$$

$$= -15 + 14 = -1$$

NOTE

Again we expand about row 3.

$$D_x = \begin{vmatrix} -8 & -2 & -3 \\ 9 & 3 & 2 \\ 2 & 0 & 2 \end{vmatrix}$$

$$= 2\begin{vmatrix} -2 & -3 \\ 3 & 2 \end{vmatrix} + 2\begin{vmatrix} -8 & -2 \\ 9 & 3 \end{vmatrix}$$

$$= 2(5) + 2(-6)$$

$$= 10 - 12 = -2$$

NOTE

Here we expand about column 1.

$$D_y = \begin{vmatrix} 1 & -8 & -3 \\ 2 & 9 & 2 \\ -3 & 2 & 2 \end{vmatrix}$$

$$= 1\begin{vmatrix} 9 & 2 \\ 2 & 2 \end{vmatrix} - 2\begin{vmatrix} -8 & -3 \\ 2 & 2 \end{vmatrix} + (-3)\begin{vmatrix} -8 & -3 \\ 9 & 2 \end{vmatrix}$$

$$= 1(14) - 2(-10) - 3(11)$$

$$= 14 + 20 - 33 = 1$$

NOTE

We expand about column 2.

$$D_z = \begin{vmatrix} 1 & -2 & -8 \\ 2 & 3 & 9 \\ -3 & 0 & 2 \end{vmatrix}$$

$$= -(-2)\begin{vmatrix} 2 & 9 \\ -3 & 2 \end{vmatrix} + 3\begin{vmatrix} 1 & -8 \\ -3 & 2 \end{vmatrix}$$

$$= 2(31) + 3(-22)$$

$$= 62 - 66 = -4$$

We can now find x, y, and z.

NOTE

The solution should be verified by substitution as before.

$$x = \frac{D_x}{D} = \frac{-2}{-1} = 2$$

$$y = \frac{D_y}{D} = \frac{1}{-1} = -1$$

$$z = \frac{D_z}{D} = \frac{-4}{-1} = 4$$

The solution for the system is $(2, -1, 4)$.

Check Yourself 7

Use Cramer's rule to solve the system.

$$\begin{aligned} x + y + z &= 7 \\ 2x - y + z &= 5 \\ x + 2y - 3z &= -3 \end{aligned}$$

NOTE

Some of these rules for simplification are suggested in exercises 35 through 43.

Note: The technique shown in this section for evaluating a 3×3 determinant can be used to evaluate a determinant of any order. Also, there are rules for simplifying determinants *before* the expansion that are particularly helpful when working with higher-order determinants.

Check Yourself ANSWERS

1. **(a)** 19; **(b)** -1 **2.** $(-1, -4)$ **3.** No real solution (inconsistent system) **4.** An infinite number of solutions (dependent system) **5.** 11 **6.** -14 **7.** $(2, 2, 3)$

Basic Skills | Advanced Skills | Vocational-Technical Applications | Calculator/Computer | Above and Beyond

App. exercises

MathZone

Boost your grade at mathzone.com!
> Practice Problems
> NetTutor
> Self-Tests
> e-Professors
> Videos

Name ________

Section ________ Date ________

< Objective 1 >

Evaluate each of the determinants.

1. $\begin{vmatrix} 3 & 4 \\ 1 & 2 \end{vmatrix}$

2. $\begin{vmatrix} 1 & -4 \\ 5 & 2 \end{vmatrix}$

3. $\begin{vmatrix} -2 & 3 \\ 4 & -6 \end{vmatrix}$

4. $\begin{vmatrix} -5 & 2 \\ 0 & 0 \end{vmatrix}$

5. $\begin{vmatrix} 9 & 7 \\ -1 & 8 \end{vmatrix}$

6. $\begin{vmatrix} 5 & -8 \\ -7 & 12 \end{vmatrix}$

< Objective 2 >

Use Cramer's rule to find the unique solution for each of the linear systems, or state whether the system is inconsistent or dependent.

7. $\begin{aligned} x + 5y &= 15 \\ x - y &= 3 \end{aligned}$

8. $\begin{aligned} 2x - 3y &= 9 \\ 2x + 5y &= -23 \end{aligned}$

9. $\begin{aligned} 4x + y &= -1 \\ -3x - 2y &= 2 \end{aligned}$

10. $\begin{aligned} x + 2y &= 7 \\ -2x - 4y &= -10 \end{aligned}$

> Videos

11. $\begin{aligned} 2x + 3y &= 8 \\ -5x + 6y &= -11 \end{aligned}$

12. $\begin{aligned} x - 5y &= 7 \\ -2x + 10y &= -14 \end{aligned}$

13. $\begin{aligned} 5x - 2y &= 0 \\ 4x + 3y &= 0 \end{aligned}$

14. $\begin{aligned} 5x - 8y &= 3 \\ 4x + 3y &= 2 \end{aligned}$

15. $\begin{aligned} 5x - 2y &= 1 \\ x &= 3 \end{aligned}$

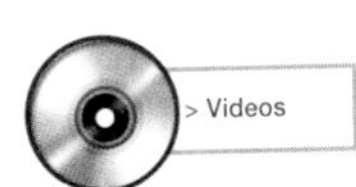

16. $\begin{aligned} 6x + 5y &= 5 \\ 3x - 4y &= 2 \end{aligned}$

Given the determinant

$$\begin{vmatrix} 2 & 3 & -5 \\ 1 & 5 & 6 \\ -3 & 4 & 7 \end{vmatrix}$$

Find the value of the minor of each of the indicated elements.

17. 2

18. -5

Answers

1. 2
2. 22
3. 0
4. 0
5. 79
6. 4
7. (5, 2)
8. $\left(-\frac{3}{2}, -4\right)$
9. (0, –1)
10. Inconsistent
11. $\left(3, \frac{2}{3}\right)$
12. Dependent
13. (0, 0)
14. $\left(\frac{25}{47}, -\frac{2}{47}\right)$
15. (3, 7)
16. $\left(\frac{10}{13}, \frac{1}{13}\right)$
17. 11
18. 19

Answers

19. −1
20. 7
21. 43
22. 17
23. 12
24. 32
25. 44
26. 0
27. −13
28. (1, 2, −3)
29. (2, −1, −5)
30. $\left(0, 1, -\frac{2}{3}\right)$
31. $\left(2, \frac{3}{2}, -2\right)$
32. $\left(9, -\frac{3}{2}, \frac{6}{5}\right)$
33. 3
34. −1, 3

19. 5

20. 7

21. −3

22. 4

Use expansion by minors to evaluate each of the determinants.

23. $\begin{vmatrix} 1 & 0 & -1 \\ 2 & 1 & 3 \\ 1 & -2 & 1 \end{vmatrix}$

24. $\begin{vmatrix} 3 & 2 & 0 \\ -1 & 2 & 0 \\ 1 & 1 & 4 \end{vmatrix}$

25. $\begin{vmatrix} 4 & 2 & 1 \\ 0 & 1 & 3 \\ 0 & -2 & 5 \end{vmatrix}$

26. $\begin{vmatrix} 2 & 1 & 2 \\ 3 & 2 & 4 \\ 5 & -2 & -4 \end{vmatrix}$

27. $\begin{vmatrix} 1 & 3 & 1 \\ 5 & 2 & 7 \\ 1 & 3 & 2 \end{vmatrix}$

Solve each of the systems by using Cramer's rule.

28.
$$\begin{aligned} x + 2y + z &= 2 \\ x + 2z &= -5 \\ x + 3y &= 7 \end{aligned}$$

29.
$$\begin{aligned} x - z &= 7 \\ 2x + y &= 3 \\ x - 2z &= 12 \end{aligned}$$

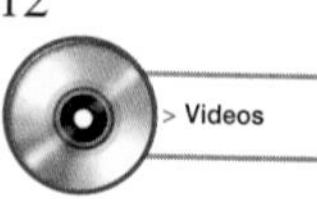

30.
$$\begin{aligned} 2x - y + 3z &= -3 \\ x + 4y - 6z &= 8 \\ 3x - 2y + 3z &= -4 \end{aligned}$$

31.
$$\begin{aligned} x + 4y - 3z &= 14 \\ 2x - 2y + z &= -1 \\ -3x + 6y + z &= 1 \end{aligned}$$

32.
$$\begin{aligned} x + 4y + 5z &= 9 \\ -2x - 8y + 5z &= 0 \\ -x + 4y + 10z &= -3 \end{aligned}$$

Basic Skills | Advanced Skills | Vocational-Technical Applications | Calculator/Computer | **Above and Beyond**

Introducing a variable in the entries of a determinant allows us to write an equation in determinant form. Solve each of the equations for x.

33. $\begin{vmatrix} 3x & 5x \\ 2 & 4 \end{vmatrix} = 6$

34. $\begin{vmatrix} x & 2 \\ x & x \end{vmatrix} = 3$

35. Evaluate the determinant.

$$\begin{vmatrix} 2 & -3 & 2 \\ 0 & 0 & 0 \\ 1 & 3 & -3 \end{vmatrix}$$

36. What do you observe from the results of exercise 35?

37. Evaluate the determinant.

$$\begin{vmatrix} 3 & 0 & 0 \\ 0 & 2 & 0 \\ 0 & 0 & 4 \end{vmatrix}$$

38. What do you observe from the results of exercise 37?
If the entries of the determinant are 0 everywhere but on the main diagonal from upper left to lower right, the determinant is the product of the entries along the main diagonal.

39. Evaluate the determinant.

$$\begin{vmatrix} 1 & 2 & 3 \\ 0 & -1 & 2 \\ 2 & 4 & 6 \end{vmatrix}$$

40. What do you observe from the results of exercise 39?
When a row (or column) is a multiple of another row (or column), the value of the determinant is 0.

41. Evaluate each of the determinants.

(a) $\begin{vmatrix} 2 & 4 & 6 \\ -1 & 0 & 3 \\ 1 & 2 & 1 \end{vmatrix}$ (b) $2\begin{vmatrix} 1 & 2 & 3 \\ -1 & 0 & 3 \\ 1 & 2 & 1 \end{vmatrix}$

42. What do you observe from the results of exercise 41?
If a row (or column) has a common factor, that number can be factored out of the row (or column).

43. Use your observation from Exercises 41 and 42 to simplify your work in evaluating the following determinant.

$$\begin{vmatrix} 1 & 3 & 5 \\ 1 & 6 & -2 \\ 4 & 12 & 8 \end{vmatrix}$$

Answers

35. 0

36. A row (or column) of zeros results in a determinant of 0.

37. 24

38. See exercise

39. 0

40. See exercise

41. (a) −8; (b) −8

42. See exercise

43. −36

Answers

44. (a) 4; (b) $-\frac{5}{3}$, 1

45. $2x + 3y = 18$

46. See exercise

44. Solve each of the equations for x.

(a) $\begin{vmatrix} x & 0 & -1 \\ 1 & 2 & 0 \\ -2 & 1 & 1 \end{vmatrix} = 3$

(b) $\begin{vmatrix} 1 & x & -2 \\ x & 1 & 2 \\ 1 & 0 & -3 \end{vmatrix} = 4$

45. Expand the determinant about row 1 to write an equation in x and y.

$$\begin{vmatrix} x & y & 1 \\ 3 & 4 & 1 \\ 6 & 2 & 1 \end{vmatrix} = 0$$

46. Write the equation of the line passing through the points with coordinates (3, 4) and (6, 2). Compare your results with that of exercise 45. What do you observe?

$2x + 3y - 18 = 0$. The equation of exercise 45 gives the line passing through (3, 4) and (6, 2).

Answers

1. 2 **3.** 0 **5.** 79 **7.** (5, 2) **9.** (0, −1) **11.** $\left(3, \frac{2}{3}\right)$
13. (0, 0) **15.** (3, 7) **17.** 11 **19.** −1 **21.** 43 **23.** 12
25. 44 **27.** −13 **29.** (2, −1, −5) **31.** $\left(2, \frac{3}{2}, -2\right)$ **33.** 3
35. 0 **37.** 24 **39.** 0 **41.** **(a)** −8; **(b)** −8 **43.** −36
45. $2x + 3y = 18$

Answers to Pretests, Reading Your Text, Summary Exercises, Self-Tests, and Cumulative Reviews

Pretest for Chapter 1

1. $\mathbb{Z}, \mathbb{Q}, \mathbb{R}$ **2.** $\mathbb{Q}', \mathbb{R}$ **3.** $\mathbb{Q}, \mathbb{R}$ **4.** $\mathbb{Q}, \mathbb{R}$ **5.** 0
6. 75 **7.** 12.25 **8.** -26 **9.** -4 **10.** -73
11. $2(n + 3)$ **12.** $\frac{2x}{z}$ **13.** -4 0
14. -7 **15.** 6 **16.** 15 **17.** $3x^2 - 8y$ **18.** $1.8m + 15$
19. $-5y$ **20.** 1 **21.** $\frac{1}{a^3}$ **22.** 0.00005

Reading Your Text

Section 1.1 **(a)** ratio; **(b)** irrational; **(c)** real; **(d)** element, member
Section 1.2 **(a)** binary; **(b)** quotient; **(c)** left, right; **(d)** addition
Section 1.3 **(a)** less than; **(b)** true; **(c)** compound; **(d)** absolute value
Section 1.4 **(a)** variable; **(b)** numerical; **(c)** like; **(d)** distributive
Section 1.5 **(a)** factor; **(b)** one; **(c)** add; **(d)** scientific notation

Summary Exercises for Chapter 1

1. $\mathbb{Z}, \mathbb{Q}, \mathbb{R}$ **3.** $\mathbb{Q}', \mathbb{R}$ **5.** $\mathbb{Q}', \mathbb{R}$ **7.** $\mathbb{Q}, \mathbb{R}$
9. 0 1 4 7
11. $-\frac{2}{3}$ 0 $\frac{5}{3}$ $\frac{7}{3}$
13. -11 **15.** 0 **17.** -18 **19.** -4 **21.** -5
23. 17 **25.** 0 **27.** 3 **29.** -70 **31.** 45 **33.** 0
35. $-\frac{3}{2}$ **37.** 5 **39.** 9 **41.** -4 **43.** $a + 4$
45. $w - 8$ **47.** $2(n - 2)$ **49.** $\frac{x + y}{3}$ **51.** 17 **53.** 17
55. 32 **57.** 112 **59.** Additive inverse
61. Associative property of addition
63. Associative property of multiplication
65. Additive identity **67.** 0 3
69. 0 $\frac{7}{2}$
71. -3 0 6 **73.** 9 **75.** -3
77. 8 **79.** -7 **81.** -7 **83.** 15 **85.** 19 **87.** 25
89. 1 **91.** -3 **93.** $4a^3, -3a^2$ **95.** $5m^2, -4m^2, m^2$
97. $12c$ **99.** $-3a$ **101.** $-3x + 10$ **103.** $19a + b$
105. $3x^3 + 9x^2$ **107.** b^5, base b, exponent 5 **109.** w^{11}
111. $x^{10}y^6$ **113.** a^6 **115.** m^8n^4 **117.** $4b^{10}$
119. $\frac{8a^6b^{12}}{c^9}$ **121.** 1 **123.** 6 **125.** $\frac{1}{x^5}$ **127.** $\frac{1}{10^4}$
129. $\frac{1}{x^2}$ **131.** a^5 **133.** $\frac{9}{m^6}$ **135.** 1.5×10^{11} m
137. 6.2×10^{-5} m **139.** 3.12×10^{25} **141.** 1.2×10^{-28}

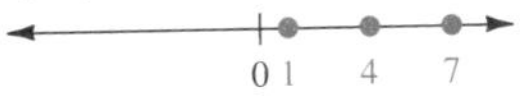

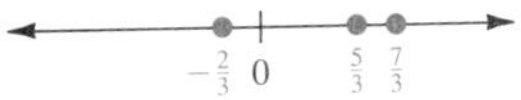

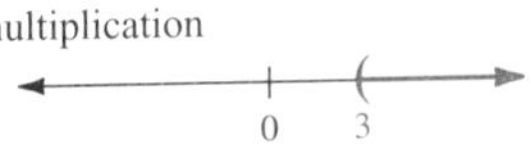

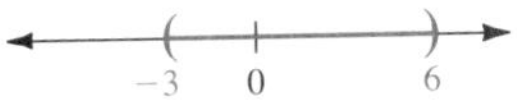

Self-Test for Chapter 1

[1.1] **1.** **(a)** 9; **(b)** $-6, 0, 9$; **(c)** $-6, -\frac{2}{3}, 4.1, 0, 9, \frac{5}{4}, 0.\overline{78}$; **(d)** $-\sqrt{3}, \pi$; **(e)** All are real numbers. **[1.2]** **2.** $2(x + y)$
3. $\frac{p - 8}{t}$ **4.** 47 **5.** -48
6. Associative property of addition **7.** Distributive property
[1.3] **8.** -5 0
9. -1 0 4 **10.** -3 **11.** 2
[1.4] **12.** -4 **13.** $21a + 13$ **14.** $-\frac{1}{3}x$ **[1.5]** **15.** $15x^3y^7$
16. $4ab^3$ **17.** $\frac{4w^4}{9t^6}$ **18.** $16x^{18}y^{17}$ **19.** 1 **20.** 6
21. $\frac{3}{b^7}$ **22.** $\frac{1}{y^4}$ **23.** 3.12×10^{-10}

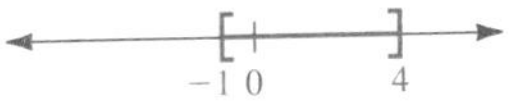

Pretest for Chapter 2

1. $x = 3$ **2.** $x = 1$ **3.** $x = -7$ **4.** $x = 1$ **5.** $x = \frac{c - by}{a}$
6. $b = \frac{2A}{h}$ **7.** Dane: \$1,280, Alicia: \$1,410 **8.** 12 cm
9. 42, 43 **10.** $x \geq -3$ -3 0
11. $x > 2$ 0 2 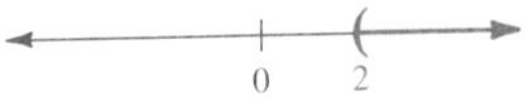
12. $x > 5$ 0 5
13. $-2 \leq x < 2$ -2 0 2
14. $x = -2$ or $x = 3$ **15.** $x = 0$ or $x = 2$
16. $x \leq -\frac{3}{2}$ or $x \geq 3$ **17.** $-2 < x < \frac{9}{2}$

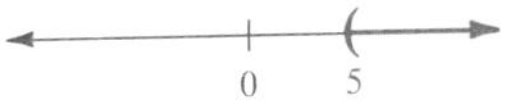

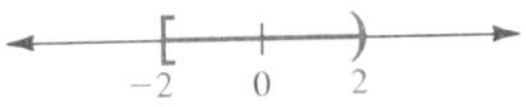

Reading Your Text

Section 2.1 **(a)** $ax + b = 0$; **(b)** equivalent; **(c)** identity; **(d)** contradiction
Section 2.2 **(a)** formulas, literal equations; **(b)** linear; **(c)** isolate; **(d)** variable
Section 2.3 **(a)** algorithm; **(b)** variable; **(c)** break-even; **(d)** $x + 1$
Section 2.4 **(a)** reversing; **(b)** bracket; **(c)** multiplication; **(d)** double, compound
Section 2.5 **(a)** two; **(b)** isolate; **(c)** compound; **(d)** $y, -y$

Summary Exercises for Chapter 2

1. $x = 7$ **3.** $x = \frac{1}{2}$ **5.** $x = 4$ **7.** $x = 4$ **9.** $x = 8$
11. $x = 6$ **13.** $x = 6$ **15.** $x = 12$ **17.** $x = 3$
19. $R = \frac{P}{B}$ **21.** $h = \frac{S}{2\pi r}$ **23.** $m = \frac{y - b}{x}$ **25.** 4 yr
27. 8% **29.** 3 h at 28 mi/h, 2 h at 24 mi/h **31.** 2:00 P.M.
33. $x > 4, (4, \infty)$
35. $x \geq \frac{2}{3}, \left[\frac{2}{3}, \infty\right)$
37. $x < -5, (-\infty, -5)$
39. $x \leq 1, (-\infty, 1]$
41. $x \geq 2, [2, \infty)$
43. $x < 7, (-\infty, 7)$
45. $-2 < x < 2, (-2, 2)$
47. $-1 \leq x \leq 4, [-1, 4]$
49. $x < -2$ or $x > \frac{8}{3}, (-\infty, -2) \cup \left(\frac{8}{3}, \infty\right)$
51. $x = -8, x = 2$ **53.** $x = 4, x = 10$ **55.** $x = -5, x = 4$
57. $x = -1, x = 3$
59. $-3 \leq x \leq 3, [-3, 3]$
61. $x < 3$ or $x > 11, (-\infty, 3) \cup (11, \infty)$
63. $x < -6$ or $x > -1, (-\infty, -6) \cup (-1, \infty)$
65. $-5 < x < \frac{7}{3}, \left(-5, \frac{7}{3}\right)$
67. $x \leq -6$ or $x \geq 9, (-\infty, -6] \cup [9, \infty)$
69. $-7 < x < 8, (-7, 8)$

Self-Test for Chapter 2

[2.1] 1. $x = \frac{4}{5}$ **2.** $x = 2$ **3.** $x = 2$ **4.** $x = \frac{3}{2}$
[2.2] 5. $r = \frac{A - P}{Pt}$ **6.** $h = \frac{2A}{B + b}$ **[2.3] 7.** 3:30 P.M.
8. 800 flashlights
[2.4] 9. $x \leq 4, (-\infty, 4]$
10. $x > \frac{17}{2}, \left(\frac{17}{2}, \infty\right)$
11. $x > 1, (1, \infty)$
12. $-2 \leq x \leq 4, [-2, 4]$
[2.5] 13. $x = -\frac{2}{3}, x = 4$ **14.** $x = \frac{2}{3}, x = 4$
15. $-\frac{3}{2} < x < 3$ **16.** $x \leq -2$ or $x \geq \frac{9}{2}$

Cumulative Review for Chapters 1–2

[1.1] 1. (a) 3, 5; **(b)** −7, −5, 0, 3, 5 **[1.2] 2.** $\frac{p - 5}{s}$
3. Associative property of addition **4.** 25 **[1.3] 5.** −14
6. (number line) **[1.4] 7.** $3x + 3$
[1.5] 8. (a) x^6y^{10}; **(b)** $\frac{y^8}{x}$ **9.** 4.37×10^9 **[2.1] 10.** $c = \frac{5}{2}$
11. $t = \frac{21}{2}$ **12.** $y = \frac{78}{7}$ **[2.2] 13.** $B = \frac{2A - hb}{h}$
14. $p = \frac{4y - 12}{7}$ **[2.3] 15.** $3\frac{2}{3}$ h **16.** 30 mi
[2.4] 17. $x < -7, (-\infty, -7)$
18. $2 \leq x \leq 5, [2, 5]$
[2.5] 19. $x = 1, x = 7$ **20.** All real numbers
21. $x < 0$ or $x > 5$ **22.** $-10 \leq x \leq -2$

Pretest for Chapter 3

1.

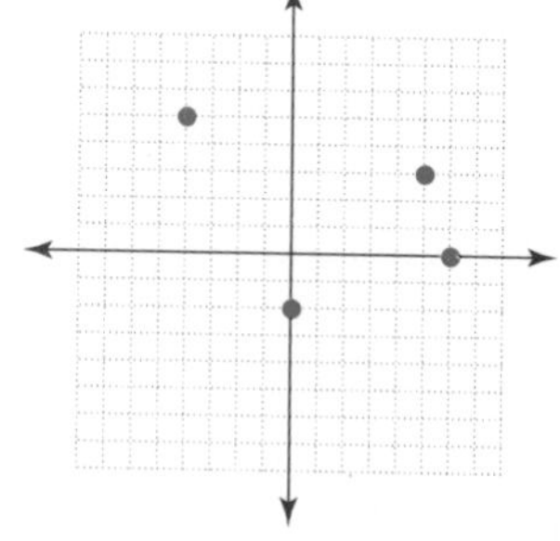

2. Answers will vary; sample: (0, −2), (3, 0), (6, 2)

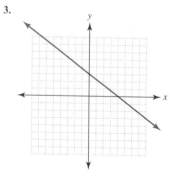

3.

4. (a) 2; **(b)** 5; **(c)** $\frac{5}{4}$
5. Function; D: $\mathbb{R}$; R: $\{y \mid y \leq 2\}$

6.

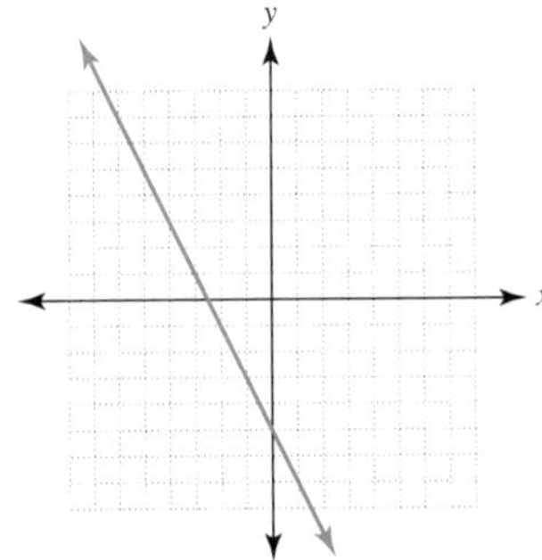
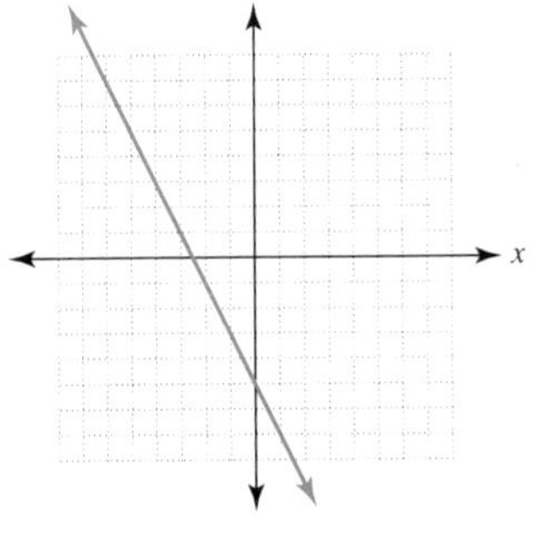

7. Parallel

8.

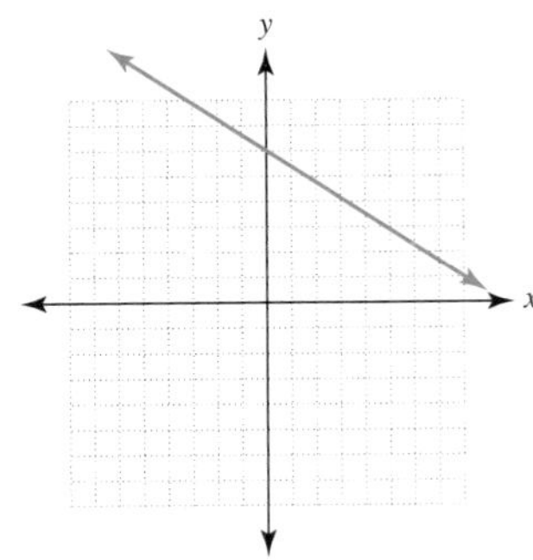

9. $x = 3$
10. $y = 2x - 8$

11.

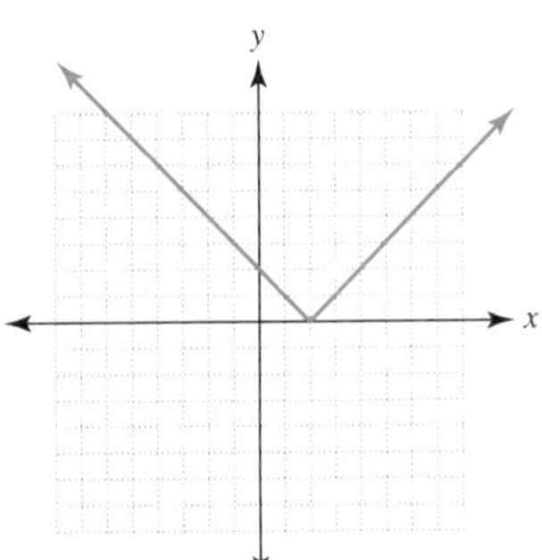

12.

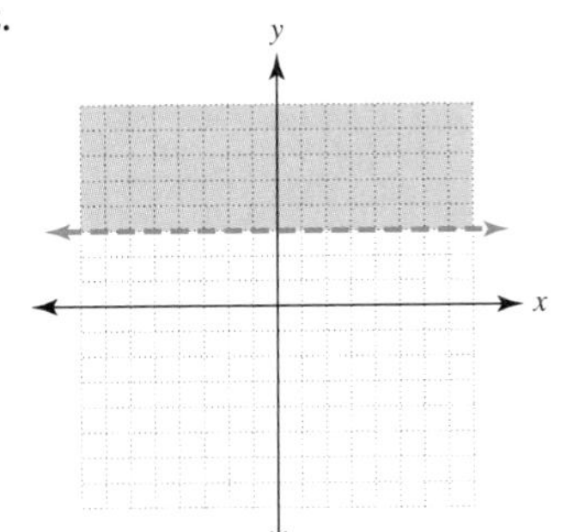

Reading Your Text

Section 3.1 **(a)** x-coordinate; y-coordinate; **(b)** graph of the equation; **(c)** standard form for a linear equation; **(d)** vertical line; horizontal line

Section 3.2 **(a)** vertical line test; **(b)** set-builder; **(c)** function; **(d)** independent variable; dependent variable

Section 3.3 **(a)** slope; **(b)** horizontal change; vertical change; **(c)** the same; **(d)** perpendicular

Section 3.4 **(a)** standard form for a linear equation; **(b)** slope-intercept form; **(c)** point-slope form; **(d)** a point (on the line); the slope (of the line)

Section 3.5 **(a)** $|x|$; **(b)** boundary line; **(c)** dashed; **(d)** origin

Summary Exercises for Chapter 3

1. (a) and (d)
3. 5. 7. 9.

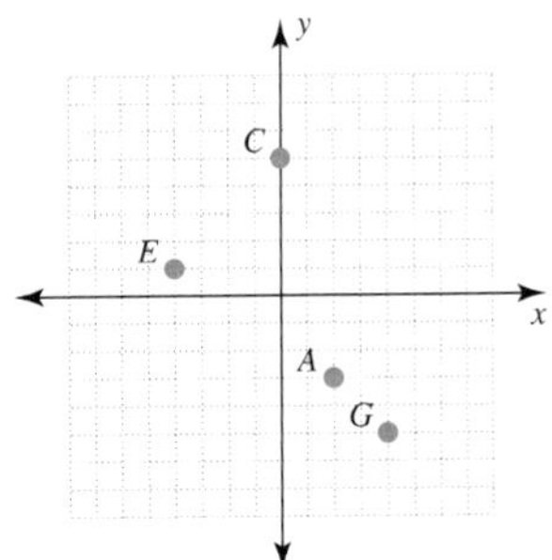

11. (2, 2) 13. (2, 0)
15. (−4, 1) 17. (0, 7)
19. Answers may vary; sample: (0, −8), (1, −6), (2, −4)
21. Answers may vary; sample: (1, 2), (3, 1), (5, 0)

23.

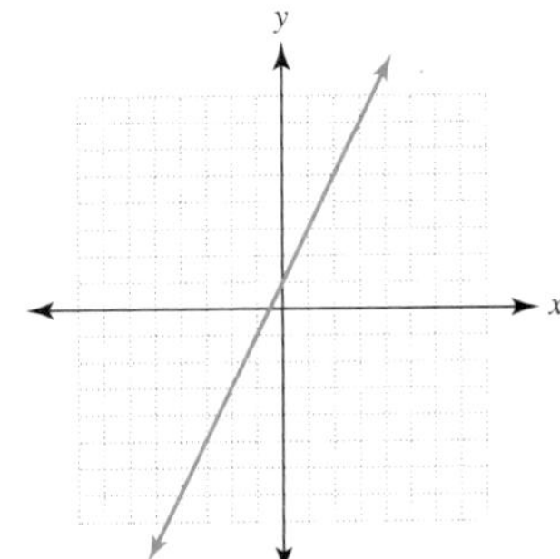

25.

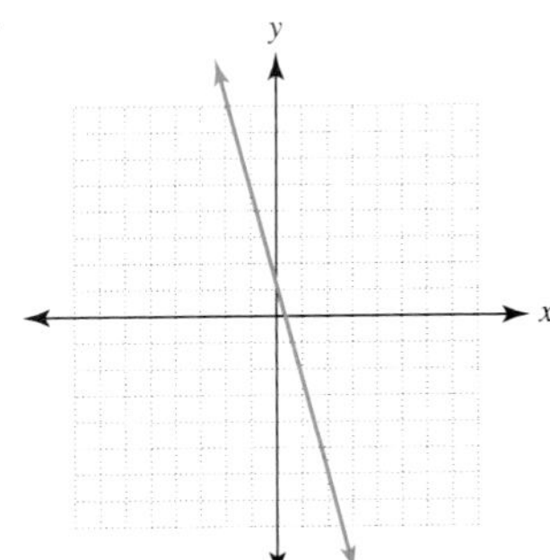

27. x-int: (6, 0), y-int: (0, 2)

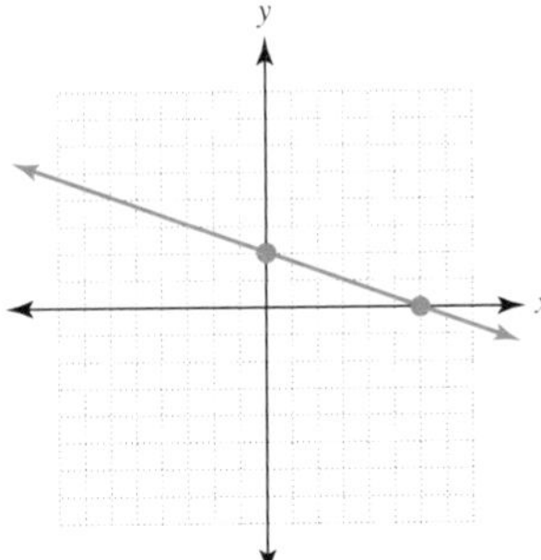

29. x-int: (4, 0), y-int: (0, 6)

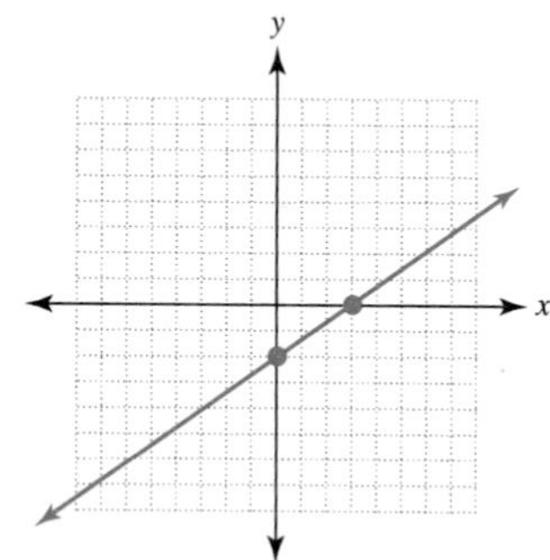

31. x-int: (3, 0), y-int: (0, −2)

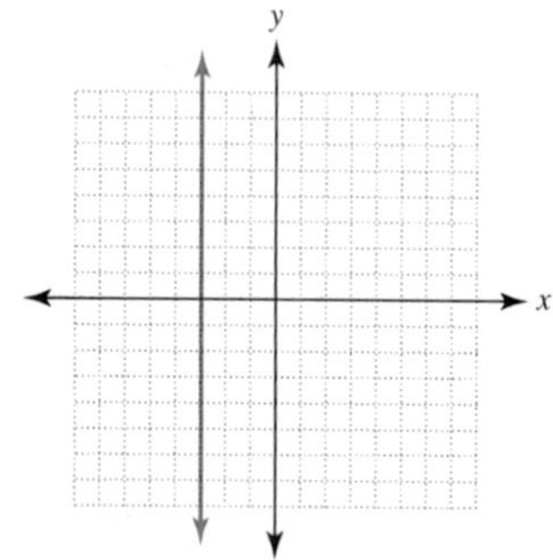

33. x-int: (−3, 0), y-int: none

35. D: {Dean Smith, John Wooden, Denny Crum, Bob Knight}, R: {65, 47, 42, 41} **37.** D: {1, 3, 4, 7, 8}, R: {1, 2, 3, 5, 6} **39.** D: {1}, R: {3, 5, 7, 9, 10} **41.** **(a)** 5; **(b)** 9; **(c)** 3.75 **43.** **(a)** 5; **(b)** $\frac{45}{8}$; **(c)** 5 **45.** **(a)** 9; **(b)** 1; **(c)** $-\frac{1}{16}$ **47.** Function **49.** Not a function **51.** Function; D: $\mathbb{R}$; R: $\{y \mid y \geq -4\}$ **53.** Not a function; D: $\{x \mid -6 \leq x \leq 6\}$; R: $\{y \mid -6 \leq y \leq 6\}$ **55.** A: (3, 4); B: (0, −2) **57.** A: (3, 6); B: (0, 1) **59.** **(a)** −2; **(b)** 0; **(c)** 2 **61.** **(a)** 1; **(b)** −3; **(c)** 1 **63.** **(a)** 3; **(b)** 0; **(c)** −3 **65.** **(a)** −2, 2; **(b)** −2.2, 2.2; **(c)** −2.5, 2.5 **67.** x-int: (7, 0), y-int: (0, 7) **69.** x-int: (6, 0), y-int: (0, 4) **71.** x-int: (2, 0) and (4, 0), y-int: (0, 8) **73.** x-int: (−5, 0) and (5, 0), y-int: (0, −5) and (0, 5) **75.** −2 **77.** $\frac{2}{3}$ **79.** 0 **81.** Undefined **83.** $\frac{1}{4}$ **85.** Perpendicular **87.** Parallel **89.** $y = -3$ **91.** $x = 4$ **93.** $y = -3$ **95.** $y = -\frac{4}{3}x - 2$ **97.** $x = -\frac{5}{2}$ **99.** $m = \frac{4}{3}$; y-int: (0, −4) **101.** $m = -\frac{1}{3}$; y-int: (0, 3) **103.** $y = -\frac{1}{5}x + 4$ **105.** $y = -\frac{5}{4}x + 2$ **107.** $y = -\frac{5}{3}x + 3$ **109.** $y = \frac{4}{3}x + \frac{14}{3}$ **111.** $C = 250 + 15h$

113.

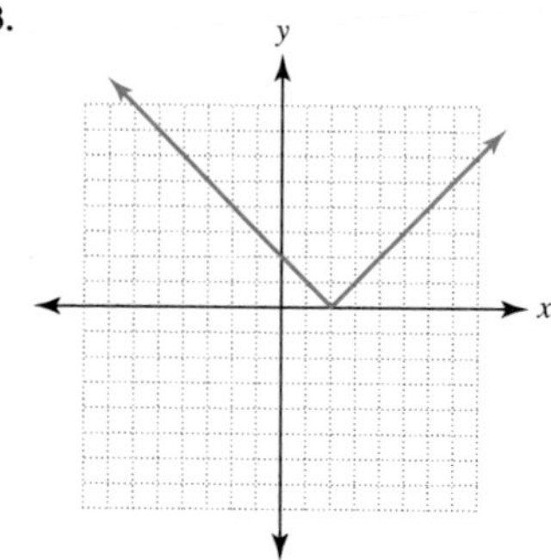

115.

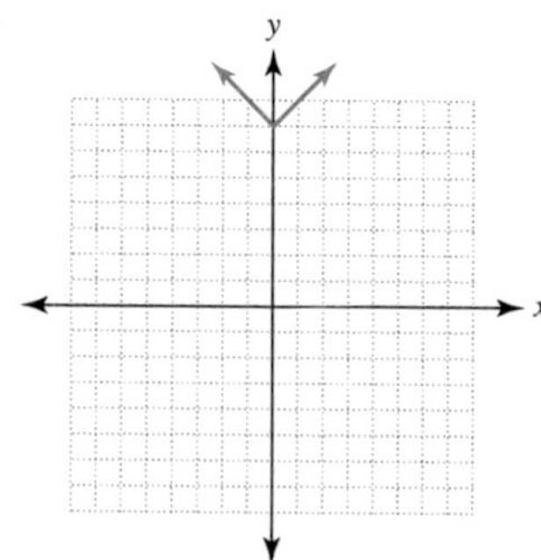

117.

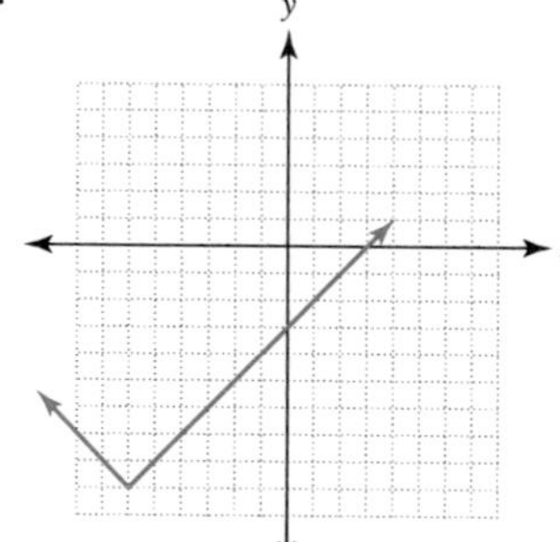

119.

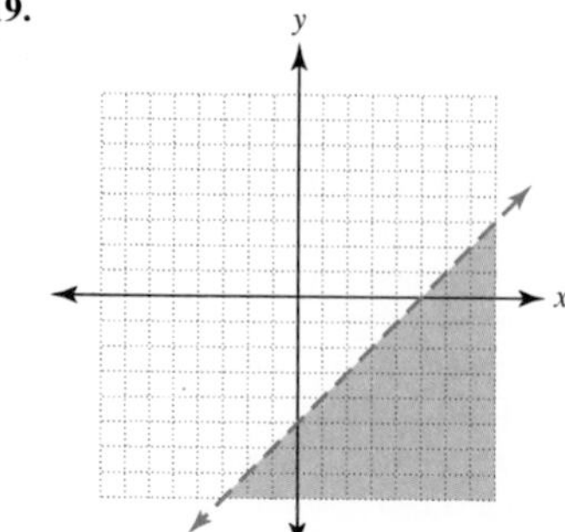

121.

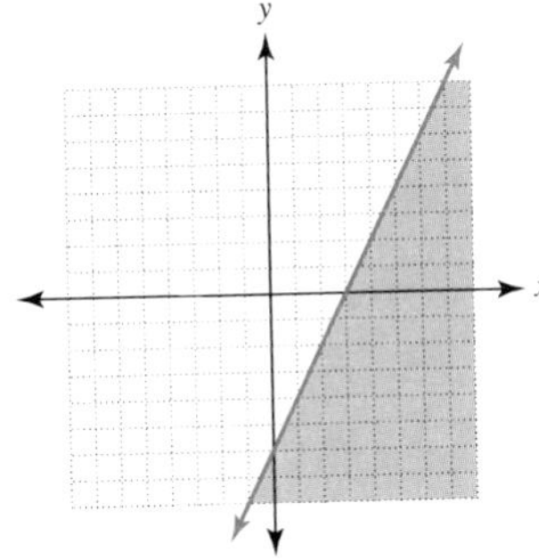

123.

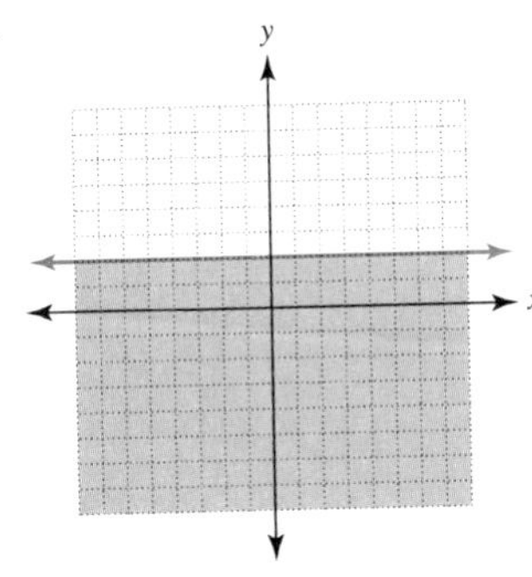

Self-Test for Chapter 3

[3.1] 1. **(b)** **2.**

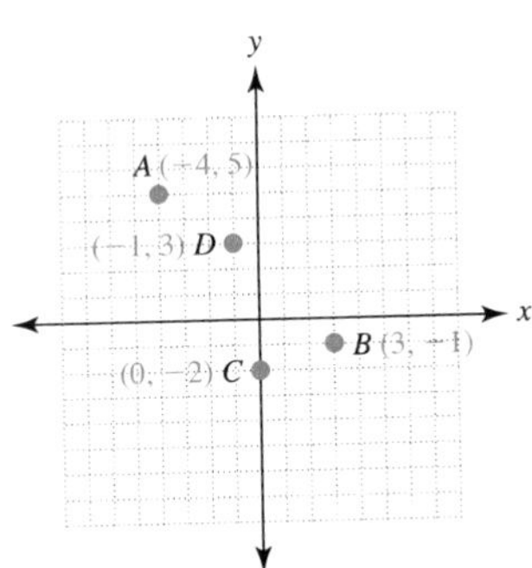

3. x-int: (6, 0), y-int: (0, 5)

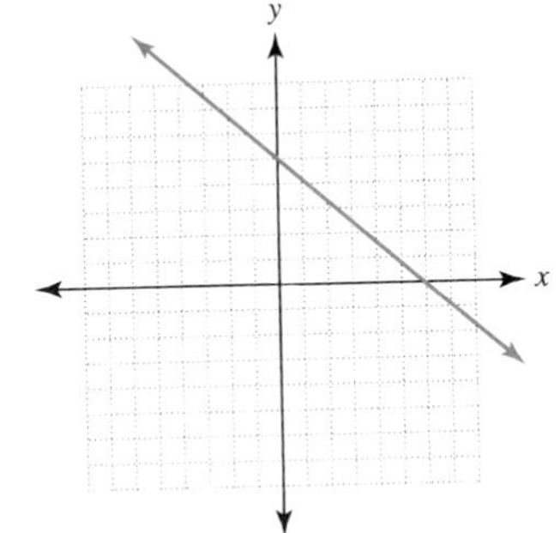

4. x-int: (3, 0), y-int: none

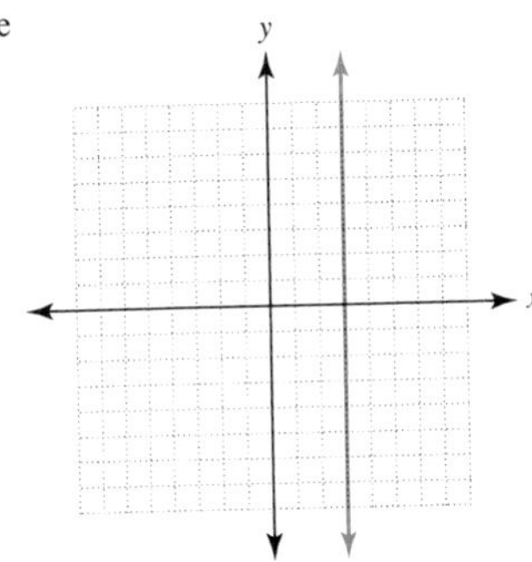

[3.2] 5. **(a)** D: $\{-3, 1, 2, 3, 4\}$, R: $\{-2, 0, 1, 5, 6\}$ **(b)** D: {United States, Germany, Russia, China}, R: {101, 65, 63, 50}
6. **(a)** 6; **(b)** 12; **(c)** 2 **7.** **(a)** 2; **(b)** −5 **8.** Function
9. Not a function **10.** A: (1, 0); B: (−3, −4)
11. A: (−4, −2); B: (1, 2) **12.** **(a)** 3; **(b)** 4; **(c)** 5
13. **(a)** −3; **(b)** −2; **(c)** 0 **14.** **(a)** 0; **(b)** 1; **(c)** 2
15. **(a)** 0; **(b)** −2, 2; **(c)** −4, 4
16. x-int: (−1, 0) and (5, 0), y-int: (0, −5)
17. x-int: (5, 0), y-int: (0, −5)
18. D: $\{x \mid -7 \le x \le 7\}$ R: $\{y \mid -7 \le y \le 7\}$
19. D: $\mathbb{R}$, R: $\{y \mid y \le 9\}$ **[3.3] 20.** 2 **21.** Undefined **22.** 0
23. $-\frac{2}{5}$ **24.** Undefined **25.** 0 **26.** Neither
27. Perpendicular **28.** Parallel **[3.4] 29.** $y = 2x - 1$
30. $y = \frac{2}{3}x - 4$ **31.** $y = -3x - 1$ **32.** $y = 4x - 2$
33. $y = \frac{2}{3}x + 3$ **34.** $C = 2.4m + 2.05$
[3.5] 35.

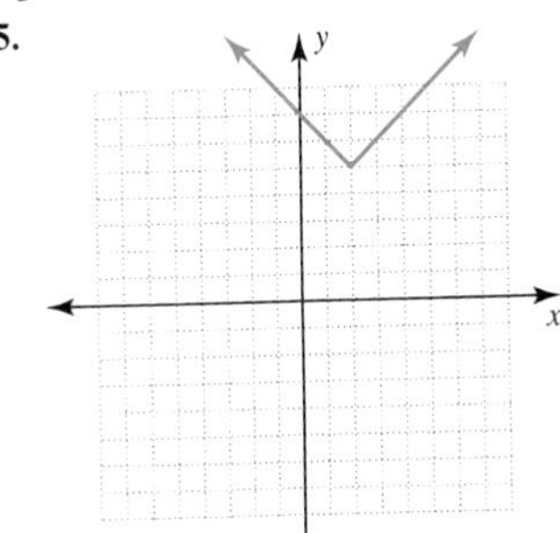

36.

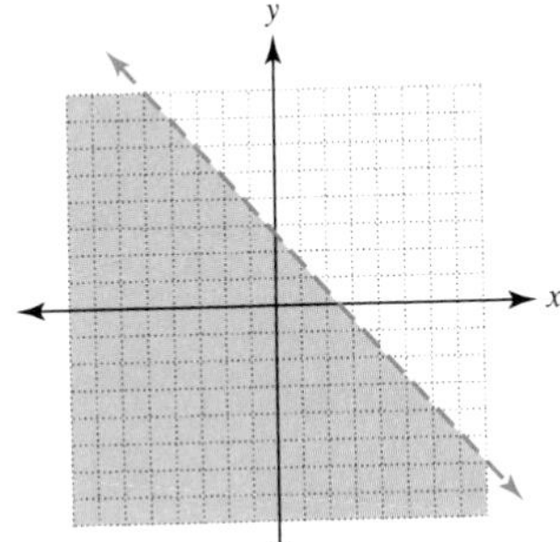

Cumulative Review for Chapters 1–3

[1.2] 1. Associative property of multiplication **2.** Commutative property of addition **3.** Distributive property

[1.3] 4. −2 0

5. −3 0 4 **[2.1] 6.** $c = \frac{5}{2}$ **7.** $x = \frac{21}{2}$

8. $x = \frac{78}{7}$ **[2.2] 9.** $B = \frac{2A - hb}{h}$ **10.** $p = \frac{4y - 12}{7}$

[2.5] 11. $x < -7$; $(-\infty, -7)$; −7 0

12. $2 \le x \le 5$; $[2, 5]$; 0 2 5

13. $x < 0$ or $x > 5$; $(-\infty, -0) \cup (5, \infty)$;

[2.3] 14. −7, −9 **15.** 94 **16.** $3\frac{2}{3}$h

17. 112 $4 tickets, 60 $5 tickets

[3.1] 18.

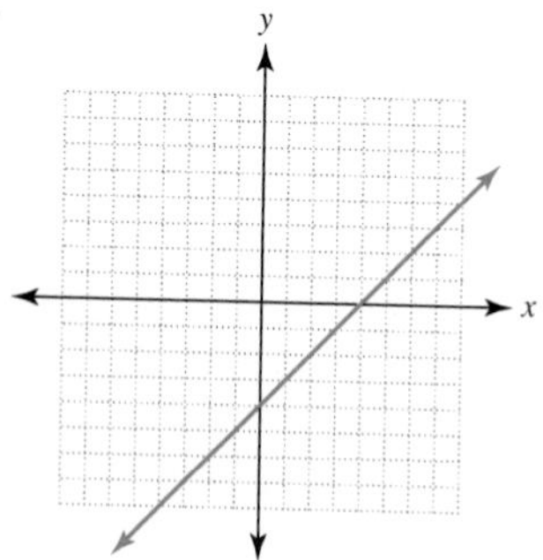

19.

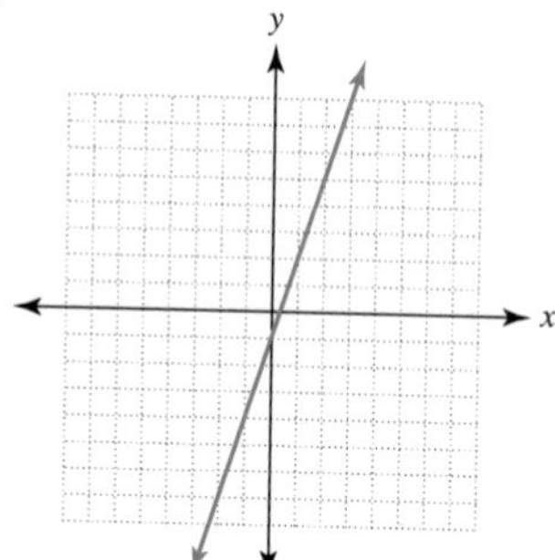

20.

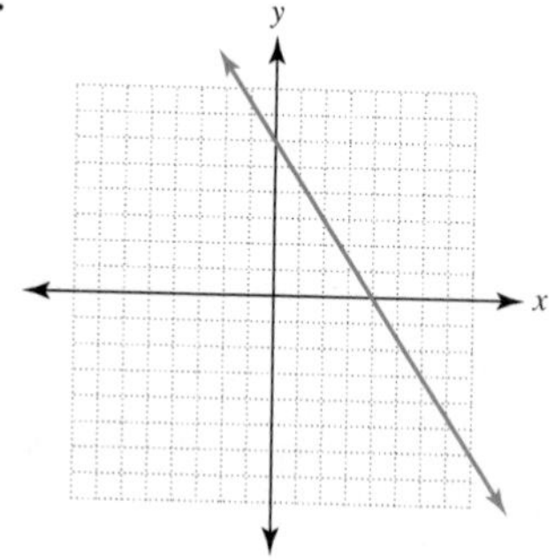

21.

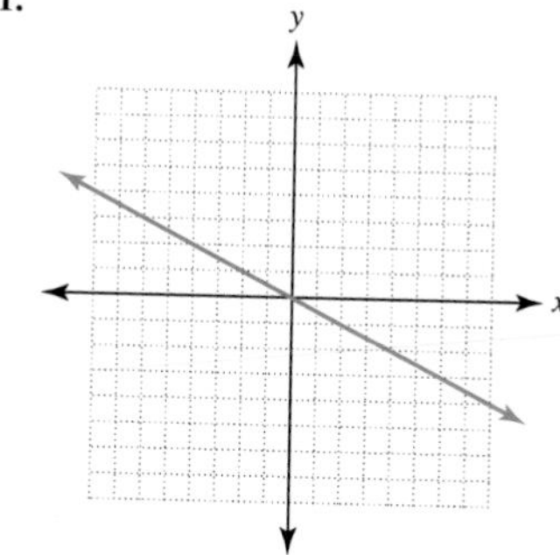

22.

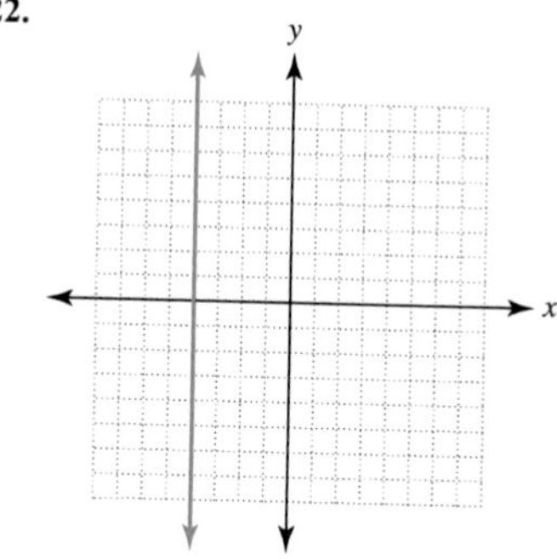

[3.3] 23. −2 **24.** Undefined **25.** $-\frac{3}{4}$ **26.** 0

27. Perpendicular **28.** Neither **[3.4] 29.** $y = 3$

30. $y = 5x - 2$ **31.** $y = \frac{1}{2}x + \frac{21}{2}$

32. $y = \frac{3}{4}x - 3$ **33.** $x = -3$

[3.5] 34.

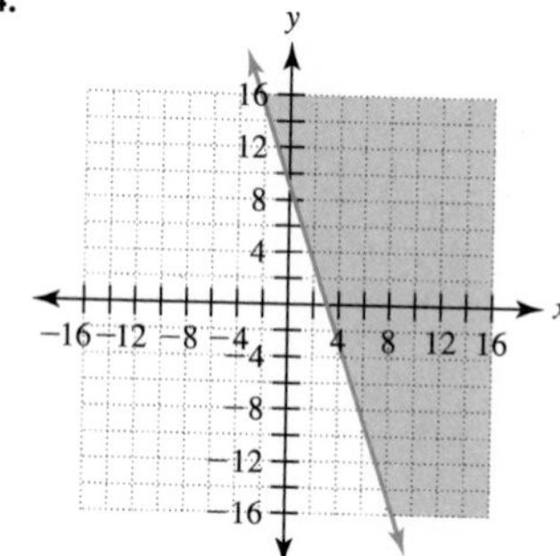

Pretest for Chapter 4

1. (2, −1) **2.** Dependent **3.** (0, 1) **4.** Inconsistent
5. 6, 9 **6.** 80 mL of 10%, 320 mL of 60%
7. Jet: 450 mi/h, wind: 50 mi/h **8.** (4, −2, −1) **9.** (0, 0, 3)
10. Savings: $3,000, Bonds: $5,000, Funds: $8,000 **11.** (2, −1)
12. (4, −2, −1) **13.**

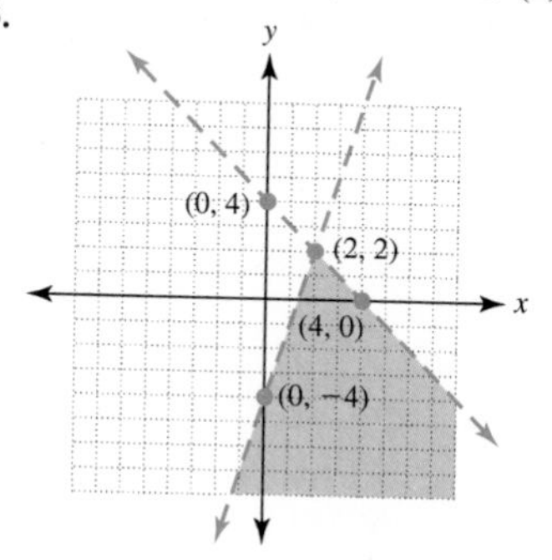

14.

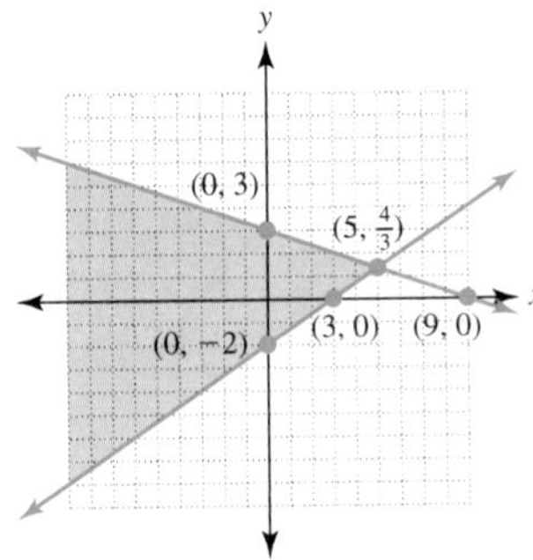

15.

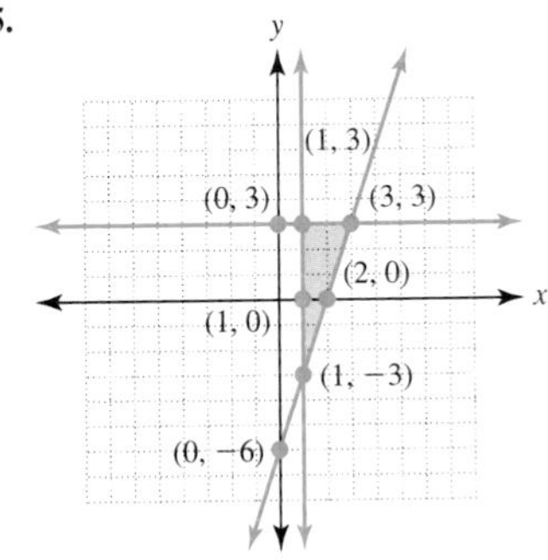

Reading Your Text

Section 4.1 **(a)** system; **(b)** solution; **(c)** consistent; **(d)** dependent
Section 4.2 **(a)** same; **(b)** no solution; **(c)** triple; **(d)** dependent
Section 4.3 **(a)** rectangular; **(b)** element; **(c)** augmented; **(d)** interchanged
Section 4.4 **(a)** intersection; **(b)** dashed; **(c)** bounded; **(d)** feasible

Summary Exercises for Chapter 4

1.

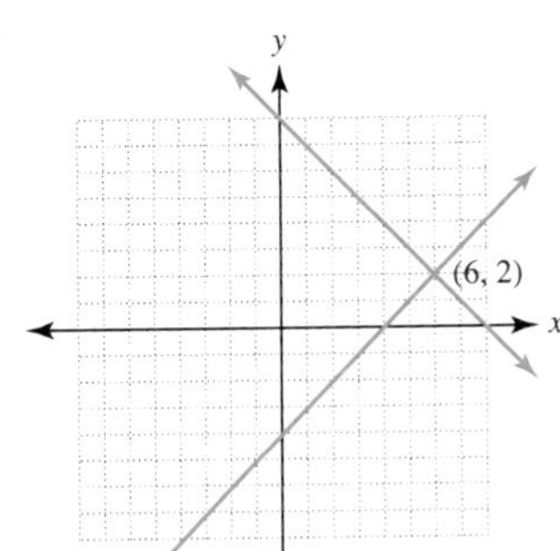

3.

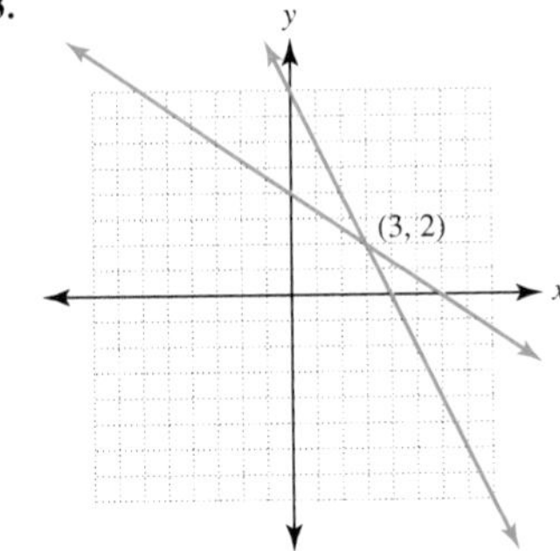

5. (3, 2) **7.** (0, −1) **9.** (−4, 3) **11.** Inconsistent
13. $\left(3, -\frac{3}{2}\right)$ **15.** (6, −4) **17.** (9, 5)
19. Inconsistent **21.** (2, −1) **23.** $\left(-\frac{2}{3}, 5\right)$
25. 7, 23 **27.** Adult: 800, student: 400
29. Length: 20 cm, width: 12 cm
31. Savings: \$8,000, time deposit: \$9,000
33. Plane: 500 mi/h, wind: 50 mi/h
35. CD-ROM drives: 15, $3\frac{1}{2}$-in. drives: 8 **37.** 300 mi
39. (6, 1, −2) **41.** (5, 2, 1) **43.** Dependent
45. 2, 5, 8 **47.** Orchestra: 200, box-seat: 120, balcony: 40
49. Savings: \$6,000, stock: \$2,000, mutual fund: \$4,000

51. 51, 93 **53.** 40 units **55.** $\left[\begin{array}{cc|c} 5 & 3 & 11 \\ -1 & -2 & 2 \end{array}\right]$

57. $\left[\begin{array}{ccc|c} 1 & 3 & 1 & 3 \\ 1 & 1 & -1 & -3 \\ 1 & -2 & -4 & -12 \end{array}\right]$ **59.** (4, −3) **61.** (2, −1, 4)

63.

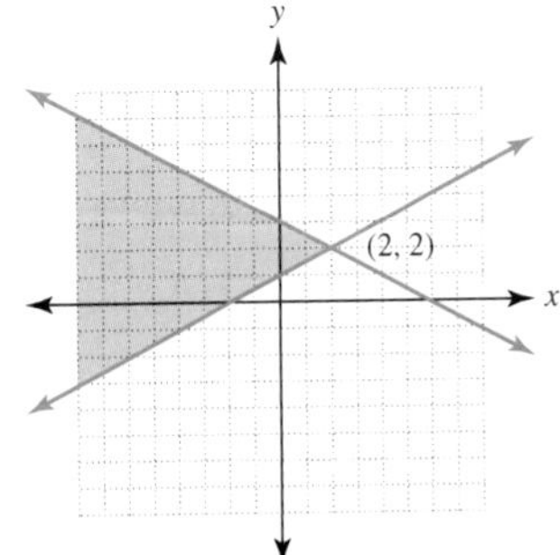

65.

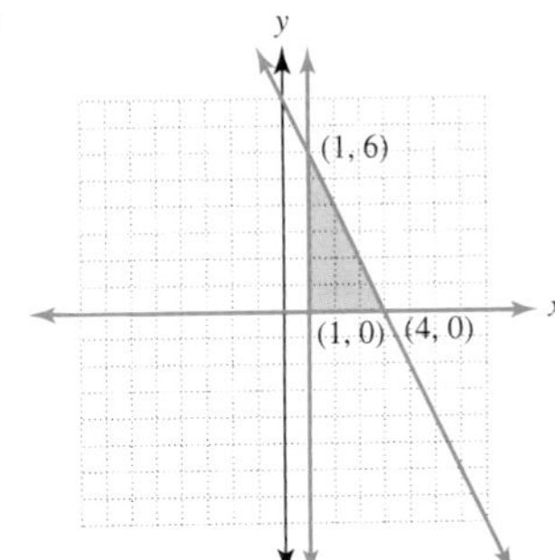

67.

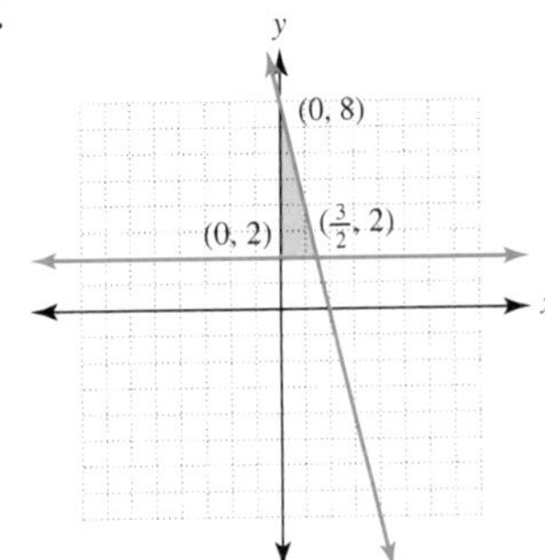

Self-Test for Chapter 4

[4.1] **1.** (−3, 4) **2.** Dependent **3.** Inconsistent
4. (−2, −5) **5.** (5, 0) **6.** $\left(3, -\frac{5}{3}\right)$

7. Disks: \$2.50, ribbons: \$6 **8.** Jawbreakers: 60 lb, licorice: 40 lb
9. Four 5-in. sets, six 12-in. sets **10.** 50 ft by 80 ft

[4.2] 11. $(-1, 2, 4)$ **12.** $\left(2, -3, -\frac{1}{2}\right)$

13. Savings: \$8,000, bond: \$4,000, mutual fund: \$2,000

[4.3] 14. $(2, 1)$ **15.** $(-1, 3, -2)$

[4.4] 16.

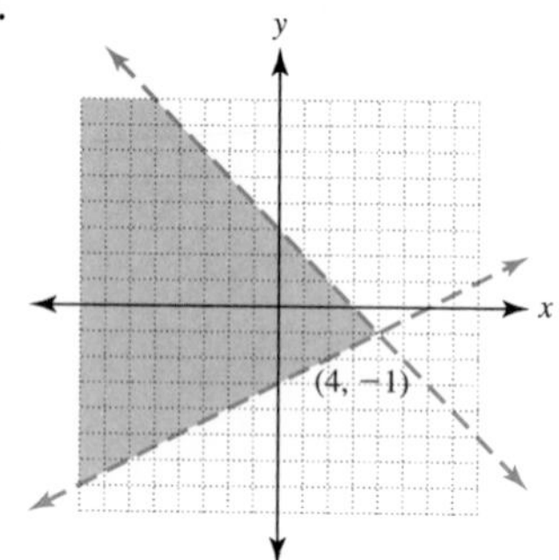

17.

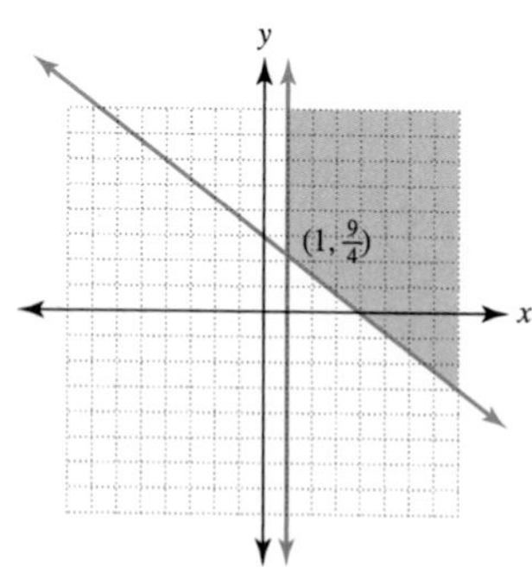

18.

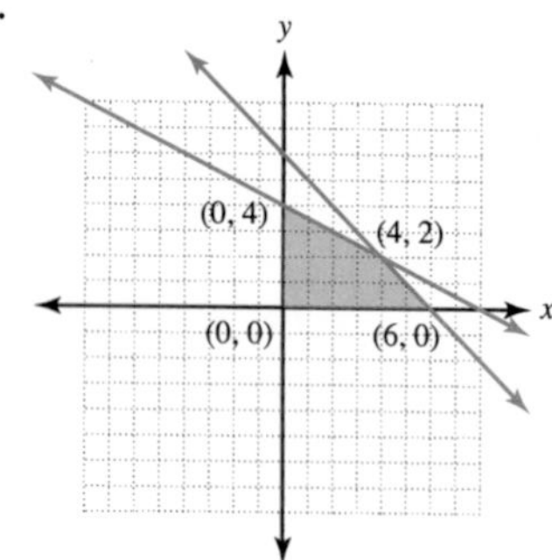

Cumulative Review for Chapters 1–4

[1.5] 1. $x^{18}y^6$ **[1.2] 2.** 62 **[3.2] 3.** 39 **[2.1] 4.** $x = 15$

[2.2] 5. $x = 5, x = -\frac{5}{3}$ **6.** $R = \frac{R_1R_2}{R_1 + R_2}$ **[2.3] 7.** $x \le 1$

8. $x < -2$ **[2.5] 9.** $-3 < x < 6$ **10.** $x > 13$ or $x < -3$

[3.4] 11. $y = 2x - 3$ **12.** $y = \frac{2}{3}x + \frac{7}{3}$ **13.** $y = -\frac{5}{4}x - 2$

[3.2] 14. Function **15.** Not a function **16.** Not a function
17. Function **[4.1] 18.** $(6, 2)$ **19.** $(-6, -3)$

20. Inconsistent **21.** Dependent **22.** $\left(-2, \frac{3}{2}\right)$

[4.2] 23. $(-4, 3, 5)$ **[4.1] 24.** Binder: \$3, paper: \$2.50
25. Bond: \$7,000, time deposit: \$3,000

Pretest for Chapter 5

1. 6 **2.** $10x^2 - 12x - 7$ **3.** $-4x^2 - 2x + 11$
4. $8d^3 - 14d^2 - 23d - 6$ **5.** $9m^2 + 12mn + 4n^2$
6. $\frac{4n^3p}{m^2}$ **7.** $x + 2 + \frac{10}{2x - 3}$ **8.** $(x + 3)(x - 3)$
9. $2z(z - 16)$ **10.** $2y(y + 1)(y^2 - y + 1)$
11. $(m - 3n)(m + 5)$ **12.** $(3w + 2)(4w - 5)$ **13.** 3, 5
14. $-1, \frac{2}{3}$ **15.** $-3, 8$

Reading Your Text

Section 5.1 **(a)** polynomial; **(b)** polynomial function; **(c)** like terms; **(d)** $-a - b; -a + b$
Section 5.2 **(a)** distributive; **(b)** perfect-square trinomial; **(c)** three; **(d)** binomials
Section 5.3 **(a)** variables; **(b)** simplify; **(c)** zero; **(d)** $x - a$
Section 5.4 **(a)** factors; **(b)** greatest common factor; **(c)** commutative; **(d)** grouping
Section 5.5 **(a)** difference of two squares; **(b)** not possible; **(c)** greatest common factor; **(d)** cubes
Section 5.6 **(a)** binomials; **(b)** first; last; **(c)** middle; **(d)** many
Section 5.7 **(a)** *ac* test; **(b)** trial and error; **(c)** greatest common factor; **(d)** zero-product principle
Section 5.8 **(a)** greatest common factor; **(b)** two; **(c)** completely; **(d)** multiply
Section 5.9 **(a)** quadratic; **(b)** zero-factor; **(c)** zeros (or roots); **(d)** zero

Summary Exercises for Chapter 5

1. Binomial **3.** Trinomial **5.** Binomial **7.** $5x^5 + 3x^2$, 5
9. $4x^4 + 6x^2 + 6$, 4 **11.** $-8, 0$ **13.** 0 **15.** -25
17. -52 **19.** **(a)** $(0, -4)$; **(b)** $(2, 10)$; **(c)** $(0, -5)$; **(d)** $(2, 19)$
21. **(a)** $(0, 0)$; **(b)** $(2, 10)$; **(c)** $(0, 1)$; **(d)** $(2, -13)$
23. **(a)** $h(x) = 2x^2 + 6x - 8$; **(b)** 0; (c) 0
25. **(a)** $h(x) = 2x^4 + x^3 - x^2 + 6x + 5$; **(b)** 13; **(c)** 13
27. **(a)** $h(x) = 5x^2 + 3x + 10$; **(b)** 18; **(c)** 18
29. **(a)** $h(x) = 4x^2 + 8x$; **(b)** 12; **(c)** 12
31. $x^2 + 10x - 1$ **33.** $-11x^2 + 11x - 10$
35. $22x^3 - 9x^2 + 4x - 8$ **37.** **(a)** $h(x) = 12x^3 - 20x^2$; **(b)** -8; **(c)** -8 **39.** **(a)** $h(x) = -6x^5 - 24x^4 + 3x^3$; **(b)** -27; **(c)** -27
41. $15x^3 - 20x^2$ **43.** $x^2 + xy - 6y^2$ **45.** $15c^2 - 19cd - 10d^2$
47. $x^3 - x^2 - 6x$ **49.** $x^2 + 16x + 64$ **51.** $4a^2 - 12ab + 9b^2$
53. $x^2 - 16y^2$ **55.** $2x^3 - 13x^2 + 19x - 6$ **57.** $3a^3$
59. $3a - 2$ **61.** $-3rs + 6r^2$ **63.** $x - 5$
65. $x - 3 + \frac{2}{x - 5}$ **67.** $x^2 + 2x - 1 + \frac{-4}{6x + 2}$
69. $x^2 + x + 2 + \frac{1}{x + 2}$ **71.** $6xy(3x + 4y)$
73. $9m^2n(5n - 3)(n + 1)$ **75.** $5(w - 3z)(1 - 2w + 6z)$
77. $(x + 7)(x - 2)$ **79.** $(4x - 3)(3x - 7)$
81. $(5a + 4)(5a - 4)$ **83.** $3w(w + 2z)(w - 2z)$
85. $(m - 4)(m^2 + 4m + 16)$ **87.** $(2c - 3d)(4c^2 + 6cd + 9d^2)$
89. $2x(x + 3)(x^2 - 3x + 9)$
91. **(a)** -8; **(b)** $-2x^2(3x + 1)$; **(c)** -8
93. **(a)** 0; **(b)** $2x(x^4 - 1) = 2x(x^2 + 1)(x + 1)(x - 1)$; **(c)** 0
95. $(a - 4)(a + 3)$ **97.** $(r - 12)(r + 3)$
99. $(a + 15b)(a + 2b)$ **101.** $(2a - 7)(a + 5)$
103. $(2c - 5)(3c - 2)$ **105.** $(2x + 5y)(4x - 3y)$
107. $5(w - 2z)(w - 3z)$ **109.** $2a(a + 3b)(a - b)$

111. $(a^2 + b^2)(a + 2b)(a - 2b)$ 113. $-2, 4$ 115. $-4, 10$
117. $-7, 4$ 119. $0, 12$ 121. $-12, 12$ 123. $-\frac{5}{3}, 3$
125. $-4, -2$ 127. $-\frac{7}{2}, 5$ 129. $-2, -1, 2$ 131. \$3 or \$25

Self-Test for Chapter 5

[5.1] 1. Binomial 2. Trinomial 3. Not a polynomial
4. $8x^4 - 3x^2 - 7$; 8, -3, -7; 4 5. 25
6. (a) $h(x) = 6x^2 - 3x + 7$; (b) $p(x) = 2x^2 - 3x + 7$; (c) 10; (d) 6; (e) 10; (f) 6 7. (a) $h(x) = -3x^3 + 3x^2 + 5x - 9$; (b) $p(x) = -3x^3 + 7x^2 - 9x - 5$; (c) -4; (d) -10; (e) -4; (f) -10
8. $5x + 12$ [5.2] 9. $6a^2 - ab - 35b^2$ 10. $25m^2 - 9n^2$
11. $4a^2 + 12ab + 9b^2$ 12. $2x^3 - 13x^2 + 26x - 15$
[5.3] 13. $x - 1 + \frac{-3}{3x + 1}$ 14. $4x^2 + 3x + 13 + \frac{17}{x - 2}$
15. $3x^2 - 5$ [5.4]–[5.8] 16. $7ab(2ab - 3a + 5b)$
17. $(x - 3y)(x + 5)$ 18. $(5c - 8d)(5c + 8d)$
19. $(3x - 1)(9x^2 + 3x + 1)$ 20. $2a(2a + b)(4a^2 - 2ab + b^2)$
21. $(x - 8)(x + 6)$ 22. $(5x - 2)(2x - 7)$
23. $3x(x + 3)(2x - 5)$ [5.9] 24. $-3, -\frac{1}{2}$ 25. $-\frac{5}{2}, \frac{2}{3}$

Cumulative Review for Chapters 1–5

[2.1] 1. 2 [3.2] 2. -77 [3.3] 3. x-int: (6, 0), y-int: (0, 4)
[3.5] 4. $y = \frac{5}{4}x - \frac{3}{4}$ [1.5] 5. $256x^{13}y^{12}$ [1.2] 6. 25
[3.1] 7. Domain: all real numbers, range: all real numbers
[3.2] 8. (a) 4; (b) 0; (c) -6 [5.1] 9. $-x^2 - 5x + 9$
[5.2] 10. $10x^2 + 7x - 12$ [5.7] 11. $x(3x + 2)(x - 1)$
[5.5] 12. $(4x + 5y)(4x - 5y)$ [5.4] 13. $(x - y)(3x + 1)$
[5.1 and 5.2] 14. (a) $3x + 7$; (b) $-13x - 5$; (c) $-40x^2 - 22x + 6$
[2.1] 15. 5 [2.5] 16. $-18, -28$ [2.1] 17. $\frac{13}{10}$
[2.4] 18. $x \geq -1$ [2.5] 19. $-13 \leq x \leq -5$
20. $-6 < x < -4$ [4.1] 21. $\left(-10, \frac{26}{3}\right)$
[2.2] 22. $R = \frac{P - P_0}{IT}$ [5.9] 23. $3, -\frac{1}{2}$
[2.3] 24. 8 cm by 19 cm 25. 16, 14

Pretest for Chapter 6

1. $\frac{-2x^2y}{3}$ 2. $\frac{3x - 1}{2x + 3}$ 3. $\frac{3a}{2b^2}$ 4. $\frac{2x - 3}{x}$
5. $\frac{3x + 3}{x(x - 3)}$ 6. $\frac{5}{(a - 1)(a + 4)}$ 7. $\frac{2}{3x}$ 8. $\frac{b + a}{b - a}$
9. $\frac{(x - 3)(x - 4)}{(x - 1)^2}$ 10. $\frac{rs}{s + r}$ 11. 5 12. 6 13. 0, 7
14. $y = 6$ 15. $r = 20$ 16. $s = 7.5$

Reading Your Text

Section 6.1 (a) factor; (b) polynomial; (c) rational; (d) hole
Section 6.2 (a) multiplying; (b) factor; (c) invert; (d) zero
Section 6.3 (a) numerators, common denominator; (b) simplified; (c) factor; (d) rational
Section 6.4 (a) fraction; (b) nonzero; (c) LCD; (d) invert
Section 6.5 (a) LCD; (b) extraneous; (c) time; (d) rate (or speed)
Section 6.6 (a) variation; (b) inversely; (c) joint; (d) combined

Summary Exercises for Chapter 6

1. Never undefined 3. $x \neq 5$ 5. $\frac{3x^2}{4}$ 7. 8
9. $-\frac{x + 3}{x + 5}$ 11. $\frac{2a - b}{3a - b}$
13.

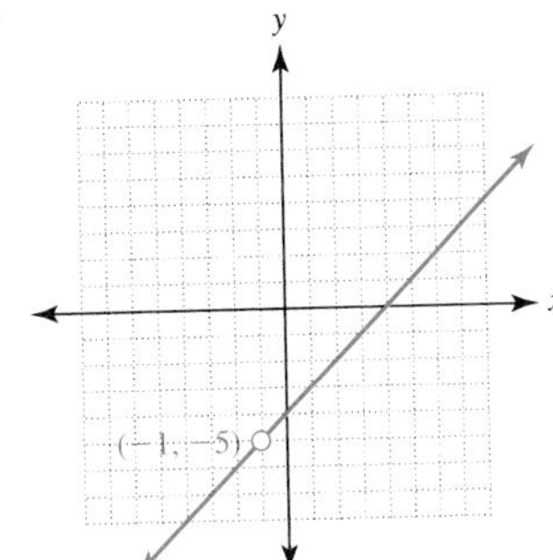

15. $\frac{5x^2}{6}$ 17. $\frac{4}{3y}$ 19. $\frac{3}{2a}$ 21. $\frac{x + 2y}{x - 5y}$
23. (a) -8; (b) $x^2 + x - 20$; (c) -8 25. 3 27. $\frac{x + 5}{x(x - 5)}$
29. $\frac{-11}{6(m - 1)}$ 31. $\frac{15x + 5}{4(x + 1)(x - 1)}$ 33. $\frac{-4}{s + 2}$
35. $\frac{3x - 1}{x + 2}$ 37. (a) 8; (b) $\frac{3x^2 - 8x}{(x - 2)(x - 3)}$; (c) (4, 8)
39. $\frac{2}{3x}$ 41. $\frac{b + a}{b - a}$ 43. $\frac{rs}{s + r}$ 45. $\frac{x - 4}{(x - 1)(x - 1)}$
47. $-y + 2$ 49. $\frac{x + 2}{(x - 1)(x + 4)}$ 51. 5 53. 6
55. 3 57. -1 59. 4 61. 0, 7 63. $\frac{TT_2}{T - T_2}$
65. $\frac{FD_1}{D_1 - F}$ 67. 5 h, 7 h 69. 6 h 71. 18 h 73. 3
75. 8 77. $d = kt^2$ 79. $y = \frac{kx}{w}$ 81. $k = 6$
83. $k = 3$ 85. $z = 12$ 87. $m = 432$ 89. 400 ft

Self-Test for Chapter 6

[6.1] 1. $\frac{-3x^4}{4y^2}$ 2. $\frac{w + 1}{w - 2}$ 3. $\frac{x + 3}{x - 2}$
4.

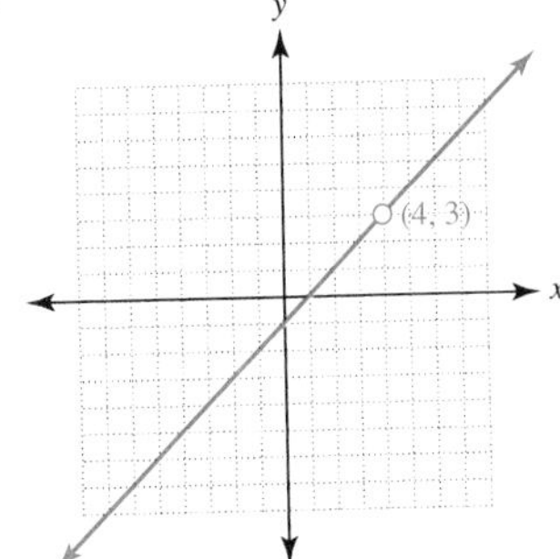

[6.2] 5. $\frac{4a^2}{7b}$ 6. $\frac{m - 4}{4}$ 7. $\frac{2}{x - 1}$ 8. $\frac{2x + y}{x(x + 3y)}$
9. $\frac{-15x - 5}{3x - 1}$ [6.3] 10. $\frac{4x + 2}{x(x - 2)}$ 11. $\frac{2}{x - 3}$
12. $\frac{4}{x - 2}$ 13. $\frac{8x + 17}{(x - 4)(x + 1)(x + 4)}$ [6.4] 14. $\frac{y}{3y + x}$

15. $\frac{z-1}{2(z+3)}$ **16.** $\frac{1}{xy(x-y)}$ **[6.5] 17.** 9 **18.** $-\frac{1}{2}, 4$
19. 3, 6 **20.** Going: 50 mi/h, returning: 45 mi/h
21. Juan: 10 days; Ariel: 40 days **22.** 3 **[6.6] 23.** 2
24. 75 **25.** 12 **26.** 500 lb/ft^2

Cumulative Review for Chapters 1–6

[2.1] 1. 12 **[3.2] 2.** -14 **[3.4] 3.** $6x + 7y = -21$
[3.1] 4. x-int: $(-6, 0)$, y-int: $(0, 7)$ **[1.4] 5.** $6x^2 - 5x - 2$
[5.2] 6. $2x^3 + 5x^2 - 3x$
[3.1] 7. Domain: $\{2\}$, range: all real numbers
[1.2] 8. 16 **[5.8] 9.** $x(2x + 3)(3x - 1)$
10. $(4x^8 + 3y^4)(4x^8 - 3y^4)$ **[6.3] 11.** $\frac{3}{x-1}$
[6.2] 12. $\frac{1}{(x+1)(x-1)}$ **[6.4] 13.** $x^2 - 3x$ **[2.1] 14.** $\frac{7}{2}$
[2.5] 15. $-\frac{8}{9}, -\frac{4}{9}$ **[2.1] 16.** $-\frac{30}{17}$ **[5.9] 17.** $-\frac{3}{2}, 4$
[2.5] 18. $x > -2$ **19.** $\frac{1}{5} < x < \frac{7}{5}$
20. $x \le -4$ or $x \ge -2$ **[6.5] 21.** $x = -5$ **[4.1] 22.** $(3, -1)$ **[1.5] 23.** $\frac{b^6}{a^{10}}$ **[6.5] 24.** Barry: 3 h, Don: 6 h
[5.9] 25. Width: 10 cm, length: 18 cm **[6.6] 26.** $y = 96$

Pretest for Chapter 7

1. $5t^3$ **2.** $\frac{\sqrt{6ab}}{4b}$ **3.** $7\sqrt{7}$ **4.** $9 + 5\sqrt{3}$ **5.** $4 - \sqrt{5}$
6. $x = 84$ **7.** $x = 4.12$ **8.** 19.21 cm **9.** $ab^2\sqrt[5]{ab^4}$
10. $2x^3y^2$ **11.** $-9 - 8i$ **12.** $5 + 5i$

Reading Your Text

Section 7.1 **(a)** principal; **(b)** approximation; **(c)** radicand; **(d)** irrational
Section 7.2 **(a)** product, sum; **(b)** factor; **(c)** fraction; **(d)** removes
Section 7.3 **(a)** radicand; **(b)** distributive; **(c)** radical; **(d)** rational number
Section 7.4 **(a)** sides; **(b)** extraneous; **(c)** lose; **(d)** three
Section 7.5 **(a)** square of the hypotenuse; **(b)** missing side (of a right triangle); **(c)** golden ratio; **(d)** divine section
Section 7.6 **(a)** rational; **(b)** principal nth root; **(c)** $a^{m/n}$; **(d)** add, subtract, multiply
Section 7.7 **(a)** $i = \sqrt{-1}, -1$; **(b)** complex number; **(c)** real part, imaginary part; **(d)** complex conjugates

Summary Exercises for Chapter 7

1. 11 **3.** Not a real number **5.** -4 **7.** $\frac{3}{4}$ **9.** 8
11. a^2 **13.** $7w^2z^3$ **15.** $-3b^2$ **17.** $2xy^2$ **19.** $3\sqrt{5}$
21. $2x\sqrt{15}$ **23.** $2\sqrt[3]{4}$ **25.** $\frac{3}{4}$ **27.** $\frac{y^2}{7}$ **29.** $\frac{\sqrt{5}}{4x}$
31. $11\sqrt{10}$ **33.** $10\sqrt[3]{2x}$ **35.** $11\sqrt{2}$ **37.** $3\sqrt{7}$
39. $13\sqrt[3]{2}$ **41.** $10a\sqrt[3]{2a^2}$ **43.** $\frac{11}{2}\sqrt{2x}$ or $\frac{11\sqrt{2x}}{2}$
45. $\frac{4}{15}\sqrt{15}$ or $\frac{4\sqrt{15}}{15}$ **47.** $6x\sqrt{3}$ **49.** $\sqrt{15} + 2\sqrt{5}$
51. $6a\sqrt{5}$ **53.** $7 + \sqrt{21} - \sqrt{14} - \sqrt{6}$ **55.** 4
57. $7 - 2\sqrt{10}$ **59.** $\frac{2\sqrt{3x}}{x}$ **61.** $\frac{\sqrt[3]{3a}}{a}$ **63.** $\frac{\sqrt[3]{x^2y}}{y^2}$
65. $\frac{5 + \sqrt{3}}{2}$ **67.** $\frac{x - 6\sqrt{x} + 9}{x - 9}$ **69.** 21 **71.** 9
73. 5 **75.** 9 **77.** $x = \pm\sqrt{r^2 - y^2}$ **79.** 11.5 in.
81. 4.9 ft **83.** 8.2 m **85.** -10 **87.** 2 **89.** 125
91. $\frac{1}{7}$ **93.** x^4 **95.** r **97.** $x^{2/5}$ **99.** x^8y^{15}
101. $\frac{x^6}{y^{7/2}}$ **103.** $\sqrt[4]{x^3}$ **105.** $3\sqrt[3]{a^2}$ **107.** $(7x)^{1/5}$
109. $3pq^3$ **111.** $7i$ **113.** $-2i\sqrt{15}$ **115.** $4 - 5i$
117. $-3 + 5i$ **119.** $23 + 14i$ **121.** 13 **123.** $\frac{6}{5} + \frac{8}{5}i$
125. $4 + 3i$

Self-Test for Chapter 7

[7.1] 1. $7a^2$ **2.** $-3w^2z^3$ **[7.2] 3.** $p^2q\sqrt[3]{9pq^2}$ **4.** $\frac{7x}{8y}$
5. $\frac{\sqrt{10xy}}{4y}$ **6.** $\frac{\sqrt[3]{3x^2}}{x}$ **[7.3] 7.** $3x\sqrt{3x}$ **8.** $5m\sqrt[3]{2m}$
9. $4x\sqrt{3}$ **10.** $3 - 2\sqrt{2}$ **[7.4] 11.** 11 **12.** 4
[7.5] 13. 9.4 cm **14.** $\approx$21.9 ft **15.** 3.7 cm **16.** 9.0 cm
17. 69.3 cm **[7.6] 18.** $64x^6$ **19.** $\frac{9m}{n^4}$ **20.** $\frac{8s^3}{r}$
21. $a^2b\sqrt[5]{a^4b}$ **22.** $5p^3q^2$ **[7.7] 23.** $3 + 10i$
24. $-14 + 22i$ **25.** $5 - 5i$

Cumulative Review for Chapters 1–7

[2.1] 1. $x = -15$ **[3.2] 2.** 5 **[3.5] 3.** $3x - 2y = 12$
[2.5] 4. $x = 3$ or $x = \frac{1}{3}$ **[5.1] 5.** $f(x) = 10x^2 - 2x$
[5.2] 6. $f(x) = 10x^2 - 39x - 27$ **[5.7] 7.** $x(x - 1)(2x + 3)$
[5.5] 8. $9(x^2 + 2y^2)(x^2 - 2y^2)$ **[5.4] 9.** $(x + 2y)(4x - 5)$
[6.1] 10. $\frac{x+5}{3x-1}$ **[6.3] 11.** $\frac{x+7}{(x-5)(x-1)}$
[6.2] 12. $\frac{a+2}{2a}$ **[6.3] 13.** 0 **[7.3] 14.** $2x^4y^3\sqrt{3y}$
15. $\sqrt{6} - 5\sqrt{2} + 3\sqrt{3} - 15$ **16.** $x\sqrt{2x}$ **[7.6] 17.** $\frac{c^{12}}{a^6b^4}$
[3.3] 18.

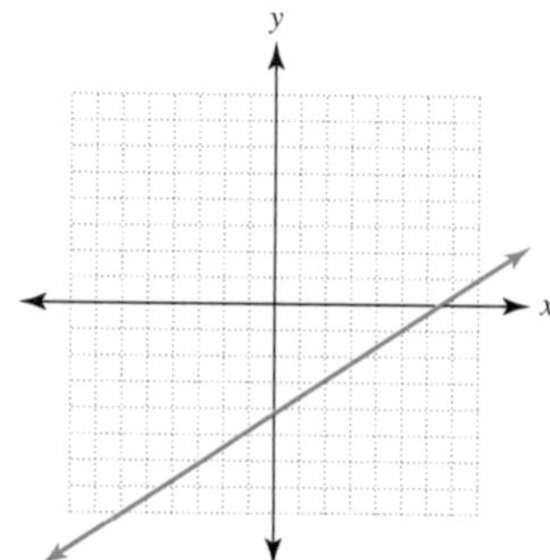

[7.7] 19. $15 + 18i$ **20.** $23 - 14i$ **[7.4] 21.** $x = 11$
[4.1] 22. $(9, 1)$ **[2.4] 23.** $x \le 17$ **[2.5] 24.** $-1 \le x \le 9$
[7.5] 25. 16

Pretest for Chapter 8

1. $\frac{2}{3}, -3$ **2.** $(-2, -16)$

3.

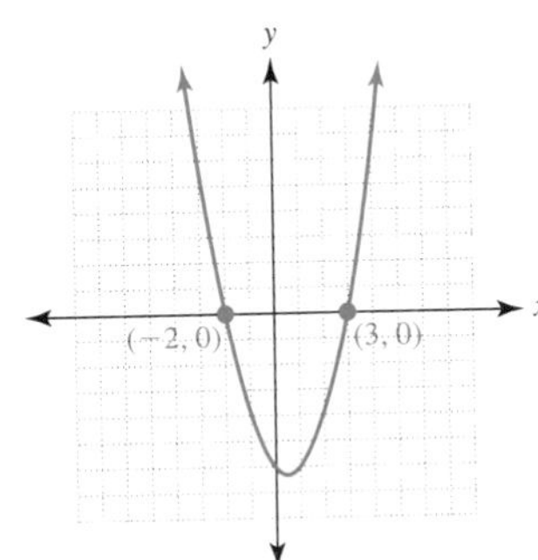

4. $\pm\sqrt{7}$

5. $-5, 2$ **6.** Width: 6 cm, length: 16 cm **7.** 1 sec, 3 sec
8. $2 \pm \sqrt{2}$ **9.** $\sqrt{7.2} \approx 2.7$ m, $2\sqrt{7.2} \approx 5.4$ m
10. $\pm\sqrt{2}, \pm 2$ **11.** 9, 36

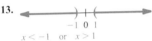

12. −5 0 2
$-5 \le x \le 2$

13. −1 0 1
$x < -1$ or $x > 1$

Reading Your Text

Section 8.1 **(a)** parabola; **(b)** downward; **(c)** vertex; **(d)** zero
Section 8.2 **(a)** square root; **(b)** completing the square; **(c)** square root; **(d)** coefficient
Section 8.3 **(a)** quadratic formula; **(b)** standard; **(c)** discriminant; **(d)** rational
Section 8.4 **(a)** quadratic; **(b)** substitution; **(c)** four; **(d)** original
Section 8.5 **(a)** algebraically; **(b)** critical; **(c)** negative; **(d)** quadratic

Summary Exercises for Chapter 8

1.

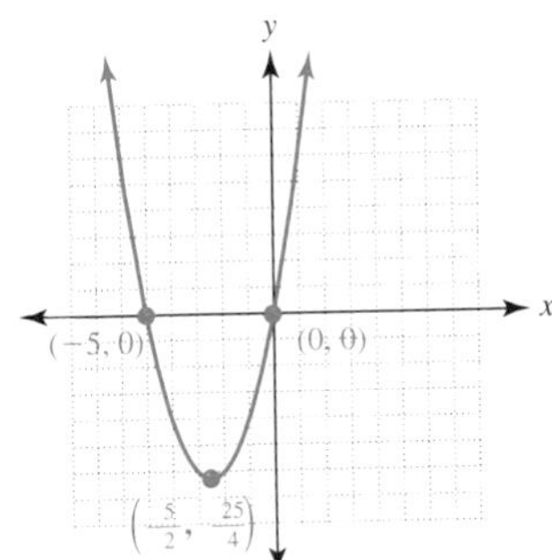

3.

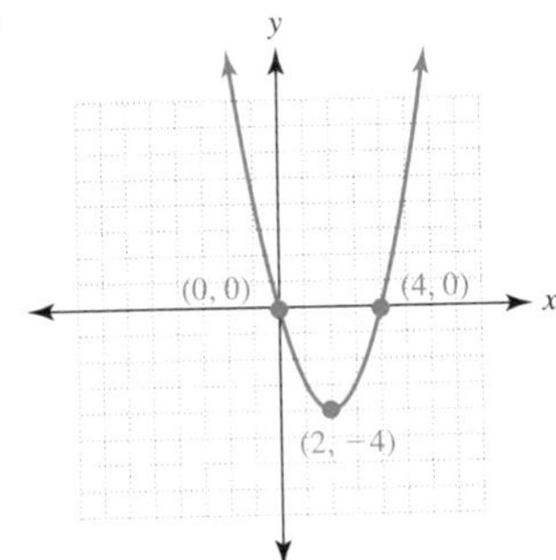

5.

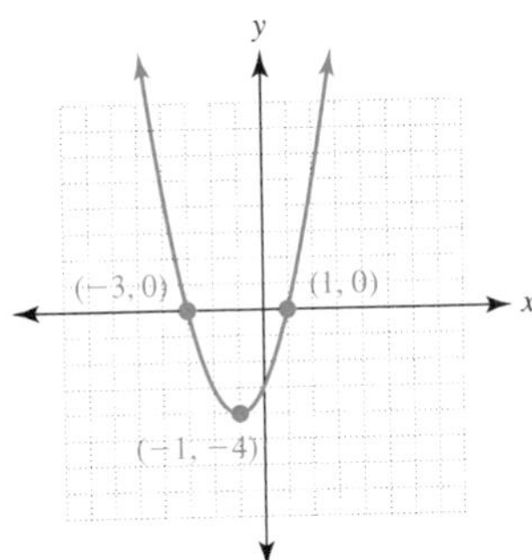

7.

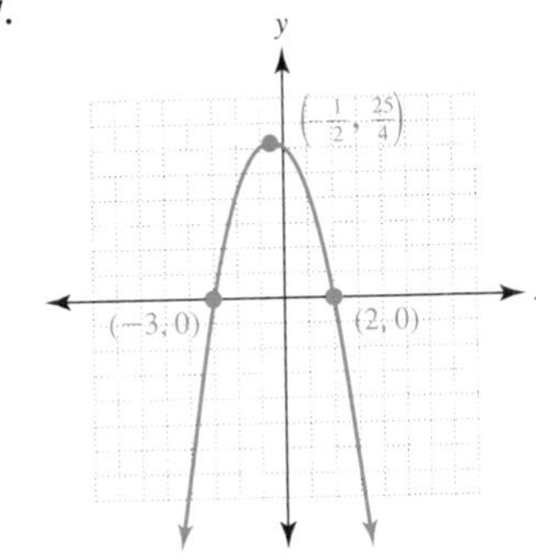

9. $(-1, -9)$ **11.** $(-1, -8)$ **13.** $(-2, 0)$ **15.** $(2, -9)$
17. $(2, -1)$ **19.** $(-1, -4)$ **21.** $(-1, 9)$ **23.** $\pm\sqrt{10}$
25. $\pm 2\sqrt{5}$ **27.** $1 \pm \sqrt{5}$ **29.** $-3 \pm \sqrt{5}$ **31.** $\frac{\pm 3i\sqrt{3}}{2}$
33. $\frac{\pm\sqrt{7}}{5}$ **35.** 36 **37.** $-1, 5$ **39.** $5 \pm 2\sqrt{7}$
41. $\frac{4 \pm \sqrt{26}}{2}$ **43.** $-3, 8$ **45.** $\frac{3 \pm \sqrt{21}}{2}$
47. $\frac{-2 \pm \sqrt{7}}{3}$ **49.** $1 \pm \sqrt{29}$ **51.** $\frac{-1 \pm i\sqrt{14}}{3}$
53. -16, none **55.** 76, two **57.** $x = 2, -1$
59. $x = -\frac{3}{2}, -2$ **61.** $\pm\sqrt{2}, \pm 3$ **63.** $0, \pm 3$ **65.** 16
67. $1 \pm \sqrt{2}, -2, 4$ **69.** $-8, 1$

71. −5 0 2 $x < -5$ or $x > 2$

73. −3 −1 0 $-3 \le x \le -1$

75. −3 0 8 $-3 \le x \le 8$

77. −8 0 8 $x \le -8$ or $x \ge 8$

79. −3 0 7 $-3 < x < 7$

81. 2 4 $x < 2$ or $x > 4$

83. −3 0 5 $-3 < x \le 5$

85. −4 0 3 $x \le -4$ or $x > 3$

87. 1 sec $\le t \le$ 3 sec **89.** Width: 8 ft, length: 10 ft
91. Width: 11 in., length: 14 in. **93.** 1 sec $\le t \le$ 5 sec

Self-Test for Chapter 8

[8.1] 1. $-\frac{2}{3}, 4$ **2.** $\left(-\frac{1}{2}, -\frac{9}{4}\right)$ **3.** (2, −9)

4.

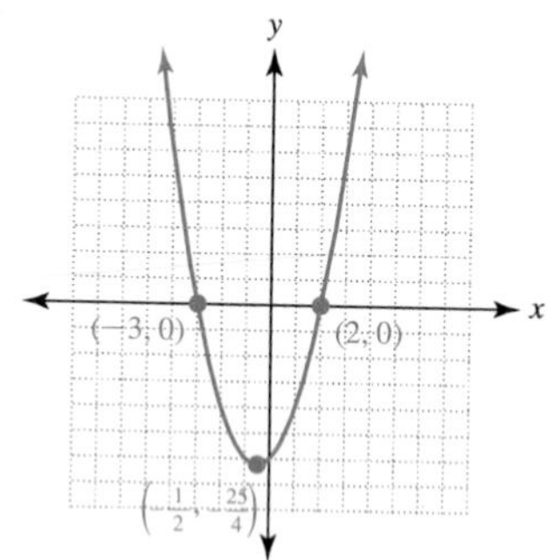

5.

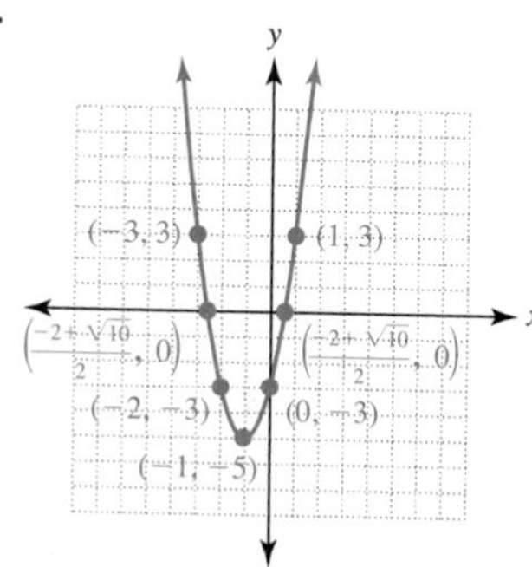

6. Width: 5 cm, length: 17 cm **7.** 2.7 sec **[8.2] 8.** $\pm\sqrt{5}$

9. $1 \pm \sqrt{10}$ **10.** $\frac{2 \pm \sqrt{23}}{2}$ **11.** $\frac{-3 \pm \sqrt{13}}{2}$

12. $\frac{5 \pm \sqrt{19}}{2}$ **[8.3] 13.** $\frac{5 \pm \sqrt{37}}{2}$ **14.** $-2 \pm \sqrt{11}$

[8.4] 15. $\pm\sqrt{3}, \pm 3$ **16.** 4, 81 **17.** −3, 5 **18.** 3, −2

[8.5] 19. −7 0 2
$-7 < x < 2$

20. −3 6
$x \le -3$ or $x \ge 6$

21. −5 0 3
$-5 \le x < 3$

22. −1 1
$x < -1$ or $x > 1$

Cumulative Review for Chapters 1–8

[3.2] 1.

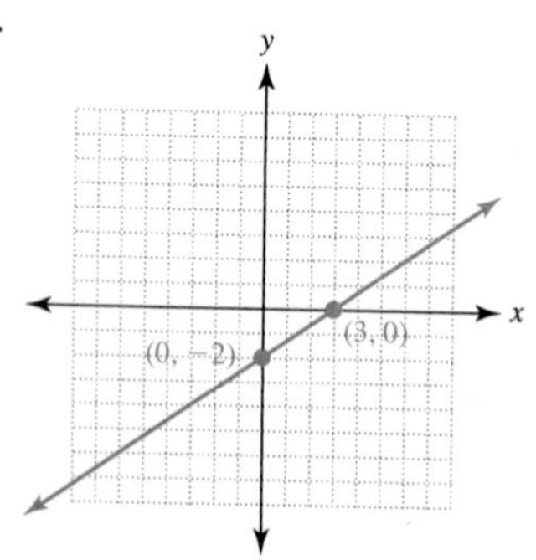

[3.3] 2. −3 **[4.1] 3.** (7, −2) **[5.3] 4.** $3x + 1 + \frac{6}{x-2}$

[5.8] 5. $x(x+3)(x-2)$ **[6.3] 6.** $\frac{-x-4}{(x-3)(x+2)}$

[7.3] 7. $\sqrt{21} - \sqrt{6} + \sqrt{42} - 2\sqrt{3}$ **[2.1] 8.** $\frac{7}{2}$ **9.** −4

[5.9] 10. −5, 3 **11.** 1, 2 **12.** −10, 3

[8.3] 13. $\frac{3 \pm \sqrt{21}}{2}$ **[8.2] 14.** $3 \pm \sqrt{5}$ **[2.5] 15.** −2, 5

[6.5] 16. 4 **[7.4] 17.** 7 **[3.5] 18.** $x + 2y = 6$

[2.5] 19. $x \le -5$ or $x \ge 13$ **[8.5] 20.** $-3 \le x \le 5$

[7.6] 21. xy^2 **[7.7] 22.** $3 - 4i$ **[2.3] 23.** −13

[8.3] 24. $-2 + 2\sqrt{97}, 2 + 2\sqrt{97}$ or 17.7 ft, and 21.7 ft

25. Between 21 and 59 units

Pretest for Chapter 9

1.

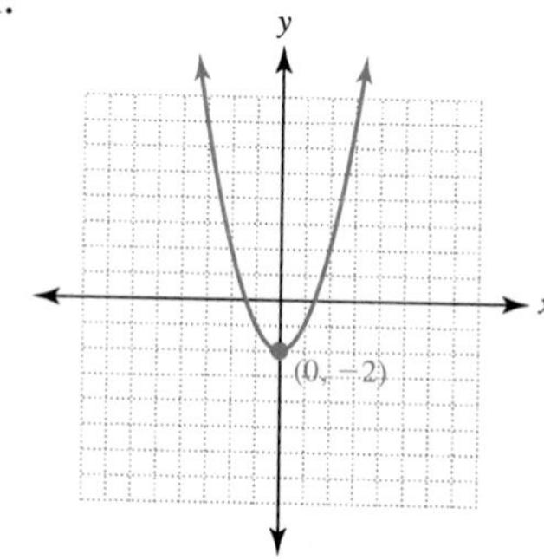

2.

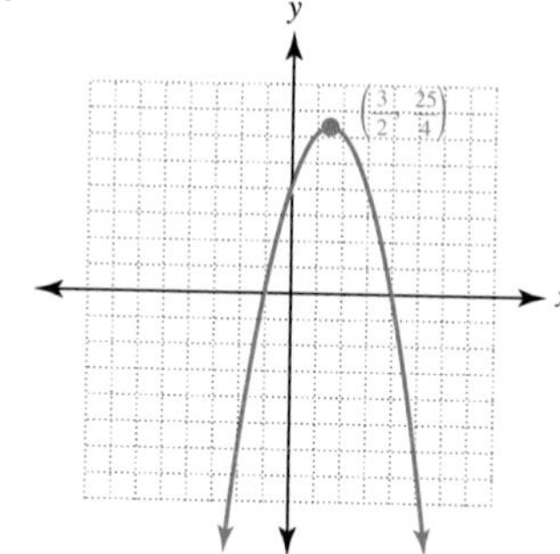

3. (0, 0); $r = 3$

4.

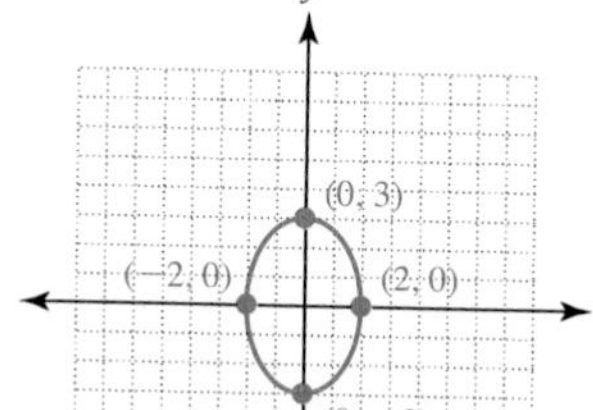

5.

6. (4, 5) and (−1, 5)

7.

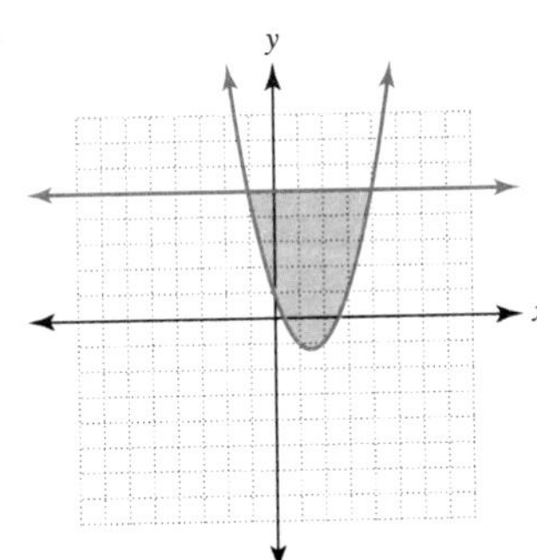

8. Circle 9. Line 10. Parabola

Reading Your Text

Section 9.1 **(a)** Conic sections; **(b)** parabola, circle, ellipse, hyperbola; **(c)** axis of symmetry; **(d)** vertex

Section 9.2 **(a)** circle; **(b)** radius; **(c)** $d = \sqrt{(x_2 - x_1)^2 + (y_2 - y_1)^2}$; **(d)** (h, k)

Section 9.3 **(a)** ellipse; **(b)** hyperbola; **(c)** asymptotes (of a hyperbola); **(d)** coefficients

Section 9.4 **(a)** conic curves; **(b)** equations; **(c)** possibly four; **(d)** inequalities

Summary Exercises for Chapter 9

1.

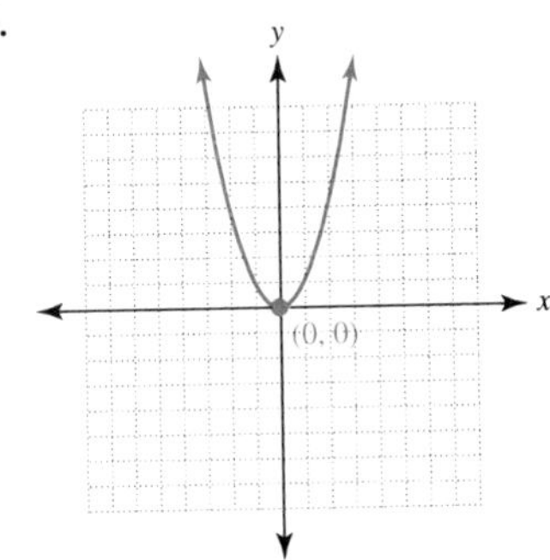

3.

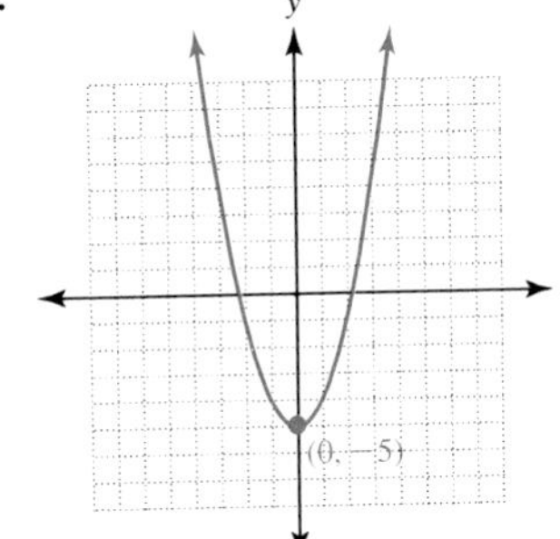

5.

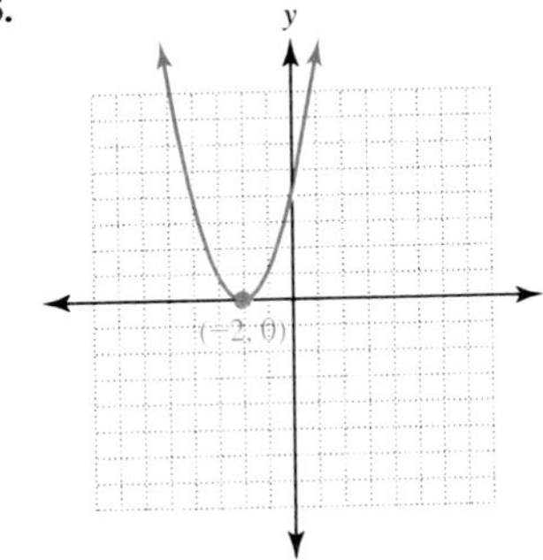

7.

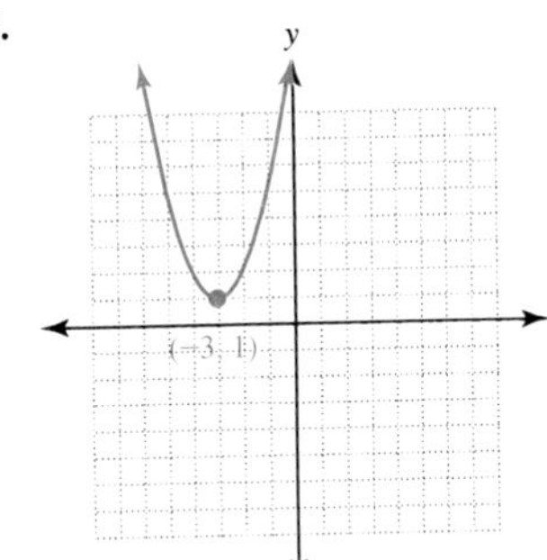

9.

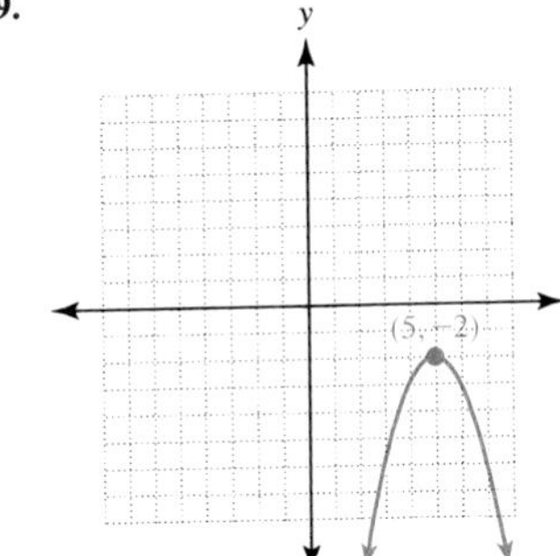

11.

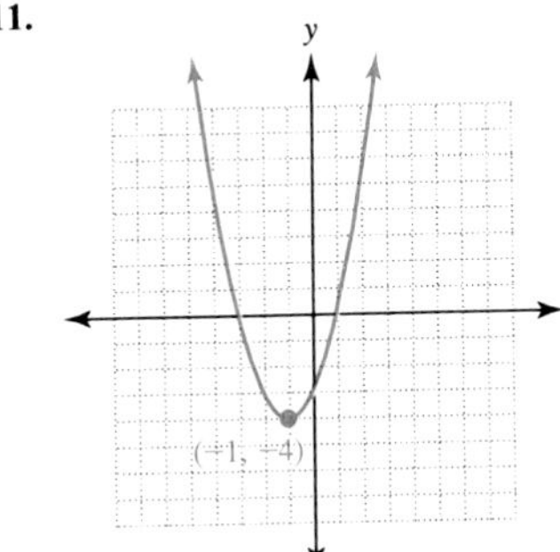

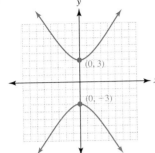

13.

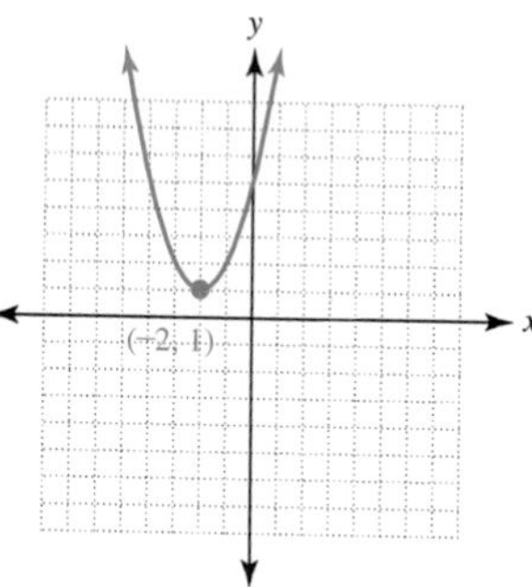

15.

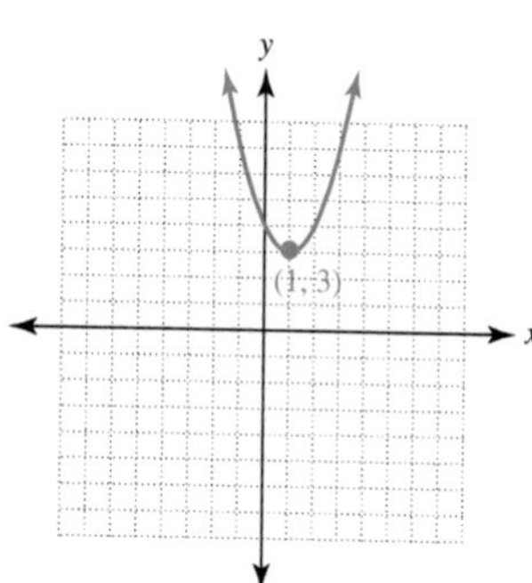

17.

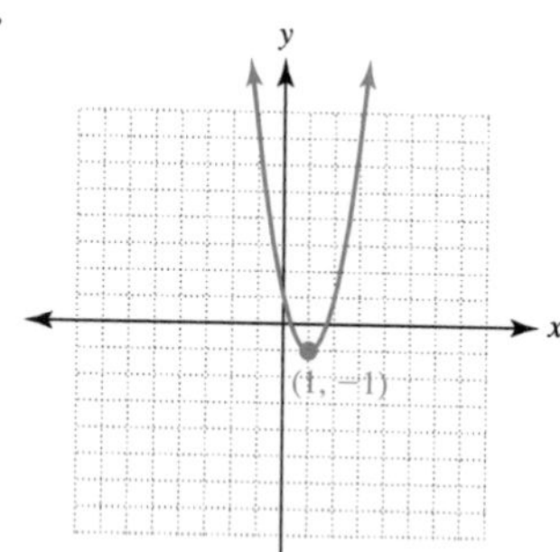

19.

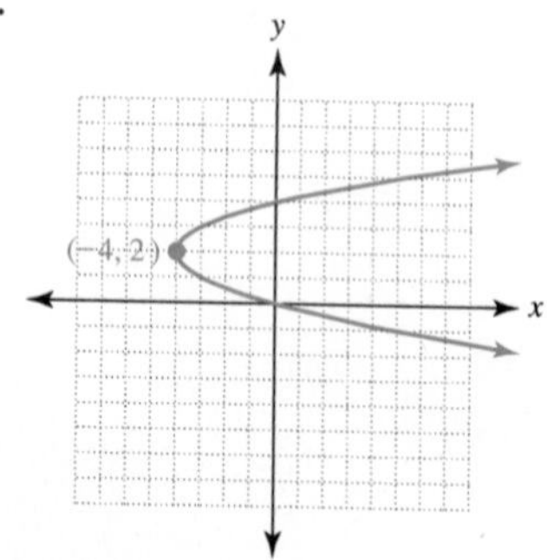

21.

23. $(0, 0), r = 4$ **25.** $(0, 0), r = 3$ **27.** $(3, 0), r = 6$
29. $(1, 2), r = 4$ **31.** $(-4, -5), r = 8$ **33.** $(0, 2), r = 3$
35.

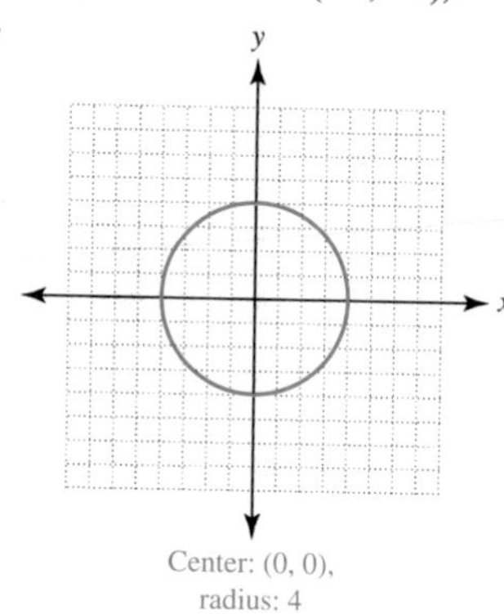

Center: (0, 0),
radius: 4

37.

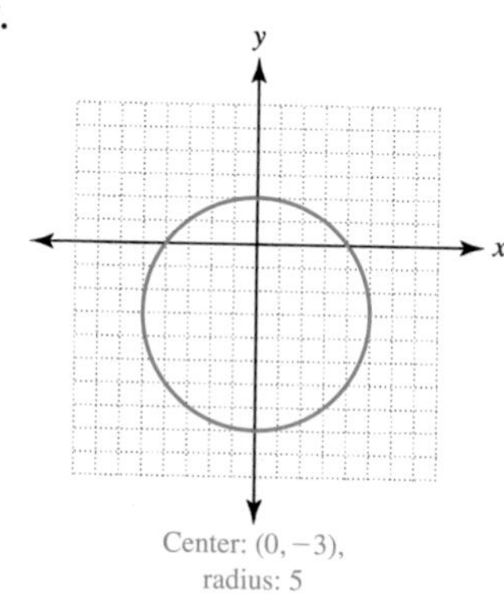

Center: (0, −3),
radius: 5

39.

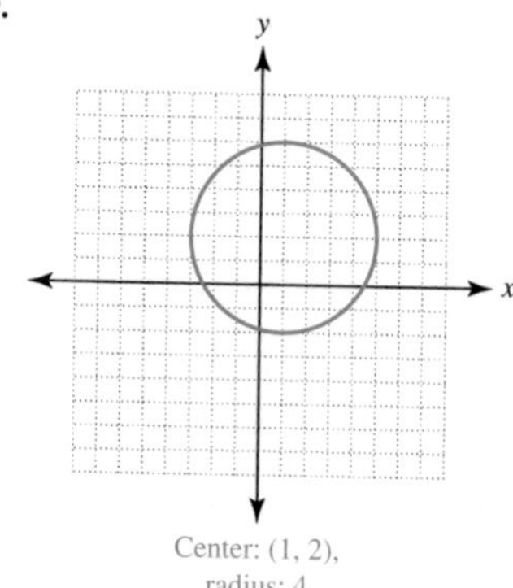

Center: (1, 2),
radius: 4

41.

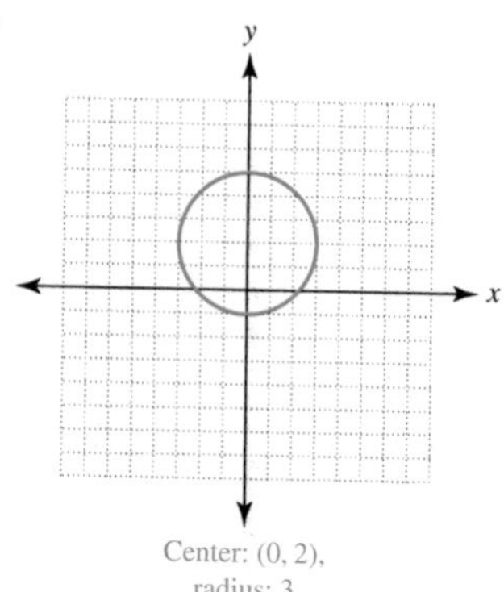

Center: (0, 2),
radius: 3

43. Line **45.** Circle **47.** Parabola **49.** Parabola

51.

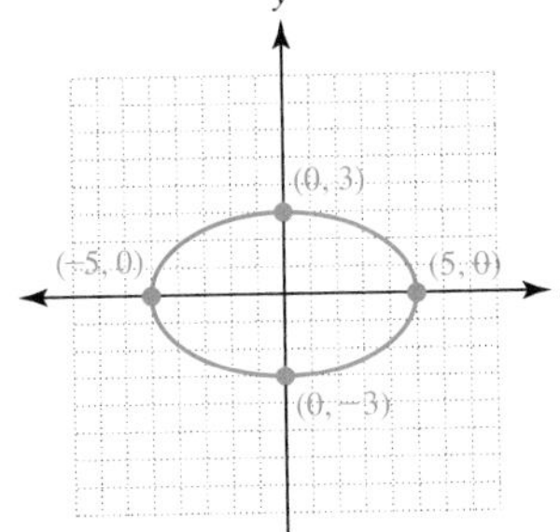

53.

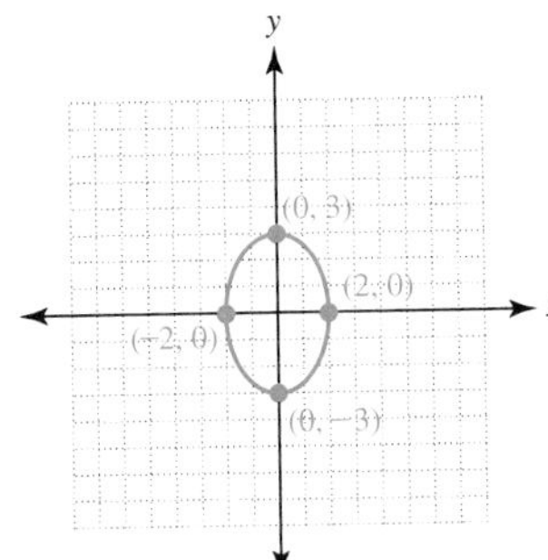

55.

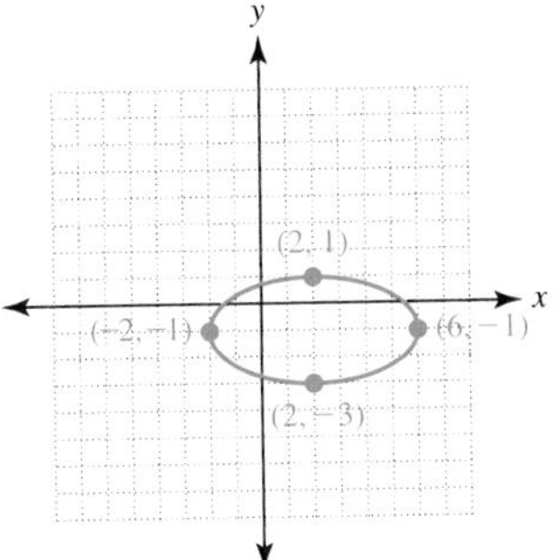

57.

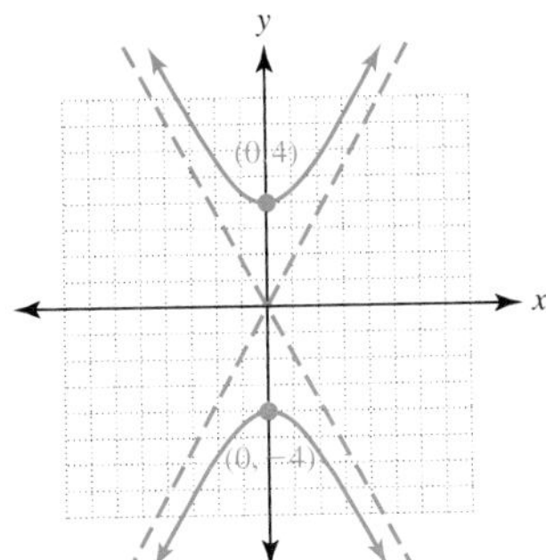

59.

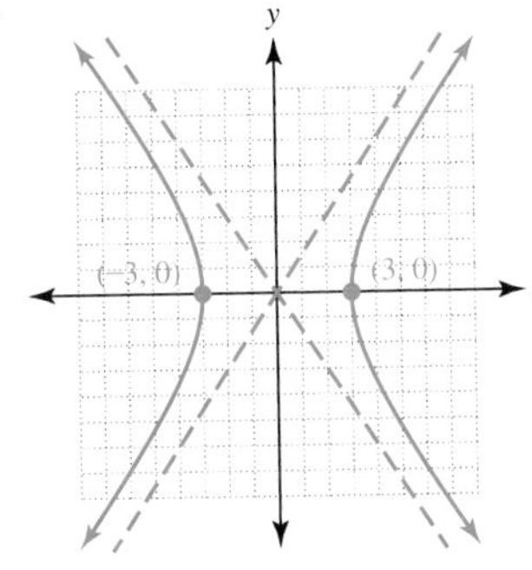

61.

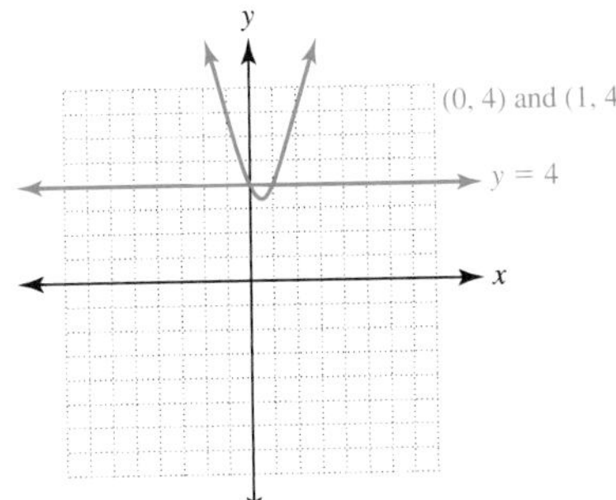

63.

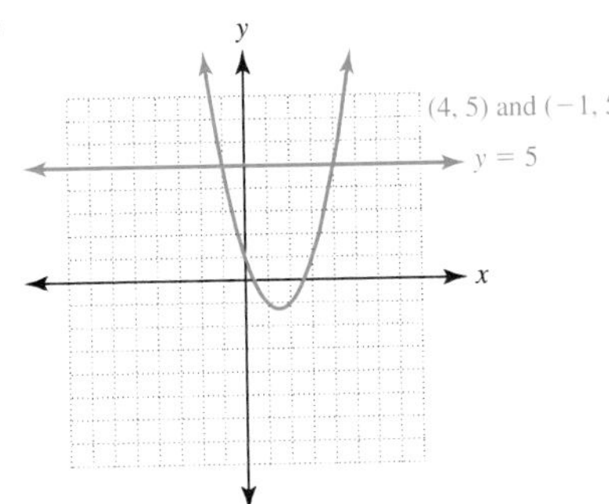

65.

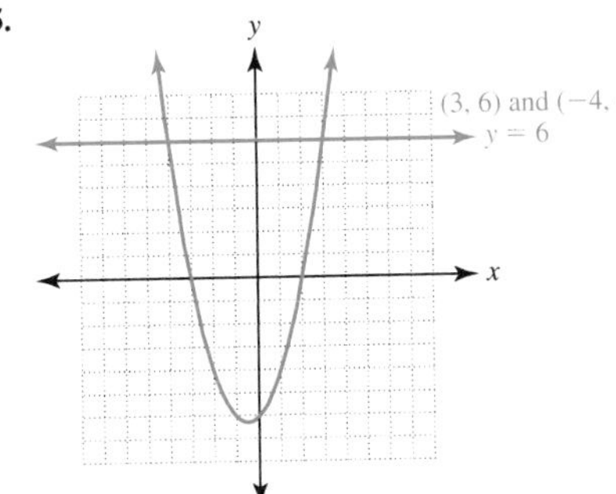

67. $(3, 3)$ and $(-4, 3)$ **69.** $(-7, 5)$ and $(-5, 5)$

71.

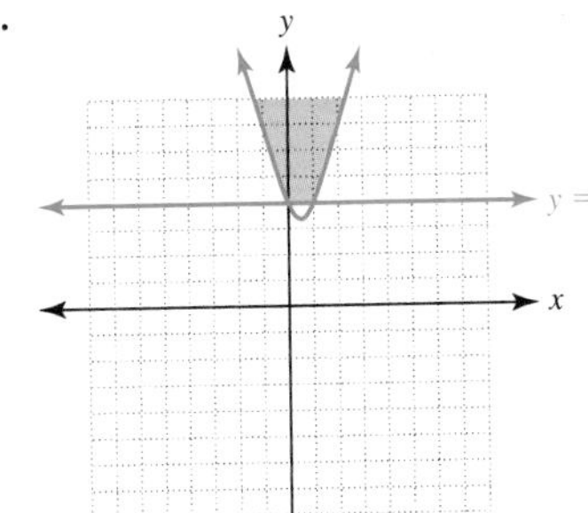

73.

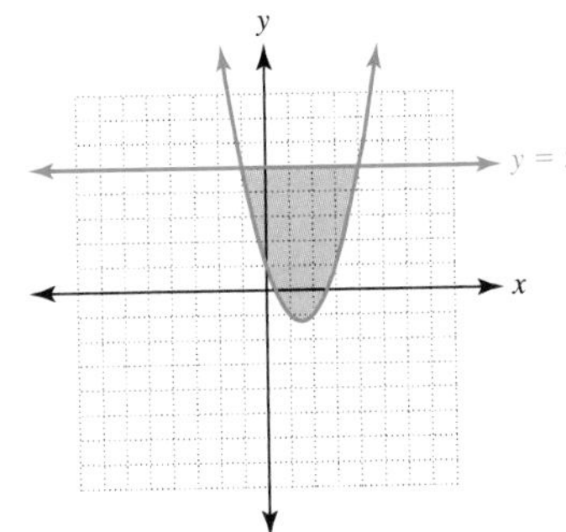

75.

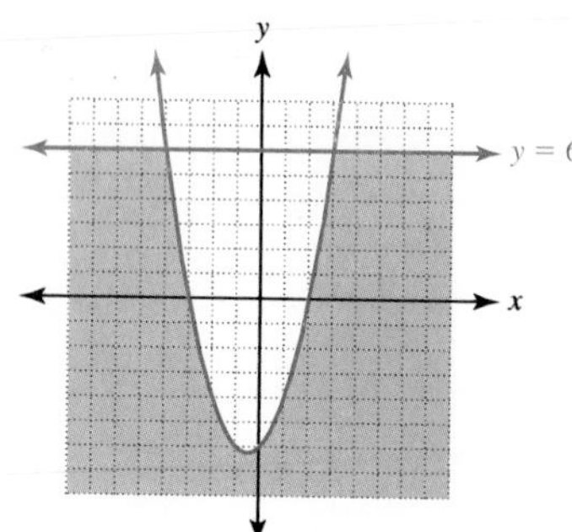

Self-Test for Chapter 9

[9.1] 1.

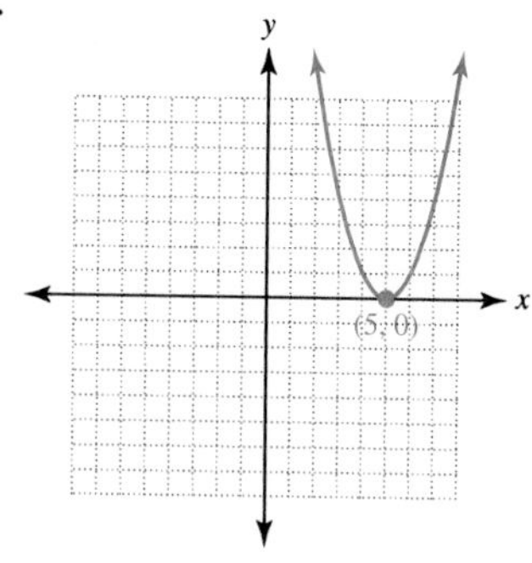

2.

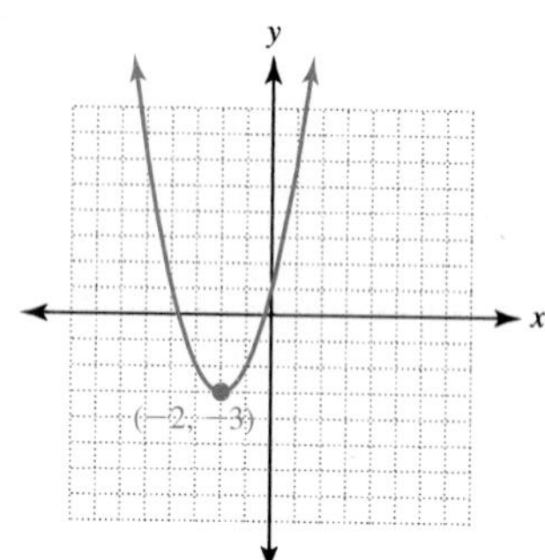

3.

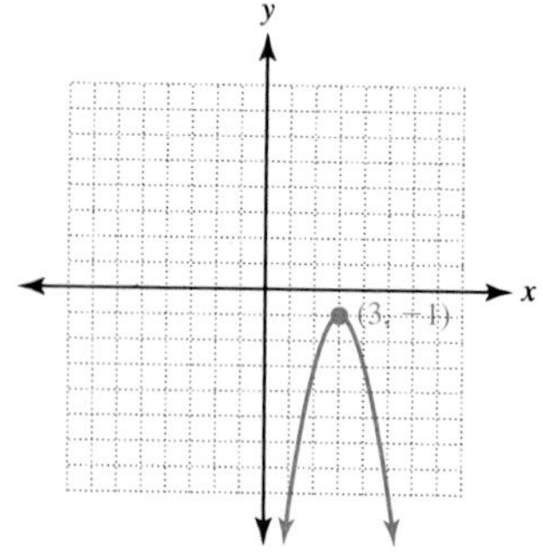

4.

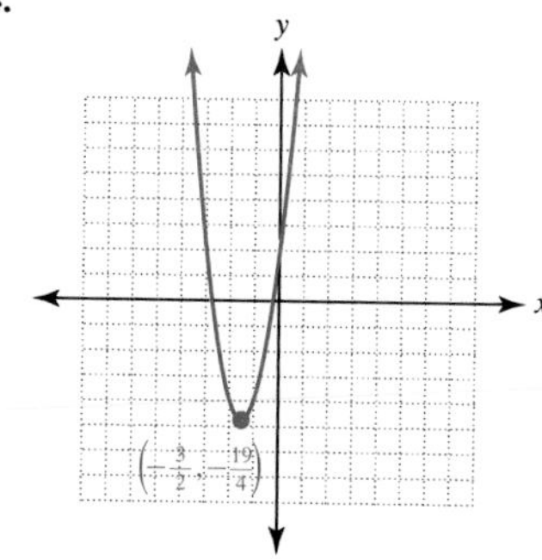

5.

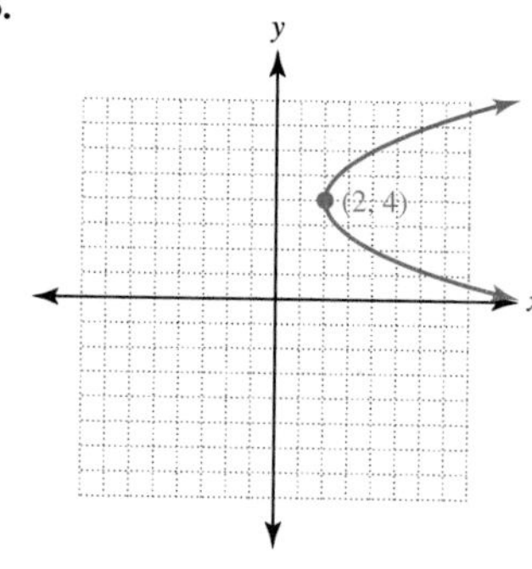

6.

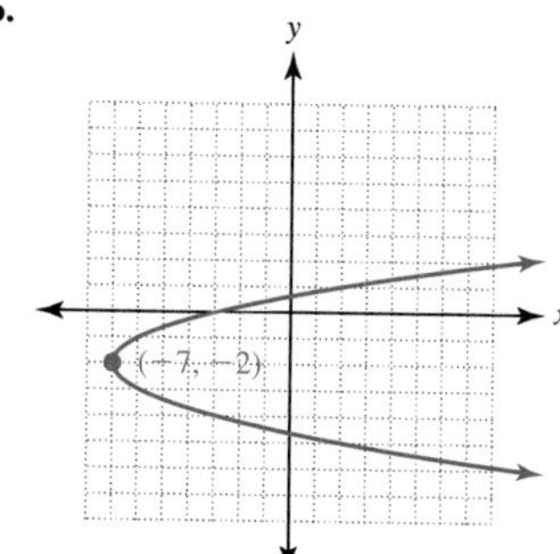

[9.2] 7. (3, −2); $r = 6$ **8.** (−1, 2); $r = \sqrt{26}$

9.

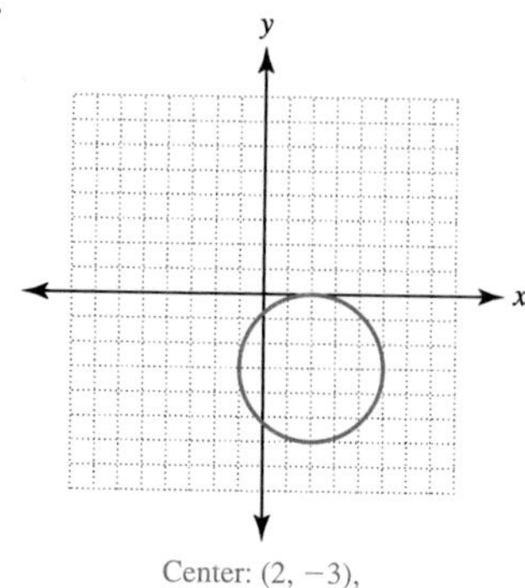

Center: (2, −3), radius: 3

[9.3] 10.

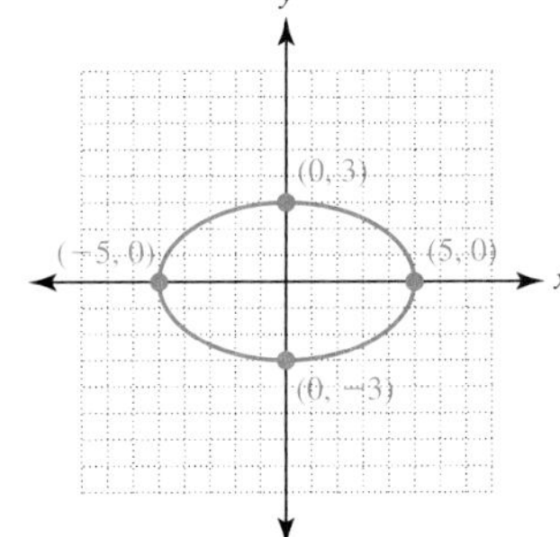

11.

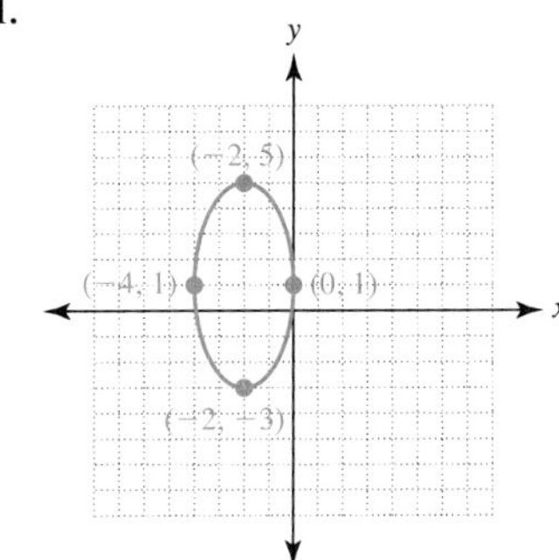

12.

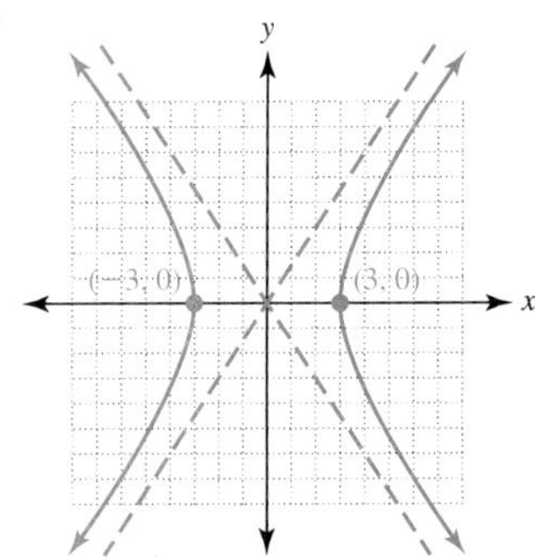

13.

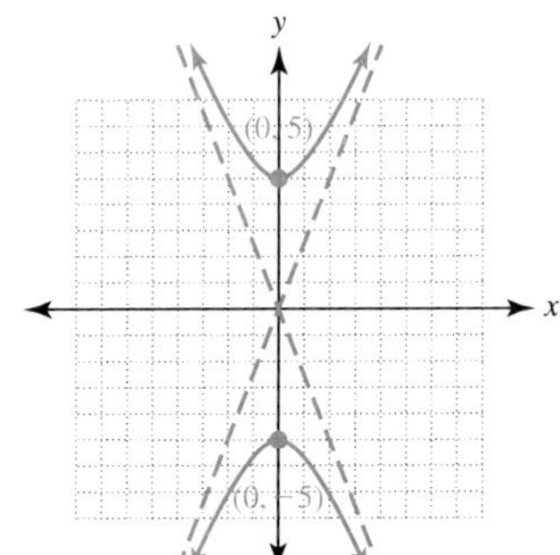

14.

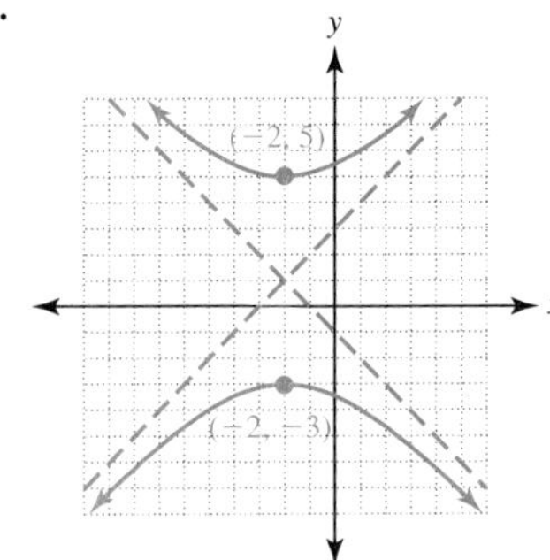

[9.4] 15.

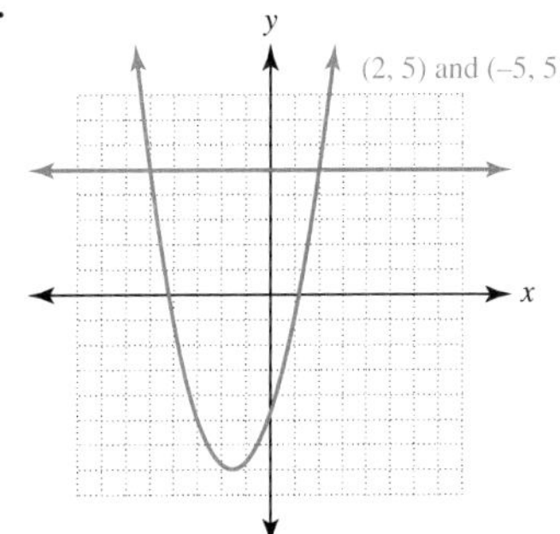

16.

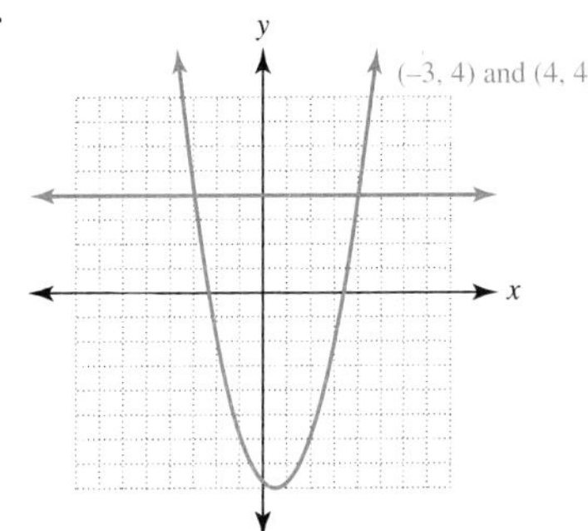

17. (2, 5) and (−5, 5) **18.** (−3, 4) and (4, 4)

19.

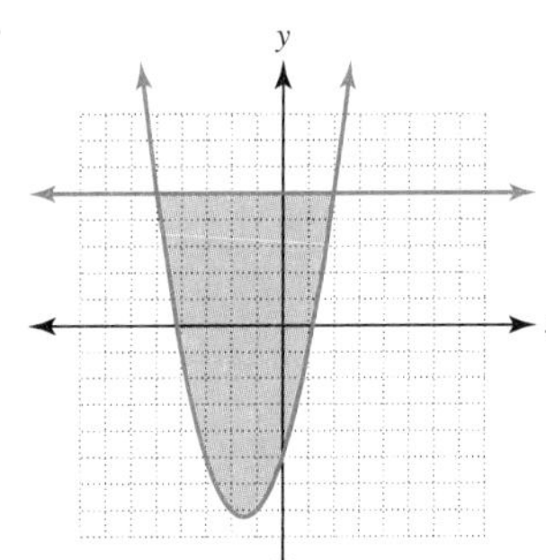

20.

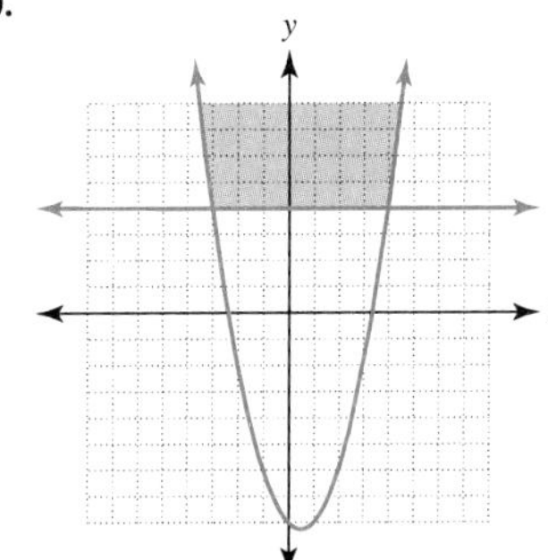

[9.1–9.3] 21. Circle **22.** Hyperbola

Cumulative Review for Chapters 1–9

[2.1] 1. $\frac{11}{2}$ **[2.4] 2.** $x > -2$ **[2.5] 3.** $-1, 4$

4. $-4 \le x \le \frac{2}{3}$ **5.** $x < -\frac{17}{5}$ or $x > 5$ **[5.9] 6.** 8, −3

[7.4] 7. 1 **[6.5] 8.** −2 **[8.2] 9.** $\frac{1 \pm \sqrt{3}}{2}$

[3.3] 10.

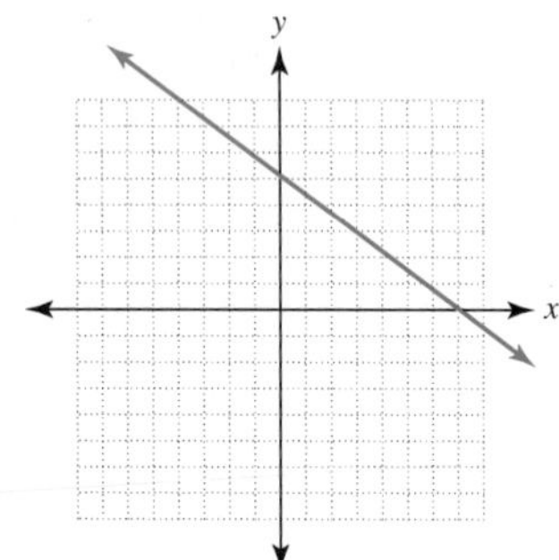

[3.6] 11.

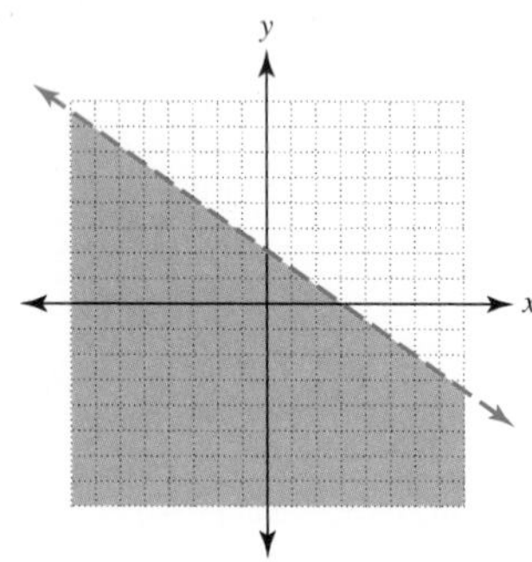

[9.2] 12. $\sqrt{601} \approx 24.5$ **[3.4] 13.** 7 **[3.5] 14.** $y = -x + 3$
[5.2] 15. $2x^2 - 5x - 3$ **16.** $9x^2 - 12x + 4$
[5.4] 17. $f(x) = (x - 3)(x^2 - 5)$

[9.1] 18.

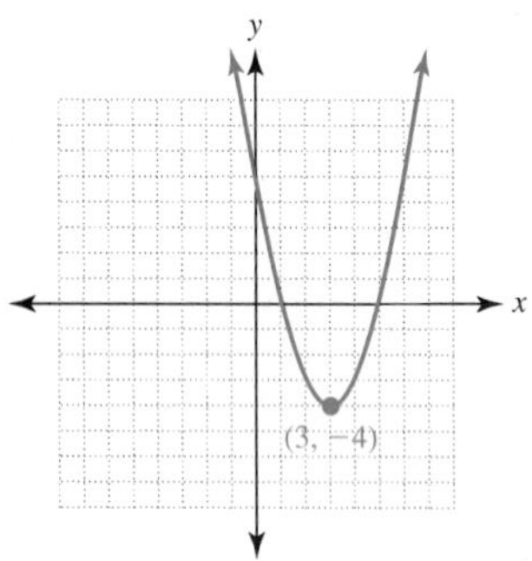

[9.2] 19.

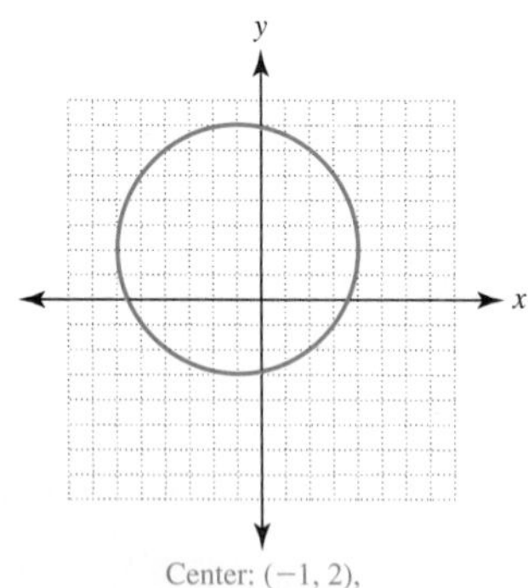

Center: (−1, 2),
radius: 5

[9.3] 20.

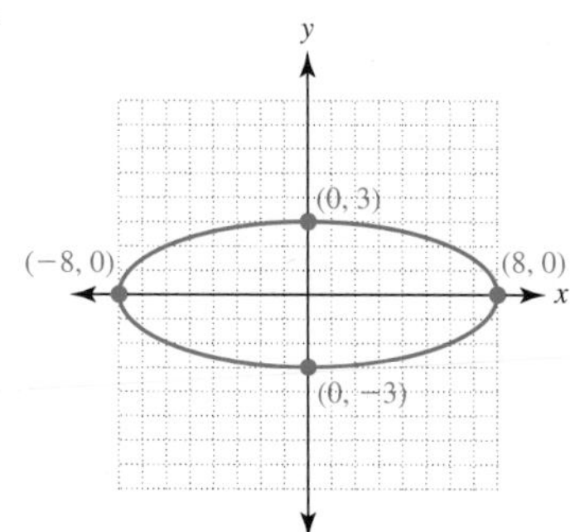

[6.3] 21. 2 **[7.3] 22.** $w\sqrt{3w}$ **[4.1] 23.** $\left(-10, \frac{26}{3}\right)$
24. 8 cm by 19 cm **25.** 73

Pretest for Chapter 10

1. $x^2 + 2x + 1$ **2.** $x^2 - 2x - 5$ **3.** $3x^3 - x^2 - 3x + 1$
4. $\frac{x^2 - 1}{3x - 1}$ **5.** 0 **6.** $\frac{3}{5}$ **7.** $x^2 + x + 1$ **8.** $\frac{1}{x^2 + x + 1}$
9. D: $\mathbb{R}$ **10.** D: $\left\{x \mid x \neq \frac{1}{3}\right\}$ **11.** $4x^2 - 4x - 2$
12. $-2x^2 + 7$ **13.** 6 **14.** −1 **15.** $f^{-1}(x) = \frac{1}{2}x + 2$, yes
16.

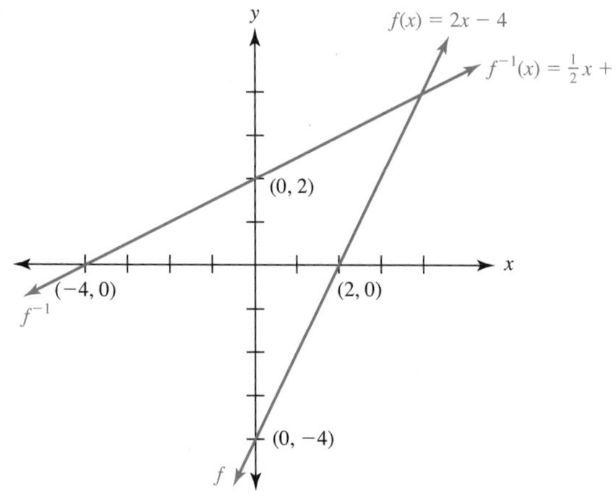

Reading Your Text

Section 10.1 **(a)** functions; **(b)** $f(x) + g(x)$; **(c)** domain; **(d)** $f(x) \cdot g(x)$
Section 10.2 **(a)** $f(g(x))$; **(b)** chaining; **(c)** $g(x)$; **(d)** $\neq$
Section 10.3 **(a)** inverse; **(b)** interchange; **(c)** symmetric; **(d)** same

Summary Exercises for Chapter 10

1. **(a)** $2x^4 + x^3 - x^2 + 6x + 5$; **(b)** 13; **(c)** 13
3. **(a)** $5x^2 + 3x + 10$; **(b)** 18; **(c)** 18
5. **(a)** $4x^2 + 8x$; **(b)** 12; **(c)** 12 **7.** $6x^2 - 10x$
9. $3x^3$ **11.** $\frac{2x}{3x - 5}$, $\left\{x \mid x \neq \frac{5}{3}\right\}$ **13.** $\frac{3x}{x^2}$, $\{x \mid x \neq 0\}$
15. **(a)** −2; **(b)** −8; **(c)** 7; **(d)** $3x - 2$
17. **(a)** 25; **(b)** 49; **(c)** 4; **(d)** $x^2 - 5$ **19.** $h(x) = (f \circ g)(x)$
21. {(5, 1), (7, 2), (9, 3)}; function
23. {(4, 2), (3, 4), (4, 6)}; not a function **25.** $y = 2x - 1$
27. $y = \frac{1}{3}x - 2$

Self-Test for Chapter 10

[10.1] 1. $x^2 + 3x - 3$ **2.** $x^2 - 3x + 5$
3. (a) $6x^2 - 3x + 7$; **(b)** $2x^2 - 3x + 7$; **(c)** 10; **(d)** 6; **(e)** 10; **(f)** 6
4. (a) $-3x^3 + 3x^2 + 5x - 9$; **(b)** $-3x^3 + 7x^2 - 9x - 5$; **(c)** -4; **(d)** -10; **(e)** -4; **(f)** -10 **5.** $(f + g)(x) = x^2 + 3x - 3, D: \mathbb{R}$
6. $(g - f)(x) = -x^2 + 3x - 1, D: \mathbb{R}$
7. $(g \cdot f)(x) = 3x^3 - 2x^2 - 3x + 2, D: \mathbb{R}$
8. $\left(\frac{f}{g}\right)(x) = \frac{x^2 - 1}{3x - 2}, D: \left\{x \mid x \neq \frac{2}{3}\right\}$ **[10.2] 9.** $9x^2 - 12x + 3$
10. $3x^2 - 5$ **11.** 48 **12.** 22
[10.3] 13. (a) $f^{-1}(x) = \frac{1}{4}x + \frac{1}{2}$, function;

(b)

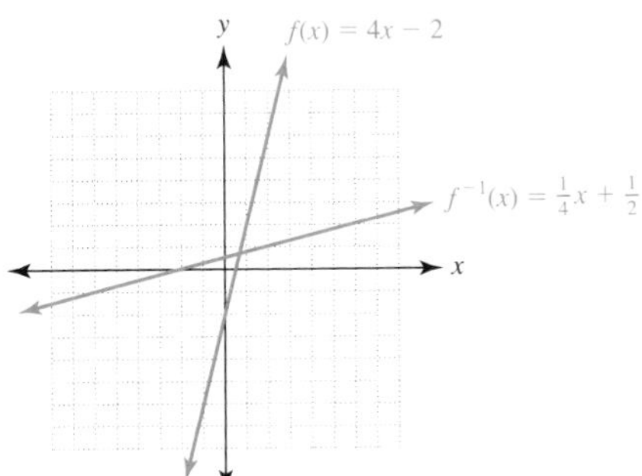

Cumulative Review for Chapters 1–10

[2.1] 1. $-\frac{1}{24}$ **[2.5] 2.** $-\frac{2}{3} < x < \frac{10}{3}$ **[2.3] 3.** 29 cm
[3.4] 4. $x = -2$
[3.5] 5.

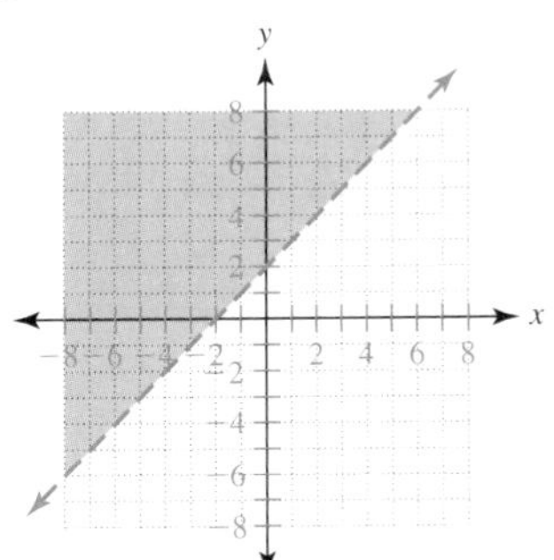

[4.1] 6. $(7, -2)$ **7.** Inconsistent **[4.2] 8.** $-2, 5$, and 7
[5.1] 9. $5x^3 - x^2 - 4x + 1$ **[5.3] 10.** $3x + 1 + \frac{6}{x - 2}$
[5.4] 11. $3mn(2mn - 3n - 1)$ **12.** $(x - 3)(2x - 5)$
[5.5] 13. $2(a + 3)(a^2 - 3a + 9)$ **[5.9] 14.** $-3, \frac{5}{2}$
[6.2] 15. $\frac{x - 5}{x - 2}$ **[6.5] 16.** $C = \frac{AB}{A + B}$
[7.2] 17. $2p^2r^4\sqrt{3pr}$ **18.** $3\sqrt{2a}$ **[7.3] 19.** $30 - 10\sqrt{5}$
[7.6] 20. $\frac{1}{m^6}$ **[7.4] 21.** $\frac{11}{5}$ **[7.7] 22.** $-\frac{9}{34} - \frac{19}{34}i$
[8.3] 23. $\frac{5 \pm \sqrt{17}}{2}$ **[8.1] 24.** $x = \frac{3}{5}, -4$ **[9.1] 25.** $(1, 3)$
[6.5] 26. $18\frac{3}{4}$ h **[3.1] 27.** $D: \{-4, -2, 6\}, R: \{-1, 3, 5\}$
[10.1] 28. $\{x \mid x \neq \pm 1\}$ **[10.2] 29.** $4x^2 - 12x + 8$
[10.3] 30. $y = 5x + 4$

Pretest for Chapter 11

1.

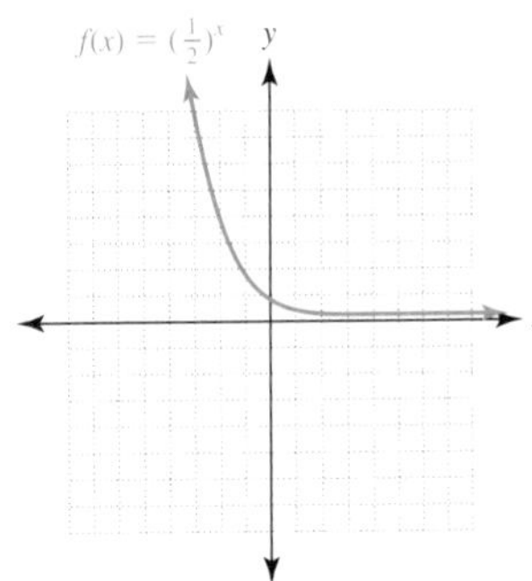

2. 3

3.

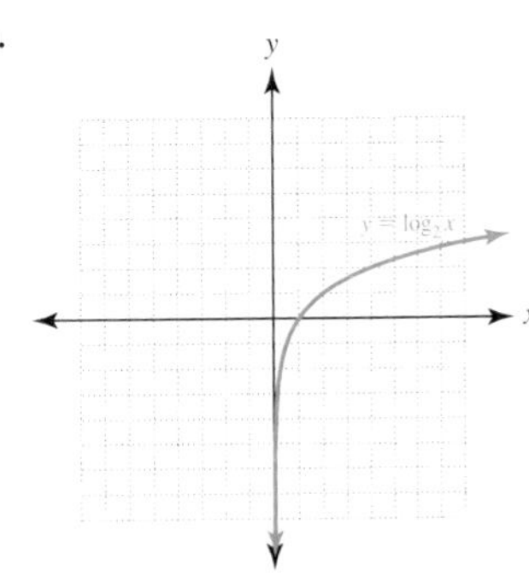

4. $\log_{64} 16 = \frac{2}{3}$ **5.** 81 **6.** $2 \log_5 x + \log_5 y - \log_5 z$
7. 3 **8.** $\frac{5}{2}$

Reading Your Text

Section 11.1 **(a)** Exponential functions; **(b)** $f(x) = b^x$, $b > 0, b \neq 1$; **(c)** growth; **(d)** decay
Section 11.2 **(a)** logarithm of x to base b; **(b)** logarithmic function; **(c)** logarithm; **(d)** logarithm
Section 11.3 **(a)** common; **(b)** antilogarithm; **(c)** natural; **(d)** natural log
Section 11.4 **(a)** logarithmic equation; **(b)** 10; **(c)** $M = N$; **(d)** Exponential equations

Summary Exercises for Chapter 11

1.

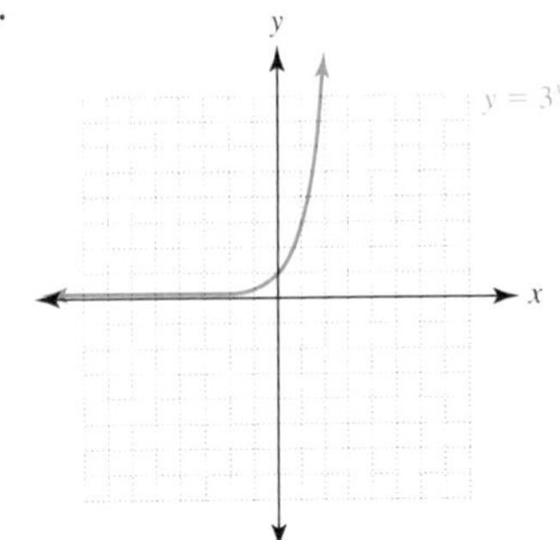

3. 3 **5.** −1 **7.** 64,000 bacteria

9.

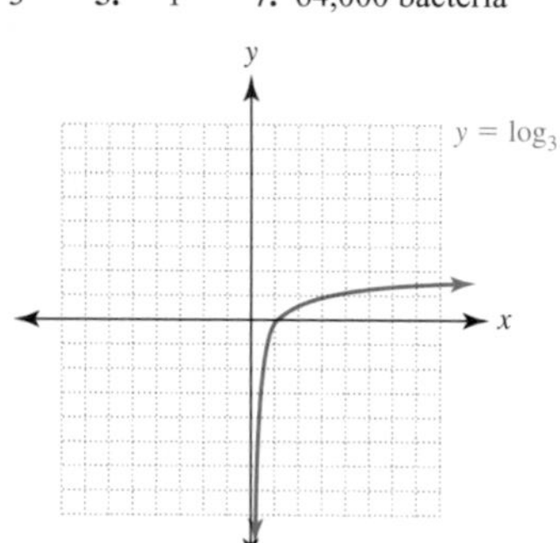

11. $\log_3 81 = 4$ **13.** $\log_5 1 = 0$ **15.** $\log_{25} 5 = \frac{1}{2}$

17. $3^4 = 81$ **19.** $81^{1/2} = 9$ **21.** $10^{-3} = 0.001$ **23.** 3

25. 64 **27.** 9 **29.** $\frac{1}{3}$ **31.** 80 dB **33.** 100 **35.** 10

37. $3 \log_4 y - \log_4 5$ **39.** $3 \log_5 x + \log_5 y + 2 \log_5 z$

41. $\frac{2}{3} \log_b x + \frac{1}{3} \log_b y - \frac{1}{3} \log_b z$ **43.** $\log_b \frac{x^3}{z^2}$

45. $\log_5 \frac{x^2}{y^3 z}$ **47.** $\log_b \sqrt[3]{\frac{x}{y^2}}$ **49.** 1.204 **51.** 0.239

53. 9.495, basic **55.** 6.3×10^{-11} **57.** 66.6

59.

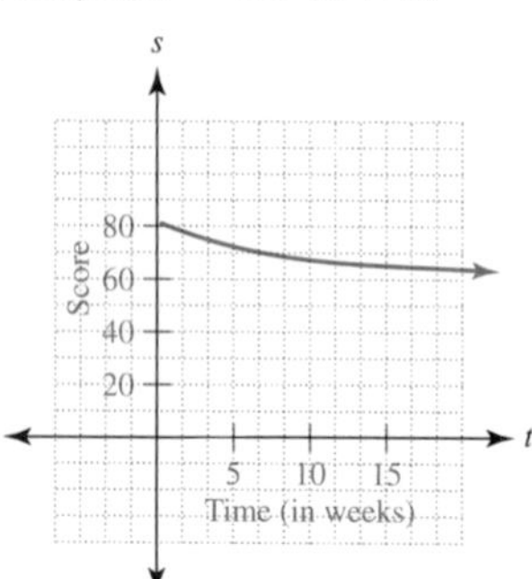

61. 1.969 **63.** 250 **65.** 2 **67.** 3 **69.** −2

71. 2.500 **73.** 4.419 **75.** 8.2 yr **77.** 166.1 yr

79. 8.7 yr **81.** 6.6 mi

Self-Test for Chapter 11

[11.1] 1.

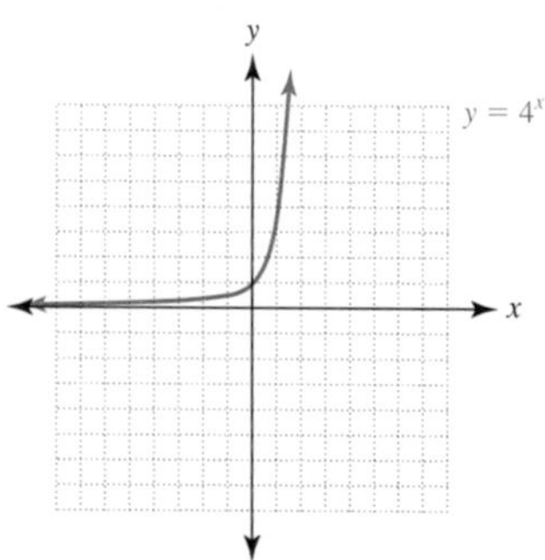

2.

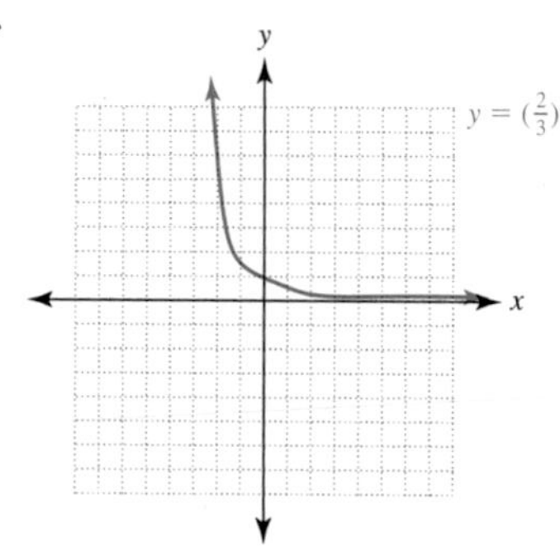

[11.2] 3. **(a)** −2; **(b)** $\frac{5}{2}$

4.

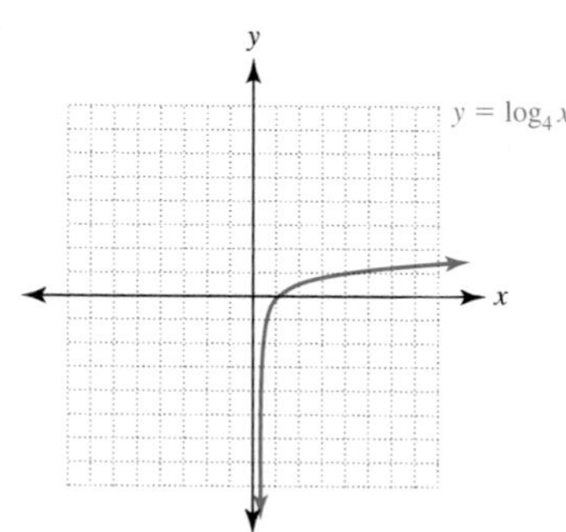

5. $\log 10{,}000 = 4$ **6.** $\log_{27} 9 = \frac{2}{3}$ **7.** $5^3 = 125$

8. $10^{-2} = 0.01$ **9.** 6 **10.** 4 **11.** 5

[11.3] 12. $2 \log_b x + \log_b y + 3 \log_b z$

13. $\frac{1}{2} \log_5 x + \log_5 y - \frac{1}{2} \log_5 z$ **14.** $\log (xy^3)$

15. $\log_b \sqrt[3]{\frac{x}{z^2}}$ **[11.4] 16.** 8 **17.** $\frac{11}{8}$ **18.** 0.262

19. 2.151

Cumulative Review Chapters 1–11

[2.1] 1. 11 **[2.5] 2.** $x < \frac{2}{3}$ or $x > 4$ **[11.4] 3.** $\frac{10}{9}$

[3.3] 4.

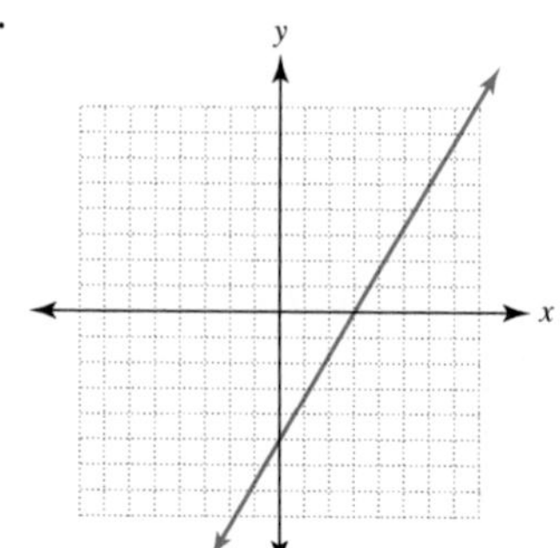

[3.6] 5.

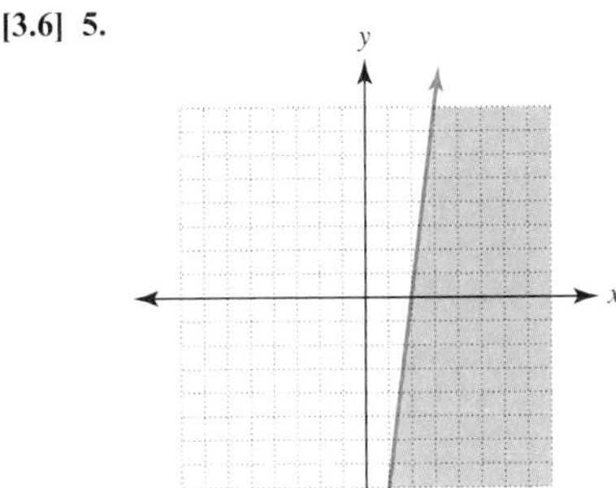

[3.5] 6. $6x + 5y = 7$ **[2.4] 7.** $x \geq 10$ **[1.4] 8.** $2x^2 - 6x + 1$
[5.3] 9. $6x^2 - 13x - 5$ **[5.7] 10.** $(2x - 5)(x + 2)$
[5.5] 11. $x(5x + 4y)(5x - 4y)$ **[6.3] 12.** $\dfrac{-x + 2}{(x - 4)(x - 5)}$
[6.2] 13. $\dfrac{x + 2}{x - 2}$ **[7.3] 14.** $-4\sqrt{2}$ **15.** $22 + 12\sqrt{2}$
16. $\dfrac{5}{3}(\sqrt{5} + \sqrt{2})$ **[2.3] 17.** 77, 79, 81 **[5.9] 18.** $-2, 1$
[8.3] 19. $\dfrac{3 \pm \sqrt{19}}{2}$ **[8.5] 20.** $-\dfrac{3}{2} \leq x \leq 1$ **[5.1] 21.** 3
[2.5] 22. $1 \leq x \leq 4$ **[9.2] 23.** $(x - 1)^2 + (y + 2)^2 = 9$
[1.5] 24. x^3w^{12} **[6.5] 25.** 6